Handbook of Semiconductor Electronics

OTHER McGRAW-HILL HANDBOOKS OF INTEREST

HANDBOOK OF SEMICONDUCTOR ELECTRONICS

*A Practical Manual Covering the Physics,
Technology, and Circuit Applications of
Transistors, Diodes, and Photocells*

Edited by

LLOYD P. HUNTER

*Professor of Electrical Engineering
Department of Electrical Engineering
University of Rochester
Rochester, New York*

SECOND EDITION

McGRAW-HILL BOOK COMPANY, INC.

New York   Toronto   London

HANDBOOK OF SEMICONDUCTOR ELECTRONICS

II

31304

PREFACE

As in the first edition the attempt is made to collect the major principles of the field of semiconductor electronics. The field has now matured sufficiently to allow a more sensible choice of subject material. This has been done without greatly expanding the size of the book but with some sacrifice of detail.

The background physics of Part I required the least revision, and for the most part, revisions to Part I consist in rectifying omissions of the original text. Advances in device and material technology required major revision of Part II but very little expansion. In Part III, the rapid development of the field has required nearly a complete rewriting of the sections on circuit applications together with a considerable expansion of the material. Two new sections have been added: Sec. 16, "Microwave Applications," and Sec. 17, "Power Supplies." The coverage of both of these areas was seriously deficient in the first edition. Part IV is reworked, and it is hoped that it is improved without much expansion. An attempt is made still to include a comprehensive bibliography, although the phenomenal volume of the literature precludes complete coverage.

This edition goes to press just as a revolution in integrated semiconductor circuitry seems to be in the making. It is unfortunate that little can yet be said about it, but such problems always attend a rapidly developing field.

The editor wishes to express his sincere appreciation to the contributors for their assistance and cooperation, to Mrs. Joan P. Moruzzi and Mrs. Mary T. Welz for the long hours spent on the preparation of the manuscript, and, finally, to the members of the IBM Laboratories for their many helpful discussions and encouragement.

LLOYD P. HUNTER

CONTRIBUTORS

J. B. ANGELL
Stanford University
Electrical Engineering Department
Palo Alto, California

W. R. BEAM
Rensselaer Polytechnic Institute
Troy, New York

G. B. B. CHAPLIN
The Plessey Company, Ltd.
Hampshire, England

W. C. DUNLAP
Raytheon Manufacturing Company
Waltham, Massachusetts

H. FLEISHER
IBM Corporation
Yorktown Heights, New York

M. B. HERSCHER
Radio Corporation of America
Camden, New Jersey

L. P. HUNTER
IBM Corporation
Poughkeepsie, New York

S. L. MILLER
Rheem Semiconductor Corporation
Mountain View, California

B. OKKERSE
N. V. Philips Gloeilampenfabrieken
Eindhoven, Netherlands

D. F. PAGE
Imperial College of Science and Technology
Department of Electrical Engineering
London, England

E. J. RYMASZEWSKI
IBM Corporation
Poughkeepsie, New York

R. F. SCHWARZ
Philco Corporation
Philadelphia, Pennsylvania

D. F. SINGER
IBM Corporation
Poughkeepsie, New York

B. N. SLADE
IBM Corporation
Poughkeepsie, New York

J. C. van VESSEM
N. V. Philips Gloeilampenfabrieken
Nijmegen, Netherlands

J. F. WALSH (deceased)
Philco Corporation

J. L. WALSH
IBM Corporation
Poughkeepsie, New York

H. J. WOLL
Radio Corporation of America
Camden, New Jersey

J. F. WOODS
IBM Corporation
Yorktown Heights, New York

CONTENTS

Part IV   Reference Material

MATRIX METHODS

GRAPHICAL METHODS

LIST OF SYMBOLS

General Rules:

Numerical subscripts usually refer to a series of similar objects. For example, T_1 and T_2 refer to transistor 1 and transistor 2, respectively. The one exception to this rule is in the matrix symbolism where 1 refers to the input and 2 refers to the output.

The matrix coefficients a_{ij}, b_{ij}, h_{ij}, r_{ij}, y_{ij}, and z_{ij} are often designated with the subscript numbers mentioned above. On some occasions, however, the subscript designations are alphabetic and refer to the input, output, and common terminal. For example, in the common-emitter connection, the input is the base and the output is the collector, so that $h_{11} = h_{ie}$, $h_{12} = h_{re}$, $h_{21} = h_{fe}$, and $h_{22} = h_{oe}$. The subscript e designates the common terminal, and the subscripts i, r, f, and o represent input, reverse, forward, and output, respectively.

Symbol	Definition	Page of First Appearance
A	Electron density above barrier with forward bias	3–10
A	Area of the junction	4–4
A	Surface area of molten zone	6–17
A	Number of atoms per milligram of impurity	7–7
A	Sample cross-sectional area	20–2
A_c	Area of the collector junction or contact	4–41
A_e	Area of the emitter junction or contact	4–7
A_i	Low-frequency current amplification factor	12–30
A_s	Area of the surface of the base immediately surrounding the emitter junction	4–7
A_v	Low-frequency voltage amplification factor	11–63
a	Channel width in unipolar transistor	4–35
a	Electron density above barrier without bias	3–10
a	Exponential parameter of base impurity gradient in a drift transistor	4–31
a_{ij}	Coefficients of generalized transistor equations	4–12
a_{ij}	Coefficient in the matrix $\begin{bmatrix} V_e \\ I_e \end{bmatrix} = [a] \begin{bmatrix} V_c \\ I_c \end{bmatrix}$	18–14
B	Hole density above barrier with forward bias	3–10
B	Bandwidth of transistor	10–2
B_{cb}	Collector-base susceptance	14–14
B_{ce}	Collector-emitter susceptance	14–14
B_{eb}	Emitter-base susceptance	14–14

Symbol	Definition	Page of First Appearance
B_F	Feedback susceptance	14–14
B_L	Load susceptance	14–9
B_L^o	Load susceptance for maximum instability	14–14
B_T	Terminal susceptance	14–7
BV_A	Avalanche-breakdown voltage	19–9
BV_a	Pseudo breakdown voltage for $\alpha = 1$	19–9
BV_{CBO}	Collector-base breakdown voltage, emitter open	4–37
BV_{CEO}	Collector-emitter breakdown voltage, base open	4–37
BV_{CER}	Collector-emitter breakdown voltage with resistance in the base circuit	11–38
BV_c	Collector-junction breakdown voltage	4–3
BV_{EBO}	Emitter-to-base breakdown voltage	19–8
b	Ratio of electron-to-hole mobility	4–32
b'	Intrinsic transistor base (see equivalent circuit, Fig. 11.22)	11–17
C	Hole density above barrier with reverse bias	3–10
c_B	Boron concentration	6–17
C_b	Barrier capacitance	3–17
$C_{b'e'}$	Intrinsic transistor base to emitter capacitance	12–11
C_c	Collector-junction capacitance	4–24
C_{cbh}	Collector-to-base interlead capacitance	12–12
C_{ceh}	Collector-to-emitter stray capacitance	12–44
C_D	Diffusion capacitance	4–24
C_{De}	Diffusion capacitance	12–6
C_F	Feedback capacitance	14–3
c_L	Concentration of impurity in the liquid	6–7
C_{Lb}	Concentration of impurity in the bulk liquid	6–7
C_{Li}	Concentration of impurity at the freezing interface	6–7
C_{L0}	Initial impurity concentration of the liquid	6–8
C_n	Concentration of donors	4–29
C_n	Neutralizing capacitance	12–44
C_{ob}	Common-base output capacitance	12–13
C_{pc}	Concentration of acceptors in the collector region	4–29
C_{pe}	Concentration of acceptors in the emitter region	4–29
C_{Tc}	Collector transition capacitance	12–6
C_{Te}	Emitter transition capacitance	12–6
C_ν	Excess-phase equivalent-circuit capacitor (see Fig. 12.15)	12–11
C'	Initial impurity concentration of the opposite type from the diffusing impurity	7–19
C_0	Surface concentration	7–19
C_1	Initial impurity concentration of the same type as the diffusing impurity	7–19
c	Velocity of light	5–2
c'	Intrinsic transistor collector (see Fig. 12.7)	12–8
$C_{b'c}$	Capacitance between collector connection and intrinsic base (see equivalent circuit, Fig. 11.22)	11–17
$C_{b'e}$	Capacitance between emitter connection and intrinsic base (see equivalent circuit, Fig. 11.22)	11–17
c_S	Concentration of impurity in the solid	6–7

Symbol	Definition	Page of First Appearance
D	Electron density above barrier with reverse bias	3–10
D	Diffusion constant	4–5
D	Density of the semiconductor	7–7
D	Diode designation	15–14
D	Pen deflection	20–37
D_B	Diffusion constant of minority carriers in the base region	12–3
D_n	Diffusion constant for electrons	3–12
D_{nb}	Diffusion constant for electrons in the base region	4–6
D_p	Diffusion constant for holes	3–7
D_{pe}	Diffusion constant for holes in the emitter region	4–6
d	Specific gravity	6–14
d	Diameter of collector junction	10–2
d	Probe spacing (four-point probe)	20–4
E_H	Hall electric field	20–13
E_s	Sweeping field in the base of a drift transistor	4–31
E_1	Constant total electronic energy	2–5
e	Napierian base	2–10
e'	Intrinsic transistor emitter (see Fig. 12.7)	12–8
ε	Applied electric field	2–11
F_b	Noise figure common-base connection	12–23
F_e	Noise figure common-emitter connection	12–23
f	Freezing rate	6–8
f	Function of Fig. 20.5	20–6
f_+	Sum of two mixed frequencies	16–13
f_-	Difference of two mixed frequencies	16–13
f_A	Fraction of acceptors ionized	20–7
f_α	Grounded-base cutoff frequency (equivalent to f_{ab})	10–1
f_α	Equivalent to f_{ab}	12–11
f_{ab}	Frequency at which $\alpha_{fb} = 0.707$ of its zero-frequency value	4–22
f_{ae}	Frequency at which $\alpha_{fe} = 0.707$ of its zero-frequency value	4–23
$f_{\alpha fb}$	Equivalent to f_{ab}	14–11
f_b	Frequency at which $\phi_{\alpha_{fb}} = 90°$	14–15
f_β	Frequency at which $\beta = 0.707\beta_0$	4–21
f_D	Fraction of donors ionized	20–9
$f(\epsilon)$	Fermi occupation probability	2–9
f_H	High-frequency cutoff	11–33
f_i	Half-power bandwidth of current amplification	12–31
f_K	Corner frequency (see Fig. 12.31)	12–24
f_L	Low-frequency cutoff	11–32
f_{max}	Maximum frequency of oscillation	12–13
f_N	Equal to $f_T \sqrt{1 + H_{FB}}$	12–24
$f_n(\epsilon)$	Fermi probability function associated with excess electrons	5–5
$f_p(\epsilon)$	Fermi probability function associated with excess holes	5–5
f_π	Frequency at which $\phi_{\alpha_{fb}} = 180°$	14–15
f_T	Frequency at which $|h_{fc}| = 1$	12–6
f'	Frequency at which $T_A^o = T_B^o = 1$	14–15
f_0	Pump frequency	16–14
f_0	Resonant frequency of tuned circuit	12–54

Symbol	Definition	Page of First Appearance
I	Intrinsic conductivity type	4–21
I_B	Base current (direct current)	11–8
I_b	Base current (small signal)	11–7
I_C	Collector current (direct current)	1–6
I_c	Collector junction current (direct current)	4–3
I_c	Collector current (small signal)	11–7
I_c	rms current in the capacitor	17–3
I_C^m	Collector current (maximum signal)	11–41
I_C^q	Collector current (quiescent point)	11–41
I_{CBO}	Collector saturation current (emitter open)	15–3
I_{CEO}	Collector saturation current (base open)	11–24
I_{cf}	Forward collector-junction current	4–27
I_{CM}	Final value of collector-current step	15–11
I_{co}	Collector saturation current (emitter open)	4–7
I_{cos}	Collector leakage reverse-biased (direct current)	13–8
I_{cr}	Reverse collector-junction current	4–27
I_D	Drain current unipolar transistor (direct current)	1–13
I_D	Dark current of a photocell	10–21
I_D	Noise diode current (direct current)	11–85
I_{DC}	Direct current	17–3
I_{DCR}	Direct current rating of rectifier	17–1
I_E	Emitter current (direct current)	1–6
I_e	Emitter junction (direct current)	4–3
I_e	Emitter current (small signal)	11–12
I_{ef}	Forward emitter-junction current	4–27
I_{EO}	Emitter saturation current (collector open)	4–12
I_{EOS}	Emitter leakage current with both collector and emitter reverse-biased (direct current)	13–6
I_{er}	Reverse emitter-junction current	4–27
I_{ESIM}	Reduced current error	13–9
I_F	Diode forward current	3–18
I_F	Fundamental component of I_e	14–20
I_{Fc}	Collector current (emitter input, collector output)	4–16
I_{Fe}	Emitter current (emitter input, collector output)	4–16
I_g	Source current (small signal)	11–44
I_L	Light flux	5–14
I_n	Noise current in noise-diode load resistor	11–85
I_{nc}	Collector-junction electron current	4–3
I_{ne}	Emitter-junction electron current	4–3
I_{nm}	Metal-barrier electron current	4–41
I_P	Current of the peak point, Esaki tunnel diode	15–78
I_p	rms current in the primary	17–3
I_{pc}	Collector-junction hole current	4–8
I_{pe}	Emitter-junction hole current	4–4
I_R	Diode reverse current	3–18
I_R	Maximum direct-current rating	17–16
I_{Rc}	Collector current (collector input, emitter output)	4–16
I_{Re}	Emitter current (collector input, emitter output)	4–16
I_s	Current due to stored charge	3–19
I_s	Surface recombination current	4–7

Symbol	Definition	Page of First Appearance
m	Excess-phase factor	4–23
m	Weight of impurity (milligrams)	7–7
m	Real part of α_{fb}	14–11
mev	Million electron volts	2–16
m_n	Mass of the electron	2–11
m_p	Mass of the hole	2–11
N	Electronic-conductivity type	1–4
N	Net doping density	4–11
N^+	Heavily N-type semiconductor material	7–2
N_A	Density of acceptors	4–6
N_A^-	Density of ionized acceptors	20–7
N_c	Density of levels in the conduction band	20–9
N_D	Density of donors	4–6
N_D^+	Density of ionized donors	20–7
NF	Noise factor or noise figure	11–83
NF_{if}	Noise figure of i-f amplifier	16–7
N_n	Density of centers occupied by electrons (empty of holes)	5–6
N_p	Density of centers occupied by holes (empty of electrons)	5–6
N_v	Density of levels in the valence band	20–9
n	Density of free electrons	2–10
n	Exponent in voltage dependence of C_b	3–17
n	Output transformer efficiency	11–48
n	Imaginary part of α_{fb}	14–11
Δn	Excess density of minority current carriers	4–7
Δn_E	Excess density of minority carriers on the base side of the emitter junction	4–7
n_b	Density of electrons in the base regions	4–3
n_{bc}	Density of electrons in the base next to the collector	4–31
n_{be}	Density of electrons in the base next to the emitter	4–31
n_c	Density of electrons in the collector region	4–3
n_e	Density of electrons in the emitter region	4–3
n_{eq}	Equilibrium density of electrons	3–19
n_i	Density of electrons or holes in an intrinsic semiconductor	3–13
n_{major}	Density of majority carriers	4–6
n_{minor}	Density of minority carriers	4–6
n_n	Density of electrons in an N region	3–10
n_P	Number of primary turns	11–47
n_p	Density of electrons in a P region	3–10
n_S	Number of secondary turns	11–47
n_0	Density of electrons in a dark photoconductor	5–5
P	Hole-conductivity type	1–5
P	Ratio of coupling coefficient to critical coupling	12–52
P	Recombination probability	20–20
P_{AB}	Transition probability (state A to state B)	3–3
P_c	Transistor power dissipation	10–9
P_{DC}	Input d-c power to the collector	11–40
P_G	Power gain	11–40
P_i	Input power	12–47

Symbol	Definition	Page of First Appearance
PIV	Peak inverse voltage	10–16
P_L	Load power	12–47
P_O	Power output	11–40
P_O^m	Power output, maximum signal	11–41
P_s	Source power	12–47
PV_c	Punch-through voltage of the collector	4–11
p	Density of free holes	2–11
p	Vapor pressure of water	6–17
P^+	Heavily doped P-type semiconductor material	7–2
p_b	Density of holes in the base region	4–3
p_c	Density of holes in the collector region	4–3
p_e	Density of holes in the emitter region	4–3
p_n	Density of holes in an N region	3–10
p_p	Density of holes in a P region	3–10
p_0	Density of holes in a dark photoconductor	5–5
ppb	Parts per billion	6–6
Q	Surface density of atoms	7–20
Q	Energy stored divided by energy lost per cycle	10–18
Q	Electric charge	17–3
Q_{Lp}	Loaded Q of transformer primary	12–52
Q_{Us}	Unloaded Q transformer secondary	12–52
q	Electronic charge	2–11
R	Dynamic resistance of crystal at operating point	16–10
R	Negative resistance value of tunnel diode	16–28
R	Hall constant (see equivalent circuit, Fig. 20.13)	20–13
R_A	Effective input noise resistance of amplifier tube	16–10
R_b	Resistance between base terminals of a tetrode transistor	12–8
R_{bs}	Base spreading resistance	4–24
R_c	Collector series resistance	4–3
R_e	Emitter series resistance	4–3
R_F	Feedback resistance	14–3
R_f	Feedback resistance	11–65
R_g	Source resistance	11–33
R_i	Input resistance	11–33
R_L	Load resistance	4–14
R_m	Measured resistance	19–18
R_n	Neutralizing resistance	12–44
R_S	Dynamic resistance of a transistor in saturation	11–40
R_s	Diode equivalent series resistance	3–18
R_s	Interstage load resistance	12–35
R_s	Series resistance	16–28
$R(V)$	Nonlinear diode resistance	3–18
r	Ratio of Hall-to-conductivity mobility	20–16
r_b	T-equivalent circuit common-emitter or common-base resistance	11–15
r_b'	Equivalent to $r_{bb'}$	12–8

Symbol	Definition	Page of First Appearance
$r_{bb'}$	Resistance between base connection and intrinsic base (see equivalent circuit, Fig. 11.22)	11–17
$r_{b'c}$	Resistance between collector connection and intrinsic base (see equivalent circuit, Fig. 11.22)	11–17
$r_{b'e}$	Resistance between emitter connection and intrinsic base (see equivalent circuit, Fig. 11.22)	11–17
r_c'	Equivalent to $r_{cc'}$ or r_{cs}	12–9
r_{ce}	Resistance between emitter connection and collector connection (see equivalent circuit, Fig. 11.22)	11–17
r_c	Common-base T-equivalent circuit collector resistance	11–15
r_{cs}	Collector spreading resistance	12–9
r_d	Common-emitter T-equivalent circuit collector resistance	11–15
r_e	T-equivalent circuit common-emitter or common-base emitter resistance	11–15
r_e'	Equivalent to $1/g_{pe}$	12–6
r_{ij}	Coefficient in the matrix $\begin{bmatrix} V_e \\ V_c \end{bmatrix} [r] \begin{bmatrix} I_e \\ I_c \end{bmatrix}$	18–11
r_o	Open impedance of chopper	13–9
r_s	Effective secondary winding resistance	17–3
r_ν	Equivalent-circuit resistor in series with the excess phase capacitor (see Fig. 12.15)	12–11
S	$h_{12}h_{21}/h_{11}h_{22}$	11–25
S	Stability factor $= dI_C/dI_{CO}$	11–70
s	Surface recombination velocity	4–7
s_n	Capture cross section of electron trap	20–21
s_p	Capture cross section of hole trap	20–21
T	Absolute temperature	2–9
T	Transformer ratio	14–8
T	Transistor designation	15–14
T_A	Ambient temperature	11–37
T_A	Transformer ratio for configuration A, Table 14.1	14–10
T_B	Transformer ratio for configuration B, Table 14.1	14–10
T_C	Transistor-case temperature	11–36
T_C	Transformer ratio for configuration C, Table 14.1	14–10
T_D	Transformer ratio for configuration D, Table 14.1	14–10
T_F	Fall time	15–11
T_i	Temperature of the idle-current loss	16–17
T_J	Junction temperature	11–11
T_n	Noise temperature	16–5
T^o	Transformer ratio for maximum instability	14–14
T_R	Rise time	15–11
T_S	Saturation or storage time	15–11
T_0	Source or reference temperature	16–6
T_1	A specific absolute temperature greater than zero	2–9
t	Time molten zone is exposed to ambient	6–17
t	Ratio of diode noise power to thermal noise power	16–7
t	Sample thickness	20–6
t_D	Delay time of transistor switch	4–26

Symbol	Definition	Page of First Appearance
V_G	Voltage gain (large signal)	11–52
V_g	Source voltage (small signal)	11–44
V_H	Hall voltage	20–13
V_I	Input voltage (direct current)	15–20
V_i	Input voltage (small signal)	15–21
V_n	Noise voltage of equivalent-voltage generator	11–85
V_O	Output voltage (direct current)	15–20
V_{OC}	Open-circuit voltage	20–28
V_P	Voltage of the peak point, Esaki tunnel diode	15–78
V_R	Voltage across internal transistor resistance	4–16
V_R	Regulated d-c voltage	17–16
V_r	Ripple voltage	17–4
V_{red}	Voltage reduction increment	17–3
V_s	Supply voltage of double-base diode	4–38
V_{so}	Open-circuit secondary voltage	17–3
V_T	Thermal noise voltage	11–83
V_U	"Up" level of input voltage	15–9
V_U	Unregulated d-c voltage	17–16
V_V	Voltage of the valley point, Esaki tunnel diode	15–78
V_0	Pinch-off voltage of unipolar transistor	4–35
V_0	Total noise voltage	11–84
V_0	Contact potential	19–27
V_1	Peak voltage of double-base diode	4–38
v	Volume of crystal in which light absorption takes place	5–14
v	Velocity of crystal growth	7–9
v	Average velocity of charge carriers	20–15
v_i	Velocity amplitude in the rate-growing equation	7–9
$\bar{v}_n$	Average electronic velocity	2–11
v_n	Average velocity of electrons in the conduction band	5–6
$\bar{v}_p$	Average velocity of holes	2–11
v_p	Average velocity of holes in the valence band	5–6
v_P	Peak inverse voltage	17–3
v_{SO}	Peak secondary voltage	17–5
W	Base-region thickness in a junction transistor	4–3
W_-	Power of the difference frequency	16–13
W_+	Power of the sum frequency	16–13
W_0	Power of the signal frequency f_0	16–13
W_1	Power of the signal frequency f_1	16–13
W_e	Thickness of the emitter region	4–6
W_f	Width of the floating region of a "hook"	4–18
W_i	Power of the idler	16–22
w	Photocell thickness	5–15
X_c	Collector reactance at $f = f_T$	12–31
ΔX_m	Measured reactance increment	19–17
x	Width of collector depletion region	4–24
x_A	Fraction of metal states which are filled	3–3
x_B	Fraction of semiconductor states which are filled	3–3
x_0	Junction depth	7–19

Symbol	Definition	Page of First Appearance
Y_L	Load admittance	11–26
Y_m	Measured admittance	19–15
Y_{nb}	Neutralizing shunt admittance (common base)	12–44
Y_{ne}	Neutralizing shunt admittance (common emitter)	12–43
Y_{rn}	Reverse transfer admittance of neutralizing path	12–43
Y_T	Terminal admittance	14–7
Y_T	Transformed device admittance y	19–15
y	Device admittance	19–15
y_m	Measured transadmittance	19–19
y_{pe}	Emitter-to-base diffusion admittance	12–6
y_{rb}	Reverse transfer admittance (common base)	12–44
y_{rc}	Reverse transfer admittance (common emitter)	12–43
Z_a	Input shunt impedance	11–31
Z_e	Impedance in emitter lead	11–31
Z_e	Emitter feedback impedance	12–35
Z_f	Collector-to-base feedback impedance	11–32
Z_g	Source impedance	11–25
Z_L	Load impedance	11–25
Z_o	Output series impedance	11–31
Z_S	Impedance of series d-c blocking capacitor	19–14
z_i	Input impedance	11–25
z_o	Output impedance	11–25
α	Grounded-base current gain	4–2
α'	Compound current gain of two transistors	4–17
α'	Constant in the rate-growing equation	7–9
α'	Intrinsic transistor common-base current gain	12–10
α^*	Innate collector efficiency	4–2
α_0	Zero-frequency grounded-base current gain	4–22
α_F	Emitter input, collector output current gain	4–12
α_{FB}	Common-base forward current gain (large signal)	1–8
α_{fb}	Common-base forward current gain (small signal)	11–9
α_{fb0}	Low-frequency value of α_{fb}	14–11
α_{fc}	Common-collector forward current gain (small signal)	18–13
α_{FE}	Common-emitter forward current gain (large signal)	13–2
α_{fe0}	Low-frequency value of α_{fe}	14–11
α_R	Collector input, emitter output current gain	4–12
α_{RB}	Common-base reverse current gain (large signal)	13–16
α_{rc}	Common-collector reverse current gain (small signal)	18–13
α_{re}	Common-emitter reverse current gain (small signal)	18–13
β	Base transport efficiency	4–2
β	Diode sensitivity in amperes per watt	16–10
β_0	Zero frequency transport efficiency	4–22
γ	Emitter injection efficiency	4–2
δ	Thickness of the liquid diffusion layer	6–8

Symbol	Definition	Page of First Appearance
ϵ	Energy of an electron in a crystal	2–9
$\Delta\epsilon$	Electronic energy gap width	2–10
ϵ_0	Fermi energy or Fermi level	2–9
ϵ_1	Energy at the bottom of the conduction band	2–10
ϵ_2	Energy at the top of the conduction band	2–10
ϵ_3	Energy at the top of the valence band	2–11
ϵ_A	Energy of acceptor states	20–7
ϵ_c	Energy of bottom of the conduction band	20–9
ϵ_D	Energy of donor states	20–9
ϵ_n	Quasi Fermi level for electrons	5–5
ϵ_p	Quasi Fermi level for holes	5–5
ϵ_v	Energy of top of the valence band	20–9
ζ_n	Capture cross section of electron traps	5–6
ζ_p	Capture cross section of hole traps	5–6
θ	Hall angle	20–28
κ	Dielectric constant	4–25
κ_0	Dielectric constant of free space	10–1
λ_0	Photoconducting threshold wavelength	5–2
μ	Current-carrier mobility	4–5
μ_D	Drift mobility	20–17
μ_H	Hall mobility $(= R\sigma)$	20–16
μ_n	Mobility of electrons	2–11
μ_p	Mobility of holes	2–11
μ_σ	Conductivity mobility	20–16
ν	Frequency of light	5–2
ν	Excess-phase factor in graded-base transistors	12–3
ν_0	Photoconducting threshold frequency	5–2
ν_e	Ionization threshold frequency	5–2
ρ	Electrical resistivity	2–13
ρ_b	Resistivity of the base region	4–5
ρ_{bc}	Base resistivity next to the collector	4–31
ρ_{be}	Base resistivity next to the emitter	4–31
ρ_c	Resistivity of the collector region	4–9
ρ_e	Resistivity of the emitter region	4–5
ρ_f	Resistivity of the floating region of a "hook"	4–18
σ	Electrical conductivity	2–11
σ	Surface tension	6–14
σ_i	Intrinsic conductivity	3–13
τ	Mean free time	3–7
τ	Current-carrier lifetime	4–7

Symbol	*Definition*	*Page of First Appearance*
τ	Duration of the current surge	17–8
τ_0	Duration of one cycle	17–8
τ_b	Lifetime in bulk material	20–22
τ_c	Transit time of collector depletion region	4–24
τ_d	Decay lifetime	10–18
τ_m	Decay time of conductivity	20–22
τ_n	Electron lifetime	3–12
τ_p	Hole lifetime	3–12
τ_R	Reverse recovery time of a diode	10–16
ϕ	Potential barrier to electrons or holes	3–10
ϕ	Contact potential	16–11
φ	Magnetic flux	17–24
$\varphi_{\alpha_{fb}}$	Phase of α_{fb}	14–11
$\varphi_{\alpha_{fe}}$	Phase of α_{fe}	14–11
ϕ_B	Metal-semiconductor barrier height	8–2
ϕ_c	Height of the collector barrier (including bias)	4–3
ϕ_e	Height of the emitter barrier (including bias)	4–3
φ_0	Equilibrium barrier height	8–12
ω	Angular frequency	3–18
ω	Angular frequency of temperature change	7–9
ω_0	Angular oscillation frequency	14–21
$\omega_{\alpha_{fb}}$	Angular frequency at which $\alpha_{fb} = 0.707\alpha_{fb0}$	15–6
$\omega_{\alpha_{RB}}$	Angular frequency at which $\alpha_{RB} = 0.707\alpha_{RB0}$	15–11
ω_c	Diode "cutoff" frequency (frequency for $Q = 1$)	16–12
ω_F	Radian cutoff frequency of α_F	4–26
ω_R	Radian cutoff frequency of α_R	4–26

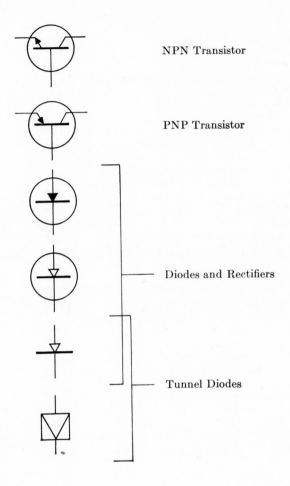

NPN Transistor

PNP Transistor

Diodes and Rectifiers

Tunnel Diodes

Handbook of Semiconductor Electronics

PART I

Physics of Transistors, Diodes, and Photocells

Section 1

TRANSISTOR CHARACTERISTICS

L. P. HUNTER

IBM Corporation, Poughkeepsie, N.Y.

The purpose of this section is to define and illustrate with a few examples the subject of this handbook. A very brief survey of transistor action and characteristics is given. The transistor and diode types selected for illustration are chosen for their value in showing the versatility of these devices rather than for their individual importance to the field. The discussions of the transistors given in this section are not meant to be explanations of their operation, but only rough descriptions of their characteristics. Proper explanations of their mechanisms of operation are given in Sec. 4.

The transistor was invented by J. Bardeen and W. H. Brattain[1] in 1948. This invention represents the discovery of a device long sought after. For many years, attempts had been made to produce an amplifier without the use of vacuum tubes. Some operable devices were invented, such as the magnetic amplifier, but their operating conditions and characteristics were such that they did not fulfill the requirement for an amplifier as versatile as a vacuum tube. The transistor from the very beginning showed characteristics which gave promise of considerable improvement over vacuum-tube amplifiers for many applications. Transistor amplifiers may have either a high or a low input impedance, they require nothing analogous to the incandescent filament of a vacuum tube, and they operate with a very low total power drain.   The two latter attributes augur well for operational lives much greater than the conventional vacuum tube.

1.1. Description of Transistor Action.   The point-contact transistor was the first transistor type discovered, and while it presently seems obsolete, it is most instructive to use it in making the initial description of transistor action, since it forms a natural link with the prior semiconductor diode art.   In Fig. 1.1 is shown a photograph and diagrams of typical point-contact transistors.   This transistor consists of a small crystal of semiconductor material (usually germanium) to which are attached two

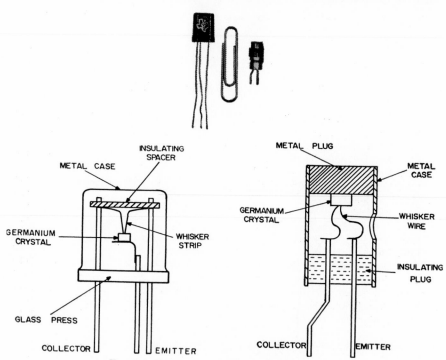

Fig. 1.1. Typical point-contact transistors.

rectifying point contacts (whiskers) in close proximity and a single nonrectifying large-area contact at some distance from the two point contacts.   Such a device exhibits a power gain of about 20 db and a frequency cutoff of the order of 10 mc.   It will handle about 150 mw total power and usually occupies a volume of about ¼ cm³. The bias voltages required range from 1 to 40 volts, depending on the applications.

Historically, transistor action was discovered in the process of attempting to explain certain aspects of semiconductor-diode action.   Transistor action can easily be described by comparing it with diode action.   Accordingly, we shall first briefly review semiconductor-diode behavior.

In Fig. 1.2 is shown the volt-ampere characteristic of a typical semiconductor diode consisting of a metal point in contact with a semiconductor crystal.   When the metal point is positive with respect to the crystal, the resistance of the contact is relatively low.   This is called the forward resistance.   When the point is negative, the resistance is high.   This is called the back or reverse resistance.   This relation of the polarity of rectification depends upon the fact that electrons dominate in carrying the current through the crystal.   Such a crystal is called N type.   If the current is carried by electron vacancies (holes), the polarity of the rectification is reversed and the crystal is said to be P type.   Point-contact-transistor action can be described as the control of the current of the high-resistance branch of the diode characteristic of one point contact to a semiconductor crystal by means of the forward current in a second rectifying point contact to the crystal.   A set of typical point-contact-transistor characteristics[2] is shown in Fig. 1.3.   From this figure it can be seen that forward current through this second point (called the emitter) lowers the back resistance of the first point (called the collector) in such a way that its dynamic resistance remains high even

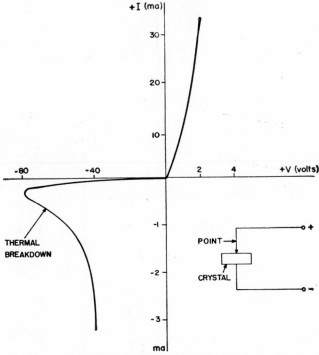

Fig. 1.2. Typical N-type semiconductor point-contact-diode characteristics.

though the total current in the collector is markedly increased.   In order to show the interaction described here, the two point contacts must be quite close together, usually of the order of two or three thousandths of an inch separation.

   A rectifying characteristic (Fig. 1.4) can also be obtained in a semiconductor diode consisting of a junction between a region of N-type conductivity and one of P-type conductivity in a single semiconductor crystal.   If such a crystal is properly prepared, the ratio of back to forward resistance is usually much greater than the same ratio for a point-contact diode.   A junction transistor can be made by preparing a semiconductor crystal consisting of two regions of the same conductivity type with a third region of opposite conductivity type sandwiched between them (NPN or PNP). If ohmic contacts are made to all three regions, the junction between one end and the center or base region can serve as an emitter controlling the current through the other junction when it is biased in its high-resistance direction, giving the set of characteristics[3] shown in Fig. 1.5.

   In Fig. 1.6 is shown a photograph and diagrams of typical junction transistors. This transistor is usually somewhat smaller than the point-contact type and typically

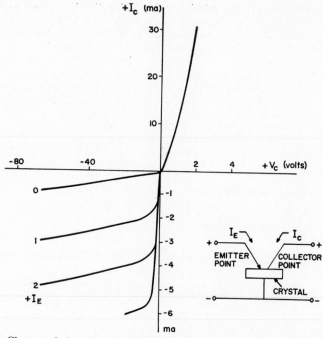

FIG. 1.3. Characteristics of typical N-type semiconductor point-contact transistor.

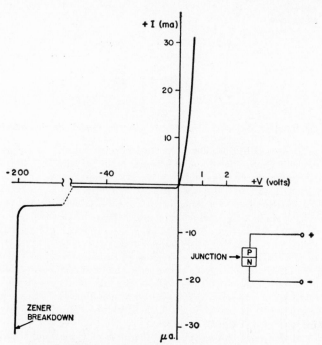

FIG. 1.4. Characteristics of typical PN-junction diode.

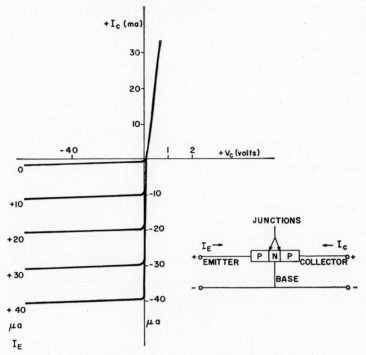

FIG. 1.5. Characteristics of typical two-junction PNP transistor.

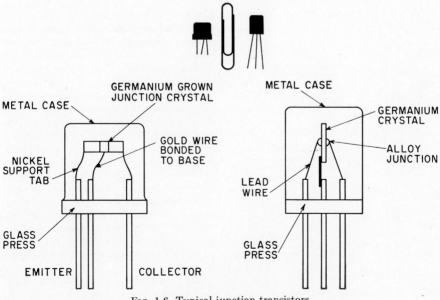

FIG. 1.6. Typical junction transistors.

handles about 50 mw of total power in its low-power version. In such a junction transistor the base region must be kept quite thin to achieve reasonably good operation.

By comparison of Figs. 1.3 and 1.5, some of the typical differences between point-contact and junction transistors can be seen. The two most significant differences are found to be the dynamic resistance of the collector characteristic and the current gain. If I_C represents collector current and I_E emitter current, the current gain is defined as $\alpha_{FB} = \partial I_C/\partial I_E$ at constant collector voltage. If the junction transistor is properly made, its current gain has a theoretical upper limit of unity. There is no theoretical upper limit for the current gain in point-contact transistors, but 2.5 is a value easy to obtain in practice. The characteristic difference in dynamic resistance is not due to any theoretical limitation but seems rather to be a limitation of present technology. Point-contact transistors have about one order of magnitude lower dynamic collector resistance than junction transistors.

Today the junction transistor has been developed into a wide variety of forms and the point-contact transistor appears to be extinct. The major reasons for this seem to be the inherent stability of the junction device and its lower leakage current. A few variations of junction devices will now be described and contrasted. In Table 1.1 a summary of their characteristics is given.

1.2. Junction Diodes. The characteristic illustrated in Fig. 1.4 is typical of an ordinary PN-junction diode. The leakage current for reasonable voltages in the reverse direction ranges between 0.01 and 1.0 μa depending on the semiconductor material and the doping level of the impurities. Several variations of this simple diode have been developed. Four will be described.

1.2a. Zener Diode.[4] This device is distinguished by very high active impurity concentration levels on both sides of the PN junction. The result of this doping is a junction with a relatively low breakdown voltage. By careful control of the doping levels this breakdown voltage can be controlled reasonably accurately. Such diodes are used as voltage regulators, since the breakdown is very sharp and gives a constant-voltage characteristic. The name derives from one of the possible mechanisms of dielectric breakdown first suggested by Clarence Zener.

1.2b. Esaki Tunnel Diode.[5] This diode is made with even higher impurity concentration levels on both sides of the PN junction than the Zener diode. The result of this is to reduce the breakdown voltage to zero. That is, at zero bias voltage the PN junction is a short circuit. The short-circuit condition exists for all reverse bias voltages and up to a small forward bias, where the characteristic reverts to a normal diode forward characteristic. A typical Esaki tunnel diode characteristic is shown in Fig. 1.7. Its principal feature is seen to be the negative resistance region between the region of the normal forward characteristic and the region of the short-circuit characteristic. These diodes are distinguished by the high speed of switching across this negative resistance region. Switching times less than 10^{-9} sec have been observed.

1.2c. Double-base Junction Diode. This device, also called a unijunction transistor,

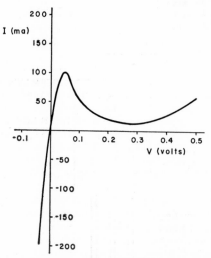

Fig. 1.7. Esaki tunnel diode characteristics.

consists typically of an N-type bar of semiconductor with a P-type alloy region on one side.[6] There are ohmic base contacts at either end of the bar and to the P region. The device is operated by applying a sweeping current between the base terminals which produces a thyratron-like characteristic between the terminal of the P region and the negative base terminal. The device can be triggered on, either by the base sweeping current or by the bias voltage on the P region. It is turned off by resetting the bias on the P region. This diode is of use in driver circuits. The turn-on and turn-off time is somewhat longer than for a simple junction diode.

1.2d. Variable-capacitance Diode.[7] This diode is distinguished by its small physical size and a junction capacity which is a rapidly varying function of the applied voltage. The small size is necessary for high-frequency performance, since the total capacitance must be minimized for high-frequency use and the capacitance is directly proportional to junction area. The principal uses of such diodes are in parametric amplifiers and subharmonic generators.

1.3. Two-junction Transistors. Two-junction transistors (NPN and PNP) have been substantially described above and compared with the point-contact-transistor triode. There are three methods of preparation of the junctions which affect the performance of the transistors significantly. By one method the junctions between the regions of opposite conductivity type are produced in the semiconductor single crystal by the addition of the appropriate impurities while the crystal is being grown from the melt.[8] By a second method the junctions are produced by a process of alloying an impurity containing metal with the opposite surfaces of a wafer of already grown semiconductor crystal.[9] There are no theoretical differences in the operation of these two types of transistors, but the method of making the junction does influence the practical performance of the transistor. For example, when two impurity regions are alloyed into the opposite sides of a thin crystalline wafer, it is very difficult to maintain plane parallel surfaces between the junctions over much more than the central three-fourths of the junction area. On the other hand, the transistor produced by the addition of impurities while the crystal is being grown from the melt usually has a base region which is quite uniform in thickness. A second difference lies in the abruptness of the change of impurity type found in crossing a junction. An alloy junction is always quite abrupt, while a grown junction may show quite a gradual transition of impurity type from one side of the junction to the other.

The third method of forming junctions is by diffusion of impurities into the surface of a wafer of already grown semiconductor crystal.[10] This is distinguished from the alloy method in that no melting and subsequent recrystallization of the surface of the semiconductor wafer take place during the diffusion process.

1.3a. Alloy Transistor. The most common type of two-junction transistor is the alloy transistor. This transistor is distinguished by the fact that the emitter and collector regions are formed by recrystallization of semiconductor material from an alloy of semiconductor material dissolved in some suitable metal mixture applied to the opposite sides of a semiconductor wafer. The impurity concentration in the undissolved base region of the semiconductor is uniform and relatively low compared with the impurity concentration in the alloy regions. Such transistors exhibit high gains, moderate collector breakdown voltages, and a frequency response good to the order of 10 mc. At the present time, the PNP type is most common in germanium and the NPN type is most common in silicon.

1.3b. Surface-barrier Transistor.[11] This device is a transistor triode in which the two rectifying contacts are formed on opposite sides of a very thin wafer of germanium by a special electroplating technique. It is not a junction transistor, since the rectifying barriers are formed by special conditions at the metal-semiconductor surface. It is not a point-contact transistor, since the effective area of the rectifying contacts is appreciably larger than that of the usual point contact. This device may have a high cutoff frequency if the germanium wafer is made thin enough. Typical values are as follows: wafer thickness, 0.0002 in.; frequency cutoff, 50 to 100 mc. Because of the extremely thin base region, these transistors have a very low power-handling capacity, usually less than 10 mw. Better performance is found if these devices are heated for a short time to a temperature sufficient to cause the electroplated contacts to "micro-alloy."[12] After such a treatment the device can reasonably be considered similar to an alloy-junction transistor.

1.3c. Drift Transistor. These devices are distinguished by a resistivity gradient in the base region which tends to speed charge carriers from the emitter to the collector. Using diffusion from the vapor phase of the impurity material it is possible to combine plane parallel junctions with a resistivity gradient in the base region between the junctions. Transistors prepared with the proper base-region resistivity gradient have shown the highest frequency response of any junction transistor reported to date. The maximum voltage which the collector junction can withstand depends upon the abruptness of the change in impurity type through the collector junction. Using a diffusion process for the formation of the collector junction it is relatively easy to produce a sufficiently gradual change in impurity type to allow a high collector-voltage rating. On the other hand, most drift transistors show a very low emitter breakdown voltage, since the impurity concentration on the emitter side of the base region is very high and conditions similar to those described for the Zener diode obtain for the emitter junction. Such transistors are widely used for high-frequency applications. Frequency responses between 100 and 2,000 mc are realized. In most cases the diffusion process used to give the base-region resistivity gradient also lends itself to the production of an extremely narrow base region. This narrow base region allows very short charge carrier transit time and hence high frequency response even though there is little effect of the base resistivity gradient.

1.3d. Mesa Transistor. This transistor is a common variation of the diffused base or drift type in which the total area of the collector junction is limited by etching away the semiconductor material surrounding the area including the base and emitter contacts. This provides a very small raised portion or "mesa" which contains the junctions of the transistor but is supported by the much more massive part of the semiconductor wafer.

1.3e. Double-base Junction Transistor. This device is sometimes called a transistor tetrode.[13] It consists of a two-junction transistor with two separate base connections on opposite sides of the central region of the transistor. The principal attribute of this device is a higher frequency response than is commonly achieved in the simple two-junction transistor (other than the drift transistor). The frequency is improved by limiting the effective cross-sectional area of the base region. This is accomplished by producing a sweeping current in the base region between the two base contacts. The sweeping current is associated with a resistive voltage drop between the two base contacts so that the area of the emitter junction which is biased in the forward direction can be limited to a very small region in the neighborhood of that base contact with respect to which the emitter bias is applied. This method of limiting the volume of the base region used for the transistor action has the effect of increasing the frequency response appreciably.

1.4. Three-junction Transistors. These devices vary in their mode of operation, but they all have the common characteristic of current gain greater than unity in the grounded-base connection [14] In a PNPN structure the emitter connection may, for example, be made to the P region at the left, the base connection to the adjacent N region, and the collector connection to the N region at the right. The remaining P region is allowed to float. Such a structure is commonly called a "hook" collector. This transistor usually shows an emitter-input current gain of the order of 100, with roughly the same input and output impedances and frequency response as a standard two-junction transistor.

If the structure is compact so that current carriers can traverse the several regions without getting lost, the device shows a uniformly high current gain at all collector currents. In this form the transistor can be used as a high-gain amplifier, or by suitable connections it can be used as a thyratron-like device.[15]

1.4a. Controlled Rectifier.[16] This three-junction device is so constructed that the floating region of the collector is usually much longer than the other regions, with the result that the grounded-base current gain at low emitter currents is less than

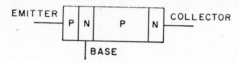

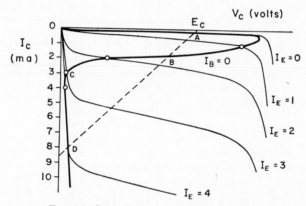

FIG. 1.8. Controlled rectifier characteristic.

unity. This device then shows a negative-resistance characteristic between the emitter and collector even for zero base current. This characteristic can be modified by the use of base current. A typical characteristic of a controlled rectifier is shown in Fig. 1.8.

1.5. Field-effect Transistor.[17] The field-effect transistor operates on a different principle from that of the conventional transistor. Stated simply, the field-effect transistor consists of a bar of semiconductor material whose resistance is modulated by varying the effective cross-sectional area of the bar by electrical means. The structure of a field-effect transistor is illustrated in the diagram of Fig. 1.9. An N-type bar of germanium is flanked by two regions of P-type germanium. The conduction current to be modulated is carried between the ends of the N-type bar. The cross-sectional area available for conduction between the two P-type regions is a function of the magnitude of the reverse bias between the two P-type regions and the N-type bar. The input impedance of this device is quite high, and the output impedance is moderately high. This is in contrast to the conventional emitter-input transistor of either the point-contact or junction type. The frequency response is significantly higher than that of an ordinary good junction transistor. This type of device shows less internal feedback between the input and output than the conventional transistor even though it is subject to Miller effect.

TABLE 1.1. QUALITATIVE PERFORMANCE OF VARIOUS SEMICONDUCTOR DEVICES

Device	Variation	Limiting frequency range	Power dissipation	Gain		Maximum signal-level range		Impedance (most usual circuit configuration)	
				Power, db	Current	Collector voltage	Collector current	Input	Output
PNP† alloy junction transistor	Power type	4–700 kc	1–100 watts	20–40	5–90	10–100	0.5–30 amp	1–100 ohms	5 k–200 ohms
	Audio type	10 kc–5 mc	10–300 mw	30–60	15–250	5–70	6–300 ma	200–3,500 ohms	70–5 k
	HF type	1–20 mc	50–200 mw	30–50	10–300	15–30	10–100 ma	100–4,000 ohms	100–5 k
PNP† drift transistor	Diffused base	50–2,000 mc	30–700 mw	30–40	10–100	20–30	10–100 ma	50–1,500 ohms	100–10 k
Surface barrier transistor	Microalloy diffused base	50–400 mc	10–30 mw	30–40	15–40	5–20	5–50 ma	50–500 ohms	70–25 k
Field-effect transistor	Unipolar type	~100 mc	300 mw	15–25	......	30	5 ma	1 megohm	100 k
Esaki tunnel diode	Germanium type	100–4,000 mc	10–200 mw	......	......	0.1–0.5	5–200 ma	Minimum: 0.2 ohms on, 15 ohms off Maximum: 10 ohm on, 500 ohms off	
PNPN-controlled rectifier	....	~1 mc	0.2–3.0 watts	......	......	30–200	1.0 amp	100 k off, ≈3 ohms on	
Variable capacity diode	Parametric amplifier type	>100,000 mc	100 mw	......	......	3.0	......	Typical capacity variation $3 \rightarrow 1 \; \mu\mu f$	

† NPN types have similar characteristics but are slightly faster due to the higher mobility of the electrons which are the operating current carriers in this case.

Table 1.1 summarizes typical operational values of the characteristics of most of the devices just described. The values given in this table are current values and will undoubtedly be surpassed sooner or later as the art develops. The purpose of including such a table is to give the uninitiated reader a basis of comparison between different semiconductor devices.

At present, various forms of the drift transistor are the highest frequency transistors. The Esaki tunnel diode shows very high frequency switching characteristics, and

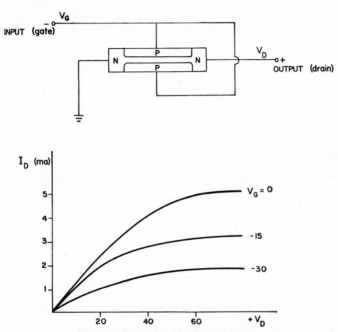

Fig. 1.9. Typical field-effect transistor.

because of its negative resistance, it can be used also as an amplifier. Variable-capacitance diodes can be used in microwave carrier systems for parametric amplification.

An unusually large range of power-dissipating capacity is listed for the alloy-junction triode. The highest power dissipation is obtained by directly alloying the collector junction to a massive heat sink, usually a copper post, which in turn is cooled by external means. This arrangement is inconvenient to use in many circuits. A somewhat lower power dissipation can be achieved by attaching the heat sink to the emitter or the base. Such structures are in many ways more convenient. In all power units the somewhat larger collector junction area and the distributed capacitance of the heat sink add appreciably to the effective capacitance of the unit so that the highest frequency response listed is not compatible with the highest powers listed.

1.6. Metal Interface Amplifier.[18] This device is a three-terminal semiconductor amplifier in which a surface barrier is formed between a thin (about 100-Å) deposited film of aluminum and an N-type germanium wafer. Upon the aluminum film a very thin oxide layer is formed and a small gold spot is deposited to form an injecting electrode. By analogy with a conventional transistor structure, the N-type wafer forms the collector region, the aluminum metal forms the base region, and the gold spot takes the place of the emitter region. The N-type germanium is biased positively with respect to the base, thus reverse-biasing the surface barrier and forming a conventional collector barrier.   The gold spot is biased negatively, and if the oxide barrier between the gold and the aluminum is thin enough, electrons will tunnel through it and enter the aluminum with significantly greater than thermal velocity.   Since the aluminum is quite thin, most of these tunnel-injected electrons will fly right through the aluminum without making a scattering collision and arrive at the collector barrier. Those electrons with energies greater than the surface-barrier height will be collected in the normal manner.   This operation is seen to be of the same nature as that of a conventional transistor except that the injection is achieved by a tunneling process and the base region is traversed by direct flight of the fast electrons rather than by diffusion or drift.   The range of operating voltages, currents, and frequencies is about the same as that of a conventional transistor.

REFERENCES

1. Bardeen, J., and W. H. Brattain: The Transistor, A Semiconductor Triode, *Phys. Rev.*, vol. 74, pp. 230–231, July 15, 1948.
2. Ryder, R. M., and R. J. Kircher: Some Circuit Aspects of the Transistor, *Bell System Tech. J.*, vol. 28, pp. 367–410, July, 1949.
3. A wide range of junction transistor characteristics is given in Sec. 11.
4. Wulfsberg, Carl N.: Zener-voltage Breakdown Uses in Silicon Diodes, *Electronics*, vol. 28, pp. 182–192, December, 1955.
5. Esaki, Leo: New Phenomenon in Narrow Germanium P-N Junctions, *Phys. Rev.*, vol. 109, pp. 603–604, Jan. 15, 1958.
6. Shea, R. F.: "Principles of Transistor Circuits," pp. 467–469, John Wiley & Sons, Inc., New York, 1953.
7. Uhlir, Jr., A.: The Potential of Semiconductor Diodes in High Frequency Communications, *Proc. IRE*, vol. 46, pp. 1099–1115, June, 1958.
8. Teal, G. K., M. Sparks, and E. Buehler: Growth of Germanium Single Crystals Containing P-N Junctions, *Phys. Rev.*, vol. 81, pp. 637–638, Feb. 15, 1951.
9. Hall, R. N., and W. C. Dunlap, Jr.: P-N Junctions Prepared by Impurity Diffusion, *Phys. Rev.*, vol. 80, pp. 467–468, Nov. 1, 1950.
10. Pearson, G. L., and C. S. Fuller: Silicon P-N Junction Power Rectifiers and Lightning Protectors, *Proc. IRE*, vol. 42, p. 760, April, 1954.
11. Bradley, W. E.: Principles of the Surface Barrier Transistor, *Proc. IRE*, vol. 41, pp. 1702–1720, December, 1953.
12. Rittman, A. D., G. C. Messenger, R. A. Williams, and E. Zimmerman: Microalloy Transistor, *IRE Trans. on Electron Devices*, vol. ED-5, pp. 49–54, April, 1958.
13. Wallace, Jr., R. L., L. G. Schimpf, and E. Dickten: A Junction Transistor Tetrode for High Frequency Use, *Proc. IRE*, vol. 40, pp. 1395–1400, November, 1952.
14. Shockley, W., M. Sparks, and G. K. Teal: P-N Junction Transistors, *Phys. Rev.*, vol. 83, pp. 151–162, July 1, 1951.
15. Mackintosh, I. M.: The Electrical Characteristics of Silicon P-N-P-N Triodes, *Proc. IRE*, vol. 46, pp. 1229–1235, June, 1958.
16. Aldrich, R. W., and N. Holonyak, Jr.: Multiterminal P-N-P-N Switches, *Proc. IRE*, vol. 46, pp. 1236–1239, June, 1958.
17. Shockley, W.: A Unipolar "Field Effect" Transistor, *Proc. IRE*, vol. 40, pp. 1365–1376, November, 1952.
18. Spratt, J. P., R. F. Schwarz, and W. M. Kane: Hot Electrons in Metal Films: Injection and Collection, *Phys. Rev. Letters*, vol. 6, pp. 341–342, Apr. 1, 1961.

Section 2

ELECTRONIC CONDUCTION IN SOLIDS

L. P. Hunter

IBM Corporation, Poughkeepsie, N.Y.

An attempt will be made to give an intuitive understanding of the physical basis of electronic conduction in solids. A rigorous presentation of this subject exists in several standard texts.[1,2] We shall proceed by relating the familiar orbital electronic structure of the atom to the electronic band structure used to account for the electronic properties of solids.

2.1. Atoms, Molecules, and Crystals. A familiar model of the atom consists of a centrally located positively charged nucleus surrounded by electrons in orbits analogous to the planetary orbits of the solar system. These individual electron orbits are associated with discrete values of total energy of the atom. We shall consider the zero of electronic potential energy to be that of an electron at rest an infinite distance from the nucleus.

Since an electron carries a negative charge, the potential energy of the atom will become negative as the electron is brought from infinity toward the positively charged nucleus. It turns out that the kinetic energy of motion of the electron in its orbit around the nucleus is numerically equal to just one-half of the potential energy of the electron in the electrostatic field of the nucleus at the position of the orbit. This is true for circular orbits, and for noncircular orbits it is true of the time averages of the kinetic and potential energies. Since the kinetic energy is positive and the potential energy negative, it is clear that the total energy of the atom must be reduced by an amount equal to the kinetic energy of the electron in its orbit when the electron returns to a bound orbit from its ionized position an infinite distance away.

The diagram of Fig. 2.1 shows a familiar orbital model of the atom and an energy-level diagram of the same atom. The vertical positions of the horizontal lines represent the levels of energy of the atom corresponding to the various electronic orbits. The lengths of these lines correspond to the diameter of the orbits. The curves bounding the system of horizontal lines therefore represent a plot of the total energy of the atom as a function of the radius of the electronic orbit.

Not all values of energy or orbital diameter are possible. Modern quantum mechanics provides a method of determining which discrete values of energy are

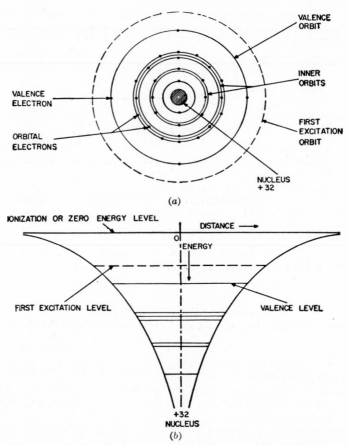

FIG. 2.1. (a) Simplified orbital model of an atom and (b) energy-level diagram of the same atom.

allowed to the orbital electrons. These particular allowed values are the ones illustrated in the energy-level diagrams by the positions of the horizontal lines. All the allowed energy levels do not necessarily contain electrons. Associated with every atom there are a number of orbital electrons just sufficient to cancel the positive charge of the nucleus. Since the total energy of the system is lower, the closer the electrons get to the nucleus, it is clear that these electrons will fill up the lowest energy levels, leaving the higher levels vacant. All the electrons will not occupy the lowest energy level, however, because of a law of physics, called the Pauli exclusion principle, which will not allow two electrons to occupy exactly the same energy level in any closed system.

If two identical atoms are brought together to form a diatomic molecule, an energy-level diagram shown in Fig. 2.2 may be drawn for the combination. It will now be noted that there are two closely spaced energy levels near the same values of energy for which single levels existed in the single isolated atom. This is the result of a coupling process and is similar to the result obtained when two oscillators of identical frequency are coupled so that the system now has two modes of oscillation of slightly different frequencies.

Another feature of the energy-level diagram of the diatomic molecule is that the highest energy levels are seen to be shared by both atoms. In the case of the diatomic molecule, the energy levels are filled with electrons to a level somewhat above the lowest level common to the two atoms. This means that the electrons in the common levels are not localized on either one of the atoms but have orbits allowing them to

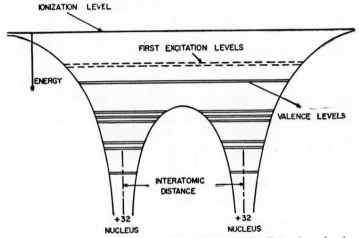

FIG. 2.2. One-dimensional energy-level diagram of a diatomic molecule.

range throughout the molecule and serve to bind the two atoms together. In any chemical system the electrons which bind atoms together are called valence electrons, and the energy levels which they fill are called valence levels. The unfilled energy levels lying above the valence levels in the individual atom or diatomic molecule are called the excitation levels of the atom or molecule. These levels may contain electrons for brief periods of time when electrons from the valence or lower-lying levels are raised in energy by the absorption of energy from light, from some bombarding particle, or from the thermal motion of the atom centers.

If a large number of identical atoms are brought together to form a solid crystal, each of the energy levels of the individual atom becomes a band of energy levels for the system of atoms comprising the crystal. In each band there is a number of energy levels approximately equal to the number of atoms in the crystal. In Fig. 2.3 is shown an energy-level diagram illustrating the bands of energy levels in such a crystal.

2.2. Insulators, Conductors, and Semiconductors. It is seen that the band of energy levels arising from the valence levels of the atom extends throughout the crystal. The next-higher band of levels arising from the lowest excitation level of the individual atom is shown to be separated from the valence band by an interval of energy in which there are no allowed energy levels. If the valence band is completely filled with electrons and there are no closely adjacent vacant energy levels, there is no possibility of changing the energy of any of the electrons in the valence band by small amounts. This means that the electrons of the valence band, even though they are free to range throughout the crystal, cannot be accelerated with an externally applied electric field to carry current. The motion of the electrons in a filled valence band is such that there is a detailed balancing of charge flow at all points in the crystal and no net current is carried. A crystal in which these conditions obtain is, therefore, an insulator.

If the energy gap between the top of the valence band and the bottom of the band of excitation levels (usually called the conduction band) is large, there will be a negligibly small number of valence electrons excited by thermal vibration to the conduction band and the crystal will be a good insulator. If, on the other hand, the energy gap is very small or does not exist at all (the latter case corresponds to the overlapping in energy of the valence and conduction bands), there will be vacant

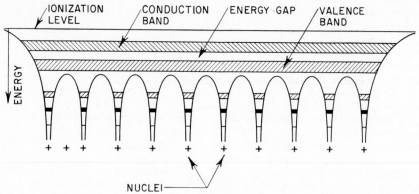

FIG. 2.3. One-dimensional energy-level diagram of a crystal.

energy levels closely adjacent to filled energy levels. It is, therefore, possible by the action of an external electric field to change the energy of some of the valence electrons by accelerating them and cause the crystal to carry a current. Such a crystal is a conducting crystal of which a metal is a good example. Still another way in which metallic conductivity may be realized is to have a valence band which is only partially filled with electrons. In such a case the overlapping of the valence and conduction bands is not necessary to obtain vacant energy levels closely adjacent to the filled levels. This is believed to be the situation in the alkali metals.

If the energy gap is intermediate between these two extremes, there will be a few electrons thermally excited to the conduction band, leaving a few vacancies in the valence band so that there are a limited number of electrons capable of cooperating with an external electric field and the crystal is capable of carrying an electric current. Such a crystal shows a resistivity several orders of magnitude higher than the resistivity of most metallic conductors and is called a semiconductor.

Practically, one can define the difference between conductors and semiconductors by the sign of their temperature coefficient of resistance. Semiconductors have a negative temperature coefficient of resistance over an appreciable range of temperature, and conductors have a positive coefficient at all temperatures. The source of this distinction can be understood by considering that there are two ways in which temperature can affect the interaction of the electrons of a solid with an external electric field. Specifically, temperature can change the total number of electrons available for conduction, and it can change their average speed of motion in a unit electric field. In a conductor with no energy gap in its electronic band structure at the valence-electron level, the number of electrons available for conduction cannot be changed appreciably. The dominant effect, then, is the scattering of the current-carrying electrons by collisions with atoms of the crystal. Since the electronic energy-band structure is determined by the positions of the atoms of the crystal in a perfect lattice, the atoms will not scatter electrons so long as the crystal lattice remains perfect. Any deviation from lattice perfection, such as thermal vibrations of the atoms or chemical impurities, will scatter electrons. As temperature is increased, the atoms vibrate about their equilibrium positions with larger and larger amplitudes. Thus at higher temperatures they are able to scatter moving electrons more effectively. This means that the average velocity of the electrons carrying a current in the material decreases as the temperature is increased and the resistivity increases, thus showing a positive temperature coefficient. In a semiconductor, since there is a finite energy gap between the valence and conduction bands, the number of electrons excited from the valence to the conduction band increases with temperature. This means that the total number of electrons available for the conduction process also increases with temperature. While it is true that these electrons are scattered more effectively at higher temperatures by the lattice atoms of the crystal and the scattering mean free path steadily decreases with increasing temperature, this effect is overcome by the effect of the rapidly increasing number of available electrons. It will be shown later that the number of electrons excited to the conduction band increases exponentially with temperature. We can then expect that the resistivity will decrease exponentially with increasing temperature, showing a negative temperature coefficient.

2.3. Fields and Energy Bands. We shall now discuss in some detail the effect of an externally applied electric field on the energy-band representation which we have developed. Our convention in drawing energy-level diagrams is one in which the energy of the system is lowered as electrons fall down toward the sources of positive potential drawn at the bottom of the diagram. If we now produce an electric field by effectively grounding one end of our crystal and applying a positive voltage to the other end, we can represent this field by tilting the energy-level diagram downward toward the positive end of the crystal, as shown at the top of Fig. 2.4. If the crystal is a conducting crystal with a band of energy levels only partially filled with electrons, these electrons will be accelerated toward the positive end of the crystal. It is a result of quantum mechanics that the kinetic energy of an electron goes to zero at a band edge.† This means that an electron must move up in the band in order to be accelerated. In our tilted-band representation, an electron will, therefore, tend to remain at a given horizontal level as it is accelerated. In the normal conduction process an electron will not move very far under the influence of the electric field until it suffers a scattering collision with one of the atoms of the crystal. This scattering collision will cause a reduction in the kinetic energy of the electron, causing it to move toward the lower band edge in the energy-level diagram. The net effect of the electric field plus the scattering process is to move the electron distribution slightly away from the lower band edge as the crystal carries an electric current.

The same type of arguments apply in the case of very localized electric fields. In Fig. 2.4 are shown two types of such local fields often encountered in semiconductors. The one in the center of the figure represents the bending of the energy bands due to the field of a dipole layer of charge on the surface of the crystal.[3] In this example it can be seen that an electron in the conduction band approaching the surface at constant total energy E_1 would slow down and be reflected at the point A as it reached the lower edge of the conduction band. In the example shown at the bottom of the figure the energy bands are distorted by a region of positive charge located in the interior of the crystal. In this example there is an energy minimum in the bottom of the conduction band which would tend to act as a trap for electrons. Such a trap can be considered much the same as the field due to the nucleus of an individual atom.

† This is hard to reconcile with previous statements about the kinetic energy of electrons in circular orbits, but the proof is beyond the scope of this book.

There will be a few discrete energy levels at the bottom of the trap rather than the high density of levels found higher up in the conduction band. When these levels are filled with just enough electrons to neutralize the positive charge originally producing the deformation of the bands, the deformation will no longer be present and the band edges will resume their normal positions.

2.4. Impurities in Semiconductors. We are now in a position to discuss the role of chemical impurities in semiconductors.[4,5] In order to make our model as explicit as possible, we shall consider the example of a single crystal of germanium with a trace

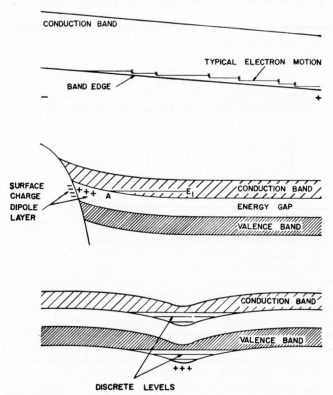

FIG. 2.4. Influence of electric charge on the form of energy bands.

of arsenic impurity. Germanium has four valence electrons and therefore falls in the IV column of the periodic system of the elements. Arsenic has five valence electrons and falls in the V column. When an arsenic atom replaces a germanium atom in the germanium crystal lattice, four of its five valence electrons are used in binding the arsenic to its neighboring germanium atoms. The extra valence electron, which is not used in the bonds between atoms, turns out to be very lightly held to the arsenic atom and is easily given up to the energy levels of the conduction band. Without its fifth valence electron the arsenic ion represents a localized positive charge in the interior of the crystal of the kind considered above. The positive charge of this ion warps the edges of the valence and conduction bands in the manner shown at the top of Fig. 2.5 and gives rise to a few rather extensive energy levels just below the edge of the conduction band. When the lowest impurity energy level is vacant, the illustrated bending of the conduction-band edges results in the reflection or scattering of electrons if they closely approach the impurity atom. This form of scattering called ionized impurity scattering is very important in semiconductor behavior. If this impurity level is occupied by an electron, the perturbation of the conduction-band edges is removed and the impurity atom is little more effective in scattering conduction electrons than is a normal germanium lattice atom. In most instances the impurity levels remain unoccupied at normal temperatures and are filled by electrons only at temperatures within a few degrees of absolute zero.

A chemical impurity with excess valence electrons giving rise to the kind of energy level described above is called a donor impurity, since it easily donates electrons to the conduction band. Filled energy levels closely adjacent to the bottom of the conduction band are called donor levels. Since the energy gap between the donor levels and the conduction band is much less than the energy gap between the valence band and

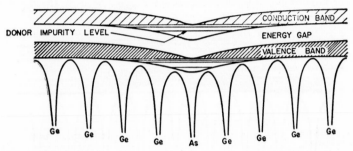

FIG. 2.5. Energy-band diagram of a crystal showing the effect of a donor-impurity atom located in a normal lattice position.

the conduction band, the donor levels will yield their electrons to the conduction band by thermal excitation at much lower temperatures than are required to excite electrons appreciably from the valence band to the conduction band. At an intermediate temperature, therefore, the donor levels will be completely ionized (having given up all their electrons to the conduction band) while the valence band remains practically filled. This means that in this temperature range there is an almost constant number of electrons available for the conduction process, since there are very few electrons excited from the valence band to the conduction band compared with the number of donor-impurity atoms. The temperature coefficient of resistance will depend only upon the scattering process and will therefore be positive. Such conductivity in semiconductors is called extrinsic conductivity. The conductivity due to the excitation of electrons from the valence to the conduction band is called intrinsic conductivity. In any practical semiconductor, both types of conductivity are exhibited in different temperature ranges. Extrinsic conductivity always occurs at a lower temperature than the intrinsic conductivity. A semiconductor with donor impurities conducts current exclusively with electrons in the conduction band in its extrinsic range and is therefore called an N-type semiconductor since the conducting particles are negative.

Continuing with the example of germanium, we shall now consider the effect of introducing a chemical impurity from the III column of the periodic table, such as gallium. Gallium has three valence electrons. When gallium replaces a germanium atom in the germanium crystal lattice, it is able to saturate its bonds to only three of its four nearest germanium neighbors. It is, therefore, quite ready to accept an electron from any available source in order to saturate the bond with the fourth neighbor. In Fig. 2.6 is shown an energy-level diagram for a gallium impurity in a germanium crystal. At ordinary temperatures the gallium atom has captured an extra electron from the valence band in order to saturate its bonds with its neighboring germanium atoms.

The field of this negative ion warps the band edges as shown. An extensive impurity energy level is found just above the top of the valence band and contains the extra electron captured by the gallium impurity. At very low temperatures this level loses its electron to the valence band. The empty level thus produced represents the unsaturated bond of the fourth nearest neighbor of the gallium. Such an energy level close to the top of the valence band is called an acceptor level. Since this energy level is separated from the valence band by an energy gap which is quite small compared with the energy gap between the valence and conduction bands, it is relatively easy to excite an electron thermally from the valence band into this vacant energy level and thus satisfy the bonding requirements of the gallium impurity. This process leaves a vacant energy level in the valence band. In the extrinsic temperature range where thermal excitation across the full energy gap is negligible and yet substantially all the acceptor impurities are ionized (the acceptor levels filled by thermal excitation

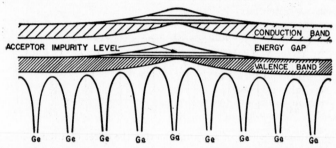

Fig. 2.6. Energy-band diagram of a crystal showing the effect of an acceptor-impurity atom located in a normal lattice position.

from the valence band), the number of vacant valence-band energy levels will be equal to the number of acceptor impurity atoms in the crystal. These vacant energy levels allow current to be carried by the electrons in the valence band, since the electrons of the valence band can now change their energy in cooperation with an external electric field.

The process of exciting a valence electron into one of these vacant energy levels obviously leaves the same total number of vacant energy levels in the valence band but changes their energy distribution. Remembering that all the electrons of the valence band are the electrons which are involved in holding the atoms of the crystal together, it is clear that a vacant energy level in the valence band may be considered to correspond to an unsaturated bond between two specific atoms of the crystal. If an electron moves in cooperation with an external field from some neighboring atom into the position which saturates the particular bond in question, the vacancy now appears in one of the bonds of the neighboring atom. If this replacement process is continued, it represents effectively the continuous motion of the vacancy under the influence of the applied electric field. It turns out that this process can best be described in terms of the motion of the vacancies (called holes) rather than in terms of the motion of the replacement electrons. These vacancies, or holes, then appear to have the property of particles which have the same mass as the electrons but with a positive rather than a negative charge. A semiconductor which in its extrinsic range carries current by means of hole conduction is called a P-type semiconductor.

2.5. Thermal Excitation and the Fermi Level. We shall now consider the thermal excitation of electrons from the valence band to the conduction band in more detail.[6] The Pauli exclusion principle is incorporated into statistical mechanics in a special branch of statistics called Fermi-Dirac statistics.[7] The probability that a given

energy level, or quantum state, is occupied by an electron is given by the so-called
Fermi function of Eq. (2.1):

$$f(\epsilon) = \frac{1}{e^{(\epsilon-\epsilon_0)/kT} + 1} \tag{2.1}$$

where ϵ is energy, k is Boltzmann's constant, ϵ_0 is the so-called Fermi energy or Fermi
level (to be defined later), and T is absolute temperature.

This function is plotted [$f(\epsilon)$ versus ϵ] for several values of temperature T in Fig. 2.7.
In the region of transition of the function,
the energy interval corresponding to kT is
indicated. At room temperature, kT corresponds to an energy of about 0.025 electron volt. (An electron volt is the kinetic
energy that an electron has when accelerated through a potential difference of 1
volt.) From the figure it is clear that the
region of transition of the Fermi probability function occupies an energy range
comparable to kT evaluated for the specific
temperature under consideration. To
apply this statistical function to our problem of determining the number of electrons
excited from the valence band to the conduction band of a semiconductor, we must
know the density of energy levels, or states,
in each of the two bands. The integrated
product of the Fermi occupation-probability function and the density function
over the conduction band will give the cor-

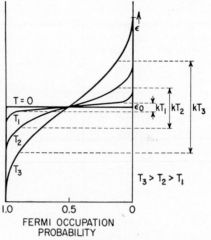

FIG. 2.7. Effect of temperature on the
Fermi occupation-probability function.

rect number of electrons excited across the energy gap at the temperature for which the
probability function is specified.

In Fig. 2.8 the product of the density and probability functions is illustrated
graphically.[8] The ordinate of this diagram is energy ϵ, as is customary in energy-level
diagrams. On the abscissas are plotted energy-level density, probability, and electron
and hole densities. Starting from left to right in the figure, the density of energy
levels or states is multiplied by the Fermi occupation-probability function to give the
density of electrons. The physical fact that every electron which is found in the conduction band has come from the valence band and left a corresponding vacancy there
is used to fix the position of the Fermi probability function relative to the density
function. It is clear that, if the energy-level density functions of the two bands are
identical in magnitude and symmetrical in form about the energy gap, the position of
the probability function will be such that the probability of occupation is one-half in
the exact center of the energy gap. This follows from the fact that the Fermi function
is antisymmetric about the one-half probability point. This one-half probability
point is called the Fermi level and occurs for $\epsilon = \epsilon_0$. Such a situation will give a
number of occupied levels in the conduction band exactly equal to the number of
vacant levels in the valence band. This corresponds to the physical situation. The
density-of-state functions are shown on the electron-density plot of Fig. 2.8 as dashed
curves. In the valence band the difference between the electron density and the
density of states is the density of vacancies or holes. This density is plotted at the
extreme right of the figure.

If the valence band, for example, contains twice the density of states or levels that
the conduction band contains, the Fermi level will of necessity be somewhat above the

center of the energy gap in order to maintain the number of electrons in the conduction band equal to the number of vacancies in the valence band.   If the conduction band contains a higher density of states than does the valence band, the situation will be reversed and the Fermi level will lie somewhat below the center of the energy gap. If reference is made to Fig. 2.7, it is clear that in all three cases mentioned above the total number of electrons in the conduction band and the vacancies in the valence band will increase with increasing temperature, since the region of transition of the probability function covers a greater energy range at higher temperatures.

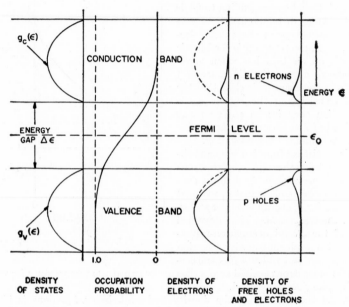

FIG. 2.8. Graphical determination of the number of free current carriers in an intrinsic semiconductor.

The movement of the Fermi level with temperature is different for the three cases. In the symmetrical case, because of the symmetry the Fermi level will not move with temperature.   In the case of higher density of states in the valence band, the Fermi level, which is located somewhat above the center of the energy gap at all temperatures, will tend to move away from the center of the energy gap with increasing temperature.   In the opposite case where the conduction band has the larger density of states, the Fermi level will also move away from the center of the energy gap with increasing temperature but will always be located somewhat below the center of the gap.

Calculating the product of the density function and the Fermi probability function, we find the number of electrons n in the conduction band to be

$$n = \int_{\epsilon_1}^{\epsilon_2} \frac{g_c(\epsilon)\,d\epsilon}{e^{(\epsilon-\epsilon_0)/kT} + 1} \tag{2.2}$$

where $g_c(\epsilon)$ represents the density of states in the conduction band and ϵ_1 and ϵ_2 are, respectively, the lower and upper edges of this band.   Under certain reasonable assumptions,[9] this integral can be evaluated to give

$$n = \left(\frac{2\pi m_n kT}{h^2}\right)^{3/2} e^{-(\epsilon_1 - \epsilon_0)/kT} \tag{2.3}$$

where m_n is the mass of the electron and h is Planck's constant. The number of electrons n is seen to decrease exponentially with the difference in energy between the Fermi level and the band edge.

Similarly, the number of holes p is given by

$$p = \left(\frac{2\pi m_p kT}{h^2}\right)^{3/2} e^{(\epsilon_3 - \epsilon_0)/kT} \tag{2.4}$$

where ϵ_3 is the energy at the top of the valence band and m_p is the mass of the holes. In a pure semiconductor in equilibrium $n = p$, showing that the Fermi level ϵ_0 must lie midway between the band edges in the center of the energy gap if $m_n = m_p$. This latter equality exists only under the assumption that the density functions in the valence and conduction bands are symmetrical about the energy gap.

From Eqs. (2.3) and (2.4) it follows that the product np depends exponentially on the gap width

$$np = \left(\frac{2\pi kT}{h^2}\right)^3 (m_n m_p)^{3/2} e^{-\Delta\epsilon/kT} \tag{2.5}$$

where $\Delta\epsilon = (\epsilon_1 - \epsilon_3)$, the energy-gap width.

The foregoing considerations apply to the intrinsic conductivity of semiconductors and show that the number of carriers available in the intrinsic-conductivity range increases exponentially with temperature.

We shall digress at this point to show just how the conductivity of the semiconductor depends upon the number of current carriers available. If a bar of semiconductor has a current I flowing in it due to a voltage V, we can write: I = number of charge carriers × charge/carrier × average velocity/carrier. If only electrons are present, $I = nq\bar{v}_n$, and if only holes are present, $I = pq\bar{v}_p$. If both are present,

$$I = nq\bar{v}_n + pq\bar{v}_p$$

The average velocities for electrons and holes $\bar{v}_n$ and $\bar{v}_p$ can be expressed as the average velocity per unit electric field μ_n and μ_p times the applied field $V/l = \mathcal{E}$, giving the general expression $I = (nq\mu_n + pq\mu_p)\mathcal{E}$. The definition of conductivity is $\sigma = I/\mathcal{E}$, giving for intrinsic conductivity

$$\sigma = nq\mu_n + pq\mu_p \tag{2.6}$$

From Eq. (2.6) it is clear that conductivity is directly proportional to the number of carriers n and p. In the case of an extrinsic N-type sample, $n \gg p$ so that $\sigma = nq\mu_n$. In the case of an extrinsic P-type sample, $p \gg n$ so that $\sigma = pq\mu_p$. The μ_n and μ_p are called the mobilities of electrons and holes, respectively, and depend on the various scattering processes encountered by these particles as they move through the crystal lattice.

We shall now consider the effects of donor impurities. The energy levels of donor-impurity atoms lie in the energy gap just beneath the conduction band. The density of these levels is determined by the density of the donor-impurity atoms and usually ranges from 10^{-6} to 10^{-9} of the density of normal semiconductor atoms (see Sec. 6). In Fig. 2.9 is shown the graphical representation of the product of the Fermi probability function and the density-of-states function, including the donor states. The diagram is drawn for some temperature in the extrinsic range where the occupation probability of the donor states is low and most of the donor electrons are found in the conduction band. As is shown by the figure, the Fermi level is considerably below the level of the donor states although it is appreciably above the center of the energy gap. In this case detailed balancing of charges must be considered between the donor states and both the conduction and valence bands. In other words, the electrons found in the conduction band must equal the vacancies in both the valence band and the donor states. This consideration determines the position of the Fermi level and thus of the Fermi distribution function.

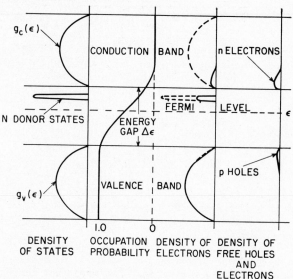

Fig. 2.9. Graphical determination of the number of free current carriers in an impurity semiconductor.

We shall consider the variation of temperature, beginning with absolute zero and going up to a temperature at which the semiconductor is well into its intrinsic conductivity range. At absolute zero all the donor states and the levels of the valence band are occupied. From Fig. 2.7 it is seen that the Fermi function exhibits a discontinuous change from unit occupation probability to zero occupation probability at the energy ϵ_0 for the absolute zero of temperature. This means that the Fermi level at absolute zero must lie somewhere between the donor states and the bottom of the conduction band. As soon as the temperature is raised ever so slightly above absolute zero, the Fermi level must be found slightly above the donor states, since their density is less by a factor of 10^8 than the density of states in the conduction band. This assumes that the donor impurities are present in a concentration of about 1 part in 10^8. As temperature is further increased, the donor states are rapidly emptied and the Fermi level moves below the level of the donor states and approaches the center of the energy gap (provided the density functions of the conduction and valence bands are equal and symmetrical about the energy gap). For a wide range of temperature, even though the Fermi level is steadily dropping toward the center of the energy gap, the actual occupation values of the donor states and the conduction band will not change appreciably. This corresponds to the extrinsic conductivity range. When the Fermi level approaches closely to the center of the energy gap, an appreciable number of electrons will begin to be excited from the valence band to the conduction band, and once this number becomes large compared with the number of donor states, the semiconductor will be well into its intrinsic range of conductivity, In Fig. 2.10 the logarithm of resistivity of a typical sample of germanium is plotted against the reciprocal of the absolute temperature, with the main conductivity regions indicated. Along the top of the figure is a plot of the position of the Fermi level as a function of the same scale of reciprocal of absolute temperature.

In the case of a P-type sample in which the impurities give rise to acceptor energy levels located in the energy gap near the top of the valence band, a similar discussion applies, and it can be easily deduced that the Fermi level starts at absolute zero just

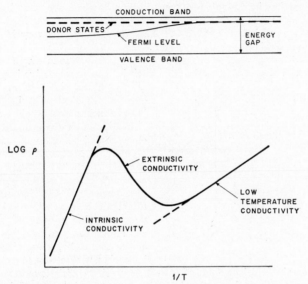

Fig. 2.10. Correlation of the position of the Fermi level with the conductivity regions of a semiconductor.

below the acceptor states and proceeds toward the center of the energy gap as temperature is raised. If both donor and acceptor impurities are present in a single crystal, the position of the Fermi level will be determined by the same considerations, with the understanding that detailed balancing of electrons must be considered between all four energy-level systems, the valence band, the acceptor states, the donor states, and the conduction band. The type of extrinsic conductivity which will be observed will depend simply upon which of the two types (donor or acceptor) of impurity states are in the majority. To a first approximation the sample will behave as though only the majority impurity were present in a concentration equal to the difference between the numbers of majority and minority impurities present.

2.6. Low-temperature Conductivity. As mentioned above, the Fermi level near absolute zero will lie between the donor impurity states and the bottom of the conduction band and the energy range of the transition of the occupation probability from unity to zero is very narrow (even compared with the energy gap between the position of the donor states and the edge of the conduction band). All this is a representation of the fact that essentially all the conduction electrons have dropped down into the donor impurity states and there are very very few left in the conduction band to carry current. The resistivity of the material at these temperatures may be 8 or 10 orders of magnitude higher than it is at room temperature. In Fig. 2.10 the rise in resistivity at low temperatures can be seen at the right-hand side of the curve.

2.6a. Impurity-band Conduction. It is a curious fact that the resistivity of most semiconductors does not increase indefinitely as absolute zero is approached. Instead there is a leveling off of the resistivity in the range of liquid helium temperatures. This phenomenon is usually attributed to impurity-band conduction.[10]

If the density of impurities is sufficiently great for their electrical fields to overlap appreciably as do those of the semiconductor atoms (see Fig. 2.3), then an impurity band of energy levels can be formed just as the valence band of the regular semiconductor was formed. In such a case there will probably always be some vacant impurity states energetically very close to the filled ones, so that a current can be carried in the impurity band without requiring ionization of the impurity centers to produce free carriers in the valence or conduction bands. Because of the relatively large separation of the impurity atoms the mobility of electrons moving between them in the impurity band is very very low. This accounts for the very high resistivity values observed in this conductivity region.

2.6b. Impact Ionization of Impurities. At low temperatures where essentially all the free holes and electrons have dropped back into their respective impurity states, it is possible to ionize them into the valence or the conduction band by impact ionization in an avalanche process.[11,12]

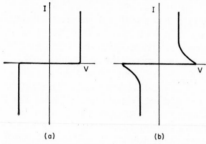

FIG. 2.11. Typical characteristic curves of a cryosar.

In Fig. 2.11 are shown two volt-ampere characteristics of uniform wafers of P-type germanium. Both of these wafers have ohmic contacts to their opposite surfaces, and both are reasonably uniform in the distribution of the impurities within them. The general breakdown phenomenon shown can be explained by assuming that as voltage is applied across the wafer, a certain critical field is reached where any stray hole or free electron can attain sufficient energy between scattering collisions so that it is capable of ionizing one of the filled acceptor impurity centers by impact. This then creates a second free carrier and the avalanche proceeds. Such an explanation is sufficient for the type of breakdown shown in Fig. 2.11a, but of course, it will not explain the type shown in Fig. 2.11b. Here the breakdown voltage is greater than the sustaining voltage, which results in a negative resistance region of the characteristic reminiscent of a gas discharge. At the present time no satisfactory explanation of this effect has been given.

Empirical methods of producing material which shows this negative resistance characteristic have been found, and devices called cryosars have been made from it.[13] The breakdown fields observed range between 40 and 200 volts/cm, while sustaining fields as low as 20 volts/cm have been found.

2.7. Radiation Effects. Some types of nuclear radiation have a marked effect on the electrical conductivity of semiconductors.[14] When an energetic nuclear particle of appreciable mass (such as a fast neutron) penetrates a semiconductor, it knocks many atoms out of their normal lattice positions by its impact. Most of these knocked-on atoms find their way back to normal lattice positions, but there are always a few lattice sites left vacant and perhaps a few atoms left in interstitial positions. If either of these lattice imperfections are capable of trapping either holes or electrons, they will have a marked effect on the electrical conductivity of the material.

In germanium of moderate resistivity it is observed that irradiation with high-energy particles always seems to produce electrically active P-type centers. This means that P-type material will lower its resistivity while N-type material will tend to convert to P-type. For very low resistivity P-type material (less than 0.1 ohm-cm) the resistivity seems to increase upon irradiation. In short, it seems that all germanium samples tend to approach a final saturation P-type state corresponding to about 10^{16} acceptors/cm³ when irradiated at room temperature.

This behavior has been explained[15] on the basis of a model which assumes that lattice vacancies and interstitial atoms are created in equal numbers by such irradiation and that each has associated with it two energy levels. The levels of the interstitial atom are widely separated in the energy gap, one near the conduction band edge and one near the valence band edge. Both are filled with an electron if the interstitial atom is to be electrically neutral. The lattice vacancy also has two associated levels which are close together below the center of the energy gap and are empty for electrical neutrality. Of course, in thermal equilibrium at room temperature for N-type material of moderate resistivity (the Fermi level near the center of the gap), the three lower levels will be filled and the upper one vacant, giving rise to singly ionized interstitials and doubly ionized vacancies. The electrons required to fill the levels of each vacancy have come one from the upper interstitial level and one from the conduction band. Taking electrons from the conduction band, of course, increases the resistivity of the N-type sample.

If the material is of moderate P-type resistivity to begin with, the electrons required to fill the levels of each vacancy will come one from the upper interstitial level as before and one from the valence band. Taking electrons from the valence band decreases the resistivity of a P-type sample by increasing the number of holes.

If the material is originally very low resistivity P-type material so that the Fermi level is nearly at the valence band edge, all the vacancy and interstitial levels must be empty and the electrons from the interstitial levels must drop into the valence band as fast as the interstitials are formed. This, of course, will decrease the number of holes available for conduction and increase the resistivity of the P-type material.

The one case in which the formation of vacancies and interstitials will have no effect on the number of conducting particles is the case of P-type material which has a Fermi level midway between the higher vacancy level and the next lower filled level. In this case the electron from the upper interstitial level will fill the lower vacancy level as pairs of vacancies and interstitials are formed, leaving each singly ionized and the position of the Fermi level unchanged. For germanium at room temperature about 3×10^{16} P-type impurities per cubic centimeter seem to place the Fermi level in this position.

When germanium is bombarded with massive particles which have a much shorter mean free path than fast neutrons or electrons, the damage to the crystal seems to consist of very badly distorted regions near the track of the particle in a matrix of relatively undisturbed material. This is, of course, quite different from the formation of relatively uniformly spaced vacancy-interstitial pairs and gives rise to a very complicated spectrum of energy levels and a complicated electrical effect of the same general character.

Table 2.1 compares the effects of various radiations on N-type germanium. An estimate of the time required to convert an N-type sample to P-type material can be obtained by calculating the time required for a given particle flux to produce an integrated total dose equal to the density of donors in the N-type sample divided by the appropriate number from the last column of Table 2.1.

In silicon the behavior is quite different in practice although it is the same in principle. Irradiation of either N-type or P-type material of moderate resistivity tends to increase the resistivity toward a saturation value roughly equal to the intrinsic value. Since silicon has a much larger energy gap than germanium, it is believed that the energy levels associated with a vacancy-interstitial pair are located much more symmetrically around the center of the gap. This is equivalent to the germanium case except that the position of the Fermi level for which no effective change in the number of current carriers takes place is very near the center of the gap. This is a consequence of the symmetry of the energy levels about the center of the gap, since, with such symmetry, it is clear that the center of the gap must lie approximately midway between the higher vacancy level and the next lower filled level. Therefore irradiation of any silicon sample will tend to move the Fermi level toward the center of the gap and the sample will tend toward intrinsic conductivity properties with the exception that the mobility will be significantly lower. The rate of current-carrier removal from irradiated silicon is somewhat greater than for N-type germanium but about the same magnitude.

TABLE 2.1. EFFECT OF RADIATION ON N-TYPE
GERMANIUM AT ROOM TEMPERATURE

Particle	Energy, mev	Number of N centers canceled/incident particle
Electrons...........	3	1.4
Neutrons...........	Reactor average	3.2
Deuterons.........	9	1×10^3
α particles.........	5	5×10^3

In the III-V intermetallic compounds the range of possible effects of radiation are much greater, since vacancies and interstitial atoms can now exist in two species and in the case of reactor irradiation the slow neutrons may cause significant transmutation and thereby chemical doping. Suffice it to say that GaSb shows an effect very similar to that of germanium and InSb shows an inverse effect (i.e., P-type is converted to N-type and N-type material approaches a low saturation resistivity). InSb under irradiation in a reactor shows a strong transmutation effect, since the thermal neutrons are captured by the In, which is then converted to Sn, a donor in the InSb lattice.

REFERENCES

1. Wilson, A. H.: "The Theory of Metals," Cambridge University Press, New York, 1953.
2. Seitz, F.: "The Modern Theory of Solids," chap. 4, McGraw-Hill Book Company, Inc., New York, 1940.
3. Torrey, H. C., and C. A. Whitmer: "Crystal Rectifiers," chap. 4, McGraw-Hill Book Company, Inc., New York, 1948.
4. Slater, J. C.: Electrons in Perturbed Periodic Lattices, *Phys. Rev.*, vol. 76, pp. 1592–1601, Dec. 1, 1949.
5. James, H. M.: Energy Bands and Wave Functions in Periodic Potentials, *Phys. Rev.*, vol. 76, pp. 1602–1610, Dec. 1, 1949.
6. Wilson, A. H.: "The Theory of Metals," chap. 5, Cambridge University Press, New York, 1953.
7. Mayer, J. E., and M. G. Mayer: "Statistical Mechanics," pp. 374–387, John Wiley & Sons, Inc., New York, 1950.
8. Shockley, W.: "Electrons and Holes in Semiconductors," p. 239, D. Van Nostrand Company, Inc., Princeton, N.J., 1951.
9. Seitz, F.: "The Modern Theory of Solids," p. 187, McGraw-Hill Book Company, Inc., New York, 1940.
10. Conwell, E. M.: Impurity Band Conduction in Germanium and Silicon, *Phys. Rev.*, vol. 103, pp. 51–61, July 1, 1956.
11. Sclar, N., and E. Burstein: Impact Ionization of Impurities in Germanium, *J. Phys. Chem. Solids*, vol. 2, pp. 1–23, March, 1957.
12. Koenig, S. H., and G. R. Gunther-Mohr: The Low Temperature Electrical Conductivity of N-type Germanium, *J. Phys. Chem. Solids*, vol. 2, pp. 268–283, 1957.
13. McWhorter, A. L., and R. H. Rediker: The Cryosar—A New Low-temperature Computer Component, *Proc. IRE*, vol. 47, pp. 1207–1213, July, 1959.
14. Crawford, Jr., J. H., and J. W. Cleland: Radiation Effects in Semiconductors, in "Progress in Semiconduction," vol. 2, John Wiley & Sons, Inc., New York, 1957.
15. James, H. M., and K. Lark-Horovitz: Localized Electronic States in Bombarded Semiconductors, *Z. physik. Chem.*, vol. 198, pp. 107–126, 1951.

Section 3

RECTIFICATION IN SOLIDS

L. P. HUNTER

IBM Corporation, Poughkeepsie, N.Y.

Rectification in solids results from the presence of potential barriers at the surface or within the crystalline solids. These barriers inhibit the flow of charged particles within the crystal in such a way that a different total number of charged particles is available for the conduction process, depending upon the direction and magnitude of current flow past the barrier. This process can best be considered by examining energy-level diagrams which include the potential-energy variations of the barrier.[1,2] Barriers may exist at the surface of crystals or in their interior. An example of the surface barrier is shown in the central diagram of Fig. 2.4. In this figure it was shown that an electron of energy E_1 cannot approach closer to the surface than the point A without being reflected by the potential barrier consisting of the bottom edge of the conduction band distorted by the presence of the dipole layer of surface charge.

3.1. Barriers—Metal-Semiconductor Contacts. In Fig. 3.1 is shown a similar barrier at the surface of a semiconductor crystal which is formed by the contact difference of potential between the semiconductor and the metal with which it is placed in contact. At the top of the figure the metal and the semiconductor are shown before the contact is made. It will be noted that the Fermi levels of the two do not fall at

---

† This section supplied by S. L. Miller.

the same value of energy. Once the contact is made and the two materials become a single thermodynamic system, there must be a single Fermi level for the system. This is accomplished by a flow of electrons from the body with the higher Fermi level to the body with the lower Fermi level. These electrons distribute themselves over the surface of the contact between the two bodies, giving rise to a dipole layer of surface charge very similar to that illustrated previously in Fig. 2.4. This barrier is shown at the bottom of Fig. 3.1.

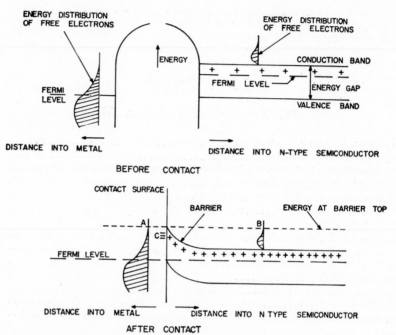

FIG. 3.1. Energy-level diagrams for a metal-semiconductor contact.

The detailed balancing of the charges is best understood by considering the energy distribution of free electrons both in the metal and in the semiconductor. At the top of Fig. 3.1 before the contact between the two substances is made, it is seen that there are free electrons in the semiconductor at higher levels of energy than in the metal. This situation follows directly from the fact that the Fermi level in the semiconductor is higher than in the metal. Since the Fermi level represents the energy at which the probability of occupation is one-half, and since the density of energy levels in the conduction band of the semiconductor and in the metal is approximately the same, the number of electrons at a given distance above the Fermi level in the conduction band should be approximately the same in either the metal or the semiconductor.

When an electrical contact is made as shown at the bottom of Fig. 3.1, the electrons of the semiconductor being at a higher level of potential energy will tend to lower their energy by flowing into the metal. This will leave the ionized donor levels of the semiconductor somewhat in excess of the number of free electrons left in the semiconductor. The semiconductor will then have a net positive electrostatic charge. We have previously noted that a positive electrostatic charge tends to lower the energy bands according to the convention of our energy-level diagrams. The energy levels of the semiconductor are, accordingly, depressed, and those of the metal are raised since the electrons which have flowed from the semiconductor into the metal cause the metal to have a negative electrostatic charge.   The electrons which have gone into the metal will remain on the contact surface, being attracted to the positive charge of the semiconductor.   These electrons are shown in position C in the figure.   The presence of this surface charge of electrons and the presence of the unneutralized charge of the ionized donor levels of the semiconductor in the barrier region create the dipole layer which forms the barrier shown in the figure.   The height of this barrier is determined by the amount the energy bands of the semiconductor are depressed and those of the metal raised when electrons flow into the metal.   The electrons will continue to flow until an equilibrium is established across the top of the barrier.   This situation will occur when the shift in the energy bands is just enough to bring the Fermi level of the semiconductor to the same value of energy as the Fermi level of the metal.[3]   Under this condition the currents in each direction over the barrier are equal.   The barrier height as seen from the semiconductor side is then exactly equal to the difference of potential produced by the initial flow of charge, provided there was no surface charge present to start with.

To prove that no currents flow when the Fermi levels of the two sides coincide, we shall consider a given energy interval above the top of the barrier with g_A states in the metal with a fraction x_A filled with electrons.   Similarly, there are g_B states in the semiconductor with a fraction x_B filled with electrons.   If P_{AB} is the probability of transition of an electron from a metallic state to a semiconductor state in the energy interval and P_{BA} is the probability for the reverse process, we can write the balance of opposing electron currents as

$$P_{AB}x_A g_A(1 - x_B)g_B = P_{BA}x_B g_B(1 - x_A)g_A \qquad (3.1)$$

Since the Fermi levels are equal, $x_A = x_B$ by definition of a Fermi level.   Similarly, $P_{AB} = P_{BA}$ by symmetry.   Therefore, it can be seen that Eq. (3.1) is satisfied regardless of the relative size of density-of-state distributions g_A and g_B or the electron densities in the energy interval $x_A g_A$ or $x_B g_B$.

In actual practice it is usually found that there is little correlation between the contact difference of potential and the measured barrier height.[4]   The explanation of this is generally considered to be that the semiconductor always carries a dipole layer of charge on its surface which determines the barrier height in conjunction with whatever adjustments of charge balancing may be necessary to bring the Fermi levels into exact coincidence.   Another way of stating this is that the surface charge of the semiconductor determines effectively the contact potential of the semiconductor, and since it is a sensitive function of surface conditions, it has no unique value for a given semiconductor material.

3.2. Barriers—PN Junctions.   We shall now consider the formation of a barrier between N- and P-type regions of a semiconductor.   Here again we shall use the principle of detailed charge balancing to bring the Fermi levels of the two semiconductor types into coincidence.   In Fig. 3.2 is shown the formation of a PN-junction barrier by bringing two pieces of the same semiconductor material but of opposite conductivity type into electrical contact.   At the top of the figure it is seen that the Fermi level of the N-type material is higher than the Fermi level of the P-type material.   When contact is made as shown at the bottom of the figure, some electrons have moved from the N-type material into the P-type material and a dipole layer of charge exists near the contact surface, creating a barrier.   In this case the dipole layer consists of ionized donor and acceptor levels near the contact surface.   The flow of electrons out of the N-type material left the charge of some of the ionized donor levels uncompensated.   When these electrons entered the P-type material, they neutralized some of the holes, thus leaving the charge of some of the ionized acceptor levels uncompensated.

This barrier as seen from the N-type material is a barrier to the motion of electrons in the conduction band into the P-type material and when viewed from the P-type material represents a barrier to the flow of holes in the valence band into the N-type material.   In all cases the detailed balancing of charge which brings the Fermi levels of two dissimilar materials into coincidence always involves both the valence and conduction bands and therefore both the free electrons and the free holes.   The charge transfer equilibrium across the PN-junction barrier involves the minority distributions of free electrons and free holes shown at A and B, respectively, in Fig. 3.2. When the Fermi levels coincide, these minority distributions balance the currents due to the portions of the majority distributions above the top of the barrier.

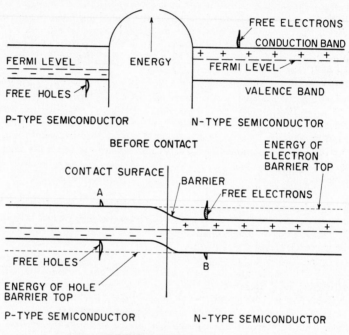

FIG. 3.2. Energy-level diagrams for a semiconductor PN junction.

3.3. Rectification in Metal-Semiconductor Contacts.   We shall now consider how barriers of this type are able to rectify currents flowing across them.   The models of the barriers considered so far have been shown without any voltage applied across them.   Since the energy-level diagrams we have been using are essentially plots of the potential energy of electrons, we can indicate an applied voltage across the barrier by lowering the Fermi level of one side relative to the other side.   Since the convention of our diagrams is such that electrons tend to fall down, the side of the barrier which is biased with a positive voltage will be lower than the negative side, thus signifying that electrons are attracted to it.   Figure 3.3 shows a metal-semi-conductor barrier which is biased in such a manner that the metal is positive with respect to the semiconductor.   In this situation the semiconductor side of the barrier is raised by the bias voltage so that a larger number of the free electrons in the conduction band are able to flow into the metal.   The higher the semiconductor side is raised, the more electrons there are at an energy above the top of the barrier, until finally, with large bias voltages, the whole distribution of free electrons in the semiconductor is able to surmount the barrier.   When this condition is reached, the current flowing can increase further only by the acceleration of these electrons to greater speeds. This acceleration process gives a linear or ohmic relation between current and voltage. At lower bias voltages the current increases more rapidly than linearly with voltage, since not only are the electrons being accelerated by increasing voltage but more of them become available to the conduction process as the voltage increases.

In Fig. 3.4 is shown a voltage-current characteristic of a semiconductor diode. The positive quadrant of this characteristic corresponds to the case just discussed (metal positive with respect to semiconductor). The dashed characteristic is the one to be expected from the considerations given so far. In this characteristic it is seen that

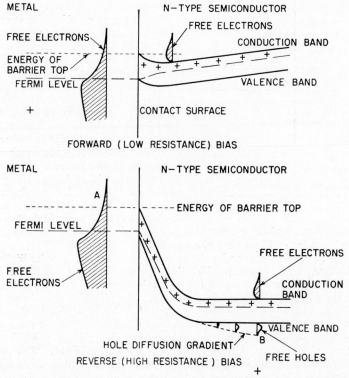

FIG. 3.3. Energy-level diagrams showing the effect of voltage bias on a metal-semiconductor contact.

the current increases much faster than linearly with voltage in the neighborhood of the origin, and then the characteristic becomes linear after the bias is sufficient to bring all the conduction electrons above the top of the barrier. The solid characteristic is the one which is actually observed for such diodes and is seen to exhibit a considerably lower resistance than the characteristic predicted by the foregoing simple theory. This phenomenon will be explained later. We shall now consider the reverse-bias characteristic. When the semiconductor is made positive with respect to the metal, the energy-level diagram is as shown at the bottom of Fig. 3.3. The semiconductor side is lowered relative to the metal side so that the tail of the free-electron distribution in the metal (A in the figure) is free to flow over the top of the barrier to the semiconductor without opposition. The number of electrons present in the metal above the top of the barrier is very small compared with the total number of free electrons in the semiconductor. The result is a very low current characteristic, as shown in the negative quadrant of Fig. 3.4. Near the origin there is a region of nonlinear current increase which is caused by the removal of the opposition current carried by the electrons in the tail of the distribution in the conduction band of the semiconductor (B in Fig. 3.1). After this voltage is exceeded, the characteristic saturates, since the electrons coming over the barrier from the metal side are not accelerated with increasing bias. The reason for this is simply that the potential drop on the semiconductor side of the barrier due to the presence of the barrier itself is so rapid that the bias voltage does not appreciably affect it.

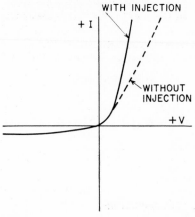

FIG. 3.4. Typical voltage-current characteristic of a metal-semiconductor point contact.

We shall now consider the effect of the minority distribution of holes in the valence band of the semiconductor. First we shall consider the case of reverse bias just considered for electrons. The energy distribution of free holes in the valence band of the semiconductor is shown at B at the bottom of Fig. 3.3. As can be seen by the diagram, there is no barrier to the passage of these holes into the metal. If the number of these holes is comparable to the number of free electrons (A) coming over the top of the barrier, they will add appreciably to the current in the negative quadrant of the rectification characteristic. In many cases the barrier is sufficiently high that the free-electron contribution of the current is negligible and the current of holes under the barrier accounts for all the reverse-bias current.

At this point we shall digress for a moment to define current-carrier lifetime for a semiconductor.[5] So far all our considerations have assumed states of thermodynamic equilibrium. We shall now consider the equilibrium between the holes in the valence band and the electrons of the conduction band. If we imagine that the equilibrium determined by the temperature and the position of the Fermi level is upset by taking a small number of electrons from the valence band and putting them in the conduction band, leaving an equal number of extra holes behind, the equilibrium will be restored by the spontaneous return of these electrons to the valence band. This process of restoring the thermodynamic equilibrium proceeds exponentially. In recombining, either the hole or the electron must be trapped in some sort of lattice defect in order that the excess momentum of the pair can be transferred to the crystal lattice when recombination takes place. Such a lattice defect is called a recombination center. This means that for a fixed concentration of recombination centers the rate of recombination will be directly proportional to the concentration of extra holes or electrons, yielding an exponential recombination law as long as the centers are not saturated. The time constant of this exponential return to the thermodynamic equilibrium in a semiconductor is called the lifetime of the current carriers in the semiconductor.

Returning now to the consideration of the minority-hole distribution in the reverse-bias condition, we note that the metal presents a sink to these holes at the contact surface. In such a situation the density of holes at the edge of the barrier must be substantially zero, since each individual hole arriving at the barrier is drawn into the metal quite rapidly by the high field existing in the barrier region under the condition of reverse bias. Deep in the semiconductor the density of holes remains the equilibrium density determined by the Fermi level. There exists therefore a density or concentration gradient of holes as the barrier is approached from the semiconductor side. This is shown at the bottom of Fig. 3.3 and is called the "hole diffusion gradient." According to simple diffusion theory the hole current into the metal is directly proportional to this gradient in the hole concentration. To make this plausible we shall give a few simple considerations regarding the diffusion process. We shall assume a one-dimensional model consisting of a bar of semiconductor material of unit cross-sectional area and with a uniform gradient (dn/dx) of hole concentration along the bar. We shall now consider the holes which flow across a plane perpendicular to the axis of the bar due to their random thermal motion. The number which cross the plane from the left in one mean free time τ will be proportional to the total number of holes within one mean free path l to the left of the plane. Similarly, the number crossing the plane from the right in the same time τ will be proportional to the total

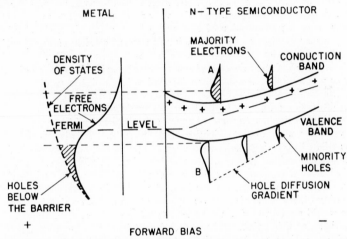

FIG. 3.5. Energy-level diagram illustrating hole injection at a metal-semiconductor contact

number of holes within one mean free path l to the right of the plane. The net hole current flowing through the plane will be the difference divided by τ.

For a uniform gradient the difference in average densities is $(dn/dx)l$ and the difference in total number within a mean free path on either side of the plane is $(dn/dx)l^2$. The hole current $J_p \sim (dn/dx)l^2/\tau$ holes/cm²/sec, or $J_p = qD_p(dn/dx)$ amp/cm², where q is the electronic charge and the constant of proportionality D_p is called the diffusion constant for holes.

Returning now to the question of the diffusion of holes under the barrier, it is clear that in the region where the hole gradient exists the number of free holes is less than the thermodynamic equilibrium requires. If the lifetime of holes in the semiconductor is quite long (return to thermodynamic equilibrium is very slow), the diffusion gradient will extend a long distance back from the contact surface (see lower diagram of Fig. 3.3), thus presenting a lower gradient than would be the case for a shorter carrier lifetime. (The lifetime of excess carriers in the metal is negligibly short.) Since the value of the gradient is lower for long carrier lifetimes, the diffusion current of holes passing under the barrier will be lower and the reverse resistance of the diode will be higher. Thus we see that current-carrier lifetime may well be the controlling factor in reverse resistance for barriers of sufficient height to render the current over the barrier negligible.

In the case of forward bias the role of the minority-carrier distribution can also be quite marked.[6] In Fig. 3.5 is shown a more detailed diagram of the forward-bias example than that given in Fig. 3.3.   At the left is shown the distribution of vacant energy levels or holes in the metal which are below the energy of the minimum of the top of the valence band of the semiconductor.   These holes give rise to an excessively large number of minority carriers in the semiconductor shown at B.   These extra holes diffuse into the semiconductor and provide extra current carriers in the neighborhood of the contact.   In order to neutralize the space charge of these extra holes, there must be an equal number of electrons in their immediate vicinity.   These electrons are shown at A and are seen to be a larger number than the usual majority electron distribution shown at the right.   These electrons occupy the potential minimum found in the bottom of the conduction band near the contact.   Whenever the density of one of the current carriers is not equal to the thermodynamic equilibrium density, the number of the current carriers of opposite charge must vary simultaneously by an equal amount so that space-charge neutrality will be preserved.   This is necessary, since the potential energy of a very few extra current carriers of one sign would cause such a perturbation of the energy-level system in their vicinity that no other like current carriers could approach and current carriers of the opposite charge would be drawn in quite rapidly to restore space-charge neutrality.

The phenomenon of the injection of extra current carriers into the semiconductor in the neighborhood of the contact when forward voltage bias is applied is responsible for transistor action and for the difference between the dashed characteristic and the solid characteristic of Fig. 3.4.[7]   If the metal-semiconductor contact is a point contact, most of the resistance to forward current flow is localized in a very small volume of the crystal in the immediate vicinity of the contact.   This is the region in which the current-flow lines are spreading out from the point and represents a region of high current density called the spreading-resistance region.   Since the resistance of a point contact is localized so near the point, the effect of current-carrier injection on the forward voltage-current characteristic is most marked in point contacts.   The effective spreading resistance is often lower by more than an order of magnitude than the value one would compute using the resistivity of the bulk semiconductor.

Summarizing at this point, we have found that in barrier rectification the reverse current of the rectifier consists of the sum of the hole and electron currents flowing over and under the barrier.   If the barrier is very high, the reverse current consists solely of the diffusion of minority carriers under the barrier and therefore depends quite critically on the current-carrier lifetime.   If the barrier is low, most of the reverse current consists of majority carriers passing over the barrier and does not depend critically on lifetime.   In the case of the forward current of the rectifier we have found that an appreciable fraction of this current is carried by injected excess current carriers, and in the special case of point-contact rectifiers this injection effect lowers the forward resistance quite markedly.   Here again current-carrier lifetime plays an important part, since it is necessary for the extra injected carriers to exist long enough to traverse most of the spreading-resistance region in order to affect the forward resistance to any great extent.   If the reader wishes to continue a study of excess carrier injection and its effects, he may refer to Sec. 5, where the injection effect is considered in relation to various photoelectric devices.   We shall continue here with a direct line of development necessary for the explanation of transistor action.

We shall now consider the operation of these factors in more detail.   The determining factor in most cases is barrier height.   We have noted that this will depend upon the surface conditions of the semiconductor and the metal in the case of metal-semiconductor contacts.   We know that in practice a contact between a given metal and a given semiconductor can be made either highly rectifying or nearly ohmic, depending on the method of preparation of the contact (see Sec. 8).   In the case of PN-junction contacts, an equally great range of rectifying characteristics is possible.

We shall consider PN-junction contacts first, since many of the ideas developed here can be carried over to the consideration of metal-semiconductor contacts.

3.4. Rectification in PN Junctions. In connection with Fig. 2.9, it was noted that the position of the Fermi level is determined by considering the conservation of electrons among the energy levels of the valence band, the impurity states, and the conduction band. That is, in an N-type semiconductor the number of electrons in the conduction band must equal the number of vacant donor-impurity levels plus the number of vacant levels in the valence band. If the total number of donor-impurity atoms is changed, it is clear that the Fermi level will have to shift in order to preserve this electron conservation. If the number of donor-impurity states is increased, the Fermi level will move toward the conduction band in order to increase the number of conduction electrons and at the same time decrease the percentage of ionized donor levels. A moment's consideration will show that both these changes tend to restore the charge balance. As the number of donor-impurity states is increased to the place where they are comparable in number to the states near the bottom of the conduction band, the Fermi level will lie very close to the bottom of the conduction band. In practice, however, such a density of impurities would fill the energy gap with energy levels and wipe out the semiconductor properties of the material. If the total number of donor levels is decreased, the Fermi level will move toward the center of the energy gap.

In the case of a P-type semiconductor, the electron conservation consists of the equality between the number of vacant energy levels in the valence band and the number of filled acceptor energy levels plus the number of electrons in the conduction band. If the number of acceptor states is increased, the Fermi level will move toward the valence band, and if the number is decreased, it will move toward the center of the energy gap. If both acceptor and donor-impurity levels are present, the electron balance will consist in the sum of the vacant energy levels in the valence band plus the vacant energy levels of the donor impurities being equal to the number of electrons in the conduction band plus the number of electrons in the acceptor impurity levels. An increase in the number of donor levels will cause the Fermi level to move as before toward the conduction band, while an increase in the number of acceptor levels will cause it to move toward the valence band.

From these considerations it is clear that the energy difference between the Fermi levels of an N-type and a P-type semiconductor before contact will depend on the densities of donor and acceptor impurities in the two semiconductor samples. As was shown in the discussion of Fig. 3.2, the barrier height of a PN junction is equal to this difference in Fermi-level energy. From this it follows that the barrier height in a PN junction may have any value between zero and the full width of the energy gap, since the Fermi level remains between the top of the valence band and the bottom of the conduction band for all practically realizable impurity concentrations. The maximum barrier height is achieved by forming a junction between two very heavily doped semiconductor samples, and the minimum barrier height is achieved by forming a junction between two samples which are nearly intrinsic.

At this point it should be noted that underlying all the discussion of barriers is the fundamental assumption that the lifetime of extra current carriers is long enough so that negligible recombination occurs while traversing the physical thickness of the barrier. If this condition is not fulfilled, the barrier region ceases to be a barrier and merely becomes an ohmic region of high resistivity.

3.5. Current-carrier Injection Efficiency. Several interesting effects occur when the concentration of impurities on the two sides of the junction is unequal. At the top of Fig. 3.6 is shown an energy-level diagram of a PN junction between a very heavily doped P-type region and a relatively lightly doped N-type region. The free-hole distribution in the P region is then much larger than the free-electron distribution in the N region. When such a junction is biased in the forward direction, as shown in the center of Fig. 3.6, electrons (A) are injected into the P-type region and holes (B) are injected into the N-type region. It is clear from the figure that with a given bias most of the forward current is carried by the holes (B) in the immediate neighborhood

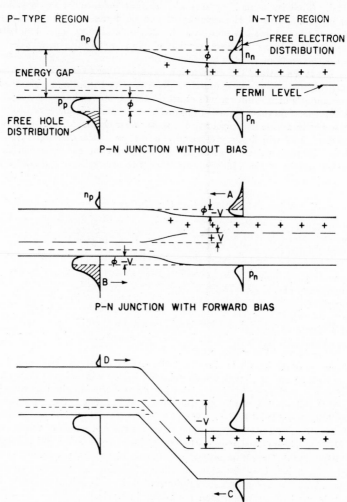

FIG. 3.6. Energy-level diagrams showing the effect of voltage bias on a semiconductor PN junction.

of the junction, since the majority distribution of holes in the P-type region far exceeds the majority distribution of electrons in the N-type region. Such a junction is, therefore, an effective hole injector and a very ineffective electron injector.[8] When this junction is biased in the reverse direction, as shown at the bottom of Fig. 3.6, it can be seen that most of the reverse current is again carried by holes (C) passing under the barrier from the N side to the P side, the electron current due to the electrons (D)

being much smaller. This means that the reverse saturation current will be quite sensitive to the excess current-carrier lifetime in the N region only.

It is not hard to visualize the effect of the reverse situation for a junction between heavily doped N-type material and nearly intrinsic P-type material. Such a junction is a good electron injector and a poor hole injector. The reverse saturation current consists mostly of electrons passing from the P region into the N region and depends strongly upon the excess current-carrier lifetime in the P region. In the case of nearly equal doping of the two regions, the junction will be about 50 per cent efficient as a minority-carrier injector of either type carrier, and the reverse saturation current depends upon the lifetime in both regions.

3.6. The Diode Equation. We shall now consider barrier rectification somewhat more quantitatively. The voltage-current relation for a PN junction will be determined in a manner which is not rigorous but is calculated to demonstrate the relationships of the physical factors to good advantage.

When the Fermi-Dirac statistics were discussed in Sec. 2, a Fermi function was introduced [Eq. (2.1)] which gave the probability of occupation of an energy level at the energy ϵ. If the energy level ϵ is above the Fermi level ϵ_0 by several times kT, the 1 in the denominator of Eq. (2.1) can be neglected and the occupation probability becomes

$$f(\epsilon) = e^{-(\epsilon-\epsilon_0)/kT} \tag{3.2a}$$

This is the occupation probability for a different type of statistics called the Maxwell-Boltzmann statistics. Fermi statistics may always be replaced by Maxwell-Boltzmann statistics when the occupation probability is small, that is, when the number of electrons in the conduction band is small compared with the number of available energy levels. By symmetry we can see that if we have a small number of holes in the valence band, they also can be treated with Maxwell-Boltzmann statistics.

Referring to the top of Fig. 3.6 we shall assume that the free electron and hole densities are sufficiently small compared with the energy-level densities in the conduction and valence bands that their distributions obey Maxwell-Boltzmann statistics and that we can calculate the number of free electrons, a, above the top of the barrier ϕ to be

$$a = n_n e^{-q\phi/kT} \tag{3.2b}$$

where n_n is the density of free electrons in the N region and q is the electronic charge. This equation is quite analogous to Eq. (2.3), except that the reference energy is the energy of the lower edge of the conduction band and $q\phi$ is the energy at the top of the barrier. If there is a forward bias voltage $+V$ across the barrier, the number of free electrons A above the top of the barrier (see center of Fig. 3.6) is given by

$$A = n_n e^{-q(\phi-V)/kT} \tag{3.3}$$

We shall now assume that the electron current J_n across the top of the barrier is governed by diffusion of the electrons into the P region. The gradient in electron concentration causing this diffusion current consists of the excess number of electrons found in the minority distribution of the P-type material at the junction interface divided by the diffusion length L_n for electrons in the P-type material. The excess number of electrons is

$$A - n_p = n_n e^{-q(\phi-V)/kT} - n_p \tag{3.4}$$

where n_p is the density of electrons in the P region normally present. Inspection of the top of Fig. 3.6 shows that at equilibrium with no bias applied the electron densities

a and n_p must be equal.† In this case from (3.2) we have

$$n_p = n_n e^{-q\phi/kT}$$ (3.5)

Substituting (3.5) in (3.4) gives

$$A - n_p = n_p(e^{qV/kT} - 1)$$ (3.6)

The diffusion current of electrons J_n into the P region is then given by

$$J_n = qD_n \frac{A - n_p}{L_n} = q \frac{D_n n_p}{L_n} (e^{qV/kT} - 1)$$ (3.7)

In an exactly similar manner the diffusion current J_p of holes into the N region can be found:

$$J_p = q \frac{D_p p_n}{L_p} (e^{qV/kT} - 1)$$ (3.8)

where D_n and D_p are the diffusion constants for electrons and holes, respectively.
The total current J across the PN junction is

$$J = J_n + J_p = q \left(\frac{D_p p_n}{L_p} + \frac{D_n n_p}{L_n} \right) (e^{qV/kT} - 1)$$ (3.9)

This equation has been derived for forward voltages less than the barrier height ϕ. When the forward bias voltage approaches or exceeds ϕ, the assumed diffusion process is superseded by a combination process involving both diffusion and conduction of the whole majority-carrier distributions, and Eq. (3.9) no longer applies. For reverse biases $-V$, however, the diffusion process is the controlling factor out to very high voltages. If both sides of the junction are at the same temperature, p_n and n_p will be simply inversely proportional to the impurity content of their respective materials. This follows from the fact that the products $n_n p_n = p_p n_p$ for a given semiconductor at a given temperature [see Eq. (2.5)] and in the extrinsic region $n_n =$ the density of donor-impurity centers of the N material and $p_p =$ the density of acceptor-impurity centers of the P material. In the illustration of Fig. 3.6, $p_n \gg n_p$ so that most of the current is carried by holes.

If the bias voltage is negative, it is clear from Eq. (3.9) that the current quickly saturates to the value

$$J = q \left(\frac{D_p p_n}{L_p} + \frac{D_n n_p}{L_n} \right)$$ (3.10)

This is the reverse saturation current of the junction. This current is dependent on the lifetime of the minority carriers through the diffusion lengths L_p and L_n, which are given by

$$L_p = \sqrt{D_p \tau_p} \quad \text{and} \quad L_n = \sqrt{D_n \tau_n}$$ (3.11)

where τ_p and τ_n are the lifetimes of holes in the N region and electrons in the P region, respectively. Equation (3.10) becomes

$$J = q \left(p_n \sqrt{\frac{D_p}{\tau_p}} + n_p \sqrt{\frac{D_n}{\tau_n}} \right)$$ (3.12)

This shows the dependence of the reverse saturation current in PN junctions on the lifetime of the minority carriers. It is analogous to the similar dependence noted

† This is not rigorous, but no significant error is introduced by assuming it.

earlier in connection with metal-semiconductor contacts. At this point it should be noted that the rectification equation of the form of Eq. (3.9) or simplified as

$$I = I_0(e^{uV} - 1) \tag{3.13}$$

holds for either PN junction barriers or metal-semiconductor barriers. The constant u is usually not found to be equal to q/kT for metal-semiconductor contacts, and I_0 does not show as complete saturation properties for such contacts as for PN junctions, but the general form still holds. Most of the detailed deviations from simple theory found in u and I_0 can be explained on the basis of heating effects in metal-point contacts or the modulation of the semiconductor spreading resistance near the point owing to extra minority-carrier injection. Some of these effects will be taken up later.

Up to this point the reverse saturation current of a PN junction has been considered the sum of the currents due to the two minority-carrier distributions diffusing over the barrier. For germanium and other low-energy gap semiconductors this model is accurate. For large-energy-gap materials, such as silicon, this current is often largely due to the regeneration of carriers in the depletion region of the junction. The size of the minority-carrier distributions depends upon the impurity concentration, the temperature, and the energy gap. At a given temperature the Fermi occupation-probability function is fixed. If the energy gap is increased, with a constant impurity concentration, the concentration of minority carriers will rapidly decrease. From Fig. 2.9 it is seen that the product of the Fermi function and the density of states in the valence band would result in more nearly total occupancy of the energy levels if the energy gap were increased by moving the edge of the valence band down. A simple mass-action law describes the relation of the concentrations of the majority and minority carriers in a given semiconductor as $np = n_i^2(T)$, where n and p are the concentrations of electrons and holes respectively, and n_i is the concentration of either electrons or holes in an intrinsic sample at the same temperature [compare Eq. (2.5)].

3.7. Effects of the Energy Gap. We shall digress somewhat at this point to give an example of the large discrepancy in the majority- and minority-carrier densities in a normal semiconductor in the extrinsic temperature range. For germanium, the intrinsic conductivity at room temperature is 0.02 reciprocal ohm-cm. Knowing the electron and hole mobilities to be 3,600 and 1,800 cm/sec/unit field, respectively, we can calculate the intrinsic concentration n_i from Eq. (2.6), letting $n = p = n_i$. We obtain $n_i = 2.3 \times 10^{13}$ carriers/cu cm, $n_i^2 = 5.3 \times 10^{26}$, so that for an extrinsic 1 ohm-cm N-type sample the majority electron density

$$n_n = \sigma/q\mu_n = 1/3{,}600 \times 1.6 \times 10^{-19} = 1.7 \times 10^{15} \text{ electrons/cu cm}$$

and the minority hole density $p_n = n_i^2/n_n = 3.1 \times 10^9$ holes/cu cm.

We are now in a position to compare two semiconductors such as germanium (gap width about 0.71 electron volt and σ_i about 0.02 at room temperature) and silicon (gap width about 1.12 electron volts and σ_i about 1.6×10^{-5} at room temperature). Considering two PN junctions produced by identical amounts of impurity in these two semiconductors, we see that the silicon junction would have a higher barrier and smaller concentration of minority carriers [n_p and p_n of Eq. (3.9)] on both sides of the junction than would the germanium diode. The consequences of this are that the silicon diode should have a much higher reverse resistance than the germanium diode for a given minority-carrier lifetime if diffusion currents alone are considered. Actually, the regeneration current in the depletion region of the junction predominates in the silicon diode, although its reverse resistance is still high compared with germanium. The forward resistances of the two diodes are quite comparable, since the majority-carrier concentrations are comparable and diffusion current predominates above 10^{-4} amperes in both cases.

To understand the temperature dependence of the reverse resistance of a PN junction, we must refer to Figs. 2.8 and 2.9 in connection with Fig. 2.7. In the case of predominant diffusion currents (as in germanium), the temperature dependence of the minority-carrier distributions on either side of the junction must be considered. In the case of predominant regeneration current (as in silicon) the equation of reverse saturation current is $I_0 = WAqn_i/2\tau$, where W and A are the width and area of the junction depletion region, and τ is the lifetime of either carrier in this region. Here the temperature dependence of n_i must be considered. It can be seen that an increase in temperature, which causes the Fermi function to include a larger energy range in its transition region (Fig. 2.7), will produce a marked increase in the density of minority carriers (Fig. 2.9) as well as a marked increase in the density of intrinsic carriers (Fig. 2.8). Equations (2.3), (2.4), and (2.5) give the quantitative exponential temperature dependence of the minority-carrier densities n_p and p_n as well as the intrinsic carrier density, $n_i = \sqrt{np}$. Consideration of these relations will show that the reverse saturation current of a PN junction increases exponentially with temperature with an activation energy essentially equal the energy-gap width for either diffusion or regeneration currents. The temperature coefficient of reverse saturation current will be higher for materials with the larger gap widths but will generally have a lower absolute value. Junction diodes made from large-gap semiconductors can therefore operate at higher temperatures before objectionable reverse leakage current appears.

3.8. The Esaki Tunnel Diode. In 1958 Leo Esaki reported the discovery of a new property of PN junctions between very heavily doped regions.[10] The unique operation of a diode made from such a junction is due to a process called tunneling. This process consists of the penetration of the energy gap by electrons in the region of the high electric field of the PN-junction barrier. This can take place only if the bottom of the conduction band on the N-type side of the junction is lower in energy than the top of the valence band on the P-type side of the junction (see Fig. 3.7). In addition to this requirement the actual barrier thickness must be very small (usually less than 100 Å). The first condition, usually called "overlapping bands," occurs in any PN junction when it is back-biased (see Fig. 3.3). In the case of the Esaki tunnel diode the bands overlap even at zero and slightly forward bias voltages. Such a situation means that the Fermi level must be located inside one or both of the allowed bands as shown in Fig. 3.7. Material in which the Fermi level is located inside the valence or conduction band is called "degenerate" material. This designation means that the material is essentially metallic in electrical behavior over a wide temperature range. That this is true can be seen from the definition of metallic conductivity given in Sec. 2, where it was pointed out that a metal is a material with a band only partially filled with electrons.

In order to obtain degenerate material it is necessary to dope the semiconductor very heavily with donor or acceptor impurities. In germanium this means an impurity concentration of about 10^{19} per cubic centimeter. In addition to the high impurity level on both sides of the junction it is necessary to have a very sharp transition from the P- to N-type impurity in order to keep the barrier region of the junction to a width of the order of 50 to 100 Å.

In Fig. 3.8 is shown a typical volt-ampere characteristic of such a junction in degenerate material. It can be seen that the characteristic near the origin has a very low resistance which decreases even more for normal reverse bias. In the forward direction the characteristic turns over and approaches the normal diode forward characteristic asymptotically. We shall now attempt to explain such a characteristic.

In Fig. 3.7a (at the top) we see the energy-level diagram for a junction between two regions of degenerate material in the absence of applied bias. The bands overlap in the sense that the bottom of the conduction band on the N-type side is below the top of the valence band on the P-type side. The density of allowed energy states in each band is shown by the dashed parabolas, and the density of filled levels is shown by the shaded areas A and C.   In the zero bias case shown it is seen that the shaded region A, representing the free-electron distribution in the N-type material, is opposite the top of the shaded region C, representing the upper part of the levels of the valence band which are filled with electrons.   Since two electrons cannot occupy the same energy level, it is clear that electrons of distribution A can tunnel through the barrier only into empty levels of distribution B which lie opposite them at the same energy level.   Similarly the electrons of distribution C can penetrate the barrier only to

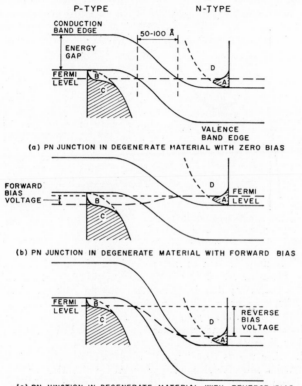

(a) PN JUNCTION IN DEGENERATE MATERIAL WITH ZERO BIAS

(b) PN JUNCTION IN DEGENERATE MATERIAL WITH FORWARD BIAS

(c) PN JUNCTION IN DEGENERATE MATERIAL WITH REVERSE BIAS

FIG. 3.7. PN junction in a degenerate material.

unoccupied levels of distribution D at the same energy.   The equilibrium condition (at zero bias) is determined by the matching of the distributions A and C so that there are equal and opposite tunneling currents.   This is fulfilled when the Fermi levels on the two sides of the junction are even.

When a slight forward bias voltage is applied, the distribution A is raised relative to the distribution C and now finds itself opposite the hole distribution B (see Fig. 3.7b).   A large tunneling current of electrons can now flow from A to B.   This situation obtains near the maximum A of the characteristic of Fig. 3.8.   If a further forward bias is applied, the distribution A is further raised relative to C and there is a progressively smaller and smaller overlap between distributions A and C.   The tunneling current now diminishes until it ceases altogether when the band edges no longer overlap.   At this point the only current carriers which can take part in the conduction process are the high-energy tails of the distributions A and B, which exceed the height of the barrier.   These are the normal contributions to the forward current of a PN junction and have been discussed before in Sec. 3.4. This then explains why the characteristic of Fig. 3.8 approaches the normal PN-junction characteristic for high forward bias.

The case of reverse bias is indicated in Fig. 3.7c. Here the distributions A and D are lowered relative to C so that there is a large overlap of C and D. The electrons in C can now tunnel freely over to D, giving a large current for reverse bias as shown in the characteristic of Fig. 3.8.

In explaining the general features of the Esaki tunnel diode volt-ampere characteristic we have made a number of oversimplifying assumptions. Among these is the assumption that the tunneling probability is relatively high and constant if the barrier is quite thin. Actually the tunneling probability drops off exponentially with increasing barrier thickness. This means that it is a strong function of bias voltage, since for forward bias the field in the barrier is reduced, resulting in an appreciable thickening of the forbidden region at a given energy level. Similarly reverse bias increases the field in the barrier and reduces the thickness of the forbidden region. Thus the tunneling probability is decreased progressively for forward bias and increased progressively for reverse bias. This, of course, will have an effect on the shape of the characteristic curve but not on its general form.

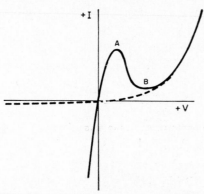

FIG. 3.8. Esaki tunnel diode characteristic (solid curve) superimposed on a normal PN-junction diode characteristic (dashed).

A more serious simplification concerns the form of the valence and conduction bands of the semiconductor. In the above discussion it was assumed that tunneling could take place directly; that is, that there was no problem of conservation of momentum during the process. Such an assumption is valid for some semiconductors such as GaAs but is not valid for germanium and silicon. In these latter materials the levels at the bottom of the conduction band are associated with values of momentum which are widely different from the values associated with the levels at the top of the valence band. This means that "direct" tunneling is not possible but that only "indirect" tunneling can take place in which a lattice vibration, or phonon, assists in satisfying the required conservation of momentum. In the case of silicon the presence of the assisting phonon can be seen in certain irregularities in the characteristic curve.[11]

One of the most difficult parts of the characteristic curve to explain is the relatively high value of the current near the minimum of the curve (point B in Fig. 3.8). At this point one would expect the tunneling current to be zero, since the bands have ceased to overlap and the normal forward diffusion current of the diode should be the only contribution to the current. Actually in most Esaki tunnel diodes the current at this point of the characteristic is many times the value to be expected from the normal forward diffusion current of the diode. This "excess current," as it is often called, is presently unexplained, although a number of probable contributing factors have been suggested. Possibly one of the most likely suggestions is that the effective energy gap of degenerate material is appreciably reduced due to the high density of donor or acceptor levels contiguous to the band edge. This would mean that the band overlap would be appreciably greater than that expected for an energy gap equal to that of the pure material, and it would therefore require a higher forward bias voltage to remove the overlap completely and bring the tunneling current to zero.

The differences among different semiconductor materials are primarily traceable to the differences in energy gap and in direct versus indirect tunneling. The wider the energy gap, the larger the voltage scale of the forward characteristic. For example, germanium diodes have the peak current at about 0.04 volt while silicon diodes peak at 0.06 volt. Both of these values are seen to be about 5 per cent of the energy gap expressed in electron volts.

The value of the peak current is determined by the area of the junction, the degree of degeneracy achieved in the doping, and the thickness of the barrier region. Since the tunneling probability increases exponentially as the barrier thickness decreases, the abruptness of the junction is the most sensitive factor in determining peak current. In practice a specified peak current is usually achieved by forming a diode with a relatively large area and then reducing the area by etching until the desired value of peak current is achieved. This results in a considerable variation in junction areas among units with the same peak current because of slight variations in barrier thickness.

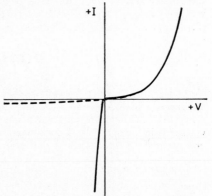

FIG. 3.9. Degenerate Esaki tunnel diode with negligible peak current.

3.8a. Backward Diode. It is possible to make a variation of the Esaki tunnel diode which consists of a PN junction between two regions doped just short of degeneracy so that at zero bias the bands do not overlap but their edges are essentially at the same level. Such a diode will have the characteristic shown in Fig. 3.9. Here again the dashed curve is a normal diode rectifying characteristic. Here any reverse bias will cause the bands to overlap and a large tunneling current will flow. A forward bias produces the normal forward characteristic of a PN junction. Such diodes have the ability of working very near the origin without appreciable minority-carrier storage effects.

3.9. Variable-capacitance Diode.[12] As stated earlier in Sec. 3.1 there is a dipole layer of charge in the region of any barrier which is necessary to create the electric field in the barrier region. If the voltage is increased (reverse bias) across the barrier, the field increases in the barrier region and the amount of charge in the dipole layer must increase also. This can be seen in Fig. 3.3; the number of ionized donors, and therefore the amount of positive charge, found in the depletion region of the barrier is much greater for reverse bias (bottom of the figure) than for the forward bias. If the charge in the depletion region changes as the bias voltage changes, it is clear that a barrier capacity C_b must exist. In an ordinary capacitor the plates remain a fixed distance apart and the dipole layer of charge on the capacitor plates is always separated by the same distance regardless of the voltage to which the capacitor is charged. Not so with a barrier involving a semiconductor junction. The dipole layer here consists of the unneutralized ionized impurity atoms found in the depletion region of the junction barrier, and since these impurities are distributed in the volume of the semiconductor, the thickness of the depletion region must always increase as the charge and voltage increase (see Fig. 4.17). This means that the junction capacitance decreases for reverse bias (high barrier field) and increases for forward bias (low barrier field). The detailed manner in which the capacitance changes with voltage will depend on the spatial distribution of ionized impurities on both sides of the junction (see Sec. 4.5e). In most cases $C_b \sim 1/V^n$, where $0.3 < n < 0.5$.

From the above it is clear that any semiconductor barrier has a variable capacitance which is a function of voltage. One of the most useful applications of this property is in parametric amplification. Since it is generally desired to use as high a pump frequency as possible, a variable-capacity diode is made to have the smallest $C_b R_s$ product possible while still retaining a reasonable value of n. (R_s is the equivalent series resistance of the diode.) The frequency at which $1/\omega C_b = R_s$ is often called the cutoff frequency of the device. At the present time this is about 100,000 mc for good units measured at zero bias voltage.

3.10. Mixer Diode. [13] The function of a mixer diode is to generate harmoni's of the local oscillator frequency with a maximum efficiency. In this process the non-linear resistance of the rectifying characteristic is most important. This is in contrast to the variable-capacitance diode described above, where the nonlinear reactance was the factor of importance to parametric amplification. From the diode equation (3.13) we can calculate the nonlinear resistance near the origin to be

$$R(V) = \frac{dV}{dI} = \frac{e^{-uV}}{uI_0} \tag{3.14}$$

From Eq. (3.14) it can be seen that the larger the value of uV, the greater is the nonlinearity of $R(V)$ and the larger will be the relative amplitude of the harmonics generated. This means that the conversion loss will decrease as the local oscillator voltage is increased. The effect saturates at voltage amplitudes of a few tenths of a volt because here the diode series resistance R_s becomes comparable to the variable resistance $R(V)$.

Any real diode will have a resistance R_s in series with the barrier and a barrier capacitance C_b shunting the variable resistance $R(V)$. In order to have the largest possible portion of the applied local oscillator voltage appear across $R(V)$, it is necessary to minimize the product $C_b R_s$ just as in the case of the variable-capacitance diode. Mixer diodes are usually of the point-contact or bonded-contact type, which helps reduce C_b because of their small barrier area but usually leaves R_s fairly high.

Since C_b decreases linearly with area of the contact and with doping level while R_s increases linearly as contact area or doping level decreases, one might wonder how the C_b and R_s can be simultaneously decreased. Several avenues are open. [14] R_s decreases as majority-carrier mobility is increased without affecting C_b; C_b decreases as dielectric constant decreases; R_s can be decreased by making the semiconductor wafer thin compared with the diameter of the contact. From this it can be seen that proper choice of material and geometry can have a significant effect.

3.11. Diode Recovery Time. The speed with which a forward-biased diode can be reverse-biased is generally limited by minority-carrier storage effects. A diode carries a forward current I_F. If this junction is suddenly switched into a circuit which draws a reverse current I_R, how long will the diode remain forward-biased and how long will this reverse current be supported?

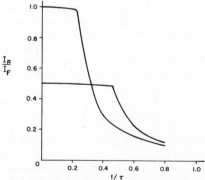

FIG. 3.10. The transient current response of a diode when max $I_R = I_F$ and $0.5I_F$.

Figure 3.10 shows the transient response of the diode in this case. The zero on the time axis corresponds to the moment of the change from forward to reverse current. The current in the reverse direction remains essentially constant at I_R until the stored carriers near the junction are depleted. It then drops and asymptotically approaches the reverse saturation current of the junction. At the same time the forward potential across the junction drops slowly as the stored charge density adjacent to it drops until the latter goes below the equilibrium density. They are tied together by the boundary condition $n = n_{eq}e^{qV/kT}$. After this the junction potential goes in the reverse direction and asymptotically approaches the reverse bias imposed by the battery.

The existence of this storage or recovery effect makes the diode a "time-division" transistor. The one junction acts as an emitter during a forward pulse and a collector during a following reverse pulse. By time sequencing or other methods of isolating the input and output, a diode amplifier which will show power gain can be made using this storage effect. In fact, ingenious schemes have even yielded time-division transistors with $a > 1$.

The mathematical solution of the recovery problem gives the following relation between the bias on the junction and currents as a function of time:[15]

$$I_s(e^{qV/kT} - 1) = I_F\left(1 - \operatorname{erf}\sqrt{\frac{t}{\tau}}\right) - I_R \operatorname{erf}\sqrt{\frac{t}{\tau}} \tag{3.15}$$

Here τ is the lifetime of minority carriers on the side of the junction in which most of the storage takes place—generally the higher resistivity side. V is the voltage across the junction. The storage period ends when the junction voltage passes through zero on its way to a reverse bias. Then the storage time

$$t_s = \tau\left(\operatorname{erf}^{-1}\frac{I_F}{I_F + I_R}\right)^2 \tag{3.16}$$

A few sample values of storage time computed with this equation are given below.

If $I_F = I_R$, $t_s = \tau(\operatorname{erf}^{-1} \tfrac{1}{2})^2 = \tau(0.47)^2 = 0.22\tau$. On the other hand, if the reverse current drawn is very much larger, then the storage or recovery time will be very much smaller because the carriers are removed from the vicinity of the junction more rapidly. If $I_R = 10 I_F$ then $t_s = \tau(\operatorname{erf}^{-1} 0.091)^2 = \tau(0.08)^2 = 0.0064\tau$.

3.12. Ohmic Contacts. An ohmic contact is one which does not rectify or inject excess carriers.

It was noted in the discussion of PN-junction barriers that a PN transition region ceased to be a barrier if the lifetime of current carriers was so short that thermodynamic equilibrium was effectively maintained throughout its thickness. In such a case the transition region becomes merely a region of high resistivity without any rectifying properties. It is essentially this model which is used to explain most ohmic metal-semiconductor contacts.

In Fig. 3.11 are shown two types of ohmic metal-semiconductor contacts. At the top of the figure is shown a typical soldered contact. It is supposed that there are a large number of recombination centers in a thin region of the semiconductor near the metal-semiconductor interface. The recombination centers are present in sufficient concentration to degrade the current-carrier lifetime to the point where thermodynamic equilibrium is maintained throughout the interface region. The contact is then ohmic.

In the solder interface region shown at the top of Fig. 3.11 the concentration of impurity energy levels at the position A is so great that effectively the semiconductor energy gap ceases to exist. At the position B the concentration of the impurity levels has dropped to the point where a semiconductor energy gap can be said to exist, but the current-carrier lifetime is extremely low.

The recombination centers may originate in two ways. The process of soldering may mechanically disrupt and strain the semiconductor crystal lattice to a point where there are enough dislocations to provide the recombination-center energy levels. A second source of centers may be energy levels associated with chemical impurities which enter the semiconductor lattice in a combination of solid-state diffusion and alloying during the soldering operation.

There are several experimental results that bear out these speculations.[16] If a clean, etched semiconductor surface is electrolytically plated with the same metals involved in the soldering operation, a rectifying contact results. This indicates that the application of heat in the soldering operation is important in producing the ohmic contact. This heat can cause the diffusion or alloying and possibly strain the semi-conductor lattice through differential thermal expansion. If, on the other hand, the surface of the semiconductor is ground without etching, the same electroplating pro-duces an ohmic contact, indicating that deformation of the surface layer of the lattice is sufficient to produce the ohmic contact.

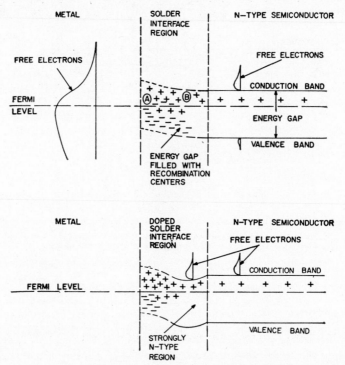

Fig. 3.11. Energy-level diagrams showing ohmic metal-semiconductor contacts.

At the bottom of Fig. 3.11 is shown the energy-level diagram of an ohmic contact which was made by deliberately adding an N-type impurity to the solder before the metal was soldered to an N-type semiconductor crystal. This contact shows a heavily doped N-type region between the main body of the N-type semiconductor and that portion of the interface region which is so heavily contaminated that it effectively exhibits metallic conductivity. The presence of this intervening strongly N-type region ensures that the contact cannot inject an excess of minority carriers into the body of the semiconductor when the junction is biased in the forward direction. This is, of course, one criterion for an ohmic contact. When the contact is biased in the reverse direction, there is no barrier impeding the flow of majority electrons from the semiconductor into the metal.

There is one property of this contact, however, which is not strictly ohmic. When the contact is biased in the forward direction, the minority-carrier distribution of the bulk semiconductor may be somewhat reduced in size because the extremely small density of holes found in the strongly N-type region will flow into the bulk semi-conductor. There is no barrier to the flow of holes from this region into the bulk semiconductor, and as the normal minority-carrier distribution is drained away by the passage of current, the holes cannot be replaced in full measure from such a small reservoir of holes as is present in the strongly N-type region. If the lifetime of minority carriers is long in the bulk semiconductor and if the resistivity is relatively high so that an appreciable amount of the conduction current is carried by the minority-carrier hole distribution, then the reduction in this hole distribution may appreciably increase the bulk resistance of the semiconductor.

3.13. Barrier Breakdown. We shall now consider the breakdown behavior of both metal-semiconductor contacts and PN-junction contacts. The various breakdown phenomena discussed here are, in general, reversible and do not lead to the destruction

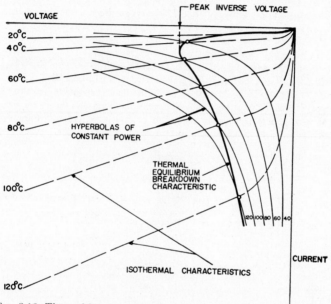

Fig. 3.12. Thermal-breakdown characteristic of a point-contact diode.

or damage of the device unless the power dissipated in the high-current region of the breakdown characteristic is sufficient to burn out the unit. There are several mechanisms of electrical breakdown possible for rectifying barriers in solids. For metal-point contacts, the most usual type of breakdown is simply due to the power dissipation of heating of the semiconductor in the region of the barrier and spreading resistance.[17] As has been noted, the temperature dependence of the reverse current is exponential, with an activation energy approximately equal to the gap width for high barriers. In the case of high barriers most of the reverse voltage appears across the barrier, and therefore most of the power dissipation occurs in the barrier region. In Fig. 3.12 the back-voltage breakdown curve is derived graphically under the assumptions of an exponential increase of the reverse current with temperature and Newton's law of cooling of the barrier region. The dashed lines represent the isothermal reverse characteristics of the diode at several different temperatures. Superimposed upon these characteristics are several hyperbolas of constant power dissipation using increments of power assumed, through Newton's law of cooling, to be proportional to the increments of temperature used in laying out the isothermal characteristics. The desired thermal-equilibrium volt-ampere characteristics can now be drawn through the intersection points of the isothermal characteristics and their respective hyperbolas. This thermal-equilibrium characteristic, which is shown as the heavy line in the figure, has a form which is quite typical of the measured breakdown characteristics often seen for metal-semiconductor point contacts. Experimental verification of this thermal-breakdown mechanism in point contacts is reasonably well established.

If a point contact is very rapidly pulsed so that the thermal-relaxation time is long compared with the pulse length, the thermal breakdown described above will not occur and other mechanisms of breakdown will take over at higher voltage. The two mechanisms which have been observed for semiconductor contacts in the absence of thermal breakdown are Zener breakdown[18] and avalanche breakdown. These two forms of breakdown are difficult to distinguish experimentally. In either of these forms there is no negative resistance region such as is usually found in a thermal-breakdown characteristic.

In avalanche breakdown the electric field across the barrier region must be large enough to produce ionization by collisions of the current carriers traversing the barrier region with electrons of the valence band. In Zener breakdown the electric field in the barrier region must be sufficiently high to cause a sort of "field emission" across the energy gap, thus increasing the number of carriers in this region by a large amount. Since there is difficulty in distinguishing these two types of breakdown experimentally, it is not always certain which of the two mechanisms is responsible for the high-voltage breakdown of a given PN junction. If thermal effects can be ruled out, the most probable cause of junction breakdown is the avalanche effect. Some empirical relations for both Zener and avalanche breakdown are given in Sec. 10.1.

REFERENCES

1. Torrey, H. C., and C. A. Whitmer: "Crystal Rectifiers," chap. 4, McGraw-Hill Book Company, Inc., New York, 1948.
2. Shockley, W.: "Electrons and Holes in Semiconductors," chap. 12, D. Van Nostrand Company, Inc., Princeton, N.J., 1951.
3. Shockley, W.: "Electrons and Holes in Semiconductors," sec. 12.4, D. Van Nostrand Company, Inc., Princeton, N.J., 1951.
4. Benzer, S.: High Inverse Voltage Germanium Rectifiers, *J. Appl. Phys.*, vol. 20, pp. 804–815, August, 1949.
5. Shockley, W., G. L. Pearson, and J. R. Haynes: Hole Injection in Germanium—Quantitative Studies and Filamentary Transistors, *Bell System Tech. J.*, vol. 28, pp. 344–366, July, 1949.
6. Swanson, J. A.: Diode Theory in the Light of Hole Injection, *J. Appl. Phys.*, vol. 25, pp. 314–323, March, 1954.
7. Bardeen, J., and W. H. Brattain: Physical Principles Involved in Transistor Action, *Phys. Rev.*, vol. 75, pp. 1208–1225, Apr. 15, 1949.
8. Shockley, W.: The Theory of P-N Junctions in Semiconductors and P-N Junction Transistors, *Bell System Tech. J.*, vol. 28, pp. 435–489, July, 1949.
9. Pearson, G. L., and B. Sawyer: Silicon P-N Junction Alloy Diodes, *Proc. IRE*, vol. 40, pp. 1348–1351, November, 1952.
10. Esaki, L.: New Phenomenon in Narrow Ge PN Junctions, *Phys. Rev.*, vol. 109, p. 603, Apr. 1, 1958.
11. Holonyak, Jr., N., I. A. Lesk, R. N. Hall, J. J. Tiemann, and H. Ehrenreich: Direct Observation of Phonons during Tunneling in Narrow Junctions, *Phys. Rev. Letters*, vol. 3, p. 167, Aug. 15, 1959.
12. Uhlir, Jr., A.: The Potential of Semiconductor Diodes in High Frequency Communications, *Proc. IRE*, vol. 46, pp. 1099–1115, June, 1958.
13. See Ref. 1, pp. 152–166.
14. Messenger, G. C.: New Concepts in Microwave Mixer Diodes, *Proc. IRE*, vol. 46, pp. 1116–1121, June, 1958.
15. Lax, B., and S. F. Neustradter: Transient Response of a PN Junction, *J. Appl. Phys.*, vol. 25, pp. 1148–1154, September, 1954.
16. Tiley, J. W., and R. A. Williams: Electrochemical Techniques for Fabrication of Surface Barrier Transistors, *Proc. IRE*, vol. 41, pp. 1706–1708, December, 1953.
17. Hunter, L. P.: The Inverse Voltage Characteristic of a Point Contact on N-type Germanium, *Phys. Rev.*, vol. 79, pp. 151–152, January, 1951.
18. McAfee, K. B., E. J. Ryder, W. Shockley, and M. Sparks: Observations of Zener Current in Germanium P-N Junctions, *Phys. Rev.*, vol. 83, p. 650, Aug. 1, 1951.

Section 4

TRANSISTOR ACTION

S. L. Miller[†]

IBM Corporation, Poughkeepsie, N.Y.

[†] Now with Rheem Semiconductor Corporation, Mountain View, Calif.
[‡] These sections are taken from the text of the first edition by L. P. Hunter.

Transistor action was defined in Sec. 1 to be the control of the reverse saturation current in one rectifying contact, called the collector, by the forward current in a second rectifying contact, called the emitter. Both contacts are made to the same piece of semiconductor material. The rectifying contacts can be either PN junctions or metal-semiconductor contacts. This definition fits all devices commonly called transistors with the exception of the "unipolar transistor," which will be discussed later.

At the present time, junction transistors of one type or another are by far the most widely used transistor devices. Their theory is quite well understood, and many of the concepts of junction-transistor theory are used to explain the operation of other types of transistors, such as the point-contact transistor. Accordingly, we shall first take up the explanation of junction transistors.[1] Later in the section, explanations of various other types of transistors will be given. The amount of space devoted to any particular transistor structure or phenomenon is not an indication of the relative importance of that structure or phenomenon to the applications field but rather reflects an attempt to cover the known physical mechanisms involved in transistor action.

4.1. The Junction Transistor. In Fig. 4.1 is shown a generalized diagram of a junction transistor. At the present time there are many alternative ways of achieving a structure like that depicted. The leading methods (described in Sec. 7) are the grown-junction, the alloy-junction, and the diffused-junction processes. There are other processes which may be considered branches of these classifications. For example, the product of the so-called "meltback" process may be considered a form of grown-junction. Similarly, it is possible that point contacts and plated contacts really induce junctions within the semiconductor and are hence methods of achieving the structure shown in Fig. 4.1. The figure actually shows the NPN structure, but all statements, calculations, and figures will be applicable to the PNP transistor when the current directions and the potentials are reversed. In general, the symmetry between the two types of transistors is complete except for properties which reflect the differences between the physical attributes of electrons and holes. One of the most important of these is the difference in their mobilities. It is for this reason that NPN transistors in germanium and silicon have higher frequency cutoffs than PNP transistors with the same dimensions. Other differences will be discussed when they arise below.

The most important feature of the structure of Fig. 4.1 is the degree of interaction between the emitter- and collector-junction diodes. This is best characterized by the current gain of the device. In ordinary operation the emitter of a transistor is forward-biased while the collector is reverse-biased. The grounded-base current gain α_{FB} is defined as $-\partial I_C/\partial I_E$ at constant collector voltage V_C. I_C is collector current, and I_E is emitter current.

This current gain α_{FB} is a circuit parameter reflecting the complete behavior of the transistor as a circuit element. This would include stray capacitances, inductances, and resistances involved with the encapsulation of the device. In this section we are concerned only with the operation of the innate device itself, and we shall, accordingly, use a current gain α without subscript to indicate this idealization. Also in this section, as in all the device sections of Parts I and II of this book, lower-case subscripts will be used to denote the electrode involved when a device idealization is concerned rather than a complete circuit parameter.

The transistor action is effected by the injection of minority carriers (electrons in the case of the NPN) into the base region by the emitter, their transport through the base region, and their collection by the collector junction. Therefore, we can consider α as the product of four factors $\alpha = \alpha^*\beta\gamma M$, where α^* is the innate collector efficiency, β is the transport efficiency, γ is the injection efficiency, and M is the multiplication

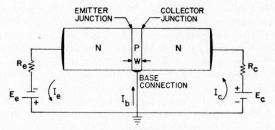

NPN TRANSISTOR DIAGRAM

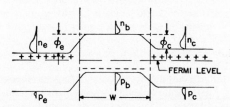

NPN TRANSISTOR ENERGY BANDS WITHOUT BIAS

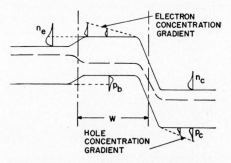

NPN TRANSISTOR ENERGY BANDS WITH BIAS

FIG. 4.1. Diagram and energy-level diagrams for an NPN grown-junction transistor.

of carriers during their traversal of the high field region in the depletion layer of the reverse-biased collector junction. These factors are defined quantitatively as follows (for NPN transistors):

$$\alpha^* = \frac{\partial I_c}{\partial I_{nc}} \frac{1}{M} \qquad \beta = \frac{\partial I_{nc}}{\partial I_{ne}} \qquad \gamma = \frac{\partial I_{ne}}{\partial I_e}$$

where I_c = total collector-junction current
I_{nc} = electron current through collector junction
I_{ne} = electron current through emitter junction
I_e = total emitter-junction current
and M is a function of V_c which can often be closely approximated by

$$M = \left[1 - \left(\frac{V_c}{BV_c}\right)^m \right]^{-1}$$

BV_c is the avalanche-breakdown voltage of the collector junction, and n is a parameter which varies with the type of transistor.

4.1a. Emitter Injection Efficiency γ. We shall first compute the injection efficiency γ. The considerations involved are most clearly and easily seen from an examination of the efficiency of an emitter junction between regions of uniform lifetime and resistivity. The emitters in both grown-junction and alloyed-junction transistors closely approximate this model. The total current through the emitter junction when it is biased in the forward direction can be calculated in a manner similar to the derivation of Eq. (3.9). This method of calculation, it will be recalled, requires first that the diffusion gradients for both holes and electrons be considered. The hole and electron currents are then found to be proportional to these gradients. There is one significant difference between the case of the single junction considered in Sec. 3 and the case of the two-junction transistor considered here. This difference consists in the fact that the base region is sufficiently thin for the bias condition of either junction to affect seriously the current in the other junction. The base-region thickness W is very much less than the diffusion length L_{nb} for electrons in the base region.

We shall consider the bias condition illustrated at the bottom of Fig. 4.1. The hole diffusion gradient in the emitter region is given by the density of holes just on the emitter side of the junction minus the density p_e deep in the emitter region divided by the diffusion length L_{pe} for holes in the emitter region. The hole density at the junction is given by $p_b \exp\left[-q(\phi_e - V_e)/kT\right]$. For $V_e = 0$ we know this density is p_e so that we see that $p_b \exp\left(-q\phi_e/kT\right) = p_e$, and the density just on the emitter side of the junction with forward bias applied is $p_e \exp\left(qV_e/kT\right)$. This gives the hole current through the emitter junction to be

$$I_{pe} = -\frac{qAD_p[p_e \exp\left(qV_e/kT\right) - p_e]}{L_{pe}} = -\frac{qAD_p p_e}{L_{pe}}\left(e^{qV_e/kT} - 1\right) \qquad (4.1a)$$

where D_p is the diffusion constant for holes. This is the same as Eq. (3.8). We shall now calculate the electron current through the forward-biased emitter junction, and here we shall see that the presence of a reverse-biased collector junction gives us a different result from that obtained in Eq. (3.7) for a single junction.

The electron diffusion gradient in the base region is given by the electron density just on the base side of the emitter junction divided by the width W of the base region. There is no residual electron density n_b to subtract, since the reverse-biased collector acts as a sink for electrons on the other side of the base region and reduces the electron density on that side to zero. The electron density on the emitter side of the base is given by $n_b \exp\left(qV_e/kT\right)$, so that the electron current I_{ne} is

$$I_{ne} = -qA\frac{D_n n_b}{W}\left(e^{qV_e/kT}\right) \qquad (4.1b)$$

where D_n is the diffusion constant for electrons. The total emitter current I_e is then

$$I_e = -qA\left(\frac{D_n n_b}{W} + \frac{D_p p_e}{L_{pe}}\right)\left(e^{qV_e/kT}\right) - q\frac{AD_p p_e}{L_{pe}} \qquad (4.2)$$

This equation for the current through the emitter junction is seen to differ from Eq. (3.9) for a single junction by the property that the current is not zero when $V_e = 0$ but rather is $-qD_n n_b/W$. This grounded emitter current flows by virtue of the reverse bias on the collector and the fact that $W \ll L_{nb}$. The charge carrier density distributions used in the preceding calculations are illustrated in the center of Fig. 4.1.

We are now in a position to calculate the injection efficiency γ. From Eqs. (4.1b) and (4.2) and the definition of γ, we obtain

$$\gamma = \frac{\partial I_{ne}}{\partial I_e} = \frac{\partial I_{ne}/\partial V_e}{\partial I_e/\partial V_e} = \frac{D_n n_b/W}{(D_n n_b/W) + (D_p p_e/L_{pe})} \tag{4.3}$$

In order to rewrite this in terms of more simply measured quantities, we want to replace the diffusion constants and carrier densities with simple resistivities. To do this we shall make use of a relation, called the Einstein relation, between diffusion constant D and mobility μ, which is given by $D = \mu(kT/q)$.

To derive this relation we will consider the region of a barrier under equilibrium conditions. In a barrier there is an electric field $-\nabla\phi$ which repels charge carriers as they approach the barrier. This means that the density of carriers drops off as the barrier is approached. The density gradient thus produced requires a diffusion current of carriers toward the barrier which just balances (at equilibrium) the field repulsion current away from the barrier. Writing this down for holes near a barrier we get

$$\begin{array}{cc} \text{field current} & \text{diffusion current} \\ -q p \mu_p \nabla\phi \quad = & q D_p \nabla p \end{array} \tag{4.4}$$

Now by analogy with Eq. (3.2b) we find that Maxwell-Boltzmann statistics give the hole density p at the potential ϕ to be

$$p = p_p e^{-q\phi/kT} \tag{4.5}$$

where p_p is the density of holes in the valence band remote from the barrier. Substituting (4.5) into (4.4) and evaluating ∇p, we get

$$-q p \mu_p \nabla\phi = q D_p \left(-\frac{q}{kT} \nabla\phi \right) p_p e^{-q\phi/kT}$$

and reducing we get

$$\mu_p = \frac{q D_p}{kT} \quad \text{or} \quad D_p = \mu_p \frac{kT}{q} \tag{4.6}$$

which is the Einstein relation.

From Eq. (2.6) and following, we find that $p_e/n_b = (\rho_e/\rho_b)(\mu_n/\mu_p)$, where ρ_b and ρ_e are the resistivities of the base and emitter regions, respectively. Substituting these relations and the Einstein relation into Eq. (4.3) gives us an expression for injection efficiency γ in a simple form:

$$\gamma = \left(1 + \frac{\rho_e W}{\rho_b L_{pe}} \right)^{-1} \tag{4.7}$$

A numerical example will show the magnitude of γ. Let us assign the following magnitudes to the parameters of the base and emitter regions:

$$\begin{aligned} \rho_e &= 0.1 \text{ ohm-cm} \\ \rho_b &= 5 \text{ ohm-cm} \\ W &= 0.002 \text{ cm} \\ L_{pe} &= 0.005 \text{ cm [10-}\mu\text{sec lifetime by Eq. (3.11)]} \end{aligned}$$

This gives $\gamma = (1 + 0.02 \times 0.4)^{-1} = 0.992$.

In assuming above that $L_{nb} \gg W$, we have effectively assumed that there is very little injected carrier recombination in the base region. Under these conditions, β, the transfer efficiency, is very nearly unity, since if there is very little recombination in the base region, nearly all the electrons injected through the emitter junction live to reach the collector junction.

In the case of an alloyed emitter it will most likely be the thickness of the regrown emitter body W_e which will determine the hole current injected into the emitter. If it is assumed that the surface of the regrown material is a region of high recombination, then the analysis remains the same with W_e replacing L_{pe}.

The calculation of emitter efficiency in the case of transistors with nonuniform emitter and base regions is more complicated. Such situations are encountered in transistors made by the diffusion process. Here, for an NPN,[1]

$$\frac{1}{\gamma} - 1 = \frac{D_{pe} \int_b (N_A - N_D)\, dx}{D_{nb} \int_e (N_D - N_A)\, dx} \tag{4.8}$$

It is assumed in the derivation of Eq. (4.8) that recombination at the free surface of the emitter is very high and that both emitter and base widths are small compared, respectively, with L_{pe} and L_{nb}. The integrals are respectively over the thicknesses of the emitter and base regions.

Up until now we have been considering the efficiency of the diffusion process for the delivery of minority carriers into the base. This is not the whole story. For example, suppose the emitter junction were shunted by a low impedance; then a good deal of what was supposedly emitter current is really just ohmic flow through the shunt which cannot possibly yield minority-carrier flow into the base. However, in general, it is difficult to shunt an emitter effectively because at reasonable emitter currents the emitter impedance $kT/qI_e = 26$ mv$/I_e$ ma is just a few ohms. The usual fabrication procedures are not likely to leave such surface shunts across the emitter.

In some semiconductors and some junctions such a shunt may be implicit in the junction itself.[2] In the ordinary diode theory, discussed in Sec. 3, only the contributions of diffusion flow to the currents were considered. There is a space-charge region of finite width which, when the junction is reverse-biased, is largely emptied of mobile carriers. Then, in this region, a net generation of carriers (electron-hole pairs) goes on. This generation rate per unit volume is larger than the generation in the neutral material on both sides of the space-charge region by the ratio n_i/n_{minor}, where n_{minor} is the number of minority carriers. These carriers are swept out by the field, emerging as majority-carrier current on both sides and adding to the ordinary diffusion saturation current. This additional current is proportional to the width of the junction and varies with voltage in the same way that the width does. It is usually necessary for the ordinary saturation current to be very small before this effect is observable. This is because $n_i/n_{\text{minor}} = n_{\text{major}}/n_i$, and since n_{major} is relatively constant, the smaller n_i, the more pronounced the effect. Consequently, it is easier to see this effect in silicon than in germanium.

Similarly, when a junction is forward-biased, there exists in the space-charge region a larger than equilibrium number of carriers giving a net recombination in this region. Thus we have majority carriers coming from both sides and annihilating each other in the junction. This looks like a shunt. Here again the significance of this shunt depends on how large its current is in comparison with the diffusion currents which would flow at the same bias. The larger the energy gap (and, therefore, the lower the diffusion current at a given voltage) and the wider the junction and the more the recombination-generation center density, the more likely that this effect will cut into γ. This effect is greater when the recombination center levels are closer to the center of the gap.

Effects possibly attributable to this mechanism are observed in silicon transistors (see Sec. 4.2). The values of α at low values of I_e are considerably lower than experience with germanium has led one to expect. If conditions are right (or rather wrong), this effect may be much more vexing in still wider gap semiconductors such as gallium-arsenide.

4.1b. Transport Efficiency β. The factor can be estimated to a first-order approximation from rather simple considerations. The rate at which carriers are lost by recombination is given, in general, by $\Delta n/\tau$, where Δn is the excess number of carriers above the equilibrium value and τ is the lifetime. Thus the rate at which carriers are lost to recombination during traversal of the base of a transistor of area A and width W is given by $(\Delta n_E/2\tau)AW$, where Δn_E is the excess over the equilibrium number of minority carriers in the base at the emitter junction. The average density of excess carriers in the base is $\Delta n_E/2$ as can be seen from Fig. 4.10. The rate at which carriers cross the base is given by $(\Delta n_E/W)D_nA$. The ratio of recombination current to diffusion current is, therefore, $W^2/2D_n\tau$ or $W^2/2L_{nb}^2$. From the definition of β we get to the first order

$$\beta = 1 - \frac{W^2}{2L_{nb}^2} \tag{4.9}$$

This evaluation of β assumes only a small amount of bulk recombination in a thin parallel-sided base region. If recombination at the surface or contacts is important and the geometry quite different, a different evaluation should be made. A more rigorous derivation of β not involving the assumption of a very small amount of recombination yields

$$\beta = \operatorname{sech} \frac{W}{L_{nb}} \tag{4.10}$$

This reduces to (4.9) when $W \ll L_{nb}$.

A numerical example will give an idea of the magnitude of β. If we have a base region of thickness $W = 2 \times 10^{-3}$ cm of P-type germanium of 30 μsec lifetime, we can calculate L_{nb} from Eqs. (3.11) to be $(90 \times 30 \times 10^{-6})^{1/2} = 5.2 \times 10^{-2}$ cm:

$$\beta = 1 - \frac{4 \times 10^{-6}}{2 \times 27 \times 10^{-4}} = 1 - 7.4 \times 10^{-4} = 0.99926$$

In many transistors the current across the base proceeds with the aid of drift in an electric field as well as diffusion. The so-called diffused-base or drift transistors are the most notable example. In this case, since the drift field shortens the transit time across the base, the β is larger than would be computed with Eq. (4.10).

In many transistor structures the β depends significantly on the surface recombination around the emitter contact. This factor is given by

$$\beta = \frac{I_{ne} - I_s}{I_{ne}} = 1 - \frac{I_s}{I_{ne}} = 1 - \frac{sA_sW}{A_eD_n} \tag{4.11}$$

where the surface recombination current $I_s = qsA_sn$; the emitter-injected electron current $I_{ne} = qA_enD_n/W$; A_s is the surface area of the base region immediately surrounding the emitter junction; A_e is the emitter-junction area; n is the density of excess electrons just beneath the emitter junction and therefore at the surface A_s; and s is the surface recombination velocity (defined by $J_s = qns$ where J_s is the recombination current density flowing into the surface and n is the excess electron density just beneath the surface).

4.1c. Collector Saturation Current I_{CO}. We shall now proceed to consider the collector current. In the absence of emitter current, we can calculate the current through the collector junction I_{CO} as follows:

The hole current through the collector barrier in the case of large reverse bias is $I_{pc} = qAD_pp_c/L_{pc}$. The electron current through the collector barrier is

$$I_{nc} = \frac{qAD_nn_b \exp \ (qV_e/kt)}{W}$$

The emitter voltage cannot be equal to zero, since we are requiring zero current from the emitter, and Eq. (4.2) shows that I_e is not zero for $V_e = 0$. Solving Eq. (4.2) for $\exp \ (qV_e/kT)$ when $I_e = 0$ gives the following equation for I_{CO}:

$$I_{CO} = I_{pc} + I_{nc} = qA \ \frac{(D_pp_c/L_{pc}) + (D_nn_b/W)(D_pp_e/L_{pe})}{(D_pp_e/L_{pe}) + (D_nn_b/W)} \tag{4.12}$$

or simplifying using Eq. (4.3):

$$I_{CO} = qA \left[\frac{D_pp_c}{L_{pc}} + \frac{D_nn_b}{W} (1 - \gamma) \right] \tag{4.13}$$

This equation holds if there is no regeneration in either the base or collector regions. Since $I_e = 0$, the emitter is slightly reverse-biased as well as the collector. The normal electron density n_b in the base region is therefore drained down and regeneration occurs tending to restore thermodynamic equilibrium. In the collector barrier depletion region such regeneration tends to restore the much larger intrinsic carrier density n_i. (See page 3-13). The result is to add two terms to I_{CO}, one for the base regeneration (the electron diffusion current qAD_nn_b/L_{nb} diminished by the ratio W/L_{nb}) and one for the collector barrier regeneration ($qAtn_i/2\tau$). I_{CO} now becomes:

$$I_{CO} = qA \left[\frac{D_pp_c}{L_{pc}} + \frac{D_nn_b}{W} (1 - \gamma) + \frac{D_nn_bW}{L_{nb}^2} + \frac{tn_i}{2\tau} \right] \tag{4.14}$$

or simplifying by the use of Eq. (4.9):

$$I_{CO} = \frac{qAD_pp_c}{L_{pc}} + \frac{qAD_nn_b}{W} [(1 - \gamma) + 2(1 - \beta)] + \frac{qAtn_i}{2\tau} \tag{4.15}$$

In this equation (qAD_pp_c/L_{pc}) is the hole current through the collector barrier from the collector region; (qAD_nn_b/W) is the electron current through collector junction with grounded emitter; and the collector-barrier regeneration current $(qAtn_i/2\tau)$ is significant only in high gap semiconductors such as silicon.

4.1d. Collector Efficiency α^*. We shall now proceed to the consideration of α^*, the collection efficiency of the collector junction defined as $\partial I_c/\partial I_{nc}$. The effect of a forward bias across the emitter junction is to increase the number of electrons in the base region. These electrons flow by diffusion across the base region and fall into the collector junction. Under normal circumstances these electrons do not affect the diffusion current of holes flowing out of the collector, so that $I_c = I_{pc} + I_{nc}$ without any cross terms. In this case $\alpha^* = 1$.

This conclusion rests on two assumptions: (1) that p_c and L_{pc} are not affected by emitter current and (2) that the conduction current of holes (conduction current as distinguished from diffusion current) in the collector region is negligible. It is very difficult to see how either L_{pc} or p_c could be modified significantly by the emitter current for normal operating conditions. We shall, therefore, consider the conduction-current assumption in more detail.

The electrons which cross the base and are collected by the collector constitute a majority-carrier current in the collector body which proceeds primarily by drift in an electric field. This field which arises from the IR drop due to this flow of ohmic current is in such a direction as to carry a drift current of holes (the minority carriers) toward the collector. Since the ohmic field is proportional to the collected current, the additional drift current of minority carriers from the collector is also proportional to the collected current and appears as an enhanced collector efficiency. The greater the resistivity of the collector body, the more pronounced this effect for two reasons: (1) There is a higher ohmic electric field, and (2) there is a larger density of minority carriers to drift in this field.

Calculating α^* taking into account the field currents in the collector region, we shall write

$$\begin{aligned} I_{nc} &= -Aq(n_c\mu_n \text{ grad } V + D_n \text{ grad } n_c) \\ I_{pc} &= -Aq(p_c\mu_p \text{ grad } V - D_p \text{ grad } p_c) \end{aligned}$$ (4.16)

Setting, grad n_c = grad p_c = p_c/L_{pc} from the space-charge neutrality condition, and eliminating grad V between Eqs. (4.16), we get

$$I_{pc} = I_{nc} \frac{p_c\mu_p}{n_c\mu_n} - qA \frac{D_p p_c}{L_{pc}} \left(\frac{p_c}{n_c} + 1 \right)$$ (4.17)

giving the total collector current

$$I_c = I_{nc} \left(1 + \frac{p_c\mu_p}{n_c\mu_n} \right) - qA \frac{D_p p_c}{L_{pc}} \left(\frac{p_c}{n_c} + 1 \right)$$ (4.18)

Taking $\partial I_c/\partial I_{nc}$, we get for an NPN transistor

$$\alpha^* = \frac{\partial I_c}{\partial I_{nc}} = 1 + \frac{p_c\mu_p}{n_c\mu_n}$$ (4.19)

For a PNP transistor

$$\alpha^* = 1 + \frac{n_c\mu_n}{p_c\mu_p}$$ (4.20)

Both of these expressions reduce to

$$\alpha^* = 1 + q^2 n_i^2 \mu_n\mu_p\rho_c^2$$ (4.21)

where ρ_c is the resistivity of the collector. Table 4.1 shows the variation of α^* with ρ_c for germanium. It is apparent from Eq. (4.21) that this effect will be negligible in silicon because n_i^2 is so much smaller.

TABLE 4.1. VARIATION OF COLLECTOR CURRENT GAIN WITH RESISTIVITY

Collector conductivity type	N	N	N	N	N	P	P	P	P	P
Collector resistivity....	1.7	4.4	8.6	16.9	37.	43.7	22.2	11.5	5.8	2.3
α^*..........	1.000	1.001	1.004	1.015	1.095	1.167	1.027	1.007	1.003	1.000

4.1e. Collector Junction Avalanche Multiplication M. When the carriers which cross the base enter the high electric fields in the space-charge region of the collector junction, they may, if the fields are high enough, achieve energies sufficiently high to knock electrons from the valence band to the conduction band.[3] This creates electron-hole pairs. These collision products are, in turn, accelerated by the high electric field and, in their turn, create more electron-hole pairs, and so on. This avalanche process results in a multiplication of the initially collected current which we shall designate by M. M is a function of the collector voltage.   It is 1 at low collector reverse voltage and infinity at BV_c, the avalanche-breakdown voltage of the collector junction.   The way in which it goes from 1 to infinity as a function of voltage depends on the way in which the electric field strengths in the space-charge region change as a function of voltage and upon whether the particles initiating the avalanche are holes or electrons.   This latter fact is important because, in general, the rate at which an electron in a given high field can create electron-hole pairs is different from that for a hole.   Specifically, in silicon the electron is more proficient in this process than the hole while in germanium the hole has the higher ionization rate.

In many cases the empirical expression[4]

$$M(V_c) = \frac{1}{1 - (V_c/BV_c)^m} \tag{4.22}$$

closely describes the variation of collector-junction multiplication with voltage.   The parameter m depends on the material, the type of junction, and whether the transistor is NPN or PNP.   It is best known in the case of alloyed-junction germanium transistors.   For PNP germanium transistors of this type, $m = 3$; for NPN germanium transistors, $m = 6$.   A numerical example of the kind of M values which may be encountered follows: A PNP germanium-alloy transistor made on 1-ohm-cm N-type material will have an avalanche-breakdown voltage of about 100 volts (see Sec. 3). At a collector reverse bias of 25 volts, $M = 1.015$, and at $V_c = 50$ volts, M would equal 1.14.

In silicon transistors m values have been observed from 1.5 for a low BV_c NPN alloyed junction to 9 for PNP transistors with graded collector junctions and breakdown voltages in the range of 20 to 200 volts.

4.1f. Other Effects of Voltage and Current on α.   The effects of collector voltage will now be discussed.   As the collector voltage is increased, the thickness of the collector barrier is increased.   (This phenomenon will be discussed in detail later in connection with the unipolar transistor.   It is illustrated in Fig. 4.17.)   This barrier thickening encroaches upon both the base region and the collector region.   If the base region is of higher resistivity than the collector region, the depletion region of the collector barrier will extend farther into the base region than into the collector region.   As collector voltage is increased, W will be decreased.   As W decreases, α will increase, giving the highest values of α at the highest practical collector voltages.

This dependence of α on collector voltage manifests itself in a higher small-signal collector conductance than would be expected on the basis of the more idealized picture.[5]   The collector conductance due to this effect is given by

$$g_c = \left. \frac{\partial I_c}{\partial V_c} \right|_{I_e} = \frac{I_e}{W} \left[2(1 - \beta) + (1 - \gamma) \right] \frac{\partial W}{\partial V_c}$$

or

$$g_c = I_e \left[\frac{W}{L^2_{nb}} + \frac{\sigma_b}{\sigma_e L_{pe}} \right] \frac{\partial W}{\partial V_c} \tag{4.23}$$

The form of these expressions can be explained by the following physical arguments: The conductance arises from the fact that as the collector voltage is increased, more carriers are collected because they traverse a thinner base.   For an increment in voltage, the increment in collected carriers will be proportional to the emitted current and to the fractional change in base width.   This accounts for the dependence on $I_e(1/W)(\partial W/\partial V_c)$.   The increment in collected carriers also must depend on how many more carriers originally emitted are recoverable.   This means that a factor like $(1 - \alpha)$ must appear in g_c.   The actual form of the expression in the parentheses of this type arises because $(1 - \beta)$ depends on the square of the base layer thickness, hence the factor of 2, while $(1 - \gamma)$ is directly proportional to W.

This conductance effect would be most pronounced in transistors with thin high-resistivity bases. $\partial W / \partial V_c$ is governed by the type of collector junction, abrupt or graded, and will be discussed later in connection with the unipolar transistor.

There is another effect of high collector voltage which should be mentioned here. If the collector voltage is increased sufficiently to cause the depletion region of the collector barrier to move entirely through the base region and at some point contact the emitter region, a relatively low-resistance path between the emitter and collector is established. This phenomenon is known as "punch-through" breakdown. In many transistors such a breakdown occurs before the collector barrier, as such, breaks down by any of the mechanisms discussed at the end of Sec. 3. There is no permanent damage done to a transistor which has undergone punch-through.

Punch-through breakdown is usually encountered in transistors which have a very low resistivity collector region and a high-resistivity base region such as the alloy-junction transistor and the surface-barrier transistor. In this case the depletion region of the collector barrier extends primarily into the base region. For such transistors with base regions of uniform resistivity we can relate the punch-through voltage PV_c to the thickness of the base region W, using a form of Eq. (4.84).

$$W = 1.65 \times 10^6 \left(\frac{PV_c}{N}\right)^{1/2} \quad \text{mils for germanium}$$

$$W = 1.43 \times 10^6 \left(\frac{PV_c}{N}\right)^{1/2} \quad \text{mils for silicon}$$

(4.24)

where PV_c is in volts, W is in mils, and N is the net doping density in the base.

There are other departures from the simplified picture of transistor operation given above. One of the principal of these is the result of a dependence of α on I_e. This dependence arises, in general, from a combination of the following factors: (1) The lifetime in the base is a function of current. Lifetime is, in general, a function of the number of carriers available for recombination.[6] This is because most recombination proceeds via a fixed number of recombination centers. As the number of carriers increases, they saturate these centers and the average lifetime per carrier increases. Therefore, one would expect α to increase monotonically with I_e owing to this mechanism whether we are dealing with surface or bulk recombination. (2) The emitter efficiency γ is a function of current. As the emitter current density goes up, a point is reached at which the density of injected minority carriers is no longer small compared with the density of majority carriers in the base. At this point, because of the requirements of charge neutrality, the number of majority carriers in the base starts to increase appreciably with I_e. When the emitter is forward-biased, majority carriers from the emitter flow into the base and majority carriers from the base flow into the emitter. Thus this increase in the base carrier density results in a decrease in γ, since a smaller portion of the emitter current consists of carriers injected into the base. (3) The geometrical distribution of current (of injection and collection) is a function of current. This results from the fact that there are appreciable lateral base resistances in the actual two-dimensional as opposed to the idealized one-dimensional transistor. A majority-carrier current flows from or into the base lead to recombine with the minority carriers lost in transit and to make up for the currents necessary to account for γ less than unity, M greater than unity, and α^* greater than unity. The ohmic IR drop due to this combined flow causes different portions of the base to be at different potentials. It should be remembered that a potential difference of 26 mv changes the emission by a factor of e at room temperature. The first two components of the base current mentioned flow from the base lead (for an NPN), while the latter two flow into the base lead.   If the first two outweigh the latter two, then the portion of the emitter closest to the base lead is forward-biased most.   If the latter two outweigh the first two, the portion of the emitter farthest from the base lead is forward-biased the most.   In other words, a transistor with $\alpha < 1$ has the center of gravity of emission shift toward the base lead with increasing I_e while a transistor with $\alpha > 1$ has the emission shift away from the base lead with increasing I_e.   Since a shift of emission toward the base lead generally means a shift of emission to a place where the carriers are more greatly affected by surface recombination, the α goes down with increasing I_e for transistors with $\alpha < 1$ while it increases with I_e for transistors with $\alpha > 1$.   Both of these effects are observed, and the fact that they are indicates that this latter geometrical effect outweighs the conductivity modulation effect discussed previously.   In transistors with $\alpha < 1$, the drop in α at high currents is a well-known phenomenon.   Figure 4.2 shows some typical data.   The negative resistance observable in two terminal avalanche transistors (these will be discussed later) is the direct result of α increasing with I_e because of a similar focusing effect for $\alpha > 1$.

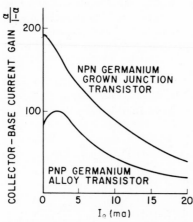

FIG. 4.2. Variation of the grounded-emitter current gain with emitter current for some sample junction transistors.

4.2. Generalized Transistor Equations.
The most general treatment of the transistor must take cognizance of the fact that fundamentally there is no difference between the emitter and collector junction.   In fact, in a symmetrical alloyed-junction transistor they are indistinguishable in detail.   Thus one would expect expressions of similar form for both the emitter current and collector current as functions of the junction voltages.   These equations are [7,8]

$$I_e = a_{11}(e^{qV_e/kT} - 1) + a_{12}(e^{qV_c/kT} - 1)$$
and
$$I_c = a_{21}(e^{qV_e/kT} - 1) + a_{22}(e^{qV_c/kT} - 1) \tag{4.25}$$

These equations are derived with no restrictions on geometry: V_e and V_c are the junction voltages.   They are positive when the junction is forward-biased. I_e and I_c are positive going, respectively, into the emitter or collector.   The derivation of these equations assumes negligible built-in fields in the base.   It can also be shown that $a_{12} = a_{21}$ under the same conditions.   The a coefficients can be given in terms of conductivities, mobilities, lifetimes, and W, the base width, in very complicated expressions.[7]   However, it is more instructive and useful to evaluate the a coefficients in terms of the easily measurable transistor parameters:

α_F = α of transistor with emitter used as emitter and collector as collector
α_R = α with collector used as emitter and emitter as collector
I_{CO} = saturation current of collector with emitter open circuited
I_{EO} = saturation current of emitter with collector open circuited

When the collector is reverse-biased so that V_c is negative and large in magnitude compared with kT/q, Eqs. (4.25) become

$$I_e = a_{11}(e^{qV_e/kT} - 1) - a_{12}$$
$$I_c = a_{21}(e^{qV_e/kT} - 1) - a_{22} \tag{4.26}$$

If the parenthetical expression is eliminated between these two equations,

$$I_c = \frac{a_{21}}{a_{11}} I_e + \left(\frac{a_{12}a_{21}}{a_{11}} - a_{22} \right) \tag{4.27}$$

Similarly if the emitter is reverse-biased, one obtains

$$I_e = \frac{a_{12}}{a_{22}} I_c + \left(\frac{a_{12}a_{21}}{a_{22}} - a_{11} \right) \tag{4.28}$$

When these latter two equations are compared with their counterparts in terms of the four measurable transistor parameters

$$\begin{aligned} I_c &= -\alpha_F I_e + I_{CO} \\ I_e &= -\alpha_R I_c + I_{EO} \end{aligned} \tag{4.29}$$

the a coefficients can be evaluated. Then Eqs. (4.25) become[8]

$$\begin{aligned} I_e &= -\frac{I_{EO}}{1 - \alpha_F\alpha_R} (e^{qV_e/kT} - 1) + \frac{\alpha_R I_{CO}}{1 - \alpha_F\alpha_R} (e^{qV_c/kT} - 1) \\ I_c &= +\frac{\alpha_F I_{EO}}{1 - \alpha_F\alpha_R} (e^{qV_e/kT} - 1) - \frac{I_{CO}}{1 - \alpha_F\alpha_R} (e^{qV_c/kT} - 1) \end{aligned} \tag{4.30}$$

In this treatment we are, of course, assuming constant values of α_F and α_R independent of both junction voltages and current levels. From the preceding discussion, we know that departures from these assumptions are encountered. The complexity of the a coefficients in terms of the physical parameters can be seen by referral to the evaluations of saturation currents and alphas in terms of these physical quantities in Sec. 4.1.

While the generality of this treatment is merely intellectually satisfying for transmission applications, it is essential for an understanding of the transistor as a switch, for in switching applications the transistor frequently exists in states where both the emitter and collector junctions are simultaneously forward-biased. Before the transistor as a switch is discussed, we shall derive some interesting general results with the aid of Eqs. (4.30).

Since it can be shown that $a_{12} = a_{21}$, it follows from Eqs. (4.30) that $\alpha_R I_{CO} = \alpha_F I_{EO}$ for all transistors within the assumptions made during the derivation. The principal one of these which is likely to cause trouble is the one about no built-in drift fields in the base region. This is because many high-frequency transistors now made by diffusion do contain such a drift field as a result of a gradient in doping. (This will be discussed in detail later.) However, careful measurements[9] in transistors having diffused bases as well as those having uniform bases do confirm this relation. In general, ordinary measurements of saturation currents at some sizable reverse bias do not agree with this relation. This is probably the result of surface-leakage effects.

When one of the interacting junctions which make up a transistor is subjected to an applied bias, this bias is transmitted in some measure to the other junction even though the intervening base is grounded and the other junction is open circuited. Briefly, this occurs because the application of a bias to one junction changes the concentration of minority carriers in the base near the other junction from the equilibrium value. This disturbs the detailed balance of currents across the other junction. Since the other junction carries no current, its potential must adjust in such a direction as to restore the balance of currents. It is easy to see from such arguments that if, say, the collector of a transistor were reverse-biased, the open-circuited emitter would also float at a reverse bias. The magnitude of this floating potential is easily computed by recourse to the general transistor equations (4.30). Let $I_e = 0$ and $-\phi_c \gg kT/q$. Then

$$0 = \frac{I_{EO}}{1 - \alpha_F \alpha_R} (e^{qV_e/kT} - 1) + \frac{\alpha_R I_{CO}}{1 - \alpha_F \alpha_R}$$

or

$$e^{qV_e/kT} = 1 - \frac{\alpha_R I_{CO}}{I_{EO}} = 1 - \alpha_F$$

Thus the floating potential saturates at

$$V_e = \frac{kT}{q} \ln (1 - \alpha_F) \tag{4.31}$$

For $\alpha_F = 0.99$, V_e at room temperature $= -26 \ln 100 \text{ mv} = -120 \text{ mv}$. For $\alpha_F = 0.9$, V_e at room temperature $= -26 \ln 10 \text{ mv} = -60 \text{ mv}$.

This floating potential constitutes a measurement of α_F at very low current levels. In germanium transistors its value corresponds quite closely to the value obtained by extrapolating the values of α versus I_e to the limit of zero I_e. In the case of silicon, anomalously low values of emitter floating potential are always observed—far smaller than 1 mv. This probably results from the space-charge regeneration and recombination effect which gives $\gamma \to 0$ at very low values of I_e. On the other hand, anomalously large floating potentials can be observed in any transistor if a surface inversion layer on the base gives an ohmic bridge between the emitter and collector bodies. Transistors in which a very small length of surface has to be bridged are particularly prone to this effect. The existence of such an effect can render some switching circuits inoperative.

4.3. The Transistor as a Switch. We have developed the picture of a transistor as being a device in which a certain emitter current gives, in general, a slightly smaller collector current and a base current which makes up the decrement between collector and emitter current. The ratio of collector current to emitter current α is to first order a constant over a large range of currents and is determined by the physics of the device.

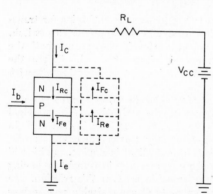

FIG. 4.3. The transistor as a switch showing the superposition which occurs when the switch is in the closed condition.

The relative values of $I_e:I_c:I_b$ are as $1:\alpha:(1 - \alpha)$. Because of this inexorable relationship it is possible to get current gain by grounding the emitter and putting current into the base. The ratio of collector current to base current is $\alpha/(1 - \alpha)$. This gain can be as high as 1,000 for very high α transistors. Such operation is frequently employed in amplifiers and other nonswitching circuits. This higher gain is, however, bought at the cost of lower bandwidth. This will be discussed later when high-frequency performance is covered.

Now consider the situation which obtains when the external collector circuit in Fig. 4.3, which consists of a battery V_{CC} and series resistance R_L, will not allow a collector current as large as $[\alpha/(1 - \alpha)]I_b$ to flow. That is, $[\alpha/(1 - \alpha)]I_b > V_{CC}/R_L$. Under these conditions the collector junction becomes forward-biased and emits minority carriers which are collected by the emitter. The transistor becomes, in essence, a superposition of two transistors, one with the emitter acting as the emitter and the collector (although it is forward-biased) acting as the collector. The other transistor consists of the collector reemitting some of its collected current and the emitter acting as the collector. The alphas appropriate to these two transistors have already been introduced in the section on the general treatment of the transistor as α_F and α_R. It can be seen from Fig. 4.3 that this superposition subtracts currents in the collector (and emitter) lead and adds them in the base lead. Thus, by an appropriate weighting of the two "transistors," the transistor can accommodate the ratio of I_c to I_b to any value less than $\alpha_F/(1 - \alpha_F)$ imposed by the external constraints. The two transistors do not interact with each other to first order because of the linearity of the diffusion equation governing the flow of carriers across the base.

With the emitter and collector junctions both forward-biased the voltage drop across the ideal transistor (from collector to emitter) becomes the difference between two small forward-bias voltages and is of the order of tens of millivolts. The a-c impedance is also very low, or about a few ohms. Thus, in this type of circuit, the application of an appropriate amount of base current will cause the impedance across the transistor to go from as high as hundreds of megohms to a few ohms. The base current necessary can be considerably smaller than the current switched. This is the closest electronic approach to the ideal switch, namely, the metallic contact which goes essentially from infinite impedance to zero with the application of a control current. The latter is limited for mechanical reasons to speeds of a few kilocycles while transistor switches of sufficiently good quality work at 100 mc.

With the aid of Eqs. (4.30) it is possible to compute the voltage drop across a "closed" transistor switch. These equations are solved for V_e and V_c.

$$
\begin{aligned}
V_e &= \frac{kT}{q} \ln\left(-\frac{I_e + \alpha_R I_c}{I_{EO}} + 1 \right) \approx \frac{kT}{q} \ln\left(-\frac{I_e + \alpha_R I_c}{I_{EO}} \right) \\
V_c &= \frac{kT}{q} \ln\left(-\frac{I_c + \alpha_F I_e}{I_{CO}} + 1 \right) \approx \frac{kT}{q} \ln\left(-\frac{I_c + \alpha_F I_e}{I_{CO}} \right)
\end{aligned}
\tag{4.32}
$$

Then using $I_c + I_b + I_e = 0$

$$
V_{ce} = \pm(V_c - V_e) = \pm \frac{kT}{q} \ln \frac{\alpha_R\left(1 - \dfrac{I_c}{I_b}\dfrac{1 - \alpha_F}{\alpha_F}\right)}{1 + (I_c/I_b)(1 - \alpha_R)}
\tag{4.33}
$$

The plus sign applies to PNP transistors and the minus sign to NPN transistors in this expression. The a-c impedance of the closed switch is easily determined by

$$
\frac{dV_{ce}}{dI_c} = \left| \frac{kT}{q} \left[\frac{1 - \alpha_F}{\alpha_F\left(I_b - I_c \dfrac{1 - \alpha_F}{\alpha_F}\right)} + \frac{1 - \alpha_R}{I_b + I_c(1 - \alpha_R)} \right] \right|
\tag{4.34}
$$

Consider the following example: an NPN transistor with $I_b = +1$ ma, $I_c = +10$ ma, $\alpha_F = 0.98$, $\alpha_R = 0.5$. Then, at room temperature, the voltage across the closed transistor switch is

$$
V_{ce} = -26 \ln \frac{0.5[1 - 10(0.02/0.98)]}{1 + 10(0.5)} \text{ mv}
$$

$$
= -26 \ln \tfrac{1}{15} \text{ mv} = 70.5 \text{ mv}
$$

The a-c impedance across this closed switch is

$$
\frac{dV_{ce}}{dI_c} = 26 \left[\frac{0.02}{0.98[1 - (0.2/0.98)]} + \frac{0.5}{1 + 10(0.5)} \right] \text{ ohms}
$$

$$
= \tfrac{34}{12} = 2.84 \text{ ohms}
$$

The above analysis holds quite well for transistors with very small series resistances in the emitter and collector bodies. Alloyed-junction and surface-barrier transistors meet this criterion best. Appreciable collector body series resistances occur in both grown-junction and diffused-base transistors. These transistors show larger voltage drops and a-c impedances than would be predicted with the above theory.

In very thin base layer transistors such as the diffused-base transistors there is an additional contribution to V_{ce} and dV_{ce}/dI_c due to the lateral base resistance. In Fig. 4.4, an idealized cross section of a diffused-base transistor is shown. In such

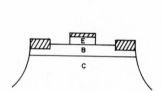

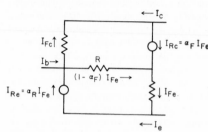

FIG. 4.4. A cross section of a diffused-base transistor.

FIG. 4.5. Equivalent circuit for a highly asymmetrical switching transistor.

thin bases, the transverse resistance in the path between the outer edge of the emitter and the base contact gives rise to a voltage drop which, in turn, biases the outer edge of the collector much more forward than the center. In fact, in extreme cases the center of the collector opposite the emitter may actually be reverse-biased while the periphery is forward-biased. The equivalent circuit for this switch is shown in Fig. 4.5.

The extra voltage drop V_R across R appears between the opposed forward biases of the effective part of the emitter and collector. It appears in both the base-to-emitter and collector-to-emitter voltages. V_R can be evaluated from the following:

$$I_c = \alpha_F I_{Fe} - I_{Fc}$$
$$I_b = (1 - \alpha_F)I_{Fe} + (1 - \alpha_R)I_{Fc} \qquad (4.35)$$

and
$$V_R = (1 - \alpha_F)I_{Fe}R \qquad (4.36)$$

When I_{Fe} is evaluated from the first two equations and substituted in the expression for V_R,

$$V_R = \frac{(1 - \alpha_F)R}{1 - \alpha_F\alpha_R}[(1 - \alpha_R)I_c + I_b] \qquad (4.37)$$

In diffused-base transistors, R can be 100 ohms and α_R as low as 0.2. For $\alpha_F = 0.98$ and $I_b = 1$ ma, $I_c = 10$ ma,

$$V_R = \frac{0.02(100)}{0.8}[(0.8)(10) + 1]\text{ mv} = \frac{18}{0.8} = 22.5\text{ mv}$$

For larger values of R and higher current levels, this contribution to V_{ce} can easily far outweigh the voltage drop given by Eq. (4.33).

The high-frequency response of the transistor switch will be discussed after the development of the high-frequency properties of the transistor in general.

4.4. Four-region Transistors. The transistor has been discussed up to now as two interacting junctions. Devices are possible which involve a third and possibly more junctions parallel to the first two and close enough to interact with them. The structure of this kind which is most widely encountered and is of the most interest is the four-region NPNP or PNPN configuration. This is shown in Fig. 4.6. Such a structure can be achieved by slight variations on the techniques used to make ordinary transistors. For example, it can be made by the grown-junction method known as rate growing, by successive diffusion of impurities, by combinations of diffusion and alloying, and frequently by accident.

These four-region transistors exist in a variety of forms. Contacts can be made to all four regions, only to the end regions and one of the middle regions, or even to only the end regions. The last two forms are the most widely used. The three-contact device constitutes the equivalent of a transistor with a large α^*. In fact, this α^* is generally large enough to give a total α far in excess of 1. This has been known as the "hook-collector" transistor.

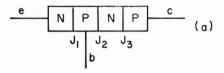

4.4a. The "Hook-collector" Transistor. This transistor consists of an emitter junction J_1, a collector junction J_2, and what amounts to another emitter J_3. The last forms the hook collector. The operation of the device shown in Fig. 4.6a can best be explained in terms of the compound structure in Fig. 4.6b which is equivalent. The collector saturation current I_{co} is divided equally between the two transistors for convenience. Any arbitrary apportionment would yield the same result.

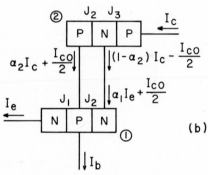

A bias is applied to this device which reverse-biases junction J_2. In the case

Fig. 4.6. The hook-collector transistor.

of the example shown, this would require that the right-hand side be at a positive potential with respect to the left side. With this polarity, junctions J_1 and J_3 are forward-biased. The properties of this structure can be obtained by solving for the relationship among I_c, I_e, and I_b.

The "emitter" current of transistor 2 is I_c, while the emitter current of transistor 1 is I_e. The collector current of transistor 1, namely, $\alpha_1 I_e + (I_{co}/2)$, is the input to the base of transistor 2 and, therefore, equal to $(1 - \alpha_2)I_c - (I_{co}/2)$. The collector current of transistor 2 and I_b combine to give the input to the base of transistor 1. In equation form,

$$(1 - \alpha_2)I_c - \frac{I_{co}}{2} = \alpha_1 I_e + \frac{I_{co}}{2} \tag{4.38}$$

or

$$\alpha_2 I_c + \frac{I_{co}}{2} - I_b = (1 - \alpha_1)I_e - \frac{I_{co}}{2} \tag{4.39}$$

These equations yield the result

$$I_c = \left(\frac{\alpha_1}{1 - \alpha_2}\right) I_e + \frac{I_{co}}{1 - \alpha_2} = \alpha' I_e + I'_{co} \tag{4.40}$$

Thus this device looks like a transistor of $\alpha' = \alpha_1/(1 - \alpha_2)$. Since α_1 and α_2 can easily each be close to 1, α' can have very large values. It should be noted that for $\alpha' > 1$, $\alpha_1 + \alpha_2 > 1$. For example, if $\alpha_1 = 0.95$ and $\alpha_2 = 0.8$, $\alpha' = 4.75$. When $I_e = 0$, the collector current $I'_{co} = I_{co}/(1 - \alpha_2)$. This means that the collector saturation current is multiplied by a factor which essentially amounts to the grounded-emitter current gain of transistor 2. The frequency variation of this compound α' will be discussed in the next section.

The components of α (β, γ, α^*, and M), previously discussed, also determine α_1 and α_2 with proper qualifications regarding the composite structure of the NPNP device. To illustrate the physical significance of the various regions of the structure, we shall calculate α' using only the injection efficiencies γ_1 and γ_2 of the two transistors to represent α_1 and α_2 to a first approximation. Here it must be remembered that the injection efficiency γ_2 is that of the junction J_3 of the composite structure considered as injecting from right to left in Fig. 4.6. If we further assume that γ_1 is essentially unity, we find that

$$\alpha' = \frac{1}{1 - \gamma_2} = 1 + \frac{\rho_f L_{nc}}{W_f \rho_c} \qquad (4.41)$$

where ρ_f and W_f are the resistivity and width of the floating N region and ρ_c and L_{nc} are the resistivity and diffusion length for electrons in the collector region.

Since we have considered the γ_1 to be unity, the α' given by Eq. (4.41) can be considered the α^* of the hook collector.

4.4b. The NPNP Diode. When contacts are made to only the end regions of the four-region transistor, a diode with interesting properties results. The general characteristic of this device is shown in Fig. 4.7. A typical load line is drawn across this characteristic to demonstrate its use as a regenerative switch. The load line, as drawn, intersects the characteristic at two stable points, namely, a and b. At point a a high voltage exists across the device and the a-c impedance of the device is very high. Depending upon the quality and cleanliness of the junctions, this a-c impedance can be hundreds or thousands of megohms.

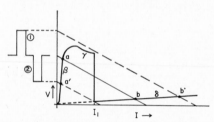

FIG. 4.7. Current-voltage characteristic of an NPNP diode.

On the other hand, at point b the voltage drop across the device will ordinarily be about a volt and the a-c impedance a few ohms. The device will stay in either of these two states until a signal sufficient to switch is applied in series with the battery. For example, consider a positive pulse 1 applied in series with the battery. For the duration of the pulse, the load line is displaced upward and the only intersection is at point b' and the switch is in that state. After the pulse ends, the switch is left in state b. Similarly, the application of a negative voltage pulse 2 in series depresses the load line so that a' is the only stable state. When this pulse ends, the device is back in state a.

The V-I characteristic depicted in Fig. 4.7 arises in the following way: We consider a properly designed hook-collector transistor whose low voltage α is less than 1 at low currents and greater than 1 above a certain current I_1 with the base open circuited. Then for $I_c = I_e$, Eq. (4.40) gives

$$I_c = \frac{M I_{co}}{1 - \alpha_1 M_n - \alpha_2 M_p} \qquad (4.42)$$

M_n is the avalanche multiplication factor for electrons entering the collector junction from the left, and M_p the factor for holes coming from the right. M is a weighted average between M_n and M_p, depending on how much of I_{co} consists of carriers from each side. As long as $\alpha_1 M_n + \alpha_2 M_p < 1$, the total α of the transistor remains less than 1. In this region, designated by β in Fig. 4.7, Eq. (4.42) essentially describes the characteristic. Since this is a two-terminal device, the α cannot exceed 1 or I_c would exceed I_e. Therefore, the peak voltage achieved by the characteristic is close to but not quite so high as the avalanche-breakdown voltage of the central junction. The peak voltage is given by the equation

$$\alpha_1 M_n(V) + \alpha_2 M_p(V) = 1 \qquad (4.43)$$

The negative resistance beyond the peak in the region designated by γ is understood in terms of the operation of the avalanche transistor (Sec. 4.9). It is simply that as the low-voltage alphas α_1 and α_2 increase with increasing current, the multiplication and hence voltage must decrease or the total α will become greater than 1.

When the current reaches I_1, the sum of the low-voltage alphas becomes greater than 1 and the transistor can no longer adjust to the situation by lowering the reverse bias on the collector junction. The only way in which the total α can remain 1 is for the collector junction to assume a forward bias. Then each one of the component transistors, the NPN and the PNP, is in the closed-switch condition discussed in Sec. 4.3. Just as in Sec. 4.3, each one of the transistors adjusts to an effective α lower than its active α to conform to external constraints. The sum of these effective alphas remains 1 at all times. This switch is regenerative, since the collector current of each one acts as the base drive of the other and they essentially hold each other in the closed condition. The voltage across the device in this region, designated by δ in Fig. 4.7, is the total drop across two forward-biased junctions in one direction and one forward-biased junction in the opposite direction. This amounts to a potential drop which is very slightly larger than the drop across a single forward-biased junction. The exact calculation is very complicated. The principal problem in the control of the characteristics of the four-region diode stems from the control of the current I_1 at which $\alpha_1 + \alpha_2 = 1$. In germanium it is difficult to get $\alpha_1 + \alpha_2$ to dip below 1 even at very low currents, and therefore most germanium units have a tendency to show no high-resistance peak at all but go right into the low-impedance condition. In silicon, however, alphas tend to be very low at low currents, and it is quite easy to see characteristics like the one discussed but generally with no great control of the turn-on current.

4.4c. The Thyratron Transistor. The hook-collector transistor is sometimes employed in switching circuits as a "thyratron transistor" or "controlled rectifier." In this application, the transistor operates as a four-region diode whose peak is controlled by an input in the base. Then switching from one stable state to another is effected by a pulse on the base of the transistor rather than by a voltage pulse in series with the battery. In general, it is possible to switch "on" a large current with a relatively small current into the base. It usually takes a drive on the base of the same order as the current switched to turn off. However, it is possible by judicious design to fabricate controlled rectifiers with turn-off gain.

The operation of this device and the principal parameters which determine its characteristics will be covered in the following discussion. Again, we consider a hook-collector transistor whose low voltage α is less than 1 at low currents and greater than 1 above a certain current I_1 with the base open circuited. The V-I characteristic is already given in Fig. 4.7 for the condition $I_b = 0$. In the circuit of Fig. 4.6, if a constant current I_b flows into the base (I_b is negative in the sign convention used in this diagram), $I_c - I_b = I_e$. When this expression is substituted into Eq. (4.40), we get $I_c = (I_{CO} - \alpha_1 I_b)/(1 - \alpha_1 - \alpha_2)$. If cognizance is taken of the current dependence of α and the multiplication of α at higher voltages, this equation becomes

$$I_c = \frac{M I_{CO} - \alpha_1(I_e) M_n I_b}{1 - \alpha_1(I_e) M_n - \alpha_2(I_c) M_p} = \frac{M I_{CO} - \alpha_1(I_c - I_b) M_n I_b}{1 - \alpha_1(I_c - I_b) M_n - \alpha_2(I_c) M_p} \qquad (4.44)$$

We now examine this equation to determine the shape of the peak in the V-I characteristic in comparison with what obtains for $I_b = 0$. In the initial high-resistance portion of the characteristic, I_c is much larger, since there is an additional term in the numerator proportional to I_b which is generally much larger than I_{CO}. Furthermore, the denominator is slightly smaller, since $\alpha_1(I_c - I_b)M_n$ is larger than $\alpha_1(I_c)M_n$ because the alphas are assumed monotonically rising functions of their respective emitter currents. The peak voltage or breakover voltage occurs when I_c begins to increase very rapidly. This happens when the denominator goes to zero or $\alpha_1(I_c - I_b)M_n(V) + \alpha_2(I_c)M_p(V) = 1$. This peak voltage is lower than that for $I_b = 0$ for two reasons. The first is that I_c at the peak is larger because of the arguments given above. This makes both α_1 and α_2 larger. Furthermore, the α_1 value is still larger because the current in transistor 1 is $I_c - I_b$, which is larger than I_c if we recall that I_b is negative. This all militates toward a lower peak voltage the larger the magnitude of I_b.

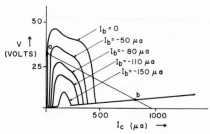

FIG. 4.8. Representative family of characteristics for a thyratron transistor.

The current at which the device goes into the low-impedance condition is now lower than I_1. The condition which must be met for this point is still that the total low-voltage a-c α is 1, since when I_b equals a constant, ΔI_c must equal ΔI_e. The collector current I_2, at which the device switches to the low-impedance state, is given by $\alpha_1(I_2 - I_b) + \alpha_2(I_2) = 1$.

Figure 4.8 gives a representative family of V-I characteristics for a thyratron transistor as a function of I_b. A sample load line is drawn across the figure. If the transistor starts in the high-impedance condition at point a, the application of any current larger than 80 μa into the base will leave only one intersection between the load line and the V-I characteristic, namely, at the low-impedance point b. From this diagram it is clear that difficulties are encountered in switching back from b to a. The best way to effect this switch is the application of a negative voltage pulse in the collector circuit. A large positive I_b in the base lead, almost as large as the current to be switched off, will also turn the device off.

A reexamination of the equation $\alpha_1(I_2 - I_b) + \alpha_2(I_2) = 1$ as the relation which determines the current at which the device switches to the low-impedance state gives some insight into the problem of turn-off gain. We essentially seek a maximum change in I_2 for a minimum change in I_b. It can be seen that

$$\frac{dI_2}{dI_b} = \frac{\partial \alpha_1}{\partial I} \bigg/ \left(\frac{\partial \alpha_1}{\partial I} + \frac{\partial \alpha_2}{\partial I} \right) \qquad (4.44a)$$

The only way in which this fraction can have a large positive value is for α_2 to be a decreasing function of current. Then the denominator can become vanishingly small when the rates of change of the two alphas with current are about equal in magnitude. Thus, in principle, it is possible to construct controlled rectifiers with arbitrarily large turn-off gains. In practice this apparently can best be achieved by construction of a device in which α_1 is quite low and α_2 is very close to 1. Then the rate at which α_1 changes with current can be quite small and approach in magnitude a decrease in gain with current which is possible in the very high gain.

The exact shape of the curves in Fig. 4.8 and how rapidly they change with successive increments of I_b are dependent on the functions $\alpha_1(I)$, $\alpha_2(I)$, $M_n(V)$, and $M_p(V)$. Multiplication as a function of V depends on the kind of collector junction and the semiconductor material, but it should be quite reproducible. On the other hand the magnitudes of α_1 and α_2 and their exact dependence on current are very difficult to control at the present time.

4.5. Frequency Response of Transistors. The high-frequency response of diodes and transistors is limited by a number of effects. A conventional circuit limitation results from the fact that junctions have a space-charge layer capacitance (discussed in Sec. 3 and under the unipolar transistor) and series resistances through which the charging current for these capacitors must flow. This results in the usual RC time limitation on frequency. In addition to the more classical kind of capacity there is a diffusion capacity associated with junctions. This arises because a change in voltage on a junction changes the diffusion current by changing the number of excess charges injected (or extracted) on both sides of the junction. The change in these stored charges with voltage also looks like a capacitance.

Since transistor action depends on the interaction of the emitter and collector, there is a frequency limitation imposed by the ability of the diffusion process to transmit a-c signals. The appreciable average transit time and the dispersion in transit time for individual particles across the base give rise, respectively, to a phase shift and attenuation (with its attendant additional phase shift) for an a-c signal. Further high-frequency effects result from the fact that the emitter efficiency γ is a function of frequency. Ordinarily, in well-designed transistors, the RC times and the diffusion cutoff combine to give the upper frequency limit of operation. However, it is possible in very thin base layer transistors with small junction areas that the upper frequency limit of operation may be limited by the transit time across the space-charge depletion region of the reverse-biased collector. This might happen in a structure with an especially thick depletion region such as NPIN or PNIP transistors.

In switching, the rapidity of response of both diodes and transistors is limited by some of the effects mentioned above as well as by storage phenomena. For example, if a diode has been forward-biased and is suddenly reverse-biased, a reverse current far larger than the saturation current and limited only by the circuit will flow at first. This current will decay after a short time to the saturation current. Similarly, the transistor switch discussed in Sec. 4.3 will not immediately go to the high-impedance condition when the signal is removed from the base. Both of these effects are due to the existence of an excess number of carriers adjacent to a junction which one is attempting to reverse-bias. It is only after these stored carriers are depleted that the junction is free to assume this reverse bias. See Sec. 3-11.

All these effects will be discussed in some detail below.

4.5a. The Frequency Cutoff of β. The d-c β or transport efficiency has been evaluated and discussed in Sec. 4.1b. It will be recalled that β is less than 1 because of the loss of some carriers due to recombination during their transit across the base. In the case of an a-c signal on top of a d-c emitter current, β_{ac} can be less than 1 without any recombination. Consider the a-c signal to be a train of rectangular pulses (for simplicity). As these pulses travel farther from the emitter, they become less rectangular in shape because the carriers of which they consist are all effectively traveling at different velocities. Some carriers begin to fill in the spaces between pulses. The closer the pulses are to each other (or the higher the a-c frequency), the shorter the distance in which the signal will decrease by a specified amount.

This specified amount is 0.707 times the low-frequency β. The frequency at which the a-c β becomes 0.707, the low-frequency β, is called the frequency cutoff f_β. The solution of the time-dependent diffusion equation gives[7]

$$\beta = \text{sech} \frac{W}{L} (1 + i\omega\tau)^{\frac{1}{2}} \qquad (4.45)$$

From this frequency, f_β, at which $\beta^2 = \frac{1}{2}$, can be shown to be

$$f_\beta = \frac{0.39D}{W^2} \tag{4.46}$$

For germanium NPN transistors $\qquad f_\beta = \dfrac{5.65}{W^2}$

For germanium PNP transistors $\qquad f_\beta = \dfrac{2.7}{W^2}$

For silicon NPN transistors $\qquad f_\beta = \dfrac{2.8}{W^2}$

For silicon PNP transistors $\qquad f_\beta = \dfrac{0.95}{W^2}$

$$(4.47)$$

where f_β is in megacycles and W is in mils.

When $W/L \ll 1$, Eq. (4.45) for β can be approximated by[10]

$$\beta = \frac{\beta_0}{1 + j(f/f_\beta)} \tag{4.48}$$

This expression makes it easy to see the phase shift in β as well as the diminution with frequency. The phase shift will be 45° at f_β. Since the frequency cutoff of β is the principal factor in the frequency cutoff of α, Eq. (4.47) is usually designated f_{ab}. Here we shall retain the designation f_β for the sake of rigor, but we can write to a first approximation

$$\alpha = \frac{\alpha_0}{1 + j(f/f_\beta)} \tag{4.49}$$

where α_0 is the low-frequency value of α.

The frequency cutoff of the grounded-emitter transistor can be determined in terms of f_β by evaluating the frequency dependence of $\alpha/(1 - \alpha)$.

$$\frac{\alpha}{1 - \alpha} = \frac{\alpha_0}{1 - \alpha_0 + j(f/f_\beta)}$$

This expression is down to 0.707 of its low-frequency value $\alpha_0/(1 - \alpha_0)$ when

$$f = (1 - \alpha_0)f_\beta$$

Thus the grounded-emitter frequency cutoff is very much lower than the grounded-base cutoff. This can be understood more easily by reference to Fig. 4.9, which depicts the collector current, emitter current, and base current in vector form. Even though the collector current has not decreased much in magnitude with frequency, the phase shift causes I_b to increase rapidly in magnitude. Therefore, the absolute magnitude of I_c/I_b decreases much more rapidly with frequency than α does.

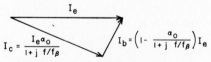

FIG. 4.9. Vector diagram showing magnitudes and phase of emitter, collector, and base currents in a transistor.

In the case of transistors with appreciable aiding drift fields, the frequency cutoff of β is, of course, higher than that given by Eq. (4.46). Such transistors will be discussed in Sec. 4.6. In these transistors, a better approximation for α as a function of frequency is

$$\alpha = \frac{\alpha_0 e^{-jm(f/f_\beta)}}{1 + j(f/f_\beta)} \qquad (4.50)$$

where m is the excess phase factor or the difference in radians between the actual phase shift and 45° at f_β. The factor $e^{-jm(f/f_\beta)}$ does not affect the magnitude of α, but it does add to the phase shift expected from pure diffusion. This phase shift affects the grounded-emitter frequency cutoff, which is now given by

$$f_{\alpha e} = \frac{(1 - \alpha_0)f_\beta}{1 + m\alpha_0} \text{ or } \frac{(1 - \alpha_0)f_\beta}{1 + m} \qquad \text{when } \alpha_0 \approx 1 \qquad (4.51)$$

The quantity $1/(1 + m)$ can be as low as 0.5 for a drift transistor in which the impurity concentration in the base at the emitter is 100 times that at the collector. At a ratio of 10 for the doping, $1/(1 + m)$ is about 0.67. In practice, the excess phase in diffused-base germanium transistors is in fair agreement with this picture. On the other hand, in silicon diffused-base transistors, the excess phase has proved to be quite variable from unit to unit.

The frequency variation of the α' of a hook-collector transistor can be discussed in a similar manner. α' is given in Sec. 4.4a as $\alpha_1/(1 - \alpha_2)$. From this expression it can be seen that the principal frequency cutoff will stem from the fact that transistor 2 is in essentially the grounded-emitter condition. We would expect the frequency cutoff of the hook-collector transistor α' to be approximately $(1 - \alpha_2)$ times the grounded-base frequency cutoff of transistor 2. It is, in fact, exactly this if the frequency cutoffs of transistors 1 and 2 are taken as the same.

4.5b. The Frequency Variation of γ. If the time-dependent diffusion equation is solved for the a-c admittance of a junction,[11] it is possible to write the frequency-dependent solution for γ. For an NPN transistor, γ is the a-c admittance for electrons over the sum of the a-c admittances for electrons and holes for the emitter junction. This becomes

$$\gamma = \left(1 + \frac{\rho_e W}{\rho_b L_{pe}} \frac{(1 + i\omega\tau_p)^{1/2}}{(1 + i\omega\tau_n)^{1/2}}\right)^{-1} \qquad (4.52)$$

which reduces to Eq. (4.7) when $\omega \to 0$. When $\omega\tau \gg 1$, γ is frequency independent at a value which is different from the d-c value. This latter high-frequency value may be either higher or lower than the d-c γ, depending on the relative values of the parameters concerned.

At relatively low frequencies where $\omega\tau \ll 1$, the a-c admittance of a junction looks like a conductance and capacitance in parallel, since it involves a quantity like $(1 + i\omega\tau)^{1/2} = 1 + i\omega\tau/2$. This latter capacitance is sometimes called the diffusion capacitance.

4.5c. The Diffusion Capacitance. The value of the diffusion capacitance and its physical interpretation can be seen quite clearly from simple physical arguments. If we consider injection primarily into the base and pure diffusion flow, Fig. 4.10 shows the density of minority carriers

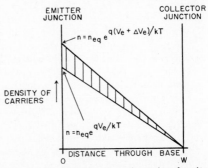

FIG. 4.10. Distribution of carrier density across the base of a diffusion transistor showing the increment in stored charge when the emitter voltage changes from V_e to $V_e + \Delta V_e$.

across the base. Here recombination is considered negligible, and therefore the density gradient must remain constant across the base. This gives a linear variation of density with distance from emitter to collector. If we use the boundary condition at the emitter that $n/n_{eq} = e^{qV_e/kT}$, it is easy to see that when the voltage on the emitter is V_e, the minority-carrier charge stored in the base is $\frac{1}{2}AqWn_{eq}e^{qV_e/kT}$. When the voltage on the emitter is raised to $V_e + \Delta V_e$, the charge stored becomes $\frac{1}{2}AqWn_{eq}(e^{qV_e/kT})(e^{q\Delta V_e/kT})$. Since capacity is $\Delta Q/\Delta V$, the diffusion capacity becomes $\frac{1}{2}AqWn_{eq}(e^{qV_e/kT})(e^{q\Delta V_e/kT} - 1)/\Delta V_e$. But

$$I_e = AqD_n \frac{dn}{dx} = AqD_n \frac{n_{eq}e^{qV_e/kT}}{W} \quad \text{and} \quad \frac{e^{q\Delta V_e/kT} - 1}{\Delta V_e} = \frac{q}{kT}$$

when $\Delta V_e \ll kT/q$. Therefore, the diffusion capacity becomes

$$C_D = \frac{1}{2} I_e \frac{q}{kT} \frac{W^2}{D_n} \tag{4.53}$$

Since this capacity varies as the base width squared, it rapidly decreases in very high frequency transistors which have very thin base widths.

4.5d. Frequency Limitation Due to Transit of the Collector Space-charge Region. After carriers arrive at the base side of the collector space-charge region, it would seem that the degradation of the a-c signal they carry would cease. One would expect perhaps a phase shift due to their transit time across the depletion region in the high drift field existing there. This traversal of the space-charge region does, however, have a frequency cutoff associated with it. This effect arises because of the equivalence of this process with the case of packets of charge traveling between two capacitor plates. The current in the circuit connecting the plates cannot resolve two packets of charge which are in the space between the plates at the same time. Therefore, the time interval between packets must be greater than the transit time. In the case of an a-c sine wave, the current in the circuit over the current entering the drift space from the base is given by[12]

$$\frac{1 - e^{-j\omega\tau_c}}{j\omega\tau_c} \tag{4.54}$$

where τ_c is the transit time. When $\omega\tau_c = \pi$ or $f = 1/2\tau_c$, the expression (4.54) becomes $-0.636j$, indicating that the amplitude of the signal is down to 0.636 and that the signal lags the current entering the drift space by 90°.

Since $\tau_c = x \text{ cm}/(5 \times 10^6 \text{ cm/sec})$, this means that if the width of the space-charge region x is 10^{-3} cm, the signal will be down to 0.636 of its low-frequency value at a frequency $f = 1/2\tau_c = 2.5 \times 10^9$ cps owing to traversal of this region alone. The limiting velocity of carriers in germanium in very high electric fields is 5×10^6 cm/sec.

4.5e. Collector Capacitance and Base Spreading Resistance. It is possible to calculate C_c and R_{bs} for special cases. Since the charge distribution in the collector barrier depends upon the gradation of resistivity in the barrier region, the capacity of a given barrier can be calculated only if the resistivity gradation is known. In the case of an alloy-junction transistor there is essentially a discontinuity in conductivity type and in resistivity at the interface between the recrystallized P-type collector region and the undissolved N-type crystal of the base region. Furthermore, the density of acceptors in the collector P region N_A is very much greater than the density of donors N_D in the N-type base region. This means, as we have stated before, that essentially all the voltage drop across the depletion layer will occur in the N-type base region.

We accordingly write Poisson's equation as

$$\frac{d^2V}{dx^2} = -\frac{qN_D}{\kappa}$$

Integrating we get

$$V_c = -\frac{qN_D}{2\kappa} x^2$$

where x is the thickness of the depletion region. The collector capacitance per unit area is

$$C_c = \frac{\kappa}{x} = \left(\frac{\kappa q N_D}{2V_c}\right)^{1/2}$$

The density of donors N_D equals the density of electrons n in the base region, so that we can substitute $1/\rho_b = q\mu_n n$, giving

$$C_c = \left(\frac{\kappa}{2V_c\mu_n\rho_b}\right)^{1/2} \tag{4.55}$$

where κ is the dielectric constant for the semiconductor material. This capacitance is also the capacitance of an alloy-junction diode. Other junction capacitances can be worked out for simple cases of impurity gradients through the depletion region, but it does not appear to be worthwhile to give more than one illustration here. Considerable success has been achieved in increasing the useful frequency range of ordinary junction transistors by thickening the collector barrier.[13] This results in lowering the collector capacitance to the same range as many point-contact devices.

R_{bs} can easily be calculated for a circular base region of uniform thickness W and a contact all around its periphery. This geometry gives

$$R_{bs} = \frac{\rho_b}{4\pi W} \tag{4.56}$$

where ρ_b is the resistivity of the base material.

4.5f. The Speed of Response of the Transistor Switch. When a pulse is applied to the base of the transistor switch of Sec. 4.3, the response is not instantaneous. Figure 4.11 shows the general behavior of the voltage across the switch as a function of time in comparison with the pulse on the base. There is, in general, a time t_0, called the turn-on time, during which the switch goes from the open to the closed, or "on," condition. This transient is determined by the parameters of the transistor and the magnitude of the base drive in comparison with $I_c(1 - \alpha)/\alpha$ or how hard the switch is driven. After the input pulse on the bases ceases, the transistor switch

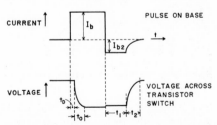

FIG. 4.11. The response of a transistor switch.

remains in the low-impedance condition for a time t_1, called the storage time. During this time the number of carriers in the base drops until there are no longer any excess carriers at the collector and that junction becomes free to assume a reverse bias. After this point is reached, an interval designated as t_2, or the decay time, elapses before the voltage across the transistor becomes approximately the battery voltage. The turn-on and decay times t_0 and t_2 are generally defined as the times required for the current through the switch to reach the 90 per cent point in its travel to its final values. The storage time and decay time can be reduced by drawing a current I_{b2} out of the base after the pulse ends.

Figure 4.11 also shows a short period called the delay time t_D during which the collector response does practically nothing after the input to the base has commenced. This delay is caused by the necessity of supplying sufficient charge to forward-bias the emitter junction so that it can begin to emit. The larger the emitter capacity, the longer this delay time.

Moll[14] has derived analytic expressions for the turn-on, storage, and decay times of a transistor switch by Laplace transform methods. He has derived the storage time in terms of four measurable parameters for a transistor α_F, α_R, ω_F, and ω_R. ω_F and ω_R are the radian cutoff frequencies of α_F and α_R. Briefly, his method consists of dividing the emitter and collector currents, respectively, into their two components— the current collected by and emitted from each. The currents emitted by the collector and collected by the emitter are then found as a function of time. The time in which these currents become zero is considered the storage time. These derived expressions are

$$t_0 = \frac{1}{(1 - \alpha_F)\omega_F} \ln \frac{I_b}{I_b - 0.9I_c(1 - \alpha_F)/\alpha_F}$$

$$t_1 = \frac{\omega_F + \omega_R}{\omega_F\omega_R(1 - \alpha_F\alpha_R)} \ln \frac{I_b - I_{b2}}{I_c(1 - \alpha_F)/\alpha_F - I_{b2}} \quad (4.57)$$

$$t_2 = \frac{1}{(1 - \alpha_F)\omega_F} \ln \frac{I_c - I_{b2}\alpha_F/(1 - \alpha_F)}{0.1I_c - I_{b2}\alpha_F/(1 - \alpha_F)}$$

These three response times can be evaluated from a consideration of the physical processes which go on during the three periods. The problem is made one-dimensional by assuming a symmetrical transistor with plane-parallel emitter and collector junctions of equal areas. Figure 4.12 shows the distribution of minority-carrier density across the base of the transistor during the closed condition. n_e and n_c are the densities at the emitter and collector, respectively. We shall begin by deriving the storage time.

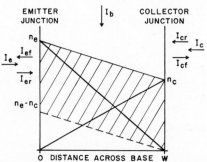

FIG. 4.12. Distribution of density of carriers across the base of a closed transistor switch.

Since the collector current remains constant (and controlled by the external circuit) during the storage period, the gradient of carriers across the base remains constant during t_1. Therefore, at the end of the storage period, the carrier density across the base varies linearly from a value of $n_e - n_c$ on the emitter side to zero on the collector side. This means that the shaded region symbolizes the carriers which must disappear from the base region during the storage period. This number of minority carriers is matched by an equal number of majority carriers which must also disappear.

The viewpoint taken here is that these minority carriers would flow out of the base and into the collector region in a time of the order of the transit time across the base if they were not restrained by the fact that the majority carriers cannot get out so easily. The trapped majority carriers keep an equal number of minority carriers constrained due to space-charge neutrality requirements. Therefore, the storage period continues until these "stored" or "trapped" majority carriers are dissipated by recombination with minority carriers or by the withdrawal of majority-carrier current through the base lead.

An equation can be written between the sum of the majority-carrier charge removed both by recombination and through the base and the stored charge represented by the shaded region. The charge lost by recombination and even perhaps by escape through the emitter and collector junctions is considered to be given by the $(1 - \alpha)$ currents made necessary by the emitted currents from both emitter and collector which continue throughout the storage period. This gives the equation

$$-I_{b2}t_1 + (1 - \alpha)[|\overline{I_{ef}(t)}| + |\overline{I_{cf}(t)}|]t_1 = An_cqW \tag{4.58}$$

where $-I_{b2}$ is the turn-off current on the base, A is the cross-sectional area of the symmetrical transistor, α is the forward and inverse alpha, and t_1 is the storage time. Also,

$$I_{ef}(0) = -qDA\,\frac{n_e}{W} \qquad I_{ef}(t_1) = -qDA\,\frac{n_e - n_c}{W}$$

$$I_{cf}(0) = -qDA\,\frac{n_c}{W} \qquad I_{cf}(t_1) = 0 \tag{4.59}$$

Therefore, if the time-average values of I_{ef} and I_{cf} are taken to be closely approximated by the arithmetic mean of the initial and final values,

$$-I_{b2}t_1 + (1 - \alpha)\,\frac{qDA}{W}\,n_c t_1 = An_cqW \tag{4.60}$$

This can be written

$$t_1[-I_{b2} + (1 - \alpha)|I_{ef}(0)|] = |I_{cf}(0)|\,\frac{W^2}{D} \tag{4.61}$$

or

$$t_1 = \frac{2}{\omega}\,\frac{|I_{cf}(0)|}{(1 - \alpha)|I_{ef}(0)| - I_{b2}} \tag{4.62}$$

Since†

$$I_{cf}(0) = -\frac{I_c + \alpha I_e}{1 - \alpha^2}$$

and

$$I_{ef}(0) = \frac{I_e + \alpha I_c}{1 - \alpha^2} \tag{4.63}$$

Eq. (4.62) becomes

$$t_1 = \frac{2}{(1 - \alpha)\omega}\,\frac{I_c + \alpha I_e}{I_e + \alpha I_c + I_{b2}(1 + \alpha)} \tag{4.64}$$

In the grounded-emitter condition this becomes

$$t_1 = \frac{2}{(1 - \alpha)\omega}\,\frac{\alpha I_b - I_c(1 - \alpha)}{I_b + I_c(1 - \alpha) - I_{b2}(1 + \alpha)} \tag{4.65}$$

This result is to be compared with Moll's result

$$t_1 = \frac{\omega_F + \omega_R}{(1 - \alpha_F\alpha_R)\omega_F\omega_R}\,\ln\frac{I_b - I_{b2}}{I_c(1 - \alpha_F)/\alpha_F - I_{b2}} \tag{4.66}$$

† These expressions are derived from the fact that $I_e = -I_{ef} + I_{er}$ and $I_c = -I_{cf} + I_{cr}$.

Equation (4.66) becomes, for a symmetrical transistor and after employment of the expansion,

$$\ln x = 2\left[\frac{x-1}{x+1} + \frac{1}{3}\left(\frac{x-1}{x+1}\right)^3 + \frac{1}{5}\left(\frac{x-1}{x+1}\right)^5 \cdots\right]$$

$$t_1 = \frac{2}{1+\alpha}\frac{2}{(1-\alpha)\omega}\frac{\alpha I_b - I_c(1-\alpha)}{\alpha I_b + I_c(1-\alpha) - 2\alpha I_{b2}} \tag{4.67}$$

The correspondence between expressions (4.65) and (4.67) is striking when α is close to unity. There are, of course, approximations in both derivations which account for the difference in the answers. For example, in the derivation proposed here, the direct recombination of stored minority and majority carriers is neglected.

It is similarly possible by the same type of physical analysis to derive approximate expressions for such times as the turn-on time, the turn-off time, and the time for the base to achieve a steady state (the last being somewhat longer than turn-on time). In all cases, we are restricted to symmetrical transistors.

For example, the turn-on time can be computed by balancing the majority-carrier charge entering the base in the form of base current with the charge resident in the triangle below the shaded area plus the $(1-\alpha)$ recombination current for the average emitter current flowing during the turn-on period.

$$I_b t_0 = AWq\frac{n_e - n_c}{2}(0.9) + (1-\alpha)(0.9)|\overline{I_{ef}}|t_0 \tag{4.68}$$

$$t_0\left[\frac{I_b}{0.9} - \frac{qDA}{2W}(n_e - n_c)(1-\alpha)\right] = \frac{2}{\omega}\frac{qDA}{2W}(n_e - n_c)$$

$$t_0 = \frac{2}{\omega}\frac{(qDA/2W)(n_e - n_c)}{(I_b/0.9) - (qDA/2W)(n_e - n_c)(1-\alpha)}$$

and using

$$I_c = \frac{qDA}{W}(n_e - n_c) \tag{4.69}$$

we get

$$t_0 = \frac{2}{\omega}\frac{I_c}{(2I_b/0.9) - (1-\alpha)I_c} \tag{4.70}$$

for the turn-on time.

Again, this is to be compared with Moll's result for a symmetrical transistor:

$$t_0 = \frac{1}{(1-\alpha)\omega}\ln\frac{I_b}{I_b - 0.9I_c(1-\alpha)/\alpha} \tag{4.71}$$

If we use the first term of the ln expansion, Eq. (4.71) becomes

$$t_0 = \frac{2}{\omega}\frac{I_c}{(2\alpha/0.9)I_b - (1-\alpha)I_c} \tag{4.72}$$

Again, the result is the same for α close to 1.

This method of accounting for the charge has proved especially valuable in devices that are too complicated to treat in other ways. Some examples of this are the treatment of some of the response properties of NPNP diodes[15] and the avalanche-transistor pulse circuit[16] by this method.

The storage problem is somewhat more complicated in transistors with reasonably high resistivity and lifetime collector bodies. This class of transistors includes the diffused-base and the grown-junction types. When the collector junction becomes forward-biased in these transistors, an appreciable injection of the minority carriers into the collector body takes place. Another way of looking at this is that the γ of the collector junction is low.

During the storage period, the carriers that have accumulated in the collector body flow back into the base and act like a continuation of the signal on the base. This, of course, prolongs the storage period. The problem can be treated as a combination of the diode recovery problem and the transistor storage problem. For reasonable parameters for a diffused-base transistor it can be shown by this analysis that the storage time remains virtually unaltered when the lifetime in the collector remains below $(\omega_F + \omega_R)/[\omega_F\omega_R(1 - \alpha_F\alpha_R)]$. When τ is several times this quantity, the storage time becomes directly proportional to the lifetime in the collector.

4.6. The Drift Transistor. The frequency response of a transistor can be materially increased by providing a sweeping field across the base to aid the transport of carriers from emitter to collector.[17] In order to produce such a field, a resistivity gradient is introduced into the base material. The direction of this resistivity gradient and its effect on the electronic band structure of the transistor are illustrated in Fig. 4.13.

At the top of Fig. 4.13 is shown an impurity concentration profile for one typical method of fabrication of such a transistor. Here the structure is produced by diffusing N-type impurities from the left side into a semiconducting wafer of original P-type impurity concentration C_{pc}. The collector junction is located at the depth where the concentration of N-type impurity C_n equals C_{pc}. As one moves to the left from this junction (back into the base region), the C_n increases, giving a resistivity gradient normal to the collector-junction surface. If a P-type alloy emitter is formed upon the left-hand surface, the N-type impurity will be effectively removed from the recrystallized P-type emitter region, giving a concentration of P-type impurities in the emitter region of C_{pe}. The physical structure of such a transistor is shown in Fig. 10.1.

Transistors with built-in impurity density gradients are also made by alloying emitter and collector dots on both sides of a wafer which has previously been diffused from one side (the emitter side). Surface-barrier (Sec. 4.7) drift transistors can be made by plating onto such material. Many transistors are made similarly to the example cited except that the emitter region is formed by another diffusion from the left face, this time of P-type impurities. The surface concentration of the P-type impurity must, of course, be greater than that for the N-type base diffusion in order that we have an emitter region. These transistors are the so-called double diffusion transistors. In transistors of this type the maximum doping concentration is not at the emitter edge of the base region but at some distance into the base from there. This means that such transistors actually have a small region containing a retarding field before the carriers reach the region of aiding drift field.

In addition to the reduction of transit time because of the aiding drift field and the consequent increase in frequency cutoff, the drift transistor has other advantages. The high impurity concentration near the emitter results in a low lateral base resistance. The low concentration at the collector reduces the collector capacitance and raises the collector breakdown voltage. The high doping density at the emitter end of the base region also makes punch-through breakdown from collector to emitter very much more improbable.

From the energy-band diagrams of Fig. 4.13, it can be seen that the effect of the resistivity gradient in the base region is to tilt the band edges in this region. This follows from the fact that the Fermi level ϵ_0 must remain level (at equilibrium) while the separation of the Fermi level from the bottom of the conduction band ϵ_1 is a function of the donor-impurity concentration. This tilting of the band edges and hence of the electrostatic potential constitutes a built-in electric field (see Fig. 2.4). When there is no collector bias applied to the structure (center of Fig. 4.13), there is no net current flow because the field current is just balanced by a diffusion current produced by the concentration gradient between the holes and electrons p_{be} and n_{be} on the emitter side of the base region and their counterparts p_{bc} and n_{bc} on the collector side of the base region.   The sweeping field in the base is given by $(1/q)(d\epsilon_1/dx)$.

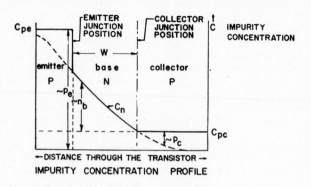

IMPURITY CONCENTRATION PROFILE

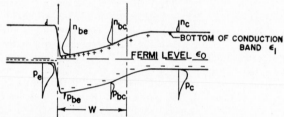

DRIFT TRANSISTOR ENERGY BANDS WITHOUT BIAS

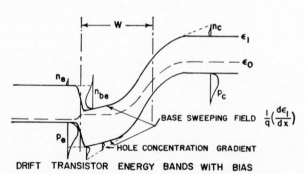

DRIFT TRANSISTOR ENERGY BANDS WITH BIAS

FIG. 4.13. PNP drift transistor energy-band diagram.

In order to calculate this field in terms of the base-region resistivity gradient $d\rho_b/dx$, we refer to Eq. (2.3),

$$n_b = \left(\frac{2\pi m_n kT}{h^2}\right)^{3/2} e^{-(\epsilon_1 - \epsilon_0)kT} \tag{4.73}$$

Differentiating with respect to distance x, we get

$$\frac{dn_b}{dx} = -\frac{n_b}{kT}\frac{d\epsilon_1}{dx} \tag{4.74}$$

giving the sweeping field

$$E_s = \frac{1}{q}\frac{d\epsilon_1}{dx} = -\frac{kT}{q}\frac{1}{n_b}\frac{dn_b}{dx} = \frac{kT}{q}\frac{1}{\rho_b}\frac{d\rho_b}{dx} \tag{4.75}$$

where the mobility is assumed to be constant and $n_b \gg n_i \gg p_b$. The transit time determined by the sweeping field alone, t_E, is given by

$$t_E = \int_0^W \frac{dx}{E_s(x)\mu_p} = \frac{1}{D_p}\int_0^W \frac{1}{d\rho_b/dx}\rho_b(x)\,dx \tag{4.76}$$

where $D_p = \mu_p(kT/q)$.

If the drift transistor is made by the diffusion process described previously, the concentration C_n will follow an error function (see Sec. 7) and $\rho_b(x) \sim 1/\{C_{n0}[1 - \text{erf}\,(x/2Dt)] - C_{pc}\}$. The integration of Eq. (4.76) can be carried out graphically. For accuracy it may often be necessary to use a variable mobility if the range of $\rho_b(x)$ is very great. In this event the form of Eq. (4.75) using n_b instead of ρ_b should be used and the D_p should be taken under the integral.

As a simple example we shall consider an exponential variation of $\rho_b(x)$ which can be used to approximate an error function. Let $\rho_b(x) = \rho_{be}e^{ax}$. Assume μ_p to be constant and $\rho_b \ll \rho_c$ over nearly the entire base thickness. We then compute

$$\frac{1}{d\rho_b/dx}\rho_b(x) = \frac{1}{a\rho_{be}}e^{-ax}\rho_{be}e^{ax} = \frac{1}{a} \tag{4.77}$$

Substituting into Eq. (4.76) and integrating, we get

$$t_E = \frac{W}{aD_p} \tag{4.78}$$

which can be compared with the diffusion transit time t_D for the same base region with uniform ρ_b.

$$t_D = \frac{W^2}{D_p} \tag{4.79}$$

The ratio $t_D/t_E = aW$ can easily be computed for different ratios of the resistivity just inside the collector to the resistivity just inside the emitter (ρ_{bc}/ρ_{be}), since by definition $\rho_{bc} = \rho_{be}e^{aW}$ or $aW = \ln\,(\rho_{bc}/\rho_{be})$. For example, if $\rho_{bc}/\rho_{be} = 100$, $aW = t_D/t_E = 4.6$. This shows that the frequency response of a drift transistor can be larger by a considerable factor than that of a uniform base transistor.

In the constant electric field which results from such an exponential impurity gradient, the exact solution of the continuity equation gives[18]

$$\beta = e^\eta \frac{Z}{\eta\,\sinh Z + Z\,\cosh Z} \tag{4.80}$$

where

$$\eta = \frac{1}{2}\ln\frac{n_{be}}{n_{bc}} = \frac{1}{2}\frac{qE_s}{kT}W$$

$$Z = (j\phi + \eta^2)^{1/2}$$

and

$$\phi = \omega\frac{W^2}{D_p}$$

For $\eta = 0$, this expression gives β for the ordinary uniformly doped base region discussed earlier. When $\eta = 1$ or $E_s W = 2(kT/q)$, the β cutoff frequency is increased by a factor of about 2 over the $\eta = 0$ case. When $\eta = 2$ or $E_s W = 4(kT/q)$, the β

cutoff is approximately three times higher than the uniformly doped base case. At $\eta = 3$ or $E_s W = 6(kT/q)$, the improvement is about a factor of 5.

This improvement in frequency cutoff cannot continue to be increased indefinitely, since the total built-in potential difference across the base can never possibly exceed one-half the energy gap if the entire base is to remain one conductivity type. In fact, the $E_s W$ value must remain several kT/q below one-half the energy gap. In germanium, one-half the energy gap is approximately $14(kT/q)$.

At the present writing it is not clear how effective the drift fields in the base are in increasing the ultimate frequency capabilities of transistors, since the impurity diffusion process which yields such fields also makes possible extraordinary dimensional control of base widths. Thus base widths of 1 micron or even less are regularly achieved. These transistors have frequency cutoffs of β so high that the ultimate frequency of operation is often limited by other factors such as RC times and it is difficult to establish the effect of the drift field. Furthermore, at higher current densities when the injected carriers outnumber the majority carriers in the base, the drift field is no longer effective and the transistor becomes a diffusion transistor. In the attempt to achieve very high frequency operation junction areas are decreased to reduce capacities. This makes the high current density effect more attainable than one would think.

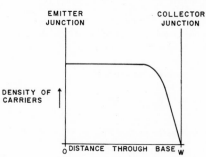

FIG. 4.14. Distribution of carrier density in the base of a drift transistor.

Figure 4.14 depicts the density of injected minority carriers as a function of position in the base for a drift transistor. This diagram is sufficiently different from the corresponding diagram for the diffusion transistor Fig. 4.10 to make it immediately apparent that many of the quantities calculated for the diffusion transistor like diffusion capacity, γ, collector conductance, etc., need reexamination.

The distribution shown in Fig. 4.14 arises because the current is carried primarily by the field through most of the base width and, therefore, the density of carriers remains almost constant. At the collector the density must be near zero because the collector is reverse-biased. Here there is no drift current and only diffusion current. This diffusion current must be equal to the drift current at the emitter end if we neglect recombination.

4.7. The Surface-barrier Transistor. The surface-barrier transistor consists of a very thin wafer of germanium with two relatively small electroplated contacts on opposing sides. A sectional view of this device is shown in Fig. 4.15. Both the collector and emitter are metal-semiconductor contacts.[19] As will be discussed under point-contact transistors, the injection efficiency γ of a metal-semiconductor contact for low currents can range from zero to unity, depending upon the height of the barrier. At high current densities $\gamma = (1 + b)^{-1}$, but since the emitter contact of the surface-barrier transistor, while small, is not nearly a point, the normal operating currents (~ 1 ma) represent relatively low current densities. Another effect of the fact that the contacts are considerably larger than points is that there is no spreading resistance region in the semiconductor immediately beneath the contacts. This means that the current flow through the semiconductor is largely governed by diffusion and that field effects are negligible. There is, therefore, very little effect of the collector bias felt at the emitter, so that the γ is not much influenced by collector voltage unless a voltage is applied which is large enough to cause the depletion region to become comparable to the thickness of the base region.

The transfer efficiency β is governed by surface recombination through Eq. (4.11). Bulk recombination in the base region is negligible, since L_{pb}, the diffusion length for holes, is very much greater than W, the separation of the emitter and collector contacts.

The collector efficiency α^* is unity for any simple metal-semiconductor rectifying contact. This means that the over-all emitter-input current gain α is equal to the $\beta\gamma$ product. The cutoff frequency of these transistors is quite high because the method

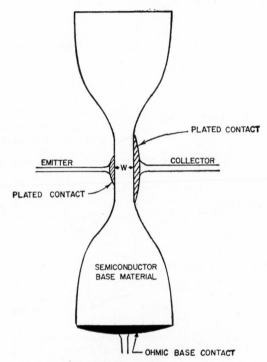

FIG. 4.15. Surface-barrier transistor.

of etching and plating the surfaces of the germanium wafer lends itself to accurate control of the very small thickness of the wafer and hence of the contact separation. Because of the very small volume in which the power dissipation of the device takes place, the power-handling capabilities are quite limited for high-frequency units made by this method.

Since γ must approach $(1 + b)^{-1}$ at high current densities, the current gain must tend to fall off as the emitter current is increased. Such an effect must be true of all emitters which have $\gamma > (1 + b)^{-1}$ at low currents. The average point-contact transistor, for example, does not show this effect in γ, since most point-contact emitters have $\gamma < (1 + b)^{-1}$ at low currents.

As temperature is increased, γ drops somewhat, since the effective barrier height decreases slowly with increasing temperature. Such an effect is the opposite of point-contact and junction transistors.

4.8. The Unipolar or Field-effect Transistor. The unipolar transistor is so called because the "working current" carried by the device is carried by one type of current carrier only. In Fig. 4.16 is shown a diagram of a unipolar transistor suggested by Shockley,[20] together with an associated energy-level diagram. The working current of this device flows between the ohmic contacts, constituting the source and the drain in the N-type semiconductor bar.   If the bias on the gate is high enough, the depletion region of the encircling PN junction becomes thick enough to "pinch off" the channel through which the working current flows.   In the illustrated energy-level diagram, the drain end of the channel is shown nearly pinched off.

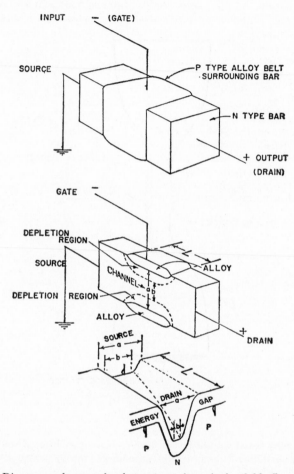

FIG. 4.16. Diagram and energy-level structure of a unipolar field-effect transistor.

In order to understand the operation of this device, we shall first consider the phenomenon of the variation in thickness of a PN-junction depletion layer.   In Fig. 4.17 are shown some energy-level diagrams of a PN junction in which the P region is much lower in resistivity than the N region.   The reverse bias across the junction increases from top to bottom in the figure.   The potential drop across the junction is produced by a dipole layer of charge.   The source of this dipole layer is the uncompensated charge of the ionized impurity atoms in the semiconductor (shown at A and B in the figure).   The total positive charge A must equal the total negative charge B so that there will be no external fields.   Since the resistivity of the P region is much lower than that of the N region, the ionized impurity density is much greater.   This means that the volume of the N region which must be involved in the depletion layer must be much greater than the volume of the P region involved. It follows then that, as the reverse bias is increased on the junction, the depletion region pushes much farther into the N region than into the P region. Figure 4.17 illustrates this effect.

In order to apply this to the unipolar transistor shown in Fig. 4.16, we shall calculate the dependence of depletion-layer thickness upon reverse bias, assuming that the whole depletion layer lies in the N region. From Poisson's equation we have, letting y be the direction perpendicular to the plane of the junction,

$$\kappa \frac{d\mathcal{E}_y}{dy} = -qN_D(y) \qquad (4.81)$$

where κ is the dielectric constant in suitable units, $\mathcal{E}$ is the electric field, and qN_D is the charge density in the N region. Integrating (4.81) under the boundary conditions of the unipolar transistor shown at the top of Fig. 4.17, we have $\mathcal{E}_y = 0$ at $y = b/2$ in the N region:

$$\mathcal{E}_y = -\frac{qN_D(y - b/2)}{\kappa} \qquad (4.82)$$

In order to get the potential difference as a function of y, we integrate again, making $V = 0$ at $y = a/2$:

$$V = \frac{qN_D}{2\kappa}\left[\left(y - \frac{b}{2}\right)^2 - \left(\frac{a}{2} - \frac{b}{2}\right)^2\right] \qquad (4.83)$$

To get the potential difference across the barrier we let $y = b/2$, which gives

$$V(b) = \frac{qN_Da^2}{8\kappa}\left(1 - \frac{b}{a}\right)^2 = V_0\left(1 - \frac{b}{a}\right)^2 \qquad (4.84)$$

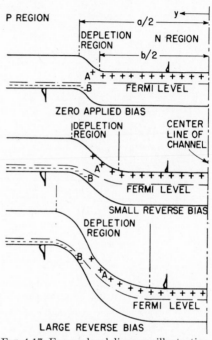

Fig. 4.17. Energy-level diagrams illustrating the widening of the depletion region with applied voltage.

Here it can be seen that for the depletion region to fill the entire channel $b = 0$ and $V(b) = V_0 = qN_Da^2/8\kappa$. V_0 is called the pinch-off voltage. Solving (4.84) for b gives

$$b = a\left[1 - \left(\frac{V}{V_0}\right)^{1/2}\right] \qquad (4.85)$$

We are now in a position to calculate the current in the channel under specific bias conditions. Let us first consider the situation where the source and the gate are both grounded and the only voltage applied is a positive voltage to the drain V_D. This will give a tapering channel of square cross section. The differential resistance of the channel is $dr = \rho\, dx/b^2 = \rho\, dx/a^2[1 - (V/V_0)^{1/2}]^2$, and by Ohm's law $I\, dx = dV$. Combining these expressions we get

$$I\int_0^L dx = \frac{a^2}{\rho}\int_0^{V_D}\left[1 - \left(\frac{V}{V_0}\right)^{1/2}\right]^2 dV \qquad (4.86)$$

which integrates to give

$$I = \frac{a^2 V_D}{\rho L}\left[1 - \frac{4}{3}\left(\frac{V_D}{V_0}\right)^{\frac{1}{2}} + \frac{1}{2}\frac{V_D}{V_0} \right] \tag{4.87}$$

A curve of Eq. (4.87) is plotted in Fig. 4.18 as the part of the $V_G = 0$ curve for

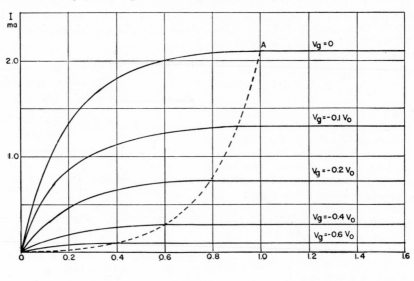

FIG. 4.18. Unipolar-transistor characteristics.

voltages less than V_0.   To give a feeling for the numbers involved, the currents for this figure were calculated using the following quantities:

$$a = 0.01 \text{ cm} \qquad L = 2 \text{ mm}$$
$$\rho = 10 \text{ ohm-cm} \qquad \kappa = 1.4 \times 10^{-12} \text{ farad/cm}$$

The pinch-off voltage V_0 comes out to be 250 volts for this case.   If a were reduced to 0.005 cm, V_0 would be reduced to 62 volts, which is more reasonable.   The saturation current of 2.1 ma would also be reduced by a factor of 16, which is rather small.   If the channel were a flat rectangle in cross section rather than square, the current-reduction factor would be 4 instead of 16.

So far we have indicated that the portion of the curve of $V_G = 0$ from the origin to the point A in Fig. 4.18 is given by Eq. (4.87).   If we consider Eq. (4.86), we see that the substitution of the gate voltage V_G for the lower limit of integration would give equations for the rest of the family of curves given in Fig. 4.18.   By inspection, it is clear that this would merely result in the substitution of $V_D - V_G$ for V_D in Eq. (4.87).   This corresponds to a horizontal shift of the original $V_G = 0$ curve to the left by the amount V_G/V_0 in the figure and a vertical lowering of the same curve by the amount $a^2 V_G/\rho L$.   The easiest way of doing this is to invert the original $V_G = 0$ curve in a point which is the center of the line joining A and the origin.   This operation gives the dashed curve of Fig. 4.18.   The rest of the family of curves can now be constructed by keeping them all parallel to the original curve and starting each number with the point A on the dashed curve.

The foregoing discussion explains only those portions of the characteristics of Fig.

4.18 which lie to the left of the dashed curve. We shall now consider the continuations of these curves to the right which are shown as horizontal lines. The dashed curve represents the locus of points on the various characteristics where the drain end of the channel has just reached pinch-off conditions. If the energy-level diagram at the bottom of Fig. 4.16 is examined, it can be seen that the total number of free electrons in the channel is very small at the drain end (b → 0) but that the field necessary to maintain the current I is quite large. As the bias ($V_D - V_G$) at the drain end is increased beyond V_0, the pinch-off condition moves toward the source. The field between the drain end and the point along the channel where pinch off is effectively reached must be large enough to maintain the current I flowing in the open part of the channel with the small trickle of electrons which are able to pass through the pinched-off section. This means that the current effectively saturates as soon as the voltage bias across the barrier at the drain end is sufficient to produce pinch off. This is the reason for extending the characteristic curves as horizontal lines to the right of the dashed curve representing initial pinch off.

An accurate analysis of the region of the channel beyond pinch off is very difficult, but one more point can be shown intuitively. Equation (4.87) indicates that the current carried by the channel in the portion which is not pinched off depends inversely on the length of this portion of the channel. As the pinch-off voltage is exceeded at the drain end, the initial pinch-off point moves toward the source, thus shortening the channel and increasing the current slightly. This shows that the saturation region of the I-V characteristics should exhibit a high positive differential resistance.

4.9. The Avalanche Transistor. The avalanche transistor[21] is any junction transistor specifically designed to have alpha greater than unity by utilization of the multiplication inherent in the breakdown of the collector junction. In appropriate circuits such transistors are capable of exhibiting negative resistances useful for both switching (in a manner similar to the NPNP diodes) and amplification.

A negative resistance is observable across such a transistor with the emitter and base tied together. This is because it is possible in a transistor to look across the avalanche discharge in the collector junction in two ways. One is directly across the avalanche region alone (from the base to the collector of the transistor, curve a in Fig. 4.19), and the other is across a source of minority carriers and the multiplication region in series (from emitter to collector with base floating, curve b in Fig. 4.19). In the former case, base-to-collector breakdown occurs at the voltage at which M becomes infinity. In the latter case, emitter-to-collector breakdown occurs

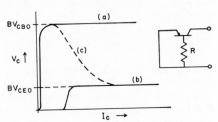

FIG. 4.19. The avalanche transistor characteristic.

at BV_{CEO}, that voltage at which the multiplication times the low-voltage alpha becomes unity. Any configuration which goes from the former to the latter condition with increasing current will exhibit a negative resistance characteristic. With the emitter and base tied together (sometimes through a resistor) as shown in Fig. 4.19, at low currents the impedance of the emitter is high and most of the current flows through the base. As the voltage increases, the characteristic follows curve a. As the breakdown voltage is reached, the current flowing through the base and thus through the base resistance (either internal or external) increases and the emitter-base bias increases in the forward direction. The impedance of the emitter becomes smaller in comparison with the base resistance. The characteristic curve c begins to depart from curve a, and as a larger and larger fraction of the total current is transferred from the base circuit to the emitter, curve c approaches curve b asymptotically.

A similar negative resistance characteristic is observed in a two-terminal avalanche transistor which is specifically designed so that α_0 shall increase with increasing current. Such a transistor is shown in

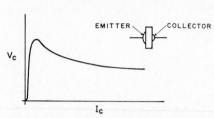

FIG. 4.20. The two-terminal avalanche transistor.

Fig. 4.20. It is nothing more than an alloyed transistor in which the emitter is much larger than the collector. At low currents α_0 is very low and BV_{CEO} across the transistor is high—near the breakdown voltage of the collector. As the current increases, a transverse voltage drop occurs in the base which biases the center of the emitter more forward than the periphery. The low-voltage alpha increases and BV_{CEO} decreases, resulting in a negative resistance characteristic. This can be thought of as a sort of focusing effect.

Very fast pulse circuits have been made by using avalanche transistors. In these the multiplication of the collector junction is used to provide rapidly the charge necessary to reduce the voltage across the junction, that is, to discharge the collector-junction capacitor.

4.10. The Double-base Junction Diode. Figure 4.21 shows the diagrams and characteristics of a typical alloy-junction double-base diode.[22] Let us assume that the measuring terminals are shorted out and that a sweeping voltage is applied to the base of the polarity shown at the top of the figure. The voltage distribution in the base will be the straight line OAV_s shown in the center of Fig. 4.21. Since the whole junction is at ground potential because of the shorted measuring terminals and the very low resistivity of the alloy region, we see that the junction is biased in the reverse direction.

If now a positive voltage is applied to the measuring terminals which is less than V_1, the junction will still be biased in the reverse direction and we shall remain on the C-V_1 branch of the characteristic shown at the bottom of the figure. When the positive voltage of the measuring terminals reaches V_1, the left end A of the junction begins to draw forward current and injects extra carriers into the semiconductor. These holes are swept to the left away from the junction by the sweeping field and lower the resistivity of the left end of the semiconductor bar. This then allows the base voltage to alter its distribution so that the voltage drop is lower in the left end of the bar than it was before, causing the left end of the junction to be biased even more in the forward direction. This positive feedback continues until the voltage distribution has shifted to one similar to the curve OBV_s shown in the center of the figure. The junction, for the case shown, is now biased in the forward direction over its entire area. The voltage on the measuring terminals is still V_1, but the operating point of the device has shifted to the point D shown on the high-current branch of the characteristic.

If the measuring voltage is now lowered, the amount of injection will decrease until finally the voltage drop in the base increases to the point where the right-hand end of the junction begins to be biased in reverse again. As more and more of the junction is cut off, the injection falls off quite rapidly so that another positive feedback process is initiated which results in cutting off the whole junction area suddenly. This occurs at E on the V_1ED branch of the characteristic shown at the bottom of the figure.

Accurate, detailed analysis of this device is quite complicated and will not be attempted here. There are several points which should be made regarding the design of double-base diodes which can be made clear without a detailed analysis. The injection efficiency of the junction primarily determines the magnitude of the negative-resistance region. An injection efficiency of nearly unity will give the maximum absolute value of the negative resistance. The best way of achieving this is to have ρ_n/ρ_p as large as convenient. If ρ_n is made quite high, the sweeping current required to hold off a given voltage V_1 will be minimized. It is easy to see that the stand-off voltage V_1 should be linearly related to V_s since the point A of Fig. 4.21 is fixed by the geometry of the device. It has been found experimentally that the reset voltage is also linear with V_s.

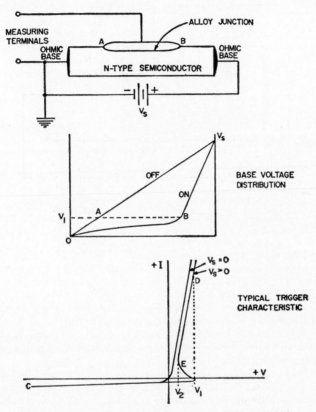

FIG. 4.21. Double-base diode, diagrams and characteristics.

Since the triggering action of a double-base diode depends on raising the conductivity in the negative end of the base material, it is clear that such a device can be triggered on by illuminating the negative end of the base or by injecting holes in that end by any other means, such as an auxiliary emitter of some sort connected in this region.

4.11. The Double-base Junction Transistor (Tetrode Transistor). If an ordinary junction transistor is prepared with two connections to opposite sides of the base region situated so that a biasing voltage can be applied between them so as to produce a current in a direction perpendicular to the direction of normal current flow between the emitter and collector, the performance of the transistor will be greatly modified when the biasing voltage is applied.[23] Figure 4.22 shows such a structure embodied in a grown-junction NPN transistor. With the bias voltages applied as shown, the emitter junction is cut off over a major portion of its area and all the transistor action is forced to take place in the immediate neighborhood of the grounded-base contact.

The most obvious effect of the bias between the base contacts is the effective reduction in cross-sectional area of the transistor. Since the transistor action is taking place in a region very close to the grounded-base connection, the conduction paths from this base connection to the effective emitter and collector barriers are very short and the base resistance is markedly reduced. The reduction in base resistance tends to increase the cutoff frequency of the device.

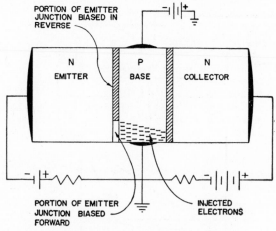

Fig. 4.22. Double-base or tetrode transistor.

This advantage must be weighed against the disadvantage of a large reduction in α due to the sweeping field in the base region. The reduction in α comes about through a reduction in the transfer efficiency β between the emitter and the collector. Before now we have always considered β to be near unity, but the double-base transistor is an exception. Since the polarity of the sweeping field tends to sweep the injected electrons toward the grounded-base connection, a substantial fraction of them are lost by flowing into the base connection before they can reach the collector. β, and therefore α, decreases linearly with the base sweeping field. A typical reduction in α is 10 per cent for a base sweeping current of about 1 ma.

In alloy-junction transistors, base sweeping fields have been used to divert injected carriers among a plurality of collecting electrodes or conversely to divert injected carriers from a plurality of emitters to one collector. Such devices are, at present, little used.

4.12. Point-contact Transistors. Historically, the point-contact transistor was the first transistor. Its discovery gave impetus to the development of the PN-junction theory and the junction transistor. Its decline in importance with the advent of junction devices is largely the result of lack of reproducibility and the lack of a good design theory. The point contact is too complex and contains too many hidden variables to yield a simple theory. First we shall briefly describe the effects of a few of the processes used in making point-contact transistors. The discussion will involve N-type point-contact transistors only.

When a point-contact transistor is assembled, the collector point is almost universally made of phosphor-bronze wire while the emitter point is made of some spring wire which does not contain a V group element such as phosphorus. After the mechanical assembly is completed, a process of electrically pulsing the collector is carried out. This process is called "electrical forming" or just "forming." Many different forming techniques are used successfully, but all of them involve heating the collector point contact to a high temperature for a short time.

The transistor before forming shows a collector resistance of the order of 10^5 ohms and an emitter-input current gain of the order of 0.2. After forming, the collector resistance is usually about 2×10^4 ohms and the emitter-input current gain α is about 2.0. Figure 4.23 shows the variation of α with emitter current which is typical of point-contact transistors after forming.

A metal-semiconductor barrier is shown in Figs. 3.3 and 3.5. The proper mathematical treatment of the injection process involving such a barrier is quite complicated.[24] The calculation of the injection efficiency for large forward currents is, however, quite simple. Let us assume strict space-charge neutrality. In this case every hole injected into the valence band will require an extra electron in the conduction band. When the injected density of holes is large compared with the original density of electrons in the N-type semiconductor,

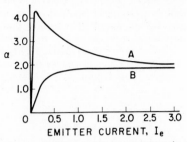

FIG. 4.23. The emitter-current variation of current gain for point-contact transistors.

the electron and hole densities will be equal near the injecting contact and the electron current I_n will equal the mobility ratio b times the hole current I_p. The injection efficiency γ is by definition

$$\gamma = \frac{I_p}{I_n + I_p} = \frac{1}{1 + b} \qquad (4.88)$$

The injection efficiency for low forward currents ranges from unity for high barriers to nearly zero for low barriers. Experimental results on pulsed point-contact diodes indicate that most point contacts typically show low initial values of γ, slowly rising to $1/(1 + b)$ at higher currents.

The foregoing discussion of γ for point contacts can be applied to the emitters of point-contact transistors if one keeps in mind that in a point-contact transistor there is a large negative bias on the collector which tends to sweep injected holes away from the emitter by electric-field action. This may have the effect of noticeably raising the γ values for low emitter currents but would not affect the saturation value of $1/(1 + b)$.

We shall assume $\beta = 1.0$ as before and now consider α^* for the collector regarded as a simple metal-semiconductor point contact shown at the bottom of Fig. 3.3. The collector current $I_c = I_{nc} + I_{pc}$, where the electron current I_{nc} is composed solely of the electrons A spilling over the top of the barrier from the metal I_{nm}. The hole current $I_{pc} = I_{pe} + qA_c(D_p p_0/L_p)$, where I_{pe} is the hole current of the emitter and $qA_c(D_p p_0/L_p)$ is the diffusion current of holes passing under the barrier and shown at B in Fig. 3.3. The collector current gain α^* is then $\partial I_c/\partial I_{pe} = 1$. The over-all current gain α is then something less than $1/(1 + b)$ or $\alpha < 0.32$ (using $b = 2.1$ for germanium at room temperature). It is supposed that this properly describes the situation for an unformed collector in a point-contact transistor.

It will now be assumed that the forming process changes the collector contact so that it can no longer be represented by the simple model of Fig. 3.3 but is more nearly represented by a "hook" structure similar to that shown in Fig. 4.6. In Fig. 4.24 is shown a diagram of the various regions of a collector contact and how they are related to the "hook" model.

It can be seen in the figure that a hemispherical shell of P-type material surrounding a hemisphere of N-type material is suggested as the structure of a formed collector contact.[25] The reasoning behind this is as follows.

The forming pulse when applied to the collector heats the germanium in the neighborhood of the collector point to a relatively high temperature. From symmetry the isothermals should be hemispherical. It is well known[26] that, when N-type germanium is heated and suddenly quenched, a conversion to P-type conductivity takes place. This process, called thermal conversion, is supposed to be responsible for the creation of a hemispherical region of P-type conductivity surrounding the collector point and extending a distance R (Fig. 4.24) into the germanium. If the metal of the collector point contained no N-type impurity, such as phosphorus, this is all that would take place in the forming process.

Since there is phosphorus in the collector-point material, it is reasonable to suppose that some of this N-type impurity diffuses into the semiconductor under the influence of the heat generated by the forming pulse. This excess N-type impurity when added to the N-type impurity which was already present in the block of semiconductor is sufficient to override the effects of the thermal conversion in a small region immediately surrounding the collector point. The process just described will produce a "hook" structure where the floating P region has a thickness $W_f = R - r$ and the collector N region has a radius r.

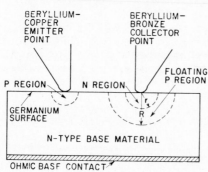

FIG. 4.24. Diagram of the structure of a point-contact transistor

With a "hook" collector we can easily account for the observed current gains of point-contact transistors. The variations of alpha with current in both component transistors can account for α versus I_e curves of type A or B in Fig. 4.23.

We have just considered the effect of a hook collector on the current gain of a point-contact transistor. It may equally well be true that the emitter contact is not a simple metal-semiconductor contact. Even though the emitters of point-contact transistors may not be deliberately formed, there is bound to be some forming action when the electrical connections necessary for the operation of the transistor are first made. Such a forming action could at most produce a small P region surrounding the emitter contact (see Fig. 4.24). This would have the effect of producing an emitter which would have an injection efficiency given by Eq. (4.7) rather than simply $1/(1 + b)$. Since most of the point-contact transistors show over-all current gains greater than unity at high emitter currents, it would seem that γ must be greater than $1/(1 + b)$, or else the hook collector is far from saturation.

There is another way of explaining the peak in α at low emitter currents which does not require the saturation of the hook collector. This mechanism[26] assumes that there is some conductivity-modulation process which will give an $\alpha^* = 1 + cb$, where c is some constant and b is the mobility ratio. The hook mechanism just considered is not a conductivity-modulation mechanism but rather a diffusion mechanism. It is proposed that there is a relatively large density of hole traps, which are not recombination centers, located in the semiconductor in the immediate region of the collector. At low emitter currents, the traps are not saturated by the relatively small number of holes flowing into the collector. Each time a trap holds a hole for a finite time and then releases it, the effective mobility of the holes in this region is reduced and the mobility ratio b is increased. At high emitter-current levels, the traps are saturated with holes and have very little effect on b. The over-all effect of the traps is to cause an artificially high b at low emitter currents which drops to the true value at high emitter currents.

A similar explanation can be given, in terms of traps which are recombination centers, to account for the point-contact transistors which have a low α at low emitter currents. In this case, it is the β factor which is affected. At low emitter currents, the recombination traps are not saturated and the hole lifetime in the base region is quite short, causing β to be relatively low. As the emitter current is increased, the recombination traps become saturated, allowing the hole lifetime and β to increase.

To summarize, it seems that most of the experimental evidence points to a hook-collector mechanism to explain the current gain of point-contact transistors. Traps of one sort or another may play a role, but the main effect appears to be due to a hook mechanism.

4.13. Integrated Devices. The improvement of understanding of transistors and the technology of their fabrication has led to the consideration of the possibility of much more complicated devices or arrays of devices made on a single piece of crystal and encapsulated together. Proposals in this area range from complete circuits involving diodes, transistors, resistors, and capacitors all made on the same silicon substrate to more modest combinations of a few interacting components. In general, it should be obvious that if the individual units in the integrated device must perform within very narrow tolerance limits, the probability for simultaneous fabrication of many different kinds of these units is low. On the other hand, if the requirements on the individual portions are relatively lax (such as in an audio amplifier), the possibilities may be quite good.

In a sense we have already discussed an integrated device in Sec. 4.4 on the four-region transistor. Since this device, the hook-collector transistor, the four-region diode, or the thyratron transistor, essentially consists of an NPN and a PNP transistor suitably interconnected, it is an integrated device. It is also probably one of the simplest of this class of devices. The difficulties already mentioned in Sec. 4.4 serve to emphasize the problems of making such devices to close tolerances. If the problem is merely to make a transistor with alpha greater than 1, it is easy to make this integrated device. However, if the current at which alpha becomes greater than 1 or the value of alpha must be controlled within very narrow limits, it seems at this writing that the combination of two separately fabricated and selected transistors offers more hope.

Two excellent examples of more complicated integrated devices are the stepping transistor[27] and the full-adder transistor.[28]

The stepping transistor is a semiconductor analogue of the gas stepping tube. In the latter a bistable gas discharge steps from one electrode (of a circular group in one envelope) to the one on, say, its right at each clock pulse. First, a pulse energizes the starting electrode and every other one from it. The next clock pulse energizes the electrodes in between these. By geometrical means the discharge is caused to shift to a predetermined side (in this case, the right) of the electrode then firing. When the voltage clock pulse is removed the discharge extinguishes. The next clock pulse energizes the other set of electrodes, which includes those to the right and left of the starting electrode. There is residual ionization left in the region of the recently extinguished discharge which favors the firing of the electrode on the right. With each succeeding clock pulse the discharge steps one to the right in this manner.

Similarly, the stepping transistor consists of a ring of bistable four-region diodes with one emitter of all of them a common junction. This structure is shown in Fig. 4.25. Again the direction of transfer is built in by the use of asymmetrical geometry.

If unit 1 is in the low-impedance condition, the stored carriers in the N base are mostly directly below the asymmetrically placed N emitter. When the clock pulse is removed from bus a, some of these carriers linger and diffuse somewhat to each side. When the next clock pulse appears on bus b, unit 2 will turn on because some of these excess carriers will already be present in its N-base region. This, in effect, will momentarily endow it with a higher α or lower turn-on current.

It would seem that this is a truly integrated device in that it would not work if separated into its component units. This is because we apparently rely on the interchange of minority carriers between neighboring PNPN diodes. This requires continuity of single crystal and close proximity. It is, therefore, disconcerting to note that this stepper would work equally well if the units were cut apart and the previously

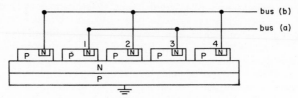

FIG. 4.25. The stepping transistor.

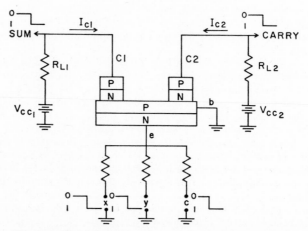

FIG. 4.26. The full-adder transistor and associated circuit.

continuous parts connected by ohmic connections.[29] This is because, in the unit which is in the low-impedance condition, a larger forward potential exists across the portion of the bottom emitter immediately below the N emitter than at the other end of the unit. These potentials are transmitted via the base leads to the units to each side. This affects the unit on the right in exactly the way in which a base current affects a thyratron (Sec. 4.4c). The peak of unit 2 is temporarily lowered and unit 2 fires when the clock pulse is applied to bus b.

The full-adder transistor is shown in Fig. 4.26 with a schematic circuit in which its properties may be utilized. It consists of a two-hook-collector transistor appropriately designed. The input signals are the indicated voltage waveforms at the terminals x, y, and c, and they represent the binary numbers to be added. The output signals are the two collector voltages which represent sum and carry.

The device operates in the following general manner: As the emitter input is increased from zero, at first, all the current flows through collector 1 (that being designed to have a higher α). At a certain value of emitter current the current in collector 1 turns off and collector 2 turns on. At a still higher value of emitter current, current flows in the collector 1 circuit again as well as in that of collector 2. A typical plot of the two collector currents versus the emitter current is given in Fig. 4.27. The switching points can be chosen so that one unit of emitter current gives a 1 in the sum output, two units give a zero sum and 1 in the carry output, and three units give a 1 in the sum and 1 in the carry output. Thus, full binary addition can be accomplished.

An understanding of the operation of this device and the complexity of a proper design can be gleaned from considering an equivalent circuit (Fig. 4.28) which experimentally duplicates the operation of the full-adder transistor. We shall assume that transistor 1 has a higher alpha than transistor 2 and that $R_1 \approx R_2$. Then, as the emitter current is raised starting from zero, the current will, at first, flow through collector 1 because current flowing in transistor 1 will give a larger feedback voltage drop across R_1. These voltages are in the direction of increasing the forward bias,

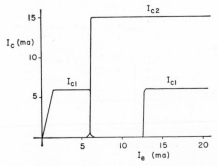

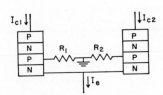

Fig. 4.27. The collector currents as a function of the emitter current in a full-adder transistor.

Fig. 4.28. Equivalent circuit for the full-adder transistor.

since $\alpha > 1$. This makes the forward bias on the emitter of transistor 1 grow so large that the emitter floats down in potential so that emitter 2 is reverse-biased or insufficiently forward-biased to emit current without the aid of a voltage drop across the base resistance R_2. As the emitter 1 current increases and the collector 1 current increases until the circuit of collector 1 is saturated (that is, $I_{c1} = V_{cc1}/R_{L1}$; I_{c1} is limited by the voltage and resistance in the circuit of collector 1), the current flowing through R_1 begins to decrease and eventually the emitter body potential floats up to the point where emitter 2 emits. Now, if the saturation current in the collector circuit of transistor 2 is larger than that in the circuit of collector 1 by a sufficient amount, the current will all switch over to transistor 2 and the emitter potential will float so that emitter 1 ceases to emit. As the emitter current continues to rise beyond this point, transistor 2 goes further into saturation, the feedback voltage across R_2 decreases, eventually the emitter potential floats up to the point where emitter 1 turns on again, but now emitter 2 does not turn off.

Hysteresis is inherent in this operation. The switching points with I_e decreasing differ from those with I_e increasing. This could cause difficulty if not taken into account in the circuit use. Close control of the characteristics of the integrated full adder requires simultaneous control of a great many parameters including the forward and inverse alphas of four transistors, I_{co}'s, and base resistances.

4.14. The Epitaxial Transistor. The epitaxial deposition of single-crystal silicon or germanium on a single-crystal substrate of the same material has recently been applied to the problem of optimizing the performance of transistors. As a process of fabrication of transistors it lies outside the scope of this section. However, epitaxial transistors will be discussed from the standpoint of their improved characteristics.

Devices can be and are being made by successive depositions of different conductivity types. In principle, this offers the possibility of achieving any arbitrary doping distribution completely unfettered by the usual restrictions imposed by fabrication methods such as diffusion, rate growing, or alloying. While this is desirable and worth working toward, the epitaxial method has not yet achieved the dimensional control to compete successfully with diffusion as a method of constructing high-frequency transistors. The transistors currently referred to as "epitaxial" are diffused junction transistors made on epitaxially deposited material. A cross section of such a transistor is shown in Fig. 4.29.

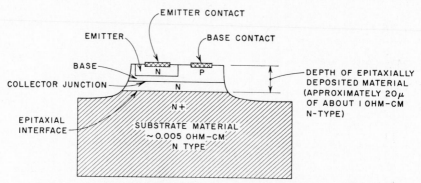

FIG. 4.29. The diffused epitaxial transistor.

This structure essentially achieves the objective of an extremely thin transistor— far beyond that obtainable by pure mechanical ingenuity. The diffused transistor, since it requires successive diffusions from the same reference surface, must start with a collector region of reasonable resistivity. Also, the wafers into which one has diffused a transistor become extremely difficult to handle when they are thinner than 0.003 to 0.004 in. Therefore, diffused transistors inherently have a series resistance in the collector body which is a function of the thickness of that body, the transverse dimensions of the transistor, and the resistivity of the starting material (which is still presumably undisturbed in the collector body).

In the epitaxial structure, only sufficient "starting" material thickness necessary to contain safely all the diffused junctions and give them their required properties is deposited on a substrate of degenerate semiconductor of the same type. This essentially moves the back contact up to the epitaxial interface and drastically reduces the effect of the previously inherent collector resistance.

The effects of this structure are more dramatic than the mere reduction of collector series resistance. Diffused junction transistors have displayed characteristics at variance with theory in many respects. For example, their transient response as a switch to a current pulse on the base departs considerably from the idealized picture in Fig. 4.11, the storage time displayed by them as a function of drive conditions is anomalous even when storage in the collector body is considered, and their collector current-voltage characteristics contain regions where the gain apparently increases rapidly with collector voltage. This latter effect is sometimes somewhat loosely called "β-crowding." All these effects are caused by transverse resistance in the collector body[30] and disappear in a properly designed epitaxial diffused transistor. In addition to a more normal switching transient in the epitaxial transistor, the storage time is shortened because of the reduction of storage in the very much thinner collector body. The obvious reduction in collector series resistance reduces the voltage drop across the closed transistor switch (discussed in Sec. 4.3) and improves the performance of the transistor as an a-c amplifier. The elimination of the apparent variation of gain with voltage at low voltages and fairly high currents makes the diffused epitaxial transistor a better linear amplifier.

REFERENCES

1. Tanenbaum, M., and D. E. Thomas: Diffused Emitter and Base Silicon Transistors, *Bell System Tech. J.*, vol. 35, pp. 1–22, January, 1956.
2. Sah, C. T., R. N. Noyce, and W. Shockley: Carrier Generation and Recombination in PN Junction Characteristics, *Proc. IRE*, vol. 45, pp. 1228–1243, September, 1957.
3. McKay, K. G., and K. B. McAfee: Electron Multiplication in Si and Ge, *Phys. Rev.*, vol. 91, p. 1079, September, 1953.
4. Miller, S. L.: Avalanche Breakdown in Germanium, *Phys. Rev.*, vol. 99, pp. 1234–1241, March, 1955.
5. Early, J. M.: Effects of Space Charge Layer Widening in Junction Transistors, *Proc. IRE*, vol. 40, pp. 1401–1406, November, 1952.
6. Shockley, W., and W. T. Read: Statistics of the Recombination of Holes and Electrons, *Phys. Rev.*, vol. 87, pp. 835–842, September, 1952.
7. Shockley, W., M. Sparks, and G. K. Teal: PN Junction Transistors, *Phys. Rev.*, vol. 83, pp. 151–162, January, 1951.
8. Ebers, J. J., and J. L. Moll: Large Signal Behavior of Junction Transistors, *Proc. IRE*, vol. 42, pp. 1761–1772, December, 1954.
9. Kulke, B., and S. L. Miller: Accurate Measurement of Emitter and Collector Series Resistances in Transistors, *Proc. IRE*, vol. 45, p. 90, January, 1957.
10. Steele, E. L.: Theory of Alpha for PNP Diffused Junction Transistor, *Proc. IRE*, vol. 4, pp. 1424–1428, November, 1952.
11. Shockley, W.: The Theory of PN Junction in Semiconductors and PN Junction Transistors, *Bell System Tech. J.*, vol. 28, pp. 435–489, July, 1949.
12. Early, J. M.: PNIP and NPIN Junction Transistor Triodes, *Bell System Tech. J.*, vol. 33, pp. 517–533, May, 1954.
13. Lax, B., and S. F. Neustradter: Transient Response of a PN Junction, *J. Appl. Phys.*, vol. 25, pp. 1148–1154, September, 1954.
14. Moll, J. L.: Large Signal Transient Response of Junction Transistors, *Proc. IRE*, vol. 42, pp. 1773–1784, December, 1954.
15. Baker, A. N., J. M. Goldey, and I. M. Ross: Recovery Time in PNPN Diodes, *IRE Wescon Conven. Record*, part 3, pp. 43–48, 1959.
16. Hamilton, D. J., J. F. Gibbons, and W. Shockley: Physical Principles of Avalanche Transistor Pulse Circuits, Solid State Circuits Conference, Philadelphia, Pa., 1959.
17. Krömer, H.: Der Drifttransistor, *Naturwissenschaften*, vol. 40, pp. 578–579, November, 1953.
    Krömer, H.: Zur Theorie des Diffusions- und des Drifttransistors, I, II, III, *Arch. Elect. Übertragung*, vol. 8, pp. 223–228, 363–369, 499–504, May, August, November, 1954.
18. Lee, C. A.: A High Frequency Diffused Base Germanium Transistor, *Bell System Tech. J.*, vol. 35, pp. 23–34, January, 1956.
19. Schwarz, R. F., and J. F. Walsh: The Properties of Metal to Semiconductor Contacts, *Proc. IRE*, vol. 41, pp. 1715–1720, December, 1953.
20. Shockley, W.: A Unipolar "Field Effect" Transistor, *Proc. IRE*, vol. 40, pp. 1365–1376, November, 1952.
21. Miller, S. L., and J. J. Ebers: Alloyed Junction Avalanche Transistors, *Bell System Tech. J.*, vol. 34, pp. 883–902, September, 1955.
    Kidd, M. C., W. Hasenberg, and W. M. Webster: Delayed Collector Conduction, A New Effect in Junction Transistors, *RCA Rev.*, vol. 16, pp. 16–33, March, 1955.
22. Lesk, I. A., and V. P. Mathis: The Double Base Diode: A New Semiconductor Device, *Conven. Record IRE*, part 6, pp. 2–8, 1953.
23. Wallace, Jr., R. L., L. G. Schmipf, and E. Dickten: A Junction Transistor Tetrode for High Frequency Use, *Proc. IRE*, vol. 40, pp. 1395–1400, November, 1952.
24. Swanson, J. A.: Diode Theory in the Light of Hole Injection, *J. Appl. Phys.*, vol. 25, pp. 314–323, March, 1954.
25. Longini, R. L.: Electric Forming of N-Germanium Transistors Using Donor Alloy Contacts, *Phys. Rev.*, vol. 84, p. 1254, December, 1951.

26. Sittner, W. R.: Current Multiplication in the Type A Transistor, *Proc. IRE*, vol. 40, pp. 448–454, April, 1952.
27. Ross, I. M., H. Loar, and L. A. D'Asaro: A Stepping Transistor, AIEE-IRE Semiconductor Device Research Conference, Purdue University, June, 1956.
28. Rutz, R. F.: Two-collector Transistor for Binary Full Addition, *IBM J. Research Develop.*, vol. 1, pp. 212–222, July, 1957.
29. D'Asaro, L. A.: A Stepping Transistor Element, *IRE Wescon Conven. Record*, part 3, pp. 37–42, 1959.
30. Miller, S. L., and R. W. Soshea: Switching Properties of Highly Asymmetrical Transistors, *Proc. IRE* (to be published).

Section 5

PHOTOCONDUCTIVITY AND PHOTOVOLTAIC CELLS

L. P. HUNTER

IBM Corporation, Poughkeepsie, N.Y.

In Sec. 4 the phenomenon of transistor collector action was discussed in some detail. In a transistor, the emitter is the source of the extra injected current carriers which act on the collector barrier. It is clear that an equally good source of extra current carriers could be produced by the optical excitation of electrons from the valence to the conduction band of the semiconductor. Optically excited extra current carriers can be used to modify the current flowing through a barrier exactly as the emitter injected carriers in a transistor modify the collector current. They can be used alternatively to charge up a floating barrier to produce a photovoltage or to modify the bulk conductivity of a bar of semiconducting material.

As a preliminary to discussing the operation of these devices, we shall consider the optical-excitation process by which excess current carriers can be produced in a semiconductor. In Fig. 5.1 is shown the energy-level diagram for a semiconductor with the optical-excitation and recombination processes illustrated. Since the density of impurity states in the energy gap is many orders of magnitude less than the density of states in the conduction and valence bands, we need consider only optical excitation between the two bands.

5.1. Photoconductivity. [1] We shall define the photoconducting process as the increase in conductivity of a semiconductor due to an increase in the number of current carriers available for the conduction process because of the absorption of light energy. Here "light energy" is used to mean the energy of photons from the ultraviolet, visible, and infrared regions of the spectrum.

The minimum energy required to raise an electron from the valence to the conduction band is the energy of the energy gap $\Delta\epsilon$. The energy of a light quantum is the frequency of the light ν multiplied by Planck's constant h. The wavelength λ_0 of the photoconducting threshold is therefore

$$\lambda_0 = \frac{c}{\nu_0} = \frac{hc}{\Delta\epsilon} \tag{5.1}$$

where c is the velocity of light. Numerically, $hc = 1.237$ to give λ_0 in microns with $\Delta\epsilon$ in electron volts. The maximum energy which can raise an electron to the conduction band from the valence band is shown in the figure as $h\nu$ max. This is the energy

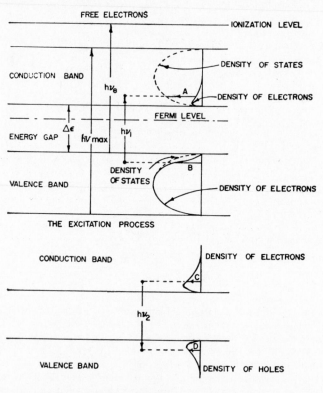

THE EXCITATION PROCESS

THE RECOMBINATION PROCESS

FIG. 5.1. Schematic optical-excitation and recombination processes.

difference between the bottom of the valence band and the top of the conduction band. All light energies between $h\nu_0$ and $h\nu_{\max}$ are capable of exciting some electrons across the energy gap, increasing the number of current carriers in both the valence and conduction bands, and thus contributing to the photoconducting process.

Considering now the specific excitation event shown as $h\nu_1$ in Fig. 5.1, we see that the number of electrons in the valence band with energies comparable to the energy of the electron excited to the conduction band by the absorption of the light quantum of energy $h\nu_1$ is proportional to the abscissa B in the electron-density function. Similarly, the number of vacant states of energy comparable to that of the excited electron is shown as the abscissa A in the density-of-states function. In the excitation process, momentum must be conserved. Every individual energy state in the valence or conduction band has a specific value of momentum associated with it just as it has a specific energy assigned to it. From this it can be seen that the probability of the excitation $h\nu_1$ taking place as shown is proportional to the number of pairs of states (one of the pair in the valence band and one in the conduction band) which have the same momentum and the energy separation $h\nu_1$. This probability is proportional to the density of electrons B in the valence band multiplied by 1 minus the occupation probability for the conduction band at A.

If we imagine the excitation vector $h\nu_1$ shifted vertically so that its base rests on the top of the valence band, it is clear that there will be no electrons at the top of the valence band with momentum large enough to equal the momentum of electrons at the upper end of $h\nu_1$ in the conduction band, since both the kinetic energy and momentum of an electron go to zero at a band edge and are maximum near the center of a band (see Sec. 2, page **2**–5). This means that no electrons can be excited from the very top of the valence band into the center of the conduction band. A similar argument shows that no electrons can be excited from the center of the valence band to the bottom of the conduction band. All the electrons capable of being excited by the radiation represented by $h\nu_1$ must therefore lie in a narrow range near B in the electron-density distribution where matching momentum states can be found at the upper end of $h\nu_1$ in the conduction band.

5.1a. Spectral Sensitivity. We shall now consider the spectral sensitivity to be expected for the photoconducting process. We have already seen that the long-wavelength threshold of the effect is the wavelength corresponding to the energy gap. As the wavelength of the exciting radiation is decreased, $h\nu$ increases and

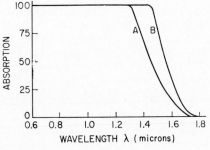

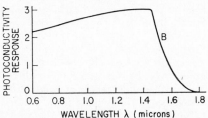

Fig. 5.2. Typical absorption and photoconductivity curves for thin germanium samples.

the appropriate abscissas A and B increase so that the probability of the excitation process increases. When the $h\nu$ is large enough to extend from the center of the valence band to the center of the conduction band, the excitation probability is largest. When the wavelength is further reduced to the point where $h\nu$ extends from the bottom of the valence band to the top of the conduction band, the direct effect ceases.

Usually before this situation is reached, other absorption phenomena begin to compete for exciting photons. In Fig. 5.1 the threshold wavelength λ_0 (corresponding to $h\nu_0$) for the photoelectric effect is seen to be reached before the photoconduction effect is over. Some of the exciting radiation will be used by the competing process, and the photoconducting process will drop off prematurely.

In Fig. 5.2 are shown the spectral-absorption curves of two samples of germanium and the photoconductivity-response curve of one of them. It is seen that the absorption curves have a threshold at the same wavelength as the threshold for the photoconductivity. This shows that the excitation of electrons from the valence to the conduction band must be at least partially responsible for the absorption. At wavelengths slightly shorter than the threshold (say 1.6 microns), the probability of excitation is such that most of the radiation is transmitted through the specimen without making an excitation collision.   Sample B is twice as thick as sample A and therefore absorbs twice as much as this wavelength (reflection at the surface of the sample is ignored in this discussion).   When the excitation probability becomes large enough to cause all the photons traversing the sample to undergo an excitation collision, the absorption will be complete.

It is seen that the photoconductivity-response curve of Fig. 5.2 falls off slowly at shorter wavelengths of the exciting radiation.   This could be due to some competing process as suggested previously.   In this case, however, the fall off in photoconductive response is probably due to surface recombination of the excited carriers.   Since the excitation probability is steadily increasing as we go to shorter wavelengths, the penetration of the radiation into the sample is much less at the short wavelengths and the excited current carriers are concentrated more and more just beneath the illuminated surface.   At 1.6 microns the excited electrons are nearly uniformly distributed throughout the thickness of the sample; at 0.6 micron they are all formed within a few thousandths of an inch of the illuminated surface.   If the surface-recombination rate is uniform over the whole surface, it will have much more of an effect where the density of extra carriers is high.   A significant fraction of the excited electrons will therefore return to the valence band before they have time to contribute much to the photoconductivity at the shorter wavelengths.

We shall now briefly consider radiative recombination.   The surface recombination previously mentioned is nonradiative, and the momentum of the electron and hole combination involved is transferred to the crystal lattice by means of trapping one of the partners of the recombination in a bound surface state.   Referring to the diagram at the bottom of Fig. 5.1, we again apply the rule that an electron in the conduction band can recombine only with a hole in the valence band which has the same momentum.   For the case shown, a photon of energy $h\nu_2$ is emitted when the recombination takes place.   The recombination probability is proportional to some fraction of C multiplied by a different fraction of D, where the fractions again depend upon the number of pairs of matched momentum states.   Since C and D are much smaller than the corresponding abscissas A and B of the excitation process, the radiative-recombination rate will be quite low.

The longest wavelength of the recombination-radiation spectrum will be equal to the excitation-threshold wavelength.   The total range of this spectrum is very small, since the energy range of the electron and hole-density distributions is small compared with the energy range covered by the whole valence and conduction bands.   At room temperature this energy range is about $\frac{1}{20}$ electron volt, which means that the entire recombination-radiation spectrum should be between 1.65 and 1.75 microns for germanium.   Actually, the electronic energy bands in germanium seem to have a very complex structure, so that the simple behavior just outlined is not exactly followed for germanium.

5.1b. Traps and Sensitization of Photoconductors.   In the foregoing discussion two types of recombination were considered, the direct recombination of free holes and electrons between the edges of the valence and conduction bands (often called edge recombination) and recombination of free holes and electrons by way of surface trapping states (called surface recombination).   In the case of edge recombination, the probability of matching the momenta of a hole and an electron in exactly the right way for a recombination collision to occur is quite low.   This means that if there were no trapping states in the crystal (either surface or bulk material states), the lifetime of excess free carriers would be very long, and indeed for germanium it is calculated to be of the order of 1 sec.

In most semiconductor materials, recombination of holes and electrons through traps is by far the most probable recombination process.   These trapping centers may exist throughout the body of the crystal as well as at the surface.   Even in the most carefully prepared germanium, for example, it is difficult to reduce the density of such trapping centers in the bulk material below about 10^{12} per cubic centimeter. Trapping centers, in order to be effective in the recombination process, must exist as energy states within the forbidden band gap between the valence and conduction bands and must not be in thermal equilibrium with the free carriers (holes and electrons). Energy states within the band gap lying between the neighborhood of the Fermi level and the nearest band edge cannot therefore act as recombination centers, since they are clearly governed by thermal equilibrium processes and any free carrier trapped by such a level will have a much higher probability of being thermally reexcited into the band than of recombining with a free carrier of the opposite type.

In Fig. 5.3 is given a graphical presentation of the relation between thermal and kinetic equilibrium of free holes and electrons under light excitation. Following Sec. 2.5 a photoconductor in the absence of light excitation will have a single Fermi

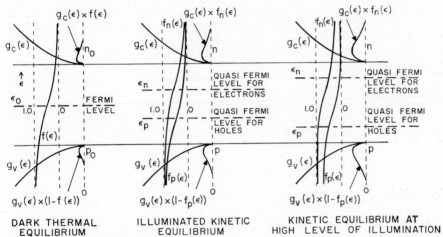

DARK THERMAL EQUILIBRIUM ILLUMINATED KINETIC EQUILIBRIUM KINETIC EQUILIBRIUM **AT** HIGH LEVEL OF ILLUMINATION

FIG. 5.3. Graphical determination of the density of free carriers in a photoconductor under conditions of thermal equilibrium and light excitation.

level, and in this dark condition all energy states within the band gap will be governed by thermal equilibrium with the free carriers in both bands. As shown in Fig. 5.3 for these conditions the number of free electrons n_0 is determined by the product of the Fermi occupation probability $f(\epsilon)$ and the density of states in the conduction band $g_c(\epsilon)$. The number of free holes p_0 is similarly given by the product $g_v(\epsilon)[1 - f(\epsilon)]$, where $g_v(\epsilon)$ is the density of states in the valence band.

For the case of light excitation we must introduce a new concept of quasi-Fermi levels. We have seen that when light strikes a photoconductor material, it raises a number of electrons from the valence band to the conduction band, thus simultaneously creating equal numbers of free holes and electrons. These carriers increase the free-carrier population in both bands. Since the temperature is not increased, the energy width of the Fermi occupation probability is the same as it was before the light excitation. And if we attempt to fit the Fermi probability function to the actual percentage occupancy of the states in the valence and conduction bands under conditions of light excitation where this occupancy is greater than thermal equilibrium would require, we see that it cannot be done with a single position in energy of the Fermi probability function but will rather require two positions, one for the conduction band and a somewhat lower position for the valence band. This state of affairs is illustrated in the second and third parts of Fig. 5.3. The upper position of the Fermi probability function is labeled $f_n(\epsilon)$ and is so located that the product $f_n(\epsilon)g_c(\epsilon) = n$, the actual density of free electrons under these conditions of light excitation. Similarly the lower position of the Fermi probability function is labeled $f_p(\epsilon)$ and is positioned so that $[1 - f_p(\epsilon)]g_{v\epsilon} = p$, the density of free holes. The 50 per cent probability points of $f_n(\epsilon)$ and $f_p(\epsilon)$ are defined as quasi-Fermi levels for electrons and holes, respectively.

From this discussion it should be clear that a greater intensity of light excitation will cause the two quasi-Fermi levels to separate farther and farther, since a greater light excitation will increase the percentage occupancy of the states of both bands and require the adjustments of both quasi-Fermi levels to a position closer to the band edges in order to match the Fermi occupation probability with the actual percentage occupancy of the states within the bands. This is illustrated in the third part of Fig. 5.3. The region of the band gap between the two quasi-Fermi levels is no longer in thermal equilibrium with the enhanced free-carrier densities, and any impurity energy states lying in this region can act as trapping centers for the recombination of holes and electrons.[2] The recombination current through these traps is determined by a kinetic process of capture of the free carriers by the traps. For example, the rate at which electrons are trapped is simply the product $nv_n\zeta_nN_p$, where v_n is the average velocity of the electrons in the conduction band, ζ_n is the capture cross section of the traps for free electrons, and N_p is the density of the traps which are empty of electrons. Similarly, the rate at which holes are trapped is $pv_p\zeta_pN_n$. Under the conditions of light excitation, the generation rates for both p and n are equal, and for kinetic equilibrium to obtain, the generation rate must equal the recombination rate. This condition will determine the densities of free carriers in both bands. Let the generation rate be g; we can now write

$$nv_n\zeta_nN_p = g = pv_p\zeta_pN_n$$

from which
$$n = \frac{g}{v_n\zeta_nN_p} \quad \text{and} \quad p = \frac{g}{v_p\zeta_pN_n} \tag{5.2}$$

A moment's reflection will show that the quantities $1/v_n\zeta_nN_p$ and $1/v_p\zeta_pN_n$ are, respectively, the electron lifetime τ_n and the hole lifetime τ_p. This follows from the definition of minority-carrier lifetime which states that it is the time constant of the exponential decay of injected free carriers toward the thermal-equilibrium value and from the fact that the time constant of an exponential is equal to the time required for complete decay at a constant rate equal to the initial rate of the exponential.

Previously, it has always been the case that the lifetimes of minority and majority carriers have been equal. This is always true when the excess free carriers of both types are equal, and such a condition exists when the excitation level is sufficiently great to excite densities of free carriers large compared with the densities of traps between the quasi-Fermi levels. In the case where the trap density exceeds the free-carrier density, the lifetimes of the two types of free carriers are not necessarily equal but depend upon the capture cross sections, the occupation densities, and the velocities of the carriers. This case would almost never be realized for a semiconductor like germanium unless it were extremely impure. However, there are many semiconductor materials in which this is the predominant case. Such materials are typified by cadmium sulfide.

It is a well-known fact that it is possible to sensitize a photoconductor or activate a phosphor by the addition of some impurity in the proper amount. For example, the photoconductive sensitivity of pure cadmium sulfide can be increased by a factor between 10^3 and 10^6 by the introduction of about two parts per million of chloride.[3] At the same time, the dark resistivity drops from about 10^{12} to about 1 ohm-cm. Since the mobility of electrons is much greater than that of holes for such materials as CdS, it is clear that increasing the number of free electrons is necessary to increase the photoconductive sensitivity. From Eq. (5.2) we see that $n = g/v_n \zeta_n N_p = g\tau_n$. This means that if we can effectively increase τ_n by decreasing either ζ_n (the capture cross section of the recombination traps for free electrons) or N_p (the number of these traps), we increase the photoconductive sensitivity.

It should be noted here that an increase in the sensitivity is directly tied to a slower response time through the increased free-electron lifetime. This is clear when one remembers that the lifetime is just the time required for the excess density of free electrons, and thus the photoconductive response, to drop to $1/e$ of its value when the exciting light is cut off.

The process of sensitizing a photoconductor such as adding a small amount of $CdCl_2$ to CdS can be explained by assuming that the sensitizing impurity functions as a recombination trap with a small cross section for electron capture and in some manner supplants the recombination centers previously present in the material. One way in which this might be accomplished would be that the energy states of the sensitizer impurity should lie somewhat higher in the energy band gap of the material so that the electrons normally carried by the sensitizer atom would fall into the somewhat lower energy states of the other recombination traps and keep them essentially full of electrons, thus rendering them unavailable for further participation in the recombination of free carriers [decreasing N_p in Eq. (5.2)]. The new recombination centers would have a very low ζ_n, so that even though their density N_p might be quite high, their over-all effect would be to decrease the effective product $\zeta_n N_p$ of the electron-trapping centers of the material.

5.2. Photoconducting Devices.[4,5] There are two general classes of photoconducting devices, those utilizing the photoconducting properties of polycrystalline films of semiconductor material and those utilizing the properties of barriers or junctions in single-crystal semiconductor material. A few interesting examples of both types will be described.

5.2a. Polycrystalline Film Photocells.[6] The simplest photoconducting device consists of a film of a highly sensitized photoconducting material bridging the gap between two suitable metal contacts. A photocell of this general type is illustrated schematically at the upper right of Fig. 5.4. In Table 5.1 is given a comparison of various semiconductor materials commonly used for this type of photocell. Ranges of sensitivity and photoconductivity decay time are given along with pertinent spectral parameters. Really quantitative information of this type is very hard to find because most investigators in the field have been interested primarily in physical and chemical mechanisms which can be deduced from qualitative comparisons as well as from much more difficult quantitative measurements. This results in light intensities being listed in foot-candles usually without specifying even the color temperature of the incandescent source. It is hoped that even this qualitative information will give the reader a feel for the kind of performance possible at the present state of the art for polycrystalline film photoconductors.

As explained in Sec. 5.1b, the sensitivity and the speed of response are inversely related. This can be seen in the behavior of CdSe as shown in the table. In the case of the "pure" CdSe shown the upper range of sensitivity and the long decay time are probably due to either lattice defects or impurities inadvertently introduced. The behavior of really pure, perfect material is most probably revealed by the insensitive, fast sample listed.

The usual photoconducting cells of this type are made by evaporating or sintering the photoconducting layer. The threshold wavelength for most of these doped materials may appear to be somewhat longer than that expected from the energy gap as discussed above. The reason for this is the relatively high impurity concentrations generally used in these materials, the impurities here providing enough extra levels inside the energy gap that direct optical excitation of electrons from these levels to the conduction band will result in an appreciable photoconductivity.   Since these levels lie within the energy gap, their separation from the conduction-band edge is less than the gap width, thus allowing their excitation by lower-energy, longer-wavelength light than that required to excite electrons clear across the energy gap.   As an example of this effect, considerable amounts of copper added to CdS will extend its photoconducting threshold wavelength to beyond 0.9 micron from the 0.5 micron shown in Table 5.1.   This effect is usually accompanied by a significant drop in sensitivity.

   5.2b. Crystal Bar Photocell.   Another very simple but interesting photoconducting cell can be made from a bar of high-purity, relatively high-resistivity semiconductor

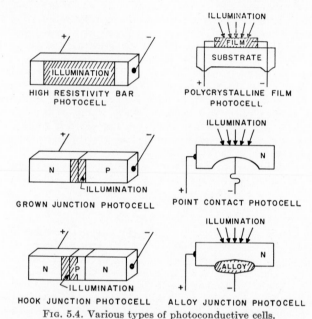

FIG. 5.4. Various types of photoconductive cells.

of either conductivity type.   The bulk resistivity of such a bar can be reduced by illuminating it with light of wavelength shorter than the photoconductive threshold of the semiconductor used.   The largest effect will be obtained if the full length of the bar is illuminated and if the lifetime of extra current carriers is long enough for them to traverse the full length of the bar in the field of the applied voltage.

   We shall give a sample calculation to give an idea of the sensitivity of such a photocell using germanium.   Let us assume that the bar is 1 mm by 1 mm by 1 cm long. If its resistivity is 20 ohm-cm and it is N type, it will contain about 8×10^{13} electrons/ cu cm in the conduction band (from $1/\rho = nq\mu_n$).   In the volume of the bar there will then be 8×10^{11} conduction electrons.   In order to lower the resistance of the bar by a factor of 2, we will have to increase the number of current carriers by about a factor of 2 (actually it must be more than 2, since holes are half as mobile as electrons in germanium).   The photoexcitation process creates equal numbers of holes and electrons, so that it turns out that we shall need enough photons per second to increase the number of electrons by 5.8×10^{11}.   If the lifetime of extra carriers is 10^{-4} sec, we must supply $5.8 \times 10^{11}(1 - 1/e) = 4.6 \times 10^{11}$ quanta every 10^{-4} sec, or 4.6×10^{15} quanta/sec.   At a wavelength of 0.54 micron, 1 lumen contains 3.8×10^{15} quanta/

TABLE 5.1. PARAMETERS OF VARIOUS SEMICONDUCTORS USED IN POLYCRYSTALLINE FILM PHOTOCONDUCTING CELLS

Material	Wavelength of peak sensitivity, microns	Threshold wavelength, microns	Sensitivity		Decay time, msec	Light/dark conductivity ratio at room temp	Illumination	References
			Conductivity, mhos/watt-cm²	Illumination at $\frac{signal}{noise}=1$, watts				
ZnS (pure)	0.338	0.400	......	......	......	$>10^6$	......	a
(Cu doped)	0.540	0.650	......	......	......	10^4	......	a
ZnSe (pure)	0.465	0.575	10^{-6}–10^{-5}	......	......	......	......	b
(Cu doped)	0.515	0.625	4×10^{-3}	......	100	......	0.2 ft-c	b
ZnTe (doped)	0.800	3.500	......	......	2–14	......	1740 ft-c	c
CdS (pure)	0.520	0.670	10^{-5}	......	110	......	3 ft-c	d, e
					15	......	900 ft-c	e
			10^{-2}		0.3	......	1740 ft-c	f
					0.4	......	1740 ft-c	f
(Cl:Cu doped)	0.620	0.670	10^{-1}	......	0.5–3.8	10^4	9 ft-c	e
(Sintered)			10^{-3}	......	2–3	5×10^5	1740 ft-c	d, f
CdSe (pure)	0.720	0.830	10^{-5}	......	<0.009	10^4	9 ft-c	e
			10^{-2}		1.5		1740 ft-c	f
(Cl:Cu doped)			10^{-1}		0.6–1.2		1740 ft-c	f, g
(Sintered)			10^{-3}		0.3–0.5		1740 ft-c	f
(Evaporated)			10^{-5}–10^{-4}		0.008		1740 ft-c	f
CdTe (pure)			......	4×10^{-11}	......	50–200	2 ft-c	i
(In doped)	0.850	1.000	......	8×10^{-11}	......	5–50	0.8 μ	h, i
							0.4 μ	i
PbS	2.900	3.400	......	3×10^{-11}	0.01	......	2.2 μ	j, l, k
PbSe	4.200	5.500	......	3×10^{-9}	0.003	......	2.5 μ	m, l, k
PbTe	4.700	6.000	......	3×10^{-9}	0.003	......	2.5 μ	n, l, k

sec. We find therefore that 1.2 lumens falling on the 0.1-cm² area of the bar would reduce its resistance from 2,000 to 1,000 ohms, provided the test voltage is too small to sweep carriers out of the bar in a time comparable to the lifetime.

An interesting property of such a bar is that it can be made to show a rectifying characteristic if the area of illumination is confined to one end of the bar and if the sweeping voltage is large enough to make the transit time from end to end short compared with the lifetime of the injected carriers. In the foregoing example, the lifetime was assumed to be 10^{-4} sec. If the voltage applied to the bar is 20 volts, the transit time for holes to flow the full length of the bar is

$$\frac{1}{\mu_p \mathcal{E}} = \frac{1}{1,800 \times 20} = 2.8 \times 10^{-5} \text{ sec}$$

This means that the extra carrier concentration has dropped only by about 20 per cent at the dark end of the bar when the illuminated end is positive. When the illuminated end is negative, the extra carriers are immediately lost to the electrical contact at that end and do not appreciably affect the resistance of the bar. For this example we must inject 5.8×10^{11} electrons in each transit time, or 2.1×10^{16} electrons/sec, in order to reduce the resistance by a factor of 2 when the illuminated end is positive. This requires 5.5 lumens falling on the positive end of the bar.

5.2c. Grown-junction Photocells.[5] In Fig. 5.4 are shown a number of photoconductive devices. At the upper left is the photoconductive bar just discussed. At left center in the figure is a single PN-junction photocell which we shall consider next.

In Sec. 3, the rectification of a PN junction was discussed in some detail. In Eq. (3.11) the reverse saturation current of such a junction was found to be

$$I = qA \left(p_n \sqrt{\frac{D_p}{\tau_p}} + n_p \sqrt{\frac{D_n}{\tau_p}} \right) \tag{5.3}$$

where p_n and n_p were the concentrations of minority carriers in the N and P regions, respectively. If we illuminate the region of the junction as shown in Fig. 5.4, we shall increase both p_n and n_p by an equal amount, provided τ_p and τ_n are nearly equal. If we let $\tau_n = \tau_p = 10^{-4}$ sec and use a 1- by 1- by 10-mm bar as before, we can maintain p_n and n_p at 5.8×10^{13} holes or electrons/cu cm if we illuminate the surface over a 2-mm² area symmetrically covering the junction with 0.24 lumen of 0.54-micron radiation. These figures substituted in Eq. (3.11) give a saturation current of 16 ma. The dark current of such a junction is usually of the order of a few microamperes.

A fixed number of exciting photons per second will give the same photoconductive response over a wide range of wavelengths. Since most photocell responses are measured using an incandescent tungsten filament at a specific color temperature (usually 2400°K), there are many times as many photons of wavelength 1.5 microns effective as there are photons of wavelength 0.54 micron. This means that a considerably greater sensitivity will be found using incandescent tungsten-filament lumens than that calculated above using monochromatic 0.54-micron lumens. Experimentally, such a PN-junction photocell shows a sensitivity of about 0.03 ma/millilumen if all the photons are striking an area of linear dimensions small compared with a diffusion length for the excess carriers and centered over the junction.

In Fig. 5.5 is shown a sensitivity profile for a grown-junction photocell. This shows clearly the effect of minority-carrier lifetime on the region of photosensitivity. The diffusion lengths L_p and L_n are by definition the distances that excess holes and electrons diffuse on the average before their densities are reduced by a factor $1/e$. As the incident light beam is moved away from the junction on either side, the photocurrent should fall off exponentially. The distance from the junction on either side where the response is down by $1/e$ is the diffusion length if proper correction is made for the finite widths of both the junction and the light beam. Since $L_p^2 = D_p \tau_p$ and $L_n^2 = D_n \tau_n$, we calculate the τ's for the example of Fig. 5.5 to be

$$\tau_p = \frac{(0.12)^2}{50} = 288 \ \mu\text{sec}$$

on the N-type side and $\tau_n = (0.18)^2/100 = 324 \ \mu\text{sec}$ on the P-type side. From this it can be seen that a very long lifetime is necessary to obtain a sensitive area of any considerable extent.

The frequency response of such a device depends on the area illuminated and upon the lifetimes of the excess carriers. A long-lifetime junction illuminated over a broad area on either side of the junction will have a low-frequency cutoff, whereas the same junction illuminated with a very sharp beam carefully centered on the junction will be reasonably good. In a very low lifetime junction a broad beam will not deteriorate the frequency response, since carriers produced at any considerable distance never reach the junction anyway.

A much more sensitive type of grown-junction photocell is the hook-junction photocell shown at the lower left of Fig. 5.4. This device uses the same hook-collector mechanism discussed in Sec. 4.

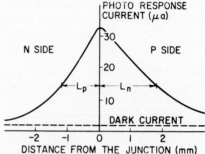

Fig. 5.5. Sensitivity contour for a grown-junction photocell.

The illuminated area must be close to the junction biased in reverse in order to obtain the maximum sensitivity. The operation of this photocell can best be understood by making an analogy between the light beam and the emitter of the hook-junction transistor. The current-multiplication factor of the hook collector was given in Eq. (4.41) to be

$$\alpha^* = 1 + \frac{L_{nc}}{W_f} \frac{\rho_f}{\rho_c} \tag{5.4}$$

where L_{nc} is the diffusion length for electrons in the P region which is not illuminated, ρ_c is the resistivity of the same P region, and ρ_f and W_f are the resistivity and thickness, respectively, of the N region. By the proper choice of L_{nc}, W_f, ρ_f, and ρ_c, α^* can be designed to have any reasonable value. Typically, $\alpha^* = 100$ is an average value. Since the hook-collector mechanism operates on the photocurrent crossing the illuminated PN junction, the sensitivity of the simple grown-junction photocell is multiplied by α^*, giving a typical value of 3 ma/millilumen. This also assumes that the total light flux falls with a fraction of a diffusion length of the reverse-biased PN junction.

The electron portion of the dark current of the reverse-biased junction is also multiplied by α^*, so that the dark current of the over-all device is usually an order of magnitude larger than the dark current of a simple-junction photocell.

The frequency response of such a hook-junction photocell is at best as good as a similar hook-junction transistor but is usually worse if the diffusion length in the illuminated P region is long and a wide light beam is used.

5.2d. Alloy-junction Photocell. The alloy-junction photocell shown at the lower right of Fig. 5.4 has a sensitivity in terms of total flux which is identical with the grown-junction photocell just discussed, provided that the wavelength of the exciting radiation is short enough to be completely absorbed in the semiconductor and that the diffusion length is large compared with the thickness of the semiconductor.

Because of the particular geometry of the structure, the sensitive area covers essentially all the surface upon which the illumination falls. There is no sensitivity profile analogous to the one just discussed for the grown-junction type, since the entire area of the surface illuminated is the same distance from the junction.

In order to maximize frequency response and sensitivity, the thickness of the semiconductor layer is made as small as practical. This has the effect of shortening the wavelength at which the sensitivity begins to fall off as the threshold wavelength is approached. This is understood by considering curves A and B of Fig. 5.2. If the thin semiconductor A cannot absorb all the radiation falling on it before it reaches the alloy region, the transmitted radiation is mostly lost to the excitation process and the sensitivity is lower than that of a photocell B with a thicker semiconductor layer.

5.2e. Point-contact Photocell.[5,7] The point-contact photocell is designed with a structure similar to the alloy-junction photocell. This device is shown at the upper right of Fig. 5.4. The area of maximum sensitivity is much less than that of the alloy photocell because the barrier under the point is much less extensive than is the alloy junction. On the other hand, the point is usually a formed phosphor-bronze whisker which exhibits considerable multiplication. The sensitivity of such a photocell is typically 0.2 ma/millilumen total flux falling entirely in the area of maximum sensitivity. The dark current of a point-contact photocell is typically 2 or 3 ma.

The same considerations regarding the thickness of the semiconductor wafer apply to the point-contact photocell as applied to the alloy-junction photocell.

Table 5.2 lists the semiconductor materials most appropriate for use in the barrier or junction types.

TABLE 5.2. THRESHOLD WAVELENGTH FOR BARRIER-TYPE PHOTOCONDUCTORS
(Wavelength in microns)

GaAs	Si	Ge	InSb
0.9	1.0	1.8	6.8

Table 5.3 summarizes the performance of typical photoconducting cells of the classes discussed above.

TABLE 5.3. PARAMETERS OF VARIOUS PHOTOCONDUCTING CELLS

Photocell type	Dark current	Sensitivity, ma/ millilumen	A-C impedance, ohms	Frequency cutoff
High-resistance bar....	1–10 ma	0.03	1.000	$1-5 \times 10^3$
Grown junction.......	1–10 μa	0.03	$1-10 \times 10^6$	$2-5 \times 10^5$
Hook junction........	10–100 μa	3.0	$1-10 \times 10^5$	$4-10 \times 10^4$
Alloy junction........	1–10 μa	0.03	$1-10 \times 10^6$	$2-10 \times 10^5$
Point contact.........	1–3 ma	0.2	$1-3 \times 10^4$	$2-10 \times 10^5$
Polycrystalline film....	1–10 μa	10.0	$1-10 \times 10^5$	$1-5 \times 10^2$

5.3. Photovoltaic Cells.[1] All the photocells discussed so far have used external power supplies, and the fundamental process involved has been the modulation of the conductivity of a PN junction or of a bar of semiconductor material. A photovoltaic cell uses no external power supply and develops a voltage across its terminals when illuminated. Photovoltaic cells can be made using either metal-semiconductor contacts or PN junctions. One typically distinguishing difference between photovoltaic cells and photoconducting cells is the area of the rectifying contact. Most photovoltaic cells have effective barrier areas one or two orders of magnitude larger than photoconducting cells. This is done because photovoltaic-cell applications usually call for a relatively large light-gathering power and require the cell to furnish sufficient current to operate some electrical device such as a microammeter. A photographic exposure meter is a good example of a photovoltaic-cell application.

The operation of a photovoltaic cell can be understood by considering the energy-level diagrams of Fig. 5.6. At the top of the figure is shown a metal-semiconductor

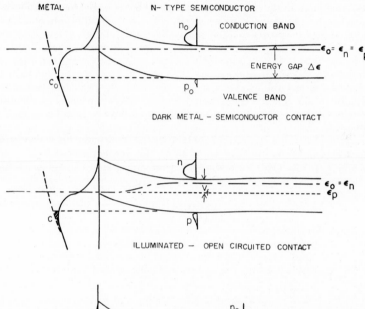

Fig. 5.6. Energy-level representation of a short-circuited and open-circuited photosensitive barrier.

contact without bias and without any illumination. Under these conditions (see Sec. 3 for details) no current will flow across the barrier, and the hole concentration p_0 in the semiconductor will balance the hole concentration in the metal c_0. It is assumed for the moment that the barrier is high enough to keep any electron interchange from taking place over the top of the barrier. The electron concentration n_0 in the semiconductor is thermodynamically in equilibrium with the hole concentration so that there is a well-defined Fermi level ϵ_0 which determines the relative sizes of n_0 and p_0.

At the center of Fig. 5.6 the same diode is shown under illumination with its terminals open-circuited. Here it is assumed for simplicity that the number of hole-electron pairs formed in the semiconductor under the excitation of the light is small compared with the normally present electron density n_0. The hole density p is much larger than it was, and thermodynamic equilibrium no longer exists across the energy gap. Since the diode is open-circuited, no current can flow; so the semiconductor side of the diagram must be raised until the enhanced hole distribution p is balanced by an equal number of holes c in the metal. The difference between the position of the Fermi level in the metal and the old Fermi level in the semiconductor is the photovoltage V_f. We still assume that the barrier is high enough to prevent electron exchange over the top of it.

Since thermodynamic equilibrium still exists in the metal, the hole distribution c is determined by the Fermi level in the metal. The new equilibrium condition was achieved by matching hole distributions under the barrier. This means that the hole distribution p in the semiconductor would be compatible with a Fermi level at the same energy as the Fermi level in the metal. Such a hypothetical Fermi level (in this case for holes only) is called a quasi-Fermi level and is shown as the dashed line ϵ_p in the figure. The electron distribution n_0 has not been appreciably increased by the light excitation so that it is still compatible with the old Fermi level ϵ_0. If the electron distribution had been appreciably increased, we would have a quasi-Fermi level ϵ_n for electrons also.

If we assume that there is a second contact to the semiconductor which is ohmic, thermodynamic equilibrium will be enforced at this contact and both quasi-Fermi levels ϵ_p and ϵ_n will coincide with the true Fermi level ϵ_0. The voltage measured between the metal and this ohmic contact will be the photoelectric voltage V_f. Under these conditions,

$$V_f = (\epsilon_p - \epsilon_0) \tag{5.5}$$

The polarity of the photovoltage V_f is such that electrons will tend to flow out of the ohmic terminal into the metal. The ohmic terminal is therefore negative with respect to the metal. If the barrier is not high enough to prohibit all electronic exchange between the semiconductor and the metal, it can be proved that the photovoltage becomes

$$V_f = \gamma(\epsilon_p - \epsilon_0) \tag{5.6}$$

where γ is the usual injection efficiency of the contact.

If the barrier is very high (greater than the energy gap), then it is clear that the maximum photovoltage obtainable would be found when ϵ_p reached its limiting position as the light intensity increased indefinitely. This limiting position of ϵ_p coincides with the edge of the valence band. Therefore, $V_{f\max} = \Delta\epsilon$. Practically, however, such barriers do not exist and $V_{f\max} \cong \frac{1}{2}\Delta\epsilon$ is a realizable limit.

5.3a. The Case of Low Light Levels. We shall now consider the factors determining V_f for the low-light-intensity case. To do this we shall first consider the case of the short-circuit current of the illuminated diode. This case is illustrated at the bottom of Fig. 5.6. When the metal and the ohmic contact to the semiconductor are shorted together (again under the assumption that no electrons flow over the top of the barrier), a hole-diffusion current density J_p flows into the metal. This current density is given by

$$J_p = q\,\frac{p - p_0}{L_p}\,D_p = q\,\frac{p}{L_p}\,D_p \tag{5.7}$$

where $p_0 \ll p$. Since the carriers of this current are holes produced by light excitation, and since each light quantum absorbed produces one hole, we can calculate the equilibrium density of holes p by equating the recombination rate p/τ to the generation rate I_L/v, where I_L is the light flux in photons per second, v is the volume of the crystal in which the light absorption takes place, and τ is the current-carrier lifetime.

This gives

$$I = \frac{A q I_{LT} D_p}{v L_p} = \frac{q I_L L_p}{w} \tag{5.8}$$

where A is the area of the photocell, w is the thickness, and $L_p = \sqrt{D_p \tau}$. This equation holds for low light levels and a photocell structure in which $w \gg L_p$. It is also assumed that the light absorption takes place throughout the thickness w adjacent to the barrier.

If the absorption of the light is confined to a layer of thickness $d \ll L_p$ adjacent to the barrier, Eq. (5.8) reduces simply to

$$I = q L_L \tag{5.9}$$

since a negligible fraction of the optically excited electrons recombine in the semiconductor but rather diffuse into the metal contact under short-circuit conditions.

In the illuminated open-circuit case the optically excited carriers must all recombine in the semiconductor or diffuse to the ohmic contact to recombine. If they are generated in a thin layer near the barrier and recombine in the semiconductor, a current $q I_L$ will diffuse into the interior of the semiconductor. In the center diagram of Fig. 5.6, the Fermi level is shifted upward in the semiconductor by the amount V_f. If the illumination is removed but a voltage equal to V_f is maintained by an external battery, the diode will be biased in the forward direction and a current density

$$J_p = \frac{q D_p c}{L_p} = \frac{q I_L}{A} $$

will flow (assuming $\gamma = 1$), where c is the density of holes in the metal above the barrier and c/L_p is the diffusion gradient in the semiconductor. Now using the diode equation (3.13) we get

$$I_p = I_0 (e^{u V_f} - 1) \tag{5.10}$$

where $I_0 = q A D_p p_0 / L_p$. Solving for V_f we get

$$u V_f = \ln \left(\frac{I_p}{I_0} + 1 \right) = \frac{I_p}{I_0} = \frac{p}{p_0} \tag{5.11}$$

for small currents. Substituting $q I_L$ for I_p and $q A D_p p_0 / L_p$ for I_0 we get

$$V_f = \frac{1}{Au} \frac{I_L}{p_0} \frac{L_p}{D_p} \tag{5.12}$$

for the open-circuit voltage at low light levels. If the thickness of the photocell w is much less than the diffusion length L_p, most of the optically excited carriers will diffuse to the ohmic contact before recombining. In this case, w is substituted for L_p in Eq. (5.12). If L_p is the governing distance, the ratio L_p/D_p in (5.12) can be written as $\sqrt{\tau/D_p}$ to show the dependence on carrier lifetime τ directly.

The unilluminated density of holes p_0 can be calculated from the resistivity of the semiconductor ($\rho = 1/n_0 q \mu_n$) and the intrinsic equilibrium constant of the semiconductor material [$n_i^2(T) = n_0 p_0$] to give

$$p_0 = n_i^2(T) \rho q \mu_n \tag{5.13}$$

In the case of a photocell with a thickness large compared with L_p, illuminated with light of a wavelength near the absorption edge so that excess carriers are excited throughout a volume of thickness much greater than L_p, we must substitute

$$I_p = \frac{qAD_p p}{L_p}$$

into Eq. (5.11) where $p = I_{L}\tau/v$; this gives an open-circuit floating voltage

$$V_f = \frac{I_{L}\tau}{uvp_0} \tag{5.14}$$

We shall now consider an example based on the structure of Fig. 5.7 to indicate the response to be expected from a photovoltaic cell. The light is absorbed near the surface of the semiconductor in the region indicated on the figure by the dotted area. If we assume that $w \ll L_p$ and that the annular ohmic contact is far enough removed from the region of illumination so that a negligible number of excess carriers reach it

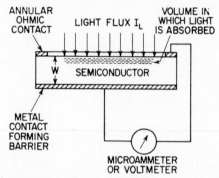

FIG. 5.7. Schematic diagram of a typical photovoltaic cell.

by diffusion, we can calculate the short-circuit current from (5.9) if there is no other loss of excess carriers.

The structure of Fig. 5.7 is such that there may be appreciable loss of optically excited carriers by recombination at the surface which is being illuminated. To take account of this properly we shall define a surface-recombination velocity s by the following relation:

$$J_s = qps \tag{5.15}$$

where J_s is a current density flowing into the surface and p is the hole density just inside the surface. Equating the current density of generated carriers qI_L/A to the sum of the loss of the illuminated surface and the current under the barrier, we have

$$\frac{qI_L}{A} = qps + \frac{qpD_p}{w}$$

giving

$$p = \frac{I_L}{A(s + D_p/w)} \tag{5.16}$$

The short-circuit current flowing under the barrier is then

$$I = I_p = \frac{ApD_p}{w} = \frac{qD_pI_L}{ws + D_p} \tag{5.17}$$

In the open-circuit case, we shall assume that all the excess carriers are lost by recombination on the surface so that $qI_L = qpsA$ or

$$p = \frac{I_L}{sA} \tag{5.18}$$

Substituting (5.18) into (5.11) we get

$$V_f = \frac{1}{Aus} \frac{I_L}{p_0}$$ (5.19)

Some typical values are as follows:

$n_i^2(300°) = 5.8 \times 10^{26}$ (for germanium)
$\rho = 1$ ohm-cm
$\tau = 100$ μsec
$I_L = 3.8 \times 10^{13}$ photons/sec (10 millilumens of 0.54-micron light)
$w = 0.10$ cm
$A = 2$ cm^2
$s = 100$ cm/sec

From this data we calculate:

$qI_L = 6$ μa
$p_0 = 3.3 \times 10^{11}$ holes/cm^3

Short-circuit current:

$I = 5$ μa [by Eq. (5.17)]

Open-circuit voltage (letting $u = q/kT \cong 40$ ev^{-1}):

$V_f = 0.014$ volt [by Eq. (5.19)]

Again it should be pointed out that approximately eight times the response calculated above will be obtained using 10 millilumens of light from an incandescent filament at a color temperature of 2400°K.

REFERENCES

1. Moss, T. S.: "Photoconductivity," Academic Press, Inc., New York, 1952.
2. Rose, A.: Lifetimes of Free Electrons and Holes in Solids, in "Progress in Semiconductors," vol. 2, John Wiley & Sons, Inc., New York, 1957.
3. Bube, R. H.: Photoconductivity of the Sulfide, Selenide, and Telluride of Zinc or Cadmium, *Proc. IRE*, vol. 43, pp. 1836–1850, December, 1955.
4. Breckenridge, R. G., B. R. Russell, and E. E. Hahn: "Photoconductivity Conference," John Wiley & Sons, Inc., New York, 1956.
5. Shive, J. N.: The Properties of Germanium Phototransistors, *J. Opt. Soc. Am.*, vol. 43, pp. 239–244, April, 1953.
6. Polycrystalline Film Photoconductivity:
   a. Cheroff, G., R. C. Enck, and S. P. Keller: *Phys. Rev.*, vol. 116, p. 1091, 1959.
   b. Bube, R. H., and E. L. Lind: *Phys. Rev.*, vol. 110, pp. 1040–1049, 1958.
   c. Braithwaite, J. G. N.: *Proc. Phys. Soc.*, vol. 64B, p. 274, 1951.
   d. Veith, W.: *Z. angew. Phys.*, vol. 7, p. 1, 1955.
   e. Bube, R. H., and S. M. Thomsen: *J. Chem. Phys.*, vol. 23, pp. 15–25, 1955.
   f. Bube, R. H.: *J. Appl. Phys.*, vol. 27, p. 1237, 1956.
   g. Bube, R. H., and S. M. Thomsen: *Rev. Sci. Instr.*, vol. 26, p. 664, 1955.
   h. Miyasawa, H., and S. Sugaike: *J. Phys. Soc. Japan*, vol. 9, p. 648, 1954.
   i. Kretshmar, G. G., and L. E. Shilberg: *J. Appl. Phys.*, vol. 28, p. 865, 1957.
   j. Moss, T. S.: *Proc. Phys. Soc.*, vol. 66B, p. 993, 1953.
   k. Wright, D. A.: *Brit. J. Appl. Phys.*, vol. 9, p. 205, 1958.
   l. Eastman Kodak and E. C. A. Manufacturer Specification.
   m. Gibson, A. F., W. D. Lawson, and T. S. Moss: *Proc. Phys. Soc.*, vol. 64B, p. 1054, 1951.
   n. Bode, D. E., and H. Levinstein: *Phys. Rev.*, vol. 96, p. 259, 1954.
7. O'Neill, C. D.: Germanium Photocells, *Proc. Natl. Electronics Conf.*, vol. 6, pp. 266–276, 1950.

PART II

Technology of Transistors, Diodes, and Photocells

Preface

In this part most of the principal techniques involved in the fabrication of semi-conductor devices are covered.   The aim is to provide the engineer with a basic understanding of the limitations imposed upon the finished devices by the various methods of fabrication.   A secondary aim is to provide enough information so that an engineer can assemble suitable equipment and make a semiconductor device by one or another of the major techniques described.   It is not meant to be detailed enough to supply a major portion of the "tricks of the trade" used in large-scale production of semiconductor devices.

In Sec. 6 the methods of purification and single-crystal preparation of semiconductors are discussed.   In this section workable methods are given which will yield crystals of reasonably reproducible properties, provided the precautions listed are properly observed.   There are many variations of the crystal-growing process, but the few given are well proved to give adequate quality crystals.

In Sec. 7 the methods of forming PN junctions are described.   Attention is given to the preparation of junctions which are good emitters, good collectors, and good rectifiers.   The various techniques of junction formation are contrasted with respect to some of the general properties of junctions.   The metal-semiconductor contacts are considered apart from junctions in Sec. 8.   In some cases it is hard to draw the line between junctions and metal-semiconductor contacts.   In this part we have placed welded and bonded contacts in the metal-contact section, along with point contacts and surface-barrier contacts.   On the other hand, alloy-junction contacts which may be microscopically identical to bonded contacts are described in the junction section.

Section 9 describes in reasonable detail some of the techniques of encapsulation of transistors and diodes.   In this section the effects of surface contamination and the importance of the protection of the crystal surface are discussed.   At the end of Part II, Sec. 10 contains several design descriptions which are intended to illustrate the proper choice of methods of fabrication to achieve four typical devices.   This section is meant to be only an illustration of the application of the principles of Part I to the techniques of Part II and is not intended to cover any appreciable part of the field of device design.

L. P. HUNTER

Section 6

PREPARATION OF SEMICONDUCTOR MATERIALS

B. OKKERSE†

Philips Research Laboratories
N. V. Philips' Gloeilampenfabrieken
Eindhoven, Netherlands

6.1. Introduction. The object of this section is to survey standard techniques presently in use for the production of the base material for germanium and silicon devices. The discussion of the preparation of semiconducting materials is consequently limited in two ways. First, no attention is given to processes which are being developed and tested with a view to producing better material more economically. Second, little account is taken of the large group of semiconducting compounds and of germanium-silicon alloys. Though several of these materials are known or may prove to be extremely useful for certain devices, the preparation problems

† ACKNOWLEDGMENT. The author wants to express his gratitude to his colleagues J. Goorissen and I. P. Penning for many enlightening and stimulating discussions before and during the preparation of this manuscript.
‡ This section prepared by G. A. Silvey, IBM Corp., Poughkeepsie, N.Y.

involved still prohibit large-scale production; the nature of these difficulties are briefly mentioned at the end of this section.

This section includes descriptions of the chemical purification of germanium and silicon, the further purification of these elements by zone refining, and the production of single crystals with a controlled impurity concentration and physical perfection. In accordance with the normal practice of manufacturers of devices, interest has been focused on the last two items. These descriptions include a theoretical introduction and a survey of the corresponding applications. It will be noted that there is still a large gap between science and technology. While the principles of the modern standard techniques are discussed at considerable length, experimental and constructional details are not given. It is also beyond the scope of this section to discuss the techniques by which the crystal is processed to the wafers required for the device production. At the end of this section some remarks are made on the technology of the semiconducting compounds.

6.2. Chemical Purification of Germanium and Silicon. The object of this section is simply to indicate how germanium and silicon are chemically processed to such a purity that these elements can be further refined by the method of zone refining or even be used without further refining. It does not seem the function of this handbook to discuss the topic intensively, because it is the common practice of manufacturers of semiconducting compounds to buy "electronic-grade" germanium (often in the form of germanium dioxide) and silicon. A recent survey of the chemical purification of germanium and silicon has been given by Wilson.[1]

6.2a. The Production of Pure Germanium Dioxide. The element germanium is as abundant in the earth's crust as common metals like zinc or lead. However, there are only a few minerals in which germanium is an important constituent (5 to 10 per cent) and these occur only in small deposits. Some zinc, copper, and silver ores contain trace amounts of germanium (0.1 to 0.001 per cent), from which the element can be economically recovered as a by-product in the recovery of the primary metals. Germanium can be recovered also from the ash of certain coals. The recovery process of germanium from the Tri-State zinc ore deposit has been described by Thompson et al.,[2] from the Congo copper, zinc, and lead ores by De Cleene,[3] from zinc ores by Boving et al.,[4] and from coal ash by Powell et al.[5]

The final product of all processes is crude distilled germanium tetrachloride (about 99 per cent pure), with arsenic trichloride and boron trichloride as major contaminants. The boiling points of these compounds are, respectively, 84, 112, and 12.5°C. Most of the arsenic trichloride and all of the boron trichloride can accordingly be separated by careful fractional distillation. Several methods have been developed to remove the final traces of arsenic trichloride. In one process use is made of the large affinity of arsenic for copper. The desired purification of the germanium tetrachloride is obtained by prolonged refluxing in a column packed with copper turnings. In modern processes the final fractionating stages are performed in an atmosphere which is saturated with hydrochloric acid and chlorine. Under these conditions the arsenic is oxidized to the pentavalent state according to the reaction:

$$AsCl_3 + 4H_2O + Cl_2 \rightleftharpoons H_3AsO_4 + 5HCl$$

The pentavalent arsenic preferentially dissolves into the aqueous hydrochloric acid phase, and the pure germanium tetrachloride can be distilled off. Theuerer[6] developed a process based on the same property by which the germanium tetrachloride is separated from the arsenic-containing aqueous layer by means of extraction. In all processes the equipment for the final stages is made from fused quartz in order to limit the chance of contamination.

Germanium can be produced by direct reduction of the germanium tetrachloride by means of hydrogen or metals. However, the efficiency of these processes is not very high. By far the most germanium is produced by hydrogen reduction of germanium dioxide, which compound is prepared by hydrolysis of the purified germanium tetrachloride, according to the reaction

$$GeCl_4 + 4H_2O \rightarrow 4HCl + Ge(OH)_4$$
$$Ge(OH)_4 \rightarrow GeO_2 + 2H_2O$$

The water used has to be deionized and distilled several times in quartz equipment. After filtering, the germanium dioxide is washed intensively, dried at 120°C, and calcinated at 400°C. Several batches of the pure germanium dioxide are mixed thoroughly to make uniform lots of about 50 kg. To evaluate the purity a sample of the lot is reduced (see Sec. 6.2b), melted, solidified by normal freezing (see Sec. 6.3a), and then zone-refined (see Sec. 6.3c), after which the resistivity of the bar is measured. The result of this analysis is given on the containers in which the germanium dioxide is packed and shipped.

6.2b The Reduction of Germanium Dioxide. Not much detailed information is available about this important process. Generally, germanium dioxide loaded in a graphite boat is reduced in streaming hydrogen at temperatures of about 650 to 660°C, according to the reaction

$$GeO_2 + 2H_2 \rightarrow Ge + 2H_2O$$

A typical design of a reduction furnace is shown in Fig. 6.1. The reaction is diffusion-controlled, and therefore the time necessary for complete reduction depends critically

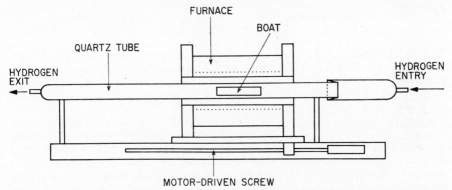

FIG. 6.1. Germanium reduction and melting unit with traveling furnace (schematically).

on the thickness of the germanium dioxide layer. For instance, if the depth of the reduction boat is 10 cm, it takes about 20 hr to complete the reduction. The reaction rate increases with increasing temperature. However, at temperatures above 675°C the following reaction becomes important:

$$GeO_2 + Ge \rightarrow 2GeO$$

The germanium monoxide is volatile at this temperature, and it disproportionates into a brown deposit at the cooler parts of the quartz reduction tube. This decreases the efficiency of the process and may clog the exit tube.

The gray metal powder is very reactive and easily contaminated. Therefore, immediately after completion of the reduction the temperature of the furnace is raised to 1000°C to melt the powder. Because of the fivefold decrease in volume in going from the oxide to the melted metal, the graphite boat has to have a special shape. A typical cross section is shown in Fig. 6.2. The dimensions of the reduced germanium bar should be adapted to the dimensions of the crucible in which the bar is going to be refined (see Sec. 6.3c).   The liquid is normally frozen by slow withdrawal of the boat from the furnace.   The over-all efficiency of the process should be better than 98 per cent.

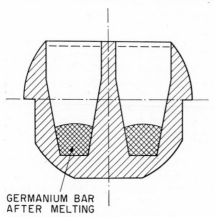

GERMANIUM BAR
AFTER MELTING

FIG. 6.2.   Typical cross section of reduction boat.

In several commercial processes the reduction, melting, and freezing steps are performed in one installation which operates continuously.   The same basic considerations apply.   The handling and loading of the reduction boats require special care to avoid contamination because of the large active surface areas involved.   When not in use the boats should be protected from dust by using plastic containers.   New boats should be prefired in chlorine at about 1100°C for several hours.

6.2c. The Production of Pure Silicon. Silicon is the most abundant solid element in the lithosphere; it is present in the form of the oxide or as silicates.   It is produced in relatively large quantities by the reduction of silica with coke in an electric furnace, according to the over-all reaction

$$SiO_2 + 2C \rightarrow Si + 2CO$$

The purity of technical silicon is of the order of 98 per cent.   The further purification to "electronic-grade" silicon presents many difficulties, which are due to (1) the large reactivity of the element, (2) the necessarily high temperatures of the processes involved, and (3) the ineffectiveness of zone refining with respect to certain impurities, notably boron, phosphorus, and arsenic (see Sec. 6.3d).   The last factor, in particular, has stimulated a good deal of research for processes to purify silicon chemically to the desired level so that the material can be used without additional refining.   At present, chemically purified silicon with a resistivity of about 500 ohm-cm at room temperature† is available in commercial quantities (the intrinsic resistivity is about 230,000 ohm-cm).   Though this purity suffices for many applications, one may expect a further need for silicon of even higher purity, especially for the production of diodes. The chemical industry is putting a great deal of effort into solving this problem.

Not much information is available about the processes presently in use for the production of electronic-grade silicon.   All processes have in common a step in which crude silicon is transformed into a silicon compound such as silane, silicon tetrachloride, trichlorosilane, or silicon tetraiodide, which compounds can be purified by fractional distillation (Lyon et al.,[7] Theuerer,[8] Van der Linden et al.[9]), by sublimation (Rubin[10]), or by zone refining.[10]   After purification, the compound is thermally cracked under reducing conditions with zinc[17] or hydrogen[8–10] and the silicon is deposited on the hot container wall (sometimes in the form of needles) or on a hot tantalum or silicon wire.[11]   The needles can be reduced in volume by melting and solidifying; the tantalum wire can be removed by etching.   The great advantage of

---

† The purity of electronic-grade silicon is characterized by the fraction (parts per billion) of electrically active impurity atoms or by the room-temperature resistivity ρ.   The relation between these two methods of characterization is (for $\rho > 1$ ohm-cm) for N-type material: ppb = $65/\rho$; for P-type material: ppb = $290/\rho$.   The resistivity can be properly used only if no compensation occurs.

the "wire process" is that the silicon forms directly in the required shape for floating-zone treatment. Naturally, depositing the silicon on a hot silicon wire offers the smallest chance for contamination. Attempts are continually being made to improve the purity of the silicon by improving the purity of the raw materials and by better control of the process parameters.

In order to characterize a lot of silicon it is common practice to grow an evaluation crystal by the vertical pulling technique (see Sec. 6.4e) and to determine the type and resistivity of the crystal. The result of this analysis is packed and shipped with the lot. A better method of evaluating the purity is to measure the resistivity after floating-zone treatment (see Sec. 6.3d).

6.3. Zone Refining. The steps necessary to reach the desired ultimate purity of the materials, which have already been purified by chemical processes, are discussed in this section. The techniques differ in detail depending on the material under consideration, but in all cases the underlying principle is that of zone refining, a process invented by Pfann.[12] Many excellent reviews on zone refining have recently been published.[13-16]

6.3a. Theoretical Considerations. The technique of zone refining makes use of the fact that at the freezing point the equilibrium concentration of an impurity in the solid differs from the concentration in the liquid. This behavior is conveniently described by the distribution constant k_0, which constant is the ratio of the concentration of impurities in the solid to the concentration in the liquid at equilibrium:

$$k_0 = \frac{\text{concentration in solid}}{\text{concentration in liquid}} = \frac{c_S}{c_L}$$

Consequently, k_0 can be calculated from the phase diagram. For the small concentrations of impurities encountered in this field, k_0 may be considered to be independent of concentration. A survey of other and usually more accurate methods for determining k_0 is given by Burton.[17]

The best-known values of k_0 for several impurities in germanium and silicon are compiled in Table 6.1. From Table 6.1 it appears that for most impurities $k_0 < 1$, indicating that the impurities are more soluble in the liquid than in the solid phase.

TABLE 6.1. DISTRIBUTION CONSTANTS IN GERMANIUM AND SILICON

	B	Al	Si	P	Ga	Ge	As	In	Sn	Sb
Ge	20	0.10	3	0.12	0.10	1	0.04	0.001	0.02	0.003
Si	0.85	0.004	1	0.35	0.01	0.3	0.3	5×10^{-4}	0.02	0.04

If one freezes a liquid, the redistribution of impurities is described by the effective distribution or segregation coefficient k instead of by k_0. This comes about because, in the case of $k_0 < 1$,† an enriched layer builds up in the liquid ahead of the moving solid-liquid interface owing to rejection of impurities by the solid.‡ In this layer the impurities can only diffuse to the bulk of the liquid because of the laminar flow pattern in the liquid adjacent to the solid. The concentration of the impurities at the interface c_{Li}, rather than the concentration in the bulk of the liquid c_{Lb}, determines the concentration in the freezing solid. The distribution coefficient c_S/c_{Lb} is closer to

† In the examples given in this article, k_0 is always assumed to be less than unity. Analogous arguments apply for k_0 larger than unity.

‡ It is assumed that the freezing rate is high with respect to the diffusion rate of the impurities in the liquid. This is always the case in the techniques under consideration.

unity than the equilibrium distribution constant c_S/c_{Li}, as can clearly be seen in Fig. 6.3.

It is clear that the distribution coefficient is a function of the freezing rate f, the diffusion constant of the impurity in the liquid D, and the thickness of the diffusion layer δ. Burton et al.[18] analyzed this problem and obtained the relation

$$k = \frac{k_0}{k_0 + (1 - k_0)e^{-f\delta/D}} \tag{6.1}$$

Because the diffusion constant D is not known in most of the cases, and because of the fact that the layer thickness δ varies with the amount of stirring and possibly also depends on the temperature gradients, the effective distribution coefficient is commonly determined experimentally for the conditions met in practice.

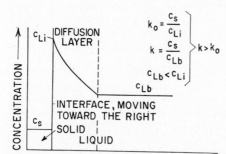

FIG. 6.3. The rejection of solute by the moving solid-liquid interface causes the distribution coefficient k to be larger than the distribution constant k_0.

A second consequence of the presence of the diffusion layer in front of the advancing solid-liquid interface is that the freezing point of the liquid in this layer increases with increasing distance from this interface, as was pointed out by Rutter et al.[19] If the temperature gradient in this region is not sufficiently steep, the temperature of the liquid at a certain distance from the interface may be lower than the corresponding freezing point and this liquid becomes supercooled. If this is the case, the smooth interface becomes unstable and dendritic growth may start, resulting in inclusion of impure liquid, or spurious nucleation centers may be formed, resulting in polycrystallinity. This phenomenon, called constitutional supercooling, is most likely to occur at high concentrations in the melt, large freezing rates, and small temperature gradients; it is comprehensively discussed by Chalmers.[20]

In normal freezing, a quantity of impure liquid material is frozen from one end. Since the freezing action rejects impurities to the liquid, the concentration of the solute in the liquid, and consequently that in the solid, continually rises. Assuming perfect mixing in the liquid except for the diffusion layer, the concentration of impurities in the solid c_S as a function of the fraction g solidified can be expressed as

$$c_S = kc_{L0}(1 - g)^{k-1} \tag{6.2}$$

where c_{L0} is the initial impurity concentration in the liquid.

In zone refining, a narrow liquid zone is caused to traverse a bar of the material to be purified. Qualitatively, one can see that a single zone pass is less effective than normal freezing, because the impurity concentration c_L in the small volume of the liquid zone increases rapidly owing to rejection of impurities by the freezing solid. As soon as c_L is equal to c_{L0}/k, where c_{L0} is the original impurity concentration of the bar, the moving zone causes no further effect. For a single zone pass the concentration $c_S(x)$ at any length x in the zone-melted bar (except for the last zone to solidify) is given by the following relation:

$$c_S(x) = c_{L0}[1 - (1 - k)e^{-kx/L}] \tag{6.3}$$

where L is the zone length. The segregation in the last zone is described by Eq. (6.2). The assumptions made in deriving Eqs. (6.2) and (6.3) are (1) perfect mixing in the bulk of the liquid, (2) no diffusion of impurities in the solid, (3) k independent of concentration, and (4) no constitutional supercooling. Except for the last, these conditions are not completely realized in practice, and, therefore, these techniques may not be so effective as expected.

In Fig. 6.4 is shown the behavior of the function (6.2) (curve a) and the function (6.3) (curve b). For many quantitative diagrams the reader is referred to the publications by Pfann.[13-15]

The effectiveness of zone refining can be tremendously increased if more zones are passed through the bar in the same direction, as a moment's reflection will show (see also Fig. 6.4, curve c). If a large number of zones is passed, the concentration gradient of impurities will eventually become so steep that the average concentration in any segment of the bar, of a length equal to that length of the liquid zone, is k times the concentration at the beginning of that segment; in that case no further movement of impurities will occur by continued zone refining. A narrow zone will, therefore, give a steeper ultimate concentration gradient than a wide zone for a given rate of traverse of the molten zone. For a given zone length, a slow rate of traverse will give a steeper concentration gradient than a fast rate because k tends to approach unity for fast rates. The ultimate impurity distribution, which depends on k and the ratio of the zone length and the length of the ingot, can be calculated theoretically.[13] The results of such calculations for some typical values are given in Fig. 6.5. In semiconductor practice, however, this ultimate impurity distribution will seldom be reached because of the unavoidable contamination of the ingot by the container or by the surrounding atmosphere during the process.

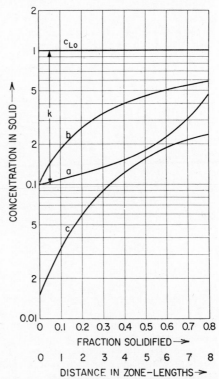

Fig. 6.4. Concentration of impurities in the solid after normal freezing (curve a) and after zone refining (curve b for one zone, curve c for two zones) for $k = 0.1$.

6.3b. Applications. During the purification process contamination of the material has to be avoided as much as is reasonably possible. This requirement sets a limit to the number of practical designs. Recognized sources of contamination are the container in which the material is to be purified, the gas ambient, and the vessel in which this gas atmosphere is maintained.

The container material must not react with the semiconductor, it should be practically free of impurities, and the cleaning should be easy. Moreover, it must be possible to fabricate the material in the desired shape. High-purity graphite and high-purity quartz have found wide application in this respect. Zone refining without a container is possible in the floating-zone technique (see Sec. 6.3*d*).

The surrounding atmosphere should be inert to the semiconductor material. The avoidance of oxygen is not so simple as it might seem. The technology to date has been built around inert atmospheres having an effective oxygen pressure of about 10^{-2} mm of Hg. Most commonly, inert gases with the highest obtainable purity are used, such as hydrogen, helium, argon, and nitrogen, or mixtures of these gases. Preferably, these gases are taken from a high-pressure tank in close proximity to the refiner in order to avoid contamination during the transport in the pipes. Immediately before use possible traces of oxygen can be eliminated by passing the gas through an oxygen getter, such as copper-impregnated kieselguhr, or by passing the gas with a small amount of hydrogen over a catalyzer like copper, platinum, or palladium and then through a drying stage, like silica gel, or still better a liquid-air trap.

Though excellent semiconductor material is obtained with the standard techniques, it should be emphasized that (1) the effect, if any, of inert gases is not very well

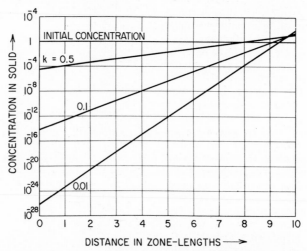

FIG. 6.5. Ultimate distribution of impurities in the solid attainable by zone refining, for several values of k, for an ingot 10 zones long. (*After Pfann.*[14])

known and (2) even very small amounts of oxygen and water vapor may have a significant effect (see Sec. 6.4e).

Alternatively, a vacuum technique can be applied. However, up to now not much seems to be gained thereby (except in special cases, see Sec. 6.3d), and the equipment is necessarily more complicated. The absence of a major improvement can be explained by assuming that, in vacuum, impurities vaporizing from the wall of the vessel hit the semiconductor material (see Hogarth et al.[21]).

In some cases, on the other hand, useful applications have resulted from the interaction between the liquid zone and a non-inert-gas atmosphere (see Secs. 6.3d and 6.4e).

The vessel in which the inert atmosphere is maintained is usually made from fused quartz because of its unique properties: purity, ease of cleaning, transparency, sturdiness, and small coefficient of thermal expansion. In a few cases water-cooled metal jackets are used (see Sec. 6.3d).

Closely connected with the problem of contamination is the choice of the method of heating. Both resistance heating and r-f induction heating have found widespread applications. The major advantage of resistance heating is its simplicity and therefore low initial cost. The advantages of r-f heating are (1) the physical separation of heat source and heated object, which simplifies the contamination problem: (2) the possibility of steeper temperature gradients; (3) the much longer life of the quartz tube; (4) the stirring action of the induced currents in the liquid; and (5) good visibility. There are two ways in which a narrow liquid zone can be arranged to traverse the length of an ingot; viz., the ingot can move, or the source of heat can move.   The latter method, however, is not widely applied.

6.3c. Zone Refining of Germanium.   On a laboratory scale and in industrial processes germanium bars are almost exclusively refined in high-purity graphite boats

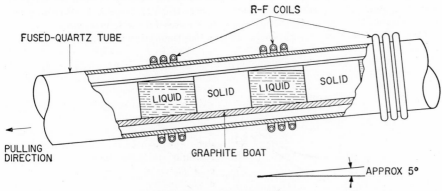

FIG. 6.6. Germanium zone refiner.

under a protective atmosphere of purified inert gases like hydrogen, helium, argon, or nitrogen (see Sec. 6.3b) contained in a quartz tube.   The graphite boat is pulled through a number of r-f induction coils arranged in series.   A typical arrangement is shown schematically in Fig. 6.6, and a commercial design of a germanium zone refiner is given in Fig. 6.7.

FIG. 6.7. Commercial design of germanium zone refiner.

The economy of the process, as far as efficiency and time are concerned, depends basically on the choice of the refining parameters: the zone length L, the interzone spacing i, the travel speed f, and the distribution coefficient k. These parameters cannot be independently fixed. They are correlated by Eq. (6.1) (k, k_0, f) on the one hand and by external conditions, like the amount of stirring (k) and the temperature gradients (f, L, i), on the other hand. From an analysis made by Burris et al.,[2e] it follows that the segregation efficiency can be increased if the zone length is decreased after a number of zones has passed. In practice the optimum conditions are determined experimentally.

The use of graphite boats presents some difficulties. First of all, graphite is porous and absorbs large quantities of air while the boats are being loaded. As the

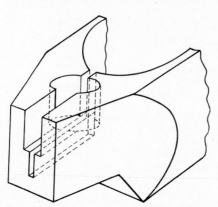

FIG. 6.8. Construction detail of front end of graphite boat provided with saw cut and hole for pulling hook.

boat is subsequently heated, the air is driven out of the graphite and the oxygen reacts with the germanium to produce germanium monoxide. The monoxide disproportionates into a mixture of germanium and germanium dioxide on the cold spots of the germanium, causing contamination, and on the quartz tube, rendering the tube opaque. These effects can be practically avoided by flushing the system with pure hydrogen or a rich hydrogen-nitrogen mixture (see Sec. 6.3b) for some time before the power is turned on and during refining. A typical gas-flow rate is 2 liters/min. The second difficulty with a graphite boat is that it represents the major load on the power source. Because of its varying cross section, the load is variable, allowing the zones to vary in width. If a saw cut is made in the front end of the boat, as shown in Fig. 6.8 (Goorissen[23]), this difficulty can be largely overcome. Arrangements in which boats made from quartz are pulled through heated carbon rings (Priest[24]) do not present these difficulties. However, they are more intricate and delicate to operate, and up to now the results do not warrant widespread application.

The shape of the boats, which are made from commercially available high-purity graphite, should be adapted to the shape of the bars of reduced germanium.

Before use the boats should be leached by pure chlorine gas at about 1000°C for 3 to 4 hr and baked in a nitrogen-hydrogen mixture at the same temperature for about the same period. It is useful to clean frequently used graphite boats regularly by the same procedure.

In order to avoid material transport during the refining operation (see Pfann[25]), due to the difference in specific density between liquid and solid germanium, the quartz tube is positioned to make an angle of a few degrees with the horizontal. The angle depends on the length and the height of the zone; the ingot is pulled toward the lower end.

The charge consists of a bar of reduced germanium or scrap germanium. The material is first rinsed with an organic solvent to dissolve greasy substances, then washed with an acid to remove possible adhering metal particles, and finally etched in one of the common etchants.† In the case of scrap material, the boat should be loaded intelligently so that the first zone melts all the material during its traverse.

† Common etchants for germanium are: (1) boil in 10 parts HNO_3 60 per cent for 5 min, then add 1 part HF 38 per cent; (2) 10 ml H_2O_2 30 per cent, 12 ml HF 38 per cent, and 38 ml distilled water, cold; (3) CP_4: 15 ml glacial acetic acid, 3 drops Br_2, 25 ml HNO_3 60 per cent, 12 ml HF 38 per cent, warm.

The boat is pulled by a quartz rod or a molybdenum wire, the sealing of which should be practically leakproof.   For instance, a simple and effective seal is the combination of molybdenum wire with a diameter of about 12 mils and a capillary with a bore slightly larger than 12 mils and 1 or 2 in. long.   It is important to have a stiff pulling system to prevent a jerky motion of the boat.   The speed is not critical and is usually of the order of 2 to 3 mm/min.   With this travel speed it is possible to maintain about 4-cm-wide zones about 5 cm apart (the distance between the centers of the coils is then 9 cm), provided that the power input is well controlled.   Little attention is required other than an occasional check.

The number of zones necessary depends on the purity of the starting material and the purity desired.   From commercially available reduced germanium it orginally

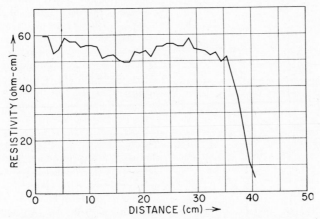

Fig. 6.9. Resistivity at room temperature versus length of a refined germanium bar after six zones, starting from commercially available reduced germanium (zone length is 4.5 cm; total length of bar is 45 cm).

takes six zones to obtain a resistivity of more than 50 ohm-cm at room temperature over 75 per cent of the length of the bar; a typical example is given in Fig. 6.9.   In intrinsic germanium obtained this way the concentration of electrically active impurity elements is less than 1 in 10^{10}.   The concentration of elements not detected by electrical measurements (except hydrogen, oxygen, and carbon) was measured by Hannay et al.[26] on the mass spectrograph and found to be less than 1 in 10^7.   By chemical analysis, Goorissen[27] found carbon in zone-refined germanium in a concentration of 1 to 2 in 10^5.[†]   It follows that zone refining is very effective in germanium, which fact can be attributed to the small distribution constants of impurities (see Table 6.1) and the availability of suitable container material.

6.3d. Zone Refining of Silicon.   The two favorable conditions just mentioned for germanium do not apply to silicon.   Three common impurities in silicon, namely, phosphorus, boron, and arsenic, have distribution constants very close to unity (see Table 6.1), which make their segregation very ineffective.   Moreover, liquid silicon reacts chemically with all known crucible materials.   Fortunately, the reaction rate of silicon with fused quartz is relatively slow even at the high temperatures involved. During this reaction silicon is contaminated notably by oxygen (Kaiser et al.[30]) and boron, which is a common impurity of quartz.   In view of these difficulties the technology of silicon is far more complicated than the technology of germanium.   Special techniques have been developed depending on the impurities involved and the ultimate

† By vacuum fusion analysis Papazian et al.[28] found hydrogen, oxygen, carbon, and nitrogen and Thurmond et al.[29] found hydrogen and oxygen in pulled germanium crystals (see Sec. 6.4d).   The concentrations observed were of the order of 1 in 10^4.

purity desired.   Because these techniques are all rather expensive, much effort has gone into the chemical purification of silicon (see Sec. 6.2c), and indeed, most silicon devices are produced from chemically purified silicon.

If the specification of the ultimate purity is not too stringent, silicon can be zone-refined in a quartz container in a process similar to that of germanium as was demonstrated by Taft et al.[31]   The wetting of quartz by molten silicon results in an intimate bonding between these materials.   On cooling, stresses build up owing to the difference in thermal expansion, which eventually crack the silicon bar and the adhering container.   Cracking of the bar is prevented by making the container wall very thin (5 to 15 mils).   As long as the temperature of the system is above 1000°C, the stresses will relieve plastically.   The fragile container is supported by silica rods. In order to keep the temperature of the silicon-quartz interface as low as possible, a protective atmosphere of argon is preferable to one of hydrogen or helium.   Nitrogen cannot be used owing to its reactivity toward molten silicon (Kaiser et al.[32]). The argon flow rate was 1.8 liters/min; the assembly was pulled at a rate of 2.3 mm/min.   This process may prove useful in the recovery of scrap material.   The contamination with boron from the quartz, combined with the large distribution constant of this impurity, prohibits the production of high-resistivity (>300 ohm-cm) silicon unless synthetic quartz is used.

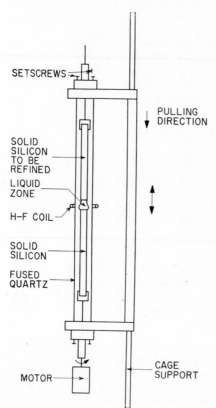

FIG. 6.10. Floating-zone refiner (schematically).

To date, high-resistivity silicon is exclusively processed in the floating-zone process, which technique was invented independently by Keck et al.,[33] Theuerer,[34] and Emeis.[35]   In this technique a molten zone is suspended by its own surface tension between two vertical colinear silicon rods.   A schematic illustration of this process is given in Fig. 6.10.   The low specific gravity d (2.33 g/cm³) and the high surface tension σ (720 dynes/cm) make silicon well suited for this process.   When the liquid zone is moved through the bar, refining action is obtained.   In the older designs[33,35] the liquid zone was maintained by radiation heat, which caused severe contamination problems. In modern designs, direct r-f induction heating is applied, as described by Keck et al.,[36] Müller,[37] Buehler,[38] and Goorissen.[39]   An example of modern commercial high-vacuum equipment is shown in Fig. 6.11.

The stability of the stationary floating zone has been analyzed mathematically by Heywang and coworkers.[40,41]   These authors showed that the maximum zone length that can be realized increases linearly with the diameter d of the bar for small diameters and approaches a limiting value for large diameters; this maximum zone length is determined by the parameter σ/d.   In practice silicon bars with a diameter of 2.5 cm have been refined by the floating-zone treatment.

The mechanical stability of the floating zone is also affected by the occurrence of levitation forces which arise from the interaction between the induced currents and the inducing electromagnetic field (see Okress et al.[42]).   Low-frequency modulation of the high-frequency currents can be especially troublesome by stimulating vibrations of the liquid zone.   Effective filtering is necessary in order to overcome this difficulty.[43]   A more elegant remedy is the use of higher frequencies, as was pointed

FIG. 6.11. Commercial high-vacuum floating-zone equipment; to the left the r-f generator, to the right the control unit and vacuum system.

out by Buehler.[38,44]   The levitation forces are small when the high-frequency currents are small.   The power P dissipated by the r-f field in the bar is given by

$$P = A\rho i^2 f^{1/2}$$

where A is a constant, i is the r-f current, f is the frequency, and ρ is the specific resistivity, and therefore, i can be small at high frequencies.   Buehler[38] found 10 per cent modulation with 360 cps at 4 mc not troublesome.   An additional advantage of high frequencies is the improved coupling of the r-f field with the bar.

The movement of the floating zone has some bearing on its stability, owing to the intricate interaction between the travel rate, the hydrostatic pressure inside the zone, the shape of the solid-liquid interface, the different surface tensions involved, and the thermal conditions, which depend on the nature of the gas atmosphere.   No quantitative information is available, but experimental evidence indicates that the downward motion of the zone is not so stable as the upward motion (see also Keck et al.[45]).

The starting of the floating-zone operation presents some difficulty, because high-resistivity silicon, if cold, does not couple sufficiently well with the r-f field owing to the small number of charge carriers.   The number of carriers can be (locally) increased by increasing the temperature of the bar.   This has been accomplished by radiation heat from a graphite ring,[37] by joule heat generated in the bar by current passage,[36] or by conduction heat from a low ohmic part of the bar which does couple directly with the r-f field.   However, the methods just mentioned are apt to contaminate the silicon.   Goorissen[46] uses a 1-kw incandescent lamp, the energy of which is focused on the silicon bar inside the r-f coil by means of a shiny metal semiellipsoid, as schematically shown in Fig. 6.12.   Once a hot (not necessarily liquid) zone is present, it can be maintained and moved through the bar by r-f heating only.   This implies that a hot zone can be returned to the head end of the bar after each zone pass by simply maintaining the r-f heating and moving the silicon rod back to its original position at a speed sufficient to keep the bar hot but not molten.

Before zone refining, the bar is etched in one of the common etchants.†   A typical bar is 40 cm long and 1.5 cm in diameter.   Means should be present to center the

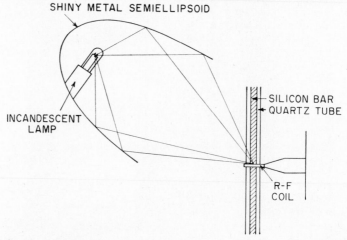

FIG. 6.12. Starting of the floating zone by the combined action of focused radiation and r-f field.

bar in the cleaned quartz tube and to position the bar on the proper level over the seed crystal.   The seed crystal can be rotated to provide for thermal symmetry and good stirring.   The system is flushed with purified argon, helium, or hydrogen (see Sec. 6.3b) at a rate of the order of 1 liter/min.   Normal travel rates of the zone are of the order of a few millimeters per minute.   After passage of one zone through the bar the procedure can be repeated without taking the bar out of the equipment by moving a hot (not molten) zone back to the starting position.   After four or five zones have passed, most of the commercially available silicon has a resistivity of a few hundred ohm-centimeters, which is mainly due to boron and phosphorus.   The segregation of these impurities (and also of arsenic) is very ineffective owing to the large distribution constants (see Table 6.1).

The removal rate of phosphorus and arsenic is much increased if zone refining is performed in vacuum (<0.1 mm of Hg).   Under these conditions phosphorus and arsenic evaporate at a measurable rate‡ from the molten zone.   Ziegler[48] modified Eq. (6.3) to include the vacuum treatment as well:

$$c_S(x) = c_{L0} \left[\frac{k}{u} - \left(\frac{k}{\iota} - k \right) e^{-ux/L} \right] \tag{6.4}$$

---

† Common etchants for silicon are (1) alkaline etchant: boil in 40 per cent NaOH solution; (2) acid etchant 1: 4 parts HNO_3 60 per cent, 4 parts HF 38 per cent, 1 part H_2SO_4 (concentrated); (3) acid etchant 2: 10 parts HNO_3 60 per cent, 1 part HF 38 per cent.

‡ Bradshaw et al.[47] showed that the evaporation rate of these impurities from silicon depends critically on the ambient gas pressure (see also Sec. 6.4e).

where $c_S(x)$ is the concentration at any length x, c_{L0} is the initial concentration, k is the effective distribution coefficient under normal pressure, L is the zone length, and u is a modified distribution coefficient:

$$u = k + \alpha \frac{L}{f}$$

where α is a measure of the evaporation rate, which depends on the geometrical conditions and the pressure, and f is the travel rate. If $\alpha = 0$, Eq. (6.4) transforms to Eq. (6.3). Experimentally, c_S/c_{L0} becomes constant after a few zone lengths. Naturally this ratio is a function of the travel speed; this is illustrated in Fig. 6.13, obtained by Goorissen.[49] After an appropriate number of vacuum treatments the silicon bar is normally P type, with a practically constant P-type resistivity of the order of 300 to 2,000 ohm-cm, depending on the boron level.

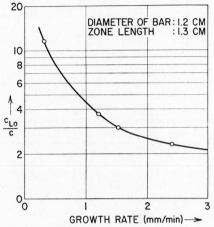

FIG. 6.13. Ratio of phosphorus concentrations before and after vacuum treatment during floating-zone refining of silicon versus travel speed.

Boron, with an effective distribution coefficient very close to unity, can be removed by passing hydrogen saturated with water vapor over the liquid zone, as was demonstrated by Theuerer.[50] The boron dissolved in the molten silicon is oxidized and carried away with the gas stream. Experimentally, the efficiency of the treatment for hydrogen saturated with water vapor between 0 and 10°C for a gas-flow rate of 1 liter/sec and for low-resistivity material is given by

$$\log \frac{c_B}{c_{B_0}} = -0.013 \frac{A}{V} t \sqrt{p} \tag{6.5}$$

where c_{B_0} = boron concentration before treatment

c_B = boron concentration after treatment

A = surface area of the floating zone, cm²

V = volume of the floating zone, cm³

t = the contact time, min ($= L/f$)

p = water-vapor pressure, mm Hg

Saturating hydrogen with water vapor at temperatures higher than 10°C causes crusting of the silicon with silica. The efficiency of the process decreases with increasing purity and is also a function of the gas-flow rate. In order to prevent contamination by the quartz tube, Buehler[38] cooled the outside of the tube with running water. Because of the large number of passes required and because of the unavoidable deposit on the inside of the quartz tube, which diminishes the visibility, Buehler developed an automatically operating floating-zone refiner. The stability of the floating zone is then especially important because even minor corrections cannot be made. With this equipment silicon with a P-type resistivity of 16,000 ohm-cm was obtained after 67 passes.

6.4. Growing of Single Crystals. The aim of this section is to describe standard techniques which are presently in use for the production of semiconducting material with a specified resistivity and physical perfection, starting from the purified raw materials.[†] Only well-developed techniques will be considered, based on the growing of crystals from the melt under controlled conditions. No attention will be given to other conceivable and sometimes tested techniques, like the growing of crystals from a solution or from the vapor phase, whether or not involving a chemical reaction. Such techniques have recently been reviewed by Tanenbaum[51] and Doremus.[52] Also not considered are techniques in which the crystal grows under conditions far from equilibrium, for instance, from a supercooled melt (Billig[53] and Bösenberg[54]). The preference for growing crystals from the melt under controlled conditions originates from the recognition that reproducible results are obtained, large growth rates can be applied, and contamination can be avoided to a very large extent. However, the method is applicable only if the material does not decompose at the temperatures involved and does not show a phase transformation between the melting point and room temperature. The subject of crystal growing has been reviewed in a symposium of the Faraday Society[55] and by Holden,[56] Buckley,[57] Neuhaus,[58] Pfann,[13] Tanenbaum,[51] Doremus,[52] and Lawson et al.[59]

6.4a. Control of Resistivity, Theoretical Considerations. For the crystal grower the control of resistivity amounts to the control of the concentration of impurities in the growing crystal. Consequently, quite similar considerations as discussed in Sec. 6.3a apply to the underlying problem. In modern practice crystals with a homogeneous concentration of N- or P-type impurities are required.[‡] Again, the concentration of impurities incorporated in the crystal is basically controlled by the distribution coefficient. In principle, two different techniques are used, namely, zone leveling and normal freezing.

In zone leveling, the liquid zone at the beginning of the bar is doped with the appropriate number of impurities and pulled through the bar of pure material. Assuming perfect mixing in the bulk of the liquid, the concentration of impurities in the solid at any length x (except for the last zone solidified) is given by the relation

$$c_S(x) = kc_0 e^{-kx/L} \tag{6.6}$$

where k is the distribution coefficient, c_0 is the concentration of impurities in the first zone, and L is the zone length. From Eq. (6.6) it follows that for $k = 0.01$ the concentration after 10 zone lengths is still 90 per cent of the concentration at the beginning of the bar. For larger distribution coefficients the concentration drops even more rapidly owing to the continuous depletion of impurities from the liquid zone. The same considerations apply to the "feed-in-pull-out technique."

In the technique of normal freezing, the crystal is grown from a doped melt. The concentration of impurities as a function of g is given by Eq. (6.2); the behavior of this function is schematically shown in Fig. 6.4. The concentration of impurities in the melt, and consequently in the bar, continually increases owing to the rejection of impurities by the solid-liquid interface. Thus crystals with a practically constant resistivity cannot be grown with this technique. To obtain at least partially a constant resistivity Burton et al.[60] made use of the fact that the distribution coefficient depends on the growth rate (see Sec. 6.3a). They programmed the growth rate in such a way that in the case of antimony dope about one-third of the crystal has a constant resistivity (technique of programmed growth rate). One can also make use of the fact that at low pressures many impurities evaporate at a measurable

---

[†] It should be emphasized that not all material characteristics determining device performance are yet recognized, let alone taken into account.

[‡] A survey of techniques by which abrupt changes in the concentration are made has recently been published by Pfann.[13]

rate from the melt, as was demonstrated by Bradshaw et al.[47]   They showed that for this case, Eq. (6.2) transforms to

$$c_S(g) = kc_{L0}(1 - g)^{k-1+AE/f} \tag{6.7}$$

where $c_S(g)$ is the concentration of impurities in the solid after a fraction g of the original volume of liquid has solidified, c_{L0} is the original concentration of impurities in the melt, k is the effective distribution coefficient, A is the area of evaporating surface, E is a measure of the rate of evaporation, and f is the growth rate.   The condition for a uniform distribution of impurities is given by

$$f = \frac{AE}{1 - k} \tag{6.8}$$

The rate of evaporation, and thus E, depends on the pressure of the ambient gas atmosphere.   When the pressure is adjusted at the proper value, crystals with a constant resistivity can be grown (vacuum technique).

Crystals with principally constant resistivity in the length direction are obtained in techniques in which the semiconducting material and the impurities are added to the melt at the same rate as they are withdrawn by the growing crystal (floating crucible technique, piston crucible technique, and gas doping technique).

In the crystals grown according to any one of the techniques discussed, local fluctuations in the concentration of impurities normally occur.   These fluctuations have been made visible by making autoradiographs from crystals doped with radioactive impurities (Burton et al.[18]) and with a selective pulse plating technique (Camp[61]). The fluctuations (striations) are attributed to variations in the effective distribution coefficient.   It appeared that intensive stirring and good temperature control reduce the inhomogeneities considerably.

6.4b. Control of Physical Perfection, Theoretical Considerations.   The electrical properties of semiconducting materials are greatly influenced by the presence of physical imperfections.   Especially grain boundaries, twin boundaries, and dislocations affect the mobility of charge carriers and the lifetime of minority carriers.   Dislocations also have a considerable influence on the wetting properties during the junction-alloying process and on the diffusion behavior of impurities.   Consequently, the object of the crystal-growing technique is to produce single crystals with the appropriate dislocation density.

In all standard techniques, single crystals of a preferred orientation are grown by solidifying the melt onto a seed crystal of the desired orientation.   It is thereby essential to prevent the occurrence of spurious nucleation which might be initiated by foreign particles floating on the liquid, by improper temperature gradients (constitutional supercooling, see Sec. 6.3a), and by unsatisfactory temperature control.

Crystals are most commonly grown in the [111] or [100] direction, sometimes in the [110] direction.   There does not seem to be any specific advantage of sufficient importance to weigh one heavily in favor of the other; the preferred orientation is normally dictated by the further processing.†   In practice, it appears to be relatively simple to prevent the formation of twin and grain boundaries‡ and to obtain single crystals. However, it is more difficult to control the density of dislocation within the single

---

† The distribution constant of an impurity may be slightly different for the orientations just mentioned, as was observed by Hall.[62]

‡ Grain boundaries in germanium and silicon are easily detectable after sandblasting or etching in one of the common etching solutions (see Sec. 6.3c).

crystal.† The most important source of dislocations is the occurrence of plastic flow. During the growth of the crystal, plastic flow is induced by thermal stresses, which result from an inhomogeneous temperature distribution. This phenomenon has been investigated by Billig,[63] Bennett et al.,[64] Cressell et al.,[65] and Penning.[66] Assuming a temperature-independent coefficient of thermal expansion and the validity of Hook's law, Penning, in developing his analysis, showed that thermal stresses are zero if the following conditions are satisfied: (1) the growth rate of the crystal must be zero; (2) the radial heat losses from the crystal must be zero; (3) the heat flux through the crystal must be constant. There appears to be a qualitative relation between the dislocation density in a crystal and the amount of deviation from

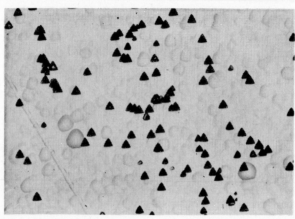

Fig. 6.14. Etch pits in a germanium (111) surface after Billig's treatment; 100×.

these conditions. Of course, plastic flow may also result from mechanical stresses in the crystal during the growing operation. Mechanical stresses are less apt to occur in growing techniques in which the crystal does not touch the container wall (vertical pulling and floating-zone technique) than in techniques in which the crystal does touch the container wall (horizontal pulling technique). In practice, it is possible to grow crystals with a low dislocation density[63-65] or with no dislocations at all (Dash,[67] Hughes,[68] Okkerse[69]), depending on the growing conditions.

6.4c. Applications. It is plain from the preceding paragraph that many parameters determine the specific resistivity and the physical perfection of the crystal. No numerical information is yet available which will guarantee optimum results. The standard techniques to be described may need modifications in order to meet the specifications of a particular demand.

From the discussion in Sec. 6.4a, it follows that in practically all techniques, the doping agent is added to the melt at the beginning of the pulling operation. The amount of impurities required is normally so small that micrograms must be weighed.

† For all practical purposes the dislocation density is equal to the number of etch pits per square centimeter. Dislocation etch pits are formed when certain crystal faces are etched with special etchants. An etch pit indicates the place where a dislocation line meets the surface. Reliable combinations are:
For germanium: (a) (111) plane and CP-4 etchant (see Sec. 6.3c), (b) (111) plane and Billig's etchant[63]: 8 g $K_3Fe(CN)_6$ and 12 g KOH in 100 ml distilled water, warm (see Fig. 6.14). For silicon: (a) (111), (100), and (110) planes and Dash's etchant[67]: 1 part HF 38 per cent, 3 parts HNO_3 60 per cent, and 10 parts glacial acetic acid, overnight; (b) (111), (100), and (110) planes and Goorissen's etchant[43] (after polishing for 3 min in 400 mg $KMnO_4$ in 25 ml HF 48 per cent): 400 mg $K_2Cr_2O_7$ in 25 ml HF 48 per cent; 5 min, stir vigorously.

In order to avoid handling of these minute quantities and also to reduce the possibility of evaporation of volatile impurities, like indium, arsenic, and phosphorus, doping pellets are used. The pellets are made from a master alloy which contains a few per cent of the impurity concerned. The composition of the master alloy can be

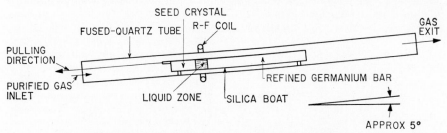

FIG. 6.15. Zone leveling of germanium (schematically).

determined analytically. In the gas-doping technique the impurities are continually added to the melt by means of the vapor phase (see Sec. 6.4e). With both techniques, crystals can be doped to any level between intrinsic and several times 10^{19} atoms/cm³. For high doping levels, steep temperature gradients and slow growth rates are required to avoid constitutional supercooling (see Sec. 6.3a).

FIG. 6.16. Germanium crystal grown by the leveling technique.

6.4d. Growing of Germanium Single Crystals. For the growing of germanium crystals variants of two different techniques are in use, namely, the horizontal and vertical pulling techniques.

In the horizontal or zone-leveling technique of Pfann,[70,71] a doped liquid zone is moved through a bar of purified germanium inside a quartz boat, starting from a single crystalline seed, as is schematically shown in Fig. 6.15. The segregation of impurities is governed by Eq. (6.6). The inside of the carefully cleaned boat is coated with soot from a cracked hydrocarbon, such as toluene, to give a nonwetting, nonnucleating layer. Radiofrequency induction heating is mostly used for similar reasons as discussed in Sec. 6.3c. Usually a graphite susceptor ring is placed inside the coil to improve the thermal conditions. The ring normally has a slot to provide for some stirring action by r-f currents in the liquid. The etching of germanium, and the purification of the gas, and the incli-

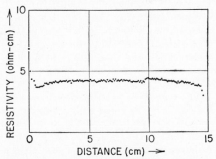

FIG. 6.17. Resistivity at room temperature versus length of a germanium crystal grown by the level technique.

nation of the quartz tube have been discussed in Sec. 6.3c. The normal travel rate is of the order of 1 to 3 mm/min. A typical zone-leveled bar is shown in Fig. 6.16; a graph of the resistivity versus length is given in Fig. 6.17. With a simple graphite ring the dislocation density is of the order of 10^4 to 10^5 per square centimeter. In order to improve the perfection of zone-leveled crystals, Bennett et al.[64] reduced the radial heat losses from the crystal by adding a fore- and after-heater. Using a growth rate of about 0.1 mm/min, these authors obtained crystals with an average dislocation density of about 1,000 per square centimeter. Cressell et al.[65] applying resistance heating under quite similar conditions grew crystals with a dislocation density of less than 10 per square centimeter. Owing to the small temperature gradients in both the latter techniques the power input has to be very well controlled in order to maintain a constant zone length, and the growth rate has to be relatively small.

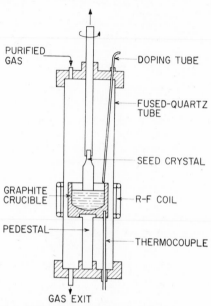

PURIFIED GAS

DOPING TUBE

FUSED-QUARTZ TUBE

SEED CRYSTAL

GRAPHITE CRUCIBLE

R-F COIL

PEDESTAL

THERMOCOUPLE

GAS EXIT

Fig. 6.18. Vertical crystal puller for germanium (schematically).

The level technique requires comparatively simple equipment and little attention after the preparatory stage, which factors make the process well adapted for automation. It is easy to obtain crystals of the desired shape and with uniform resistivity. However, the contact of the growing crystal with the container wall increases the possibility of contamination and makes the avoidance of mechanical stresses difficult. Radial thermal symmetry is difficult to achieve, and stirring is possible only by induced r-f currents and by thermal convection currents. Notwithstanding these inherent difficulties, a very large fraction of the germanium crystals is, at present, being grown with this technique.

In the vertical pulling or Czochralski technique (Teal et al.[72]) a crystal is grown by the slow withdrawal of a seed crystal from a doped melt contained in a crucible. The method is schematically shown in Fig. 6.18 and has been described by Teal et al.,[73] Teal,[74] Lehovec,[75] Bradley,[76] Marshall et al.,[77] and many others. The amount of germanium solidifying per second depends on the amount of heat that can be transported from the solid-liquid interface to the solid. This amount again depends on the geometrical conditions, the temperature of the melt, the ambient gas atmosphere (composition and flow rate), the pulling rate, and the rotation speed. The crystal can be shaped by adjusting the growing parameters, most commonly the temperature of the melt. In the stationary state the pulling rate is equal to the freezing rate.

The crucible is usually made from high-purity graphite (see Sec. 6.3); the inside of the crucible is covered with a hard layer of graphite, which is deposited by cracking of hydrocarbons in situ. The etching of germanium and the ambient gas atmosphere have been discussed in Sec. 6.3c. Both r-f heating and resistance heating are used. A thermocouple is placed in a well in the wall of the crucible. The temperature should be very carefully controlled (to within about 0.1°C) because temperature variations result in resistivity and diameter variations. To ensure a radially symmetric temperature distribution and sufficient stirring of the melt, the seed crystal is rotated at about 100 rpm. Before the seed is inserted, the temperature of the melt is adjusted to slightly above the melting point. Care should be taken that the melt wets the crystal completely. The pulling is then started; usual pulling rates are of the order of 1 to 2 mm/min. Because the shape and the electric properties of the crystal depend critically on the growing conditions, the parameters involved should be very well controlled. With the use of this technique, crystals with diameters up to 15 cm have been grown (Runyan[78]).

The dislocation density depends primarily on the pulling speed, the temperature gradients, and the perfection of the seed crystal. With a simple crucible like the one shown in Fig. 6.18, the dislocation density is usually of the order of a few thousands per square centimeter. With a deep crucible provided with an extra bottom to prevent a cold spot near the crucible bottom, the dislocation density may be as low as a few dislocations per square centimeter if small growth rates are applied (0.25 mm/min). Crystals without dislocations can be grown from any crucible if (1) the seed is dislocation-free, (2) the surface of the melt is free from floating particles, and (3) the growth parameters are changed only very gradually. The method is based on the experience that dislocations have difficulty in nucleating in dislocation-free germanium. The seed crystal can be made dislocation-free in the initial stage of the growing operation by necking the seed down to a diameter of about 1 mm. The dislocations already present will grow out of the seed because of its small diameter, and no new dislocations will be generated because the thermal stresses are necessarily small in small-diameter crystals.[67,69]

The segregation of impurities is governed by Eq. (6.2) if a simple crucible is used. Several methods have been developed to grow crystals with a constant impurity concentration in the length direction (see Sec. 6.3a). For the technique of the programmed growth rate[60] and the "feed-in-pull-out" technique[79] the reader is referred to the original literature. Crystals with essentially a constant resistivity are obtained with the floating-crucible technique (Goorissen et al.[80] and Leverton[81]). A typical design is shown in Fig. 6.19. The small inner crucible floats on the melt contained in a larger outer crucible. By means of a capillary the inner and outer reservoir form a system of communicating vessels. The buoyancy of the inner crucible can be adjusted by the weight on the "tail." After the charge is melted, the inner crucible is pushed upward to float on the liquid. Once the growth of the crystal has started, the melt in

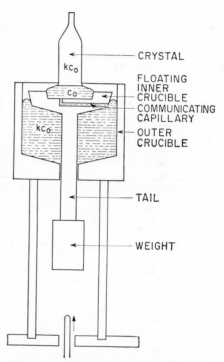

CRYSTAL

FLOATING
INNER
CRUCIBLE

COMMUNICATING
CAPILLARY

OUTER
CRUCIBLE

TAIL

WEIGHT

FIG. 6.19. Floating crucible (schematically). (*After Goorissen et al.*[80])

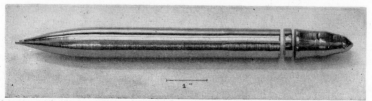

FIG. 6.20. Germanium crystal grown by the floating-crucible technique.

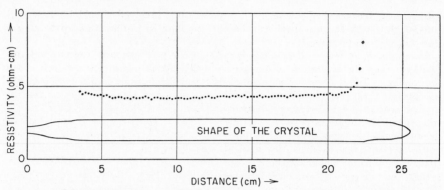

FIG. 6.21. Resistivity at room temperature versus length of an antimony-doped germanium crystal grown by the floating-crucible technique.

the large crucible is doped to a concentration kc_0 and the melt in the small crucible to a concentration c_0, where k is the distribution coefficient and kc_0 is the desired impurity concentration of the crystal. Back diffusion of impurities from the inner to the outer crucible is prevented by the flow of liquid germanium through the capillary. A crystal grown with this technique is shown in Fig. 6.20; a typical resistivity curve is given in Fig. 6.21. A variant of this technique is the pistonc-rucible tech-

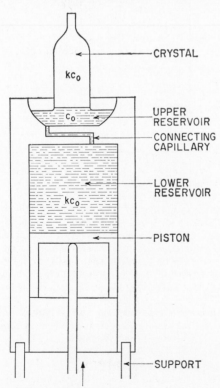

FIG. 6.22. Piston crucible (schematically). (*After Okkerse.*[69])

nique[69] as shown schematically in Fig. 6.22. Here the doped liquid germanium is pushed from the lower to the upper reservoir by means of a piston and at the same rate as the crystal is withdrawn.

6.4e. Growing of Silicon Single Crystals. The techniques for the production of silicon crystals follow essentially the same principles as discussed for germanium. However, the number of practical designs is limited because of the reactivity of molten silicon with all known crucible materials. Two different techniques are used, namely, the vertical pulling technique and the floating-zone technique. As both techniques have been discussed extensively (see Secs. 6.3*d* and 6.4*d*) and because much relevant information is given in Sec. 6.3*b*, only details will be considered here.

In the vertical pulling technique silicon crystals are grown from a quartz crucible which is placed inside a high-purity graphite crucible. As a rule, commercially available electronic-grade silicon is used as such without etching. When quartz reacts with silicon, volatile silicon monoxide is formed which disproportionates on the cold parts of the equipment into a brownish mixture of silicon and silicon dioxide. This deposit seriously diminishes the visibility during the course of the operation.   More serious is the unavoidable uptake of oxygen by the growing crystal.[30]   Oxygen incorporated in the silicon crystals gives rise to complicated phenomena on heat-treatment, which affect the number of charge carriers.   Much relevant information is given by Kaiser et al.[82]   Because the amount of oxygen built into the growing crystal increases with increasing rotation speed, silicon crystals are normally pulled at a low rotation speed (1 rpm).

The average dislocation density[†] of crucible-grown crystals is of the order of a few thousands per square centimeter.   Dislocation-free crystals are grown under similar conditions as discussed for germanium.   Contamination of dislocation-free crystals with oxygen is prevented in the floating-zone equipment by means of the pedestal technique suggested by Dash.[84]   Here the required temperature gradients are

TABLE 6.2

	P	As	Sb	B	Al
f from Eq. (6.8), mm/min............	0.75	45	310	0.23	0.45

obtained by heating only the liquid zone.   Coupling of the r-f field with the solid bar is prevented by several slots across the bar.

Crystals with constant resistivity can be made if the crystal is pulled under vacuum (see Sec. 6.4a).   The growth rate required to obtain a crystal with a uniform distribution of impurities has been determined by Bradshaw et al.[47] for some typical conditions (evaporating surface 30 cm², charge of silicon 100 g, crystal diameter 2 cm, 10^{-4} cm Hg).   Their results are given in Table 6.2.   This technique is suitable for the production of relatively low ohmic material where the unavoidable contamination with boron from the quartz is not serious.

High-resistivity silicon crystals are grown in the floating-zone equipment.   Doping can be accomplished by dissolving a doping pellet in the liquid zone.   Segregation is governed by Eq. (6.6).   A disadvantage of this technique is that the liquid zone is rapidly depleted of impurities, especially if the distribution constant is large, which is the case for many important impurities.   Goorissen et al.[85] solved this problem by

Fig. 6.23. Silicon crystal grown by the floating-zone technique.

adding impurities to the liquid zone at the same rate as they are incorporated in the crystal.   This is done by mixing with the inert-gas flow an apportioned flow of impurity atoms in the form of a volatile compound.   On passing the hot region of the tube the compound decomposes and the impurities dissolve into the liquid zone. The growing of the crystal is started as soon as the concentration of impurities in the liquid zone is equal to c_1/k, where c_1 is the desired impurity concentration of the crystal.   A photograph of a crystal grown by this technique is shown in Fig. 6.23; a typical resistivity curve is given in Fig. 6.24.

The dislocation density of crystals grown by the floating-zone technique is of the order of 10^4 per square centimeter.   It is difficult to obtain a lower dislocation

[†] See Sec. 6.4b for recipes.   Logan et al.[83] found that the presence of oxygen in the crystals may obstruct the identification of etch pits.

density because of the inherent unfavorable thermal conditions. Twinning and polycrystallinity are frequently observed if the starting material is contaminated with carbon. When carbon reacts with silicon, silicon carbide is formed; in large concentrations this is insoluble and gives rise to spurious nucleation centers. Silicon carbide tends to deposit on the surface of the bar, but it can be removed by sandblasting and etching. The same treatment is successful in the removal of silicon dioxide and

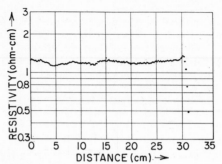

Fig. 6.24. Resistivity at room temperature versus length of a silicon crystal doped with phosphorus by gas-phase doping.

silicon nitride, which may form in the event of faulty contact of molten silicon with oxygen and nitrogen.

6.5. Semiconducting Compounds. A large number of predominantly covalent intermetallic compounds have been found to be semiconductors. The wide variety of these materials that have been investigated during the past decade has made a systematic classification difficult. Primary attention has been given to binary compounds having the following generalized formulas: $A^{III}B^V$, $A_2^{II}B^{IV}$, $A^{II}B^{VI}$, $A_2^V B_3^{VI}$, and $A_x^{II}B_y^V$. Several ternary semiconducting compounds have also been investigated, though less extensively. The semiconducting compounds possess at least one common chemical characteristic, namely, thermal dissociation at elevated temperatures. The synthesis, purification, and crystal growth of these materials have been considerably more difficult than in the case of germanium and silicon. Much work remains to be done in this field before the full potential of the compounds as semiconductors is realized. Silicon carbide, for example, shows considerable potential as a high-temperature semiconductor, though preparation problems are particularly severe. At present, no satisfactory method exists for producing large, single crystals of semiconductor quality. The subject of silicon carbide as a semiconductor is comprehensively reviewed in a volume containing the entire proceedings of the 1959 Boston Conference on Silicon Carbide.[86]

The $A^{III}B^V$ compounds deserve particular attention because they have been extensively studied during the past decade and because several of them show potential as materials for device applications. Welker first noted their semiconductor properties in 1952.[87] A comprehensive review of preparation of the $A^{III}B^V$ compounds has been given recently by Folberth.[88] As compared with germanium and silicon, these compounds provide a considerably wider range of semiconductor properties and, hence, their investigation has proved to be of great interest from both scientific and technological points of view.

A primary consideration for the preparation of the compounds is the use of constituent elements having impurity concentrations of less than 1 part per million. During the past several years, much effort has been expended toward the use of standard chemical and physical methods of purification. Because of the wide interest in the III-V compounds, commercial sources of the constituent elements are now available in purities of 99.999% or better. When further purification is desired, distillation, sublimation, extraction, or zone refining may be employed. In addition, a knowledge of the phase diagram of the binary system under consideration is of the utmost importance. Diagrams for the more common binary systems have been compiled by Hansen.[90] For many compounds, the vapor pressure of the more volatile component is significant at the temperatures required during the process of preparation and adequate precautions must be taken to maintain compound stoichiometry. The III-V compounds which have been investigated more thoroughly fall into two classifications: (a) compounds with low vapor pressure at the melting point (of the order of 1 mm), such as InSb, GaSb, and AlSb; (b) compounds with significant vapor pressure at the melting point, such as GaAs, InAs, GaP, and GaAs. The technology of compounds of class a is similar to that of germanium and silicon. Zone refining and crystal pulling may be carried out in an inert-gas atmosphere with a minimal loss of volatile components. The synthesis, purification, and crystal growth of class b compounds is much more complicated. Representative compounds of each class are considered below.

Indium antimonide has been studied more extensively than other III-V compounds and was the first in this family of materials to be characterized in detail. Relatively pure single crystals are quite easily prepared by standard pulling procedures (Sec. 6.4) because of the low melting point (523°C) and correspondingly low vapor pressures of the indium and antimony. The compound is isoelectronic with α tin. The discovery of extremely high electron mobility stimulated further work on the material. InSb lends itself to zone refining. This, together with ultrapure handling and crystal-growth methods, has led to carrier concentrations of $\sim 10^{14}$ per cubic centimeter. The following distribution coefficients [k, see Eq. (6.2)] have been reported by Strauss[89] for InSb crystals pulled from the melt at an extraction rate of 1.3 cm/hr and a rotation rate of 130 rpm; Cd, 0.26; Zn, 3.38; Se, 0.17; Te, 0.54. The distribution coefficient for zinc was found to vary with extraction and rotation rates. Mullin[91] has made similar determinations for k when pulling InSb crystals in the (111) crystallographic direction at an extraction rate of 2 cm/hr and a rotation rate of 100 rpm, and arrived at the following values: Cu, 6.6×10^{-4}; Ag, 4.9×10^{-5}; Au, 1.9×10^{-6}; Zn, 2.3; Cd, 0.26; Ga, 2.4; Sn, 0.057; P, 0.16; As, 5.4; Se, 0.35; Te, ~ 1; Fe, 0.04.

The chemical etching characteristics of III-V compounds differ from those of germanium and silicon due to polarity along the (111) crystallographic directions. Gatos and Lavine[92] have studied surface etching of the (111) crystallographic planes of InSb and other III-V compounds. They observed that dislocation etch pits form on (111) surfaces (terminating with group III atoms) but do not form on ($\overline{111}$) surfaces (terminating with group V atoms). At low temperatures, (111) surfaces exhibit appreciably smaller etching rates and more noble electrode potentials than the ($\overline{111}$) surfaces. Etching methods may be used to easily differentiate one (111) surface from the other. Dislocation etch pits are observed on both (110) and (100) surfaces of InSb.

As a class b compound, gallium arsenide presents several technological problems. The compound melts at 1240 ± 2°C. The dissociation pressure at that temperature is 0.9 atm.[93] The compound may be prepared by subliming arsenic into gallium held at elevated temperature, with suitable precaution being taken to regulate the arsenic pressure during synthesis. Single crystals have been prepared by floating-zone, pulling, and Bridgeman methods, within closed vessels under the appropriate arsenic pressure. An apparatus for pulling GaAs within a sealed quartz tube has been described by Gremmelmaier[94] wherein the seed crystal is supported within the tube by an external magnetic field. A crucible containing GaAs is heated inductively while the entire tube is maintained at the temperature required to maintain the appropriate arsenic vapor pressure. Piston pullers are also successful in producing single crystals by maintaining a slow, controlled leak of arsenic vapor around the piston.   With both Bridgeman and pulling methods, the choice of crucible materials presents some difficulty.   Though quartz is more commonly used, it is slowly reduced by elemental gallium at elevated temperatures, resulting in silicon contamination.   Thus, it is important to minimize the time during which gallium is held at elevated temperature during synthesis.   The use of a sandblasted quartz surface not only minimizes this problem, but also reduces wetting of the quartz crucible surface by molten gallium arsenide.   Graphite is not particularly desirable as a crucible material because of the slight solubility of graphite in gallium arsenide.   The solubility of other group IV elements, Si, Ge, Sn, and Pb, has been reported by Kolm[95] as about 0.5 atom per cent.   Quartz has been shown to introduce copper which diffuses rapidly and behaves as an acceptor.   This contamination is reduced through the use of high-purity quartz.   Alumina also shows considerable promise as a crucible material.   In spite of these problems, crystals of GaAs may be pulled with a carrier concentration of $\sim 10^{16}$ per cubic centimeter and with a room-temperature electron mobility of approximately $5{,}000$–$6{,}000$ cm^2/volt-sec.

Zone refining of GaAs is not particularly effective because of the necessity of using a sealed system at $\sim 600°$C to maintain arsenic pressure over the melt.   Since several electrically active impurities have high vapor pressures at this temperature, the efficiency of one zone pass decreases with the increasing number of zone passes. This is due to the interaction between the resultant contaminated vapor phase and the liquid zone.

Gallium phosphide is of interest as an electroluminescent material and as a semiconductor for high-temperature applications.   High-purity, single-crystal material is difficult to produce.   Frosch et al.[96] have reported the use of a pressure-chamber apparatus for growing controlled single-crystal GaP by the floating-zone technique. GaP melts at approximately $1500°$C under a phosphorus pressure of 25 atm.   Polycrystalline ingots may be prepared under less severe conditions by growth from gallium solution at temperatures between 1200 and $1400°$C under a pressure of 5 to 10 atm phosphorus vapor.   The gallium is contained in a quartz boat, sealed inside a quartz tube, together with elemental phosphorus.

Vapor growth of class *b* III-V compounds shows considerable promise as a means of purification and preparation of single-crystal material at low temperatures and pressures.   Antell and Effer[97] have reported the growth of small crystals of InAs, InP, GaAs, and GaP from the vapor phase compound of the monochloride or monoiodide of the metal and phosphorus and arsenic.   This type of reaction has been employed for the epitaxial growth of GaAs on single-crystal substrates of GaAs and of Ge.[98]   The transport of GaAs by means of a reaction with iodine is accomplished by imposing a decreasing temperature gradient between the source material and the monocrystal seeds.   The reactions have been carried out in sealed quartz tubes under various iodine pressures and with a growth temperature of approximately $550°$C. It has been observed that while epitaxial growth easily occurs on the (111) faces of GaAs from the gas phase reaction, growth under similar conditions on the $(\overline{1}\overline{1}\overline{1})$ face is negligible or polycrystalline.   Due to the low volatility of various metal iodides, the process affords a degree of GaAs purification during transport from source to seed.

REFERENCES

1. Wilson, J. M.: The Chemical Purification of Germanium and Silicon, in "Progress in Semiconductors," vol. 3, pp. 27–51, John Wiley & Sons, Inc., New York, 1958.
2 Thompson, A. P., and J. R. Musgrave: Germanium, Produced as a Byproduct, Has Become of Primary Importance, *J. Metals*, vol. 4, pp. 1132–1137, November, 1952
3. De Cleene, P. B.: Le Germanium, Metal Industriel, *L'Onde électrique*, vol. 37, pp. 701–722, 1957.

4. Boving, T., and J. Andre: Germanium, Zinc's Important Byproduct, *J. Metals*, vol. 10, pp. 659–661, October, 1958.
5. Powell, A. R., F. M. Lever, and R. F. Walpole: Extraction and Refining of Germanium and Gallium, *J. Appl. Chem.*, vol. 1, pp. 541–551, 1951.
6. Theuerer, H. C.: Purification of GeCl$_4$ by Extraction with HCl and Chlorine, *J. Metals*, vol. 8, pp. 688–690, May, 1956.
7. Lyon, D. W., C. M. Olson, and E. D. Lewis: Preparation of Hyper-pure Silicon, *Trans. Electrochem. Soc.*, vol. 96, pp. 359–363, 1949.
8. Theuerer, H. C.: Purification of Silicon, *Bell Labs. Record*, vol. 33, pp. 327–330, September, 1955.
9. Van der Linden, P. C., and J. de Jonge: The Preparation of Pure Silicon, *Rec. trav. chim.*, vol. 78, pp. 962–966, November. 1959.
10. Rubin, B., G. H. Moates, and J. R. Weiner: Transistor-grade Silicon. I. The Preparation of Ultrapure Silicon Tetraiodide, *J. Electrochem. Soc.*, vol. 104, pp. 656–660, November, 1957.
11. Van Arkel, A. E.: "Reine Metalle," p. 27, Springer-Verlag, Berlin, 1939.
12. Pfann, W. G.: Principles of Zone Melting, *J. Metals*, vol. 4, pp. 747–754, July, 1952.
13. Pfann, W. G.: "Zone Melting," John Wiley & Sons, Inc., New York, 1958.
14. Pfann, W. G.: Techniques of Zone Melting and Crystal Growing, *Solid State Phys.*, vol. 4, pp. 423–521, 1957.
15. Pfann, W. G.: Zone Melting, *Metall. Rev.*, vol. 2, pp. 29–76, 1957.
16. Graf, R.: *Métaux Corrosion Inds.*, vol. 30, p. 463, 1955.
17. Burton, J. A.: Impurity Centers in Ge and Si, *Physica*, vol. 20, pp. 845–854, 1954.
18. Burton, J. A., R. C. Prim, and W. P. Slichter: The Distribution of Solute in Crystals Grown from the Melt, part I, Theoretical, *J. Chem. Phys.*, vol. 21, pp. 1987–1991, November, 1953.
19. Rutter, J. W., and B. Chalmers: A Prismatic Substructure Formed during Solidification of Metals, *Can. J. Phys.*, vol. 31, pp. 15–39, January, 1953.
20. Chalmers, B.: Melting and Freezing, *J. Metals*, vol. 6, pp. 519–532, May, 1954.
21. Hogarth, C. A., and P. J. Hoyland: Radial Variation of Minority Carrier Lifetime in Vacuum-grown Germanium Single Crystals, *J. Elect. and Control*, vol. 4, pp. 60–62, 1958.
22. Burris, L., C. H. Stockman, and I. G. Dillon: Contributions to Mathematics of Zone Melting, *J. Metals*, vol. 7, pp. 1017–1023, September, 1955.
23. Goorissen, J.: Philips Research Laboratories, patent applied for.
24. Priest, H. F., and G. L. Priest: *Lincoln Lab. MIT Tech. Rept.* M 35–20, May 27, 1954.
25. Pfann, W. G.: Change in Ingot Slope during Zone Melting, *J. Metals*, vol. 5, pp. 1441–1442, 1953.
26. Hannay, N. B., and A. J. Ahearn: Mass Spectrographic Analysis of Solids, *Anal. Chem.*, vol. 26, pp. 1056–1058, June, 1954.
27. Goorissen, J.: Philips Research Laboratories, private communication.
28. Papazian, H. P., and S. P. Wolsky: Volatile Impurities in Silicon and Germanium, *J. Appl. Phys.*, vol. 27, p. 1561, December, 1956.
29. Thurmond, C. D., W. G. Guldner, and A. L. Beach: Hydrogen and Oxygen in Single-crystal Germanium as Determined by Vacuum Fusion Gas Analysis, *J. Electrochem. Soc.*, vol. 103, pp. 603–605, November, 1956.
30. Kaiser, W., P. H. Keck, and C. F. Lange: Infrared Absorption and Oxygen Content in Silicon and Germanium, *Phys. Rev.*, vol. 101, pp. 1264–1268, February, 1956.
31. Taft, E. A., and F. H. Horn: Zone Purification of Silicon, *J. Electrochem. Soc.*, vol. 105, pp. 81–83, February, 1958.
32. Kaiser, W., and C. D. Thurmond: Nitrogen in Silicon, *J. Appl. Phys.*, vol. 30, pp. 427–431, March, 1959.
33. Keck, P. H., and M. J. E. Golay: Crystallization of Silicon from a Floating Liquid Zone, *Phys. Rev.*, vol. 89, p. 1297, 1953.
34. Theuerer, H. C.: French Patent 1,087,946.
35. Emeis, R.: Tiegelfreies Ziehen von Silicium-Einkristallen, *Z. Naturforsch.*, vol. 9a, p. 67, 1954.
36. Keck, P. H., W. van Horn, J. Soled, and A. MacDonald: Floating Zone Recrystallization of Silicon, *Rev. Sci. Instr.*, vol. 25, pp. 331–334, 1954.
37. Müller, S.: Siliciumreinigung durch Tiegelfreies Zonenschmelzen, *Z. Naturforsch.*, vol. 9b, p. 504, 1954.
38. Buehler, E.: Contribution to the Floating Zone Refining of Silicon, *Rev. Sci. Instr.*, vol. 28, pp. 453–460, June, 1957.
39. Goorissen, J. Preparation of Single Crystals of Silicon by the Method of Zone Refining, *Acta Electr.*, vol. 1, pp. 201–206, 1956.
40. von Heywang, W., and G. Ziegler: Zur Stabilität senkrechter Schmelzzonen, *Z. Naturforsch.*, vol. 9a, p. 561, 1954.

41. von Heywang, W.: Zur Stabilität senkrechter Schmelzzonen, *Z. Naturforsch.*, vol. 11a, pp. 238–243, 1956.
42. Okress, E. C., D. M. Wroughton, G. Comenetz, P. H. Brace, and J. C R. Kelly: Electromagnetic Levitation of Solid and Molten Metals, *J. Appl. Phys.*, vol. 23, pp. 545–552, May, 1952.
43. Goorissen, J.: Philips Research Laboratories, private communication.
44. Buehler, E.: *Electrochem. Eng. Abstrs.*, p. 144, 1957.
45. Keck, P. H., M. Green, and M. L. Polk: Shapes of Floating Liquid Zones between Solid Rods, *J. Appl. Phys.*, vol. 24, pp. 1479–1481, December, 1953.
46. Goorissen, J.: Philips Research Laboratories, patent applied for.
47. Bradshaw, S. E., and A. I. Mlavsky: The Evaporation of Impurities from Silicon, *J. Electronics*, vol. 2, pp. 134–144, 1956.
48. Ziegler, G.: Quantative Berücksichtigung der Abdampfung beim Tiegelfreien Zonenschmelzen, *Z. Metalk.*, vol. 49, pp. 491–494, 1958.
49. Goorissen, J.: Philips Research Laboratories, private communication.
50. Theuerer, H. C.: Removal of Boron from Silicon by Hydrogen Water Vapor Treatment, *J. Metals*, vol. 8, pp. 1316–1319, October, 1956.
51. Tanenbaum, M.: in N. B. Hannay, "Semiconductors," Reinhold Publishing Co., New York, 1959.
52. Doremus, R. H., B. W. Roberts, and D. Turnbull: "Growth and Perfection of Crystals," John Wiley & Sons, Inc., New York, 1958.
53. Billig, E.: Growth of Monocrystals of Germanium from an Undercooled Melt, *Proc. Roy. Soc.*, ser. A, vol. 229, pp. 346–363, 1955.
54. Bösenberg, W.: Kokillenguss von Dünnen, Einkristallinen German um-Platten, *Z. angew. Phys.*, vol. 9, p. 347, 1957.
55. "Crystal Growth," Discussions of the Faraday Society, No. 5, Guerney & Jackson, London, 1949.
56. Holden, A. N.: Preparation of Metal Single Crystals, *Trans. Am. Soc. Metals*, vol. 42, pp. 319–346, 1950.
57. Buckley, H. E.: "Crystal Growth," John Wiley & Sons, Inc., New York, 1951.
58. Neuhaus, A.: Methods and Results of Modern Single-crystal Growth Processes, II, Special Growth Methods, *Chem. Ing. Tech.*, vol. 28, pp. 350–365, 1956.
59. Lawson, W. D., and S. Nielsen: "The Preparation of Single Crystals," Butterworth & Co. (Publishers) Ltd., London, 1958.
60. Burton, J. A., E. D. Kolb, W. P. Slichter, and J. D. Struthers: Distribution of Solute in Crystals Grown from the Melt, Part II, Experimental, *J. Chem. Phys.*, vol. 21, pp. 1991–1996, November, 1953.
61. Camp, P. R.: Resistivity Striations in Germanium Crystals, *J. Appl. Phys.*, vol. 25, pp. 459–463, 1954.
62. Hall, R. N.: Segregation of Impurities during the Growth of Germanium and Silicon Crystals, *J. Phys. Chem.*, vol. 57, pp. 836–839, 1953.
63. Billig, E.: Some Defects in Crystals Grown from the Melt, I, Defects Caused by Thermal Stresses, *Proc. Roy. Soc.*, ser. A, vol. 235, pp. 37–55, 1956.
64. Bennett, D. C., and B. Sawyer: Single Crystals of Exceptional Perfection and Uniformity by Zone Leveling, *Bell System Tech. J.*, vol. 35, pp. 637–660, May, 1956.
65. Cressell, L. G., and J. A. Powell: The Production of High Quality Germanium Single Crystals, in "Progress in Semiconductors," vol. 2, pp. 137–164, John Wiley & Sons, Inc., New York, 1957.
66. Penning, P.: Generation of Imperfections in Germanium Crystals by Thermal Strain, *Philips Research Repts.*, vol. 13, pp. 79–97, April, 1958.
67. Dash, W. C.: Growth of Silicon Crystals Free from Dislocations, *J. Appl. Phys.*, vol. 30, pp. 459–474, April, 1959.
68. Hughes, R. C.: North American Philips Corporation, private communication.
69. Okkerse, B.: A Method of Growing Dislocation-free Germanium Crystals, *Philips Tech. Rev.*, vol. 21, pp. 340–344, 1959–1960.
70. Pfann, W. G., and K. M. Olsen: Purification and Prevention of Segregation in Single Crystals of Germanium, *Phys. Rev.*, vol. 89, pp. 322–323, January, 1953.
71. Pfann, W. G., K. M. Olsen, and B. Sawyer: In H. E. Bridgers, J. H. Scaff, and J. N Shive, "Transistor Technology," vol. I, chap. 2, D. Van Nostrand Company, Inc., Princeton, N.J., 1958.
72. Teal, G. K., and J. B. Little: Growth of Germanium Single Crystals, *Phys. Rev.*, vol. 78, p. 647, 1950.
73. Teal, G. K., M. Sparks, and E. Buehler: Single-crystal Germanium, *Proc. IRE*, vol. 40, pp. 906–909, 1952.
74. Teal, G. K.: In H. E. Bridgers, J. H. Scaff, and J. N. Shive, "Transistor Technology," vol. I, chap. 4, D. Van Nostrand Company, Inc., Princeton, N.J., 1958.

75. Lehovec, K., J. Soled, R. Koch, A. MacDonald, and C. Stearns: Apparatus for Crystal Pulling in Vacuum Using a Graphite Resistance Furnace, *Rev. Sci. Instr.*, vol. 24, pp. 652–655, August, 1953.
76. Bradley, W. W.: In H. E. Bridgers, J. H. Scaff, and J. N. Shive, "Transistor Technology," vol. I, chap. 4, D. Van Nostrand Company, Inc., Princeton, N.J., 1958.
77. Marshall, K. H. J. C., and R. Wickham: An Improved Czochralski Crystal Pulling Furnace, *J. Sci. Instr.*, vol. 35, pp. 121–125, 1958.
78. Runyan, W. R.: Growth of Large Diameter Silicon and Germanium Single Crystals, *J. Appl. Phys.*, vol. 27, p. 1562, December, 1956.
79. Nelson, H.: In "Transistors," p. 66, Radio Corporation of America, Princeton, N.J., 1956.
80. Goorissen, K., and F. Karstensen: Das Ziehen von Germanium-Einkristallen aus dem "schwimmenden Tiegel," *Z. Metallk.*, vol. 50, pp. 46–50, January, 1959.
81. Leverton, W. F.: Floating Crucible Technique for Growing Uniformly Doped Crystals, *J. Appl. Phys.*, vol. 29, pp. 1241–1244, August, 1958.
82. Kaiser, W., H. L. Frisch, and H. Reiss: Mechanism of the Formation of Donor States in Heat-treated Silicon, *Phys. Rev.*, vol. 112, pp. 1546–1554, December, 1958.
83. Logan, R. A., and A. J. Peters: Diffusion of Oxygen in Silicon, *J. Appl. Phys.*, vol. 28, pp. 819–820, July, 1957.
84. Dash, W. C.: Silicon Crystals Free of Dislocations, *J. Appl. Phys.*, vol. 29, pp. 736–737, April, 1958.
85. Goorissen, J., and A. M. J. G. van Run: Gas-phase Doping of Silicon, *Proc. Inst. Elec. Engrs.*, vol. 106, pt. B, suppl. 17, pp. 858–860, 1959.
86. O'Connor, J. R., and J. Smiltons (eds.): "Silicon Carbide," Pergamon Press, New York, 1960.
87. Welker, H.: *Z. Naturforsch.*, vol. 7a, p. 744, 1952.
88. Folberth, O. G.: to be published in "Halbleiterprobleme."
89. Strauss, A. J.: *J. Appl. Phys.*, vol. 30, pp. 559–563, 1959.
90. Hansen, M., and K. Anderko: "Constitution of Binary Alloys," McGraw-Hill Book Company, Inc., New York, 1958.
91. Mullin, J. B.: *J. Electronics*, vol. 4, p. 358, 1958.
92. Gatos, H. C., and M. C. Lavine: *J. Electrochem. Soc.*, vol. 107, p. 427, 1960.
93. Van den Boomgaard, J., and K. Schol: *Philips Research Repts.*, vol. 12, p. 127, 1957.
94. Gremmelmaier, R : *Z. Naturforsch.*, vol. 11a, p. 511, 1956.
95. Kolm, C., S. A. Kulin, and B. L. Averback: *Phys. Rev.*, vol. 108, p. 965, 1957.
96. Frosch, C. J., M. Gershenzon, and D. F. Gibbs: *J. Electrochem. Soc.*, vol. 107, p. 65c, 1960.
97. Antell, G. R., and D. Effer: *J. Electrochem. Soc.*, vol. 106, p. 509, 1959.
98. Lyons, V. J.: Private communication.

Section 7

METHODS OF PREPARING PN JUNCTIONS

W. Crawford Dunlap

Raytheon Company, Waltham, Mass.

† This section compiled by G. A. Silvey, IBM Corporation, Poughkeepsie, N.Y.

7.1. Introduction and Definitions. The active region of most semiconducting devices is a PN junction. It is our purpose in this section to discuss the methods in common use for preparing such junctions. Although we shall attempt to keep the discussion as general as possible, the fact remains that most junction studies have been carried out with germanium, with silicon having received somewhat less attention. These are the only two semiconductors which are in commercial use as far as junction devices are concerned.

No attempt is made here to discuss the fabrication or testing of completed PN junction devices, and indeed only a fraction of the problems of making PN junctions can be mentioned.

Much of the technology of junctions has become highly proprietary, and much of the published information is restricted to general rather than specific information. There are, however, a number of good reviews of the state of the art, of which the articles and reviews in "Transistor Technology"[1] are particularly noteworthy. Thurmond[2] has given an excellent survey describing the foundations of various crystal-growing and junction-forming techniques, while articles by Fuller[3] and Frosch[4] describe in some detail various diffusion techniques. Smits[5] has also given a more general review of diffusion techniques. Dacey and Thurmond[6] have given a rather comprehensive review of the entire subject of PN-junction technology.

Although most of our discussions will be devoted to PN junctions, there are other types of junctions that we shall discuss, and it is important that the distinctions be clear. The PN junction is a boundary between two parts of a semiconductor, one of which is P type, or hole conducting, the other N type, or electron conducting. The semiconductor is usually a homogeneous single crystal, but not always. Also, it often happens, but not necessarily, that the individual regions of the semiconductor are homogeneous in resistivity.

A junction may be more generally defined as the surface separating two parts of a semiconductor having different properties. Thus we may have NN^+ junctions, PP^+ junctions, NI junctions (where I refers to intrinsic material), and so on. It would also be possible in principle to have junctions separating such regions of different lifetime, although the utility of such structures has not yet been demonstrated.

Junction-fabrication methods can be divided into two general classes:

1. The first includes those methods (grown junctions) in which the impurities leading to the desired properties are incorporated into the crystal during growth. These methods have the advantage of producing junctions with superior properties in some instances. Junction diodes made in this way are often superior to those made by other methods. Also, growth and part of the processing are achieved in one step rather than two. However, there are disadvantages in that the method is somewhat inflexible in the geometry of the junction produced, since proper crystal structure is so important that the conditions of growth must be closely controlled.

2. The other class of methods involves treatment of a piece of homogeneous crystal so as to incorporate the desired regions of conductivity in secondary processes. Typical of this class is the fused-junction method, in which small wafers are heated with the impurity element needed to make junctions, contacts, etc. Another less widely used method is that in which parts of the sample are bombarded with nuclear particles so as to create junctions.

Another method in which a piece of crystal is treated after formation of the ingot is the diffusion method, which will be discussed in greater detail below.

Historically, PN-junction devices got their start with the "surface" junctions of the "formed" point contacts used for the earliest transistors. These were very poorly understood, and they have now become of minor interest. The first junction transistors were made by use of grown junctions. When transistors came into mass production, the fusion method supplanted the grown-junction method to a great extent because of its economy of material and greater flexibility. During the last few years diffusion has become increasingly important as a commercial process, and although most rectifiers and transistors are still made by the alloy process, it remains a question if to a great extent diffusion may not become the most important of all commercial processes.

It must be stressed that all the techniques outlined are important tools in the kit of the device designer, and various combinations of alloying, diffusion, and other methods are usually required to make a new device having optimum properties.

In addition to the sequential use of various methods, the last few years have seen the increasing development of combination techniques for making multiple-junction

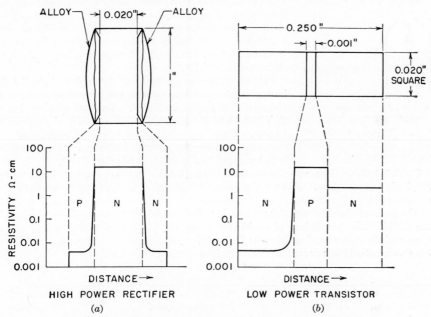

FIG. 7.1. Schematic specifications of two junction devices.

structures. Typical of these are "double diffusion," "grown-diffused" methods, "alloy-diffusion," "diffuse-meltback," and other hyphenated processes combining one or more of the basic processes in a single step. These methods are also treated in detail in what follows.

Junction and Device Specification. To make a good PN-junction device, the electrical characteristics (resistivity, type, mobility, lifetime) and the geometry of the junctions must be kept under close control. Specifications for two basic junction devices are indicated schematically in Fig. 7.1 for (1) a high-power junction rectifier and (2) a low-power NPN-junction transistor. We discuss here methods of meeting these specifications and of making the junction of the highest possible quality.

In the case of the rectifier, the junction must be of high quality (low reverse leakage current), the area must be large, and low-resistance (highly doped) regions must be provided on both sides. These regions are necessary to provide a high density of injected minority and majority carriers for efficient rectifier performance. Devices of this type can be made by a variety of the known methods of making junctions, although the fused-junction method is preferred for making junction rectifiers above a certain size and power rating.

In the case of the transistor of Fig. 7.1b the desired cross section is only about 20 mils square; the end regions can be fairly wide, but the center (base region) must be extremely thin, preferably less than 1 mil. Transistors of this type can be made either by double doping or by rate growing, while transistors of similar characteristics but different geometry can be made by the fused-junction method. Transistors of high power are made mostly by the fused-junction method because of the greater control over large areas, although diffusion is becoming increasingly competitive as a technique for making large-area devices.

7.2. Production of PN Junctions by Doping. One of the simplest and in some ways one of the best methods of making junctions is the direct doping of the melt during growth of the single crystal.[7] Such junctions are particularly useful for low-power high-quality diodes and photodiodes. A similar application of the technique is the double-doping method for making transistors, as is discussed in Sec. 7.3.

Figure 7.2 shows an ingot of germanium in which is incorporated a PN junction formed by adding gallium to the melt at the point indicated. The surface of the junction is not usually planar, as the result of various growth factors. This lack of planarity is a complication for large-area devices but is not too serious if the junction is to be sawed into small bars (dashed lines).

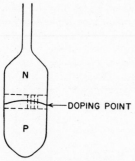

Fig. 7.2. Cross section of germanium ingot containing PN junction.

Table 7.1 shows the properties of various impurity elements of particular importance for doping germanium. Among the properties included are the atomic weight; the maximum impurity content generally attainable; the distribution constant,[8] defined as the ratio of the content of impurity in unit mass of solid to that in unit mass of the liquid, under conditions of equilibrium; and some information on the ionization energy of the states produced by the impurity.[9] Donor levels (N) are measured from the conduction band; acceptor levels (P) from the valence band.

TABLE 7.1[9]

Element	Atomic weight	Atoms/mg	Distribution or segregation constant in Ge, C_S/C_L	Max content in Ge (940°C), atoms/cu cm	Melting point, °C	Boiling point, °C	Energy of deep states, electron volts
B............	10.82	5.55×10^{19}	~20.	$>10^{19}$	2300	>2550	None > 0.01
Al...........	26.97	2.23×10^{19}	0.10	$>10^{18}$	660	1800	None > 0.01
Ga..........	69.22	8.69×10^{18}	0.10	$>10^{19}$	29.8	1600	None > 0.01
In...........	114.76	5.25×10^{18}	0.001	10^{17}	155	1450	None > 0.01
Tl...........	204.39	2.68×10^{18}	4×10^{-5}	10^{15}	304	1650	None > 0.01
P............	30.98	1.94×10^{19}	0.12	$>10^{19}$	44	280	None > 0.01
As...........	74.91	8.03×10^{18}	0.03	10^{19}	Sublimes	......	None > 0.01
Sb...........	121.76	4.94×10^{18}	0.003	5×10^{17}	630	1380	None > 0.01
Bi...........	209.00	2.88×10^{18}	4×10^{-5}	?	271	1450	?
Zn...........	65.38	9.22×10^{18}	0.01	10^{17}	420	907	0.03, 0.1 P
Cu...........	63.57	9.47×10^{18}	1.5×10^{-5}	2×10^{15}	1083	2300	0.04, 25 P
Au...........	197.2	3.05×10^{18}	3×10^{-5}	2×10^{15}	1063	2600	0.15, 0.55 P
Pt...........	195.23	3.08×10^{18}	5×10^{-6}	5×10^{14}	1773	4300	0.04, 0.55 P
Fe...........	55.84	1.08×10^{19}	10^{-6}	2×10^{14}	1535	3000	0.25, 0.45 P
Ni...........	58.69	1.02×10^{19}	2.5×10^{6}	2×10^{14}	1455	2900	0.24, 0.4 P
Co...........	58.94	1.02×10^{19}	10^{-6}	2×10^{13}	1495	3000	0.2, 0.4 P
Li...........	6.94	8.69×10^{19}	>0.01	$>10^{16}$	186	>1220	0.01 N

As discussed in Sec. 6.3a the distribution or segregation coefficient differs from the distribution constant in that it applies to nonequilibrium conditions. Its value always lies between the value of the distribution constant and unity.

It is seen that the various impurities range widely in their solubilities and segregation constants. For heavy doping, arsenic and gallium are often used. These elements, with phosphorus and aluminum, are the only elements with which 10^{19} atoms/cu cm can be incorporated into germanium. Table 7.1a shows segregation constants of some elements in silicon, as well as their ionization energies.

Since the normal segregation process which governs the changes in impurity content with distance along the ingot is discussed in Sec. 6, we shall not attempt further discussion here.

Impurities are commonly added to germanium either in the form of the pure element or in the form of an alloy. For impurities such as arsenic or gallium, having high segregation coefficients, the use of the alloy method is recommended because of the difficulty of weighing out directly the small quantities needed (often 1 mg or less).

TABLE 7.1a[8]

Element	Distribution or segregation constant in silicon, C_S/C_L	Ionization energy, electron volts
Boron..................	0.9	0.045 P
Aluminum..............	0.004	0.057 P
Gallium...............	0.01	0.065 P
Indium...............	0.0004	0.16 P
Phosphorus............	0.35	0.044 N
Arsenic...............	0.3	0.049 N
Antimony.............	0.04	0.039 N
Tin..................	0.02	
Gold..................	3×10^{-5}	0.35 P

When elements with smaller segregation coefficients are used, the quantities needed are larger, and these are often weighed out directly.

The problem of purity is particularly important for the very small segregation-coefficient materials. Presence of even a trace of a high segregation-coefficient impurity in a low segregation-coefficient additive can strongly affect the results obtained on doping.

Also of importance is the volatility of the elements used for doping. Appreciable quantities may be lost if a volatile element such as phosphorus is added directly rather than in the form of an alloy. Such elements can also contaminate the furnace for appreciable periods of time in a way not observed when involatile impurities are used. Antimony is the least volatile of the usual donors. Gallium and boron are the least volatile acceptors of the third-column group.

Also of importance in doping is the question whether the impurity element produces secondary states that may affect the lifetime of the minority carriers. Gold, iron, and copper, for example, have deep states in the forbidden energy band that seriously affect lifetime and, hence, should not be used for most doping work unless it is specifically desired to lower the lifetime.

7.2a. The Single-reservoir Method. Let us consider in detail the making of a particular grown junction in germanium, as an example. Let us suppose that we wish to fulfill the following conditions and that we have chosen gallium and antimony as suitable impurity elements:

$$\begin{array}{ccc} & \text{N} & \text{P} \\ \text{Resistivity} & \text{20 ohm-cm} & \text{0.01 ohm-cm} \end{array}$$

Assuming we have 100 g of germanium, let us dope the melt first with antimony and follow this, before much of the crystal has been grown, with gallium.

The first problem in doping is to determine the impurity content required for a given resistivity. There is a major uncertainty here, when really accurate experiments are desired, since the desired relation depends on the mobility of the carriers. The mobility not only apparently varies with resistivity itself, but also is not uniform from sample to sample depending on growth conditions, etc. These variations may be as great as 50 per cent. The mobilities shown in the accompanying table represent results on some of the better crystals that have been made.

HALL MOBILITY OF CARRIERS IN SILICON AND GERMANIUM

Element	Mobility, sq cm/volt sec	
	Holes	Electrons
Germanium...............	1,800	3,800
Silicon..................	400	1,750

Using these figures, the following relations tell us the desired impurity density for the specific resistivity. We assume that all impurity atoms will be electrically active in the crystal and will all be ionized. This is a good approximation for germanium at all temperatures and for silicon, for practically all the "ordinary" doping elements, above liquid-air temperature.

For resistivities above 1 ohm-cm (Ge) and 10 ohm-cm (Si), the following approximate relations will hold, since the mobility is practically independent of resistivity there:

$$\begin{array}{cc} \text{Ge} & \text{Si} \\ N_D = 1.64 \times 10^{15}/\rho/\text{cu cm} & N_D = 4 \times 10^{15}/\rho/\text{cu cm} \\ N_A = 3.47 \times 10^{15}/\rho & N_A = 1.8 \times 10^{16}/\rho \end{array}$$

Below 1 ohm-cm for Ge, 10 ohm-cm for Si, the impurities begin to interfere with the carrier motion, and the mobility drops with decreasing resistivity. The following relations describe the effect approximately:

$$\begin{array}{cc} \text{Ge} & \text{Si} \\ \mu_n = 3,800 + 1,000 \log_{10} \rho & \mu_n = 1,750 + 470 \log_{10} \rho/10 \\ \mu_p = 1,800 + 535 \log_{10} \rho & \mu_p = 400 + 100 \log_{10} \rho/10 \end{array}$$

Thus for our purposes we can calculate the required impurity density for obtaining a given resistivity for both Ge and Si from the formulas

$$\begin{array}{cc} \text{Ge} & \text{Si} \\ N_D = \dfrac{1.64 \times 10^{15}/\rho}{1 + 0.26 \log_{10} \rho} & N_D = \dfrac{4 \times 10^{15}/\rho}{0.73 + 0.27 \log_{10} \rho} \\[2mm] N_A = \dfrac{3.47 \times 10^{15}/\rho}{1 + 0.33 \log_{10} \rho} & N_A = \dfrac{1.8 \times 10^{16}/\rho}{0.73 + 0.25 \log_{10} \rho} \end{array} \tag{7.1}$$

Having the desired impurity content in the solid crystal, we use the values of segregation coefficient from Tables 7.1 and 7.1a. Equation (7.2) gives the results, applying only to the first part of the melt to be frozen. In case the experiment involves the compensation of a previous impurity of the opposite type, the amounts must be increased appropriately.

The required amount of impurity m, in milligrams, is given by the following equation:

$$m = \left(\frac{W}{kAD} \right) C_1 \qquad (7.2)$$

where W is the weight in grams of the germanium in the melt, k the segregation coefficient, A the number of atoms per milligram of the particular impurity used as tabulated in Table 7.1, C_1 the impurity content (atoms per cubic centimeter) needed to produce the desired value of N_D or N_A as calculated from the formulas of Eq. (7.1), and D the density of germanium in grams per cubic centimeter.

Returning now to the particular problem we wish to solve, we find, on assuming that the germanium is initially perfectly pure intrinsic material, that 1.5 mg of antimony should be added to 100 g of germanium to produce an initial resistivity of 20 ohm-cm. In this case, since the P-type region is so much more heavily doped than the N-type, we can neglect the compensating effect of the donors already present and calculate that the gallium content should be 6.7 mg to produce our 0.01-ohm-cm material.

Equally important is the diffusion coefficient. This limits the sharpness of the junction, since diffusion of impurities is greatest when the concentration gradients are high, as in sharp junctions. Substitutional acceptors† diffuse the least rapidly and hence should be used as the element of variable concentration where maximum sharpness is needed. Interstitial impurities, such as copper or lithium, diffuse the most rapidly, and substitutional donors take up an intermediate range. Because of rapid diffusion at the melting point, even when gallium and antimony are used for making a junction, it is difficult to make grown junctions having the sharpness of fused junctions. Thus grown junctions are almost always of the "graded" variety; in such junctions the transition from P to N type takes place in a distance comparable to the width of the space-charge layer. For copper or other fast-diffusing impurities, the junction may be 1 to 2 cm away from the doping point.

The distinction between "grown," "fused," and "diffused" junctions is seen to be arbitrary in some ways. The test of sharpness of a junction is usually made by measurements of the capacity versus voltage of the junction biased in the inverse (blocking) direction. $1/C$ varies as $V^{1/3}$ for junctions with "linear crossover," compared with $V^{1/2}$ for sharp junctions. Figure 7.3 shows a typical PN-junction impurity profile and the corresponding resistivity.

Further discussion of diffused junctions is given in Sec. 7.7.

7.2b. *The Split-reservoir Method.*[11] In principle the ingot of Fig. 7.2 could have been subdivided indefinitely into PN junctions by continual reversal of type through doping with the proper amount of donors and acceptors. In practice, this has the bad result that with each reversal the impurity content continually increases and the properties (lifetime and mobility, particularly) become continually more inferior. In addition, accurate compensation to produce the desired resistivities becomes progressively more difficult as the total impurity content increases. A means of growing large numbers of junctions in a single ingot is obtained if the reservoir is split into two portions, the one containing the donor, the other containing the acceptor impurity (Fig. 7.4). By dipping the seed, or growing ingot, successively into the proper pool of

† Substitutional impurity atoms are those which enter the lattice and replace a germanium parent lattice atom. Interstitials, on the other hand, may be added to an already complete lattice and are wedged in between the lattice atoms. For small ions, this may be quite easy, and they may have considerable freedom in movement. This accounts for the high diffusion rates of copper, lithium, and nickel in Ge.

liquid germanium, the reversal of type can be made with little or no deterioration or loss of accuracy and with little added complication. This method has not been widely used, and thus operating experience with it is limited.

It should be clear from the foregoing that junctions between regions of the same type, but differing conductivity, can easily be made by the same methods.

7.3. Transistors Prepared by Double Doping. Special problems are encountered in the production of transistors by doping methods. In particular, good characteristics require that the base region be very thin, preferably less than 1 mil (see Sec. 4). Also, somewhat better control is needed over the resistivities of the various portions of the transistor bar than is needed for most diodes.

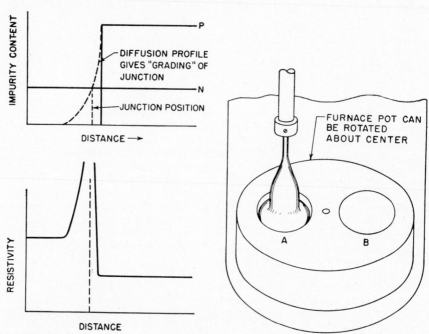

FIG. 7.3. Characteristics of a typical PN junction.

FIG. 7.4. Split-reservoir furnace.

Because of the importance of good lifetime and the need for good crystal structure, as well as the requirements mentioned previously, furnace equipments for transistor production are often more elaborate than those used for simple crystal growing or diode production. The temperature control and arrangements for stirring are, in particular, likely to be more elaborate.

The procedure for making NPN transistor blanks (the variety usually made by double doping) is to produce the collector region first, usually of high resistivity ($\sim$10 ohm-cm N type), then dope with gallium so as to produce a medium-resistivity P-type base region[12] ($\sim$1 ohm-cm). After a time during which the crystal has grown 1 mil or so, the melt is doped with a donor (arsenic) so as to produce a low-resistivity N-type emitter ($\sim$0.001 ohm-cm). Rather high rotation speeds ($>$4 rps) are desirable during these processes, and special stirrers are often used. The growth rate must be very slow and steady during growth of the base region to allow complete stirring. Among the stirring means most widely used are rotation of the crucible, with a quartz paddle immersed in the molten germanium to provide the stirring.

As in the case of junction diodes, very few good transistor junctions (usually only one) can be made in one ingot by the double-doping process. Transistors, in particular, are sensitive to the build-up of compensating impurities. Again, the multiple-reservoir method offers a means of getting around this difficulty.

Figure 7.1 shows a typical cross section of an NPN transistor bar and the profile of impurity content, assuming no acceptor present before doping. As in the case of the single PN junction, the resistivity profile is modified by diffusion. In the case of thin base regions, diffusion may considerably change the thickness of the base region. This offers a means of controlling base thickness, although it may be difficult to prevent deleterious effects associated with heat-treatment (see Sec. 7.7).

7.4. Rate Growing. The method of rate growing was first announced by Hall,[13] who succeeded in making good transistor junctions with a thin base region by this method. Following his original work he made further investigations into the basis of the process.[14] A number of similar investigations has also been made by investigators at the Bell Laboratories.[15-17]

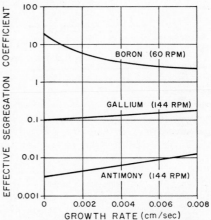

FIG. 7.5. Segregation coefficients of impurities in germanium as a function of growth rate.

A primary requisite of rate growing is that both donor and acceptor impurities in nearly equal amounts must be incorporated into the growing crystal. Whether the one or the other type predominates is determined by the rate of growth.

In his original studies Hall had used antimony and gallium as the two impurities. His work indicated that the segregation coefficient of gallium was independent of rate of growth while that of antimony increased markedly with growth rate. More recent studies have indicated that both segregation coefficients increase with growth rate, with antimony increasing more rapidly. Work at Bell Laboratories, as well as later work by Hall, indicated that best results with germanium might be obtained with boron and antimony, since, as Fig. 7.5 shows, the segregation of boron actually drops with increasing growth rate.

In practice, rate growing has been most extensively applied to the making of double transistor barriers, although it can also be used for the making of simple PN junctions in both silicon and germanium. For making transistor barriers, temperature control is used to vary the growth rate and the pulling rate is generally kept constant. The temperature is varied periodically by changing the power input to the furnace heater. This requires rather low thermal inertia and good thermal transfer. As the temperature of the melt rises, the growth slows, and as temperature falls, the rate of growth increases. Depending upon the magnitude of the power pulse, there may be modulation of the antimony content by as much as a factor of 5. Figure 7.6 shows the segregation coefficient, and thus the impurity content, as a function of the fraction of the crystal grown in each cycle of temperature change. The curves depend upon the parameter α', which is defined by the equation

$$v = v_i(1 - \alpha' \cos \omega t) \tag{7.3}$$

where v is the velocity of growth assumed to vary sinusoidally with time, v_i an intrinsic velocity determinable theoretically for the given conditions of growth. If $\alpha' < 1$, the growth rate is always positive and the curves are smoothly varying cycloid-like curves.   The larger α' is, the greater the swing of the impurity content during the cycle, and when $\alpha' = 0$, there is no growth-rate variation and no rate growing.

When $\alpha' = 1$, the situation changes, for here the growth rate becomes zero for part of the cycle.   For $\alpha' > 1$, the crystal melts back and the velocity of growth is negative.   This leads to a discontinuity in the impurity content.   After melting back, the

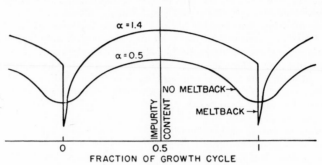

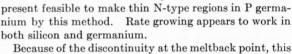

FIG. 7.6. Typical variation of impurity content in a rate-grown crystal.

growth rate always starts off at a value of 0 and increases more rapidly the larger the value of α'.

Junctions are produced if the acceptor level is not modulated by the temperature cycle or if, though modulated, its range lies within the range of modulation of the donor content.   In an N-type bar, thin P-type regions may be produced at each minimum of the growth curve.   The smaller the acceptor density, the thinner the regions will be.   Values of a few tenths of a mil are easily obtained.   It is not at present feasible to make thin N-type regions in P germanium by this method.   Rate growing appears to work in both silicon and germanium.

Because of the discontinuity at the meltback point, this junction appears well suited for the emitter junction.   On the other hand, the more gradual crossing of the donor and acceptor densities at the other junction makes it well suited for "graded" collector junctions, particularly in giving good peak-inverse properties and low collector capacity.

Thus by periodic cycling of the temperature at intervals of a few minutes, many double junctions of excellent quality for transistors can be built into a single ingot, without undue build-up of compensating impurities.   A picture of such an ingot (sectioned) is shown in Fig. 7.7.   The junctions have been made visible by spreading a suspension of barium titanate in carbon tetrachloride over the face of the section while a small current was passing through the crystal.   The barium titanate collects at the regions of high fields, namely, the junctions.   Note the typical scalloped edges of the ingot, produced by the periodic temperature change.

FIG. 7.7. Double junctions in a rate-grown ingot.

Rate-grown Diodes.   The rate-growing method is somewhat more suitable for transistors than for diodes.   Although experience with diodes is not great, it appears that many successive PN junctions can be made along an ingot of silicon or germanium by periodic increase of pulling rate or temperature.   Suitable methods must be used to separate the junctions sufficiently so that diodes can conveniently be made.   In the case of the transistor junctions, if strong temperature cycling is used, the junctions will tend to be alternately "sharp" and "graded," with different sets of characteristics. With more moderate cycling (no meltback) or with the pulling rate as the controlling variable, the successive junctions can be made nearly identical. Rate-grown junction diodes are not so likely to be heavily doped as fused or doped junctions, and thus they may lack the high efficiency needed for power rectifiers. They can, however, be made with graded characteristics that are very suitable for high inverse-voltage properties.

7.4a. Mechanism of Rate Growing. Hall attempted to set up a model explaining the observed effects of rate growing by assuming that the pickup of impurity atoms is determined by the rate of adsorption of the atoms at the growing crystal face and by the rate of diffusion of these nonequilibrium concentrations into the interior of the crystal. Such a process is determined by a relaxation time determined by the atomic spacing of germanium and by the diffusion coefficient in the solid at the melting point. The corresponding rate of growth beyond which rate-growth effects occur should be about 12 in./hr, in reasonable agreement with observed effects.

Burton, Slichter, and coworkers have carried out experiments to show that liquid transport processes are more important than those in the solid. Two important basic facts of the process are thus explained, which were somewhat obscure in Hall's theory:

1. The rate of stirring is almost as important as the rate of growth.
2. The difference in characteristics between donors and acceptors is an artificial one, the facts indicating that the rate-growth effect depends primarily upon the order of magnitude of the distribution coefficient and upon the diffusion coefficient in the liquid. Boron has a large distribution constant (20) which decreases markedly with growth rate, gallium has a smaller distribution constant (0.1) which increases slightly with growth rate, and antimony has an even smaller distribution constant and correspondingly large dependence on growth rate.

7.4b. Stirring-modulation Method. Bridgers[16] has used the dependence of distribution coefficient upon stirring rate to develop another technique of making transistor barriers of the NPN type. The method suffers from the fact that it is not so flexible as techniques for changing temperature, which can combine the rate-growing effect with the meltback technique.

Rate-growing Silicon. Rate growing has been found to be successful for making NPN transistors using silicon.[17] Again, the principles involved appear to be identical with those used for germanium, and only the details of the equipment will vary because of the higher melting temperature of silicon.

Advantages and Disadvantages of Rate Growing. As has already been pointed out, the rate-growing process is characterized by the large number of equivalent junctions or pairs of junctions that can be made in an ordinary ingot—as many as 50 or more in a 5-in. ingot. Furthermore, because of the inherent effects of melting back, these junctions, both emitter and collector, are well suited for transistors, both triode and tetrode. The control over the base-region width is excellent, and many junctions have been made with a base region only a few tenths of a mil thick. Such transistor junctions are excellent for high-alpha high-frequency transistors.

The drawbacks of rate growing lie mainly in the limited range of conductivity that is available in any one ingot, and indeed, it appears that the absolute range of impurity content available is limited to a factor of 5 or so. Also, rate growing, being a crystal-growth method, is subject to inflexibility in the geometry of the junction. The lack of strong doping attainable in the base region limits the effectiveness of rate-grown transistors in the high-current high-frequency region.

Rate-grown tetrode transistors having excelling high-frequency properties were made several years ago. However, they lacked the feasibility in mass production inherent in other methods using the simpler triode structure, including the alloy, diffused, and surface-barrier types. The method has not received much attention during the last few years.

7.5. Remelt and Segregation Junctions. Remelt junctions represent a class of devices made by melting a portion of a piece of semiconductor material so as to produce a junction at the boundary of the melted and unmelted portions. Various processes of this type are known as "remelt,"[18] "surface melting,"[19] "meltback,"[20] and "melt quench,"[21] depending upon the particular aspect stressed, as, for example, the use of nonequilibrium and rate-growing effects to influence the results. Remelt-junction processes may also involve doping procedures during the remelt operation.

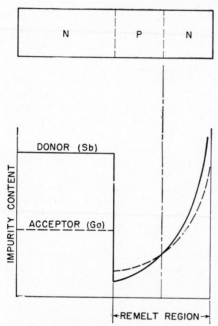

FIG. 7.8. Distribution of donor and acceptor concentration after a remelt operation.

A block of germanium is heated to a high temperature at one end. This germanium contains both donor and acceptor elements. The heating is done in a special fixture or small furnace having high-temperature gradients. With proper precautions, the one end is melted before the other end has become hot enough to heat-treat appreciably. (Preliminary treatment of the block with potassium cyanide for removal of copper may be advisable.)

After the end of the block is melted, the block is cooled and a junction is formed at the contact with the melted region, provided there is the proper impurity content in the original block. There may be formed a transistor NPN structure with a thin base region well suited for high-alpha high-frequency transistors.

Impurity Distributions. Figure 7.8 shows the distribution of antimony and gallium, each of which was present uniformly throughout the block before melting. Antimony is in excess by an amount determinable from the desired final characteristics. When the block is melted, these impurities remain in their same proportions. However, when the block freezes again, the antimony and gallium now become reduced according to their normal segregation properties. Since the gallium has the larger segregation coefficient, it is in excess at the beginning of the remelt region. However, its segregation in the solid is somewhat less rapid than that of antimony, and a second junction may be formed as the antimony predominates. This is a "segregation junction." Thus, on the basis of normal segregation alone (Fig. 7.8), the concentrations can be chosen so that an NPN structure is formed. This will have the characteristics of low emitter resistance, high base resistivity, abrupt emitter junction, and graded collector junction, all desirable features. However, the rate-growth effect may also play an important role. This will, in general, reduce the distance required for the formation of the second PN junction and will aid in the formation of a thin base layer. In addition, control of characteristics can be aided by doping the remelted region with donor or acceptor impurities during the remelt.

Remelt Diodes. Diodes can also be made by the remelt process. However, since antimony must be present in relatively large quantities because of its small segregation coefficient, the "sprout" end will tend to be N type regardless of other factors, and this end will have to be removed by sawing or grinding before contact is made. Special care has to be taken in using antimony and gallium to produce the desired spacing between junctions. A typical distribution is shown in Fig. 7.9. The antimony now is only slightly in excess of the gallium, so that after the meltback it remains the minority component until the end of the bar freezes.

7.6. Alloy or Fusion Junctions. Among the methods of making junctions in which a homogeneous wafer of semiconductor is treated so that junctions are formed, the more important are those variously labeled as "fusion," "alloying," and "diffusion" techniques. Because of the wide variations in terminology used by various workers in this field, we shall give a short discussion of the terms used and the principles involved.

Alloying or Fusion. Alloying junctions are junctions made by heating a wafer of semiconductor in contact with an impurity element which becomes liquid at the temperature used or which forms a liquid alloy with germanium at the heating temperature being used. This method is also referred to as the fusion technique.

Diffusion. When the impurity remains solid, forms no liquid alloy or eutectic, or when the wafer is heated in a vapor of impurity at such low pressures that there is no appreciable liquid formation, we say we are making a diffusion junction. If an alloy or fused junction is heated long enough for its properties to be appreciably modified by solid-state diffusion, it may be considered to be a diffused junction.

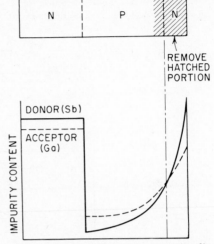

Fig. 7.9. Donor and acceptor impurity distribution after a remelt operation designed for diode production.

Both the alloy and diffusion methods are special cases of the general method of heating a semiconductor wafer in contact with an impurity, originally called diffusion by Hall and Dunlap,[22] who first discussed its application to PN-junction devices. We shall now discuss the nature of the contact made by heating a wafer of, say, germanium in contact with solid, liquid, or vapor impurity. The most widely used elements with germanium are indium and antimony, although alloys have been used and probably will be more widely used.

Figure 7.10 shows a cross section of an alloy junction[23] on germanium, made by heating a pellet of indium on a slice of germanium at a temperature of, say, 500°C for 1 min. The molten indium very rapidly attacks the germanium and forms a liquid germanium-indium solution. The germanium continues to dissolve into the indium until the saturation limit appropriate to the given temperature is reached. This can be determined approximately for any impurity if the phase diagram of the impurity germanium system is known. Such a diagram for In-Ge is indicated in Fig. 7.11. This diagram gives the equilibrium concentration of liquid indium-germanium solutions in contact with solid germanium at the temperature indicated. It is seen that the saturation solution of indium-germanium at 600°C contains about 20 per cent indium.

When the heating is completed and the wafer cools, several processes take place:

1. The liquid solution is now supercooled and begins to freeze.

2. Germanium begins to precipitate out, usually in the form of a single crystalline layer deposited upon the unattacked germanium. This is called the recrystallized

layer, first noticed in indium-germanium contacts by English.[24] Because of the high concentration of indium, the recrystallized layer is highly doped with indium. Thus a junction is formed, assuming that the underlying layer is N type. At 600°C, it is estimated that the recrystallized layer contains about 10^{18} atoms In per cubic centimeter.

3. After the liquid has reached its farthest penetration, solid diffusion takes place into the solid crystal. The diffusion produces a PN junction inside the undisturbed

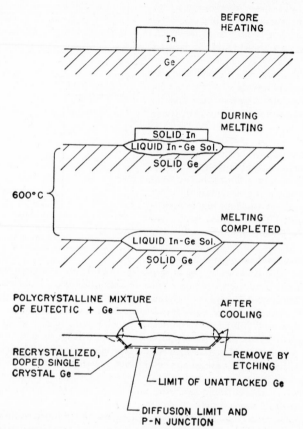

Fig. 7.10. Cross section of an alloy junction showing the alloying process.

crystal whose depth depends upon the time and temperature and which may range from a few lattice spacings to several mils.

We see from the values of Table 7.2 that the PN junction can be made to lie at any desired distance from the recrystallized region, depending upon the kind and amount of impurities present and upon the time-temperature cycle used in heating.

For most commercial applications, good results have been obtained if the diffusion layer is small compared with the barrier potential depth in the junction. Since such junctions have capacity-voltage relationships that indicate a sharp barrier, the importance of the diffusion zone is problematical, although there is some probability that the higher perfection of the lattice in the diffusion layer may lead to higher voltage breakdown and better back-leakage characteristics of the junctions.

7.6a. Materials for Alloy Junctions. Of the various acceptors that can be used for making alloy junctions on N-type germanium, indium alone has won wide acceptance. This is because a number of factors enter into the quality of a junction, including low back current, good forward injection, stability, and good mechanical properties. Indium appears to be soft enough so that the mechanical strains that usually occur in the germanium during the cooling stage of the process are not deleterious. The softness of indium is somewhat of a drawback, however, because the lead wires in the indium may pull out. For making transistor emitter junctions, small amounts of gallium or aluminum are often added to the indium to increase the doping level in the recrystallized layer. This leads to better emitter efficiency and to higher current amplification, particularly for large emitter currents.

Aluminum, on the other hand, has been tested extensively for junction contacts on germanium without outstanding success. Gold gives somewhat better results, and it may be used, particularly if alloyed with an acceptor such as gallium that will dope the germanium strongly. At the present time, however, gold is mainly used for silicon alloy junctions and for welded ("gold-bonded") contacts to germanium.

Similar problems are met when making donor alloy contacts to germanium. Early work was done with pure antimony, which was soon found to make brittle, unstable contacts. More recent work has indicated that a rather narrow range of concentration (10 to 15 per cent) of antimony in lead produces an acceptable junction on P-type germanium.[25] Another question of importance is the "recombination rate" appropriate to various contacts. Tin, for example, appears to be superior to alloys containing lead.[26]

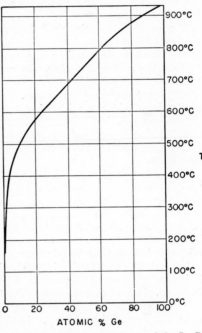

FIG. 7.11. The phase diagram of the In-Ge system.

7.6b. Details of the Alloy Process. Alloy contacts for experimental purposes or production are generally made in either (1) electrical fixtures or (2) ovens. For experimental work, a fixture is often used. The heating is done by a strip heater of molybdenum, mounted between heavy conducting bars. The germanium wafer rests on the molybdenum plate. A thermocouple close to the plate is used for obtaining reproducible results; however, unless it is carefully used, the readings may not indicate accurately the temperature of the pellet. A protective atmosphere (argon, hydrogen) is required. Forming gas (90 per cent N_2, 10 per cent H_2) is also widely used.

It is recommended that fairly slow, uniform heating be used in furnace alloying, a steady well-controlled temperature be maintained at the alloying temperature, and slow and uniform cooling of the order of $10°$/min be used.

Alloying agents are applied in one of several ways: (1) The most common is the use of buttons, held in place by special jigs, often pressed by special fixtures. Such buttons are usually kept perfectly clean. (2) Plated contacts are often used, although there is some question about their cleanliness. (3) Evaporated contacts are often used for silicon, since vacuum processes are often desirable to maintain a clean silicon surface.

Good control of semiconductor material is required for making acceptable junctions. Grain boundaries and lineage appear to be highly deleterious; in addition, it is generally felt that the proper crystal face must be used for best results. The shape of the alloy contact may vary with the crystalline face used. For example, the (111) face may tend to give a triangular contact area and the (100) face a square area. Many transistor development engineers find that a wafer cut from the (111) face of a germanium crystal gives the best plane-parallel junctions if the alloying process must penetrate the surface of the wafer to a considerable depth. If the alloying process barely removes the surface, good junctions can be made using other crystalline faces.

Tunnel ovens are also used for mass production of PN junctions by the alloy process. These are probably more suitable for high-quantity production than the fixture method, since units can travel through the oven on a conveyor belt with comparatively little handling. In any case, the procedures used are identical in principle with those of the fixture method.

7.6c. Control of the Alloy Process. The critical aspects of alloying, particularly for production, include the following aspects: (1) wetting, (2) control of penetration, (3) area control.

1. Wetting is most easily guaranteed by perfect cleanliness of both alloying agents and semiconductor wafers. High purity in furnace gases or heating fixtures may also be critical.

Strangely enough, a particularly serious problem with alloying, particularly with very clean systems, is the tendency of indium-type alloys to wet germanium too easily and to spread unduly over the semiconductor wafer or to assume other than circular alloy dot shapes. It has been found that a density of dislocations between 10^3 and 10^4 seems useful in helping to "pin" the wetting action to about the size of the original button, with little or no deleterious effect on the device properties, at least for industrial-type indium-alloy transistors.

2. Control of penetration is mostly the result of careful technique and experience. It is now fairly easy to control the depth of penetration through a 3- to 4-mil wafer, from two sides, so that the base width is not more than 0.4 mil.

The microalloy technique[27] is an approach to alloying which has a number of advantages relative to control. In this technique other means than alloying itself are used to reduce the wafer thickness at the desired spots, in this case by jet etching. A plated, very thin layer of indium or other alloying agent is then deposited, and the alloying is carried out at the lowest possible alloying temperature, further limiting the penetration and sidewise flow. Penetration depths were found by Rittmann et al. to be of the order 0.001 mil.

Still another approach where very small penetration is desired is the use of germanium-rich alloys. If the alloy button contains germanium such that the temperature of melting is very close to the equilibrium composition for this temperature, the penetration can be held to arbitrarily small values. Usually, unfortunately, such alloys are difficult to prepare and use, being in particular very brittle.

Figure 7.12 shows a typical cross section of an alloy-junction transistor. The regularity of the penetration is not exaggerated, and in any case it is not difficult to obtain nearly planar emitter and collector contacts.

3. Various techniques are used for controlling the location of the junction and the exact area. Among these are the use of jigs, often made of graphite, into which the germanium wafers are fastened and the indium pellets positioned in suitable holes. Then when heating takes place, the indium wets the germanium (presumably) always in the same place and the same area. It is not always easy to guarantee that indium

will wet the entire area desired.   This is a particularly difficult problem if the junctions are intricate in shape and have very close tolerances, as, for example, in a power transistor.

A technique developed by Armstrong[28] appears especially suited to solve this problem.   A mask is made and gold or silver is evaporated onto the germanium in just the places where the indium is wanted.   Then indium either is evaporated heavily over the same area or simply flows over the evaporated layers, to which it alloys quite accurately, without spreading over onto the lightly oxidized germanium.

Naturally, there are many techniques of this kind that must be incorporated into any practical process of making transistors and other semiconductor devices, and we cannot, in the space available, go into the subject in any great detail.

7.6d.   Temperature-gradient Zone Melting.   An ingenious method, reported by W. G. Pfann,[29] for controlling the positioning and other properties of the alloy junction is "temperature-gradient zone melting."   In this method, the fused contact can be

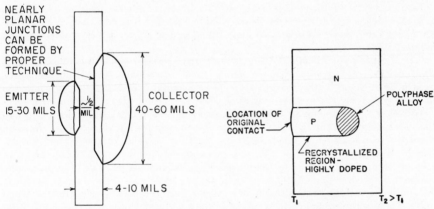

FIG. 7.12. Cross section of an alloy-junction transistor.

FIG. 7.13. Temperature-gradient zone melting.

driven into the interior of the crystal and replaced by doped germanium, merely by heating the fused contact between two plates of germanium in a temperature gradient.

The method depends upon the greater solubility of many metals in germanium at higher temperatures, as shown in Fig. 7.13.   When a layer of indium is sandwiched between two plates of germanium in a temperature gradient, the lower-temperature side tends to come to equilibrium with a smaller concentration of germanium in indium than on the higher-temperature side.   This concentration gradient creates a diffusion flow of germanium, but this flow makes the melting point rise, and thus indium-germanium deposits on the left-hand side, and conversely, the loss of the germanium means a more unsaturated solution at the right-hand side, and thus further attack of germanium by the indium takes place there.   Therefore the thin molten region can move through large distances in the direction of higher temperatures. Pfann has also shown this method to work for gold in silicon, where it probably has special advantages in removing the actual junction region from the region of the metal-silicon contact, where mechanical strains have a tendency to disrupt the junction.   The method, while interesting, is still in the experimental stage.

7.6e.   Alloy Junctions on Silicon.   Silicon poses special problems in the formation of alloy junctions.   Silicon appears to be much more difficult to wet with liquid metals than germanium.   This is probably owing to the tough and refractory, though very thin, film of silicon dioxide (silica) that forms on silicon after even very short exposure to air.   Generally, methods of making alloy junctions on silicon depend primarily upon the technique used in breaking through this barrier layer.   Mechanical methods (pressure, grinding) and chemical methods (fluxes and similar agents) are both used.

A critical problem with silicon-alloy junctions is brittleness, since nothing so satisfactory in this respect as the indium-germanium junction has yet been developed. This brittleness may not show up in immediate poor characteristics or failure but may show up only after repeated temperature cycling has caused damage to the junction through repeated expansion and contraction.   Mounting of silicon on base material of suitable coefficient expansion is also necessary (molybdenum is suitable).   Use of evaporated-alloyed contacts is recommended on silicon because it removes most of the problems of brittle contacts.

Gold-antimony alloys have been widely used for alloy junctions on P-type silicon, and aluminum probably has been the most successful for junctions on N-type silicon.

No detailed attention will be given to techniques of silicon-junction fabrication, around which a whole technology is developing.   Suffice it to say that, as in germanium, a liquid alloy is first formed and, after freezing starts, a recrystallized region is formed.[30,31]

7.7. Diffusion Junctions. Diffusion junctions have been made in germanium and silicon with a large variety of doping agents[32,33] and compounds.   Such junctions have been made for use in the fabrication of diodes and transistors.[34-37]   Diffusion has now become one of the most promising of the general methods of junction formation.

Diffusion junctions can be made by exposing a P-type block of semiconductor to the vapor of an N-type impurity at elevated temperature (or vice versa).   In some cases where the diffusing impurity is not volatile at ordinary temperatures (e.g., boron), it can be deposited on the surface of the semiconductor at low temperature and subsequently heated to a temperature at which diffusion will take place at a reasonable speed.

Junctions produced by diffusion of a vapor into the solid semiconductor move uniformly into the crystal surface, retaining the contour of the crystal surface.   If the surface is very flat, the junctions will be very flat.   The depth beneath the surface at which the junction is formed is determined by the time, temperature, and amount of impurity.   The depth of penetration together with the initial impurity content of the semiconductor crystal determines both the location of junction and its thickness. Such junctions have been made within 2 microns of the surface and of the proper grading (see Sec. 4, page 4-11) to withstand more than 50 volts.

Diffusion has at the present time developed into a very flexible technique.   It can be used for both high-power and high-frequency devices.   It has been used in conjunction with practically all the other junction-forming techniques, and as will be discussed below, "grown-diffused," "diffused-meltback," "alloy-diffused," and similar processes are now quite important.   Additional modifications of the diffusion technique have appeared, including "outdiffusion" and "diffusion with evaporation in a vacuum."

The art of diffusion for junctions has also led to a great variety of specific techniques involving the manner of diffusion, the nature of the diffusing impurities, carrier gases for protection of the semiconductor surfaces, and masking techniques for controlling the location of the diffused region on the surface.   We shall discuss a few of these.

All these varieties of conditions require different boundary conditions for the solution of the diffusion equation if complete accounting of the results is desired. We shall be unable to do more than give theoretical results for a few of the simpler boundary conditions, then summarize the technical details of some of the processes mentioned.

7.7a. Theory of Diffusion. Diffusion into the solid crystal is governed by the differential equation[38]

$$\frac{\partial C}{\partial t} = D \frac{\partial^2 C}{\partial x^2} \tag{7.4}$$

The particular initial and boundary conditions determine the nature of the solution. For the one-dimensional "step-function" solution, applying to many diffusion problems of interest, we assume that there is an infinite source of the diffusing impurity at

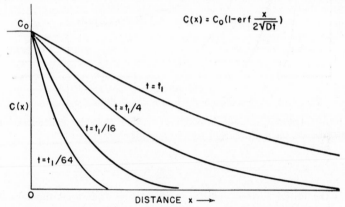

$$C(x) = C_0 \left(1 - \text{erf} \frac{x}{2\sqrt{Dt}}\right)$$

FIG. 7.14. Step-function solution of the diffusion equation.

the plane $x = 0$ and that it maintains a concentration in the germanium of $C = C_0$ at $x = 0$, for all t. The solution of the diffusion equation is

$$C(x) = C_0 \left[1 - \text{erf} \left(\frac{x}{2\sqrt{Dt}} \right) \right] \tag{7.5}$$

and is indicated in Fig. 7.14. The solution can be simplified in the case, as often occurs, that the interesting range of $C(x) \ll C_0$. Then we can approximate

$$1 - \text{erf} \left(\frac{x}{2\sqrt{Dt}} \right) \approx \frac{e^{-x^2/4Dt}}{\sqrt{\pi}\,(x/2\sqrt{Dt})} \tag{7.6}$$

To apply this equation to the formation of junctions, we consider that if the crystal contains an impurity of opposite type to that diffusing, with uniform concentration C', then the diffusion curve will cross $C = C'$ at the value $x = x_0$, the junction depth. Again assuming $C(x) \ll C_0$, we find for the penetration of the junction

$$x_0 = 2\sqrt{Dt} \left[\ln \frac{C_0}{C'} - \ln \sqrt{\pi} \left(\frac{x_0}{2\sqrt{Dt}} \right) \right]^{1/2} \tag{7.7}$$

For typical values of $C' \sim 10^{14}$/cu cm and $C_0 \sim 10^{20}$/cu cm, this expression reduces to the simple approximation

$$x_0 \approx 8\sqrt{Dt} \tag{7.8}$$

If the diffusion proceeds into a base already containing the diffusing impurity in the concentration $C = C_1$, then

$$C(x) = C_1 + C_0 \left(1 - \text{erf} \frac{x}{2\sqrt{Dt}} \right) \tag{7.9}$$

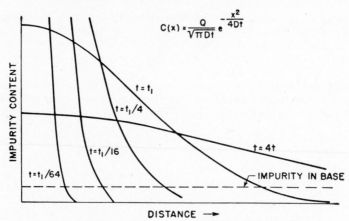

$$C(x) = \frac{Q}{\sqrt{\pi D t}} e^{-\frac{x^2}{4Dt}}$$

FIG. 7.15. Constant-source solution of the diffusion equation.

If the total impurity amount is constant, rather than its concentration at the germanium surface, then a different solution applies:

$$C(x) = \frac{Q}{\sqrt{\pi D t}} e^{-x^2/4Dt} \tag{7.10}$$

where Q is the initial surface density of atoms (per square centimeter). Typical results are shown in Fig. 7.15.

The penetration of the PN junction can again be determined by substituting x_0 for x and C' for C:

$$x_0 = 2 \sqrt{Dt} \left[\ln \left(\frac{Q}{C' \sqrt{\pi D t}} \right) \right]^{1/2} \tag{7.11}$$

For typical values we can take $C' = 10^{14}$/cu cm, $Q = 10^{17}$/sq cm,

$$D = 10^{-10} \text{ sq cm/sec}$$

and $t = 10^4$ sec. We then find that the penetration varies nearly as

$$x_0 \sim 8 \sqrt{Dt} \qquad \text{cm} \tag{7.8}$$

Thus for this range of values the penetration is about the same for either the "step-function" or the "constant-source" solution. In Table 7.2 are listed the junction depths of several common N- and P-type impurities for diffusion into germanium with an impurity concentration of about 10^{14} atoms/cu cm. Values are calculated using Eq. (7.8).

TABLE 7.2. IMPURITY DIFFUSION DISTANCES IN GERMANIUM[39]

D sq cm/ sec	Temperature, °C					Penetration, Angstroms				
	Sb, As	P	Zn	Ga	In	$t = 1$ sec	10	100	10^3	10^4
10^{-10}	875	925	...	...	...	8,000	2.5×10^4	8×10^4	2.5×10^5	8×10^5
10^{-12}	700	725	800	900	875	800	2,500	8,000	2.5×10^4	8×10^4
10^{-14}	550	575	650	725	700	80	250	800	2,500	8,000
10^{-16}	450	475	550	600	575	8	25	80	250	800

Another method of considerable importance is double or simultaneous diffusion, by means of which two junctions can be built into a semiconductor wafer.   It is generally assumed that the same results are obtained if the two diffusions are done simultaneously or in sequence.   There are some advantages in using sequential diffusion, since different temperatures or surface concentrations C_0 or surface conditions may be desirable in the two cases.

Some of the best high-frequency transistors, the "mesa" types operating in the 100-mc frequency range, are made by the double-diffusion method.[40]

Figure 7.16 shows two diffusion profiles, obtained by simultaneous diffusion from the surface, which can yield two junctions separated by very small distances so as to provide a very thin transistor base layer and a highly doped emitter.   These are two of the primary requirements of good high-frequency transistors, and the thin base layer is also valuable for low-frequency power transistors because it minimizes deleterious effects due to the degradation of lifetime during the diffusion heating.

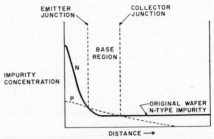

Fig. 7.16. Double-diffused NPN structure for silicon, where acceptors diffuse more rapidly than donors.

The III-V compounds are useful sources of diffusant for simultaneous diffusion, gallium arsenide being a good example. For sequential diffusion, the pure elements or, more frequently, the oxides are used.   Phosphorus pentoxide and boric oxide are widely used for supplying diffusant in regular, controllable amounts, since they decompose slightly at diffusion temperatures to give a proper supply of diffusant.

7.7b. Techniques of Vapor Diffusion.[3–5]   For proper control of diffusion from the surface the following factors are important:

1. Preparation of sample
2. Method of supplying the diffusing impurity or impurities
3. Method of heating
4. Protection of the surface, particularly for silicon

1. Surface preparation is extremely important for such devices as mesa units, where the penetration is only a few microns.   For such devices the smoothness of the surface must be on a comparable scale, and great care is needed to polish out scratches and imperfections.   For rectifier junctions and other deep penetrations less care is needed.

2. Methods of supplying impurity for diffusion include the following:

a. Evaporation of thin films of impurity on the sample.

b. Inclusion of small pieces of the (volatile) impurity element in the diffusion system.

c. Passing of the carrier gas over the impurity element or an oxide in a secondary furnace before the gas reaches the samples.

d. Painting or spraying the samples with a slurry or mixture containing the impurity element or its oxides.   This method is particularly useful for silicon rectifiers, since glasses formed by painting oxides protect the surfaces and make possible the simultaneous formation of a PN junction on one side and an NN junction on the other. (In some processes, the N layer is first formed by phosphorus diffusion, a face is lapped off, then boron diffusion is used.)

3. Several distinct methods of carrying out the diffusion process are in common use. These are of three general types:

   a. The closed gas-filled tube
   b. The open tube with carrier gas
   c. The vacuum system with impurity reservoir and constricted access

   a. The closed-tube system is used, of course, with samples either containing the impurity as an evaporated or sprayed layer or with a piece of impurity present in the tube.   In this method, quartz tubes are most widely used.

   Usually the tube, especially for experimental purposes, is small and is kept at constant temperature.   It is also possible to use a two-temperature system with closed tubes when the tube is small so that one end can extend into a second-temperature zone.   The impurity supply will be governed, to some extent at least, by the lowest temperature in the tube.

   4. Protection of the surface becomes of great importance, particularly for silicon, since an excess of diffusant or even thermal etching due to excessive diffusion time can corrode the surface and render diffusion uneven and evaluation difficult.   There are two prime methods for protection of the surface:

   a. Use of glassy oxides not only provides a controlled source of diffusant, but the glass also protects the surface from evaporation and thermal etching.   The action probably includes the effect of SiO_2.

   b. Direct use of a silicon oxide (silica) layer on the silicon is provided by adding oxygen, water vapor, or other oxygen-bearing gases to the carrier gas.   A common method is through bubbling a part of the carrier gas supply through water at known temperature.

   7.7c. Masking and Other Control Means for Area Control in Diffusion.   Glasses and silica layers may be used not only for the general protection of silicon surfaces but also for masking off certain areas against diffusion.   Additional flexibility is given to these techniques because of the fact that silica acts preferentially in inhibiting the passage through it of certain impurities but not of others.

   For more details on the use of these techniques the reader is urged to consult the literature.[41]

   7.7d. Outdiffusion.   A method of applying diffusion which so far has had little impact upon the industrial technology but which may be useful is that of outdiffusion.[42-44]   Figure 7.17 illustrates the basic principles.   Using a wafer which is

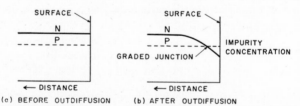

FIG. 7.17. Impurity profiles before and after outdiffusion.   The acceptor is assumed to have much smaller diffusion coefficient than the donor.

N type by reason of the excess of a rapidly diffusing donor impurity over a slowly diffusing acceptor impurity, then heating of such a sample in a vacuum for appreciable periods of time will create a thin P-type skin on the surface.

   Outdiffusion is specified in terms of (1) the surface evaporation velocity K of the particular impurity and (2) the diffusion coefficient.   Evaporation velocities K of the order of 10^{-8} cm/sec are found.

   Because of the small concentration gradients existing inside the semiconductor surface, the PN junctions formed by outdiffusion are highly graded in comparison with PN junctions formed at the same depth by indiffusion.   Halpern and Rediker report junctions at a depth of 1 to 2 microns, which are made by diffusing antimony out of antimony-indium doped germanium heated for 4 hr at 600°C. The built-in field associated with this grading makes diodes made upon these junctions especially well suited for high-speed switching. Switching times of the order 20 millimicroseconds are found.

By combining indiffusion with outdiffusion, Halpern and Rediker have been able to make 200-mc transistors.

Although the outdiffusion process seems to have great possibilities for extremely fine control of junction depth, little has been done with it in industrial device development.

7.7e. Grown-diffused Junctions. We begin here a short series of discussions of the combination of diffusion with other standard techniques of junction formation. The grown-diffused junction process, first discussed by Statz,[45] is illustrated in Fig. 7.18,

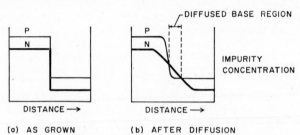

(a) AS GROWN   (b) AFTER DIFFUSION

FIG. 7.18. Impurity profiles for grown-diffused transistors.

where we see the impurity distributions of an N and a P impurity incorporated into a grown crystal. The impurity profiles are adjusted so that on subsequent diffusion after the growth of the crystal an N-type region is formed between the two P regions (for germanium), a thin P region for silicon.

The grown-diffusion process has certain advantages over double-doped transistor junctions. It has been used to some extent for silicon transistors.[46] On the other hand it also has many of the disadvantages of other grown junctions, such as lack of flexibility in the characteristics obtained and poor economy of material, since few junctions capable of transistor formation can be made by the method.

7.7f. Diffused Meltback. Figure 7.19 shows the impurity profiles for the diffused-meltback method. The principles used are similar to those for the grown-diffused

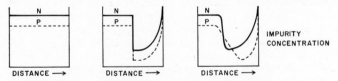

(a) BEFORE MELTBACK   (b) AFTER MELTBACK   (c) AFTER DIFFUSION

FIG. 7.19. Impurity profiles for diffused-meltback process.

method, but the meltback process is used for the formation of the emitter-base junction, the diffusion process then forming the base-collector junction.

Lesk and Gonzalez,[47] who have developed the diffused-meltback method, have found that the requirements of the technique do not allow making the proper combination of characteristics, namely, highly doped emitter, moderately doped base, and lightly doped collector. They found, however, that such a desired combination of characteristics could be obtained by using three impurities, namely, two acceptors and one donor, rather than the two ordinarily used.

Silicon NPN transistors of good quality as well as PNP germanium transistors have been made by the diffused-meltback method.[48] The technique appears well suited for high-frequency transistors.

Unlike the grown-diffused method, the meltback technique uses small rods approximately 3 mm long by 30 mil square cross section. Thus a large number of units can be made with small amounts of material.

7.7g. Alloy-diffusion Methods. When the diffusion process in the semiconductor bulk proceeds from an alloy or from the regrown region formed underneath an alloy contact, we have an alloy-diffused contact. Such contacts have been used for a variety of purposes, including both single- and double-diffused zones, for high-frequency and power transistors. In a sense the method differs only slightly from the grown-diffused and the diffused-meltback. Since the primary requirement is to build into the regrown region the desired concentrations of donor and acceptors, the diffusion steps are very similar. This is sometimes called "postalloy diffusion."

Figure 7.20 shows schematically the construction and impurity concentrations in a transistor structure formed by diffusing a single impurity from the alloy, which acts as the emitter, into the bulk. Thus the diffused zone acts as the base region. In most alloy-diffused devices the alloy region remains and is used for forming contacts.

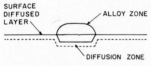

FIG. 7.20. Diffusion from alloy region.

In the work of Navon and de Beurs, with silicon alloy-diffused transistors, a slightly different method of carrying out the alloy-diffusion process was used. In this case both the emitter and the base were formed by diffusion. The alloy contact was applied in the initial phase of the program primarily to put the N and P impurities into the silicon.

After the regrown region was formed, the alloy region was etched away and a diffusion cycle was carried out. The formation of the base region by diffusion proceeds in the same way as in the simple form.

7.8. Natural and Artificial Surface Junctions. Historically, surface junctions have played an important role in semiconductor technology. Germanium high-voltage diodes were long made by making pressure contacts to N-type crystals.[52] These were shown by Bardeen to be PN-junction devices, arising from a very thin P layer on the N-type base.[53] Although Bardeen postulated "surface states" as the source of the junction, similar layers can also be produced by diffusion of an impurity into the surface or by evaporation of an impurity away from the surface.

Most commercial point-contact diodes have been subjected to an electrical pulsing treatment called "forming." The power dissipated at the point contact during this treatment in most cases is sufficient to produce a junction more or less deep in the material—either by fusion and alloying of the impurities in or on the actual material of the whisker or by diffusion of a component of the whisker into the crystal.

An interesting application of surface junctions is in the "surface-barrier" transistor.[54] In the making of this device, plated contacts are made by "jet-plating," after the wafer has been etched to a very small thickness by electrolytic "jet-etching." It appears that the plating is for contact only and does not enter into the formation of the junction, since a wide variety of metals give similar results, including indium, tin, zinc, and cadmium, which are not all acceptors. Tin, in particular, has no direct electrical activity in germanium.

Unfortunately, instability of "surface-barrier" transistors has led to their replacement by "microalloy" types.

Preparation of Surface for Junction Work. The nature of the states responsible for the P layer on N-type germanium is not yet clear. It may be due to adsorbed ions, structure imperfections, oxide layers, etc. Regardless of the source, these states absorb electrons from the interior of the semiconductor to produce the energy-band picture of Fig. 7.21.   The curvature of the energy bands results from the space charge of the ions left behind by the electrons absorbed at the surface.   The depth of the P layer and the distribution of conductivity in the P layer are determined by the magnitude and variation with distance from the surface of the impurity (donor) concentration, as well as the surface conditions.

Although the P layer may have a high density of carriers, it may also be extremely thin (10^{-6} cm), and thus the resistance along the surface may be quite high, high enough to prevent short-circuiting the PN junction itself.   Also, the mobility for motion along the surface may be smaller than in the bulk because of scattering from the surface imperfections.

Etched surfaces show the most pronounced rectification, although freshly cleaved surfaces are also quite effective.   Polished and ground surfaces, however, are very poor in rectification, indicating that the poor structure nullifies the strong P-type character of distorted layers, through poor lifetime.

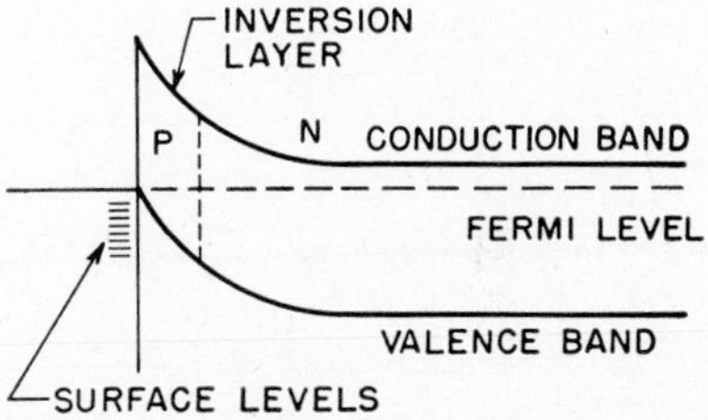

Similar effects are observed with silicon, except that on silicon the surface states appear to have donor (hole-trapping) character; hence, for practical rectifiers, P-type silicon is used.   In both silicon and germanium, the nature of the surface states and the type of conducting layer appear to be modified in the presence of moisture, electrolytic contamination, or active atmospheres such as oxygen, ozone, or ionized gases.

Fig. 7.21. Surface inversion layer on N-type germanium.

Grain-boundary Junctions.   Just as the surface of germanium tends to be P type, possibly because of the disorder present, so also grain boundaries tend to be P type, so that N-type germanium containing a grain boundary may also have a P-type layer sandwiched between the N-type regions.

Such a structure can be used for preparation of NPN transistors.   The P layer formed is extremely thin (1 micron), so that in some ways the resulting characteristics are good.   Unfortunately, the P region, being a region of disorder, is also a region of high carrier recombination, and this seriously limits the alpha of the transistor to values that are too low for most commercial transistors today.

A topic related to grain-boundary junctions is that of junctions produced by plastic deformation.   Treuting[55] has shown that junctions formed by use of either compressive or tensile deformation can be used for making devices.   Graded junctions are produced by a gradual change, step junctions by a sharp change in the deformation.

A wide variety of devices has now been produced by use of dislocations including grain boundaries in various forms.[56,57]   None of these has become commercially significant at the present writing.

7.8a. "Welded" and "Formed" Whisker Contacts.   Welded and formed whisker contacts are important ones in semiconductor technology, although they are also perhaps the most complicated and least understood ones being made.   They probably involve the properties of surface junctions, alloy contacts, and diffused junctions and probably also the effects of impurities (copper, platinum) possessing deep states and therefore permitting occurrence of trapping phenomena.   Such effects may be involved, for example, in the high-alpha values (2 to 10) commonly associated with the point-contact transistor.

Figure 7.22 shows the probable structure of a formed phosphor-bronze contact such as is used for the collector of point-contact transistors.   Results obtained are similar, although perhaps not identical, when forming is carried out by direct currents, a-c discharges, or capacitor discharges.   Under the influence of the heat, a tiny region of doped germanium containing an excess of phosphorus is formed under the point contact. This is highly doped N-type germanium. Beyond this is a second PN-junction region formed by the diffusion of copper from the bronze whisker. Below this is the undisturbed high resistivity in N-type material.

Such a structure forms a PN hook, which has the ability to trap holes in the middle P region, and allows a considerable number of electrons to pass through the region for each hole which enters the P region. The high alphas may also be accounted for if electron traps are formed in the collector region.

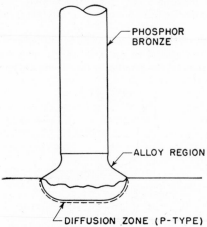

FIG. 7.22. Typical "welded" or "formed" contact-transistor collector point.

7.9. Pressure-welded Junctions. Nowhere in the present discussion has it been suggested that an acceptable junction could be made by putting two pieces of germanium in contact, the one N and the other P type. Although rectifying characteristics may be obtained in this way, there is generally a high resistance in both directions because of the surface barriers, and surface recombination has an especially bad effect. Thus such contact junctions suffer from the same defects as the grain-boundary junctions previously discussed. It appears definitely advisable that a single crystal be present at the junction.

A modification of the simple pressure method is the pressure-welded technique of Shulman and Van Winkle,[58] who pushed two pieces of germanium into contact at very high temperatures, so close to the melting point that under the influence of the pressure actual melting and welding of the two pieces took place. Little further has been done with this method. Shulman and Van Winkle observed acceptable rectification, with reverse resistances of the order of 50,000 ohms and a peak inverse of 100 volts.

Since the volume of germanium decreases on melting, addition of pressure lowers the melting point. According to the Clausius-Clapeyron equation, 1,000 kg/cm² is sufficient to lower the melting point about 2°C. Pressures of this order of magnitude were obtained by making the one surface optically flat, the other rough. When loads of 1 to 2 kg were applied to the contact, localized melting took place and the two pieces became bonded.

Although there was evidence in the characteristics of high recombination in the imperfect welded region, this is not too serious for some applications. In particular, higher reverse currents may be tolerated to obtain a minimum storage effect for high-frequency work.

7.10. Ion- and Nuclear-bombardment Junctions. Among the first large-area rectifying junctions were those produced at Purdue University[59] by bombardment of N-type germanium surfaces with alpha particles and deuterons. These projectiles create a region of disorder close to the surface, depending upon their range. If enough particles are used so that uniform regions of disorder are produced, acceptable junctions can be made. However, since the disordered region is also a region of very high recombination, the characteristics are inferior to those of junctions in good single-crystal material. For this reason, but little further work has been done with these junctions.

A similar technique is that of ion bombardment developed by J. W. Moyer.[60] In this method, ions of, say, a donor element such as arsenic are accelerated to a voltage of perhaps 50 kv and allowed to impinge upon a germanium surface.   They penetrate perhaps 500 Å, sufficient to create a junction as in the case of diffused junctions.   They also create a disordered region, and the surface layer may initially have P-type characteristics.   Heat-treatment at 450°C (too low a temperature to permit much diffusion) converts the surface layer to N type.   It is possible that this heat-treatment allows the donor ions to find sites in the lattice where they become electrically active; this would involve a diffusion for only perhaps a few lattice spacings at the most.

Both the foregoing techniques are possible ones where good characteristics are not paramount and where ability to control the location and area of the junction is important.

7.11. Junctions Formed by Vapor Deposition.   Several vapor growth processes have been developed for the formation of junctions in both silicon and germanium devices. These processes involve reduction or disproportionation reactions of gaseous halides at elevated temperature on a substrate crystal, resulting in epitaxial growth of suitably doped crystal layers.

In the case of silicon, Allegretti and Shambert[61] have investigated a variety of reaction systems having the common feature that a hot single-crystal surface is exposed to a gas atmosphere which, by suitable interaction, produces silicon atoms on the surface.   The generalized reaction may be represented as

$$SiH_4 - xY_x + \frac{x}{2} H_2 \rightleftharpoons Si + HY + \frac{4 - x}{2} H$$

where Y is Cl, Br, I and x varies from zero to 4.   Reaction temperatures from 700 to 1300°C have been used successfully, depending on the silicon compound used. Growth rates vary from 0.25 to 5.3 microns/min, the rate generally increasing with substrate temperature and with silicon-compound concentration.   The substrate silicon may be in the form of filaments, rods, or wafers.   The condition of the initial substrate surface is an important variable in the success of the growth process.   The (111) oriented substrate produced the highest yield of usable single-crystal areas. This orientation was used predominantly in the work reported by Allegretti et al. of the formation of electrically active layers and junctions.   Silicon layers with P-type doping and resistivities as low as 0.004 ohm-cm were obtained by the addition of BCl_3 into the reaction system in suitably low concentrations, with no adverse effect on single-crystal growth.   The N-type doping was accomplished satisfactorily by the addition of known concentrations of arsenic or phosphorus halides to gaseous reactants.   Contiguous N- or P-type layers of desired thickness and carrier concentration were obtained by alternating the type and concentration of doping agent during the growth process for known periods of time.

Epitaxial growth of both silicon and germanium crystal layers with N- or P-type doping has been reported by Theurer and Christensen,[62] by means of hydrogen reduction of either $SiCl_4$ or $GeCl_4$.   Silicon growth was achieved by first treating the substrate surface at 1295°C by means of induction heating on a graphite or silicon support for $\frac{1}{2}$ hr in dry hydrogen to remove surface oxide.   For film deposition, substrate treatment in hydrogen containing 2 mole per cent $SiCl_4$ at a flow rate of 1 liter/min for 5 min at 1270°C resulted in an epitaxial layer 6 to 8 microns thick. At temperatures below 1100 to 1200°C, the crystal perfection of the deposit diminished, and at lower temperatures the deposit was no longer epitaxial.   Deposits were made on a (111) substrate surface.   The film thickness is usually controlled by reagent concentration or by substrate temperature.   A minimal thermal gradient across the wafer is essential in order to obtain a uniform crystal growth.   In the case of germanium, the substrate surface pretreatment was carried out at 830°C, again with hydrogen.   Subsequent treatment in hydrogen containing 0.2 mole per cent

$GeCl_4$ with a hydrogen flow of 1 liter/min for 10 min resulted in a film of about 5 microns thick.   In the case of silicon, doping was achieved by the addition of PCl_3 or BCl_3 to the $SiCl_4$ used for reduction.

The epitaxial growth of silicon and germanium crystal layers can also be carried out by means of the disproportionation of their iodides on crystal seeds at temperatures considerably below the melting point of the elements.   The general reaction may be represented as $2MI_2 \rightleftharpoons MI_4 + M\downarrow$; thus, by means of suitable thermal gradients within a reaction system, source material may be transported as the diiodide to a seed wafer where disproportionation occurs and epitaxial growth proceeds.

In the case of germanium, the properties of layers produced by this process have been given by Dunlap, Ruth, and Marinace.[63]   Marinace[64] has subsequently described a closed-tube process whereby source and seed germanium are contained within a sealed quartz tube, together with a quantity of iodine.   The source germanium is maintained at 550°C while the substrate is at 300°C.   The rate of epitaxial growth is a function of initial iodine concentration, an I_2 concentration of 5 mg/cm^3 giving $\sim$10 microns/hr.   The growth rate also depends upon crystal orientation, with the (110) surface giving the best rate and the most uniform deposit.

Doped deposits can be produced by using previously doped germanium as the source material or by adding the elemental impurity together with intrinsic germanium as the source.   A wide range of doping levels is achieved for both N- and P-type materials.   PN junctions are produced by placing the seed crystals in the center of a quartz reaction tube with oppositely doped sources at either end.   When the temperature profile is shifted, contiguous conductivity types of crystal layers are produced at will.   The impurity concentration can be controlled by the doping level of the germanium sources.

An iodide disproportionation process for silicon has been described by Wajda et al.[65] The reagents and substrate are contained within a sealed quartz tube.   The source silicon is maintained at about 1000°.   The substrate temperatures can range to very low values for simple silicon transport, but to achieve uniform crystalline growth, the substrates should be slightly below the effective disproportionation temperature of SiI_2, or about 900°C.   The quantity of iodine in the reaction tube must be sufficient to create a total pressure in excess of the critical disproportionation pressure, which in turn is temperature dependent.   Using the iodide disproportionation process, Glang and Kippenhan[66] have extended Wajda's process by incorporating doping elements into the deposited crystal layers in order to form large-area PN junctions. This can be done by (1) loading a small, weighed quantity of the desired impurity element together with high-purity silicon into the source zone or (2) using as source material silicon master alloys with known impurity concentrations.

7.11a. Junctions Formed by Vacuum Evaporation.   The vacuum evaporation of single-crystal thin films of silicon on a silicon substrate crystal has been reported by Hale and James.[67]   The evaporation was carried out at 10^{-5} to 10^{-6} mm Hg pressure. The single-crystal substrates were etched, polished, ultrasonically cleaned, and ion bombarded at 400 volts with 10 microns of argon for $2\frac{1}{2}$ hr.   The source material was maintained at 1650°C.   The substrates were kept at approximately 1100°C. Substrate temperatures below 1000° gave polycrystalline deposits.   The source-to-substrate distance was 2 cm with a growth rate of about $\frac{1}{2}$ micron/min.   For deposits less than 10 microns in thickness, the deposit surfaces were usually as smooth as the initial substrate.   The imperfection density of the deposit was dependent upon growth and surface conditions.   P-type doping was accomplished by the use of a doped silicon source using a single boat.   For N-type doping, a source of pure silicon was contained in one boat while a second boat contained pure antimony.   Considering the deposition rate obtained by this method and the substrate temperature required, impurity diffusion becomes a significant problem.   However, junctions were obtained which were suitable for device use.

7.12. Junctions in Heavily Doped Material. The recent development of the Esaki tunnel diode,[68] presaging as it does an extremely active future for this device resulting from its high-frequency capabilities, requires attention to a topic not specifically covered. This is the problem of preparing junctions both sides of which are extremely heavily doped. For Esaki tunnel diodes it appears that the present limitations depend to some extent on the limits of doping by present techniques.

At the present writing, little has been published on the Esaki tunnel diode and nothing at all on the methods of greatest promise in preparing it. Thus the present review will consist mostly of suggestions and little of direct experimental results.

In order to observe the tunneling effect in PN junctions, the material on both sides of the junction must be degenerate; that is, the carriers become packed so densely in the material that they cannot any longer be regarded as classical particles obeying Maxwell statistics but rather as particles obeying Fermi (quantum) statistics. Practically speaking, the most striking effect of this increased concentration is a change in temperature dependence of resistivity. Degenerate material is more nearly metallic in its behavior and shows, usually, a small positive temperature coefficient of resistance.

Degeneracy is not a state that is clearly defined, and the transition takes place over wide ranges of temperature and carrier concentration. It also depends markedly upon the effective mass of the carriers; such substances as indium antimonide containing carriers of low effective mass become degenerate at lower carrier concentrations than others, such as germanium or silicon. At room temperature, germanium tends to become degenerate when the carrier concentration exceeds 10^{17}.

In order to produce good junctions for germanium Esaki tunnel diodes, material doped to at least 10^{19} carriers/cu cm must be prepared. The presence of this concentration of carriers, however, does not necessarily ensure that satisfactory degenerate junctions can be made. For example, gallium-doped germanium with a concentration of 10^{20} carriers/cu cm exhibits very poor degenerate junctions when alloyed with tin-arsenic dots.

The base material intended for good degenerate junctions should preferably be single-crystal material doped to degeneracy. Polycrystalline-base material sometimes yields good degenerate junctions but usually shows poor reproducibility. The techniques for preparation of base material vary somewhat depending upon the volatility of the impurity. In particular, phosphorus and arsenic, when properly used, have been found to be the most satisfactory doping agents for N-type base material. Antimony appears to have too low a limit of solid solubility to be particularly useful. Gallium, boron, and aluminum are satisfactory impurities for P-type base material.

We shall now discuss two methods which have been successfully used for the preparation of degenerately doped germanium crystals.[69]

Crystal Pulling. Certain modifications of the usual crystal-pulling technique are necessary, although the normal considerations regarding temperature gradients apply. In order to achieve a high level of doping, growing conditions must be adjusted to give the optimum segregation coefficient. In addition, care must be exercised that inclusions of the elemental impurity do not become incorporated in the crystals. In the case of germanium, pull rates of 1 in./hr or less and rotation rates of 30 to 50 rpm have been found necessary to prevent the formation of inclusions. For the preparation of arsenic- and phosphorus doped crystals, the impurity is usually added as an alloy of germanium previously prepared in an evacuated sealed system. Even though these impurities are normally considered quite volatile, their volatility in the liquid alloy at its melting point is sufficiently low that crystals doped to 4×10^{19} impurities/cu cm can be grown without pressurizing the crystal pulling. On the other hand, without control of the partial pressure of impurity vapor over the melt, it is not possible to grow uniformly doped crystals. Therefore, in order to pull uniformly doped crystals, it is better to use a pressurized system with a controlled impurity vapor partial pressure which maintains the liquid composition constant. Since the doping level desired is so close to the limit of solid solubility, it is very difficult to do this by simply programming temperature and pull rate. Under these conditions, any slight change in growth conditions may cause the limit of solid solubility to be exceeded. In spite of these difficulties, it turns out to be somewhat easier to get uniform highly doped crystals by a pulling technique than by a zone-leveling technique in which the maintenance of the constant impurity concentration in the molten zone is achieved by regulating the partial pressure of the impurity vapor in the sealed apparatus.

Diffusion. Impurities normally used as doping elements for degenerately doped material generally show a higher solid solubility at some temperature below the melting point of the pure germanium. Therefore, a greater concentration of impurity can be incorporated into the material by diffusion at the temperature of maximum solid solubility. Diffusion of volatile impurities can be carried out in a furnace with two separately controlled temperature zones, one zone being maintained at the temperature of maximum solid solubility and the second zone at a somewhat lower temperature which is used to control the partial pressure of the impurity vapor in the sealed system. This method of doping is much slower than crystal pulling, and for maximum efficiency the semiconductor should be prepared in as thin slices as possible. Diffusion should proceed long enough to ensure that the doping is quite uniform throughout the wafer thickness; otherwise the control of the penetration of the alloy during junction formation becomes quite critical. One marked advantage of diffused-base material over melt-grown crystal-base material is that the perfection of the former can be much greater, since all the modern techniques for producing high-quality crystals can be used in its preparation.

The principal method for the fabrication of the degenerate junction necessary for an Esaki tunnel diode is to alloy a small contact into a piece of degenerately doped base material. The alloy dot must contain sufficient material of the opposite impurity type to overdope the base material after recrystallization. In order to minimize series resistance, the wafers should remain as thin as possible. In practice, good junctions are usually achieved in wafer thicknesses of 2 mils or less. In order to get proper tunneling action, the depletion layer of such a junction should be approximately 100 Å or less in thickness. This necessitates a technique which will prevent any appreciable postalloy diffusion. It is also advantageous to use a technique which will minimize the depth of penetration of the alloy. It has been found that adjusting the composition of the alloy dot in such a manner that its melting point is lowered will alloy the alloying process to proceed at a lower temperature where the rate of solution of the base material is lower. This, with a given time cycle, permits a better control of the small depth of penetration referred to above. The total time cycle itself must be fast enough to prevent appreciable postalloy diffusion beyond the recrystallized region. At the present time there is much yet to be learned about the metallurgical structure of heavily doped PN junctions.

7.13. Junctions in Compound Semiconductors. Although compound semiconductors of the III-V type (gallium arsenide is typical) have been enthusiastically studied as possible transistor materials since 1952, little progress has been achieved in development of a commercial PN-junction device using these materials. The closest approach is in the development of PN-junction photovoltaic detectors of indium antimonide. These detectors have been made by various methods.[70] Gallium arsenide point-contact diodes containing no deliberately fabricated junctions are acquiring increasing interest for parametric diodes. These devices probably contain surface-type natural junctions such as those discussed in Sec. 7.8.

All the standard techniques for the preparation of junctions in the elements such as germanium and silicon have been applied to the preparation of junctions in the compounds. In addition, new methods are also available, since lack of stoichiometry in the junctions also has electrical effects.   Thus control of the vapor pressure of phosphorus or arsenic during the preparation of gallium phosphide appears to be a possible means of junction formation.

The technology of PN junctions in compound semiconductors has been reviewed by Jenny.[71]   He has found that zinc alloying upon gallium arsenide has produced good junctions.   In this process he has also used the phenomenon of surface diffusion to spread the junction over large areas, creating very thin base regions for transistor action and simplifying the problem of making base contacts.

Jenny has also carried out a number of studies using diffusion not only to produce the PN junctions needed for transistor action but also to change the band gap in the emitter so as to increase emitter efficiency.   Since gallium phosphide, for example, has a higher band gap than gallium arsenide, diffusion of phosphorus into the arsenide creates just the effect that is desired.   Diffusion of sulfur simultaneously makes possible the incorporation of the emitter-base PN junction.

Junction rectifiers made by alloying zinc into aluminum antimonide have been discussed by Henkel.[72]   The AlSb wafer was heated to 900°C with a 0.1-mm-thick foil of pure aluminum on one side for the ohmic contact, a 0.1-mm-thick foil of aluminum containing 2 per cent zinc on the other surface for forming the PN junction. Characteristics of such rectifiers are not such that they form promising competition for silicon or germanium rectifiers at the present state of the art.

7.14. Multiple-junction Structures.   PN hooks are double junctions with floating inversion layers that have interesting properties for making high-current-gain transistors and photocells (see Sec. 4, page 4-17).   They can be made by any of the techniques described so far or by a combination of these methods.   Figure 7.23 shows formulations of such devices appropriate to the various methods.   These diagrams

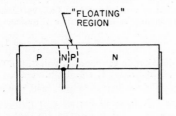

(a) GROWN HOOK TRANSISTOR.

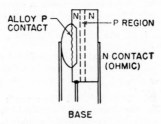

(b) P-N HOOK TRANSISTOR USING JUNCTION EMITTER AND RATE GROWN P REGION.

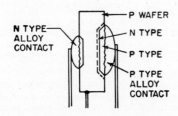

(c) P-N HOOK WITH ALLOY JUNCTION EMITTER AND COLLECTOR, PLUS HOOK CREATED BY DIFFUSION FROM COLLECTOR.

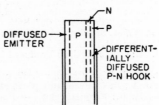

(d) P-N HOOK TRANSISTOR WITH DIFFERENTIALLY DIFFUSED COLLECTOR AND HOOK, PLUS DIFFUSED EMITTER.

Fig. 7.23. Multijunction devices.

also illustrate methods of making complex structures by a single method or a combination of previously discussed methods.

In the first of these, the alternating P and N regions are obtained by successive doping. In the second, a wafer is used in which a thin P region has been incorporated by doping during growth or by rate growing. The emitter and collector junctions are obtained by the alloy techniques.

Figure 7.23c shows that the emitter and collector are both alloy junctions, but the hook is obtained by incorporating in the collector contact an element which diffuses relatively rapidly compared with the primary contact material and is of opposite type.

In Fig. 7.23d another modification is shown. This consists of an ohmic contact, a collector junction and hook produced by differential diffusion of two different impurities, and a diffused junction plus ohmic contact for the emitter.

The process of differential diffusion has been observed experimentally to occur, although it has been little used for device work. It involves the use of an impurity of low solubility and high diffusion and another of opposite type, of high solubility and small diffusion. If these are deposited on the surface, for example, as plated or evaporated layers, and the wafer is heated, the penetrations and impurity contents can be proportioned so as to form a double junction.

With the further development of transistor technology, it is probable that such specialized techniques will be used more widely than at present. Clearly, there are many other modifications and combinations of the available methods than can be used for special conditions and requirements.

REFERENCES

1. "Transistor Technology," in 3 volumes, D. Van Nostrand Company, Inc., Princeton, N.J., 1958. This is essentially a compilation of reprints of Bell Laboratories papers published between 1952 and 1957. It also contains a large number of articles written especially for the series.
2. Thurmond, C. D.: Impurity Control and Junction Formation, in reference 1, vol. 3, pp. 3–31.
3. Fuller, C. S.: Formation of Junctions by Diffusion, in reference 1, vol. 3, pp. 64–85.
4. Frosch, C. J.: Silicon Diffusion Technology, in reference 1, vol. 3, pp. 90–99.
5. Smits, F. M.: Formation of Junction Structures by Solid-state Diffusion, *Proc. IRE*, vol. 46, pp. 1049–1061, 1958.
6. Dacey, G. C., and C. D. Thurmond: P-N Junctions in Silicon and Germanium—Principles, Metallurgy, and Applications, *Met. Rev.*, vol. 2, pp. 157–193, 1957.
7. Teal, G. K., M. Sparks, and E. Buehler: Growth of Germanium Single Crystals Containing P-N Junctions, *Phys. Rev.*, vol. 81, p. 637, 1951.
8. Burton, J. A.: Impurity Centers in Ge and Si, *Physica*, vol. 20, pp. 834–854, 1954.
9. Dunlap, W. C.: Impurities in Germanium, in "Progress in Semiconductors," vol. 2, pp. 167–209, Heywood and Co., London, 1957.
10. Kohn, W.: Solid State Physics, in "Shallow Impurity States in Silicon and Germanium," vol. 5, Academic Press, Inc., New York, 1957.
11. Moore, A. R.: The Preparation of Single and Multiple P-N Junctions in Single Crystals of Germanium, "Transistors I," RCA Laboratories, Princeton, N.J., 1956.
12. Shockley, W., M. Sparks, and G. K. Teal: P-N Junction Transistors, *Phys. Rev.*, vol. 83, pp. 151–162, 1951.
13. Hall, R. N.: P-N Junctions Produced by Rate Growth Variation, *Phys. Rev.*, vol. 88, p. 139, 1952.
14. Hall, R. N.: *J. Phys. Chem.*, vol. 57, p. 836, 1953.
15. Burton, J. A., R. C. Prim, and W. P. Slichter: *J. Chem. Phys.*, vol. 21, p. 1987, 1953.
16. Bridgers, H. E.: Formation of p-n Junctions in Semiconductors by the Variation of Crystal Growth Parameters, in reference 1, vol. 3, pp. 32–43, reprinted from *J. Appl. Phys.*, vol. 27, p. 746, 1956.
17. Tanenbaum, M., L. B. Valdes, E. Buehler, and N. B. Hannay: *J. Appl. Phys.*, vol. 26, p. 686, 1955.
18. Pfann, W. G.: Redistribution of Solutes by Formation and Solidification of a Molten Zone, in reference 1, vol. 3, pp. 43–51, reprinted from *J. Metals*, vol. 6, p. 294, 1954.
19. Lehovec, K., and E. Belmont: *J. Appl. Phys.*, vol. 24, p. 1482, 1953.

20. Hall, R. N.: "Melt-back Transistors," presented at AIEE-IRE Semiconductor Device Research Conference, Philadelphia, Pa., June, 1955.

21. Pankove, J. I.: "Transistors I," p. 82, RCA Laboratories, Princeton, N.J., 1956.

22. Hall, R. N., and W. C. Dunlap, Jr.: P-N Junctions made by Impurity Diffusion, *Phys. Rev.*, vol. 80, p. 467, 1950.

23. Saby, J. S., and W. C. Dunlap, Jr.: Impurity Diffusion and Space Charge Layers, in "Fused-impurity" P-N Junctions, *Phys. Rev.*, vol. 90, pp. 630–632, 1953.

24. English, A. C.: IRE-AIEE Conference on Electron Devices, Durham, N.H., June, 1951.

25. Jenny, D. A.: A Germanium N-P-N Alloy Junction Transistor, *Proc. IRE*, vol. 41, pp. 1728–1734, 1953.

26. Burcham, N. P., L. E. Miller, T. R. Robillard, N. C. Vanderwal, and R. W. Westberg: Germanium Alloy Junction Transistors, in reference 1, vol. 3, p. 181.

27. Rittmann, A. D., G. C. Messenger, R. A. Williams, and E. Zimmerman: Microalloy Transistor, *IRE Trans. on Electron Devices*, vol. ED-5, pp. 49–54, 1958.

28. Armstrong, L. D.: P-N Junctions by Impurity Introduction through an Intermediate Metal Layer, *Proc. IRE*, vol. 40, pp. 1341–1342, 1952.

29. Pfann, W. G.: Temperature-gradient Zone-melting, *J. Metals*, vol. 7, p. 961, 1955.

30. Goldey, J. M.: Evaporation and Alloying to Silicon, in "Transistor Technology," vol. 3, pp. 231–244.

31. Pearson, G. L., and B. Sawyer: Silicon P-N Junction Alloy Diodes, in reference 1, vol. 3, pp. 220–229, reprinted from *Proc. IRE*, vol. 40, November, 1952.

32. Dunlap, W. C.: Measurement of Diffusion in Germanium by Means of P-N Junctions, *Phys. Rev.*, vol. 86, p. 615A, 1952.

33. Dunlap, W. C.: Diffusion of Impurities in Germanium, *Phys. Rev.*, vol. 94, p. 1531, 1954.

34. Pearson, G. L., and C. S. Fuller: Silicon P-N Junction Power Rectifiers and Lightning Protectors, *Proc. IRE*, vol. 42, p. 760, 1954.

35. Lee, C. A.: A High-frequency Diffused-base Germanium Transistor, *Bell System Tech. J.*, vol. 35, p. 23, 1956.

36. Prince, M. B.: Diffused P-N Junction Silicon Rectifiers, in "Transistor Technology," vol. 3, pp. 245–265, reprinted from *Bell System Tech. J.*, vol. 35, May, 1956.

37. Aldrich, R. W., R. H. Lanzl, D. E. Maxwell, J. O. Percival, and M. Waldner: An 85 Watt Dissipation Silicon Power Transistor, *IRE Trans. on Electron Devices*, vol. ED-5, pp. 211–214, 1958.

38. Barrer, R. M.: "Diffusion in and through Solids," Cambridge University Press, New York, 1950.

39. Saby, J. S., and W. C. Dunlap, Jr.: Impurity Diffusion and Space Charge Layers, in "Fused-impurity" P-N Junctions, *Phys. Rev.*, vol. 90, pp. 630–632, 1953.

40. Tanenbaum, M., and D. E. Thomas: Diffused Emitter and Base Silicon Transistors, in reference 1, vol. 3, pp. 287–305, reprinted from *Bell System Tech. J.*, vol. 35, January, 1956.

41. Frosch, C. J., and L. Derick: Surface Protection and Oxide Masking during Diffusion in Silicon, *J. Electrochem. Soc.*, vol. 104, pp. 547–552, 1957.

42. Smits, F. M., and R. C. Miller: Rate Limitation at the Surface for Impurity Diffusion in Semiconductors, *Phys. Rev.*, vol. 104, pp. 1242–1245, 1956.

43. Lehovec, K., K. Schoeni, and R. Zuleeg: Evaporation of Impurities from Semiconductors, *J. Appl. Phys.*, vol. 28, pp. 420–423, 1957.

44. Halpern, J., and R. H. Rediker: Outdiffusion as a Technique for the Production of Diodes and Transistors, *Proc. IRE*, vol. 46, pp. 1068–1076, 1958.

45. Statz, H.: Paper presented at AIEE-IRE Semiconductor Device Research Conference, Philadelphia, Pa., June, 1955; U.S. Patent 2,899,343.

46. Cornelison, B., and W. A. Adcock: Transistors by the Grown-diffused Technique, *IRE WESCON Conv. Record*, pt. 3, pp. 22–27, 1957.

47. Lesk, I. A., and R. E. Gonzalez: Germanium and Silicon Transistor Structures by the Diffused-meltback Process Employing Two or Three Impurities, *IRE Trans. on Electron Devices*, vol. ED-5, pp. 121–126, June, 1958.

48. Phillips, A. B., and A. M. Intrator: A New High-frequency npn Silicon Transistor, *IRE Natl. Conv. Record*, pt. 3, pp. 3–13, 1957.

49. Beales, J. R. A.: Alloy-Diffusion, a Process for Making Diffused-base Junction Transistors, *Proc. Phys. Soc. (London)*, ser. B, vol. 70, pp. 1087–1089, 1957.

50. Jochems, P. J. W., O. W. Memellinck, and L. J. Tummers: Construction and Electrical Properties of a Germanium Alloy-diffused Transistor, *Proc. IRE*, vol. 46, pp. 1161–1165, 1958.

51. Navon, D., and P. deBeurs: An Alloy-diffused Silicon High Current Transistor with Fast Switching Possibilities, *IRE Trans. on Electron Devices*, vol. ED-6, pp. 169–173, April, 1959.

52. Benzer, S.: High Inverse Voltage Germanium Rectifiers, *J. Appl. Phys.*, vol. 20, pp. 804–815, 1949.
53. Bardeen, J.: Surface States and Rectification at a Metal-to-Semiconductor Contact, *Phys. Rev.*, vol. 71, pp. 717–727, 1947.
54. Bradley, W. E.: The Surface Barrier Transistor. Part I. Principles of the Surface Barrier Transistor, *Proc. IRE*, vol. 41, pp. 1702–1706, 1953.
55. Treuting, R. G.: U.S. Patent 2,840,495, issued June 24, 1958.
56. Matare, H. F.: Dislocation Planes in Semiconductors, *J. Appl. Phys.*, vol. 30, p. 581, 1959.
57. Sosnowski, L.: Electronic Processes at Grain Boundaries, *J. Phys. Chem. Solids*, vol. 8, pp. 142–146, January, 1959.
58. Shulman, G. C., and D. M. Van Winkle: Pressure Welded P-N Junctions in Germanium, *J. Appl. Phys.*, vol. 24, p. 224, 1953.
59. See, for example, K. Lark-Horovitz: Conductivity in Semiconductors, *Elec. Eng.*, vol. 68, pp. 1047–1056, 1949.
60. Moyer, J. W.: U.S. Patent 2,842,466.
61. Allegretti, J. E., and D. J. Shambert: "Silicon P-N Junctions for Device Applications by Direct Deposition from a Vapor Phase," AIME Boston Conference on Metallurgy of Elemental and Compound Semiconductors, 1960.
62. Theuerer, H. C., and H. Christensen: *J. Electrochem. Soc.*, vol. 107, pp. 268–269C, 1960.
63. Dunlap, W. C., R. P. Ruth, and J. C. Marinace: Properties of Vapor-deposited Germanium Layers, *Bull. Am. Phys. Soc.*, ser. II, vol. 1, no. 6, 1956. See also *J. Appl. Phys.*, vol. 31, p. 995, 1960.
64. Marinace, J. C.: Vapor Growth of Germanium in a Closed Tube, *IBM J. Research and Develop.*, vol. 4, no. 2, April, 1960.
65. Wajda, E. S., B. W. Kippenhan, and W. H. White: Epitaxial Growth of Silicon, *IBM J. Research and Develop.*, vol. 4, pp. 288–295, 1960.
66. Glang, R., and B. W. Kippenhan: Impurity Introduction during Epitaxial Growth of Silicon, *IBM J. Research and Develop.*, vol. 4, pp. 299–301, 1960.
67. Hale, A. P., and B. D. James: 1960 Electron Devices Meeting, sponsored by Professional Group on Electronic Devices, Washington, D.C., Oct. 27–28, 1960.
68. Esaki, L., and Y. Miyahara: A New Device Using the Tunneling Process in Narrow p-n Junctions, *Solid-state Electronics*, vol. 1, pp. 13–31, 1959.
69. Brock, G. E.: Private communication, IBM Research Laboratory, Poughkeepsie, N.Y.
70. Rieke, F. F., L. A. DeVaux, and A. J. Tuggolino: Single Crystal Infrared Detectors Based upon Intrinsic Absorption, *Proc. IRE*, vol. 47, pp. 1475–1481, 1959.
71. Jenny, D. A.: The Status of Transistor Research in Semiconductor Compounds, *Proc. IRE*, vol. 46, pp. 959–968, 1958.
72. Henkel, H. J.: The Production of Barrier Layers in Aluminum Antimonide by the Alloying Process, *Z. Metallk.*, vol. 50, pp. 51–53, January, 1959.

Section 8

METAL-SEMICONDUCTOR CONTACTS

J. F. WALSH[†]

Philco Corporation

8.1. Introduction. Rectification phenomena originating at the contact between a metal and a semiconductor have been observed for many years. These contacts have long been used as rectifiers and photodetectors. Metal points served as the injectors and collectors in the first transistors. Such contacts, however, found themselves playing second fiddle in transistor technology soon after methods for fabricating PN junctions were developed. This is not surprising, for while PN junctions are well understood and well behaved, metal contacts have a somewhat notorious history of being not too predictable or reproducible.

It is only in more recent years that broad-area contacts (i.e., large compared with a point) have shown any significant rectification on Ge and Si. Such contacts have by now been studied fairly extensively on these two materials. On the other hand

---

† Revised by Ruth F. Schwarz, Philco Corporation.
‡ Adapted from the original text of W. R. Sittner.

little or no information exists about the rectifying properties of large-area contacts on the host of intermetallic semiconductors now available for use.

This section will first give a brief review of the theory of such contacts in that it may aid as a guide in obtaining the desired type of contact (i.e., rectifying or ohmic) on a given material. Since the surface condition before deposition of the metal is known to be of such importance in these contacts, the theory will be followed by a section on etching. Experimental results as well as the applications for broad-area contacts on Ge and Si will then be discussed in detail. This will be followed by a section on methods of fabricating ohmic contacts, which are required for at least one of the contacts in nearly every device. Finally, point contacts and their uses will be discussed.

8.2. Theory. *8.2a. Majority-carrier Flow.* The first accepted theory of rectification was proposed in 1938 by Schottky (Mott, Davydov).† This theory postulated the existence of a space-charge region in the semiconductor adjacent to the

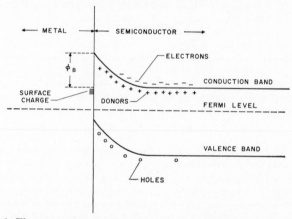

FIG. 8.1. Electron energy-level diagram of a metal-semiconductor contact.

metal which formed a barrier to electronic flow. This barrier is depicted for N-type material in Fig. 8.1. The establishment of such a barrier would be expected to occur if the work function of the metal was higher than that of the semiconductor. This would imply that as the metal and semiconductor were originally brought into close proximity, it would be easier for an electron to escape from the semiconductor to the metal than vice versa, so that the previously neutral semiconductor would soon acquire a net positive charge and the metal would acquire a corresponding net negative charge. The dipole set up by these charges would create an electric field which would enhance the escape rate of electrons from the metal and retard the escape rate of electrons from the semiconductor. When the field has become just sufficient to make the two escape rates equal, no further net transfer of charge would occur and the system would have reached thermal equilibrium. Because of the relatively low concentration of free carriers in the semiconductor, this space-charge region can extend a considerable depth into the semiconductor ($\approx 10^{-6}$ to 10^{-3} cm) whereas the charge residing in the metal will more precisely constitute a surface charge.

If a voltage is now applied across the contact in such a direction as to drive electrons from the metal to the semiconductor (i.e., the metal is negative with respect to the semiconductor), this bias will appear almost entirely across the space-charge region, since this region is very nearly depleted of electrons and thus offers a high resistance to electron flow. The bias will have the effect of reducing still further the

† For a complete historical summary, see Henisch.[1]

small number of electrons in the already depleted region as well as increasing the depth of the space charge and the height of the barrier. The escape rate of electrons from the metal to the semiconductor will be disturbed very little if at all by this bias, since the concentrations of carriers in the metal are in no way disturbed by it. On the other hand, Fermi statistics show that an increase in barrier height of only 0.1 volt at room temperature should be sufficient to reduce the density and hence the escape rate of electrons from the semiconductor to the metal to only a few per cent of its equilibrium value. For biases of this polarity above 0.1 volt the diode current should thus saturate out to the equilibrium escape rate of electrons from the metal to the semiconductor. This direction is known as the reverse direction of the diode. If the metal is made positive with respect to the semiconductor, the diode is said to be forward-biased. The space-charge region will then have a concentration of carriers which is higher than it was at equilibrium but which is still small compared with the concentration of carriers in the bulk of the semiconductor. The bias will reduce the width of the space-charge region and the height of the barrier. The rate of transfer of electrons from metal to semiconductor will again be undisturbed by the bias, while many more electrons can escape to the metal owing to the increased carrier concentration in the immediate vicinity of the contact. Rectification will thus occur as a result of the modulation of the density of electrons in the space-charge region with applied bias.

Many versions of the expected current-voltage relation of such a diode have been given over the years.[1-3] Nearly all of these can be condensed into an equation of the following form:

$$J_n = \bar{v}qN_D e^{-q(\varphi_B/kT)}(e^{qV/kT} - 1) \tag{8.1}$$

where J_n is the electron current per unit area of contact, q is the electronic charge, N_D is the concentration of impurities in the semiconductor, φ_B is the height of the barrier in the semiconductor at thermal equilibrium, k is Boltzmann's constant, T is the absolute temperature, and V is the applied voltage, which appears across the barrier. The multiplying parameter $\bar{v}$ which we let absorb the differences in the various theories has the dimensions of a velocity and in many analyses shows a mild voltage dependence. The simplest theory equates $\bar{v}$ to the mean component of thermal velocity perpendicular to the contact. The factor $(e^{qV/kT} - 1)$, which appears in nearly all rectification theories, gives a measure of how much the bias modulates the concentration of electrons in the semiconductor region immediately adjacent to the metal. Since the energy required to transfer an electron across the barrier is supplied by thermal processes, we would expect the diode characteristics to have a strong temperature dependence. The characteristic thermal energy to which electrostatic potentials are compared is kT. This corresponds to 0.025 electron volt at room temperature. Thus, according to Eq. (8.1), the ideal diode at room temperature should have a rectification ratio of about 50 at 0.1 volt and 2,500 at 0.2 volt.

The above description assumed that the work function of the metal was higher than that of the N-type semiconductor. If the work function of the metal is lower than that of the semiconductor, the net transfer of electrons in the process of establishing equilibrium should be from the metal to the semiconductor. This will result in an accumulation of electrons in the semiconductor region adjacent to the metal. The impedance of this region will thus be lower than the N-type bulk, resulting in a low-resistance contact. If an I-V characteristic is taken, the voltage will in the main appear across the bulk of the semiconductor and one will thus obtain an ohmic curve. This does not imply that the I-V characteristic of the contact itself is linear. It is most likely not linear. It is simply difficult to establish any voltage across it, since it is in series with the higher resistance bulk.

If the semiconductor is P type, the role of the work function will be reversed. If the metal has a higher work function than the semiconductor, there will be an accumulation of holes in the P-type semiconductor and a low-resistance contact will be obtained. If the work function of the metal is lower than that of the semiconductor, a depletion of holes will occur and a high-resistance rectifying contact will be obtained.

The nature and degree of rectification thus depend strongly on the work function of the metal used to make the contact. Low-work-function metals rectify best on P-type material and poorly if at all on N-type. High-work-function metals rectify best on N-type and poorly if at all on P-type material. The work functions of the various metals differ by a few volts, while according to Eq. (8.1), only a few tenths of a volt variation in φ_B will cause changes of several orders of magnitude in the impedance of a contact-to-current flow. The dramatic variations in the impedance of a diode with the work function of the metal as predicted by Eq. (8.1) have never been observed. In fact, point-contact impedances seem quite indifferent to the metal used.[4] On the other hand, studies on broad-area contacts have indicated a very mild dependence of work function on the impedance of the diode in the case of Si[5,6] and only the vaguest suggestion of a work-function dependence in the case of Ge.[7] This lack of correlation can be explained in part by the fact that we have thus far ignored minority-carrier flow across the contact. More effective in explaining the lack of correlation, however, is the role of the semiconductor surface in establishing the barrier.

These two subjects will now be discussed.

8.2b. The Effect of Surface States on Barrier Formation. The lack of correlation between the work function of the metal and the observed properties of point-contact diodes led Bardeen[8] to postulate the existence of a space-charge region at the surface of the semiconductor even in the absence of a metal contact. He suggested that this dipole layer existed because of the discrete electronic states lying within the forbidden band at the surface of the crystal. By now it is well known that such surface states and surface barriers exist. In fact their properties have been studied extensively.[9] These states can occur either from the termination of the periodic structure of the crystal at the surface or from the presence of adsorbed species on the surface. The levels can act as acceptor or donor states. For the free semiconductor surface, these levels have no place to accept electrons from or donate electrons to other than the semiconductor region immediately adjacent to the surface. Because of the difference in the density-of-states diagram at the surface, such a transfer of charge must occur in order simultaneously to conserve charge and maintain the Fermi statistics throughout. The reasoning is precisely the same as that for the transfer of charge across a PN junction in establishing equilibrium. Once a surface-state type, density, and location is known, the height and type of surface dipole will be uniquely determined on a semiconductor of known resistivity. A potential barrier such as that shown in Fig. 8.1 can thus exist at the free surface of the semiconductor.

Surface-state densities of the order of 1 per surface atom are certainly realizable. Thus, one can easily obtain densities of the order of $3 \times 10^{14}/cm^2$. Such large surface-state densities will tend to lock the Fermi level at the surface near the center of gravity of their energy distribution. Thus, there will be a large number of both full and empty states in the surface layer when the free surface is in equilibrium with the bulk.

If a metal is now brought into contact with the semiconductor, thermal equilibrium can be established by transferring charges between the metal and the surface states of the semiconductor, thus establishing a thin dipole layer about the contact plane. If this transfer of charge can establish a sufficient dipole to satisfy contact potential differences without drastically altering the fraction of surface states occupied, the barrier inside the semiconductor will remain nearly unchanged during the transfer. The surface barrier can thus be shielded from the influence of the metal by the surface states. Since a transfer of only about 10^{13} electrons/cm^2 is necessary to establish a volt across about 10^{-7} cm, there should usually be an ample number of surface states to shield the surface barrier efficiently from the influence of the metal.

8.2c. Minority-carrier Flow. If a potential barrier is established to majority-carrier flow, this barrier will automatically offer less impedance to minority-carrier flow than the bulk of the semiconductor. For example, since the barrier region of Fig. 8.1 constitutes a region depleted of electrons, it must have an enriched supply of holes at thermal equilibrium. This follows from the fact that at thermal equilibrium, the PN product is a constant throughout the semiconductor.† Hole flow across the contact should therefore be limited more by the bulk of the N-type semiconductor than by the barrier region. For the same reason, it is also the bulk of the N-type semiconductor which limits the flow of holes across the barrier at a PN junction. The hole flow across the contact is thus given precisely as in Eq. (3.8) for a PN junction by

$$J_p = \frac{qD_pp_n}{L_p}(e^{qV/kT} - 1) \tag{8.2}$$

where J_p equals the current of holes per unit area crossing the contact, D_p equals the diffusion constant of holes, p_n equals the equilibrium density of holes in the N-type bulk, and L_p is the effective diffusion length of holes in the N-type bulk.

In using Eq. (8.2), one should keep in mind that the effective diffusion length of a hole can in a sense be quite dependent on the geometry of the diode. Any spreading effects due to nonplanar geometries will increase concentration gradients, thus causing a smaller effective diffusion length. In a point contact, for example, where spreading effects are high, the effective diffusion length is limited to the radius of the contact at most.[10] Equation (8.2) also assumes that holes move only by diffusion. If the surface of the semiconductor adjacent to the contact is more P type than the bulk, holes may prefer to move via conduction for a while along the surface before being injected or extracted from the bulk. Since the effective surface-to-volume ratio increases as the area of a contact decreases, any such effects should be more noticeable in small-area contacts. These modifications in Eq. (8.2) are also applicable to PN junctions. They are stressed here because the small dimensions achieved with metal contacts can make them of considerable importance.

The total current crossing the junction is, of course, given by the sum of (8.1) and (8.2). The role of electrons and holes would be reversed if the barrier were on P-type material.

8.3 Etching. *8.3a. Objectives.* Proper etching of the semiconductor surface is essential if good rectification is to be obtained with a metal contact. The function of the etching is to remove any of the material damaged by the mechanical processes, usually sawing and lapping, used to prepare the crystal. Such highly disturbed regions will result in very large rates of thermal recombination and generation of hole-electron pairs (i.e., short lifetimes). These high recombination and generation rates act as shunting paths whereby the current can be transferred freely from the conduction to the valence band. If a barrier to electrons is established, there will be a thin P-type layer at the surface containing an appreciable concentration of holes (see Fig. 8.1). The current can thus, at least partially, bypass the barrier by crossing the contact in the enriched hole region and then transferring to electron current when the hole density begins to get low. A low-resistance contact will result.

Etching processes can be purely chemical or electrochemical in nature. The latter process is used more to shape the semiconductor into a desired geometry than as a cleaning process.

---

† Constancy of the PN product prevails at thermal equilibrium provided there are no degenerate regions. Degeneracy, however, will not affect the qualitative argument given here.

8.3b. Chemical Etching. Practically all the chemical etch mixtures used with germanium or silicon have the common features of a constituent for oxidizing the surface, a constituent for dissolving the oxide, and an additional substance for controlling the reaction rate.

An etching solution which leaves germanium and silicon surfaces in a highly polished state is called CP4.† This etch consists of equal parts of concentrated (46 per cent) hydrofluoric and glacial acetic acids, about 1.5 parts of concentrated nitric acid for each previous part, and a few drops of liquid bromide for each 50 cm³ of etchant. A germanium surface, after treatment with this etch, is so highly polished that it has a mirror-like appearance. The etch has been used extensively for etching junction diodes, used as both rectifiers and photocells, as well as transistors.

An etchant which removes damaged germanium but which leaves the surface, particularly the (100) plane, in a roughened condition is superoxol etch. After

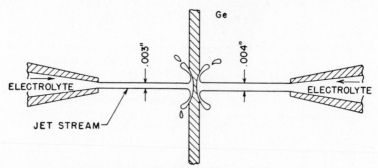

Fig. 8.2. Jet etching of a semiconductor transistor blank. (*Courtesy of the Proceedings of IRE.*)

etching, the (100) plane of germanium has an "orange-peel" appearance, resulting from the etch attacking some crystalline planes more rapidly than others. It is compounded of equal parts of superoxol‡ and concentrated hydrofluoric acid; these are mixed with three to four times their total volume of distilled water.

In these solutions the hydroxide peroxide and nitric acid are the oxidizing agents. The acid acts as the oxide solvent. In the CP4 etch, bromine acts as an accelerator while the acetic acid serves to moderate and control the reaction possibly through buffering the ionization of the acids. The reaction is violent in the absence of the moderator.

8.3c. Electrochemical Etching. Etching of the semiconductor can also be achieved by passing a current through it if the semiconductor serves as the anode in an electrolyte and another inert electrode is used as the cathode. If the electrolyte is directed in a stream onto the semiconductor, the etching will be confined principally to the regions of the semiconductor where the current density in the stream striking it is high. The streams of electrolyte can thus be used to shape the semiconductor into desired configurations without introducing disturbances in the crystal structure.

Such an etching process was employed in the fabrication of the first transistors using broad-area metal-semiconductor contacts as the electrodes.[11] Such transistors were made on N-type Ge. To achieve the transistor structure, the electrolyte is directed onto opposite sides of a semiconductor blank through two axially aligned glass jets§ (see Fig. 8.2). The jets are placed about ½ cm from the blank. The blank should be about 3 to 5 mils thick, and the jet diameters about those of the

† Chemical Polish No. 4.
‡ An aqueous solution of 30 per cent hydrogen peroxide.
§ A typical etching solution for Ge is 0.2 N H_2SO_4, plus 1 cm³ enthone per liter of solution.

electrode sizes desired in the finished product (in practice from 3 to 5 mils, with the collector slightly larger). A low-resistance ohmic contact is required for the application of potentials to the semiconductor. The electrolyte is forced through the jets under a pressure of approximately 10 psi. Currents in the range of a few milliamperes are used. To produce these currents several hundreds of volts are required because of the high resistance of the jets.

The rate of etching is determined to a large degree by the availability of holes in the semiconductor.[12] On N-type crystals the hole concentration can be supplemented by shining light on the semiconductor electrolyte interface, thus speeding up the

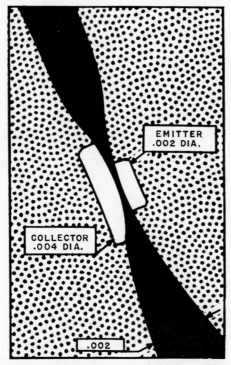

EMITTER
.002 DIA.

COLLECTOR
.004 DIA.

.002

Fig. 8.3. Schematic of the transistor made by jet-etching techniques.

etching rate. When the semiconductor has reached the desired thickness, etching is stopped. Figure 8.3 depicts a Ge blank which has been etched by this process.

Various methods exist for controlling the final thickness of the etched-down region. If a very thin region is desired, the width can be controlled by observing the frequency or intensity of radiation near the absorption edge which is transmitted through it.

For Ge the absorption edge lies in the infrared. Thus after a blank is etched to approximately the proper dimensions, one of the nozzles can be replaced by an infrared detector. Light is then introduced into the remaining electrolyte stream, and when the intensity recorded on the infrared detector reaches the proper level, etching is stopped. Because the system is not plane parallel, a lens effect occurs and the proper cutoff intensities must be determined by calibration.

On N-type Si, the hole density is much lower than in Ge, so that intense light must be focused on the region being etched in order to obtain reasonable etching rates.† Control of the thickness is relatively easy in Si because it transmits visible light

† A typical etching solution for silicon is 8.4 g NaF, 6 cm³ HF per liter of H_2O.

when thin enough.   For example, when a microscope light is used as a source, dull red can be seen when the blank is 1 mil thick.   This light becomes bright red at 0.5 mil and yellow at 0.2 mil.   A photoelectric detector can thus easily be devised for controlling the thickness.

Area contacts can be plated onto the blank by using the same system as that described above for etching if the electrolyte used contains the ion of the metal to be plated.†   If the Ge is then made the cathode of the electrolytic system, plating will result.   Currents are maintained in the same range as for etching.   After a metallic dot a few tenths of a mil thick has been deposited, plating is stopped. Contact can then be made to the metallic dots.   A brief cleanup etch after plating will give a well-defined area of contact.

8.4.   Area   Contacts. *8.4a.   Germanium.*   Broad-area contacts (as compared with point contacts) have been studied fairly extensively on Ge.[7,13-17] The results all indicate that as long as a good adhering metal contact is obtained on a freshly etched surface, rectification, can easily be obtained on N-type material while ohmic contacts are obtained on P-type material.   The metal may be deposited by electroplating, evaporation, or even by painting contacts on with a substance such as silver paste.   The I-V characteristics of an indium contact plated onto a thick 5 ohm-cm N-type Ge blank are shown in the low-voltage range in Fig. 8.4 and over the entire voltage range in Fig. 8.5.   The current-voltage dependence at low levels is seen to be essentially of the form given by Eqs. (8.1) and (8.2).   A relatively large percentage of the reverse current in this diode, however, can be accounted for by Eq. (8.2).   Hence the good agreement between experiment and theory is more a verification of Eq. (8.2) for minority-carrier flow than of Eq. (8.1) for majority-carrier flow.   All experiments on contacts made on freshly etched Ge indicate that Eq. (8.2) for the hole flow is as valid for this case as for a PN junction.[7]   On the other hand, it would seem that there has not been as yet any conclusive experimental verification of the coefficient in front of the exponential term of Eq. (8.1) or of the coefficient multiplying the voltage within the exponent of Eq. (8.1) for the majority-carrier flow.

Reverse curves for 10 different metals electroplated on 5 ohm-cm N-type Ge blanks are shown in Fig. 8.6.   The reverse currents are seen to vary by about a factor of 20 for the various metals shown.   About the only correlation that can be seen between

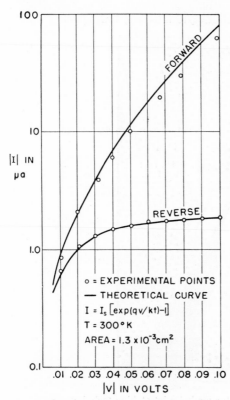

FIG. 8.4. Comparison of theoretical and experimental   current-voltage   characteristics for an indium contact plated onto 5-ohm-cm N-type germanium.   (*Courtesy of the Proceedings of IRE.*)

† A typical plating solution for an indium contact on Ge is 7.7 g $In_2(SO_4)_3$, 11 g NH_4Cl, 0.11 ml enthone per liter of H_2O.

the work function of the metal and the reverse current is that platinum, which is known to have one of the highest work functions, gave the lowest current. It should be stressed, however, that the results in Fig. 8.6 are not unique but simply show what sort of values could be obtained under the best plating conditions reached for each particular metal.

The experimental evidence leads one to conclude that when the freshly etched Ge surface is brought into intimate contact with a metal, a relatively high barrier to

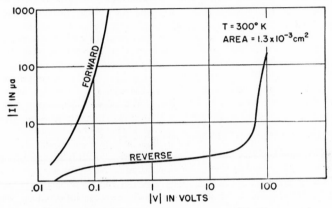

FIG. 8.5. The current-voltage characteristics of the diode of Fig. 8.4 over the entire range (*Courtesy of the Proceedings of IRE.*)

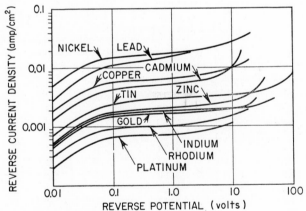

FIG. 8.6. Reverse characteristics of various metals electroplated onto 5-ohm-cm N-type germanium. (*Courtesy of Journal of Applied Physics.*)

electron flow exists. The height of the barrier varies only slightly with the metal used. That is, the surface of the germanium is strongly P type. This fact explains the ohmic nature of plated contacts on P-type germanium, since the only junction produced is a PP^+ junction which has a negligible barrier. This result is not exactly that which would be expected from the surface-state model of Sec. 8.2b. Surface studies have shown that while the truly free germanium surface is very P type, a freshly etched germanium surface which contains about a monolayer of oxygen is moderately N type. One is led to conclude that if a monolayer of oxygen is sandwiched between a metal and germanium, the metal tends to neutralize the effect of the oxygen on the germanium, thus leaving the semiconductor surface more nearly in its free condition. As pointed out by Bardeen,[8] for such intimate contact as is obtained in this case, the surface double layers of atomic dimensions which create the work functions and surface states probably all become intermingled. The work functions as defined for the individual materials therefore tend to lose their meaning.

A few studies have been made by Harrick[17] on metal contacts to germanium with thick oxides sandwiched in between. He has, at least, demonstrated the complexity of such a system by proving injection for some samples independent of the polarity and extraction for others independent of the polarity. Rectification at such contacts may or may not occur.

Since good surface barriers exist on N-type germanium with metal contacts, these contacts can be used as emitters and collectors in transistors fabricated in the manner described in Sec. 3. The common metal used for such contacts is indium because it is easily plated and produces low current densities. However, even for the best contacts obtained, the electron current density crossing the emitter is considerably higher than in a good alloyed PN junction at the same bias. Respectable α's can be obtained only by designing the unit so that comparably larger hole currents can flow. This can be accomplished by going to high resistivities or very thin base widths [see Eq. (4.7)]. Both directions lead to a high base resistance, so that the over-all performance of the device is not so good as could be accomplished with alloyed junctions fabricated on the same dimensions. Nevertheless, quite respectable transistors can be achieved with base resistivities of the order of 1 ohm-cm and base widths of the order of 0.1 mil. Microalloying of the contacts after plating will improve

TABLE 8.1. WORK FUNCTIONS AND RECTIFICATION PROPERTIES OF METALS
PLATED ONTO 2.5-OHM-CM N- AND P-TYPE SI
(O stands for ohmic, R for rectifying, * for the better rectifier of the two
when both types rectified)

Metal	Work function, electron volts[20]	N-type silicon	P-type silicon
K..........	2.15	O	R
Na.........	2.27	O	R
Li..........	2.39	O	R
Mg.........	3.46	O	R
Al..........	3.74	O	R
Zn..........	3.74	O	R
In..........	4.00	O	R
Pb.........	4.02	O	R
Sn.........	4.11	O	R
Cd.........	3.92	R	R*
Sb.........	4.08	R	R*
Co.........	4.18	R*	R
Bi.........	4.28	R*	R
Ag.........	4.28	R*	R
Cu.........	4.47	R*	R
Ni.........	4.84	R*	R
Fe.........	4.36	R	O
Au.........	4.58	R	O
Rh.........	4.65	R	O
Pt.........	5.29	R	O

the injection efficiency, thus leading to a relatively high-α transistor as well as a high-frequency unit.[†][18] Introducing some gallium into the indium contacts before alloying has been shown to improve the injection efficiency.

8.4b. Silicon. Considerable data also exist on broad-area contacts on Si.[5,6] Table 8.1 lists the results of various metals electroplated onto 2.5 ohm-cm N- and

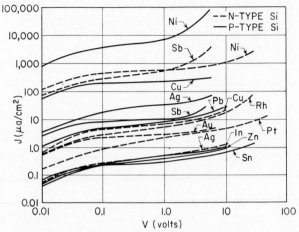

FIG. 8.7. Reverse characteristics of various metals electroplated onto 2.5-ohm-cm N- and P-type silicon. *(Courtesy of Journal of Applied Physics.)*

P-type Si along with the work functions of the metals. An obvious correlation exists between the rectifying properties of the contact and the work function of the metal. Such a correlation also was found by Brattain for evaporated contacts. Figure 8.7 shows the reverse characteristics of the various rectifiers obtained by electroplating, while Fig. 8.8 shows the entire I-V characteristic of one of the higher-resistance diodes. The current voltage characteristic of this diode does not follow the theoretical form of Eqs. (8.1) and (8.2) as well as the Ge rectifier shown in Fig. 8.4. This is not too surprising, however, since high-resistance Si PN junctions also do not reach the high degree of rectification indicated by Eq. (8.2). This has been explained by the fact that as the gap width of the semiconductor is increased, recombination and generation in the space-charge region decrease, but not so rapidly as the impedance to flow over the barrier is increasing.[19] Thus, the high barriers which can be established in high gap materials have a greater tendency to be shunted out by recombination and generation processes, leading to a reduction in the rectification ratio.

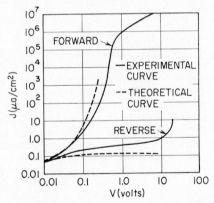

FIG. 8.8. Comparison of experimental and theoretical characteristics of a Zn contact plated onto 2.5-ohm-cm P-type silicon. *(Courtesy of Journal of Applied Physics.)*

† Microalloying is a very brief heat-treatment leading to extremely shallow recrystallized regions.

The data imply that the freshly etched Si surface is fairly near intrinsic. However, since the oxide forms much more readily on Si than on Ge, such a freshly etched surface probably contains two to three atomic layers of oxide before the plating is accomplished. The thin layer of dielectric sandwiched between the metal contact and the semiconductor may be the reason that a correlation between the work function and the rectifying properties of the contact was obtained.

Transistor action was reported on both N- and P-type Si for at least some of the metals plated. However, the reverse current densities did not always give a good indication of the injection efficiency obtainable. α's higher than 0.1 were never achieved on N-type silicon transistors with any of the contacts. On the other hand, α's of 0.95 to 0.99 could easily be obtained with Zn and In contacts on P-type material.

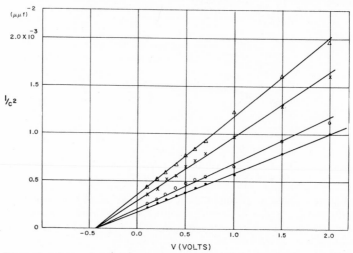

FIG. 8.9. Data of voltage versus capacitance for nickel contacts plated onto 2.5-ohm-cm N-type silicon.

The oxide layer thus appears to block the hole flow while offering little to no impedance to electron flow. The diode characteristics on N-type material should thus give a good measure of the silicon surface-barrier impedance to electron flow. On the other hand the characteristics on P-type material are measuring the sum of the oxide impedance and the silicon surface-barrier impedance, the former apparently being much higher than the latter.

These conclusions are substantiated by capacitance data taken on the diodes of Fig. 8.7. The capacitance per unit area of contact for a reverse bias V should be given as in Eq. (4.54) by

$$C = \left(\frac{\kappa q N_D}{2(V + \varphi_0)}\right)^{1/2} \tag{8.3}$$

Here κ is the dielectric constant and φ_0 is the equilibrium barrier height φ_B, provided the concentration of minority carriers at the surface is less than the net impurity concentration (i.e., provided there are no inversion layers).[13] The behavior of the capacitance near zero bias should thus allow for a determination of the barrier height provided the concentration of minority carriers at the surface is not too high. While this condition was not met on most of the Ge contacts studied, it should be met at least on the lower-resistance Si samples. Capacitance data were taken on all the diodes shown in Fig. 8.7. Particularly consistent data from sample to sample were obtained with Ni contacts. Capacitance data of four different nickel contacts on N-type Si are shown in Fig. 8.9 and of two different nickel contacts on P-type Si are shown in Fig. 8.10.† No unusual behavior was noted in the capacitance data on the N-type samples with any of the metals, while the P-type samples often showed an erratic behavior below 0.2 volt. Below this bias some metals showed a considerably higher capacitance and others a slightly lower capacitance than predicted by Eq. (8.2). Values of φ_0 extrapolated from the data at biases above 0.2 volt usually were higher than expected. Values of φ_0 as high as 1.5 electron volts were obtained. This behavior would again tend to point to the oxide layer as playing an important role on the P-type samples.

From the capacitance data of Fig. 8.9, a barrier height of 0.42 electron volt is indicated for the Ni contacts on N-type Si. These data combined with the reverse

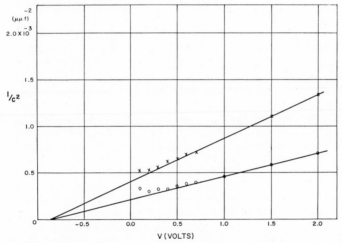

FIG. 8.10. Data of voltage versus capacitance for nickel contacts plated onto 2.5-ohm-cm P-type silicon.

current density permit a calculation of $\bar{v}$ in Eq. (8.1). Such a calculation gives a velocity of about 10^7 cm/sec. For reverse biases, at least, the value of $\bar{v}$ thus appears to be of the order of the limiting velocity achievable in the semiconductor material.

While good transistors with metal contacts on P-type Si were obtained, they showed serious degradation with time. The degradation consisted in a lowering of the collector breakdown voltage and an eventual decrease in current gain. It has been demonstrated that this degradation was in part associated with the removal of water vapor from the device. It can thus be concluded that no useful silicon counterpart of the germanium surface-barrier transistor has been developed.

8.5. Broad-area Ohmic Contacts. This section should be more properly headed "low-resistance contacts." As has been indicated in the previous sections, such contacts will be obtained if an accumulation of majority carriers exists near the surface or if there are a large number of recombination centers in the immediate vicinity of the contact. In practice most large-area ohmic contacts are made by using a solder containing a dopant of the same type as is contained in the bulk of the semiconductor. When the solder joint is made, an alloyed contact results which is probably both heavily doped and filled with recombination centers. Table 8.2 lists some of the common procedures used in making ohmic contacts to Ge and Si.

Ohmic contacts can be made by electroplating under certain specific conditions, for

† These data were taken at Philco Corporation by E. C. Wurst, Jr., in 1956.

example, on P-type germanium. A relatively low-resistance plated contact can be made on N-type germanium if the surface has been properly mutilated. This procedure obviously depends on shorting out the barrier to electrons by producing a region of high recombination rate in the barrier region. The degree of ohmicness achieved this way is usually of marginal utility.

TABLE 8.2. PROCEDURES FOR MAKING OHMIC CONTACTS TO
GERMANIUM AND SILICON

	Solder	Temperature, °C	Atmosphere
Germanium:			
N type.........	Pb-Sn-Sb	225	Air
P type.........	In	180	Air
Silicon:			
N type.........	Pb-Sn-Sb	800	H_2
P type.........	Au-B	750	H_2

8.6. Point Contacts and Bonded Contacts. *8.6a. I-V Characteristics.* If a sharpened metallic point is placed in contact with a semiconductor, the current-voltage characteristic generally shows some rectification which is independent of the metal used. If the resistivity of the semiconductor is not too high, the sign of the rectification is always that expected for a barrier to majority-carrier flow. However, there is some qualitative correlation between the behavior of an unformed point and the broad-area contacts. Unformed points on P-type germanium, for example, show much poorer rectification than on N-type germanium.[1] The dimensions achievable with a point (i.e., radius $\approx 4 \times 10^{-4}$ cm) lead to high spreading resistances which could allow appreciable fields to exist even across an accumulation layer established at the point. Such fields could thus lead to low breakdown voltages which would show a preferred direction on an accumulation layer due to the presence of the built-in field and would allow for injection. Thus, the sign of the rectification and even injection do not unambiguously determine the sign of the dipole layer existing at the contact.

Most point-contact rectifiers are improved by subjecting them to a forming process. The current-voltage characteristics of formed points generally show a fairly poor saturation in the reverse direction and an exponential dependence in the forward direction. However, the coefficient of the voltage in the exponent is always less (by a factor of two to five times) than the theoretical values of q/kT. The reverse dynamic impedance of a formed point is of the order of 5 to 50 kilohms, and the forward dynamic impedance is in the 50- to 100-ohm range.

8.6b. Forming Processes. All the methods of forming consist basically of the application and dissipation of electrical power in the vicinity of the point in an amount far in excess of the normal maximum rating value. The methods differ in the amount and duration of the power application, as well as in the detailed procedure for successive applications.

Since the forming process is found to be a progressive one, with the application of pulses of increasing power producing generally monotonic changes in the diode characteristics, it can be used to "tailor" one or more characteristics of the units The most important characteristic for a particular type of diode is selected as the forming objective, and pulses of increasing power are applied, with measurement of the forming objective between successive pulses. Whether this tailoring process or a standard "one-shot" pulsing process is more desirable is an economic question.

One method of forming is by capacitor-discharge pulsing. As shown in Fig. 8.11, a capacitor is charged through a large series resistance R_1 by a power supply.   To form the diode, the capacitor is discharged through the diode in series with another resistor R_2.   In order to vary the size of the forming pulse, one can vary the potential to which the capacitor is charged, the capacitance of the capacitor, or the amount of series resistance.   Variations in series resistance are usually most effective.

A typical forming procedure might be to discharge a 0.1-μf capacitor charged to 300 volts through a resistance of 1,000 ohms.   One "shot" might produce the desired result, or it might be necessary to reduce R_2 to 250 ohms or perhaps even 50 ohms to get the desired degree of forming.

The only additional forming method to be described is "a-c pulsing."   In this case a low-impedance source of high-voltage (100 to 300 volts) alternating current is connected through a series resistor to the diode for a short time.   A 60-cycle current is normally used, and the pulsing occurs for a small fraction of a second.

A common feature of the most effective forming methods is that the pulse applied to the point is negative (reverse direction) and is large enough to "break down" the diode; hence the current flow is limited principally by the series resistor.   Since

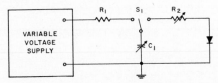

FIG. 8.11. Circuit for capacitor-discharge forming of point contacts.

both the current and voltage are high, the peak power dissipated in the region of the point is quite large.   In the capacitor-discharge method the times involved are quite short, being of the order of 10 to 100 μsec.   These very high power pulses produce a number of marked changes in the physical structure of the point contact. These, in turn, produce the changes in electrical characteristics.   One significant change that occurs on forming is that the reverse characteristics exhibit a multiplication effect.   Thus, the α's of point-contact transistors can be greater than unity. This multiplication is usually ascribed to some sort of hook being developed in the forming process (see Sec. 4.4a).

8.6c. Bonded Contacts.   A procedure similar to that of forming a point contact can be used to create small-area PN junctions under a metal contact if the mixture of the semiconductor and the metal has a melting point lower than either of the individual constituents, i.e., there is a eutectic in the metal-semiconductor phase diagram.   The heat created in the passage of a high current pulse through a wire making the contact will then result in a bond between the semiconductor and the metal.   If small percentages of suitable impurities to act as donors or acceptors are introduced into the metal, a junction will be formed after the heat-treatment.   The metallurgical process involved is essentially that of the alloying procedure described in Sec. 7.   There is a dissolving of the semiconductor and then a recrystallization onto the parent crystal, with the recrystallized region freezing the impurities into it.

In practice, a common metal used to make the bond is gold containing the desired impurity.   A small wire of this, a few mils thick, welded to another wire is used to make the contact.   The gold-germanium phase diagram has a eutectic at a composition of 12 per cent Ge, the eutectic mixture having a melting point of 356°C.   The bond on Ge can thus be achieved at any temperature between 356°C and the melting point of Ge, which is 958°C.   Depending on the doping used in the gold, PN, N$^+$N, or P$^+$P junctions can be formed on both Ge and Si.   Thus both small-area rectifying junctions and low-resistance contacts can be obtained by this process.

8.6d. Applications of Point Contacts and Bonded Contacts.   All small-area contacts will have an inherent high spreading resistance in series with the contact unless another ohmic contact is brought within the dimensions of the radius of the contact. This spreading resistance R is given by

$$R = \frac{1}{4\sigma a} \tag{8.4}$$

where σ is the conductivity of the semiconductor material and a is the radius of contact. The spreading resistance will limit the rectification ratio at high biases where the contact resistance is small in comparison.   The barrier capacitance of such contacts, however, will be proportional to the square of the radius of contact.   Hence the RC time constant of the contacts will be proportional to the radius.†   Small-area contacts thus find their applications in areas where fast response times are needed.   Point contacts are used primarily as microwave mixer diodes.   Bonded contacts, which trade an improved rectification ratio for a slight loss in speed, have applications in the computer field.

REFERENCES

1. Henisch, H. K.: "Rectifying Semiconductor Contacts," Oxford University Press, New York, 1957.
2. Torrey, H. C., and C. A. Whitmer: "Crystal Rectifiers," McGraw-Hill Book Company, Inc., New York, 1948.
3. Gunn, J. B.: The Theory of Rectification and Injection at a Metal-Semiconductor Contact, *Proc. Phys. Soc.*, ser. B, vol. 67, pp. 575–581, July, 1954.
4. Meyerhoff, W. E.: Contact Potential Difference in Silicon Rectifiers, *Phys. Rev.*, vol. 71, pp. 727–735, May, 1947.
5. Wurst, Jr., E. C., and E. H. Borneman: Rectification Properties of Metal-Silicon Contacts, *J. Appl. Phys.*, vol. 28, pp. 235–240, October, 1956.
6. Brattain, W. H.: Unpublished work done at Bell Telephone Laboratories in 1940. (This work is quoted in Ref. 8.)
7. Borneman, E. H., R. F. Schwarz, and J. J. Stickler: Rectification Properties of Metal-Semiconductor Contacts, *J. Appl. Phys.*, vol. 26, pp. 1021–1028, August, 1955.
8. Bardeen, J.: Surface States and Rectification at a Metal-Semiconductor Contact, *Phys. Rev.*, vol. 71, pp. 717–727, May, 1947.
9. Kingston, R. H.: "Semiconductor Surface Physics," University of Pennsylvania Press, Philadelphia, 1957.
10. Swanson, J. A.: Diode Theory in the Light of Hole Injection, *J. Appl. Phys.*, vol 25, pp. 314–323, 1954.
11. Tiley, J. W., and R. A. Williams: Electrochemical Techniques for Fabrication of Surface-barrier Transistors, *Proc. IRE*, vol. 41, pp. 1706–1708, December, 1953.
12. Garrett, C. G. B., and W. H. Brattain: Experiments on the Interface between Germanium and an Electrolyte, *Bell System Tech. J.*, vol. 34, pp. 129–176, January, 1955.
13. Schwarz, R. F., and J. F. Walsh: The Properties of Metal to Semiconductor Contacts, *Proc. IRE*, vol. 41, pp. 1715–1720, December, 1953.
14. Gunn, J. B.: Measurement of the Surface Properties of Germanium, *Proc. Phys. Soc.*, ser. B, vol. 67, pp. 409–421, May, 1954.
15. Hartig, P. A., and R. N. Noyce: Effects of Low Energy Gas Discharges on Evaporated Metal-Semiconductor Contacts, *J. Appl. Phys.*, vol. 27, pp. 843–847, August, 1956.
16. Bray, R.: Purdue University Report, September, 1950.
17. Harrick, N. J.: Metal to Semiconductor Contacts: Injection or Extraction for Either Direction of Current Flow, *Phys. Rev.*, vol. 115, pp. 876–882, August, 1959.
18. Rittmann, A. D., G. C. Messenger, R. A. Williams, and E. Zimmerman: Microalloy Transistor, *IRE Trans. on Electron Devices*, vol. ED-5, pp. 49–54, April, 1958.
19. Sah, C., R. W. Noyce, and W. Shockley: Carrier Generation and Recombination in p-n Junctions and p-n Junction Characteristics, *Proc. IRE*, vol. 45, pp. 1228–1243, September, 1957.
20. Michaelson, H. B.: Work Functions of the Elements, *J. Appl. Phys.*, vol. 21, pp. 536–540, June, 1950.

† At high forward biases where appreciable injection can occur, storage effects can also affect the response time of the diode.

Section 9

ENCAPSULATION

J. C. VAN VESSEM

Semiconductor Development Laboratories
N. V. Philips' Gloeilampenfabrieken
Nijmegen, Netherlands

9.1. Basic Encapsulation Problems. Most changes which occur in semiconductor devices during life and during storage can be attributed to changes of the surface condition of the device. As a result, changes in reverse currents, reverse voltages, and current amplification, together with instability and runaway, can be observed. Thus it can be said that the quality of a semiconductor device depends a great deal upon its encapsulation and the previous surface treatment.

9.1a. Surface Protection. Nowadays nearly all units are hermetically sealed. A true hermetic seal is desirable for two reasons: (1) to maintain the carefully created surface condition, preventing molecules on the surface getting away from it, and (2) to prevent outside contamination from upsetting the surface structure.

The nature of the surface is slowly beginning to be better understood. It seems that oxide layers are present, but also layers of adsorbed water molecules play a role. Excess moisture can induce increased surface conductivity, owing to so-called "channels," N-type layers formed on P-type surfaces and vice versa.[1] Until now it is unknown whether interaction between the germanium or silicon oxides and water takes place, although chemically a hydrated surface layer does not seem impossible.[2]

Recent work by Atalla[3] has shown that a thick oxide layer on silicon may serve to keep the surface-conduction phenomena separated from the PN junction itself, thus stabilizing the device. With thick protective oxide layers silicon devices, both transistors and diodes, have been successfully encapsulated without hermetic sealing. These devices have, in addition to the oxide layer, some overcoating of plastic or glass.

The effect of water vapor on a device depends on many factors: the nature of the device (diode or transistor), the polarity of the device (P or N type), and the previous surface treatment of the device. Point-contact germanium diodes on N-type material can show good characteristics while being exposed to a relative humidity of 40 to 60 per cent, but excess humidity may cause instability, flutter, and decrease in back resistance.

PNP and NPN germanium transistors are very sensitive to changes in water-vapor pressure. Reverse current and current amplification will improve or deteriorate, depending upon the previous surface condition.[2,4] Very generally, however, it seems that NPN transistors are more sensitive to moisture when being encapsulated than PNP transistors.

Thus, it once more must be stressed that the purpose of the encapsulation is to maintain the original surface condition the designer has created. Realizing, however, that even if we seal our device hermetically without changing the surface structure, there must exist a temperature-dependent sorption-desorption equilibrium on the surface. The problem of maintaining the electrical parameters of our device constant under all conditions of storage or use at various ambient temperatures seems to be a very difficult one. For very critical applications three obvious solutions now exist to help us with this problem: (1) Heat the device on a pump and backfill with a very dry, inert atmosphere after pumping. This shifts the surface condition entirely to one side. There will be no change of vapor pressure with change of temperature because everything has been pumped away. Generally, the α_{FB} (and α_{FE}) will be rather low and reverse currents can increase somewhat during the operation. Furthermore, having "dried" the surface thoroughly, one must be very careful not to admit any water vapor during the life of the transistor. Therefore special water-vapor "getters" are used in this process (e.g., Vycor glass). (2) Operate the device at as low a junction temperature as possible by the use of a lower rating for maximum collector dissipation and ambient temperature. This method guarantees an excellent performance but is costly because of the reduced ratings. (3) Try to put a substance in the can which helps to maintain a temperature-independent water-vapor pressure. Several manufacturers have tried various inorganic compounds for this purpose, such as calcium sulfate, molecular sieve, and many others. None of these admixtures until now have solved the problem entirely, but some improvement certainly has been obtained. Much depends for each recipe upon the previous surface treatment, however.

9.1b. Thermal Considerations. Most semiconductor devices are temperature-sensitive devices. In nearly all cases a steep increase of reverse currents with increasing temperature is observed. This results in the development of more internal heat; thus the junction temperature is raised further, etc., and unless by way of the encapsulation the developed heat can be transported away in time by radiation, conduction, or convection, the device will destroy itself.

So, when designing the package, we have to consider the maximum dissipation and maximum allowable ambient temperature. From them we can calculate the thermal requirements our construction must fulfill. If our unit must be able to operate at 55°C ambient temperature and will have to dissipate 150 mw, we can quickly calculate the thermal requirement for our envelope. With the aid of Fig. 10.6, we can determine directly the limiting operating junction temperature. We find, for instance, 85°C. This means that the maximum temperature difference between ambient and junction can be 30°C. This situation will occur when 150 mw is being dissipated. Or, in other words, the maximum rate at which the junction temperature of the transistor can increase is $30°/150$ mw $= 0.2°C/mw$. We often refer to this figure as the "thermal coefficient" of the transistor. The symbol K is often used for this parameter. The K is one of the most important transistor parameters. It depends directly on the mechanical construction of the device. In Sec. 9.4 we shall further analyze the relationship between K and the mechanical construction.

For devices with a low collector dissipation (below 100 or 200 mw), the unit can usually be operated in free air without a heat sink. If we consider medium-power units in the range of 200-mw to 1-watt dissipation, cooling fins or a simple clamp to bolt the unit to the chassis or some other heavy metal part become necessary. For high-power devices (more than 1-watt dissipation), the envelope must be fixed very tightly to a good heat sink and internally the thermal path from collector junction to envelope must be made as conducting as possible. Sometimes it seems worthwhile to improve the power dissipation of a unit by attaching it to a better heat sink. The latter will always improve the dissipation, but we must never forget that if we want to operate the transistor with a higher collector dissipation, which usually means at a higher collector current or voltage, the characteristic behavior of the transistor may change. (For instance, the α_{FE} of an alloyed power unit will show a strong tendency to fall off at higher collector currents, resulting in more distortion if we use the device as an amplifier or output transistor.) This means that the electrical and the thermal design must be matched. It does not pay to have more reserve on the one or on the other side because we shall not be able to use it at an advantage in most cases.

9.1c. Choice of Materials and Techniques. The choice of encapsulating materials and techniques depends upon many factors: (1) desired degree of hermetic sealing, (2) thermal properties of the envelope, (3) price of the envelope, (4) mechanical requirements, and (5) geometrical requirements.

The degree of hermetic sealing depends directly upon the choice of technique and materials. Of course, a hermetically sealed unit is always in danger of "leaking" or becoming permeable to external influences under standard or extreme conditions. Thus, different encapsulations can show different degrees of hermetic sealing. For one thing, metals can be or become porous at higher temperatures or glass-to-metal seals can show minute leaks after having been subjected to temperature cycling. Another danger to the seal is the repeated bending of the leads. Further considerations will be the matching of the coefficients of thermal expansion of all materials used.

The importance of the thermal properties of the envelope has been already explained. For high-power units copper is practically the only material used. Some arrangement to clamp a copper base against a cooling plate or chassis with or without an electrically insulating layer in between is very important. Copper envelopes can be closed very elegantly by "cold welding." Medium-powered units can be manufactured in all sorts of envelopes. Here, in contrast to the high-power units, none of the electrodes of the transistor is, in general, internally connected to the envelope. Often provisions for simple cooling fins have to be made. For low-power units the thermal conductivity of the envelope becomes less important because the radiation properties of the outer transistor shell here are the determining factor together with the conductivity of the material between junction and envelope. The heat is conducted from junction to outer envelope, and the envelope loses most of its heat by radiation. To illustrate our point: A glass envelope radiates as well as a metal envelope. If we compare a transistor in a glass envelope filled with a good conducting material with a transistor in a metal can of the same size filled with gas, then we shall find a better thermal behavior for the glass transistor. If we fill the metal can with the same material as the glass envelope, we shall find roughly the same K value for both types of encapsulation.

The price of the encapsulation is today beginning to play a more and more important role because the transistor no longer is a novelty but is being used in almost the same quantity as vacuum tubes. In considering the price of a package we shall also have to consider the effect the package can have on final yield. Some packages can be the cause of reject transistors when the sealing of the envelope influences the transistor. To illustrate this: A glass package generally is cheap and dependable. If we make the glass envelope very small, the price is still further reduced, but the chances are that many devices when being sealed will be spoiled by the high temperatures necessary to melt the glass. Another possibility: If the price of a welded envelope can be reduced by the use of another can or base material, we also shall have to consider the percentage of welded cans that do not pass the leak-detector test.

It is nearly impossible to give a general rule for the prices of the different types of encapsulation. Very generally, we can say that ceramic-to-metal sealed cases are rather expensive. In the range of metal envelopes the size and number of sealed-in insulated electrode leads will play an important role. All-glass envelopes are for low power and are a cheap way of encapsulation. Here, sealing is more difficult. Plastic encapsulation can also be a very cheap method but is not a very dependable one.

Mechanical requirements are important. One of the first of these requirements is to be able to bend the leads several times without their breaking off. Also, leads must be capable of being soldered, without damaging the device internally, by heat conduction. Furthermore, dropping the device from the table to the floor must leave it unaltered. For heat-sink- or chassis-cooled units the flatness and mechanical strength of the underside of the diode or transistor must not be neglected. If the bottom is not flat, thin layers of air will increase the resistance of the heat path between junction and heat sink. If the mounting base is not strong enough mechanically, it can be deformed when bolting it to the heat sink, thus breaking the device parts which internally have been soldered to the base. The bolt which clamps the base against the heat sink also must be strong enough to guarantee the right pressure.

Geometrical size can be the consequence of many different reasons. Space sometimes sets an upper limit to the size of the envelope. Nevertheless, one will find that the transistor or diode very often is smaller than many other of the components used. Extreme miniaturization will cost money and nowadays is used only when the circuit designer needs it. Lead arrangements can be an important requirement too. Automation machinery, for instance, must be able to "feel" the orientation of the leads. Also, interelectrode capacities can be the cause of a special lead arrangement. Sometimes the requirement of interchangeability with already existing devices will determine the manufacturer's or customer's choice. The variation in geometry of the different designs being offered is tremendous. Some degree of standardization has been reached, but the whole situation still is far from satisfactory.

9.2. Typical Encapsulation Structures. In this section we shall give a survey of the different sorts of structures used for encapsulation of diodes and transistors and discuss their advantages and disadvantages, whereas in Sec. 9.3 we shall describe the mechanical and fabrication aspects of the various techniques. The envelopes will be divided in groups, each group being characterized by the device which is being encapsulated.

9.2a. Germanium Diodes. The oldest form of germanium diode consists of a ceramic tube in each end of which a brass slug has been fixed with a kit or solder. One slug supports the crystal, while the cat whisker has been welded on the other slug (see Fig. 9.1a). A variation upon this form is a phenolic tube with cast-in metal bearings. The electrodes with whisker and crystal are pressed into each bearing until

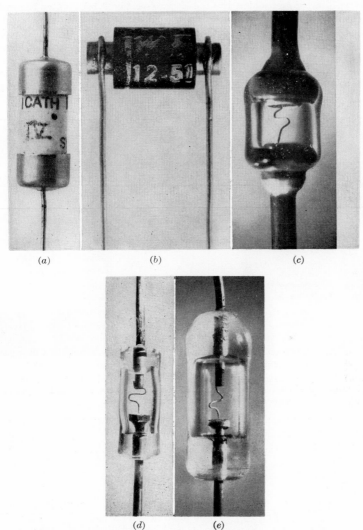

(a)   (b)   (c)

(d)   (e)

FIG. 9.1. (a) Ceramic encapsulated germanium diode. (b) Phenolic-resin envelope for germanium diode. (c) All-glass diode with Kovar seals. (d) All-glass subminiature diode. (e) All-glass European germanium diode.

electric contact between the electrodes has been established (see Fig. 9.1b). Both forms are not absolutely moistureproof. We must keep in mind, however, that under normal circumstances the device can perform well and that a germanium diode is not so sensitive to water vapor as a transistor.

An advantage of the envelopes shown is that they all have electrode leads (or slugs) of large thermal capacity which helps to increase the dissipation or to keep the junction temperature low. To improve the moisture resistance of the diode, a solder seal was used to close the package. Because all organic plastic materials are more or less permeable to water vapor, however, a glass body became desirable. Kovar tubes were sealed to the glass (a Corning type 7052). Through the ends the whisker and crystal shanks were inserted and soldered to the Kovar (see Fig. 9.1c). Often the solder seal here spoiled the diode quality because minute amounts of solder flux necessary to make a good seal sometimes penetrated into the diode case and accelerated the deterioration of the diode during life. Finally, lead wires containing crystal and whisker were soldered directly into a cylindrical glass tube without the use of fluxes.

The miniature all-glass diode nowadays seems to be the preferred standard envelope in the United States. Dumet leads are sealed into a Corning 0-120 type of glass as shown in Fig. 9.1d. Also, in Fig. 9.1e, bigger glass cases are being used.

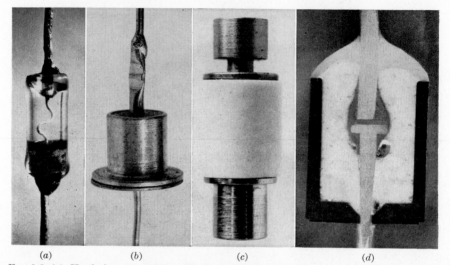

(a)   (b)   (c)   (d)

FIG. 9.2. (a) Hard-glass case with molybdenum lead wires, used for miniature silicon diode. (b) Medium-power silicon diode. (c) Metal-to-ceramic case for medium-power silicon diode. (d) Plastic encapsulated medium-power silicon diode.

When the glass seal has been carefully made, the all-glass diodes have a true hermetic seal. The maximum diameter of the wires which can be sealed into a thin glass tube sets a limit, however, to their maximum dissipation. Thanks to the more stable diode surface, higher operating junction temperatures can be tolerated, thus partly compensating this disadvantage. All structures shown are called "double-ended." The leads are arranged axially. Most users prefer this for easy mounting, the diodes being often supplied on reels of tape which can be fed directly into a mounting machine. A few manufacturers are also offering "single-ended" packages with both leads coming off one end. Especially for gold-bonded diodes this structure allows a final surface treatment after mounting and bonding but before final encapsulation. This can improve the reliability of the diode.

9.2b. Silicon Diodes (Small and Medium). Here the encapsulation design considerations, more often than for the germanium diode, include thermal requirements because the silicon diode is often used when a small device with a high permissible ambient temperature and a higher power rating is needed. Low-power units are encapsulated in the standard miniature all-glass package as shown in Fig. 9.1d. An improved version of this consists of an envelope of a special high-melting glass into which, on one side, a molybdenum crystal support has been sealed (see Fig. 9.2a). Thermally, the conductivity is not much higher than that of a Dumet wire of smaller cross section. For somewhat more power dissipation, a simple metal envelope is used with one electrode insulated by a glass seal in the top of the can as shown in Fig. 9.2b. The crystal is soldered to the metal base directly, care being taken to match the expansion coefficient of the silicon with the base metal (Kovar is often used). The whole now also acts as a cooling fin. No heat sink is used. This same envelope is also used for somewhat larger germanium diodes.

Some diodes are mounted in a metal-to-ceramic case (Fig. 9.2c) which can be clipped into a holder. The slugs at the end serve as a heat sink. When the metal end parts are soldered to the ceramic, with the help of a thin silver layer which has been

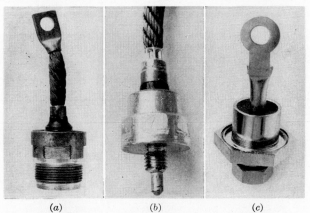

(a)   (b)   (c)

Fig. 9.3. Several models of silicon power diodes.

predeposited upon the ceramic,[5] this encapsulation is hermetically sealed. Sometimes the slugs are stuck with epoxy resin to the case. This seal is less reliable than a solder seal.

Recently, some firms have returned to plastic encapsulation in order to reduce costs. Two kinds of plastic are mostly used: one to cover the diode surface and another for casting the envelope as shown in Fig. 9.2d. Some of these encapsulations will withstand many moisture tests, although until now no plastic materials are known which are entirely impermeable to water vapor.

9.2c. Germanium and Silicon Power Diodes. This field seems to lack any tendency to standarize. The principal design requirements here are (1) lowest heat resistance between junction and mounting base, (2) large contact area between mounting base and heat sink, (3) low electrical and thermal resistance for the top contact, (4) an effective method to clamp or screw the mounting base against a heat sink or radiator, and (5) a method to close the case without damaging the diode surface. Several models are shown in Fig. 9.3. They all, more or less, fulfill the requirements just mentioned. For detailed techniques see Sec. 9.3.

9.2d. Transistors (Low-power and Subminiature). During the first years of the existence of the transistor, very often sockets were used for transistor mounting. Nowadays a transistor is considered to be such a stable circuit element that it is nearly always soldered into the circuit. Generally, the small and miniature transistors are encapsulated in a metal can, pressed or soldered to a metal-to-glass header. For comparison a range of small metal cans in different sizes is shown in Fig. 9.4, the smallest can being less than $\frac{1}{8}$ in. high and $\frac{1}{10}$ in. in diameter. Small metal cans can also be welded to the header (Fig. 9.4), but sometimes the protruding rim increases the maximum external diameter considerably.

Glass envelopes are widely used in Europe (Fig. 9.5). A well-sealed glass encapsulation is one of the most hermetic seals imaginable. The sealing, however, is an operation which needs some time and locally a high temperature. Therefore, the

(a)   (b)   (c)

(d)   (e)   (f)

FIG. 9.4. Several sorts of metal cans used for low-power transistor encapsulation.

length of the glass envelope has a lower limit of about $\frac{1}{2}$ in. If we make the envelope shorter, the risk of ruining a considerable percentage of transistors during the sealing becomes too great.

Plastic envelopes are not used any more for transistor encapsulation. The transistor is such a surface-sensitive device that any form of plastic encapsulation sooner or later fails, usually because they are all permeable to water vapor.

9.2e. Transistors for Medium-power Dissipation. The medium-size metal or glass envelope needs some additional cooling to raise its power dissipation from the 50-mw level to the level of a few hundred milliwatts. Metal clips to fasten the envelope to the heat sink (Fig. 9.6) are sometimes used for this purpose. In this case it helps considerably if we also reduce the internal heat resistance between junction and can,

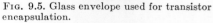

FIG. 9.5. Glass envelope used for transistor encapsulation.

FIG. 9.6. Transistor with metal clip to connect to heat sink.

for instance, by the use of thermally good conducting "fillers." Mixtures of silicon oil with powdered Al_2O_3, SiC, BeO, or metal powder are sometimes used for this purpose.

Another way to improve the K of a medium-sized metal can is by means of a bolt soldered to the cap of the can which allows one of the transistor electrodes to be internally connected to the envelope. Many medium-power transistors are nowadays encapsulated in the standardized case shown in Fig. 9.4d (Jedec T05 or T09). Many computer firms and the military are using this envelope extensively.

9.2f. Transistors for High-power Dissipation. One of the most widely used envelopes here is the diamond-shaped case (Fig. 9.7a). It can be closed by pressing and swaging, by welding the steel cap to a steel ring which has been brazed to the copper base, or it can be cold-pressed with soft metal seals. For high collector and emitter currents, the resistance of the emitter lead becomes very critical and special seals will become necessary. Mostly, the insulated emitter lead-through consists of a Kovar eyelet, filled with glass,

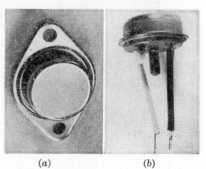

(a)   (b)

FIG. 9.7. (a) Diamond-shaped power transistor envelope. (b) Round power transistor envelope.

with a Kovar contact pin in the middle. This pin has a resistance which cannot be neglected. To improve this, one can solder a hollow Kovar tube inside the eyelet to replace the pin. In this tube a copper pin can be soldered. Some companies use a special sort of glass which enables them to solder copper leads directly to glass. This makes the construction simpler. The glass seal is more critical, however. Also, the envelope shown in Fig. 9.7b is often used for high-power transistors.

At the present time, nearly all manufacturers make the power transistor single-ended (leads and bolts on one side), although some double-ended envelopes still are being made.

9.3. Typical Encapsulation Techniques and Materials. *9.3a. Metal Envelopes.* Metal envelopes can be joined to metal bases by several methods: (1) projection welding, (2) cold welding (direct method), (3) cold sealing with a soft interposed layer, and (4) soldering.

1. PROJECTION WELDING. In this operation the parts to be welded are pressed together between the electrode jaws, after which the welding current flows through the

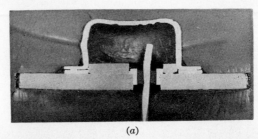

(a)

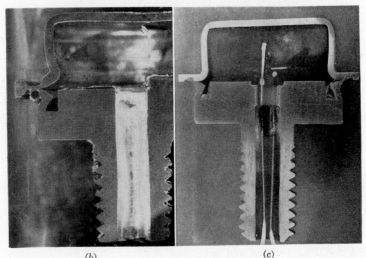

(b)   (c)

FIG. 9.8. (a) Cross section of power transistor with copper base, steel ring, and welded steel cap. (b) Cross section of a power transistor in a cold-welded copper case. (c) Cross section of power transistor with copper base, cold-welded to steel cap.

parts. The time of this current flow must be accurately controlled to prevent burning of the metal parts. Frequently, electronic-control devices driven by thyratrons or ignitrons are used. Thus, the welding time can be accurately set to within a hundredth of a second, and the welding energy regulated. A good weld can be obtained only when the metal surfaces to be welded have been properly cleaned by wire brushing, etching, or other means.

Metals with a high melting point are difficult to weld. Metals that oxidize easily must be protected by a reducing atmosphere. Generally, in our semiconductor technique mostly iron and nickel are used for caps and bases. When copper bases have to be used, a steel ring can be brazed upon it and then a steel cap can be welded to the ring (see Fig. 9.8a).

2. COLD WELDING (DIRECTLY). When two clean metal surfaces are placed in contact and a pressure applied, there is a migration of atoms between the two surfaces, giving rise to bonding. The extent of the bonding depends on the properties of the metal. If the pressure is sufficiently high to give rise to plastic flow in the metal in sideways direction, the two surfaces flow together to give a region of homogeneous metal in which an interface is no longer observable. This region forms a bond which may be as strong as or stronger than the original metal.

Since the cold weld involves the flow of metal, the metal must initially be in a ductile state. Work hardening by any process prior to the cold-welding process must be prevented or has to be removed by annealing. Furthermore, the surfaces to be welded must be absolutely clean and free from oxide. Especially with aluminum and copper special steps have to be taken to ensure that the oxide film is completely

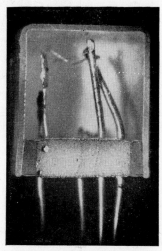

FIG. 9.9. Cross section of silicon power rectifier with a steel cap with compression seal and copper base with soft interposed layer.

FIG. 9.10. Cross section of envelope closed with a cold-pressed soft solder seal.

removed immediately prior to the formation of the weld. Wire brushing is a good method but can be a danger to semiconductor parts mounted to the header. To overcome this difficulty, the parts can be cleaned in an earlier stage of assembly and gold-plated. The welding tool consists of a pair of hard-steel ring dies suitably mounted in a press. The total load applied to the press must be such that the pressure applied to the die faces is well above the yield point of the metal used. Depending on the width of the tool face, a deformation of 60 to 85 per cent seems to be necessary to form a vacuumtight joint for welding copper (Fig. 9.8b). OFHC copper is generally used.

3. COLD SEALING WITH INTERPOSED LAYER. Sometimes it is necessary to use steel parts for an envelope. For power diodes, for instance, steel caps have the advantage that glass-insulated electrodes can be sealed directly to the cap with a compression seal. (The glass radially compresses the center lead. See Fig. 9.9.) Steel cannot be cold-welded to softer metals directly in the way which has just been described. If a groove is cut in both header and cap, a soft interposed metallic layer can be used which fills the groove and unites the two parts. A migration of atoms between the two surfaces does not take place here. Therefore, the weld is mechanically weaker than the direct cold weld. This can easily be overcome by swaging the base metal over the rim of the cap. This is shown in Fig. 9.9, where a steel cap is welded to a

copper base.   A lead, tin, lead-tin, or tin-indium ring can be used for the intermediate layer.   In some cases the copper itself can be used as the soft metal to fill the groove in the steel counterpart (Fig. 9.8c).   A special flange has to be used on a copper header; otherwise the deviations from flatness of the bottom due to the deformation of the welding will spoil thermal performance of the device.   For small envelopes a header with a slightly conical steel rim is often used.   The outer side of the rim and the inner side of the steel cap are covered with a soft solder.   Cap and rim are joined together by pressing (Fig. 9.10).

4. SOLDERING.   Many semiconductor devices are still being assembled in soldered envelopes.   Basically, soldering is an elegant and safe method to join parts.   However, the condition for good soldering is an oxide-free surface and a reducing atmosphere during the soldering operation.   To ensure this, fluxes are used which clean the metal parts but which often can be very harmful to the surface of the device in the can.   Therefore, soldering preferably must be done after preclosing the can in such a way that during the short soldering operation which follows no fluxes can enter in the interior of the can.   This can be done, for instance, by giving header and cap a tight fit.   More and more manufacturers are going over to other techniques, however.

9.3b. Glass Sealing.   Glass seals are an important method in the encapsulation technique.   We need glass-to-metal seals to insulate electrode leads.   Also, many diode and transistor cases are closed with a glass-to-glass seal.   Essential points for a good glass-to-metal seal are freedom from strain in the glass, vacuumtight adherence of the glass to the metal, and freedom from gas bubbles in the molten part.   To avoid strain, the thermal-expansion coefficients of the metal and the glass must be matched over a wide temperature range.   To obtain a good adherence between metal and glass, it is necessary that the oxide skin of the metal be wetted by and dissolved in the molten glass, thus forming a sort of thin intermediate glass layer.   The temperature for making the oxide skin dissolve in the glass, however, is rather high for a semiconductor device (960°C for powder glass).   Therefore, the glass-to-metal seals are usually performed on the piece parts and the final sealing consists only of glass-to-glass seals.   This procedure also enables one to anneal all glass-to-metal seals before mounting the semiconductor device.   The best metal oxide soluble in glass is cuprous oxide (Cu_2O).   The thermal expansion of copper does not match that of most glasses.   Therefore, nickel-iron wire is used, clad with a copper skin (Dumet wire).   Plain nickel-iron has an oxide skin which dissolves less readily in glass, although it is still well wetted by the glass.   In some alloys cobalt is used to replace part of the nickel, cobalt oxide being soluble in glass.   This material is known as Kovar or Fernico.

Nickel-iron alloys (50/50) are matched to soft glass (expansion coefficient 110×10^{-7}).   Replacing some nickel by cobalt to FeNiCo (54/28/18) gives matching to hard glass (expansion coefficient 55×10^{-7}).

In Table 9.1, the most important characteristics of metals and alloys for glass-to-metal seals are shown.   For further information on glass seals see reference 6.

In practice, nearly all germanium diodes are sealed in thin glass tubes with Dumet end seals.   In order to keep the final sealing temperature low, the Dumet leads are first sealed in glass beads.   Then the beaded leads are sealed in the glass tube (see Fig. 9.1d).   Electric or gas heating can be used for the final seal.

In Europe, a very large part of the total transistor production is sealed in glass envelopes (Fig. 9.5).   It is essential to keep the inner temperature low during the sealing.   Therefore, a low-vapor-pressure silicon grease is used as a filler and, when the lower half of the transistor is clamped in a water-cooled chuck during sealing, serves to lower the inner thermal resistance and to keep the junction cool.[7]   Gas or electric heating can be used for sealing.

9.3c. Other Encapsulation Techniques.   Ceramic materials, plastics, and low-melting glasses are compounds which are less frequently used for encapsulations, ceramics because they are difficult to machine to size and expensive, plastics because they are always somewhat permeable for moisture, and low-melting glasses because they are new and relatively untried for encapsulation and/or surface stabilization. For a vacuumtight seal chiefly hard porcelain (Mg silicate, "steatite," "calite") can be used. During baking and glazing, shrinkage occurs which makes it difficult to control the sizes of the fired parts.

Porcelain parts, in general, cannot be soldered directly to metals. First, an intermediate layer of a thin film of metal or alloy has to be applied to the ceramic body in such a way as to become an integral part of it. This usually entails a firing operation at elevated temperature. Several processes are possible. One process coats the ceramic parts, in those places where a solder contact to a metal is desired, with a paste of fine molybdenum and iron powder. After this paste is sintered to the ceramic in a hydrogen atmosphere at about 1400°C, a paste of nickel powder is applied in a similar manner and fired at 1000°C. The metallic parts then can be silver-brazed to the metallized ceramic. Other processes use different combinations of metals, but all methods depend upon the principles mentioned above.[5] For devices such as silicon power rectifiers this technique is sometimes used.

Plastic materials are no longer considered to be very dependable encapsulation materials. At the present time, the best known method for encapsulation with plastic is to protect the semiconductor surface of the device first with a layer of silicone lacquer or silicone plastic, after which the device is cast in an epoxy resin. Epoxy resins are known under various trade names, such as Araldite, Carboline, Epibond, Epons, Pylene, and 3M.[8]

Recently, a new method was announced[9] whereby germanium or silicon devices are dipped in a molten glass. The glasses used are a new series of inorganic sulfide glasses which are fluid in the temperature range 200 to 400°C. They show very low permeability to gases and water vapor, as do the vacuumtight seals which are formed between the glasses and certain metals. A variation of this method which shows considerable promise for silicon devices consists in growing an SiO_2 layer about 1 micron thick before glassing. Care must be exercised in the glassing operation to ensure that the SiO_2 layer is not completely dissolved away since many of the glasses used contain metals which act as semiconductor doping agents and can radically affect properties of the device. Glass-coated devices have been exposed to 100 per cent relative humidity for months causing no deterioration in electrical characteristics. The method is still new and has not yet found widespread use in industry.

9.4. Thermal Design Considerations. *9.4a. The Measurement of Thermal Resistance.* The IRE definition of thermal resistance is:[10] "The thermal resistance of a semiconducting device is the quotient of the temperature drop and the heat generated through internal power dissipation under steady state conditions; the temperature drop is to be measured between the region of heat generation and some reference point."

As reference points, the mounting base, heat sink, envelope, and ambient temperature are generally used. For the point of heat generation the collector junction temperature of a transistor or the diode junction temperature of a diode is usually taken. Although it can be a point of discussion whether all the heat is always generated exactly at the junction, we assume that the actual point of heat generation is sufficiently near the junction that the error introduced is negligible. The temperature of mounting base, heat sink, or envelope can be measured with a thermocouple, but the junction temperature cannot so easily be measured directly.

Fortunately, the transistor and diode characteristics are strongly temperature dependent and can be used as an effective thermometer.[11,12] The forward or reverse current-voltage relationship of a single diode or of the collector or emitter diode of a transistor has to be measured at different temperatures. After a load is applied to

Table 9.1. Physical Characteristics of Metals and Alloys for Glass-to-metal Seals

Ser. No.	Metal or alloy	Type composition	Practical shape available W—Wire B—Ribbon R—Rod S—Sheet T—Tubing F—Formed	Thermal expans. coefficient, $\Delta l/l/\Delta t \times 10^7$ cm/cm/°C	Thermal conductivity, cal/cu cm sec °C	Electrical resistivity, ohm-cm $\times 10^6$ (20°C)	Glass type H—Hard S—Soft	Sealing glasses* Commonly used	Sometimes used
1	Platinum	Essentially pure Pt	W-T-B-S-F	91 (25–300)	0.166	10	S (H)	0120, 0010, 0080, 8160 LG-12; LG-12-7; GEC-L1; GEC-X4; BTH-C12; Ch-GWA	
2	Dumet	Core: Ni-43; bal: Fe Sheath: borated copper	W (0.040 in. diam. max)	80–100 (radial) 61–65 (axial)	~0.4	4.6	S	0120, 0010, 0080, 8160 LG-12; LG-12-7; GEC-L1; GEC-X4; BTH-C12; Ch-GWB	
3	Copper	Essentially pure Cu (ofhc)	W-R-T-B-S-F	164 (25–300)	0.92	1.724	S H	Almost any glass for thin copper in form of sheet, ribbon, or tubing	
4	Steel (SAE 1010) (plated or bare)	Mn: 0.30–0.50; C: 0.08–0.13; S: 0.050 max; P: 0.040; bal: Fe	W-R-T-B-S-F	125 (25–300)	0.11	18	...	1990, 1991 GEC-R16: BTH-C41/76	0080; 0240
	Nickel-iron G.E. alloy	Ni: 41.5; Mn: 0.5; C: 0.06; Si: 0.2; bal: Fe	W-R-T-B-S-F				...	G.E. 1075	
5	Allegheny 42 4750	Ni: 42; bal: Fe Ni: 47–50; bal: Fe		78 (20–500) 98 (20–500)	0.026 0.037	66 50	...	0010, 0080, 0120, 8160	
	Driver Harris 142 52	Ni: 41.5; bal: Fe Ni: 50–51; bal: Fe	W-R-B-S W-R-B-S	78 (20–500) 95 (20–500)	0.026 0.0399	66 43.22			
	Carpenter 42 49	Ni: 42; bal: Fe Ni: 49; C: 0.10 max; bal: Fe		50 (20–350) 90 (20–350)	......	71 43			
6	Low-chrome nickel iron: Sylvania 4	Ni: 42; Cr: 6; Mn: 0.29; C: 0.04; Si: 0.12; bal: Fe		79 (20–300)	0.032	34	...	0010, 0080, 0120, 8160	
	"Sealmet" 4	Ni: 42; Cr: 6; bal: Fe		111 (20–500)	0.029	34	S	LG-12; LG-12-7; BTH-	

No.	Material	Composition						Code
	Driver Harris 14	Ni: 42; Cr: 6; bal: Fe	....	92 (25–350)	0.032	34		C12; GEC-L1
	Carpenter 426 (Stanworth)	Ni: 42; Cr: 6; bal: Fe	....	93 (20–350)		94		
		Ni: 47; Cr: 5; bal: Fe	W-R-T-B-S-F	99 (20–400)				0010
	High-chrome iron:							
7	Sealmet 1	Cr: 28; bal: Fe	....	110 (20–500)	0.059	72		0240 GEC-L14; Ch-GWA/B
	Carpenter 27	Cr: 28; bal: Fe	....					0010
	Driver Harris 446	Cr: 28; bal: Fe	....					Window glass
	Allegheny Telemet	Cr: 16–23; Mn: 2 max; C: 0.25 max; S: 0.030 max; P: 0.040 max; Si: 1 max; bal: Fe	....	117 (30–530) (max. value)			S	0120; 0010
	Nickel cobalt chrome iron:							
8	Fernichrome	Ni: 30; Co: 25; Cr: 8; bal: Fe	....				H	0010; 0120; 0050; 7040; 7052; 7060 L-704 705 650; GEC-FGN; BTH-C40; Ch-GSB
	Fernico II	Ni: 31; Co: 15; bal: Fe	....					
9	Kovar (Nilo K)	Ni: 29; Co: 17; bal: Fe	....	50 (25–300)	0.046	49		GEC-HH H26; BTH-C11; 1137 46; Ch-GSC 7720; 3320; 7991; 7750 L-772; GEC-W1 WQ31; BTH-C9; Ch-GSD
	Molybdenum	Essentially pure Mo	W-R-T-B-S-F	55 (25–300)	0.35	5.7	H	
10	Tungsten	Essentially pure W	W-R-B	46 (0–500)	0.38	5.5	H	7050; 7740

* Four-number code: Corning Glass Works, Corning, N.Y.
LG: Libbey Glass Division, Owens-Illinois Glass Company (formerly Kimble glass), Toledo, Ohio.
GEC: General Electric Company, Ltd., Wembley, England.
BTH: British Thomson-Houston Company Limited, London, England.
Ch: Chance Brothers, Limited, Smethwick, England.
Reprinted from Kohl's "Materials Technology for Electron Tubes," by permission.

the device, the current-voltage relationship is measured again and thus the increase in junction temperature (ΔT_j) is known. Before and after the load is applied, the reference point temperature (usually the mounting base temperature) is also measured. If the generated power is P watts and the temperature change of the mounting base is $\Delta T_m °C$, the thermal resistance between junction and mounting base K_{j-m} becomes

$$K_{j-m} = \frac{\Delta T_j - \Delta T_m}{P} \qquad °C/watt$$

In practice, some difficulties arise: (1) Some diode and transistor characteristics are not temperature stable. They "drift away," and especially when the reverse characteristics are used, only very stable units can be measured and the measurement has to be repeated two or three times to exclude errors. (2) The generation of power has to be interrupted to take the "temperature reading." This must be done very quickly or the device cools down again.

As a remedy in case (1), the forward current-voltage dependence is generally used which is much less sensitive than the reverse characteristic. The calibration must be very accurate because the temperature effect in the forward direction is less pronounced than that in the reverse direction.

To measure the junction temperature correctly, during dissipation the power is interrupted only for a very short time (2 msec) to prevent too much cooling of the junction. In this short interval the forward voltage necessary for a given forward current is amplified with a d-c amplifier and read from an oscilloscope. Before the measurement is started, the change of forward voltage (with a constant forward current) as a function of junction temperature is determined. From a graph the new T_j is read.

9.4b. Analysis of the Internal and External Heat Resistance of a Device. Around the spot inside our device, where the heat is generated, we can distinguish a number of isothermal surfaces. In accordance with the definition of "thermal resistance" given at the beginning of Sec. 9.4, we can, in theory, determine the individual resistance K_n of each region between two isothermal surfaces. If we add all individual resistances, we find the total thermal resistance

$$K_{\text{total}} = \Sigma K_n$$

If we try to calculate our K_{total} (from now on referred to as K), we see that it is very difficult to establish the positions of the isothermal surfaces.

As a first approximation we can draw the first isothermal surface close around the spot where the heat is developed, the second surface as close as possible to the outer side of the envelope, and the third surface near infinity (ambient atmosphere). Thus we have a rough first approximation in three steps: K_1 is the thermal resistance between the heat source and the first isothermal surface. K_2 is the thermal resistance of the region between the first isothermal surface and the second surface, of which we, for simplicity's sake, now assume that it coincides completely with the outer envelope surface. This approximation is reasonably accurate for a thermally well-conducting envelope, for instance, a copper can. K_3 is the resistance of all the material around the envelope.

$$K = K_1 + K_2 + K_3$$

K_1 will depend upon the geometry and construction of the internal transistor element: collector and emitter diameter and thickness, size and material of base contact, nature and thickness of the semiconductor material (germanium or silicon). K_2 depends upon the material between transistor or diode and envelope and upon the material of the envelope itself. K_3 depends upon the whole situation around the transistor envelope and has to be further analyzed.

For simplicity's sake we first rewrite $K = K_1 + K_2 + K_3$ as $K = K_i + K_e$. Here $K_1 + K_2 = K_i$ represents the total thermal resistance from the internal part of the device (junction to envelope) and K_e represents the total external thermal resistance. K_e depends upon all possible manners in which we can conduct the heat away from the envelope. This is done in three different ways simultaneously: (1) by black-body radiation, (2) by conduction (through the leads or by conduction from other parts of the envelope which are in direct thermal contact with a large body, such as a chassis), and (3) by convection of the surrounding air in contact with the envelope. These three effects work together (in parallel) to carry the heat away from the envelope. If we define the external thermal conductance as $1/K_e$, the radiation conductance as $1/K_{er}$, the convection conductance as $1/K_{ev}$, and the conductance conductance as $1/K_{ed}$, we can write

$$\frac{1}{K_e} = \frac{1}{K_{er}} + \frac{1}{K_{ev}} + \frac{1}{K_{ed}}$$

Depending upon external conditions, each one of those three factors can be relatively more important than the others. For instance, $1/K_{er}$ is a very important factor for medium- and small-power units, which operate without an additional heat sink. In case an external heat sink is used, $1/K_{ed}$ becomes very important. If we use forced-air cooling, then $1/K_{ev}$ is the determining factor.

While the K_i and K_e values can be roughly calculated, when we assume certain approximations, the actual measurement is relatively simple. K_e can be determined indirectly if we measure K_i by immersing the transistor in an oil bath of constant temperature and determine K along the lines indicated in Sec. 9.4a. In this case, $K_1 = K_i$, because K_e approaches 0. After measuring the same transistor in air ($K_2 = K_i + K_e$), we find

$$K_e = K_2 - K_1$$

To illustrate this, in Table 9.2 the K measurements in air and in oil are given for a glass transistor ($\frac{3}{5}$ in. high and $\frac{1}{5}$ in. diameter, collector diameter 18 mils, emitter diameter 14 mils, base contact a gold-plated wire, case filled with silicon grease, 10-mc germanium alloy type, 0.0023-in.-thick germanium crystal). For metal cans of the same size, the K values are of the same order of magnitude. The values show that the internal heat resistance represents here nearly 60 per cent of the total K.

We can improve the internal heat conductance for a given collector and emitter diameter by the use of larger contact elements to the base, emitter, and collector. The effect of using a larger base contact is shown in Table 9.2, second line. Here we see that K_i is reduced by as much as 50 per cent if we use the base contact as a sort of internal cooling fin.

TABLE 9.2. ANALYSIS OF INTERNAL THERMAL RESISTANCES IN A
10-MC GERMANIUM ALLOY TRANSISTOR

Type of transistor	K in air, °C/mw	K in oil = K_i, °C/mw	$K_e = K - K_i$, °C/mw
Standard 10-mc alloy (see text)........	0.47	0.28	0.19
Same type but large metal base contact ($\pm 3 \times 6$ mm)....................	0.31	0.14	0.17
Standard type but with better conducting filler.........................	0.32	0.15	0.17
Large base contact with better conducting filler......................	0.25	0.10	0.15

Another way to reduce K_i is to reduce the thermal resistance of the filling substance, in this case a silicone grease. The third line of Table 9.2 shows this effect. If we combine the better-conducting grease with the internal cooling fin, the K_i is further reduced (fourth line of Table 9.2). Generally, it is found that the best K is always obtained by making the heat resistance directly around the heat-developing area as low as possible. A thin sheet of high resistance (for instance, a thin layer of air) will be relatively more harmful when it is very near the heated junction than when it is near the periphery of the envelope. For this reason high-power devices always have a direct contact between the heated electrode and the envelope.

9.4c. The "Heat Sink." After the manufacturer has spent so much effort on the inner thermal structure of the transistor and has tried to minimize the internal heat resistance K_i, in comparison with the external K_e, a good understanding of K_e by the user of the transistor is very important. To illustrate this, let us consider the internal and external K of a germanium power transistor with a collector diameter of $\pm \frac{1}{6}$ in. which has been shaved to a thickness of 8 mils. The internal K consists of the following components:

	$°C/watt$
Indium.....................	± 0.5
Germanium.................	0.1
Thin solder layer.............	0.1
Copper base.................	0.2
Total K_i..................	0.9

The insulating washer between case and heat sink can be made, for instance, of mica, Mylar, or anodized aluminum and will vary in K value depending on thickness and material used. A normal value is about 0.5°C/watt. A normal heat sink as an aluminum chassis or plate (8 by 8 by 0.1 in.) will have a K of about 2 to 3°C/watt. An iron chassis will be much worse. So for the case where all conditions have been fulfilled, the total K will vary between 4 and 5°C/watt. This means that for a collector dissipation of 5 watts and an ambient temperature of 60°C, the collector junction temperature will rise to

$$60 + 5 \times 5 = 85°C$$

This is about the upper maximum which can be allowed for normal use. If the screws have not been well tightened, or if a thin air layer is present between transistor base, insulator, and heat sink, the K can easily increase 1°C/watt. Also, the use of a chassis of different material and/or thickness may add 1 or 2°C. Thus, if K is not properly controlled, $5 \times (1 + 2) = 15°C$ increase in T_j can be found and the transistor will be damaged or can burn out by thermal instability.

Much can be gained by the construction of effective cooling fins with or without forced-air cooling. For the efficient use of very high power devices such as silicon power rectifiers, the whole result depends on the use of the cooling fin or heat sink. Unfortunately, thermal calculations and measurements for these cases are difficult, and the result also depends strongly upon the way of mounting (horizontal or vertical), density of the ambient air (altitude correction), torque on the bolts, form of the fin, surface of the fin, etc. With the aid of monographs the thermal calculations can be carried through.[13]

9.5. Encapsulation Standardization. At the present time, the number of different forms of encapsulation is tremendous. Nearly every manufacturer has tried to make his own form of envelope and tried to convince others that his should be the standard. For some years the Joint Electron Device Engineering Council has been trying to achieve a certain standardization in the field of semiconductor devices. Although as a first result the most important outlines and base connections of the products of the major American manufacturers have all been accepted as standard, there are certain envelopes which are becoming more and more an accepted standard for everybody.   The outlines as well as the bases have been coded in the following way.

Outline (example, TO − 1):

TO = transistor outline
 1 = serial order assignment of outlines as they are registered
DO = diode outline

Base (example, E3 − 15)

E = terminals integral with envelope.   Index may be partial and indicated by terminal position, reference mark, or noncentral index member
3 = number of terminals or contact members provided
15 = serial order assignment within the "E" group

Some of the most used transistor outlines and base standards are:

TO − 1 with E3 − 39 for miniature, low-power low- and high-frequency transistors
TO − 7 with E4 − 48 for miniature, low-power high-frequency transistors
TO − 3 with E2 − 42 for power transistors
TO − 5 with E3 − 44 and TO − 9 with E3 − 51 for computer and industrial transistors and many other types

For small diodes the subminiature all-glass encapsulation is used by nearly all manufacturers.   For power diodes the standardization has started but will still take some time.

In Europe, generally no standardization has been achieved yet but some JEDEC standards are used by several manufacturers.

9.6. Testing of Encapsulated Units.   With every technique for making semiconductor devices a certain possibility always exists that some units have not been hermetically sealed.   For long-life applications it is, however, of the greatest importance to eliminate faulty units right away.   Several methods exist to test for leaks in the hermetic seal.   The principles of leak detection are based upon the following techniques: (1) penetration of the envelope by a low-viscosity fluid and (2) penetration of the envelope by gas molecules.   The detection of the penetration always forms the difficult part of the operation.   When we use a low-viscosity fluid, the problem is easy for all-glass envelopes.   If we dissolve some sort of colored or fluorescent dye in the fluid, the penetration can be readily observed.   In the case of a metal envelope we shall have to use the sensitivity of the transistor or diode for water vapor and eliminate the leaky devices by testing the reverse characteristics for hysteresis, flutter, or increased leakage current.

As a fluid, we can use water with a detergent or alcohol, which has a low viscosity by itself.   The units can first be placed in a desiccator or other vacuum system to be evacuated and then immersed in the fluid, after which atmospheric pressure or overpressure is admitted into the system to force the fluid inside.

Another alternative is to expose the units to a fluid of low viscosity under a few atmospheres overpressure.   The advantage of the use of water and detergent or alcohol is that the semiconductor surfaces are very sensitive to these polar molecules and the electrical characteristics react strongly.

A very simple test is the boiling test whereby the units are immersed in boiling water and alternately boiled and cooled for two days.   The cooling cycle gives the water molecules an opportunity to suck in if the envelope leaks.

The detection of special gas molecules is done with a mass spectrograph (or "leak detector"). When we expose the units to some atmospheres overpressure of hydrogen or helium, these molecules can penetrate the smallest leaks. Then the units are brought in the mass spectrometer or leak detector and tests for H_2 or He are made. This method is very sensitive but involves rather costly equipment. An advantage of this method is that the device characteristics do not have to be used to detect the leaks. Therefore, the method can be used on empty envelopes as well. As a variation upon the method, the unit can be encapsulated in an H_2 or He atmosphere and then be checked with a leak detector straight away.

REFERENCES

1. de Mars, G.: Some Effects of Semiconductor Surfaces on Device Operation, *Semicond. Prod.*, vol. 2, pp. 24–29, 1959.
2. Wallmark, J. T., and R. R. Johnson: Influence of Hydration—Dehydration of the Germanium Oxide Layer on the Characteristics of p-n-p Transistors, *RCA Rev.*, vol. 18, pp. 512–524, 1957.
3. Atalla, M. M., E. Tannenbaum, and E. J. Scheibner: Stabilization of Silicon Surfaces by Thermally Grown Oxides, *Bell System Tech. J.*, vol. 38, pp. 749–785, 1959.
4. Wahl, A. J., and J. J. Kleimack: Factors Affecting Reliability of Alloy Junction Transistors, *Proc. IRE*, vol. 44, pp. 494–502, 1956.
5. Kohl, W. H.: "Materials Technology for Electron Tubes," chap. 16, pp. 403–422, Reinhold Publishing Corporation, New York, 1951.
6. Espe, W., and M. Knoll: Werkstoffkunde der Hochvakuumtechnik, in "Glass-Metall-Einschmelzungen," p. 337, Springer-Verlag, Berlin, 1936.
7. Koets, A. A. M., W. A. Roovers, and J. C. van Vessem: Dutch Patent 87,748, U.S. Patent 2,877,392.
8. Knoll, M.: "Materials and Processes of Electron Devices," p. 288, Springer-Verlag, Berlin, 1959.
9. Pearson, A. D., and S. S. Fluschen: Program of the Fall Meeting of the Electrochemical Society (A), September, 1958.
10. JEDEC Meeting No. 22, pp. 14–16, Jan. 16, 1958.
11. Gates, R. F., and R. A. Johnson: The Measurement of Thermal Resistance, *Semicond. Prod.*, vol. 2, pp. 21–27, 1959.
12. Reich, B.: Measurement of Transistor Thermal Resistance, *Proc. IRE*, vol. 46, pp. 1204–1206, 1958.
13. Luft, W.: Taking the Heat off Semiconductor Devices, *Electronics*, vol. 32, p. 53, 1959.

Section 10

DEVICE DESIGN CONSIDERATIONS

B. N. Slade

IBM Corporation, Poughkeepsie, N.Y.

In Part I the physical principles governing device operations are given. In the preceding sections of Part II a catalogue of material- and device-fabrication techniques is described. In this section it is intended that the kind of choice which can be made between the various techniques will be illustrated. Only a few devices are considered for illustration, and no attempt will be made to present detailed design calculations. The detail which is presented should be considered to be illustrative rather than complete. Furthermore, many of the equations used in the designs are approximations at best. In the actual final design of the devices considered here, a certain amount of empirical experimentation is required to achieve the geometry and process required to give a specific set of electrical performance parameters.

10.1. High-frequency Transistors. The first illustration of device design considerations will be used to show the design capabilities of alloy- and diffused-junction transistors. Devices using germanium will be considered, but the same design considerations apply to silicon with the use of the appropriate values of the different parameters. In Sec. 4, the limitations of the high-frequency response of transistors were given as

$$\text{Current gain cutoff frequency } f_\alpha = \frac{D}{\pi W^2} \tag{10.1a}$$

$$\text{Collector capacitance } C_c = A_c \left(\frac{\kappa \kappa_0}{2 V_C \mu_n \rho_b} \right)^{\frac{1}{2}} \tag{10.2a}$$

and

$$\text{Base spreading resistance } R_{bs} = \frac{\rho_b}{4\pi W} \tag{10.3a}$$

† These sections from the original text of L. P. Hunter.

10–1

where W is the width of the base region, A_c is the area of the collector junctions, and κ_0 is the dielectric constant of free space in the mks system. Equation (10.1a) is the alpha-cutoff frequency as V_C approaches zero. For the case of germanium, these formulas can be reduced to the following conveniently usable forms using the following constants:

$$\kappa_0 = 16$$
$$\mu_p = 1,700$$
$$\mu_n = 3,600$$
$$D_p = 44 \text{ cm}^2/\text{sec}$$
$$D_n = 94 \text{ cm}^2/\text{sec}$$

	For PNP transistors	For NPN transistors	
$f_\alpha =$	$\dfrac{2.67}{W^2}$ mc	$\dfrac{5.58}{W^2}$ mc	(10.1b)
$C_c =$	$\dfrac{0.071d^2}{\sqrt{V_{C\rho_b}}}$ $\mu\mu\text{f}$	$\dfrac{0.103d^2}{\sqrt{V_{C\rho_b}}}$ $\mu\mu\text{f}$	(10.2b)
$R_{bs} =$	$\dfrac{31\rho_b}{W}$ ohms	$\dfrac{31\rho_b}{W}$ ohms	(10.3b)

where d, the diameter of the collector junction, and W are in mils; ρ_b is in ohm-centimeters; and V_C is in volts. These formulas are restricted by certain conditions. Equation (10.1a) assumes that injected carriers are transported across the base region solely by diffusion and that there are no sweeping fields in the base region. Equation (10.2a) assumes that the collector region is of very low resistivity at the collector junction. Equation (10.3a) is given for a disk-shaped base region with an ohmic contact entirely around its periphery.

In discussing the device design, we must also consider the junction-voltage limitations. One such limitation is the avalanche-type voltage breakdown. Also, in Sec. 4, it was noted that in a transistor structure a voltage failure could be present when the depletion region of the collector barrier moved through the base region and made contact with the emitter. This was called punch-through. The punch-through voltage PV_C can be calculated under the same assumptions that were used for the C_c calculations. We can summarize the avalanche and punch-through failures with the following empirical relations:

	For PNP transistors	For NPN transistors	
$PV_C =$	$\dfrac{630W^2}{\rho_b}$ volts	$\dfrac{1340W^2}{\rho_b}$ volts	(10.4a)
$BV_{CBO} =$	$87\rho_b^{0.725}$ volts	$51\rho_b^{0.725}$ volts	(10.4b)

In order to have some specific design objective, let us arbitrarily pick the following specifications for the common emitter connection:

$$\text{Low-pass bandwidth } B > 0.5 \text{ mc}$$
$$h_{fe} > 20$$
$$C_c < 3 \ \mu\mu\text{f}$$
$$BV_{CBO} > 40 \text{ volts}$$

We shall assume that these specifications have been evolved with all due consideration of various circuit techniques and that we are now faced with the problem of choosing the best way to make a transistor to meet them.

The minimum allowable h_{fe} will require an alpha-cutoff frequency of

$$f_\alpha = \frac{B}{1 - \alpha} \approx 10 \text{ mc} \tag{10.5}$$

Also, the bandwidth specification imposes a limit on the load resistance because of the collector capacitance, but here again we shall assume that this has been considered by the circuit designer. We must be certain, however, that the charging resistance for C_c is the load resistance and that the base spreading resistance is small compared with the load resistance. Furthermore, we must be sure that the cutoff frequency of the R_L and C_c is well above the required bandwidth so that the frequency will not be limited by the $R_L C_c$ product. For our requirements, then, we shall calculate an R_L for a bandwidth B about ten times as large as the bandwidth objective of 0.5 mc. We can calculate the maximum load resistance from the formulas of Sec. 12 as

$$R_L = \frac{1 - \alpha}{2\pi B C_c} = \frac{0.05}{2\pi \times 3 \times 10^{-12} \times 5 \times 10^6} = 530 \text{ ohms} \qquad (10.6)$$

This means that the R_{bs} must be about 50 ohms or less so that it will not require an even smaller R_L than the circuit designer planned for.

Let us first examine the alloy transistor to determine if it will meet these requirements. We shall plan to design for a minimum alpha so that the $f_\alpha = 10$ mc holds. Since this f_α has been determined by the design requirement on B, we can use (10.1b) to calculate that a base width

$$W = \sqrt{\frac{2.67}{10}} = 0.52 \text{ mil}$$

is required for the PNP structure. From this base width we next calculate the base resistivity required to satisfy the collector-voltage requirements. From Eq. (10.4a) we can calculate

$$\rho_b = \frac{630 \times 0.267}{40} = 4.2 \text{ ohm-cm}$$

With a ρ_b of 4.2 ohm-cm we calculate from Eq. (10.4b) an avalanche-breakdown voltage of

$$BV_{CBO} = 87\rho_b^{0.725} = 87 \times 2.84 = 247 \text{ volts}$$

In actual practice it is difficult to achieve the theoretical value of avalanche breakdown. Surface leakage across the junction usually results in a junction breakdown somewhat below the theoretical value even when the transistor is subjected to the most careful and rigorous surface processing. Therefore, in the transistor design, it is advisable to allow for this decrease in voltage. In the above case, however, it is obvious that there is far more than enough safety factor, since our required voltage is only 40 volts.

We now calculate the collector diameter required to achieve a collector capacitance of 3 $\mu\mu$f using ρ_b of 4.2 ohm-cm and a collector voltage of 5 volts.

$$C_c = \frac{0.071d^2}{V_C\rho_b} = \frac{0.071d^2}{\sqrt{5 \times 4.2}} = 3 \ \mu\mu\text{f}$$

$$d = 13.8 \text{ mils}$$

Calculating the base spreading resistance from (10.3b),

$$R_{bs} = \frac{31\rho_b}{W} = \frac{31 \times 4.2}{0.52} = 250 \text{ ohms}$$

Since we require a value substantially lower, approximately 50 ohms, we can reduce ρ_b to about 0.7 ohm-cm to obtain a value of R_{bs} of 42 ohms. This will result in a

BV_{CBO} of 67 volts and a PV_C of 240 volts, still well above our minimum requirements. Therefore, it appears that these specifications can be met by a PNP alloy transistor. However, the required base width is approaching the lower limit which can be effectively controlled by the alloy process. Consequently, it appears that for the frequency and voltage requirements, we are approaching the limit of design capability of the PNP alloy type. For the required f_α, the base width of the NPN type would be

$$W = \sqrt{\frac{5.58}{10}} = 0.75 \text{ mil}$$

It appears that there is a greater degree of flexibility in designing an NPN alloy transistor for the frequency range of 10 mc and greater, but even in the NPN case we soon approach a limit.

Now let us select another set of design objectives with a higher frequency of operation.

$$\text{Low-pass bandwidth } B > 2 \text{ mc}$$
$$h_{fe} > 20$$
$$C_c < 3 \ \mu\mu\text{f}$$
$$BV_{CBO} > 40 \text{ volts}$$
$$R_{b\varepsilon} < 40 \text{ ohms}$$

The minimum allowable α (≈ 0.95) will require an alpha-cutoff frequency of

$$f_\alpha = \frac{B}{1 - 0.95} = 40 \text{ mc}$$

We immediately can see from the base width required to achieve this cutoff frequency that a degree of control beyond the alloy process capabilities is required.

$$W = \sqrt{\frac{2.67}{40}} = 0.258 \text{ mil}$$

Even the base width calculated for the NPN alloy case, 0.377 mil, is too small to make fabrication of such a device practical.

It is obvious then that a severe frequency limitation exists in the alloy-junction-type transistor because of the difficulty in achieving the proper combination of base width, base resistivity, and punch-through voltage. We shall now discuss a far more effective method of achieving high-frequency response in a structure which lends itself to a considerable amount of design flexibility. Such a device is a diffused-base transistor[1,2] in which a drift field is built into the transistor by forming a base region of an exponentially graded impurity distribution. Because of the high impurity concentration in the base region adjacent to the emitter, base regions of extremely narrow dimensions, on the order of 0.1 mil, can be achieved without encountering serious emitter-to-collector punch-through voltage problems.

Let us explore a few techniques which enable us to achieve such base-width control. Figure 10.1a illustrates the "post-alloy-diffusion" technique[3] of making a PNP diffused-base transistor. In this technique a narrow N-type region is diffused in a P-type germanium pellet. This region can be formed by antimony or arsenic diffusion and serves as the external base ring contact. A lead-alloy dot containing small amounts of an acceptor and donor impurity is now placed on the N-type skin. The acceptor impurity must have a considerably higher segregation coefficient than the donor impurity, and the donor impurity must have a considerably higher diffusion constant than the acceptor impurity. Gallium and antimony are examples of typical acceptor and donor impurity metals which fill these requirements. The alloy is now heated at approximately 750°C and penetrates the N-type skin as in Fig. 10.1*b*. The molten Pb-Ga-Sb-Ge alloy is held at this temperature for several minutes, during which time the antimony atoms diffuse ahead at a much faster rate than the gallium atoms, thus forming a thin N-type exponentially graded base region. Since the diffusion constant of antimony is approximately 230 times that of gallium at 750°C, the degree of gallium diffusion is negligible. This technique provides a closely controlled method of obtaining a thin base region, since the diffusion is controlled only by time and temperature. In the remaining portion of the process, a base ring is

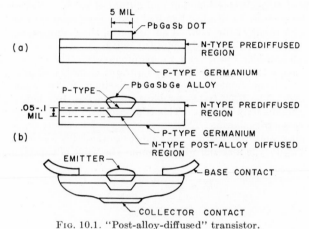

FIG. 10.1. "Post-alloy-diffused" transistor.

soldered to the prediffused N-type skin, leads are attached to the emitter and collector alloy dots, and the transistor is electrolytically etched in order to (1) clean the emitter region and remove some of the highly doped material adjacent to the emitter junction in order to achieve a high emitter breakdown voltage and (2) remove enough of the germanium in order to reduce the collector diameter and to achieve a sufficiently low collector capacitance.

Alternate techniques to the post-alloy-diffusion process will achieve the same results. Figure 10.2 illustrates the cross section of a device where a closely controlled base region is formed by diffusion of impurities into germanium in the vapor phase. An alloy dot of opposite impurity type is mechanically positioned on the surface or evaporated through a mask, then alloyed at a sufficiently low temperature to assure that it will not penetrate the base region. The dimensions of the dot and the temperature of alloying must be adjusted in order to assure control of penetration and

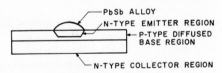

FIG. 10.2. NPN diffused-base transistor.

base width. This technique is applicable to either the PNP or NPN types. In the case of the PNP type, arsenic or antimony diffusion onto P-type germanium will form the N-type base and indium, gallium, or aluminum will form the emitter alloy material. In the NPN case, indium or gallium diffusion onto N-type germanium will form the P-type base and a lead alloy containing antimony or arsenic will form the emitter.

Let us now determine if our requirements can be met with the diffused transistor made by these techniques. Even if we completely neglect the effects of the sweeping field in the base region, it is possible to obtain a 40-mc response with a base region of approximately 0.26 mil. This base thickness is easily achieved by alloy-diffusion techniques.

Throughout this chapter calculations involving frequency cutoff and base width of diffused-base transistors ignore the effects of the drift field in the base region resulting from the graded impurity distribution.   For several reasons it is difficult to calculate accurately the frequency enhancement due to the field.   First, the field varies depending upon the actual impurity distribution in the base region and this distribution varies considerably with the process.   Second, at high current densities the effects of the drift field decrease considerably.   Finally, in the higher-frequency designs, the frequency cutoff is limited not by the base width and drift field but by the capacitance and resistance of the collector junction and output circuitry.   Nevertheless, at low currents and frequencies up to a few hundred megacycles, some increase in frequency cutoff occurs as a result of the field.   Consequently, the design examples given here can probably be treated with a little more flexibility.

Now we shall consider the C_c and R_{bs} requirements.   The exponentially graded junction will have a lower capacitance per unit area than will an abrupt alloy junction, so that it will be quite safe if we calculate a maximum collector-junction diameter from Eq. (10.2b).   The PNP transistor illustrated in Fig. 10.1 indicates a collector diameter of approximately 14 mils.   This is a practical dimension using the emitter and base ring geometries shown.   Therefore, we can now calculate the required P-type resistivity to obtain our required C_c.   We must use the NPN formula in Eq. (10.2b), since our starting P-type material will determine the value of capacitance.

$$C_c = 3 = \frac{0.103 \times 14^2}{\sqrt{\rho_t \times 5}}$$

$$\rho_t = 15 \text{ ohm-cm}$$

Since the capacitance per unit area for a graded junction is approximately 33 per cent lower than that for an abrupt junction, we could, in practice, use a lower value of ρ_b, say 10 ohm-cm, in this example.

From (10.6) we calculate the value of R_L for a bandwidth which is ten times the design value,

$$R_L = \frac{0.05}{2\pi \times 3 \times 10^{-12} \times 2 \times 10^7} = 135 \text{ ohms}$$

In order to maintain a low value of R_{bs}, say about 15 ohms, the average ρ of the base region must also be low.   For a value of $R_{bs} = 15$ ohms and $W = 0.26$ mil,

$$\rho_t = \frac{0.26 \times 15}{31} = 0.13 \text{ ohm-cm}$$

Although this value is quite low, it can be obtained by properly controlling the surface concentration and steepness of the gradient during the diffusion process.

It appears from the foregoing discussion, however, that the above design would be marginal for frequencies much higher than these objectives.   Even though base-width control to much smaller values is no problem, some limitations are apparent owing to the difficulty in selecting a proper combination of R_L and R_{bs} values.   For requirements having somewhat higher frequencies and/or lower capacitances, either higher values of collector resistivities are required or other geometries must be employed to reduce the C_c.   The "mesa" transistor[2] appears to offer the best solution to this problem by permitting the evaporation or diffusion of emitters and bases of extremely small dimensions and the formation of collectors of very small area.   Figure 10.3 shows a schematic diagram of a mesa transistor.   One technique consists of the following steps shown in Fig. 10.3 which show the formation of an NPN mesa transistor.[4]

First, a graded region of P type is formed by diffusion of an indium vapor onto an N-type germanium wafer. A matrix of Ag-Al base strips is next evaporated onto the P-type region through a mask. A suitable mask with apertures lined up over the base strips is now placed onto the wafer, and silicon monoxide evaporated through the mask as in Fig. 10.3a. The mask is now removed, and an N-type vapor diffusion is carried out. Since the silicon monoxide acts as a mask against the diffusion of donor impurities, the diffusion has occurred only in selected regions. As shown in Fig. 10.3b, we now have several NPN diffused-base transistors which need contacts made to the

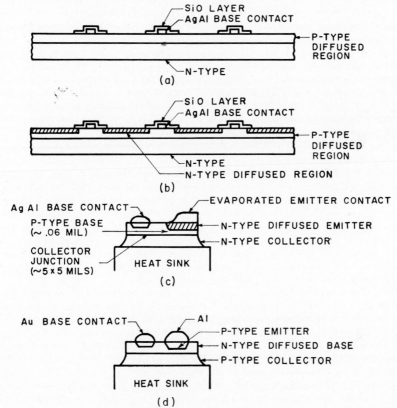

Fig. 10.3. Germanium mesa transistors.

emitter and collector. Evaporation techniques are used to make contact to these two regions. After the individual transistor assemblies are separated, the collector is attached to a heat sink and a mesa is now etched to reveal the collector as in Fig. 10.3c and reduce the collector to its final desired area. This technique permits extremely small emitters and collectors to be formed through masks with apertures of desired dimensions and geometry; furthermore, the transistors can be made in large batches on one wafer by simultaneous diffusion through one mask. Another technique widely used for the fabrication of PNP mesa diffused transistors is illustrated in Fig. 10.3d. An N-type region is diffused onto a P-type wafer. Aluminum is now evaporated through a mask having appropriate apertures. Another evaporation of gold doped with a donor impurity is subsequently carried out through another mask to form the base region.

The above techniques not only have provided a low-cost method of assembling transistors but also permit the formation of junctions of very small geometry on transistors having frequency capabilities greater than 500 mc. Thus we have a practical method of further enhancing the frequency response of the transistor.

As an example, consider an NPN mesa transistor made by the double-diffusion technique with the dimensions shown in Fig. 10.3. We calculate the frequency cutoff to be

$$f_\alpha = \frac{5.58}{W^2} = \frac{5.58}{(0.06)^2} = 1{,}540 \text{ mc}$$

Here again we have neglected the effects of the accelerating field, and depending upon the magnitude of this field, the frequency cutoff could be somewhat higher. However, this value should be considered only as the intrinsic cutoff, i.e., the value determined by the transit time between the emitter and collector. The measured cutoff frequency will be somewhat less than this value owing to the frequency limitations of the collector-plus-can capacitance and the circuit load. For the geometry of the mesa transistor shown in Fig. 10.3, measured cutoff frequencies on the order of 600 to 700 mc are realizable. For higher values of frequency, further reduction in geometry is required as well as different packaging techniques.[5]

In the above description of a mesa transistor it is seen that the primary effect of the mesa structure is to limit the geometrical area of the collector junction while still maintaining mechanical strength. This allows a reduction in C_c and, therefore, a higher operating frequency. It is possible to produce the same effect by diffusing the P-type base region through the openings of a suitable masking material coating the surface of the wafer. If these openings are of the desired collector junction area, a mesaless structure can be obtained with the same electrical characteristics as a mesa structure. In this case, of course, the base and emitter contacts must be entirely within the area of the base diffusion. Double-diffused structures of this type are possible in both germanium and silicon and lend themselves to the use of surface protective coatings better than does the mesa structure.

If the high-frequency transistor is to be used for switching, a further improvement is possible in the so-called "epitaxial" structure.[6] In this structure, the starting material consists of a two-layer wafer, the main bulk of the material being very low resistivity (less than 0.001 ohm-cm) and a thin layer of normal-resistivity, high-quality material in which the transistor structure is formed. This latter layer is formed by epitaxial vapor deposition upon a polished surface of the bulk material (see Sec. 7.11).

The resulting transistor preserves the collector junction qualities of a transistor made with normal collector material and yet shows a very low collector series resistance because of the close proximity of the low-resistivity material to the collector junction. The structure may have the usual thickness to preserve mechanical strength. An additional switching advantage lies in the possibility of making the bulk material very low lifetime so that the transistor is capable of coming out of saturation very quickly.

Such a layer structure formed in the initial wafer is possible only in PNP germanium transistors and NPN silicon transistors, since the impurity diffusion constants are such that the resistivity of the epitaxial layer would be radically altered by subsequent processing heat-treatments in NPN germanium or PNP silicon transistors.

10.2. Power Transistors. For our next illustration, we shall choose a transistor capable of dissipating and handling relatively high power levels. In a power transistor the criteria of greatest importance are the power-dissipating capacity and the maintenance of a high current gain at high values of emitter current. Again we shall arbitrarily choose some specifications in order to set definite design objectives. The common-emitter connection is the circuit configuration specified:

Low-pass bandwidth $B = 10$ kc
$$h_{fe} = 50 \text{ at maximum}$$
$$h_{fe} = 30 \text{ at } I_c = 3 \text{ amp}$$
$$BV_{CBO} = 100 \text{ volts}$$
$$P_c = 20 \text{ watts at mounting base temperature of } 25°C$$

We shall first consider germanium-alloy junction technology to determine if these specifications can be met. The bandwidth requires an $f_\alpha = 10 h_{fe} = 500$ kc at the low emitter currents. This, in turn, requires a base width of 2.32 mils. Since the collector rating is 100 volts, it is desirable to allow for some safety factor, say 150 volts. Furthermore, as pointed out before, junction breakdown voltages are usually limited to values below that determined by theoretical avalanche breakdown due to surface leakage across the junction. This problem obviously gives us some difficulty in the design, and a certain degree of empiricism must be used in determining the actual practical voltage breakdown which can be obtained with a given surface treatment and value of resistivity. However, for this purpose, we shall use a value of 150 volts for calculations. With this value we calculate the value of base resistivity to be

$$BV_{CBO} = 87 \rho^{0.725}$$
$$\rho^{0.725} = {}^{150}\!/_{87}$$
$$\rho_b = 2.1 \text{ ohm-cm}$$

Using this value of resistivity we now can calculate a value of PV_C. Although the value of the base width is 2.32, the PV_C will be determined by the point of closest spacing between emitter and collector. Thus, if the alloy process forms uneven junctions, PV_C can be considerably less than that determined by the average base width. Assuming, however, a transistor of flat and uniform junctions, the PV_C is calculated to be

$$PV_C = \frac{630 \times (2.32)^2}{2.1} = 1,600 \text{ volts}$$

Obviously, there is no problem with voltage punch-through in this case, and we see that the frequency and voltage requirements are compatible.

We shall now consider the h_{fe} requirements. In Sec. 4 there are expressions given for the various components of $h_{fe} = \alpha/(1 - \alpha)$; γ, the injection efficiency [Eq. (4.7)]; β, the transport efficiency [Eq. (4.9)]; and α^*, the intrinsic collector efficiency [Eq. (4.20)]. It was further mentioned that there is an effect of surface recombination around the emitter rim which causes the h_{fe} to fall off as I_E is increased. This effect can be calculated to a first approximation as follows:[7]

The surface recombination velocity s is defined by $J_s = qps$ (where J_s is the recombination current density flowing into the surface and p is the density of excess carriers just beneath the surface). A_s is the area of the annular ring of base surface surrounding the emitter which is effective in carrying the recombination current I_s. Now we have

$$I_s = qsA_s p$$

where p is the density of injected holes just on the base side of the emitter junction of a PNP transistor. The emitter hole current is

$$I_{pe} = \frac{qA_e D_p p}{W}$$

where A_e is the area of the emitter junction. Solving for p and substituting in the expression for I_s we get

$$I_s = \frac{sA_sI_{pe}W}{A_eD_p}$$

and the transport factor β is given by

$$\beta = \frac{I_{pe} - I_s}{I_{pe}} = 1 - \frac{I_s}{I_{pe}} = 1 - \frac{sA_sW}{A_eD_p}$$

Combining with Eqs. (4.7), (4.9), and (4.20), we find the following expression for $1/h_{fe}$ for a PNP transistor:

$$\frac{1}{h_{fe}} = \frac{\rho_e W}{\rho_b L_{ne}} + \frac{A_s s W}{A_e D_p} + \frac{W^2}{2L_{p5}^2} - \frac{n_c \mu_n}{2p_c \mu_p} \tag{10.7}$$

The first two terms are the dominant terms and the only ones sensitive to large emitter currents. The first term arises from the injection efficiency of the emitter, and since it contains ρ_b it is clear that the conductivity modulation of the base region at high emitter currents will affect it. We shall first calculate the dependence of this first term on I_E.

If we let Δp be the injected hole density at the emitter, the emitter hole current will be

$$I_{pe} = A_e q D_p \frac{\Delta p}{W} \approx I_E \tag{10.8}$$

From Ref. 7 we find that D_p is effectively increased at high emitter currents because of the electric field set up in the base region. The correction factor which is applied to D_p is given as $(1 + M)/(1 + M/2)$, where $M = WI_E bq/kTA_e\sigma_b$. The additional electron density at the emitter side of the base region is $\Delta n = \Delta p$ because of space-charge neutrality.

We shall now calculate a correction factor for the first term of Eq. (10.7) to take account of the effects of high emitter currents. The original form of the first term of Eq. (10.7) can be obtained from Eq. (4.3) of Sec. 4 by division and appropriate substitution to change from an NPN structure to the PNP structure considered here.† This yields

$$\frac{D_n n_b W}{D_p p_e L_{ne}} = \frac{1}{\gamma} - 1 \tag{10.9}$$

At low emitter currents $\Delta n = \Delta p \ll n_b$ and D_p is not increased by the field effect, so that the ratio $D_n n_b / D_p p_e = \rho_e/\rho_b$. At high emitter currents, however, $\Delta n = \Delta p$ is comparable to n_b and D_p is also increased. It is not proper directly to substitute $(n_b + \Delta p)$ for n_b and $D_p(1 + M)/(1 + M/2)$ for D_p since both M and Δp [see Eq. (10.8)] are functions of I_E and $\gamma = \partial I_{pe}/\partial I_E$. If we make the substitutions in the ratio I_{ne}/I_{pe} and then differentiate to get $(1/\gamma - 1)$ we find the following result:

$$\frac{1}{\gamma} - 1 = \frac{\rho_e W}{\rho_b L_{ne}} \left[1 + \frac{M}{2} + \frac{M}{2(1 + M)^3} \right] \tag{10.10}$$

The correction factor in brackets is practically $(1 + M/2)$. In our usual units M becomes $41.5 W\rho_b I_E/d^2$, where d is the diameter of the emitter in mils, W is in mils, and I_E is in milliamperes.

† The fact that D_p is implicit in the first term of Eq. (10.7) was pointed out by Dr. Gardiner L. Tucker.

The second term of (10.7) must be corrected for the variation of D_p with emitter current,[4] giving

$$\frac{A_s s W}{A_e D_p} \frac{(1 + M/2)}{(1 + M)} \tag{10.11}$$

We are now in a position to compute the change of h_{fe} with emitter current for our example transistor provided we know the relative sizes of the first two terms of (10.7) at zero emitter current. We will assume that the last two terms are negligible. In Fig. 10.4 is shown the effect of changing the relative size of the first and second terms but keeping their sum at zero emitter current constant. From these curves it can be seen that the h_{fe} requirement can be met by choosing a relatively large ratio

$$r = \frac{A_s s W / A_e D_p}{\rho_e W / \rho_b L_{ne}} \tag{10.12}$$

and allowing M to range up to about 20, or alternatively limiting M to about 4 and using a relatively small ratio r.

In practice, using alloy techniques, both M at a given I_E and r can be varied by varying d, the diameter of the emitter junction. To make this clear we will reduce r to a more usable form. A_s is the area of an annular ring of crystal surface around the periphery of the emitter alloy spot. A good approximation to its width is W because the fringing of the hole flow lines must be comparable to the width of the base region. Therefore we may write $A_s = \pi d W$ and $A_e = \pi d^2/4$, which gives the ratio

$$r = \frac{4 \rho_b s W L_{ne}}{\rho_e d D_p} \tag{10.13}$$

Now we see that as d is increased both M and r are reduced, but M is reduced much faster since d^2 appears in the denominator.

Returning to the numerical analysis

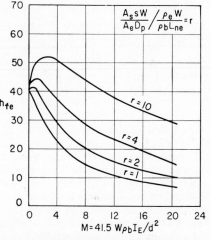

FIG. 10.4. Effect of the relative size of the surface-recombination term and the injection-efficiency term on h_{fe}.

of our transistor specifications we have established $\rho_b > 2.1$ ohm-cm and $W < 2.32$ mils. From the α requirement we have seen that the h_{fe} can vary only between 50 and 30. If we make $r \sim 8$ and limit M to 14 at $I_E = 3$ amp, we shall meet this requirement as far as per cent variation of h_{fe} is concerned. This limitation on M sets a limit on d since

$$d = \sqrt{41.5 W \rho_b I_E / M} = \sqrt{41.5 \times 2.32 \times 2.1 \times {}^{300}\!/_{14}} = 208 \text{ mils minimum}$$

The requirement that h_{fe} maximum be less that 50 means that the injection-efficiency term $\rho_e W / \rho_b L_{ne}$ plus the surface-recombination term $A_s s W / A_e D_p$ be $\geqq 0.025$. The requirement that $r \sim 8$ means that the injection-efficiency term $\rho_e W / \rho_b L_{ne} = 0.003$ and the surface-recombination term $A_s s W / A_e D_p = 4 s W^2 / d D_p = 0.022$. We have determined all the quantities in this last expression except s, the surface-recombination velocity. Calculating s we find

$$s = \frac{0.022 \times 44 \times 208 \times 2.5 \times 10^{-3}}{4 \times (2.32)^2 \times 6.25 \times 10^{-6}} = 3{,}740 \text{ cm/sec}$$

This is a reasonable value for s.

In order to achieve the high value of injection efficiencies required in the design of such a high-current transistor described here, it is necessary that the value of ρ_e/L_{ne} be quite high. By highly doping the recrystallized region of an alloy power transistor, satisfactory values can be achieved. Such high doping levels are achieved by using alloys doped with acceptor impurities (or donor impurities in the case of the NPN transistor) having high values of segregation coefficients such as gallium or aluminum.[8]

Junction diameters of 0.200 in. are readily achieved with relative uniformity permitting spacings on the order of 2 mils.

Before we leave the discussion of h_{fe} in alloy transistors, it should be pointed out that if the volume recombination term [third term of Eq. (10.7)] is comparable to the surface recombination term and both of these terms are large compared with the injection efficiency term, the h_{fe} crowding will be greatly reduced. However, this would be obtained at the expense of a lower level of h_{fe}.

It should also be pointed out that the values used for the emitter areas are approximate at best. It has been shown in the literature that the actual effective area of

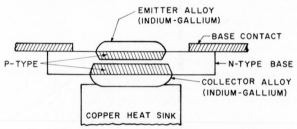

Fig. 10.5. PNP germanium alloy power transistor.

emission is somewhat less than the physical emitter area owing to the biasing off of the center of the emitter at high currents. This tends to concentrate the minority-carrier emission toward the outer edge of the emitter junction.[9]

We shall now consider the power-dissipation requirement. For the removal of heat from a small volume it is most effective to use a heat sink of good thermal conductivity thermally connected directly to the volume closest to the area where the heat is being dissipated.

To obtain the highest dissipation, we connect the heat sink directly to the collector alloy material. The cross section of the structure is shown in Fig. 10.5. From our previous discussion we shall assume a collector diameter of 0.210 in., slightly larger than the 0.190 in. for the emitter. This makes our collector area about 0.22 cm². The thickness of the recrystallized germanium between the collector junction and the alloy material is approximately 2 mils, and we shall assume that the In-Ga-Ge alloy layer between the germanium and the copper heat sink is about 4 mils thick. We shall also assume that the heat has to travel about 1 cm down the copper before it is dissipated in the chassis to which it is attached.

We can now calculate the temperature differences appearing across the various parts of the structure as 20 watts of heat flows out of the collector junction. First, the germanium layer has a thermal conductivity of 0.14 cal/(sec)(°C)(cm²)(cm); so we have

$$20 \text{ watts} = 4.8 \text{ cal/sec} = \frac{0.14 \times 0.22 \text{ cm}^2}{0.005 \text{ cm}} \Delta T$$

giving $\Delta T = 0.8°C$ across the recrystallized region. The indium alloy has a thermal conductivity about 0.4 that of germanium, so that the thermal drop across the alloy region of twice the thickness as the germanium is 4.0°C. The thermal drop in 1 cm of copper with the sink diameter approximately equal to the collector diameter [the thermal conductivity of copper is 1.0 cal/(sec)(°C)(cm²)(cm)] is

$$20 \text{ watts} = 4.8 \text{ cal/sec} = \frac{1 \times 0.22 \text{ cm}^2}{1 \text{ cm}} \Delta T$$

$$\Delta T = 22°C$$

The total temperature difference between the collector junction and the chassis is then 27°C. If the chassis is held at 25°C, the collector junction will be 52°C when dissipating 20 watts.

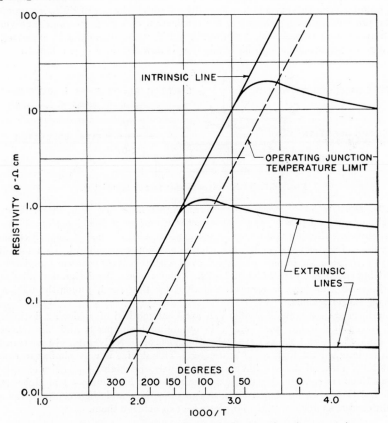

Fig. 10.6. Limiting operating temperature for junctions in germanium.

In Fig. 10.6 is shown the temperature dependence of germanium resistivity. The dashed curve gives the limiting operating temperatures for a PN junction in germanium as a function of the larger resistivity next to the collector junction. In the case of our alloy transistor, the base resistivity is the larger resistivity next to the collector junction, and because of the voltage limitation it can be no lower than 2.1 ohm-cm. Such a transistor cannot be operated much above 70°C before appreciable changes in electrical characteristics set in. Thus we can tolerate approximately a 45°C rise in temperature between the junction and the chassis. Our design meets this requirement with ease.

In germanium, transistors of higher power-handling capabilities could be designed with very low base resistivities on the order of a few tenths of an ohm-centimeter.

However, this increase would be gained at the expense of lower emitter efficiencies, resulting in low h_{fe} as well as much lower breakdown voltages.

A substantial increase in power-handling capabilities can be obtained by using silicon because of its greater energy gap. For example, silicon would allow a junction temperature of nearly 400°C in the 1-ohm-cm range, thus allowing about 150 watts dissipation in a structure the size of the one we have been considering. This presupposes that this much heat can be removed from the heat sink and its base temperature still be maintained at 25°C. Although carrier mobility is somewhat lower in silicon than in germanium, a compensating factor is the ability to obtain large junctions of good uniformity with very small base widths through the use of diffusion processes. At the present state of technology, the fabrication of high-power and high-voltage silicon transistors is practical, but there are still some difficulties in achieving the high current performance with high gain that is now obtained in germanium.

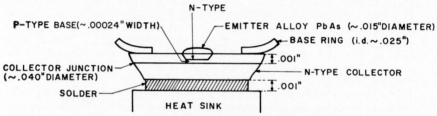

FIG. 10.7. NPN diffused-base power transistor.

10.2a. High-frequency Power Transistors.   As we have just seen, the achievement of high current and power capabilities by the use of large-area junctions is realized by present-day alloying techniques in germanium with the use of impurities having high values of segregation coefficients, such as gallium or aluminum. Junction diameters of 0.100 to 0.250 in. are readily achieved with relatively uniform junction fronts permitting spacings on the order of 2 mils. Nevertheless, the design flexibility of the alloy-junction transistor is somewhat limited by the speed, punch-through, alpha trade-off considerations.

The diffused-base transistor offers an excellent method of achieving flexibility in power transistor design, particularly in obtaining high speeds and high operating voltages. Figure 10.7 shows a cross-sectional view of an NPN diffused-base transistor which is designed for high-speed switching. This device is very similar to conventional NPN diffused devices for low power levels and high frequencies except that the junctions are considerably larger in area to permit high current and higher power characteristics. Let us choose some design objectives and then compare the alloy and diffused-base devices to see how best we can achieve them.

$$f_\alpha = 80 \text{ mc}$$
$$h_{fe} = 100 \text{ at } 500 \text{ ma}$$
$$BV_{CBO} = 100 \text{ volts}$$
$$BV_{EBO} = \text{greater than 3 volts}$$
$$P_c = 3 \text{ watts}$$

To achieve the desired frequency cutoff in an NPN alloy power transistor would require a base width of 0.27 mil. If we now compute the base resistivity required to enable us to obtain a punch-through voltage greater than 100 volts, we find that with the 0.27-mil base width we require a 0.94-ohm-cm resistivity. Now, if we compute the avalanche breakdown from (10.4b) using this value of resistivity, we obtain a value of only 50 volts, well below the minimum collector breakdown we specified. Therefore, even if we were able to obtain base widths as low as 0.27 mil with large junction alloy processes, it would be impossible to meet both the punch-through and breakdown requirements.

Now let us analyze the diffused-base structure for the same requirements. As we discussed in the previous section, it is relatively easy to obtain base widths on the order of 0.27 mil by diffusion. Consequently, even if we ignore the effects of the drift field in the base region resulting from the graded impurity distribution, an 80-mc frequency cutoff can be achieved without difficulty. In determining the punch-through voltage we first assume a surface concentration of approximately 10^{19} atoms/cm^3 of acceptors. Since some penetration of the emitter alloy occurs, we can assume that the acceptor concentration of the base region opposite the emitter front is lower, say approximately 3×10^{16} atoms/cm^3. This concentration would result in a resistivity at the edge of the base region of approximately 0.1 ohm-cm. From Eq. (10.4b) the calculated value of avalanche breakdown for the emitter is 9 volts, allowing for considerable safety factor over our 3-volt requirement. In actual practice the periphery of the emitter alloy junction will contact the surface of the base region where the impurity concentration is much higher, approximately 10^{19} atoms/cm^3 as pointed out above. This would tend to short-cut the interior portion of the emitter and result in much lower breakdown voltage. However, in actual practice, etching this portion of the emitter-base region will result in BV_{CBO} values approaching the one calculated above.

Since our collector breakdown voltage requirement is 100 volts, we chose the value of 150 volts for which we calculated a resistivity of 2.1 ohm-cm in the previous section. Using this value of collector resistivity and a base graded exponentially from a value of 0.1 ohm-cm next to the emitter, it is practical to obtain an average base resistivity of 0.94 ohm-cm which is needed to obtain the 100-volt punch-through value with the 0.27-mil spacing. Consequently, the voltage and frequency requirements are compatible in this type transistor.

We next determine the value of h_{fe} at 500 ma using the geometry of the transistor shown in Fig. 10.5. Using an emitter diameter of 0.015 in. we calculate an approximate h_{fe} directly from Eqs. (10.10) and (10.11). We also calculate the value of M from our previous expression $M = 2.1 \times 41.5 W \rho_b I_E / d^2$. We have multiplied this expression by 2.1, the ratio of electron-to-hole mobilities, to convert M for an NPN transistor. In calculating the injection efficiency term, a value of 2.2 ohms is used for ρ_e / L_{ne}. This value has previously been experimentally determined for an arsenic-doped emitter in an NPN alloy-junction transistor.[10]

$$M = \frac{2.1 \times 41.5 \times 0.27 \times 0.1 \times 500}{15^2} = 5.2$$

$$\frac{1}{h_{fe}} \approx \left(1 + \frac{M}{2}\right)\left[\frac{\rho_e W}{\rho_b L_{ne}} + \left(\frac{A_{ss} W}{A_e D_p}\right)\left(\frac{1}{1 + M}\right)\right] = 8.6 \times 10^{-3}$$

where $A_s = \pi \times 15 \times 10^{-3} \times 0.27 \times 10^{-3} = 9.4 \times 10^{-6}$ in.^{2} and $s = 2,000$ cm/sec. Therefore, $h_{fe} = 116$.

The value of h_{fe} which we have calculated is the small-signal value. Since the large-signal h_{fe} is the integrated value of h_{fe} over the 0- to 500-ma range, its value will be somewhat larger owing to the fact that h_{fe} is larger at lower currents.

We next calculate the thermal-dissipation capabilities of the device. First, we calculate the temperature difference across the germanium between the collector junction and the bonding material to the heat sink.

$$\Delta T = \frac{3 \times 0.005}{4.8 \times 0.14 \times 0.008} = 2.8°C$$

Next, we calculate the drop across the 1-mil lead bonding region between the germanium and copper heat sink using a value of 0.083 for lead.

$$\Delta T = \frac{3 \times 0.0025}{4.8 \times 0.083 \times 0.008} = 2.4°C$$

Finally, the thermal drop across the copper sink is

$$\Delta T = \frac{3 \times 0.5}{4.8 \times 0.008} = 39°C$$

The total thermal drop for a 3-watt dissipation at 25°C is 44.2°C, resulting in a junction temperature of 69.2°C if the chassis is held to 25°C, thus fulfilling our requirements.

10.3. Switching Diodes. For the third illustration we choose a diode suitable for high-speed switching. A good switching diode should have a low forward resistance and a high reverse resistance. When it is switched rapidly between the forward and reverse bias conditions, it should recover its equilibrium characteristic quickly. Again we choose an arbitrary set of specifications to discuss.

Peak inverse voltage	$PIV > 100$ volts
Reverse saturation current	$I_0 < 1$ μa at 5 volts
	$I_0 < 20$ μa at 100 volts
Forward current at 1 volt	> 200 ma
Reverse recovery time	$\tau_R < 1$ μsec

where the reverse current must fall to $2I_0$ in 1 μsec after switching from 50 ma forward current. We shall analyze these specifications in terms of a germanium gold-bonded diode structure.

Considering first the PIV requirement we can calculate that the avalanche breakdown (>150 volts) will put a lower limit of 2.2 ohm-cm on the germanium resistivity [see Eq. (10.4b)]. The forward current will put a minimum size on the area of the junction. When the effect of hole injection on the spreading resistance R_s of a small contact is considered, the following relation can be deduced:[11]

$$I = \frac{1+b}{2b} \frac{V}{R_s} \left(1 + \frac{V}{2kT}\right) \tag{10.14}$$

Solving this for R_s gives

$$R_s = \frac{1+b}{2b} \frac{V}{I} \left(1 + \frac{V}{2kT}\right) \tag{10.15}$$

where b, the mobility ratio, equals 2.1 for germanium. Our forward current specification of 200 ma at 1 volt allows us to calculate R_s.

$$R_s = \frac{3.1}{4.2} \frac{1.0}{0.2} (1 + 20.1) = 78 \text{ ohms}$$

The spreading resistance of a flat circular contact of diameter d is given by $R_s = \rho/2d$, so that we can calculate the minimum diameter which will give the required forward current as $d = \rho/2R_s = 2.2/156 = 0.0141$ cm $= 5.5$ mils.

It must be pointed out that the low effective resistance of this contact (200 ma at 1 volt = 5 ohms) is due to the modulation of the 78 ohms spreading resistance by massive hole injection. This can be effective only if the lifetime of the injected holes is longer than their transit time through the spreading-resistance region. We can get an idea of the extent of the spreading-resistance region if we consider the resistance between two concentric hemispherical surfaces of diameter a and A, respectively. The resistance between them is given by $R_s = \rho/\pi(1/a - 1/A)$. If we let $A \to \infty$, $R_s \to \rho/\pi a$, which is the same as the spreading resistance for a flat circular contact except that the π must be replaced by 2. If $A = 10a$, the resistance will be 90 per cent of the true spreading resistance, so that we can say that the spreading-resistance region of a crystal is the volume of a hemisphere centered at the contact and having a diameter about ten times the diameter of the contact. Since the diameter of the contact is 5.5 mils, the depth of the spreading-resistance region must be about 55 mils. An estimate of the required lifetime can be made by calculating the lifetime associated with a 55-mil diffusion length. $L_p = \sqrt{D_p \tau_p}$, giving $\tau_p = L_p^2/D_p$, so that here $L_p = 55$ mils $= 0.141$ cm and $D_p = 44$ for holes in germanium. This gives

$$\tau_p = 450 \ \mu\text{sec}$$

It seems quite clear that a 450-μsec lifetime will not permit a 1-μsec recovery time. We must accordingly find another means of getting our high forward current.

One way to do this is to make the germanium wafer very thin so that we have planar geometry. In this case $R_s = \rho W/A$, where W is the thickness of the wafer and A is the area of the contact. We have already calculated from (10.15) that we need $R_s = 78$ ohms to meet the forward voltage requirement; so we will pick W thin enough so that if we set $W = L_p$ we get an effective diffusion transit time of about 0.1 μsec. This gives $W = \sqrt{44 \times 10^{-7}} = 2.1 \times 10^{-3}$ cm ~ 1 mil. From this W, $R_s = 78$ ohms, and $\rho = 2.2$ ohm-cm we calculate a contact area of 4.6×10^{-5} sq cm, giving a contact diameter of 7.6×10^{-3} cm, or 3 mils.

We must now check the reverse saturation current requirement. Referring to Sec. 3 we find that Eq. (3.10) can be written in shortened form as

$$I_0 = \frac{qAD_p p_n}{L_p} \tag{10.16}$$

since $P_n \gg n_p$ because of the very much smaller resistivity in the recrystallized region. We have also made L_p effectively very small by making the germanium wafer thin. Before we can use this expression we must express p_n in terms of ρ. For this purpose we remember that $n_n p_n = n_i^2 = 7 \times 10^{26}$ at room temperature. Also, $\rho = 1/n_n q \mu_n$, so that $p_n = 7 \times 10^{26} \rho q \mu_n = 4 \times 10^{11} \rho$ holes/cu cm. Substituting this in (10.16) along with $A = \pi d^2/4$ and $L_p = W$, we get

$$I_0 = \frac{5.5 \times 10^{-3} d^2 \rho}{W} \tag{10.17}$$

where d and W are in mils and I_0 is in microamperes. This equation allows us to calculate our I_0 requirement. We have determined $W = 1$ mil, $\rho = 2.2$ ohm-cm, and $d = 3$ mils, giving the I_0 at low voltage as 0.11 μa, which is well within our specification of 1 μa at 5 volts.

We will now examine our recovery specification more carefully. We have assumed that an effective diffusion transit time of about 0.1 μsec would be sufficient to meet it. To check this we must calculate the extent of the injection for 50 ma of forward current. Using Eq. (10.15) we may calculate that for $R_s = 78$ ohms and $I = 0.050$ amp the voltage is 0.5 volt. This gives an effective resistance of $V/I = 10$ ohms. Since the zero current resistance is 78 ohms, there has been an 8-to-1 increase in total carrier density. The minority-carrier density p_n was originally about $n_n/700$ ($n_n p_n = 7 \times 10^{26}$ and $n_n = 6 \times 10^{14}$ for 2.2 ohm-cm). When carrying the 50-ma forward current, the hole and electron density are about equal so that the injected level of hole density is about $(\frac{2}{3})8 n_n$. ($\frac{2}{3}$ is used instead of $\frac{1}{2}$ because the electrons are twice as mobile as holes.) The injected hole density p is then $5.3 \times 700 = 3{,}700p_n$. In order for the reverse current to recover to 2 μa, p must drop from $3{,}700p_n$ to $20p_n$ (since $1p_n$ gave the I_0 of 0.1 μa).

The effective diffusion transit time for a 1-mil semiconductor thickness is

$$\tau = \frac{W^2}{D_p} = 0.13 \ \mu\text{sec}$$

We see that the decay lifetime of carriers under the junction will be much less, since after the junction is reverse-biased, the excess carriers may diffuse to either side of the semiconductor and the carrier concentration in the center is drained off in both directions. It turns out that the decay lifetime $\tau_d = W^2/\pi^2 D_p = 0.013 \ \mu$sec. Now for our specified recovery the carrier concentration must decrease by a factor of

$$\frac{3{,}700}{20} = 185$$

so that by the definition of lifetime we can write $185 = e^{\tau_R/\tau_d} = e^{\tau_R/0.013}$. Solving for τ_R, we get $\tau_R = 0.08 \ \mu$sec, which is well within our recovery-time specification.

In addition to the carriers under the junction, which we have seen are cleaned up very rapidly, there will be some carriers stored in the region of the crystal surrounding the junction. These fringing carriers will extend only about a distance W beyond the edge of the junction because the ohmic contact acts as a sink for excess carriers and it extends far beyond the junction. Assuming that the current from these stored carriers is comparable to that from the carriers stored directly under the junction, we can estimate their cleanup time by using a decay lifetime comparable to τ. This gives $185 = e^{\tau_R/\tau} = e^{\tau_R/0.13}$, yielding $\tau_R = 0.7 \ \mu$sec, which is still within our specification. Actually the current from the fringing stored carriers is probably much less than the current from the carriers stored immediately beneath the junction. This would then reduce our required decay factor of 185 and hence the calculated value of τ_R.

We have seen how it was necessary to go to extremes in the geometry of this diode in order to meet the specifications theoretically. Practically, it would seem almost impossible to operate such a diode at 200 mw and not have serious heating problems. Since I_0 is theoretically a factor of 5 lower than the specification, it presumably would be permissible to have a junction temperature of about 65°C without exceeding $I_0 = 1 \ \mu$a. This would probably require a base connection consisting of a solid copper rod with suitable thermal contact with its surroundings. It should be pointed out that the diameter of the spot cannot be more than doubled, or the I_0 specification will not be met. Here again better and safer performance could be obtained by using a semiconductor with a larger energy gap such as silicon.

The specification of $I_0 < 20 \ \mu$a at 100 volts is met only by making sure that the avalanche-breakdown voltage is greatly in excess of 100 volts and that the semiconductor surfaces are clean and show no leakage current. This last is very difficult to assure at the present stage of the art. The resistivity cannot be increased beyond about 4 ohm-cm, or punch-through voltage breakdown will occur below 150 volts. The optimum resistivity for voltage effects ($PV_C = BV_{CBO} = 200 \text{ volts}$) is 3.2 ohm-cm. The specifications chosen are very difficult to meet with present technology, although they are theoretically possible for a germanium device.

10.4. Variable-capacitance Diodes. We now turn to another type of diode which makes use of the variation in capacitance of the reverse-biased PN junction. Applications of such diodes are found in automatic frequency control at ultrahigh frequencies and in parametric amplifiers. Both of these types of applications require that the device have a high Q at frequencies of several hundred megacycles and beyond. Expressing $Q = 1/\omega CR$, it is obvious that the design must emphasize a very low product of junction capacitance and series resistance. For our example, we consider an alloy-junction diode having the geometry shown in Fig. 10.8. We choose a value of frequency cutoff at 20 kmc, where f_c is defined as the frequency at which $Q = 1$. We add the further condition that this value be measured at a bias of 1 volt. From Q, we calculate

$$CR = \frac{1}{2\pi \times 20 \times 10^9} = 8 \times 10^{-12}$$

R can be expressed as $\rho_b(500l/d^2)$, where l and d are in mils. Therefore,

$$CR = \rho_b \frac{500l}{d^2} \frac{0.071d^2}{\sqrt{\rho_b}}$$

$$= 500 \times 0.071l \sqrt{\rho_b} = 8 \times 10^{-12}$$

and

$$\rho_b = 0.013 \text{ ohm-cm}$$

If we choose a value of C at 1 volt of 8 $\mu\mu$f to be satisfactory for this design and a value of l to be 2 mils, the thickness between the junction and ohmic contact, we can calculate the junction diameter to be

$$d = \sqrt{500 \times 2 \times 0.013} = 3.6 \text{ mils}$$

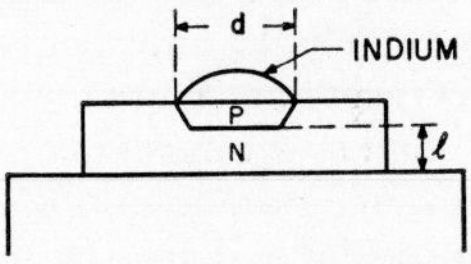

The breakdown voltage of this design would be

$$87 \times (0.013)^{0.725} = 3.9 \text{ volts}$$

Fig. 10.8. Variable-capacitance diode.

For the same requirements a higher breakdown voltage could be achieved by decreasing l, thus allowing for a higher resistivity.

10.5. Photocells. For our fourth and final illustration we shall choose a semiconductor photocell. Our specifications will be

Sensitivity   > 0.02 ma/millilumen
Dark current   < 5 μa
Spectral response flat from 4,000 to 10,000 Å
Frequency cutoff > 500 kc

Referring to Table 5.3, we see that the required sensitivity is within the range of a single junction device. The value of sensitivity = 0.03 ma/millilumen given in the table assumes efficient use of the optically injected carriers as well as the usual spectral distribution of the exciting light (radiation from a tungsten filament of color temperature 2400°K). We can therefore calculate the efficiency of utilization of injected carriers for our photocell, and unless it is less than 70 per cent, we can be sure that the sensitivity will exceed the specification of 0.02 ma/millilumen. We shall choose an alloy-junction photocell of the same general type of configuration shown in Fig. 5.4 at the lower right. The detailed configuration is shown in

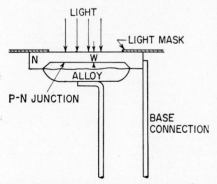

FIG. 10.9. Diagram of an alloy-junction photocell.

Fig. 10.9. We shall consider first the frequency-response requirement.

The cutoff frequency of such a photocell of semiconductor thickness W will be the same as the f_α of a transistor with base thickness W. This can be seen from the fact that most of the excess carriers produced by light injection must diffuse substantially across W before being collected at the reverse-biased PN junction. Accordingly, we find frequency cutoff $= 2.67/W^2 = 0.5$ mc, giving $W = 2.30$ mils.

We can now check the long-wavelength end of the spectral-response curve, using the W determined above. From the results of Brattain and Briggs,[12] it appears that the absorption of 10,000 Å light in a film of germanium 3.9×10^{-5} cm thick is about 80 per cent. Since the transmitted intensity should be given by the usual expression

$$I = I_0 e^{-\mu W}$$

we can calculate the absorption coefficient μ at 10,000 Å as $\ln (I_0/I) = \mu W$, giving $\ln (^{100}\!/_{20}) = \mu \times 3.9 \times 10^{-5}$ cm or $\mu = 4.1 \times 10^4$/cm. In terms of mils, $\mu = 104$/mil. From this it is easy to see that essentially all the light incident upon the germanium surface is either reflected or absorbed, only $e^{-104 \times 2.3}$ is transmitted. This is true over the entire spectral range of the specification.

The reflection coefficient[6] of germanium varies from 0.46 at 10,000 Å to 0.54 at 4,000 Å so that the photo response should fall off about 20 per cent toward the blue end of the spectrum. Since the excess carriers generated photoelectrically are generated in a layer nearer and nearer the surface as we move toward the blue, the residual surface recombination may somewhat increase this drop off in blue sensitivity.

We shall now consider the effect of surface recombination on the over-all sensitivity. The surface-recombination current $I_s = Aqps$, where p is the density of excess carriers generated by the light in a layer just beneath the surface, s is the surface-recombination velocity, and A is the illuminated area which is about equal to the junction area. The current through the junction $I = AqpD_p/W$ [see Sec. 5, Eqs. (5.16) and (5.15)]. Now modern surface-treatment technology can easily produce surfaces with $s < 200$ cm/sec. Using this figure we will calculate the ratio I/I_s. (Inserting W in centimeters)

$$\frac{I}{I_s} = \frac{D_p}{sW} = \frac{44}{200 \times 5.2 \times 10^{-3}} = 42$$

This shows that only about 2 per cent of our optically excited carriers are lost by surface recombination. We are therefore assured of an over-all sensitivity of about 0.03 ma/millilumen (see Table 5.3).

The final specification to check is the dark-current requirement. This is the reverse saturation current of the PN junction. The effective distance to the base contact may have a bearing on the dark current if this distance is less than a diffusion length from the junction. We shall assume, however, that the base contact is much more than a diffusion length away from the junction. We have already tacitly assumed that the diffusion length $L_p \gg W$, since we assumed that optically injected holes were lost only by surface recombination. There are two sources of dark current left. One is due to the surface generation of carriers when the junction bleeds off the equilibrium minority density p_0, and the other is the usual diffusion of carriers in from the base region. This latter current can be computed by assuming that these diffusing carriers reach an annular ring of the junction of area $W\pi d$, where d is the diameter of the junction. It is given by

$$I_1 = \frac{W \pi d p q_0 D_p}{L_p}$$

The surface generation current is

$$I_2 = Aqp_0 s = \frac{\pi d^2 q p_0 s}{4}$$

This can be understood by remembering that there is no net current flowing into the surface when the equilibrium density of minority carriers p_0 is present. When p_0 is bled away by the junction, the current of holes I_2 flows out of the surface since its counterbalancing current has been removed.

The total dark current is the sum of I_1 and I_2:

$$I_D = \pi dq p_0 \left(\frac{D_p W}{L_p} + \frac{ds}{4} \right) \tag{10.18}$$

Expressing p_0 in terms of ρ and reducing to our usual units we find

$$I_D = 4.8 \times 10^{-4} d\rho \left(\frac{44W}{L_p} + 6 \times 10^{-4} ds \right) \tag{10.19}$$

where d, W, and L_p are in mils; s is in centimeters per second; ρ is in ohm-centimeters; and I_D is in microamperes. If we assume $W/L_p = 0.1$ to satisfy our previous assumption, and if we take $d = 100$ mils and $\rho = 5$ ohm-cm, we get $I_D = 4.0$ μa. This is close to our specification limit, but the resistivity can be lowered if we find it necessary.

This concludes our discussion of semiconductor-device design examples. It is hoped that the calculations given here in some detail will indicate the procedures to be followed in considering the limitations of other types of devices.

REFERENCES

1. Kromer, H.: Theory of Diffusion-type and Drift-type Transistors, part I, The Quadripole Matrix for Low Frequencies, *Arch. elektrotech. Übertragung*, vol. 8, pp. 223–228, May, 1954.
2. Lee, C. A., and D. E. Thomas: "A New High Frequency PNP Transistor," IRE Semiconductor Device Research Conference, Philadelphia, Pa., June, 1955.
3. Schwartz, R. S., and B. N. Slade: "High-speed PNP Alloy-diffused Transistor for Switching Applications," IRE Electron Devices Conference, Oct. 31, 1957.
4. Berger, A. W., R. M. Folsom, W. E. Harding, and W. E. Mutter: "Diffusion Masking and All Diffused Germanium NPN Mesa Transistors," IRE Electron Devices Conference, Oct. 31, 1959.
5. Rutz, R. F.: Some Properties of Experimental 1000 mc Transistors, *IBM J. Research and Develop.*, vol. 3, p. 230, July, 1959.
6. Theuerer, H. C., and H. Christensen: *J. Electrochem. Soc.*, vol. 107, pp. 268–269C, 1960.
7. Webster, W. M.: On the Variation of Junction Transistor Current Amplification Factor with Emitter Current, *Proc. IRE*, vol. 42, pp. 914–920, June, 1954.
8. Armstrong, L. D., M. Bentivegna, and C. L. Carlson: PNP Transistors Using High Emitter Efficiency Alloy Materials, in "Transistors I," pp. 144–152, Radio Corporation of America, Princeton, N.J., March, 1956.
9. Fletcher, N. H.: Self-bias Cutoff Effect in Power Transistors, *Proc. IRE*, vol. 43, p. 1660, 1955.
10. Slade, B. N.: Recent Advances in Power Transistors, in "Transistors I," pp. 153–171, Radio Corporation of America, Princeton, N.J., March, 1956.
11. Swanson, J. A.: Diode Theory in the Light of Hole Injection, *J. Appl. Phys.*, vol. 25, pp. 314–323, March, 1954.
12. Brattain, W. H., and H. B. Briggs: The Optical Constants of Germanium in the Infrared and Visible, *Phys. Rev.*, vol. 75, pp. 1705–1710, June, 1949.

PART III

Circuit Design and Application for Transistors, Diodes, and Photocells

Section 11

LOW-FREQUENCY AMPLIFIERS

H. J. WOLL AND M. B. HERSCHER

Radio Corporation of America, Camden, N.J.

11.1. Equivalent Circuits. *11.1a. Four-terminal Linear Networks.* Numerous equivalent circuits for junction transistors are possible. The question of which equivalent circuit to use is not a clear-cut issue. A good equivalent circuit must fit easily and conveniently into circuit design, the parameters must be readily obtainable from the commonly used graphical characteristics, they must be easy to measure, and if possible they should be simply related to the physics of the device. This viewpoint is that of the circuit designer who uses the transistors. He is interested in having controls and limits applied to those quantities which are directly related to circuit performance. The device designer and manufacturer, on the other hand, find it easy to work with parameters that are directly related to the physical quantities that they control in the construction of a transistor. Since Sec. 11 is devoted to the transistor as a low-frequency circuit element, the circuit designer's point of view will prevail in the selection of equivalent circuits. It should be noted, however, that certain low-frequency equivalent circuits are more readily extended to include high-frequency operation than others.

From the point of view of the circuit designer, the transistor is a device with three terminals, one of which may be used as an input terminal, the second as an output terminal, and the third as the common or ground terminal. However, in certain cases such as split input or output none of the transistor terminals is common. It is generally more convenient to analyze the transistor as a four-terminal device, i.e., two pairs of terminals, since there is available a wealth of information for the analysis of this type of circuit element.

Consider a general four-terminal linear network or "black box," as shown in Fig. 11.1. If the equations relating these currents and voltages are known, everything that is needed in a linear-network calculation can be determined from them. Since the transistor is an active network, four independent parameters are needed to define the network as contrasted with

FIG. 11.1. Four-terminal linear network.

the three independent parameters needed to define a passive four-terminal network.

The following are some of the relationships that can be used to define the input characteristics of a transistor considered as a four-terminal network. The input voltage can be defined in terms of the short-circuit admittance and the open-circuit reverse voltage-amplification factor as in Fig. 11.2. The input voltage can be defined in terms of the open-circuit impedance and the reverse transfer impedance as in Fig. 11.3. The input current can be defined in terms of the open-circuit impedance and the short-circuit reverse current-amplification factor as in Fig. 11.4. The input current can be defined in terms of the short-circuit admittance and the reverse transfer admittance, as in Fig. 11.5. Similarly, the output characteristics of the transistor can be defined by a corresponding set of equations and equivalent circuits.

Any combination of one of the preceding input equivalent circuits and one of the output equivalent circuits is a valid equivalent circuit for a four-terminal active linear network and hence for a transistor. There are 16 such combinations of circuits. Four of these correspond to equations commonly used in matrix analysis of networks.[1]

The z's and the y's referred to above correspond to the z's and the y's in Sec. 18. For example, if both the input and output equivalent circuits are of the form shown in Fig. 11.3, the loop equivalent circuit using the z parameters is obtained. Likewise

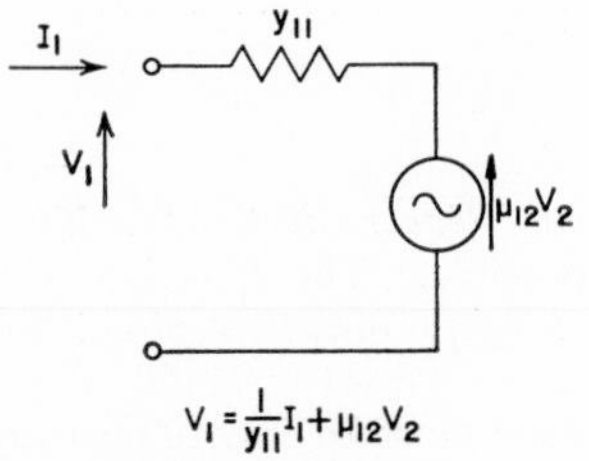

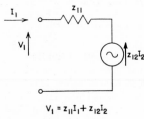

$$V_1 = \frac{1}{y_{11}}I_1 + \mu_{12}V_2$$

FIG. 11.2. Input equivalent circuit using voltage-amplification factor.

$$V_1 = z_{11}I_1 + z_{12}I_2$$

FIG. 11.3. Input equivalent circuit using transfer impedance.

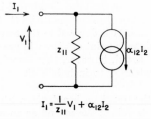

$$I_1 = \frac{1}{z_{11}}V_1 + \alpha_{12}I_2$$

FIG. 11.4. Input equivalent circuit using current-amplification factor.

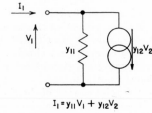

$$I_1 = y_{11}V_1 + y_{12}V_2$$

FIG. 11.5. Input equivalent circuit using transfer admittance.

if both input and output conform to Fig. 11.5, the nodal equivalent circuit using the y parameters is obtained.[2]

From the circuit designer's point of view, certain of these parameters are inconvenient to use for the analysis of transistor circuits. The output-voltage generators $\mu_{21}V_1$ and $z_{21}I_1$ act in series with the output impedance of the transistor. In most circuits, a transistor has an output impedance that is much greater than the load impedance. Therefore, it is generally more convenient to use an output-current generator in parallel with the output impedance because in this configuration the output impedance can be ignored whenever it is much greater than the load impedance. This is analogous to the fact that it is usually more convenient to use g_m rather than μ when analyzing a pentode-tube circuit. The input-current generators $\alpha_{12}I_2$ and $y_{12}V_2$ are inconvenient to measure, although suitable bridges have been built.[3]

If those equivalent circuits which contain μ_{21}, z_{21}, α_{12}, or y_{12} are eliminated, only 4 circuits remain out of the original 16. These are shown in Figs. 11.6 to 11.9. Also shown are single-generator variations of these circuits in the common-emitter connection. Typical values of these common-emitter parameters for a low-frequency, low-power transistor with a short-circuit forward current gain h_{21} (or α_{fe}) of 50 are given in Table 11.1. The parameters of these equivalent circuits for the common-emitter connection can be read directly from collector and base characteristics taken in this connection. For example, the graphical characteristics of Figs. 11.10 and 11.12 are associated with the equivalent circuit of Fig. 11.6; Figs. 11.11 and 11.12 with Fig. 11.7; Figs. 11.10 and 11.13 with Fig. 11.8; and Figs. 11.11 and 11.13 with Fig. 11.9.

11.1b. Common-emitter h Parameters. The parameters of the equivalent circuit in Fig. 11.6 are particularly easy to measure, are directly obtainable from the commonly used graphical characteristics, and are convenient to use in circuit design. For these

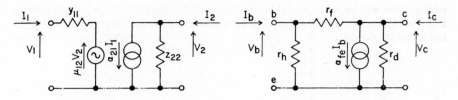

TWO GENERATOR

$$V_1 = \frac{1}{y_{11}}I_1 + \mu_{12}V_2$$

$$\equiv h_{11}I_1 + h_{12}V_2$$

$$I_2 = a_{21}I_1 + \frac{1}{z_{22}}V_2$$

$$\equiv h_{21}I_1 + h_{22}V_2$$

SINGLE GENERATOR

$$V_b = r_h I_b + \frac{r_h}{r_f}V_c$$

$$I_c = a_{fe}I_b + \frac{1}{r_d}V_c$$

$$\left(\begin{array}{c} r_f \gg r_h \\ r_f \gg r_d \end{array} \right)$$

FIG. 11.6. Equivalent circuits.

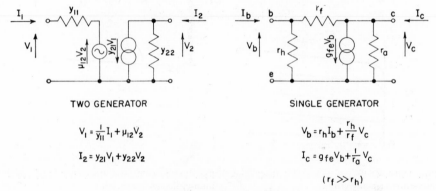

TWO GENERATOR

$$V_1 = \frac{1}{y_{11}}I_1 + \mu_{12}V_2$$

$$I_2 = y_{21}V_1 + y_{22}V_2$$

SINGLE GENERATOR

$$V_b = r_h I_b + \frac{r_h}{r_f}V_c$$

$$I_c = g_{fe}V_b + \frac{1}{r_a}V_c$$

$$(r_f \gg r_h)$$

FIG. 11.7. Equivalent circuits.

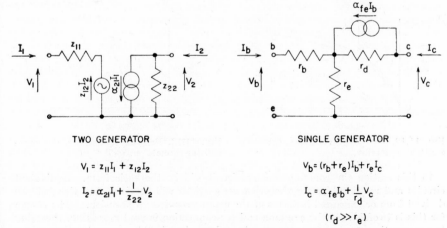

TWO GENERATOR

$$V_1 = z_{11}I_1 + z_{12}I_2$$

$$I_2 = \alpha_{21}I_1 + \frac{1}{z_{22}}V_2$$

SINGLE GENERATOR

$$V_b = (r_b + r_e)I_b + r_e I_c$$

$$I_c = \alpha_{fe}I_b + \frac{1}{r_d}V_c$$

$$(r_d \gg r_e)$$

FIG. 11.8. Equivalent circuits.

reasons, they will be fundamental in Sec. 11.   It is felt that they have a slight advantage over the parameters in the equivalent circuits of Figs. 11.7 to 11.9 (see Sec. 19 for measurement details).

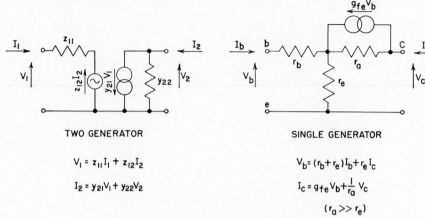

TWO GENERATOR

$$V_I = z_{11}I_1 + z_{12}I_2$$

$$I_2 = y_{21}V_1 + y_{22}V_2$$

SINGLE GENERATOR

$$V_b = (r_b + r_e)I_b + r_e I_c$$

$$I_c = g_{fe}V_b + \frac{1}{r_a}V_c$$

$$(r_a \gg r_e)$$

Fig. 11.9. Equivalent circuits.

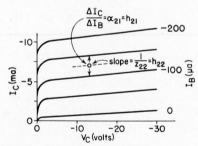

Fig. 11.10. Collector characteristics, common-emitter connection.

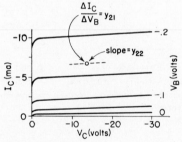

Fig. 11.11. Collector characteristics, common-emitter connection.

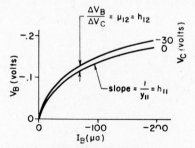

Fig. 11.12. Base characteristics, common-emitter connection.

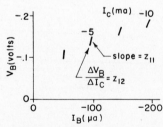

Fig. 11.13. Base characteristics, common-emitter connection.

In this section the common-emitter circuit will be the basic form.   Equivalent circuits and relationships for the other connections will be given, but they will be derived from or expressed in terms of the common-emitter connection.   The reason for this is twofold: (1) the common-emitter connection is used more than the other two connections for low-frequency work, and (2) since in this connection the current gain is much higher than the common-base connection, the voltage gain much higher than the common-collector connection, and the power gain higher than either connection, it affords a better insight into what the transistor is doing in the circuit; i.e., the

TABLE 11.1. TYPICAL VALUES OF COMMON-EMITTER
EQUIVALENT-CIRCUIT PARAMETERS

$$\frac{1}{y_{11}} = h_{11} = 2,000 \text{ ohms} \qquad r_h = h_{11} = 2,000 \text{ ohms}$$

$$\mu_{12} = h_{12} = 600 \times 10^{-6} \qquad r_f = \frac{h_{11}}{h_{12}} = 3.3 \text{ megohms}$$

$$\alpha_{21} = h_{21} = 50 \qquad \alpha_{fe} = h_{21} = 50$$

$$\frac{1}{z_{22}} = h_{22} = 25 \text{ } \mu\text{mhos} \qquad r_d = \frac{1}{h_{22}} = 40 \text{ kilohms}$$

$$z_{11} = h_{11} - \frac{h_{12}h_{21}}{h_{22}} = 800 \text{ ohms} \qquad r_b = z_{11} - z_{12} = 776 \text{ ohms}$$

$$z_{12} = \frac{h_{12}}{h_{22}} = 24 \text{ ohms} \qquad r_e = z_{12} = 24 \text{ ohms}$$

$$y_{21} = \frac{h_{21}}{h_{11}} = 0.025 \text{ mho} \qquad g_{fe} = y_{21} = 0.025 \text{ mho}$$

$$y_{22} = h_{22} - \frac{h_{12}h_{21}}{h_{11}} = 10 \text{ } \mu\text{mhos} \qquad r_a = \frac{1}{y_{22}} = 100 \text{ kilohms}$$

other connections may be considered to be a transistor in the common-emitter connection with the current or voltage gain reduced by feedback. As an example of the sensitivity of the common-emitter presentation, compare the common-base collector characteristics shown in Fig. 11.18 with the common-emitter collector characteristics shown in Fig. 11.14. In fact, such data as α_{fb} (or h_{fb}), the common-base

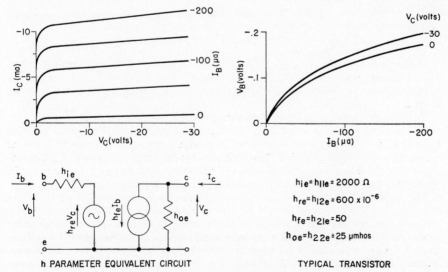

$$h_{ie} = h_{11e} = 2000 \text{ } \Omega$$

$$h_{re} = h_{12e} = 600 \times 10^{-6}$$

$$h_{fe} = h_{21e} = 50$$

$$h_{oe} = h_{22e} = 25 \text{ } \mu\text{mhos}$$

h PARAMETER EQUIVALENT CIRCUIT   TYPICAL TRANSISTOR

FIG. 11.14. Common-emitter connection.

short-circuit current gain, are usually measured in the common-emitter connection and then transformed to the common-base representation.

The parameters used in the equivalent circuit of Fig. 11.6 are known as h parameters. They are shown in the common-emitter connection in Fig. 11.14.

As can be determined from either the equations or the equivalent circuit, h_{ie} (or h_{11e}) is the input impedance when the output is short-circuited (V_C = constant). Since the h parameters and their corresponding equivalent circuit are small-signal quantities, the term "output is short-circuited" does not mean zero voltage from collector to emitter but rather zero incremental or signal voltage from collector to emitter. The desired d-c operating point is maintained, and the "short circuit" is obtained by a large capacitor or similar means. Thus in determining h_{ie} (or h_{11e}) graphically from the base characteristics of Fig. 11.12

$$h_{ie} = \frac{\partial V_B}{\partial I_B} \qquad \text{with } V_C = \text{constant}$$

$$= \text{slope of curve} \qquad V_C = \text{constant}$$

h_{re} (or h_{12e}) is the ratio between the open-circuit (I_B = constant) voltage at the base and the applied voltage at the collector. It is the feedback factor or reverse μ. From Fig. 11.12

$$h_{re} = \mu_{re} = \frac{\partial V_B}{\partial V_C} = \frac{\Delta V_B}{\Delta V_C} \qquad \text{with } I_B = \text{constant}$$

h_{fe} (or h_{21e}) is the ratio between the short-circuit (V_C = constant) collector current and the applied base current. It is the current amplification β or α_{fe}. From Fig. 11.10

$$h_{fe} = \beta = \alpha_{fe} = \frac{\partial I_C}{\partial I_B} = \frac{\Delta I_C}{\Delta I_B} \qquad \text{with } V_C = \text{constant}$$

h_{oe} (or h_{22e}) is the output admittance when the base is open-circuited (I_B = constant). From Fig. 11.10

$$h_{oe} = \frac{\partial I_C}{\partial V_C} \qquad \text{with } I_B = \text{constant}$$

$$= \text{slope of curve} \qquad I_B = \text{constant}$$

In the equivalent circuit of Fig. 11.14, h_{ie} is an impedance, $h_{re}V_c$ a voltage generator, $h_{fe}I_b$ a current generator, and h_{oe} an admittance. For this set of h parameters to be consistent and to represent a realistic equivalent circuit, they must all be taken at the same d-c operating point.

The collector and base characteristics shown in Fig. 11.14 not only present data for the determination of the small-signal h parameters at any operating point but also form the basis for graphical analysis of large-signal operation. These two sets of curves give all the information regarding the low-frequency operation of this transistor at a given temperature, regardless of operating point or signal amplitude. In most cases they present data on parameters with sufficient accuracy.

The variation of common-emitter h parameters of a typical low-level germanium alloy-junction PNP transistor with emitter current is given in Fig. 11.15, with collector voltage in Fig. 11.16, and with temperature in Fig. 11.17. Although these curves were taken on an average transistor, some variation is to be expected from unit to unit. The variation of h parameters for typical low-level silicon transistors will, in general, follow the same basic trends.

As shown in Fig. 11.15, h_{fe} and h_{re} are relatively independent of emitter current,

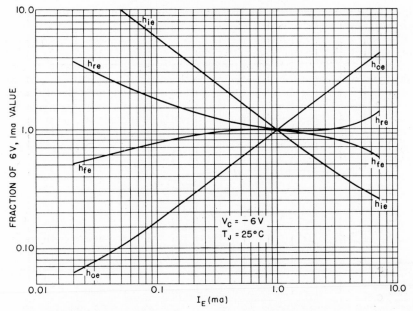

FIG. 11.15. Variation of common-emitter h parameters with emitter current for typical alloy-junction germanium transistor.

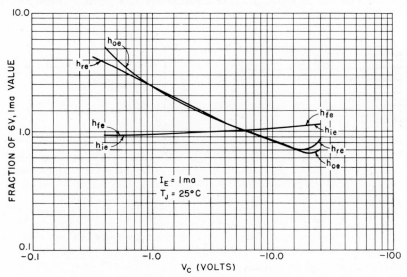

FIG. 11.16. Variation of common-emitter h parameters with collector voltage for typical alloy-junction germanium transistor.

h_{ie} varies inversely with the emitter current, and h_{oe} varies directly with emitter current. This can be determined for h_{ie} and h_{fe} by reference to Fig. 11.23 and for h_{ie} and h_{oe} by reference to the approximate formulas in Fig. 11.22.

From Fig. 11.16, it is seen that h_{ie} and h_{fe} are relatively independent of collector voltage. This can be seen by reference to Fig. 11.23. The variation of h_{re} and h_{oe}

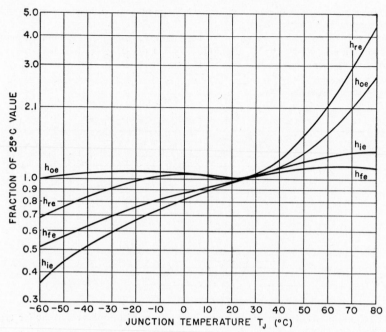

Fig. 11.17. Variation of common-emitter h parameters with junction temperature for typical alloy-junction germanium transistor.

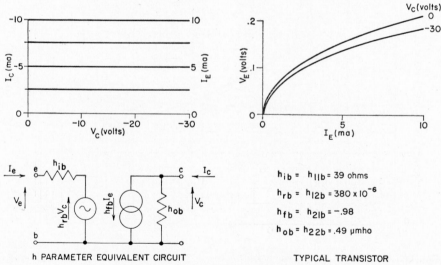

h PARAMETER EQUIVALENT CIRCUIT   TYPICAL TRANSISTOR

$h_{ib} = h_{11b} = 39$ ohms

$h_{rb} = h_{12b} = 380 \times 10^{-6}$

$h_{fb} = h_{21b} = -.98$

$h_{ob} = h_{22b} = .49$ μmho

Fig. 11.18. Common-base connection.

with collector voltage is difficult to read in Fig. 11.23.   The equations of Fig. 11.22 indicate that at constant emitter current there is a close relationship between h_{ie} and h_{fe} and between h_{oe} and h_{fe}.   This can be observed in the temperature curves of Fig. 11.17.   The variation of h_{ie} and h_{fe} with temperature can be determined by reference to Fig. 11.23.   Again, h_{re} and h_{oe} are difficult to read accurately in Fig. 11.23.

The common-emitter h parameters in terms of the parameters from other equivalent circuits are given in Table 11.2.

11.1c. Common-base h Parameters. The common-base h parameters and the accompanying equivalent circuit are analogous to the respective counterparts in the common-emitter arrangement. The equivalent circuit is shown in Fig. 11.18. As before, h_{ib} is an impedance, $h_{rb}V_c$ is a voltage generator, $h_{fb}I_e$ is a current generator, and h_{ob} is an admittance.

TABLE 11.2. COMMON-EMITTER h PARAMETERS

In Terms of CE T Parameters

$$h_{ie} = r_b + (1 + \alpha_{fe})r_e$$

$$h_{re} = \frac{r_e}{r_d}$$

$$h_{fe} = \alpha_{fe}$$

$$h_{oe} = \frac{1}{r_d}$$

In Terms of CB h Parameters	*In Terms of CB T Parameters*
$h_{ie} = \dfrac{h_{ib}}{1 + h_{fb}}$	$h_{ie} = r_b + \dfrac{r_e}{1 - \alpha_{fb}}$
$h_{re} = \dfrac{h_{ib}h_{ob}}{1 + h_{fb}} - h_{rb}$	$h_{re} = \dfrac{r_e}{(1 - \alpha_{fb})r_c}$
$h_{fe} = -\dfrac{h_{fb}}{1 + h_{fb}}$	$h_{fe} = \dfrac{\alpha_{fb}}{1 - \alpha_{fb}}$
$h_{oe} = \dfrac{h_{ob}}{1 + h_{fb}}$	$h_{oe} = \dfrac{1}{(1 - \alpha_{fb})r_c}$

In Terms of CC h Parameters	*In Terms of Low-frequency Hybrid-pi Parameters*
$h_{ie} = h_{oc}$	$h_{ie} = r_{bb'} + r_{b'e}$
$h_{re} = 1 - h_{rc}$	$h_{re} = \dfrac{r_{b'e}}{r_{b'c}}$
$h_{fe} = -(1 + h_{fc})$	$h_{fe} = g_m r_{b'e}$
$h_{oe} = h_{oc}$	$h_{oe} = \dfrac{1}{r_{b'c}}(1 + g_m r_{b'e}) + \dfrac{1}{r_{ce}}$

The common-base h parameters can be read directly off the common-base characteristics shown in Fig. 11.18, but the collector characteristics are not very informative, since they indicate primarily that the output current is about equal to the input current. The common-base h parameters in terms of other circuits are given in Table 11.3.

11.1d. Common-collector h Parameters. The common-collector h parameters and their accompanying equivalent circuit are shown in Fig. 11.19. They can be read directly off the common-collector characteristics shown in Fig. 11.19. The output characteristics are very similar to those for the common-emitter connection. The input characteristics are not very informative, since they indicate primarily that the input voltage is about equal to the output voltage.

The common-collector h parameters in terms of other circuits are given in Table 11.4.

11.1e. Common-base T Equivalent Circuit. The common-base T equivalent circuit shown in Fig. 11.20, as a result of its initial application to point-contact transistors, has been widely used for junction transistor circuit analysis. It can be extended to comprise high-frequency effects by including a capacitor across r_c and considering

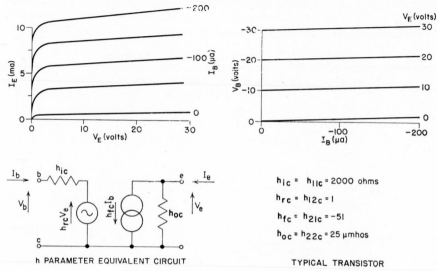

$h_{ic} = h_{11c} = 2000$ ohms

$h_{rc} = h_{12c} = 1$

$h_{fc} = h_{21c} = -51$

$h_{oc} = h_{22c} = 25$ μmhos

h PARAMETER EQUIVALENT CIRCUIT   TYPICAL TRANSISTOR

FIG. 11.19. Common-collector connection.

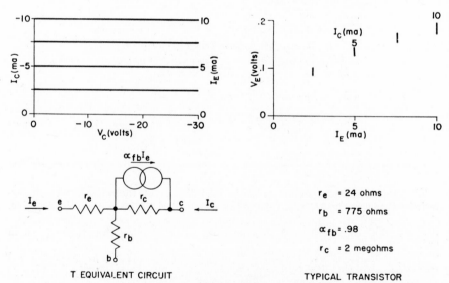

$r_e = 24$ ohms

$r_b = 775$ ohms

$\alpha_{fb} = .98$

$r_c = 2$ megohms

T EQUIVALENT CIRCUIT   TYPICAL TRANSISTOR

FIG. 11.20. Common-base connection.

α_{fb} as a function of frequency. An important defect is the fact that junction transistors are generally used in the common-emitter connection. It is to be noted that the common-base T can be used for calculations in the common-emitter and common-collector connections also.

α_{fb} and r_c can be read directly off the common-base collector characteristics shown in Fig. 11.20. α_{fb} is equal to h_{fb} (common-base), and r_c is practically equal to $1/h_{ob}$ (common-base) since $r_c \gg r_b$. Since $r_b = \partial V_E/\partial I_C$ with $I_E = $ constant, r_b can be read directly off the emitter characteristics shown in Fig. 11.20. The slope of the emitter curves at constant collector current is equal to $r_e + r_b$, i.e., $\partial V_E/\partial I_E = r_e + r_b$ with $I_C = $ constant.

The common-base T parameters in terms of other circuits are given in Table 11.5.

TABLE 11.3. COMMON-BASE h PARAMETERS

In Terms of CE h Parameters	*In Terms of CE T Parameters*
$h_{ib} = \dfrac{h_{ie}}{1 + h_{fe}}$	$h_{ib} = r_e + \dfrac{r_b}{1 + \alpha_{fe}}$
$h_{rb} = \dfrac{h_{ie}h_{oe}}{1 + h_{fe}} - h_{re}$	$h_{rb} = \dfrac{r_b}{r_d(1 + \alpha_{fe})}$
$h_{fb} = -\dfrac{h_{fe}}{1 + h_{fe}}$	$h_{fb} = -\dfrac{\alpha_{fe}}{1 + \alpha_{fe}}$
$h_{ob} = \dfrac{h_{oc}}{1 + h_{oe}}$	$h_{ob} = \dfrac{1}{r_d(1 + \alpha_{fe})}$

In Terms of CB T Parameters

$$h_{ib} = r_e + r_b(1 - \alpha_{fb})$$

$$h_{rb} = \frac{r_b}{r_c}$$

$$h_{fb} = -\alpha_{fb}$$

$$h_{ob} = \frac{1}{r_c}$$

In Terms of CC h Parameters	*In Terms of Low-frequency Hybrid-pi Parameters*
$h_{ib} = -\dfrac{h_{ic}}{h_{fc}}$	$h_{ib} = \dfrac{r_{bb'} + r_{b'e}}{1 + g_m r_{b'e}}$
$h_{rb} = h_{rc} - \dfrac{h_{ic}h_{oc}}{h_{fc}} - 1$	$h_{rb} = \dfrac{r_{bb'}}{r_{b'c}} + \dfrac{r_{bb'} + r_{b'e}}{(1 + g_m r_{b'e})r_{ce}}$
$h_{fb} = -\dfrac{h_{fc} + 1}{h_{fc}}$	$h_{fb} = -\dfrac{g_m r_{b'e}}{1 + g_m r_{b'e}}$
$h_{ob} = -\dfrac{h_{oc}}{h_{fc}}$	$h_{ob} = \dfrac{1}{r_{b'c}} + \dfrac{1}{r_{ce}(1 + g_m r_{b'e})}$

11.1f. Common-emitter T Equivalent Circuit. The common-emitter T equivalent circuit shown in Fig. 11.21 is a derivation of the common-base T that came about because junction transistors are generally used in the common-emitter connection and because α_{fe} (beta) is the quantity that generally is measured experimentally. It is not so easy to extend the common-emitter T equivalent circuit to high-frequency operation as the common-base T.

α_{fe} and r_d can be read directly off the common-emitter collector characteristics shown in Fig. 11.21. α_{fe} is equal to h_{fe}, and r_d is practically equal to $1/h_{oe}$ since $r_d \gg r_e$. The slope of the base curves at constant collector current is equal to $r_e + r_b$, i.e., $\partial V_B/\partial I_B = r_e + r_b$ with $I_C = $ constant. Since $r_e = \partial V_B/\partial I_C$ with $I_B = $ constant, r_e can be read directly off the base characteristics shown in Fig. 11.21.

The common-emitter T parameters in terms of other circuits are given in Table 11.6.

11.1g. Hybrid-pi Equivalent Circuit. The hybrid-pi equivalent circuit[4] is shown in Fig. 11.22. This circuit has the advantage that it represents a transistor rather well over its useful frequency range. All the parameters, including the transconductance, are relatively independent of frequency. For this reason, it is quite useful, since it can be extended to include high-frequency operation. Another advantage of the hybrid-pi equivalent circuit is that its parameters are directly and easily related to

TABLE 11.4. COMMON-COLLECTOR h PARAMETERS

In Terms of CE h Parameters	In Terms of CE T Parameters
$h_{ic} = h_{ie}$	$h_{ic} = r_b + (1 + \alpha_{fe})r_e$
$h_{rc} = 1 - h_{re} \cong 1$	$h_{rc} = 1 - \dfrac{r_e}{r_d} \cong 1$
$h_{fc} = -(1 + h_{fe})$	$h_{fc} = -(1 + \alpha_{fe})$
$h_{oc} = h_{oe}$	$h_{oc} = \dfrac{1}{r_d}$

In Terms of CB h Parameters	In Terms of CB T Parameters
$h_{ic} = \dfrac{h_{ib}}{1 + h_{fb}}$	$h_{ic} = r_b + \dfrac{r_e}{1 - \alpha_{fb}}$
$h_{rc} = 1 - \dfrac{h_{ib}h_{ob}}{1 + h_{fb}} + h_{rb} \cong 1$	$h_{rc} = 1 - \dfrac{r_e}{(1 - \alpha_{fb})r_c} \cong 1$
$h_{fc} = -\dfrac{1}{1 + h_{fb}}$	$h_{fc} = -\dfrac{1}{1 - \alpha_{fb}}$
$h_{oc} = \dfrac{h_{ob}}{1 + h_{fb}}$	$h_{oc} = \dfrac{1}{(1 - \alpha_{fb})r_c}$

In Terms of Low-frequency Hybrid-pi Parameters

$$h_{ic} = r_{bb'} + r_{b'e}$$

$$h_{rc} = 1 - \frac{r_{b'c}}{r_{b'e}} \cong 1$$

$$h_{fc} = -(1 + g_m r_{b'e})$$

$$h_{oc} = \frac{1}{r_{b'c}}(1 + g_m r_{b'e}) + \frac{1}{r_{ce}}$$

the physics of the device. Various techniques are available for measuring these parameters.

Figure 11.22 is a common-emitter version of this equivalent circuit. A very low frequency version would not include capacitors $C_{b'e}$ and $C_{b'c}$. Actually, however, for many low-frequency transistors and particularly for power transistors, the reactive elements will not be negligible. Although the alpha-cutoff frequency f_{ab} (where h_{fb} falls to 0.707 of its low-frequency value) of the transistor may be above the audio range, the beta-cutoff frequency f_{ae} (where h_{fe} falls to 0.707 of its low-frequency value) may fall in the audio range, since

$$f_{ab} = \frac{1}{2\pi r_e C_{b'e}} \quad \text{and} \quad f_{ae} = \frac{1}{2\pi r_{b'e} C_{b'e}} = f_{ab}(1 - \alpha_{fb}) = \frac{f_{ab}}{h_{fe} + 1}$$

where r_e is the emitter resistance of the T equivalent circuit and $r_e = r_{b'e}(1 - \alpha_{fb})$.

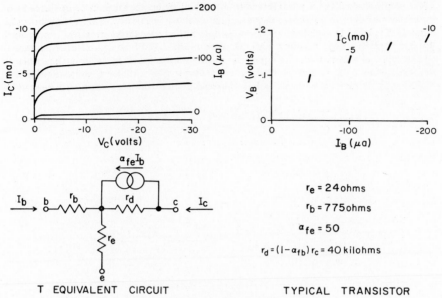

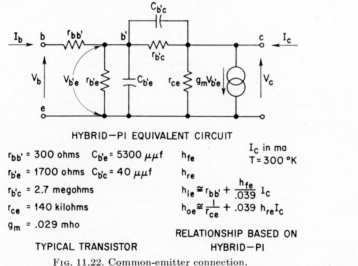

$r_e = 24\,\text{ohms}$

$r_b = 775\,\text{ohms}$

$\alpha_{fe} = 50$

$r_d = (1 - \alpha_{fb})\,r_c = 40\,\text{kilohms}$

T EQUIVALENT CIRCUIT   TYPICAL TRANSISTOR

FIG. 11.21. Common-emitter connection.

HYBRID—PI EQUIVALENT CIRCUIT

TYPICAL TRANSISTOR		RELATIONSHIP BASED ON HYBRID—PI
$r_{bb'}$ = 300 ohms	$C_{b'e}$ = 5300 $\mu\mu f$	h_{fe}
$r_{b'e}$ = 1700 ohms	$C_{b'c}$ = 40 $\mu\mu f$	h_{re}
$r_{b'c}$ = 2.7 megohms		$h_{ie} \cong r_{bb'} + \dfrac{h_{fe}}{.039}\,I_c$
r_{ce} = 140 kilohms		$h_{oe} \cong \dfrac{1}{r_{ce}} + .039\,h_{re}I_c$
g_m = .029 mho		

I_c in ma
$T = 300\ ^{\circ}K$

TYPICAL TRANSISTOR   HYBRID—PI

FIG. 11.22. Common-emitter connection.

A more complete description of the effect of high-frequency cutoff on low-frequency amplifiers is given in Sec. 11.3f.

The ohmic-base lead resistance $r_{bb'}$ is predominantly in the base lead connection to the intrinsic transistor base b'. Although only four parameters are needed to define the intrinsic transistor at low frequencies, the total number of parameters in the low-frequency hybrid-pi equivalent circuit is five. This is one more quantity than is strictly necessary for a low-frequency equivalent circuit. Thus the transformation from common-emitter h parameters to hybrid-pi given in Table 11.7 requires additional knowledge; in this case, it is assumed that $r_{bb'}$ is known.

11.2. Typical Transistors. The collector and base characteristics for several typical transistors are given in Figs. 11.23 to 11.30. While every effort was made to obtain typical transistors, the curves were taken on a small sample and may not be representative. They are plotted in the form of Fig. 11.14. The base-to-emitter voltage V_B is plotted versus the base current I_B for the base characteristics. The

TABLE 11.5. COMMON-BASE T PARAMETERS

In Terms of CE h Parameters   *In Terms of CE T Parameters*

$$\alpha_{fb} = \frac{h_{fe}}{1 + h_{fe}} \qquad\qquad \alpha_{fb} = \frac{\alpha_{fe}}{1 + \alpha_{fe}}$$

$$r_c = \frac{1 + h_{fe}}{h_{oe}} \qquad\qquad r_c = r_d(1 + \alpha_{fe})$$

$$r_b = h_{ie} - \frac{h_{re}}{h_{oe}}(1 + h_{fe}) \qquad r_b = r_b$$

$$r_e = \frac{h_{re}}{h_{oe}} \qquad\qquad r_e = r_e$$

In Terms of CB h Parameters

$$\alpha_{fb} = -h_{fb}$$

$$r_c = \frac{1}{h_{ob}}$$

$$r_b = \frac{h_{rb}}{h_{ob}}$$

$$r_e = h_{ib} - \frac{h_{rb}(1 + h_{fb})}{h_{ob}}$$

In Terms of   *In Terms of Low-frequency*
CC h Parameters   *Hybrid-pi Parameters*

$$\alpha_{fb} = \frac{h_{fc} + 1}{h_{fc}} \qquad\qquad \alpha_{fb} = \frac{g_m r_{b'e}}{1 + g_m r_{b'e}}$$

$$r_c = -\frac{h_{fc}}{h_{oc}} \qquad\qquad \frac{1}{r_c} = \frac{1}{r_{b'c}} + \frac{1}{r_{ce}(1 + g_m r_{b'e})}$$

$$r_b = h_{ic} + \frac{h_{fc}(1 - h_{rc})}{h_{oc}} \qquad r_b = r_{bb'} + \frac{r_{b'e}}{1 + r_{ce}/r_{b'c}(1 + g_m r_{b'e})}$$

$$r_e = \frac{1 - h_{rc}}{h_{oc}} \qquad\qquad r_e = \frac{r_{b'e}}{(1 + g_m r_{b'e}) + r_{b'e}/r_{ce}}$$

family of curves represents various collector voltages V_C, starting at zero and increasing by equal steps. The lowest curve and, in many cases, the only curve separated from the rest is $V_C = 0$.

Collector current I_B is plotted versus collector voltage V_C for the collector characteristics. The family of curves represents various base currents I_B, starting at zero and increasing by equal steps. The lowest curve is $I_B = 0$.

The common-emitter h parameters can be read off these curves in the manner shown in Figs. 11.10 and 11.12. Although h_{ie} and h_{fe} can be read with considerable facility, it is difficult to read h_{re} and h_{oe} unless the curves have a great deal of precision.

TABLE 11.6. COMMON-EMITTER T PARAMETERS

In Terms of CE h Parameters

$$\alpha_{fe} = h_{fe} = \beta$$

$$r_d = \frac{1}{h_{oe}}$$

$$r_e = \frac{h_{re}}{h_{oe}}$$

$$r_b = h_{ie} - (1 + h_{fe})\frac{h_{re}}{h_{oe}}$$

In Terms of CB h Parameters

$$\alpha_{fe} = -\frac{h_{fb}}{1 + h_{fb}}$$

$$r_d = \frac{1 + h_{fb}}{h_{ob}}$$

$$r_e = h_{ib} - \frac{h_{rb}(1 + h_{fb})}{h_{ob}}$$

$$r_b = \frac{h_{rb}}{h_{ob}}$$

In Terms of CB T Parameters

$$\alpha_{fe} = \frac{\alpha_{fb}}{1 - \alpha_{fb}}$$

$$r_d = (1 - \alpha_{fb})r_c$$

$$r_e = r_e$$

$$r_b = r_b$$

In Terms of CC h Parameters

$$\alpha_{fe} = -(1 + h_{fc})$$

$$r_d = \frac{1}{h_{oc}}$$

$$r_e = \frac{1 - h_{rc}}{h_{oc}}$$

$$r_b = h_{ic} + \frac{h_{fc}(1 - h_{rc})}{h_{oc}}$$

In Terms of Low-frequency Hybrid-pi Parameters

$$\alpha_{fe} = g_m r_{b'e}$$

$$\frac{1}{r_d} = \frac{1}{r_{b'c}}(1 + g_m r_{b'e}) + \frac{1}{r_{ce}}$$

$$r_e = \frac{r_{b'e}}{(1 + g_m r_{b'e}) + r_{b'c}/r_{ce}}$$

$$r_b = r_{bb'} + \frac{r_{b'e}}{1 + r_{ce}/r_{b'c}(1 + g_m r_{b'e})}$$

TABLE 11.7. HYBRID-PI PARAMETERS

In Terms of CE h Parameters and $r_{bb'}$

$$r_{b'e} = h_{ie} - r_{bb'}$$

$$r_{b'c} = \frac{h_{ie} - r_{bb'}}{h_{re}}$$

$$g_m = \frac{h_{fe}}{h_{ie} - r_{bb'}}$$

$$\frac{1}{r_{ce}} = h_{oe} - \frac{(1 + h_{fe})h_{re}}{h_{ie} - r_{bb'}}$$

However, since these curves are the input and output characteristics of the transistor in the common-emitter connection, the factors that are unimportant in the curves are those which are generally unimportant in circuits. For example, if a load line is drawn on the collector characteristics and then transferred to the base characteristics, the input resistance of the stage is obtained as described in Sec. 11.5g. If h_{re} is small,

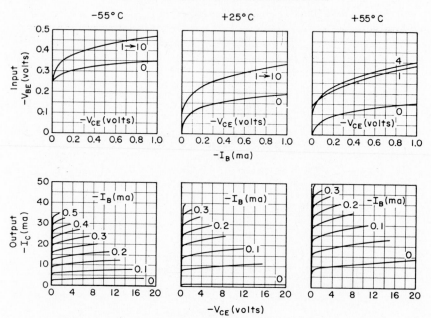

FIG. 11.23. Germanium alloy junction, PNP.   RCA 2N217.   Input and output characteristics (common-emitter).

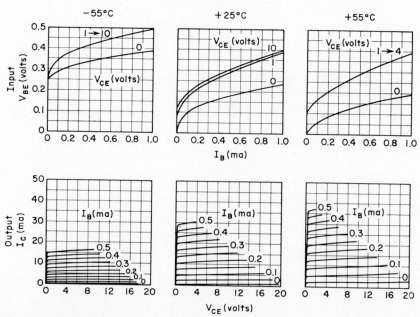

FIG. 11.24. Germanium alloy junction, NPN.   RCA 2N647.   Input and output characteristics (common-emitter).

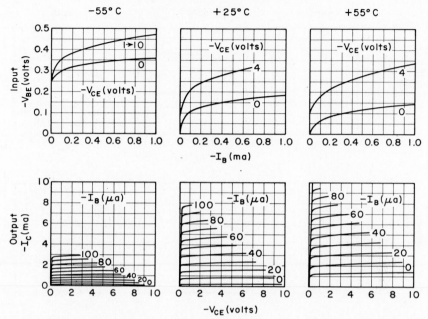

FIG. 11.25. Germanium alloy junction (low noise), PNP.   RCA 2N220.   Input and output characteristics (common-emitter).

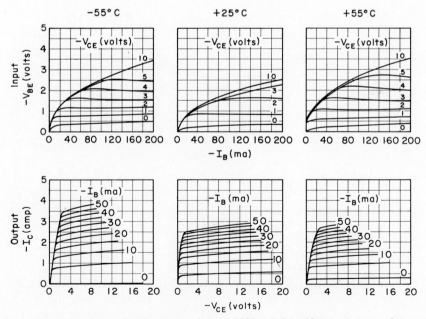

FIG. 11.26. Germanium alloy junction (power), PNP.   RCA 2N561.   Input and output characteristics (common-emitter).

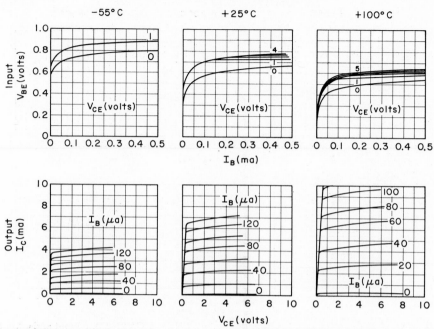

FIG. 11.27. Silicon grown junction, NPN.   Texas Instruments 2N335.   Input and output characteristics (common-emitter).

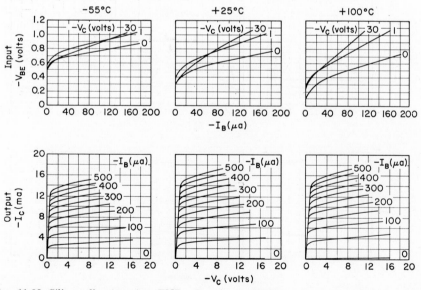

FIG. 11.28. Silicon alloy junction, PNP.   Raytheon 2N329A.   Input and output characteristics (common emitter).

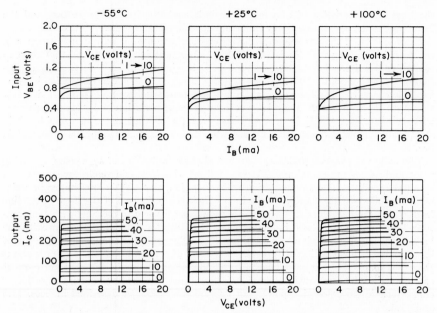

FIG. 11.29. Silicon single diffused-junction mesa (medium power), NPN. RCA 2N1092. Input and output characteristics (common-emitter).

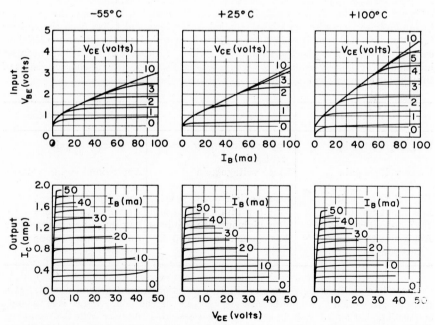

FIG. 11.30. Silicon single diffused-junction mesa (power), NPN. RCA 2N1069. Input and output characteristics (common-emitter).

the base characteristics will be relatively independent of collector voltage and the input resistance will be relatively independent of load resistance.

Examination of the base characteristics will indicate if h_{re} is an important factor in the transistor. It generally is much more important in power transistors than in small-signal units. The base characteristics will give the input resistance as a function of operating point. They show that the input resistance decreases with increasing base current. The base current with zero base-to-emitter volts is approximately the I_{co} of the transistor. Especially noticeable is the variation in d-c input resistance with temperature. This is a very important factor that must be considered in stabilizing a stage for operation over a wide temperature range and is discussed in Sec. 11.9c.

The collector characteristics at a glance give an indication of h_{fe} versus operating point and versus temperature. Thus h_{fe} fall off with increasing collector current can be determined. Collector saturation resistance, i.e., the effective resistance in series with the collector, also can be determined. It is the reciprocal of the slope of the line from which the base-current lines emanate and can be seen to increase with temperature. The curve of $I_B = 0$ indicates I_{CEO}, the collector current that flows with the base open. It is approximately h_{fe} times I_{co}. The collector current is a function of base current below the line of $I_B = 0$. The lines of constant base current have about the same spacing, but reverse base current flows. In the limit, the collector current can be reduced to approximately I_{co}. Load lines can be drawn on the collector characteristics to determine power output and distortion, as described in Secs. 11.5 and 11.6.

If the collector characteristics are extended to sufficiently high voltages, breakdown will be seen. This limits the peak voltage at which the transistor can be operated.

11.3. Simple Amplifier Circuits. *11.3a. Single-stage Amplifier.* A transistor can be operated with the signal applied to the base and taken from the collector (common-emitter), with the signal applied to the emitter and taken from the collector (common-base), or with the signal applied to the base and taken from the emitter (common-collector or emitter follower). The characteristics of these three connections correspond roughly to the three tube connections, with the exception that the input impedance is generally lower in the transistor circuit. The general characteristics of these three connections are given in the accompanying table.

Common emitter	Common base	Common collector
Large current gain	Approximate unity current gain	Large current gain
Large voltage gain	Large voltage gain	Approximate unity voltage gain
Highest power gain	Intermediate power gain	Lowest power gain
Low input resistance	Very low input resistance	High input resistance
High output resistance	Very high output resistance	Low output resistance
Analogous to grounded cathode	Analogous to grounded grid	Analogous to cathode follower generally

In audio amplifiers the common-emitter connection is most generally used. It is the only connection that affords both voltage and current gain. Hence it is the only connection that affords gain in a conventional cascaded amplifier with R-C coupling. The other two connections require interstage transformers to obtain gain in such an amplifier. In amplifier circuits, the transistor is a circuit element connected to external impedances. The following definitions are convenient:

Source impedance, Z_g—the impedance seen looking to the left of the line aa' in Fig. 11.31

Input impedance, z_i—the impedance seen looking to the right of the line aa' in Fig. 11.31 with load connected

Output impedance, z_o—the impedance seen looking to the left of the line bb' in Fig. 11.31 with source connected and source voltage equal to zero

Load impedance, Z_L—the impedance seen looking to the right of the line bb' in Fig. 11.31

Corresponding definitions apply for admittances.

The following tabulations give some of the quantities that are of general use in analyzing transistor amplifiers in terms of the h parameters of the stage. These quantities include input impedance, output impedance, current amplification, voltage

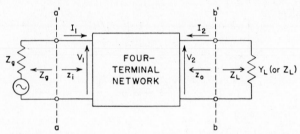

FIG. 11.31. Four-terminal network and external impedances.

amplification, power gain, and insertion gain. The equations are general, with the exception of those concerning matched power gain, which assume resistive low-frequency transistor parameters, resistive source, and resistive load. Matched power gain for low-frequency amplifiers is usually only of academic interest, since it is seldom that either low-level or power stages are operated under matched conditions.

A quantity $S = h_{12}h_{21}/h_{11}h_{22}$ is used in the relations that follow. Although the open-circuit feedback-voltage ratio h_{12} expresses the magnitude of the feedback factor, it does not give an indication of how important this feedback is. For example, if $h_{12} = 0.01$, the performance of a low-gain stage is relatively unaffected. On the other hand, the same value of h_{12} would have considerable effect on the performance of a high-gain stage. S is a measure of the effect that h_{12} has on the performance of the transistor. It is a measure of how much the load affects the input impedance and how much the source affects the output impedance.

Table 11.8 gives these relations for a general four-terminal network such as is shown in Fig. 11.31 in terms of the h parameters of the network. Insertion gain[5] is the gain "resulting from the insertion of a transducer in a transmission system, the ratio of the power delivered to that part of the system following the transducer to the power delivered to that same part before insertion." Table 11.9 gives the same quantities for the common-emitter connection of Fig. 11.32, Table 11.10 for the common-base connection of Fig. 11.33, Table 11.11 for the common-collector connection of Fig. 11.34. In Tables 11.9, 11.10, and 11.11 the quantities are expressed in terms of *common-emitter h parameters.*

TABLE 11.8

Input impedance =
$$\frac{V_1}{I_1} = h_{11} - \frac{h_{12}h_{21}}{h_{22} + Y_L} = h_{11}\left(1 - \frac{h_{22}S}{h_{22} + Y_L}\right)$$

Output admittance =
$$\frac{I_2}{V_2} = h_{22} - \frac{h_{12}h_{21}}{h_{11} + Z_g} = h_{22}\left(1 - \frac{h_{11}S}{h_{11} + Z_g}\right)$$

Current gain =
$$\frac{I_2}{I_1} = \frac{h_{21}Y_L}{h_{22} + Y_L}$$

Voltage gain =
$$\frac{V_2}{V_1} = \frac{-h_{21}}{h_{11}Y_L + h_{11}h_{22} - h_{12}h_{21}} = \frac{-h_{21}/h_{11}}{Y_L + h_{22}(1 - S)}$$

Transfer impedance =
$$\frac{V_2}{I_1} = \frac{-h_{21}}{h_{22} + Y_L}$$

Insertion gain† =
$$G = \left[\frac{h_{21}}{h_{11}h_{22}} \times \frac{1 + R_g/R_L}{(1 + 1/h_{22}R_L)(1 + R_g/h_{11}) - S}\right]^2$$

Power gain† =
$$G = \frac{h_{21}^2}{h_{11}h_{22}} \frac{1}{1 + h_{22}R_L} \frac{1}{1 - S + \dfrac{1}{h_{22}R_L}}$$

Matched input resistance† =
$$R_{mi} = h_{11}\sqrt{1 - S}$$

Matched output conductance† =
$$G_{mo} = h_{22}\sqrt{1 - S}$$

Matched power gain† =
$$G = \frac{h_{21}^2}{h_{11}h_{22}} \frac{1}{(1 + \sqrt{1 - S})^2}$$

---

† Low-frequency case where h parameters are real.

$$\left(S = \frac{h_{12}h_{21}}{h_{11}h_{22}}\right)$$

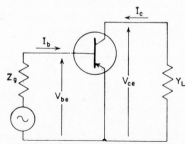

FIG. 11.32. Common-emitter amplifier stage.

The following relations apply to the common-emitter stage shown in Fig. 11.32 and are in terms of common-emitter h parameters.

TABLE 11.9

Input impedance =

$$\frac{V_{be}}{I_b} = h_{ie} - \frac{h_{re}h_{fe}}{h_{oe} + Y_L} \cong h_{ie} \qquad (Y_L \gg h_{oe}S)$$

Output admittance =

$$\frac{I_c}{V_{ce}} = h_{oe} - \frac{h_{re}h_{fe}}{h_{ie} + Z_g} \cong h_{oe} \qquad (Z_g \gg h_{ie}S)$$

Current gain =

$$\frac{I_c}{I_b} = \frac{h_{fe}Y_L}{h_{oe} + Y_L} \cong h_{fe} \qquad (Y_L \gg h_{oe})$$

The following relations apply to the common-base stage shown in Fig. 11.33 and are in terms of common-emitter h parameters.

TABLE 11.10

Input impedance =

$$\frac{V_{eb}}{I_e} = \frac{1}{1 + h_{fe}}\left[h_{ie} + \frac{h_{ie}h_{oe} - h_{re}(1 + h_{fe})}{h_{oe} + Y_L(1 + h_{fe})} h_{fe} \right]$$

Output admittance =

$$\frac{I_c}{V_{cb}} = \frac{1}{1 + h_{fe}}\left[h_{oe} + \frac{h_{ie}h_{oe} - h_{re}(1 + h_{fe})}{h_{ie} + Z_g(1 + h_{fe})} h_{fe} \right]$$

Current gain =

$$\frac{I_c}{I_e} = -\frac{h_{fe}}{1 + h_{fe}}\left[\frac{Y_L}{h_{oe}/(1 + h_{fe}) + Y_L} \right] \cong 1 \qquad \left(\begin{matrix} Y_L \gg \dfrac{h_{oe}}{h_{fe}} \\ h_{fe} \gg 1 \end{matrix} \right)$$

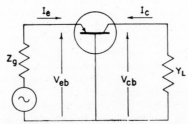

FIG. 11.33. Common-base amplifier stage.

The following relations apply to the common-collector stage shown in Fig. 11.34 and are in terms of common-emitter h parameters.

TABLE 11.11

Input impedance =

$$\frac{V_{bc}}{I_b} = h_{ie} + \frac{1 + h_{fe}}{h_{oe} + Y_L}$$

Output admittance =

$$\frac{I_e}{V_{ec}} = h_{oe} + \frac{1 + h_{fe}}{h_{ie} + Z_g}$$

Current gain =

$$\frac{I_e}{I_b} = -\frac{(1 + h_{fe})Y_L}{h_{oe} + Y_L}$$

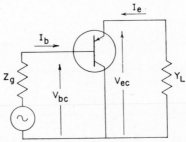

FIG. 11.34. Common-collector amplifier stage.

11.3b. Two-stage Amplifier. The question often arises as to what are the characteristics of two or more transistor amplifier stages in cascade. This can be handled by matrix analysis, as shown in Sec. 18. Although equations for input impedance, output admittance, power gain, etc., can be derived for any of the possible combinations, these equations are complicated, and in most cases the usage does not justify a tabulation of them. In this section, cascaded stages, stages with various types of feedback, or stages with impedances to ground will be handled in terms of the stage h parameters. Two stages in cascade will be consolidated as a single circuit element whose h parameters are easily calculable from the h parameters of the individual stages. A stage with feedback elements or some similar perturbation will be considered as a new circuit element whose h parameters can be calculated from the h parameters of the transistors being used.

Figure 11.35 shows two stages in cascade. The parameters of the first stage are h'_{nn}, those of the second stage are h''_{nn}, and those of the combination are h_{nn}. The parameters of the two stages in cascade are given in terms of the parameters of the individual stages. It is to be noted that these parameters are the h parameters for the configuration in which the transistor is being used. If one of the stages is common-base, common-base h parameters must be used. If one of the stages has an unbypassed emitter resistor or a small collector resistor, perturbed h parameters must be used that reflect these additional elements.

Since a transistor can be connected in three different ways, there are nine different ways in which to connect two transistors in cascade, as shown in Fig. 11.36. To illustrate the attributes of these various connections, typical transistor h parameters, given in Table 11.12, were used in the calculations of the various two-stage amplifiers.

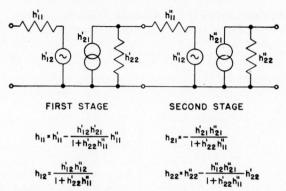

FIRST STAGE   SECOND STAGE

$$h_{11} = h'_{11} - \frac{h'_{12}h'_{21}}{1+h'_{22}h''_{11}}h''_{11} \qquad h_{21} = -\frac{h'_{21}h''_{21}}{1+h'_{22}h''_{11}}$$

$$h_{12} = \frac{h'_{12}h''_{12}}{1+h'_{22}h''_{11}} \qquad h_{22} = h''_{22} - \frac{h''_{12}h''_{21}}{1+h'_{22}h''_{11}}h'_{22}$$

Fig. 11.35. Two stages in cascade. The h parameters of the combination in terms of the h parameters of the individual stages.

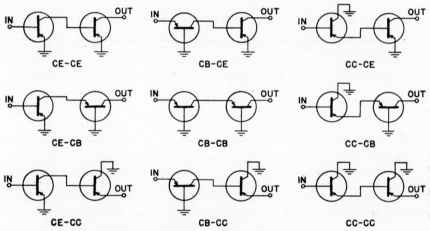

Fig. 11.36. Two-stage transistor amplifier configurations.

TABLE 11.12. TYPICAL TRANSISTOR PARAMETERS

Common Emitter	Common Collector
$h_{11} = 2,000$ ohms	$h_{11} = 2,000$ ohms
$h_{12} = 600 \times 10^{-6}$	$h_{12} = 1$
$h_{21} = 50$	$h_{21} = -51$
$h_{22} = 25$ μmhos	$h_{22} = 25$ μmhos
$(S = 0.6)$	$(S = -1,020)$

Common Base
$h_{11} = 39$ ohms
$h_{12} = 380 \times 10^{-6}$
$h_{21} = 0.98$
$h_{22} = 0.49$ μmho
$(S = -19.4)$

The values of the h parameters of the two-stage cascade considered as a single circuit element are given in Table 11.13. The four connections of common-emitter and common-base stages have an h_{12} of less than 10^{-6}. These connections have very little interaction between input and output and are essentially unilateral. Thus the

TABLE 11.13. h PARAMETERS OF TYPICAL TWO-STAGE AMPLIFIERS

1st stage / 2d stage	Common emitter	Common base	Common collector
Common emitter	$h_{11} = 1{,}940$ ohms $h_{12} = 0.34 \times 10^{-6}$ $h_{21} = -2{,}380$ $h_{22} = 24.3$ μmhos $S = -0.017$	$h_{11} = 40$ ohms $h_{12} = 0.23 \times 10^{-6}$ $h_{21} = 49$ $h_{22} = 25$ μmhos $S = 0.011$	$h_{11} = 99{,}000$ ohms $h_{12} = 570 \times 10^{-6}$ $h_{21} = 2{,}430$ $h_{22} = 24.3$ μmhos $S = 0.58$
Common base	$h_{11} = 2{,}000$ ohms $h_{12} = 0.23 \times 10^{-6}$ $h_{21} = 49$ $h_{22} = 0.50$ μmho $S = 0.011$	$h_{11} = 39.2$ ohms $h_{12} = 0.14 \times 10^{-6}$ $h_{21} = -0.96$ $h_{22} = 0.49$ μmho $S = -0.007$	$h_{11} = 4{,}000$ ohms $h_{12} = 380 \times 10^{-6}$ $h_{21} = -50$ $h_{22} = 0.50$ μmho $S = -9.5$
Common collector	$h_{11} = 1{,}940$ ohms $h_{12} = 570 \times 10^{-6}$ $h_{21} = 2{,}430$ $h_{22} = 1{,}240$ μmhos $S = 0.58$	$h_{11} = 40$ ohms $h_{12} = 380 \times 10^{-6}$ $h_{21} = -50$ $h_{22} = 50$ μmhos $S = -9.5$	$h_{11} = 99{,}000$ ohms $h_{12} = 0.95$ $h_{21} = -2{,}480$ $h_{22} = 1{,}240$ μmhos $S = -19.2$

input impedance is approximately h_{11} and the output admittance approximately h_{22} under all conditions. The connections which include a common-collector stage have considerable feedback; therefore, the input and output impedances are influenced considerably by the terminating impedance. High and low input impedances are obtained when the first stages are common-collector and common-base, respectively. High and low output impedances are obtained when the last stages are common-base and common-collector, respectively. High gain is obtained by using one or more common-emitter stages.

11.3c. Modified Amplifier. A resistor, capacitor, or other impedance associated with a transistor can be considered part of the stage or amplifier by altering the h

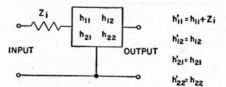

FIG. 11.37. Impedance in series with input.

parameters to include the effect of the additional element. The transformations given in Figs. 11.37 to 11.44 list the effect of an impedance connected in series with any terminal or connected between any two terminals. If more than one impedance is involved, the combined effect can be determined by successive transformations.

The particular case of a transistor in the common-emitter connection with an impedance in the emitter lead is shown in Fig. 11.40. Usually $|h_{22}Z_e| \ll 1$, and the transformations given with Fig. 11.39 reduce to those given with Fig. 11.40. In particular, Z_e may be the reactance of the emitter bypass capacitor.

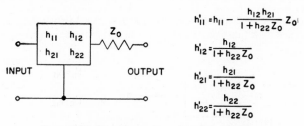

$$h'_{11} = h_{11} - \frac{h_{12}h_{21}}{1+h_{22}Z_0}Z_0$$

$$h'_{12} = \frac{h_{12}}{1+h_{22}Z_0}$$

$$h'_{21} = \frac{h_{21}}{1+h_{22}Z_0}$$

$$h'_{22} = \frac{h_{22}}{1+h_{22}Z_0}$$

FIG. 11.38. Impedance in series with output.

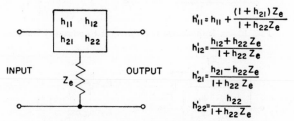

$$h'_{11} = h_{11} + \frac{(1+h_{21})Z_e}{1+h_{22}Z_e}$$

$$h'_{12} = \frac{h_{12}+h_{22}Z_e}{1+h_{22}Z_e}$$

$$h'_{21} = \frac{h_{21}-h_{22}Z_e}{1+h_{22}Z_e}$$

$$h'_{22} = \frac{h_{22}}{1+h_{22}Z_e}$$

FIG. 11.39. Impedance in series with common lead.

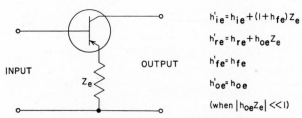

$$h'_{ie} = h_{ie} + (1+h_{fe})Z_e$$

$$h'_{re} = h_{re} + h_{oe}Z_e$$

$$h'_{fe} = h_{fe}$$

$$h'_{oe} = h_{oe}$$

$$(\text{when } |h_{oe}Z_e| \ll 1)$$

FIG. 11.40. Impedance in emitter lead.

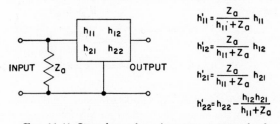

$$h'_{11} = \frac{Z_a}{h_{11}+Z_a}h_{11}$$

$$h'_{12} = \frac{Z_a}{h_{11}+Z_a}h_{12}$$

$$h'_{21} = \frac{Z_a}{h_{11}+Z_a}h_{21}$$

$$h'_{22} = h_{22} - \frac{h_{12}h_{21}}{h_{11}+Z_a}$$

FIG. 11.41. Impedance from input to common lead.

If a common-emitter transistor has feedback from collector to base, the general circuit shown in Fig. 11.43 reduces to that shown in Fig. 11.44 and the transformations reduce to those associated with Fig. 11.44 if $|Z_f| \gg |h_{11}|$ and $1 \gg |h_{12}|$.

11.3d. Frequency Response. The frequency response of an amplifier is often an important design consideration. Since the device characteristics of many transistors (particularly power transistors) often are such that the high-frequency cutoff may fall in the audio-frequency range, it is important to consider the limitations on transistor frequency response as they affect the design of low-frequency amplifiers. Some general considerations for both the low-frequency and high-frequency cutoffs for typical circuits will be discussed.

11.3e. Low-frequency Cutoff. There is no low-frequency cutoff for the transistor device, per se, since basically it can operate down to direct current. The low-frequency cutoff is only a function of the circuit in which the transistor operates. Thus,

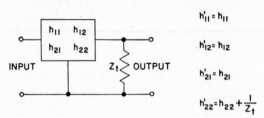

$$h'_{11} = h_{11}$$
$$h'_{12} = h_{12}$$
$$h'_{21} = h_{21}$$
$$h'_{22} = h_{22} + \frac{1}{Z_t}$$

Fig. 11.42. Impedance from output to common lead.

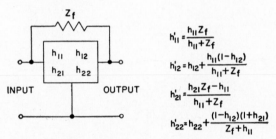

$$h'_{11} = \frac{h_{11} Z_f}{h_{11} + Z_f}$$
$$h'_{12} = h_{12} + \frac{h_{11}(1 - h_{12})}{h_{11} + Z_f}$$
$$h'_{21} = \frac{h_{21} Z_f - h_{11}}{h_{11} + Z_f}$$
$$h'_{22} = h_{22} + \frac{(1 - h_{12})(1 + h_{21})}{Z_f + h_{11}}$$

Fig. 11.43. Impedance from input to output.

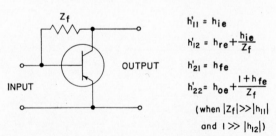

$$h'_{11} = h_{ie}$$
$$h'_{12} = h_{re} + \frac{h_{ie}}{Z_f}$$
$$h'_{21} = h_{fe}$$
$$h'_{22} = h_{oe} + \frac{1 + h_{fe}}{Z_f}$$
$$\text{(when } |Z_f| \gg |h_{11}|$$
$$\text{and } 1 \gg |h_{12}|)$$

Fig. 11.44. Collector-to-base feedback.

a direct-coupled transistor amplifier can amplify frequencies down to direct current. This section will discuss the circuit limitations on low-frequency response for both R-C-coupled amplifiers and transformer-coupled amplifiers.

The 3-db low-frequency cutoff for the R-C-coupled amplifier stage T_2, shown in Fig. 11.45, is given by the following expression: $f_L = 1/[2\pi C(R_{o1} + R_{i2})]$, where R_{o1} is the output resistance of the first amplifier and R_{i2} is the input resistance of the second amplifier.[6] Thus, the low-frequency cutoff will occur where the total series a-c loop resistance is equal to the reactance of the coupling capacitor.

The low-frequency response of the transformer-coupled amplifier, shown in Fig. 11.46, will fall off because the shunt reactance of the transformer decreases at low frequencies. The following expression is given for the low-frequency 3-db cutoff for a transformer-coupled amplifier:

$$f_L = \frac{1}{2\pi L_P[(N_2/N_1)^2 G_L + G_o]}$$

where L_P is the transformer primary inductance, G_L is the load conductance equal to $1/R_L$, and G_o is the transistor output conductance equal to $1/R_O$. In this case it is important that the transformer be selected such that the impedance of the primary

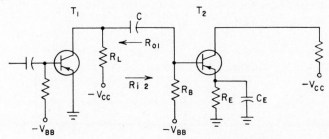

FIG. 11.45. R-C-coupled amplifier with fixed bias.

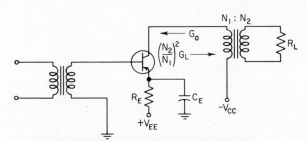

FIG. 11.46. Transformer-coupled amplifier.

is larger than the reciprocal of the total of the load conductance referred to the primary $(N_2/N_1)^2 G_L$ plus the output conductance G_o at the lowest frequency of interest.

One other consideration may be important in determining the low-frequency response of an amplifier. This will arise if the amplifier has a bypass capacitor in the emitter circuit as in Figs. 11.45 and 11.46. The capacitor C_E not only has to bypass the external emitter resistance R_E but also must be larger than the resistance reflected to the emitter which is $(R_g + R_i)/h_{fe} = (R_g + r_{bb'})/h_{fe} + r_e$, where r_e is the internal a-c emitter resistance, $r_{bb'}$ is the base resistance, and R_g is the source resistance. Thus, where the reactance of C_E is equal to $r_e + (R_g + r_{bb'})/h_{fc}$, the low-frequency response will be down 3 db.

The actual low-frequency cutoff therefore will depend on the particular circuit, since the effects of the decoupling capacitor C_E, the coupling capacitor C, or the transformer primary inductance may predominate.

11.3f. High-frequency Cutoff. The high-frequency characteristics of transistors are important particularly for transistors with large junction areas such as power units. The cutoff for these transistors will often be in the passband of the amplifier to be designed. Many times, this factor will lead to an increase in distortion at higher frequencies as described in Sec. 11.6f. The high-frequency cutoff f_H of a transistor amplifier will be determined both by the intrinsic frequency cutoff of the transistor and by the circuit in which it is used.

The alpha-cutoff frequency f_{ab} is a measure of the frequency at which the small-signal short-circuit common-base current gain is down 3 db from its low-frequency value. A corresponding frequency for the common-emitter connection may be defined as f_{ae} (sometimes designated f_β), the beta-cutoff frequency (Sec. 11.1g). For most low-frequency transistors,† f_{ae} will be related to f_{ab} by the following equation: $f_{ae} = f_{ab}/(h_{fe} + 1) = f_{ab}(1 + h_{fb})$. Thus, the intrinsic high-frequency cutoff of a transistor used in the common-base connection always will be greater than the cutoff for the same transistor used as a common-emitter amplifier.

Another device limitation which may reduce the high-frequency cutoff is the collector-to-base capacitance $C_{b'c}$, shown in Fig. 11.22. This is essentially the same as

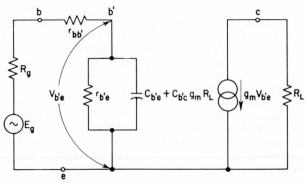

FIG. 11.47. Common-emitter equivalent circuit for determining high-frequency cutoff.

the collector capacitance which would appear in parallel with the collector resistance r_c for the T equivalent circuit, shown in Fig. 11.20 (modified for high frequencies).

From the common-emitter hybrid-pi equivalent circuit shown in Fig. 11.22, it can be seen that the effective high-frequency cutoff can be related to the internal base-emitter voltage $V_{b'e}$, since the current delivered to the load is directly proportional to this voltage. For a common-emitter connection, the effective shunt input capacitance[7] is $C = C_{b'e} + g_m R_L C_{b'c}$, as shown in Fig. 11.47. This appears in parallel with $r_{b'e}$ and will influence the base-emitter voltage $V_{b'e}$, thereby tending to reduce the effective high-frequency cutoff from the beta-cutoff frequency $f_{ae} = 1/2\pi r_{b'e} C_{b'e}$ (Sec. 11.1g). The relative importance of $C_{b'c}$ compared with $C_{b'e}$ can be seen to depend upon the load R_L and g_m, which is determined by the operating point.

For many low-level transistors, the high-frequency cutoff will be above audio frequencies. For amplifiers employing power transistors, the load resistance R_L will generally be small and the effect of $C_{b'c}$ on frequency response will usually be negligible. In this case, $C_{b'e}$ alone will generally be the important factor in determining the high-frequency cutoff. From the equivalent circuit shown in Fig. 11.47, it may be seen that the effects of the input shunt capacity are greatly reduced when the amplifier is driven from a voltage (low-resistance) source. The effective high-frequency cutoff will increase under these conditions, being limited only by the $r_{bb'}$ of the transistor. On the other hand, if the common-emitter amplifier is driven from a current (high-resistance) source, the high-frequency cutoff will be f_{ae} or lower.

The high-frequency characteristics for a common-collector amplifier are essentially the same as those of a common-emitter amplifier. The high-frequency cutoff also will improve as the source resistance is decreased.

† This equation may not hold for drift transistors or diffused-base units.

The high-frequency cutoff for a common-base amplifier will essentially be the alpha-cutoff frequency f_{ab} unless the shunting effect of the output capacity causes the response to fall off more rapidly. Which effect predominates will depend on the particular transistor and circuit parameters. As the source impedance of a common-base amplifier is decreased, the high-frequency cutoff will also decrease.

There is one additional practical limitation on the high-frequency response of the transformer-coupled amplifier in Fig. 11.46. This is the leakage reactance between the primary and secondary of the transformer. The 3-db cutoff frequency which occurs when this factor predominates is given by the following expression:

$$f_H = \frac{R_O + (N_1/N_2)^2 R_L}{2\pi L_S}$$

where L_S is the total leakage inductance. Furthermore, the output capacitance of the transistor may resonate with the leakage reactance and cause peaking in the high-frequency response. It, therefore, follows that wideband frequency response is easier to obtain for R-C-coupled amplifiers than for equivalent transformer-coupled stages.

It should be noted that the frequency response of many circuits can be extended through the judicious use of feedback. The increased frequency response, however, will be at the expense of a reduction in gain at mid-frequencies. A more complete discussion of the use of feedback techniques is given in Sec. 11.8.

11.4. Device Ratings and Circuit Considerations. *11.4a. General.* A transistor operating in a circuit is normally limited by the maximum ratings of the device. It is important to understand these limitations in order that the transistor can be optimally utilized without reducing the circuit reliability. There are several device limitations which are important for transistors. These are usually given in terms of maximum voltage, current, and power ratings. Implied in the maximum power rating is a maximum temperature rating for the device.

11.4b. Maximum Junction Temperature $T_{J,\max}$. The upper limit of junction temperature is usually specified by the transistor manufacturer. For germanium transistors, this upper limit may range from 75 to 100°C, whereas for silicon devices the upper temperature range may vary from 140 to 215°C. There are several factors which may contribute to establishing an upper temperature range for transistors. One may be that the materials used in constructing the device cannot be raised above a certain temperature without destroying their properties. Another factor may be that the transistor characteristics will change as temperature is increased, sometimes irreversibly. These factors will usually lead to a decrease in reliability of the device or even a catastrophic failure. Although each manufacturer determines the maximum junction temperature by a different criterion, it is good practice not to exceed this rating.

11.4c. Maximum Power Dissipation. The power output of a transistor amplifier (particularly a power amplifier) is usually limited, so that the dissipation does not raise the junction temperature to an unsafe value. The heat from the transistor can be dissipated by refrigeration, by forced-air cooling, and more commonly by radiation and convection to the surroundings. For a given temperature rise, the amount of heat that can be dissipated by radiation and convection is determined by the size of the object and to a lesser extent by its shape. A germanium transistor the size of a $\frac{1}{2}$-in. cube in free air may be limited to a dissipation in the order of a watt. A silicon transistor of the same size may allow a dissipation of several watts, since the device can stand a greater temperature rise.

If the transistor is thermally joined to a metal chassis or some other heat sink, the allowable dissipation can be increased many times. The limitations are the thermal drop between the collector junction and the transistor case, the thermal drop between the transistor and the chassis, and the temperature rise of the chassis itself.   If the chassis is not large enough to lose sufficient heat by radiation and convection, an appreciable temperature rise will occur in the chassis itself.   Power transistors usually are clamped to the chassis, as shown in Fig. 11.48, with studs or screws to ensure a low thermal drop between the transistor and the chassis.   Generally, a bearing surface is provided to transmit the heat.   The internal construction of a good power transistor provides a low thermal drop between the collector junction and the case. A power transistor clamped to a heat sink may have a thermal rise (generally called

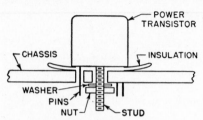

FIG. 11.48. Power transistor clamped to chassis.

thermal resistance θ) above the ambient temperature as low as 1°C/watt, while a low-power transistor may have a thermal resistance of 1000°C/watt.

For the chassis to be an efficient heat sink, it must be sufficiently large in area to dissipate the heat without undue temperature rise.   It must be constructed of material with a high thermal conductivity and sufficient thickness to distribute the heat throughout the chassis.   Proper form factor and orientation to ensure good ventilation are highly desirable.   Even a slight amount of forced convection can lower the size requirement of the heat sink considerably.

The heat-conducting surface of a transistor is generally electrically connected to the collector of the transistor.   Therefore, an electrical insulator that is a good conductor of heat is usually needed between the transistor and the chassis.   This insulator may be a thin sheet of mica or plastic or an anodized aluminum chassis. Silicone oil and clean flat surfaces facilitate the transfer of heat.

The thermal resistance between the collector junction and connected heat sink or the temperature rise of the transistor in free air can be readily measured.   The most reliable temperature-sensitive parameter to use for this measurement is the voltage drop across a forward-biased junction.   This will be accurate for both silicon and germanium transistors.[8]   The use of I_{CO} as a calibration device is not recommended for silicon units, since the leakage current may dominate the temperature-sensitive saturation current and give erroneous results.

To calibrate the transistor, it is heated in an oven and the forward voltage drop across the collector-base junction V_{CB} is measured at various temperatures (with the emitter open).   The voltage drop across a forward-biased diode will decrease with increasing temperature, as described in Sec. 11.9c.   For these measurements, the collector-to-base diode should be driven from a high-impedance d-c source.   Initially, the forward diode current should be adjusted at room temperature (30°C) to make the voltage drop about 0.25 volt for germanium transistors and 0.5 volt for silicon transistors.   These values will minimize the errors introduced by the bulk and series lead resistance of the diode.

The transistor is then operated at a given power dissipation, and the V_{CB} is measured.   It is necessary to make this measurement very rapidly because the transistor may have a low thermal inertia (capacity) and its temperature will change rather quickly.   In practice, a switching arrangement which alternately applies d-c power and measures V_{CB} is generally employed.

If, for example, under the following conditions,

$$T_{\text{case}} = T_C = 30°C$$
$$P_{\text{dissipation}} = P_C = 5 \text{ watts}$$

the junction temperature T_J is 80°C, as determined by measuring V_{CB}, the thermal resistance of the transistor can be calculated as follows:

$$\theta_t = \text{thermal resistance} = \frac{T_J - T_C}{P_C} = \frac{80 - 30}{5} = 10°C/\text{watt}$$

It can then be calculated that the same transistor with the same heat sink would have a junction temperature of 100°C at 7 watts dissipation. In a like manner the thermal resistance of a transistor in free air can be determined and used. The maximum power dissipation can then be expressed in terms of the total thermal resistance from junction to air and the maximum allowable junction temperature.

$$P_{C,\max} = \frac{T_{J,\max} - T_{\text{ambient}}}{\theta_{\text{total}}} = \frac{T_{J,\max} - T_A}{\theta_t + \theta_i + \theta_a} = \frac{T_{J,\max} - T_A}{\sum_n \theta_n}$$

where θ_t is the thermal resistance from junction to case, θ_i is the thermal resistance from case to chassis (through an insulator), and θ_a is the thermal resistance from chassis to air. The thermal equivalent circuit for such a transistor is shown in

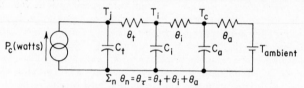

$$\sum_n \theta_n = \theta_\tau = \theta_t + \theta_i + \theta_a$$

C_t = junction thermal capacity (depends on mass associated with junction and mounting base)
C_i = insulator thermal capacity and is negligible
C_a = chassis or heat sink thermal capacity (depends on mass)

FIG. 11.49. Thermal equivalent circuit.

Fig. 11.49, where the power dissipation is equivalent to a thermal current and the temperature is equivalent to a thermal voltage.

In practice, however, another limitation on the maximum transistor power dissipation will be encountered. This is the limitation due to the circuit thermal stability. As described in Sec. 11.9k, if a circuit is not stabilized against temperature, it is possible that it may exhibit thermal runaway. This is a particularly important consideration for power transistors. If too much power is dissipated by the transistor, its junction temperature may rise regeneratively, causing increased dissipation and finally destroying the unit. This limitation must be considered apart from the $T_{J,\max}$ limitation.

Another factor may be important for reliability considerations.[9] If the thermal time constant $\theta_t C_t$ of a transistor is low, there is the possibility that a large temperature differential will exist between the junction and the case. This is often the situation when the case is tied to a heat sink which has a high thermal inertia. This temperature differential may create strains in the device each time the junction temperature is cycled and can reduce the useful transistor life expectancy. In addition, where the junction temperature can follow the instantaneous dissipation (i.e., at low frequencies), peak power dissipation rather than average dissipation may be the dominant consideration.

Although the previous discussion considered only the dissipation occurring at the collector junction, in some applications the dissipation occurring at the emitter junction may be significant. Heat arising at the emitter junction may be more difficult to remove, since the collector is normally the element connected to the transistor case. The thermal resistance from emitter to case, therefore, will be much greater than the corresponding collector-to-case thermal resistance. Thus, in some instances, the emitter dissipation may restrict the power-handling capabilities of the transistor.

11.4d. Maximum Collector Current. The maximum collector-current rating given by most manufacturers should be closely examined, since a large collector current in itself usually is not the limiting factor. More realistically, a peak current limitation might be imposed by the fact that the instantaneous power dissipated from the junction may be excessive owing to the small thermal time constant for the transistor.

Also, high currents may lead to overheating in isolated "hot spots" in the junction, since it is not a perfectly homogeneous surface. The peak current may also be limited by the current-handling capability of the internal lead connections.

Peak operating currents may also be limited by the physical sizes of the junctions, since the current density may be excessive and lead to a reduction of current gain. Therefore, a practical design criterion for limiting the amount of peak collector current may be that the current gain in the transistor has decreased to such an extent at high collector currents that the device no longer has sufficient gain for satisfactory circuit operation. This reduction in current gain may also lead to an intolerable increase in distortion.

11.4e. Maximum Collector Voltage. No uniform specifications for the maximum permissible collector voltage are given for transistors. There are, however, certain basic limitations on the maximum collector voltage of a transistor. Manufacturers present this information in various forms. For the collector-to-base junction, the important limitations are avalanche breakdown and punch-through. Punch-through is the effect caused by the collector depletion region gradually widening with increasing collector voltage until it reaches the emitter region and results in an electrical short circuit between the collector and emitter.

For most transistors, however, avalanche breakdown is usually the major limitation regarding collector voltage. This is caused by excessive electric fields in the transistor and is similar to the Townsend avalanche found in gaseous-discharge devices. Regardless of whether collector breakdown occurs because of avalanche or punch-through, it is important not to exceed this collector voltage. If there are no current-limiting resistances in the collector circuit (such as in a power amplifier or transformer-coupled amplifier) and breakdown occurs, excessive currents may flow and cause overheating of the transistor and permanent damage.

It should be noted that the avalanche breakdown of silicon transistors decreases as the temperature is lowered. This factor should be kept in mind when designing circuits employing silicon transistors which must be operated over wide temperature ranges.

The avalanche breakdown voltage for the common-emitter connection BV_{CEO} (from collector to emitter with base open) will be lower than that for the common-base connection BV_{CBO} (from collector to base with emitter open) due to the alpha multiplication factor.[10] This factor increases the charge carriers and reduces the breakdown voltage. It is important in designing common-emitter circuits to recognize this lower voltage limitation. In addition, the collector-to-emitter breakdown voltage is a function of temperature. As temperature increases, the breakdown voltage BV_{CEO} will decrease above room temperature for most transistors. With silicon transistors, the breakdown voltage also may decrease slightly at very low temperatures.

The breakdown voltage for a common-emitter circuit also is a function of the d-c resistance between the base and emitter of the transistor. Figure 11.50 shows that the breakdown voltage BV_{CER} decreases rapidly as the external base-emitter resistance R_{BE} is increased for several typical germanium power transistors. R_{BE}, therefore, should be as small as possible in order to avoid early collector-to-emitter voltage breakdown.

For some circuits, such as class B amplifiers, a reverse voltage is applied to the base-emitter junction while the transistor has a high collector-emitter voltage across it. If the transistor does not have an appreciable internal base resistance r_{bb}', the breakdown voltage for this condition approaches that of the higher common-base avalanche-breakdown voltage.

11.4f. Maximum Base-Emitter Breakdown. A discussion of transistor voltage breakdown should also include the effects of excessive reverse voltage at the base-emitter junction. This type of breakdown is important in large-signal applications,

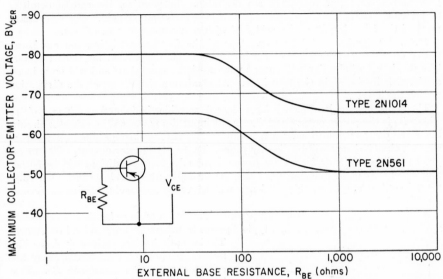

Fig. 11.50. Maximum collector-emitter voltage versus external base resistance. (*RCA Data Sheet* 2N561, 2N1014, 12-58.)

particularly in class B amplifiers where a high inverse signal voltage can appear at the input junction.

The factors which cause base-emitter voltage breakdown are similar to those occurring in the base-collector junction, as previously described. The significant feature regarding breakdown in the emitter-base junction is that it may occur at much lower voltages than the corresponding base-collector breakdown. This is due to the low-resistivity material used in the emitter. Diffused transistors, in particular, will exhibit a very low breakdown voltage, some breakdowns being as low as 1 volt.

In general, therefore, it is good procedure to ascertain that the peak inverse input voltage will be less than the base-emitter breakdown voltage.

11.5. Class A Power Amplifiers. *11.5a. Introduction.* Class A power amplifiers are often used in circuits requiring high linearity where a moderate amount of power output is desired. The main disadvantage of using a class A power amplifier is that the collector current flows continuously,[11] resulting in higher transistor dissipation for a given power output compared with a class B amplifier.

The load impedance rarely is matched to the output impedance of a power amplifier. The choice of the load resistance is usually governed entirely by the maximum output power desired and by the supply voltage that is available, although, in some cases, the allowable distortion may also influence this choice. Most power amplifiers must work over a wide range of voltage and current, and the input resistance and transfer characteristics may change considerably over this range, so that it is generally necessary to compute the gain and power output of a class A power amplifier on a large-signal basis or by graphical techniques.

The power gain of a class A amplifier can be expressed as $P_G = h_F^2(R_L/R_i)$, where h_F is the large-signal current transfer ratio, R_L is the collector load resistance, and R_i is the large-signal a-c input resistance of the transistor. In practice, since the load resistance for a class A power amplifier will be much smaller than the output impedance, the static current-transfer curves can be used to determine the large-signal current gain h_F. For a high power gain, it may be noted that a large current gain and small input resistance are desirable. In practice, the common-emitter amplifier is usually employed, since it has the greatest power gain. For this reason, most of the following discussion will deal with common-emitter amplifiers.

11.5b. Dissipation and Efficiency. One of the factors restricting the maximum power output for class A amplifiers is the allowable dissipation for the transistor. The maximum dissipation will occur under no-signal conditions and will be reduced as signal is increased in the transistor. At maximum signal output the dissipation will be the lowest.

The collector circuit efficiency for a class A amplifier is defined as $\text{Eff} = P_O/P_{DC}$ where P_O is the power output and P_{DC} is the input d-c power to the collector circuit. Since the d-c power into a class A amplifier is constant (disregarding temperature effects), the efficiency will be directly proportional to the power output. The maximum possible efficiency for a class A amplifier under ideal conditions will be 50 per cent when the collector current can swing the entire length of the load line. Actually, for a practical amplifier, this efficiency will never be approached owing to several considerations.

As shown in Fig. 11.51, there is a practical limitation on how far the collector current may increase or decrease in a typical power transistor for a given load resistance. The lower limit is approximately I_{CO}. The maximum current swing is limited by the collector saturation resistance R_S. This is an equivalent ohmic resistance in series with the collector of the transistor. The reciprocal of the slope of a line drawn from the origin to the intersection of the load line and the active-saturation region boundary is defined as the d-c saturation resistance (for a given collector current). For many transistors, the active-saturation region boundary is a linear function, and R_S will be independent of the collector current.

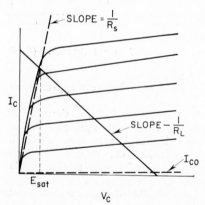

Fig. 11.51. Limitations of collector-current swing for load resistance R_L.

Current in the transistor cannot swing beyond the saturation region, so that the minimum collector voltage will be limited to the equivalent saturation voltage $E_{sat} = R_S I_C$.† For germanium transistors, the saturation resistance may be as low as 0.01 to 0.1 ohm. On the other hand, the saturation resistance may be quite high in some silicon units and may range from 1 to 20 ohms or more. Large saturation resistances will substantially lower the maximum efficiency.

---

† Actually, E_{sat} depends upon the base current I_B for any given I_C. This can be seen if the saturation region is plotted on an expanded scale. Up to a point, E_{sat} will decrease as I_B is increased. In many cases, E_{sat} will be specified rather than the saturation resistance R_S.

In addition to the limitations imposed by the collector saturation resistance and I_{co}, the maximum collector current swing may intentionally be restricted in order to obtain better linearity and reduced distortion.

There are various methods by which a class A amplifier may be connected to the a-c load. These are described in the following sections for an ideal transistor (i.e., no saturation resistance). The restrictions on signal swing described in this section, however, must be considered in designing a practical amplifier.

11.5c. Direct-coupled Amplifier. A common-emitter class A amplifier may be coupled directly to the load, as shown in Fig. 11.52. As seen from Fig. 11.53 the

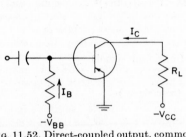

FIG. 11.52. Direct-coupled output, common-emitter stage.

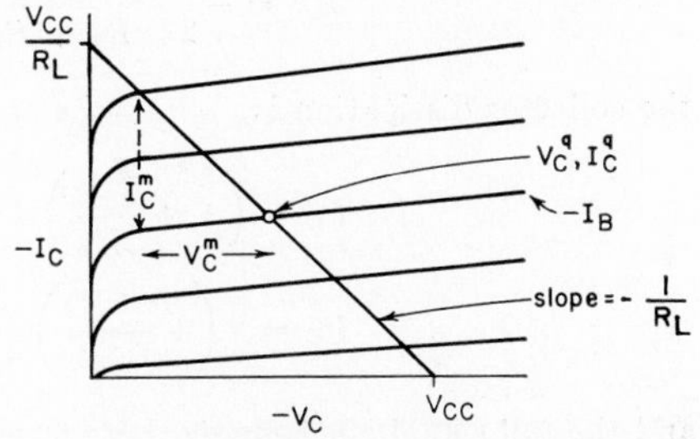

FIG. 11.53. Load line, direct-coupled output.

load line intersects the abscissa at $V_C = V_{CC}$ and has a slope equal to the negative of the load conductance. Since the a-c and d-c resistance of the collector load are the same, there is only one load line. The power output is

$$P_O = \frac{V_C^m I_C^m}{2}$$

Ideally the collector characteristics are linear, and the collector voltage can be driven to zero. Under these conditions, the maximum power output is

$$P_O^m = \frac{V_C^q I_C^q}{2} = \frac{V_{CC}^2}{8R_L}$$

the collector dissipation is

$$P_C = P_O^m \qquad \text{(maximum signal)}$$
$$P_C = 2P_O^m \qquad \text{(zero signal)}$$

and the full signal efficiency is

$$\text{Eff} = 25\%$$

11.5d. R-C-coupled Amplifier. If the transistor is R-C-coupled to the load, as in Fig. 11.54, both an a-c and a d-c load line are involved. As shown in Fig. 11.55 the

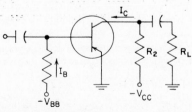

FIG. 11.54. R-C-coupled output, common-emitter stage.

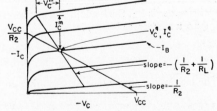

FIG. 11.55. Load line, R-C-coupled output.

d-c load line has a slope that is the reciprocal of the d-c collector resistance. The a-c load line has a slope that is the reciprocal of the parallel combination of the load and d-c collector resistances. The power output is

$$P_O = \frac{V_C^m I_C^m}{2} \frac{R_2}{R_2 + R_L}$$

The maximum power output under ideal conditions is

$$P_O^m = \frac{V_C^q I_C^q}{2} \frac{R_2}{R_2 + R_L} = \frac{V_{CC}^2}{8R_L(1 + R_2/2R_L)^2}$$

the collector dissipation is

$$P_C = \left(1 + \frac{2R_L}{R_2}\right) P_O^m \qquad \text{(maximum signal)}$$

$$P_C = 2\left(1 + \frac{R_L}{R_2}\right) P_O^m \qquad \text{(zero signal)}$$

and the full signal efficiency is

$$\text{Eff} = \frac{R_2 R_L \times 100\%}{2(R_2 + R_L)(R_2 + 2R_L)}$$

$$= 8\% \text{ maximum when } \frac{R_2}{R_L} = \sqrt{2}$$

11.5e. Transformer-coupled amplifier. In the case of choke or transformer coupling, as shown in Fig. 11.56, the resistance of the transformer primary is usually negligible

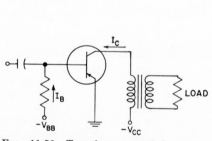

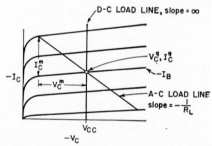

FIG. 11.56. Transformer-coupled output, common-emitter stage.

FIG. 11.57. Load line, transformer-coupled output.

and the d-c load line vertical. If the load resistance reflected in the primary of the transformer is R_L, the load lines are as shown in Fig. 11.57. The power output, assuming no transformer losses, is

$$P_O = \frac{V_C^m I_C^m}{2}$$

The maximum power output assuming an ideal transistor is

$$P_O^m = \frac{V_C^q I_C^q}{2} = \frac{V_{CC}^2}{2R_L}$$

the collector dissipation is

$$P_C = P_O^m \qquad \text{(maximum signal)}$$
$$P_C = 2P_O^m \qquad \text{(zero signal)}$$

and the full signal efficiency is

$$\text{Eff} = 50\%$$

11.5f. Nonlinear Distortion. Distortion in a class A stage may arise from non-linearities in the transfer characteristics of a transistor. It is a function of the power output, the source resistance, and the load resistance. As seen in Figs. 11.58 and 11.59, the common-emitter transfer characteristics become nonlinear at high currents owing to the effect of current-gain fall off with increasing current and at low currents owing to the nonlinear input resistance. These nonlinearities cause second-harmonic distortion in class A stages. The amount of distortion can be computed graphically

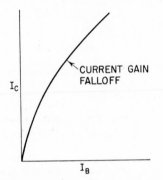

FIG. 11.58. Common-emitter current-transfer characteristic.

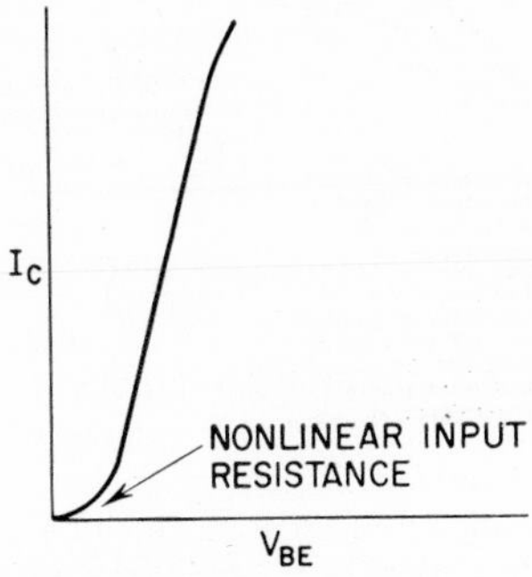

FIG. 11.59. Common-emitter transconductance characteristic.

by conventional methods.[11] If low distortion is the prime requisite, push-pull operation can be used to cancel much of the even harmonic distortion.

Limiting takes place at the high-current end of the load line because of zero or near-zero collector voltage (saturation voltage). It takes place at the other end of the load line because the transistor is cut off. Maximum undistorted power output can be obtained if the output stage is limited at both ends of the load line for approximately the same signal level. This is accomplished by proper biasing of the stage. Techniques to maintain the bias at the proper value are discussed in Sec. 11.9.

11.5g. Nonlinear Input Impedance. From Fig. 11.59, the transfer characteristics of collector current versus base-to-emitter voltage can be seen to become nonlinear at low current levels. This is due to the nonlinear input resistance of the transistor. At low levels, the input resistance is very strongly a function of the current. With most power transistors, however, except for this small region, the linearity of the transconductance characteristic (I_C versus V_{BE}) is greater than that of the current-transfer characteristic (I_C versus I_B) shown in Fig. 11.58. This means that a low-resistance source should be used to drive a power amplifier in order to minimize the distortion. Thus, if the stage can be driven from a constant-voltage source (where the source impedance is much less than the input resistance of the transistor) and the signal excursion is limited (which will reduce the maximum efficiency), the distortion can be reduced.

The distortion due to the input impedance can be determined from the base characteristics. When the load line has been drawn on the collector characteristics as in

Fig. 11.57, it is transferred to the base characteristics as shown in Fig. 11.60. This then gives input voltage as a function of input current. The nonlinearity of the input resistance of the stage is then known. If the stage is driven from a high-impedance source, the input resistance of the stage has little effect and the nonlinearity is that shown in the collector characteristics.

If the transistor is driven from a known source resistance, assumed to be constant, the input signal to the transistor can be determined graphically. For example, if as in Fig. 11.61 the driving stage is considered to be a constant-voltage generator V_g in series with a source resistance R_g, the load line of R_g can then be drawn on the base characteristics, Fig. 11.60. The position of the input load line of R_g is adjusted so that its intercept with the ordinate is $V_B = V_g$. V_g is the total applied voltage. It is the

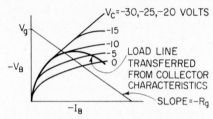

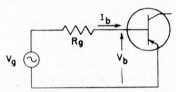

FIG. 11.60. Load lines, base characteristics.   FIG. 11.61. Equivalent circuit of driver and transistor.

sum of the bias and the signal voltages. The intersection of the load line transferred from the collector characteristics with the input load line is the operating point for the transistor with the aforementioned applied voltages.

As the instantaneous value of V_g changes, the input load line moves up and down in order to maintain V_g as its end point. If the intersection of the input load line with the collector load line is noted, the base current can be determined as a function of the driving voltage. When the base current is used as a function of driving voltage, the portion of the distortion due to the nonlinear input resistance can be calculated. The base current can be transferred to the collector characteristics in order to determine the collector voltage or current as a function of the driving voltage. From this the distortion of the stage can be computed.

If the driving stage is considered to be a constant-current generator I_g in parallel with a source resistance R_g, the same type of analysis can be used, with the exception that the position of the input load line of R_g is adjusted so that its intercept with the abscissa is $I_B = I_g$.

In order to reduce distortion further, negative feedback can be used, as described in Sec. 11.8. If an emitter resistor is used in order to obtain negative feedback, the magnitude of the emitter resistor will be limited, since the available d-c supply voltage will be reduced by the product of the resistance and the current flowing through it. This will limit the available output power and reduce the over-all circuit efficiency. In addition, the a-c power gain of the stage will be reduced unless the resistance is bypassed by a capacitor.

11.5h. Reactive Load. As in vacuum-tube amplifiers, the load line is an ellipse if the load is reactive. If the stage is overloaded, the output voltage will show the distortion as a notch in the side of the wave when the load is reactive rather than as a clipping of the peaks when the load is resistive. Reactive-load impedances are generally encountered at low audio frequencies, which may range from 20 to 300 cycles, depending upon the quality and the use of the amplifier. It is desirable to make the primary inductance of the output transformer as low as possible because the size of the output transformer is dependent upon the primary inductance of the winding. A rough rule of thumb is to make the primary impedance (no load) of the output transformer at the lowest frequency that rated power output is desired, from one to two times the reflected a-c resistance of the load. If low distortion is desired, considerable feedback is required. When the no-load primary impedance of the output transformer is equal to the reflected load resistance, the transformer is feeding a complex impedance whose magnitude is 70 per cent of that in the middle-frequency range; yet the maximum power output is only about 1 db lower than that obtainable in the middle-frequency range.

11.5i. Maximum Voltage. In a vacuum-tube amplifier, the maximum voltage rating usually applies to the d-c or average plate voltage. In a transformer-coupled amplifier, the peak plate voltage may be almost double the average voltage and no harm results. However, in transistor amplifiers, the maximum voltage rating is generally a peak rating. Thus in a transformer-coupled stage, the supply voltage should not exceed half the maximum allowable peak voltage. A discussion of maximum voltage ratings for transistors is given in Sec. 11.4e.

11.5j. Common-emitter Stage. A common-emitter stage is easy to drive, has high power gain, and has an input resistance of h_{ie} or less. This kind of output stage is desirable when the driver is R-C coupled, since the current gain is large in this connection and a driver transformer is not needed. Although the preceding paragraphs have concerned common-emitter stages, much of this analysis can be used for any of the connections. With only slight error, the same collector characteristics and load line can be used to analyze a common-base or common-collector stage.

11.5k. Common-base Stage. The common-base connection has medium power gain and a low input resistance. A driver transformer is usually needed with this connection, since the current gain is less than unity. Because of the linearity of the common-base collector characteristics, as illustrated in Fig. 11.18, this type of output stage has low distortion when driven from a current source. Another way of saying this is to say that a common-base output stage inherently has a considerable amount of negative feedback. Because of this low distortion and the ease of stabilization, it is often desirable to use a common-base stage if the amplifier has a driver transformer.

The common-emitter collector characteristics shown in Fig. 11.57 plot I_C as a function of V_{CE}, whereas common-base characteristics plot I_C as a function of V_{CB}. Ordinarily, the difference between these two voltages, the base-to-emitter voltage, is considerably smaller than the collector voltage. As a result of this, the common-emitter collector characteristics, load lines, collector dissipations, power outputs, and efficiencies given in Secs. 11.5a to 11.5i are nearly true for common-base stages. The input impedance of a common-base stage can be determined from Figs. 11.57 and 11.60 since the input voltage is $-V_B$ and the input current is $-(I_C + I_B)$. The input resistance is then $\Delta V_B / \Delta (I_C + I_B)$ measured along the load line. Since both these quantities are not available in the same graph, both Figs. 11.57 and 11.60 must be used for this calculation. However, if the load line is plotted in both cases, the results are obtainable directly.

11.5l. Common-collector Stage. The common-collector stage has low power gain, less than unity voltage gain, high current gain, a low output impedance, and a high input resistance. It also has low distortion because of the large amount of negative feedback. The common-collector stage can be conveniently driven from an R-C-coupled driver because the driving current is small. The fact that a large driving voltage is required is often no difficulty, since the input resistance is correspondingly high. When the preceding stage is a current source, a high driving voltage is automatically obtained across this high input resistance.

Ordinarily the emitter current and the collector current of a transistor are approximately equal. Under these conditions, common-emitter collector characteristics can be used to analyze common-collector stages. Therefore, the data given in Secs. 11.5a to 11.5i apply to common-collector stages.

The driving requirements of a common-collector class A stage are available directly from Figs. 11.57 and 11.60. Figure 11.60 gives the input voltage and current of the transistor itself. The input current of the stage is the same as that of the transistor, while the input voltage of the stage is equal to $V_B - V_C$. In most cases V_C is much larger than V_B, and $-V_C$ can be taken to be the input voltage of the stage. V_C and V_B are both given directly in either Fig. 11.57 or 11.60. For example, from either figure, the input resistance can be obtained directly if it is assumed that V_B is small compared with V_C. In this case, the input resistance is $\Delta V_C / \Delta I_B$ measured along the load line.

11.5m. Split-load Stage. The split-load base-input stage shown in Fig. 11.62 has a number of advantages as a class A power amplifier. It is intermediate between the common-emitter and the common-collector stages. It applies a certain controlled amount of negative feedback to the output stage without much loss in over-all amplifier gain when the driver transistor has a high output impedance. It overcomes the limitation of insufficient driver supply voltage that is encountered with common-collector output stages. It provides a point, i.e., the emitter, from which feedback can be applied to earlier stages with a reduction in high-frequency instability caused by phase shift in the output transformer.

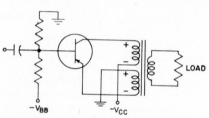

FIG. 11.62. Split-load, common-emitter stage.

As in the case of the common-collector stage, it is easily analyzed using common-emitter graphical characteristics.

11.6. Class B Power Amplifiers. *11.6a. Introduction.* Ideal class B push-pull amplification is characterized by signal flow through each transistor during only one-half of the input cycle. Class B amplifiers are at present used to a greater extent in transistor circuits than in tube circuits because it is easier and simpler to build class B amplifiers with transistors, because many transistor applications require low battery drain and hence high efficiency, and because maximum power dissipation is a severe limitation with available transistors.

Transistors can be operated with a very small idling current, and many can be driven to nearly zero collector voltage, with the result that output-stage efficiencies approaching the theoretical maximum of 78.5 per cent sometimes can be realized in practice. As is the case with class A amplifiers, class B stages can be operated common-emitter, common-base, or common-collector or in intermediate connections such as with a split load. They can be driven by transformer-coupled, R-C-coupled, or direct-coupled drivers. Their output can be coupled to the load through a transformer or can be transformerless. For optimum design of class B amplifiers, thermal considerations (Sec. 11.4c) as well as electrical limitations become important.

11.6b. Power Output and Dissipation. A transformer-coupled common-emitter stage is shown in Fig. 11.63. A small amount of forward bias is supplied by the voltage divider R_1 and R_2. Stabilization of operating point against variations in I_{co} resulting from changes in transistors or temperature requires that R_2 be low. This, however, has the accompanying disadvantage that a substantial amount of power is lost in the voltage divider. Also a low value of R_2 does not compensate for the change in transistor input resistance with temperature. This factor is commonly compensated by making either R_1 or R_2 a thermistor or other temperature-sensitive element. Techniques for compensation of class B amplifiers are further described in Sec. 11.9j.

The composite collector characteristic shown in Fig. 11.64 is obtained in the same way that composite characteristics[12,13] for push-pull tube amplifiers are obtained. The load line has a slope equal to the negative of the reciprocal of the load resistance

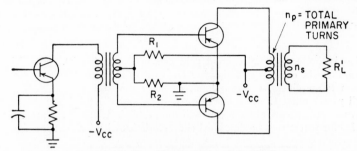

FIG. 11.63. Class B common-emitter stage.

referred to one of the transistors, i.e., the resistance reflected to half the output-transformer primary just as in tube circuits. Thus if the output transformer has $n_P/2$ turns on each side of the primary center tap and n_S turns on the secondary, the load line has a reciprocal negative slope equal to $R_L = \frac{1}{4}(n_P/n_S)^2 R'_L$, where R_L is the

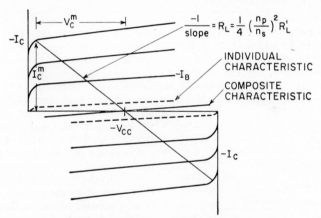

FIG. 11.64. Composite collector characteristics.

load referred to one transistor and R'_L is the actual load resistance. Assuming no losses in the output transformer, the power output of the stage is

$$P_O = \frac{V_C^m I_C^m}{2}$$

Assuming ideal characteristics, the voltage across one transistor can swing twice the supply voltage V_{CC} and the maximum power output is

$$P_O^m = \frac{V_{CC}^2}{2R_L}$$

with a corresponding peak collector current of

$$I_C(\text{peak}) = \frac{V_{CC}}{R_L}$$

Under these conditions, the peak base current is

$$I_B(\text{peak}) = \frac{I_C(\text{peak})}{h_{FE}}$$

where h_{FE} is the large-signal current gain measured at $I_C(\text{peak})$. The driver stage, therefore, must be capable of supplying $I_B(\text{peak})$ to the class B output stage.

In class B amplifiers, the maximum collector dissipation usually occurs at less than full power output. The power output P_O and the total collector dissipation (both transistors) P_C are given in the following table in terms of the maximum power output P_O^m for transistors having ideal characteristics with a sine-wave signal input.

	Zero signal	Maximum dissipation	Maximum output
P_O..............	0	$0.4P_O^m$	P_O^m
P_C..............	0	$0.4P_O^m$	$0.3P_O^m$
Efficiency........	0	50%	78.5%

The highest dissipation for a class B transistor will occur when the signal is a square wave whose output amplitude is one-half the peak output voltage. Under this condition, the total dissipation in the two transistors is $0.5P_O^m$.

Lines of constant collector dissipation on the collector characteristics are hyperbolas, as shown in Fig. 11.65. The collector dissipation (one transistor) can be estimated conveniently by averaging the dissipation values along the load line, weighting each in proportion to the amount of time that the operating point is in that region of the characteristics.

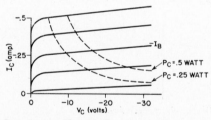

The actual power delivered to the load by a class B amplifier, however, will be less than the power delivered by the transistors, since the output transformer is not lossless. The maximum power delivered to the load is

FIG. 11.65. Hyperbolas of constant dissipation.

$$P_L^m = \eta P_O^m$$

where η is the efficiency of the output transformer. Thus, for a given maximum power delivered to the load, the maximum transistor dissipation will be slightly higher than theoretical for a transformer-coupled class B amplifier.

It should be noted that for a given power output, a center-tapped class B transformer can be smaller than the equivalent transformer used for class A operation. This is a result of a cancellation of the d-c magnetization caused by direct current flowing in the primary. For perfectly matched class B transistors, the resultant d-c magnetization will be zero.

11.6c. Dissipation and Efficiency for Nonideal Devices.[14] The discussion in Sec. 11.6b considered the case of a class B amplifier using ideal transistors in which the output signal could swing along the entire load line, reaching zero voltage across each transistor. As described previously in Sec. 11.5b, in practical devices the collector saturation resistance will limit the lower value of collector voltage which may appear across the transistors.

For many germanium power transistors, the saturation resistance can be very low (Sec. 11.5b) and nearly ideal class B amplification can be obtained. The use of silicon transistors in power amplifiers, however, with their higher saturation resistance, requires that the dissipation and efficiency for nonideal devices be investigated. This d-c saturation resistance and the collector a-c load resistance will strongly influence the efficiency and dissipation of the class B transistors. In particular, the ratio of load resistance to d-c saturation resistance R_L/R_S will determine the power output at which maximum dissipation will occur for the transistors with a sine-wave input. This ratio will also determine the maximum conversion efficiency of the collector circuit.

The maximum power output P_O^m of a class B amplifier may be defined as that power output obtained when the collector voltage swings to its lowest value determined by the saturation resistance (where $V_C^m = V_{CC} - E_{sat}$). The following normalized relationship can be derived for the power dissipation of both output transistors as a function of the maximum power output:

$$\frac{P_C(\text{two})}{P_O^m} = \frac{4}{\pi}\left[\frac{(R_L/R_S)+1}{R_L/R_S}\right]\sqrt{\frac{P_O}{P_O^m}} - \frac{P_O}{P_O^m}$$

where

$$0 \le \frac{P_O}{P_O^m} \le 1$$

and

$$0 < \frac{R_L}{R_S} < \infty$$

This equation has been plotted in Fig. 11.66 for various values of R_L/R_S as a function of normalized power output P_O/P_O^m. Because R_L is normally low in a power amplifier, it can be seen that when R_L/R_S approaches infinity, the transistors perform as ideal devices, since their saturation resistances must approach zero. Thus, the lower curve is plotted for ideal transistors, and the dissipation values given in the table in Sec. 11.6b can be taken from this curve. As the saturation resistance increases in a transistor operating with a given R_L, the point at which the maximum dissipation occurs will shift closer to the maximum power output for the amplifier, as indicated by the locus of maximum dissipation in Fig. 11.66. When R_L/R_S equals 1.76 or less, maximum dissipation will occur at maximum power output.

The collector efficiency for a nonideal device can be written as

$$\text{Eff} = \frac{\pi}{4}\frac{R_L/R_S}{(R_L/R_S)+1}\sqrt{\frac{P_O}{P_O^m}}$$

where

$$0 \le \frac{P_O}{P_O^m} \le 1$$

and

$$0 < \frac{R_L}{R_S} < \infty$$

This equation is plotted in Fig. 11.67 for various values of R_L/R_S as a function of normalized power output P_O/P_O^m. Again, for an ideal device, R_L/R_S approaches infinity (top curve) and at maximum power output the maximum ideal efficiency of 78.5 per cent will be obtained. For nonideal devices, the maximum efficiency will be less and will depend on the magnitude of R_L/R_S.

In addition to the restrictions placed upon dissipation and maximum efficiency by the saturation resistance, the dissipation in an actual amplifier circuit will generally be higher than the curves indicate, since the transistors normally will be biased slightly in the forward direction to prevent crossover distortion (discussed in Sec. 11.6d). Nevertheless, good experimental verification of the preceding equations can be made.[14]

Thus, it is important in determining the maximum transistor dissipation in a class B amplifier that the ratio of R_L/R_S be considered. It should also be noted that the collector saturation resistance has a positive temperature coefficient of approximately

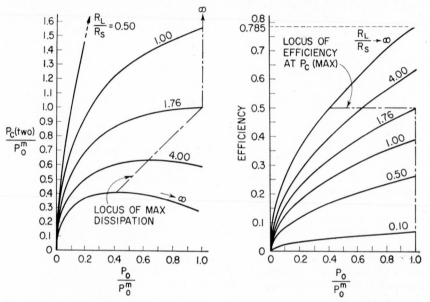

FIG. 11.66. Normalized power dissipation.   FIG. 11.67. Normalized conversion efficiency.

0.4 per cent/°C (Figs. 11.27 to 11.30). Therefore, at higher temperatures, the transistor dissipation will increase and the collector efficiency will decrease.

11.6d. Nonlinear Distortion. Distortion in a class B amplifier may arise from various factors. The nonlinearities in the transfer characteristics of the transistor will give rise to odd-order harmonic distortion, whereas differences between the two halves of the amplifier will give rise to even-order harmonic distortion. Only odd-order distortion would be present for transistors which are perfectly matched in push-pull class B operation. It is quite difficult, however, to match exactly the transfer characteristics of each transistor for all the characteristics which produce distortion. The over-all distortion will be a function of the power output, supply voltage, load impedance, and driving source.

The distortion which arises from these various factors will be most severe in common-emitter power amplifiers, since there is no internal degeneration. For this reason and because of the widespread use of common-emitter amplifiers, most of the following discussion will concern this configuration.

As discussed in Sec. 11.5f, the transconductance characteristic I_C versus V_{BE} (Fig. 11.59) is more nearly linear than the corresponding current-transfer characteristic I_C versus I_B (Fig. 11.58) for a power transistor. Nevertheless, the region near zero input voltage will be quite nonlinear for the transconductance characteristic. The type of distortion which arises from the rapidly changing nonlinear input impedance at low input signals is known as crossover distortion and is shown in Fig. 11.68.

If a small amount of forward bias is applied, however, the distortion which arises from this nonlinearity can be greatly reduced. Figure 11.69 shows how a composite transconductance transfer characteristic would appear with a small amount of forward bias to eliminate non-linearities. For a germanium transistor at room temperature, the forward base-

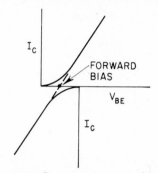

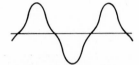

FIG. 11.68. Crossover distortion.

FIG. 11.69. Composite transconductance characteristic.

to-emitter voltage which should be applied to reduce crossover distortion is about 0.15 to 0.25 volt. For a corresponding silicon transistor, this voltage will be about 0.6 to 0.7 volt.

Since the transconductance characteristic is more nearly linear than the current-transfer characteristic, a class B power amplifier should be driven from a voltage source for reduced distortion. This means that the source resistance should be much less than the large-signal input resistance of the amplifier.

If the proper amount of forward bias is not applied, the distortion will increase at low signal levels. Also, unless the stage is compensated properly for temperature (Sec. 11.9*j*), the crossover distortion will increase at lower temperatures. This can be seen from Fig. 11.70, which shows the transconductance characteristic at various temperatures for a typical germanium power transistor. These curves show that a greater forward bias must be applied at lower temperatures in order to maintain reasonably linear operation.

11.6e. Distortion Due to Unbalance. One of the major problems in the design of class B amplifiers using present-day transistors is the wide range of tolerances in large-signal current gain and transconductance that must be met. If the

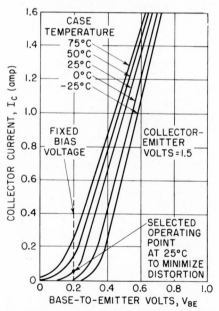

FIG. 11.70. Transconductance characteristics as a function of temperature.

common-emitter current gain is held within 2 to 1, it is considered reasonably good for a commercial type. If the transistors used in a class B push-pull amplifier are not identical, however, even-order harmonic distortion will arise, since the half cycles of the input signal will be unequally amplified. Mismatching can arise from several causes. These can be separated into two parts, those which are frequency independent and those which are frequency dependent.[15]   The latter effects are discussed in Sec. 11.6*f*.

The second harmonic distortion arising from transistor mismatch is given by the following expression:[15]

$$\% \text{ 2d harmonic } = 42 \frac{1 - N}{1 + N}$$

where N is equal to the voltage gain of one-half of the amplifier divided by the voltage gain of the second half ($N = V_{G1}/V_{G2}$), the large-signal common-emitter voltage gain being

$$V_G \cong \frac{h_{FE}R_L}{R_g + R_i}$$

If a small amount of forward bias has been applied to the base-emitter junction, the input resistance will not change appreciably at low current levels. At high emitter currents the input resistance will decrease slightly until it is equal to the large-signal input resistance of $r_{bb'}$ (if no external emitter resistors are used), and the voltage-gain expression becomes

$$V_G \cong \frac{h_{FE}R_L}{R_g + r_{bb'}}$$

Thus, a mismatch in $r_{bb'}$ may give rise to some second-harmonic distortion at high output levels. However, it still remains preferable to drive the transistors from a low-impedance source, since the greatest linearity will occur under these conditions. In addition, as discussed in Sec. 11.3*f*, when the transistor is driven from a low-impedance source, the frequency response will be improved for the common-emitter configuration. It should be noted that for perfect matching, both the large-signal current gain and the rate at which the current gain falls off with increasing emitter current should be identical for both transistors of the push-pull stage. Under these conditions, the distortion will be predominantly third harmonic owing to the fall off of current gain.

11.6f. Distortion at Higher Audio Frequencies. The voltage gain of a class B amplifier was shown to be directly proportional to the transistor current gain. Even if both transistors are perfectly matched at lower frequencies, distortion may rise at higher frequencies owing to the mismatch of beta-cutoff frequency and the variation of current gain with frequency. Distortion arising from these effects is predominantly second harmonic and is essentially independent of signal level.

Another type of distortion which may occur at high frequencies is due to minority-carrier storage and results in a high-frequency ringing in the input and output transformers[15] if the coupling between each half of the transformers is not sufficient (Sec. 11.6*g*). For transformerless class B circuits, the carrier storage effect will result in a shift of the zero crossing for the output of the amplifier. It should be noted that this may give rise to an increase in collector current for each half of the transistor. Thus, at frequencies where carrier storage is significant, the transistor dissipation as well as the distortion may increase appreciably.

11.6g. Distortion Arising from Coupling. In a class B amplifier, for a sine-wave input, the collector current of each transistor ideally is a half sine wave. In a transformer-coupled stage, the collector currents of both transistors are added in the output transformer. If the two halves of the primary winding are not sufficiently well coupled, switching transients and distortion may result, including ringing caused by carrier storage at higher frequencies. The same type of distortion may arise in the driver transformer (even to a greater extent) if the input impedance changes rapidly in the crossover region.   The use of bifilar windings in both the driver and output transformers will increase coupling and thus reduce these switching transients.

Transformerless or complementary-symmetry class B stages avoid this difficulty because either they do not have an output transformer or else the collector currents from both transistors flow through the same winding.   There is, however, another type of distortion which may arise in these amplifiers if they are coupled to the load through a capacitor as shown in Figs. 11.81, 11.85, and 11.88.   At low frequencies,

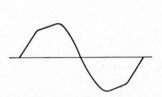

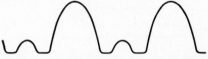

FIG. 11.71. Distortion due to low-frequency phase shift.

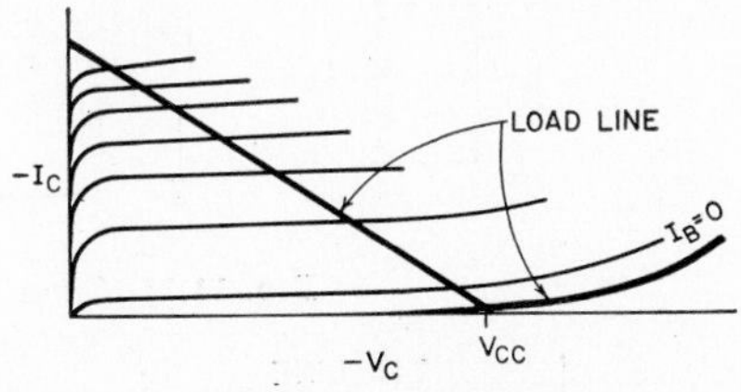

FIG. 11.72. Transistor near collector breakdown.

where the effect of the coupling capacitor is important, the load on the output stage may become complex and an elliptical load line will result.   At high signal levels, the output will be clipped diagonally as shown in Fig. 11.71.   This type of distortion is similar to that which results from the primary inductance of the output transformer being too low in transformer-coupled amplifiers as discussed in Sec. 11.5h.   In transformerless circuits this distortion can be reduced by increasing the value of the capacitor which couples the load.

11.6h. Maximum Voltage.   As seen in Fig. 11.72, the collector current increases disproportionately for sufficiently high collector voltage.   This breakdown at high collector voltages may be due to any of several causes and is discussed in Sec. 11.4e.   If the supply voltage of a class B amplifier is too high, collector current will flow during the "cutoff" portion of the cycle even if the base is biased beyond cutoff.   The load line in this case is shown in Fig. 11.72.   The collector current of one transistor in a normal class B amplifier is shown in Fig. 11.73.   If the transistor is being driven into the

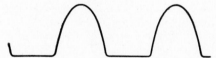

FIG. 11.73. I_C of each transistor in normal amplifier.

FIG. 11.74. I_C of each transistor in amplifier near collector breakdown.

breakdown region, the collector current is as shown in Fig. 11.74.   The current drawn during the normally off portion of the cycle reduces the power output of the stage and materially increases the collector dissipation of the transistor.   The increased collector dissipation raises the temperature of the transistor, thereby further increasing the current that flows during the normally off portion of the cycle.   This process often becomes cumulative, resulting in destruction of the transistor, especially if the stabilization is poor.

11.6i. Common-base Stage.   The preceding discussion on class B amplifiers has been limited to common-emitter stages.   However, as in the case of class A power amplifiers, most of it applies directly to common-base and common-collector stages.   For most practical cases, the same collector characteristics can be used and the same load lines apply.   The difference between the three connections is feedback, which does not change optimum loading or power output. Since both the common-base and the common-collector connections have considerable feedback, they inherently have less distortion than the common-emitter connection. Of much more importance is the fact that the degeneration or gain reduction accomplishes much in stabilizing stage gain and thereby balancing transistors with unequal h_{fe} (beta).

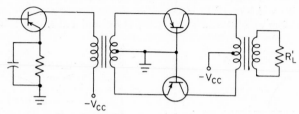

FIG. 11.75. Class B common-base stage.

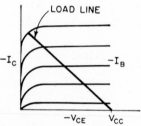

FIG. 11.76. Load line for common-base or common-collector operation.

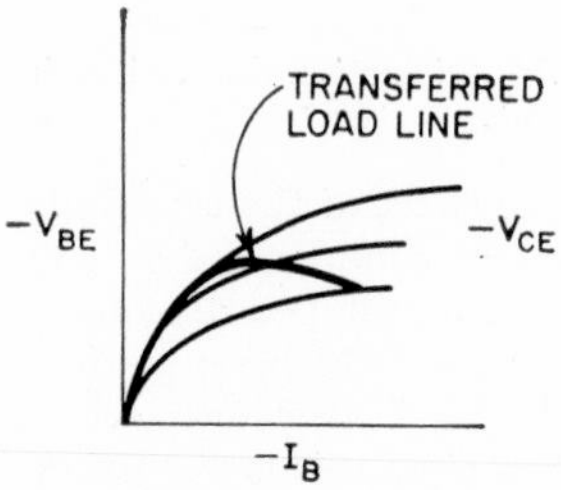

FIG. 11.77. Load line for common-base or common-collector operation.

If a driver transformer is to be used as in Fig. 11.75, a common-base output stage is highly desirable. The collector current is very nearly equal to the emitter current, so the distortion is low and there is little unbalance. The stage should ideally be driven from a high impedance, since the collector-current versus emitter-current transfer characteristic is quite linear beyond a few milliamperes. A small amount of forward bias will materially increase the linearity over the operating range in the event that the stage is driven from a voltage source, since the transconductance characteristic (I_C versus V_{BE}) is the same for both the common-base and common-emitter connections. Both the common-emitter graphical characteristics can be used. The load line shown in Fig. 11.76 has a slope equal to the reciprocal of the load reflected across half the primary winding if the base-to-emitter voltage is small compared with the collector voltage. The emitter current is equal to $I_C + I_B$. The base-to-emitter voltage V_{BE} given in Fig. 11.77 is the negative of the emitter-to-base voltage or input voltage.

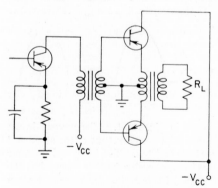

FIG. 11.78. Class B common-collector stage.

11.6j. Common-collector Stage. The common-collector stage shown in Fig. 11.78 is well adapted for use with driver stages that must be lightly loaded, since it has a high input resistance. Distortion due to nonlinearity of characteristics and unbalance between transistors is reduced considerably by the feedback inherent in the common-collector stage. The common-emitter collector characteristics shown in Fig. 11.76 are useful in analyzing the stage, since their use involves the assumption that $I_C \cong I_E$, which is reasonably accurate. The base characteristics of Fig. 11.77 give V_B, which when added to the output voltage gives the input voltage. V_B is usually small, so that the input and output voltages are roughly equal.

11.6k. Split-load Stage. The split load is intermediate between a common-emitter and a common-collector stage. It was described in Sec. 11.5m for the class A single-ended case. It has an advantage over the common-collector stage in that the driver is

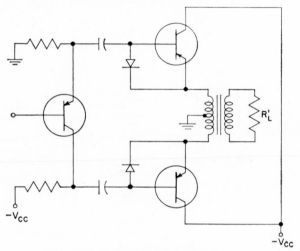

Fig. 11.79. Class B common-collector stage.

not required to supply as high peak voltage and therefore is not so severely limited by lack of V_{CC} supply. The split-load arrangement allows full choice in the amount of local feedback that is applied to the output stage.

11.6l. Transformerless Class B Amplifiers. Transformerless class B stages are possible without resorting to the use of complementary symmetry. It is possible (using transistors of only one polarity) by proper circuit design to eliminate either the input transformer or the output transformer or both. Often, the saving in weight and size, as well as the elimination of the phase shift caused by transformers, will compensate for the loss of gain which may arise when transformers are not used.

For example, by the use of a phase inverter (several varieties are discussed in Sec. 11.11), the input transformer can be eliminated. Such a circuit for a common-collector class B amplifier is shown in Fig. 11.79. When coupling capacitors are used, however, it is possible that crossover distortion in the output stage can occur, since the charge and discharge paths of the coupling capacitor will be different during conduction and cutoff for each half of the amplifier. This difference causes a reverse d-c bias to be applied to the bases of the output stage which is dependent upon the signal level and results in increased distortion. As shown in Fig. 11.79, a diode can be placed from base to emitter to provide a discharge path. A low-value resistance can also be used in place of the diode. If the proper value of resistance is used, the input impedance presented to the driver stage can be effectively linearized during both conduction and nonconduction.[16]

The output transformer can also be eliminated. The circuit of Fig. 11.80, which uses a pair of PNP transistors, is a common-emitter class B amplifier. With an input signal of one polarity, transistor T_2 conducts; with the other polarity, transistor T_1 conducts. With the use of appropriate circuits, common-collector and common-base stages can be realized. If auxiliary transistors are used for phase splitting, the input transformer can be eliminated. This type of operation can be realized with vacuum tubes, and the technology is rather well developed. The disadvantages of this circuit are that the power supply must be split and that power-supply ripple appears in the input circuit.

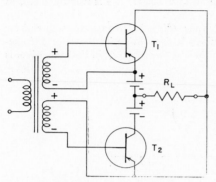

FIG. 11.80. Transformerless class B output using a pair of PNP transistors.

A completely transformerless class B amplifier using all PNP transistors is shown in Fig. 11.81.[17] In this amplifier, the direct current flows in series with both transistors in the output stage while the alternating signal current is in parallel, since the output and driver stages are push-pull, class B. Phase inversion is accomplished by means of the phase inverter transistor T_1. Resistors R_{13} and R_{11} linearize the input impedance for the driver stages.

The voltage across R_{10} and R_{12} due to the current flowing through transistors T_2 and T_3 provides forward bias for the output transistors. The output transistors for this amplifier essentially operate in the common-emitter configuration, while the driver transistors T_2 and T_3 are common-collector stages. The common-collector

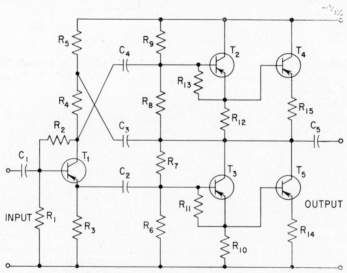

FIG. 11.81. Series-type transformerless amplifier.

stages provide a low source resistance for the output transistors, thus minimizing distortion and improving the high-frequency response. R_{10} and R_{12} provide low values of d-c resistance which help to increase the collector-to-emitter breakdown voltage of the output transistors as described in Sec. 11.4e.

Half of the d-c supply voltage will appear between R_7 and R_8 when the amplifier is biased properly. The peak collector voltage appearing across each output transistor will be approximately equal to the supply voltage. This is in contrast to a transformer-coupled class B amplifier where the peak collector voltage is twice the supply voltage.

11.6m. Power Supplies. Power supplies for class B amplifiers must be low-impedance, since the current drain varies tremendously from no signal to full signal. The variation is greater than with tube amplifiers, since the efficiency of transistor amplifiers is greater. It is important in both the collector and the bias supplies to avoid filters or bypass circuits with time constants that interfere with the proper action of the amplifier. For example, it would be desirable from the viewpoint of stabilization to have resistors in the emitter leads of the amplifier of Fig. 11.63. However, the power

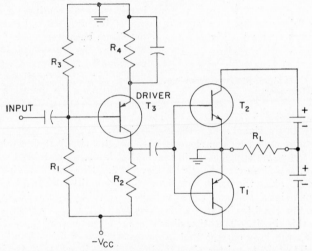

FIG. 11.82. Complementary-symmetry, common-emitter stage.

loss in these resistors would be too great unless they were bypassed. If they are bypassed, a d-c voltage is developed under full signal that will cut the transistor off at low levels. This situation occurs in the reproduction of music whenever a low-level passage immediately follows a high-level passage.

Since the current drain increases with signal, the power-supply regulation should be such that sufficient supply voltage is available for the transistors under all operating conditions. This implies that the power supply must be designed to provide a slightly higher supply voltage under quiescent conditions in order that sufficient voltage is available at maximum power output. As a result, the transistor dissipation must necessarily be higher under quiescent conditions than would be the case when the circuit is operated from an ideal power supply. Also, the operating point may shift slightly as signal increases owing to a decrease in supply voltage and introduce additional distortion.

11.7. Complementary Symmetry. *11.7a. Common-emitter Stage.* In a vacuum tube, the direct current flows only from plate to cathode. In the case of transistors, the direct current may flow from collector to emitter (NPN) or from emitter to collector (PNP), depending upon which type of transistor is being used. This added degree of freedom permits the use of many new and novel circuits.

Figure 11.82 illustrates the use of a pair of transistors in common-emitter complementary-symmetry connection. As shown, the transistors are biased near cutoff so that class B amplification is obtained. When the bases are driven positive, transistor

T_2 conducts, thereby passing a half sine wave of current through the load R_L.   In like manner, when the bases are driven negative, transistor T_1 conducts, passing a half sine wave of current through the load in the opposite direction.   Thus no net direct current passes through the load R_L.   The direct current flows through the two transistors in series.   Like all class B amplifiers, the power-supply drain increases under drive.   This type of arrangement is well suited for R-C coupling, since the input or base circuit also operates on a class B basis.   When transistor T_2 conducts, current passes into its base; on the other hand, when T_1 conducts, current passes out of its base, with the result that no net direct base current need be supplied. This is a big advantage since a knotty problem in R-C-coupled class B ampli-

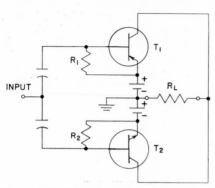

Fig. 11.83. Complementary-symmetry, common-emitter stage.

fiers is to prevent the direct base current from changing the operating point.   The major disadvantage that makes this con-figuration impractical is the fact that both power supplies float at signal level; i.e., they are connected to the signal side of the load resistor.

Another common-emitter complementary-symmetry circuit is shown in Fig. 11.83. In this case the power supplies are in the emitter leads, overcoming the difficulty of floating power supplies experienced with Fig. 11.82.   However, this circuit has other disadvantages.   Since the power supplies are in the emitter leads, they are in series with the input signal and any ripple voltage that exists across the supply will be impressed on the transistor input.   Thus a very high degree of power-supply filtering is needed with this circuit.   The other disadvantage is that special precautions must be taken to keep the base current that occurs under heavy drive from changing the operating point of the transistor, since the input circuit is not class B as in Fig. 11.82.

11.7b. Common-collector Stage.   If the ground point of the stage in Fig. 11.82 is changed from the emitters to the common point of the power supplies, the foregoing disadvantages are overcome.   The power supplies are grounded, power-supply ripple requirements are normal, and there is little tendency for the d-c voltage at the bases of the transistors to change under drive.   The stage is now a common-collector stage rather than a common-emitter stage and is shown in Fig. 11.84.   The required driving current is the same as the circuit of Fig. 11.82, but a much larger driving voltage is required.   The required driving voltage is approximately equal to the output voltage developed across the load.   Although the power gain of the common-collector stage is less than that of the common-emitter stage, the loss in gain can be considered negative feedback, with the accompanying reduction in distortion and high-frequency phase shift.   In particular, the degree of balance required between the two transistors is relaxed considerably in the common-collector connection.

11.7c. Comparative Gain, CE-CE and CE-CC.   If the common-collector output stage is driven through R-C coupling by the preceding transistor, this loss in power gain does not necessarily mean an equivalent loss in over-all gain for the amplifier, since the high impedance of the common-collector output stage results in a better match with the driver.   For example, compare the amplifiers of Figs. 11.82 and 11.84, using transistors with the following characteristics in all stages:

$$h_{ie} = 2,000 \text{ ohms} \qquad h_{fe} = 50$$
$$h_{re} = 600 \times 10^{-6} \qquad h_{oe} = 25 \text{ } \mu\text{mhos}$$

Figure 11.82 is a common-emitter–common-emitter amplifier. Figure 11.84 is a common-emitter–common-collector amplifier. Single transistor parameters should be used for the push-pull stages since they are class B, and ideally only one transistor is conducting at any one time. The resistors R_1, R_2, and R_3 are assumed large. In a more exact calculation, their effect may be considered by altering the h parameters of transistor T_3 to include them. From Table 11.13, the h parameters of the network

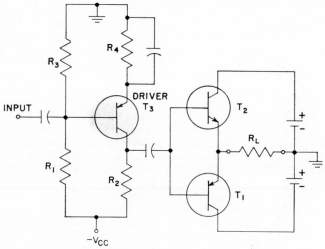

FIG. 11.84. Complementary-symmetry, common-collector stage.

that results when two common-emitter transistors with the foregoing characteristics are cascaded are

$$h'_{11} = 1{,}940 \text{ ohms} \qquad h'_{21} = -2{,}380$$
$$h'_{12} = 0.34 \times 10^{-6} \qquad h'_{22} = 24.3 \ \mu\text{mhos}$$

The current gain with a 600-ohm load is

$$\frac{I_2}{I_1} = \frac{(1 + h'_{21})Y_L}{h'_{22} + Y_L} = 2{,}340 \text{ or } 67 \text{ db}$$

The input resistance is

$$R_i = h'_{11} + \frac{1 + h'_{21}}{h'_{22} + Y_L} = 1{,}940 \text{ ohms}$$

The voltage gain is

$$\frac{V_2}{V_1} = \frac{I_2}{I_1} \times \frac{1}{R_i} \times \frac{1}{Y_L} = 724 \text{ or } 57 \text{ db}$$

If two transistors of the same type are cascaded in a common-emitter–common-collector connection, from Table 11.13 the characteristics of the combination are

$$h'_{11} = 1{,}940 \text{ ohms} \qquad h'_{21} = 2{,}430$$
$$h'_{21} = 570 \times 10^{-6} \qquad h'_{22} = 1{,}240 \ \mu\text{mhos}$$

The current gain with a 600-ohm load is

$$\frac{I_2}{I_1} = \frac{(1 + h'_{21})Y_L}{h'_{22} + Y_L} = 1{,}390 \text{ or } 63 \text{ db}$$

The input resistance is

$$R_i = h'_{11} + \frac{1 + h'_{21}}{h'_{22} + Y_L} = 1{,}465 \text{ ohms}$$

The voltage gain is

$$\frac{V_2}{V_1} = \frac{I_2}{I_1} \times \frac{1}{R_i} \times \frac{1}{Y_L} = 569 \text{ or } 55 \text{ db}$$

Thus the gain and input resistance of the two configurations are essentially the same.

11.7d. Unbalance. The preceding discussion presupposes that the two transistors in the output stage are truly complementary. In practice, the two units will differ in h_{fe} (beta), rate of fall off in h_{fe} with increasing collector current, input resistance, and I_{CO}. These are the same factors that cause unbalance in conventional transformer-coupled class B amplifiers; so much of the general discussion in Secs. 11.6d and 11.6e applies to complementary symmetry, too.

In complementary-symmetry operation the two transistors are in series so that the two collector currents are equal. However, the collector voltages are interdependent. A satisfactory biasing scheme will adjust the bias so that the two collector voltages are equal. This is the inverse of the conventional transformer-coupled push-pull output where the two collector voltages are equal and where the bias is adjusted so that the two direct collector currents are equal.

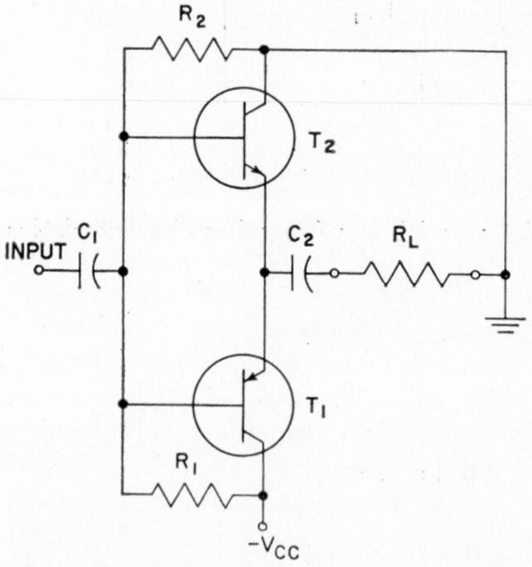

Fig. 11.85. Complementary-symmetry, common-collector stage. Single power supply.

To meet requirements of distortion and power output, the unbalance between the two transistors in a power-output stage must be held within certain limits which are determined by the performance desired from the amplifier. One approach to the problem is matched transistors or tight-tolerance transistors in which the parameters that affect the balance are held within the required limits. The other approach is to use feedback to make the amplifier insensitive to dissimilarities between the two transistors. A combination of the foregoing two approaches has much to offer in the way of obtaining high performance using transistors with reasonable manufacturing tolerances.

The circuit of Fig. 11.85 has feedback which has a strong tendency to balance the output-stage transistors. The common-collector connection relaxes the requirements on balance in h_{fe} (beta) and h_{ie}. The resistors R_1 and R_2 are equal, thereby biasing the two transistors so that their collector voltages are approximately equal.

11.7e. Emitter Follower. The circuit of Fig. 11.84 is a push-pull emitter follower somewhat analogous to a vacuum-tube cathode follower. However, a cathode follower is single-ended and the output voltage cannot fall rapidly. When a cathode follower is turned off rapidly, the tube is cut off and the charge in output and load capacities must be discharged through the passive circuit elements that are present. The complementary-symmetry emitter follower can be driven in both directions and hence is capable not only of fast rise time but of fast fall time also.

11.7f. Common-base Stage. Transformers are generally needed to drive common-base output stages, since the common-base connection has no current gain. Therefore there is not much point in considering a complementary-symmetry common-base stage because the same type of operation can be realized with a pair of PNP transistors if a driver transformer is used.

11.7g. Single Power Supply. The circuit of Fig. 11.84 can be revised to use a single power supply by putting a blocking capacitor C_2 in series with the load as in Fig. 11.85. The power-supply voltage should be twice that of each power supply in Fig. 11.84. The path of normal d-c flow through the power supply and transistors in series is undisturbed. The load is still connected from the emitters to ground. The blocking capacitor C_2 does not disturb the circuit, since normally direct current does not flow through the load. The bias is adjusted so that the d-c collector-to-emitter

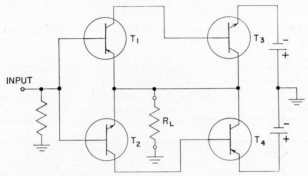

Fig. 11.86. Complementary-symmetry. Direct-coupled driver.

voltages of the two transistors are equal. Thus the operation of the circuit of Fig. 11.85 is equivalent to that of Fig. 11.84.

11.7h. Direct-coupled Driver. One of the big problems in class B transistor amplifiers is obtaining proper drive for the output stage. Simple direct-coupled circuits are available using complementary types of transistors, thereby opening the possibility of elegant driver-output stage configurations. Such an amplifier[18,19] is shown in Fig. 11.86. To make calculations concerning the power gain and input impedance of this amplifier, one needs values of the parameters taken from the composite characteristics of T_1 and T_2 for the first stage and T_3 and T_4 for the second stage. Values of the parameters taken at a typical class A operating point for one of the transistors will approximate the composite values. None of the small-signal parameters need be doubled or halved to take care of the fact that they will be used to represent the action of two transistors. This is true because the transistors are being operated class B; hence when one is conducting, the other is nonconducting. The first stage in this amplifier may be considered to be common-emitter and the second stage common-collector. The input signal is applied in series with the load resistor to obtain feedback over both stages.

If the transistors in this amplifier have the following characteristics,

$$h_{ie} = 2,000 \text{ ohms} \qquad h_{fe} = 50$$
$$h_{re} = 600 \times 10^{-6} \qquad h_{oe} = 25 \ \mu\text{mhos}$$

the h parameters from Table 11.13 of the common-emitter–common-collector cascade are

$$h'_{11} = 1,940 \text{ ohms} \qquad h'_{21} = 2,430$$
$$h'_{12} = 570 \times 10^{-6} \qquad h'_{22} = 1,240 \ \mu\text{mhos}$$

Since the load is connected between the input and what is normally the common lead, as shown in Fig. 11.87, the formulas for input impedance and gain can be obtained from Table 11.11.   The current gain with a 2,000-ohm load is

$$\text{Current gain} = \frac{(1 + h'_{21})Y_L}{h'_{22} + Y_L} = 700 \text{ or } 57 \text{ db}$$

The input resistance is

$$R_i = h'_{11} + \frac{1 + h'_{21}}{h'_{22} + Y_L} = 1.4 \text{ megohms}$$

The voltage gain is

$$\text{Voltage gain} = \text{current gain} \times \frac{1}{Y_L} \times \frac{1}{R_i} = 1 \text{ or } 0 \text{ db}$$

11.7i. Quasi-complementary-symmetry Amplifier.   It is possible to combine the features of complementary symmetry with a series output stage to produce a class B amplifier.   Figure 11.88 shows one combination. This is known as a quasi-complementary-symmetry amplifier.[20,17]   This amplifier uses similar polarity transistors in the output stage and obtains phase splitting by virtue of the complementary pair T_2 and T_3.   The output stage operates push-pull and is capacitively coupled to the load.   Both the driver and output stages act as class B amplifiers.   Transistor T_2 operates as a common-collector amplifier, whereas T_4 operates as a common-emitter amplifier. T_3 and T_5 operate somewhere between the common-emitter and common-collector modes.   The input impedance to the driver stage T_2T_3 is, however, reasonably constant, regardless of which half of the amplifier is conducting by virtue of the bootstrapping obtained across capacitor C_1.

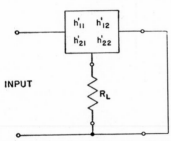

FIG. 11.87. Equivalent circuit of amplifier shown in Fig. 11.86.

The input stage, using transistor T_1, need only be a low-level class A amplifier, since phase splitting occurs in the following stage.   Bias for stage T_1 is obtained from the amplifier side of C_2.   The voltage at this point should be approximately $V_{CC}/2$.

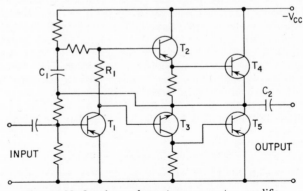

FIG. 11.88. Quasi-complementary-symmetry amplifier.

R_1 is a low value of resistance used for biasing T_2 and T_3.   It can be made a temperature-sensitive element such as a thermistor or a diode for better temperature compensation (Sec. 11.9*j*).

11.8. Feedback. *11.8a. Introduction.* In basic principles, feedback in transistor ampliers is the same as feedback in vacuum-tube amplifiers. The well-developed concepts of the vacuum-tube art can be used as a guide in the design and development of transistor amplifiers with feedback. In general, distortion is reduced and frequency response is improved by degenerative feedback. In most cases the distortion reduction is about equal to the gain reduction. The input and output impedances of the amplifier, or section of amplifier, over which the feedback has been placed are either increased or decreased, depending upon the particular way in which the feedback is applied.

11.8b. High-frequency Instability. One major problem in applying feedback to transistor audio amplifiers is the poor high-frequency response of present-day "audio" transistors. This is especially true when the transistors are connected common-emitter. In the region just above the top audio frequencies where gain and phase

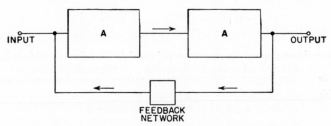

Fig. 11.89. Two-stage amplifier with feedback over both stages.

must be controlled within narrow limits, the transistors are contributing to the over-all phase shift. The easiest solution and perhaps the long-range solution to this problem is to use high-frequency transistors. Terman[21] gives the general rule of thumb that the transmission characteristics of the feedback loop must be controlled an octave beyond the amplifier-frequency range for each 10 db of useful feedback plus one or two octaves for safety factor and for loss due to nonoptimum cutoff characteristics. Thus a 15,000-cycle amplifier with 20 db of feedback must have controlled loop gain out to about 240 kc. Therefore the transistors should have relatively low phase shift out to this frequency when used in such feedback amplifiers.

11.8c. Local Feedback Loops. One method of applying feedback in a stable manner is to use multiple local feedback loops which may or may not be enclosed in an over-all feedback loop. The use of common-base or common-collector stages instead of common-emitter stages may be considered to be the application of local feedback. Other types of local feedback are a resistor in the emitter lead of a common-emitter stage as shown in Fig. 11.40, a resistor from collector to base as shown in Fig. 11.44, and a split-load output transformer as shown in Fig. 11.62. All these types of local feedback reduce the distortion and the phase shift of the stage, with a penalty being paid in the form of loss in gain and in increase in distortion due to higher operating level of earlier stages. For example, consider the amplifiers in Figs. 11.89 and 11.90. The two stages shown in Fig. 11.89 each have a voltage gain of A_v resulting in an over-all voltage gain of $A_v^2/2$ after 6 db of over-all feedback has been applied. The over-all phase shift is cut to half, and the same is true of the distortion when measured with the output level adjusted to the same value as before the application of feedback. On the other hand, if the feedback is applied locally as in Fig. 11.90, the over-all voltage gain is $A_v^2/4$ after 6 db of feedback has been applied to each stage. As before, the phase shift is cut to half, but the distortion is not necessarily cut to half since the first stage is operating at twice its former level in order to obtain a given output level. Thus local feedback requires more gain reduction, and even then it may not supply equivalent performance because of the increased output required from the earlier stages.

11.8d. Gain Reduction. In a feedback amplifier, the amount of gain reduction depends not only upon the constants of the amplifier but also upon the terminating impedances, i.e., the source impedance and the load impedance. Many vacuum-tube

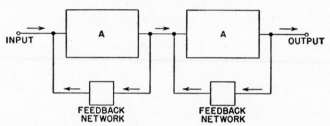

FIG. 11.90. Two-stage amplifier with local feedback over each stage.

feedback amplifiers present the special case in which the gain reduction is independent of one or both of the terminating impedances. For example, if feedback is obtained by means of an unbypassed cathode resistor, the input and output impedances of the stage are increased, but they are usually large enough to be neglected anyway. This approximation is usually not true in transistor amplifiers.

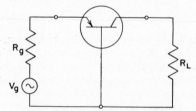

FIG. 11.91. Common-base stage.

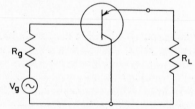

FIG. 11.92. Common-collector stage.

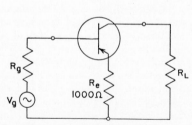

FIG. 11.93. Unbypassed emitter resistor.

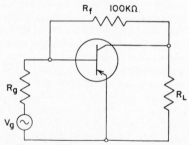

FIG. 11.94. Collector-to-base feedback.

A statement concerning the amount of gain reduction in a feedback amplifier is based upon an arbitrary definition. Some particular configuration is assumed to be "without feedback." Thus a common-base stage can be considered to be a common-emitter stage with negative feedback, or on the other hand a common-emitter stage can be considered to be a common-base stage with positive feedback. In the first case, the distortion and gain variations are reduced by feedback; in the second case, they are increased.

Consider the four single-stage amplifiers shown in Figs. 11.91 to 11.94. They are all common-emitter stages with feedback. In all cases the gain reduction (compared with a common-emitter stage) drops to zero for sufficiently high or sufficiently low terminating resistances.

TABLE 11.14. GAIN REDUCTION FOR TYPICAL FEEDBACK CIRCUITS

R_g, kilohms	1	1	100	100
R_L, kilohms	10	100	10	100
Insertion gain, db:				
Common-emitter connection	44	57	33	29
Gain reduction, db:				
Common-base connection (Fig. 11.91)	24	18	32	24
Common-collector connection (Fig. 11.92)	43	56	14	23
Common emitter, $R_e = 1,000$ ohms (Fig. 11.93)	24	18	3	1
Common emitter, $R_f = 100$ kilohms (Fig. 11.94)	8	19	14	24

For example, if a typical transistor with the following common-emitter h parameters,

$$h_{ie} = 2,000 \text{ ohms} \qquad h_{fe} = 50$$
$$h_{re} = 600 \times 10^{-6} \qquad h_{oe} = 25 \text{ } \mu\text{mhos}$$

is connected in the common-emitter connection, it would have the insertion gain given in Table 11.14. Power gain is not used here, since power gain is independent of the source impedance and hence gives no indication of the mismatch between the source and the amplifier input. The amplifier stages shown in Figs. 11.91 to 11.94 have less insertion gain than a common-emitter stage using the same transistor and terminating impedances. The reduction in gain is due to the feedback that has been applied to the transistor, with the exception of a small error due to losses in the feedback resistors R_e and R_f. Table 11.14 shows the amount of gain reduction that is obtained in each of the cases with specified terminating resistors.

The insertion gain for the subject stages was computed by substituting the h parameters for that stage in the formulas of Table 11.8. The h parameters of the stages were obtained from the common-emitter h parameters by the transformations of Tables 11.3 and 11.4 and Figs. 11.40 and 11.44.

As an example, consider Fig. 11.93. The transformed h parameters from Fig. 11.40 are approximately

$$h_{11} = h_{ie} + (1 + h_{fe})R_e = 53,000 \text{ ohms}$$
$$h_{12} = h_{re} + h_{oe}R_e \qquad = 25,600 \times 10^{-6}$$
$$h_{21} = h_{fe} \qquad = 50$$
$$h_{22} = h_{oe} \qquad = 25 \text{ } \mu\text{mhos}$$

From Table 11.8, the insertion gain of the stage with $R_g = 100,000$ ohms and $R_L = 10,000$ ohms is

$$G = \left[\frac{h_{21}}{h_{11}h_{22}} \frac{1 + R_g/R_L}{(1 + 1/h_{22}R_L)(1 + R_g/h_{11}) - S} \right]^2$$
$$= 950 \text{ or } 30 \text{ db}$$

11.8e. Distortion Reduction. In the general case, the amplifying and feedback portions of a feedback amplifier are not easily separable, there may be several feedback loops, the distortion reduction (and other benefits of feedback) will not be the same for all parameters or all components, and the distortion reduction cannot be easily correlated with the gain reduction. A complete and thorough method for the analysis of such amplifiers has been developed[22] and is directly applicable to the problem of transistor feedback amplifiers.

In essence this method consists of calculating the insertion gain of the amplifier. The reduction in the insertion gain by the application of feedback is, of course, the gain reduction. The distortion reduction or amount of gain stabilization effective on any particular circuit element or parameter can be determined exactly by varying this element a small amount and noting the effect on the insertion gain. To obtain the improvement it is necessary to make the same calculation for the case of no feedback applied to the amplifier. The change in amplifier gain caused by the perturbation divided by the change in reference amplifier gain caused by an equal perturbation is the distortion reduction. It is important to use insertion gain, since the characteristics of the source as well as the load influence the performance of the amplifier.

In an amplifier the gain is directly proportional to certain parameters while others have little effect on the gain. When feedback is applied, the elements that contribute most to the direct transmission are generally stabilized the most. When the gain reduction is due primarily to feedback and the losses in the feedback elements are small, the distortion reduction is generally about equal to the gain reduction.

11.8f. Specific Configurations. The split-load output stage shown in Fig. 11.62 is intermediate between a common-emitter and a common-collector stage. The amount of feedback is dependent upon the percentage of the primary winding that is in the emitter circuit. The feedback is also dependent upon the terminating impedances. If this stage is fed from a current source or is very heavily loaded, there is little feedback. The emitter of a split-load output stage is a convenient point to use in supplying feedback voltage to an earlier stage, inasmuch as feedback from this point reduces power-supply ripple. Feedback from the collector of this amplifier would increase power-supply ripple in the load. Feedback from the emitter introduces less phase shift from the transformer in the feedback loop than does secondary or tertiary feedback.

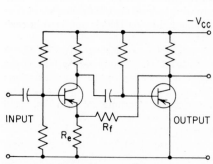

FIG. 11.95. Two-stage amplifier with feedback from collector to preceding emitter.

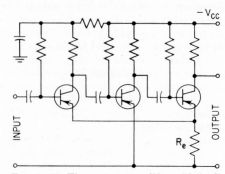

FIG. 11.96. Three-stage amplifier with feedback from output-stage emitter to first-stage emitter.

Figure 11.95 shows a resistance-coupled two-stage amplifier with feedback from collector to the preceding emitter. This arrangement has a high input impedance and a low output impedance. The feedback is not effective when the amplifier is operated from a constant-current source.

Figure 11.96 is a three-stage amplifier having a common-emitter resistor between the first and the last stage, resulting in feedback that is proportional to the load current. This amplifier has a high input and a high output impedance. The feedback is not effective when the amplifier is operated from a constant-current source. This amplifier has enough stages that stability is an important consideration. If the amplifier is unstable, the conventional techniques of controlling the high-frequency and low-frequency attenuation and phase characteristics can be applied. If it is a servo or similar amplifier where only a limited high-frequency response is needed, it can be stabilized by inserting a high-frequency cutoff R-C filter at some point in the circuit. If this is unsatisfactory and high-frequency transistors are unavailable, the phase shift can be reduced by local feedback over the individual stages, using an emitter resistor or collector-to-base feedback.

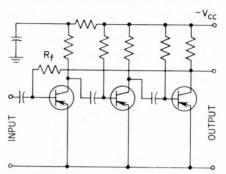

Fig. 11.97. Three-stage amplifier with feedback from output-stage collector to first-stage base.

Figure 11.97 shows a three-stage amplifier with feedback from collector to base. This amplifier has a low input and a low output impedance. The feedback is not effective if the amplifier is driven from a constant-voltage source. The same stability considerations apply to this amplifier that apply to the amplifier of Fig. 11.96.

11.9. Operating-point Stability. *11.9a. General Considerations.* The choice of a suitable d-c operating point (generally in terms of collector current and collector voltage for the common-emitter connection) for a transistor low-frequency amplifier is usually determined by considering the magnitude of the a-c and/or d-c signal which must be handled. Additional considerations often are necessary for low-noise amplifiers (see Sec. 11.10).

Once a d-c operating point is chosen, it is highly desirable to maintain this bias point constant, despite ambient-temperature changes and variations of d-c gain and cutoff collector current I_{co} for a given transistor type. Without some form of bias stabilization or compensation, the operating point may shift from one end of the d-c load line to the other and thereby introduce distortion by limiting the desired signal swing. In addition, thermal runaway may occur in circuits which have small d-c load resistors (such as transformer-coupled circuits). Many circuit techniques which provide a relatively constant operating point with changes in ambient temperature will also allow the circuit to perform satisfactorily for transistors which have relatively large variations in current gain and I_{co}. Thus, transistor interchangeability in a circuit generally is improved by the proper use of d-c bias stabilization.

The techniques which are normally employed to maintain a relatively constant operating point may be divided into two categories: (1) stabilization techniques and (2) compensation techniques. Stabilization is a linear technique and refers to the use of d-c feedback (usually by resistive networks) to maintain the operating point constant. For example, by connecting resistors in series with the emitter or from collector to base, d-c degeneration will be provided which will help to stabilize the operating point. Compensation is a nonlinear technique and refers to the application of temperature or voltage-sensitive devices (such as thermistors, diodes, transistors, etc.) which provide a compensating voltage or current change that tends to maintain the d-c operating point constant. In general, stabilization techniques are used in low-level class A amplifiers while compensation techniques are normally employed in power-amplifier stages, particularly class B amplifiers.

The transistor is basically a temperature-sensitive device. Therefore, it is important to understand the factors which cause the d-c operating point to change with temperature in order that proper techniques can be employed to counteract these changes. The temperature effects generally considered are caused by changes in the saturation current and input conductance.[23] Another factor which is usually neglected is the change of short-circuit common-emitter d-c gain h_{FE} (or beta) with temperature. The last two factors are particularly important for silicon transistors.

11.9b. Cutoff Collector Current I_{CO} (I_{CBO}). In a junction transistor, the collector-base junction is reverse-biased for normal operation. The collector current is almost equal to the emitter current, and when the emitter current is zero as in Fig. 11.98, the

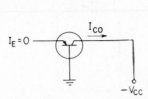

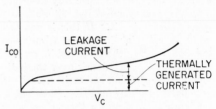

FIG. 11.98. Measurement of I_{CO}.   FIG. 11.99. Components of I_{CO}.

collector current ideally is zero. Actually, the collector current will not be zero, since the back resistance of the collector-base diode is finite. The current that flows in the connection of Fig. 11.98 is called I_{CBO} or, more commonly, I_{CO}. It is one of the measures of the quality of a transistor. I_{CO} is composed of two parts: (1) the thermally generated reverse current (saturation current) and (2) the leakage current. The thermally generated current is an exponential function of temperature and will double approximately every 10°C rise in junction temperature. (This rise actually may vary from 8 to 12°C, depending on the transistor type.) The saturation current is essentially independent of collector voltage. The leakage current, however, is voltage dependent. It may or may not vary with temperature. These two components can be separated as shown in Fig. 11.99.

The effect of I_{CO} on operating point is prevalent at high temperatures owing to the exponential dependency on temperature. At lower temperatures (below room temperature) the effects of I_{CO} on the operating point correspondingly are reduced. Although I_{CO} behaves similarly with temperature for both silicon and germanium transistors, it is usually three to four orders of magnitude smaller for silicon units and is generally negligible below room temperatures. Typical values of saturation current for low-power germanium units would be about 1 μa at room temperature (25°C), whereas the corresponding silicon unit might have a saturation current of only 0.001 μa.

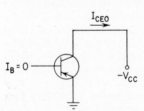

FIG. 11.100. Measurement of I_{CEO}.

For silicon units, particularly, the leakage current will probably be the dominant current at and below room temperatures.

When a transistor is connected in the common-emitter connection as in Fig. 11.100, a much larger collector current I_{CEO} flows. I_{CEO} is the collector current with zero base current. I_{CO} can be assumed injected into the base as shown in Fig. 11.101 by a fictitious constant-current generator representing the thermal current in parallel with a resistance representing the leakage. The collector current I_{CEO} that flows as a result of I_{CO} being injected into the base is $I_{CO}(1 + h_{FE})$, where h_{FE} is the common-emitter short-circuit d-c gain (beta). This condition will exist when the transistor is biased for a constant base current.

11.9c. D-C Input Conductance. The d-c input conductance is highly sensitive to temperature variations and will increase as a function of temperature. Effectively, this is the change in forward conductance of a diode with temperature. The variation will be substantially the same for both germanium and silicon transistors, although some silicon units may change more rapidly. As temperature increases, for a fixed base-to-emitter d-c bias voltage, the base-emitter diode current will increase, resulting in a greater increase of collector current.

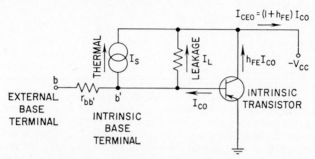

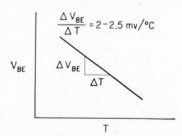

FIG. 11.101. Transistor equivalent circuit showing effect of $r_{bb'}$ and I_{CO} on collector current.

The effects of the change in input conductance on collector current (with temperature) may be more conveniently analyzed by considering the corresponding change in V_{BE}, the d-c base-to-emitter voltage which results. For silicon transistors, V_{BE} ideally will be about 0.6 to 0.7 volt at room temperature, although if an internal d-c series resistance is present, this voltage may be somewhat higher. Corresponding germanium transistors may have a V_{BE} of about 0.1 to 0.2 volt. As temperature increases, Fig. 11.102 shows that V_{BE} will decrease almost linearly approximately 2.0 to 2.5 mv/°C, depending on the transistor type employed. In many applications, particularly power amplifiers, the changes in input conductance may be counteracted by employing temperature compensation, i.e., the use of a device which supplies a voltage to the base-emitter junction which decreases at 2 to 2.5 mv/°C (Sec. 11.9j). As can be seen from the input characteristics in Figs. 11.23 to 11.30, the d-c input resistance varies throughout the entire temperature range and therefore can be an important contributor to a change in operating point, regardless of the temperature range involved.

FIG. 11.102. Change in V_{BE} with temperature.

11.9d. Common-emitter D-C Gain h_{FE}. The collector current and therefore the d-c operating point are dependent upon the d-c gain of the transistor. Any changes in the current gain h_{FE} (beta) will produce corresponding changes in the operating point. In addition, for the common-emitter connection, since I_{CEO} is strongly dependent upon the common-emitter d-c gain h_{FE}, the I_{CO} current component will also vary with changes in current gain and tend to change the bias point. Although the common-base d-c gain h_{FB} (alpha) is one of the more stable transistor parameters with temperature, a small change in h_{FB} can lead to a large change in beta (h_{FE}), since $h_{FE} = -h_{FB}/(1 + h_{FB}) = \alpha_{FB}/(1 - \alpha_{FB})$. For example, if h_{FB} changes from -0.98 to -0.99, h_{FE} will change from 49 to 99, a factor of 2. For the extreme temperature limits of a transistor, a change of this magnitude or more is not unusual. With rising temperature, h_{FE} will usually increase for most transistors. For certain transistors (e.g., Fig. 11.30), however, h_{FE} may actually decrease above room temperature. For a particular transistor type, therefore, it is important to check the manufacturer's data sheet for this information or to measure this characteristic. Particularly with silicon, where wide temperature ranges are encountered, the change in h_{FE} will be an important factor in influencing changes in collector current.

11.9e. Collector-current Stability Factors. In order to determine analytically, a priori, the changes in operating point which may be encountered in a given circuit and to design the circuit so as to minimize these changes, it is convenient to introduce the concept of d-c stability factor. In the literature, the stability factor normally encountered is the change in collector current for a change in I_{CO}. This was introduced by Shea[24] and given the notation S (where $S = dI_C/dI_{CO}$), where a smaller value of S indicates a more stable circuit. In order to be completely general and to take into consideration the changes in collector current caused by factors other than I_{CO}, it is necessary to introduce additional definitions for the analysis of d-c stability.[25] Together with Shea's definition, these supplemental factors can almost completely specify the shift in operating point which can be expected for a transistor when the temperature is changed over a given operating range. These additional mathematical expressions are particularly important for circuits employing silicon transistors, since I_{CO} in itself, although an exponential function of temperature, is not the major contributor to a shift in operating point owing to its low value over most of the operating temperature range.

Stability factors will be defined which consider the change in collector current I_C (since this is the important parameter for the common-emitter circuit) as a function of the three temperature-dependent variables previously discussed. Similar stability factors could be defined for emitter current if desired. The stability factors for collector current are:

$$S_1 = \frac{\Delta I_C}{\Delta I_{CO}} \cong \frac{dI_C}{dI_{CO}} \qquad \text{Collector-current change for unit change in } I_{CO}$$

$$S_2 = \frac{\Delta I_C}{\Delta V_{BE}} \cong \frac{dI_C}{dV_{BE}} \qquad \text{Collector-current change for unit change in } V_{BE}$$

$$S_3 = \frac{\Delta I_C}{\Delta h_{FE}} \cong \frac{dI_C}{dh_{FE}} \qquad \text{Collector-current change for unit change in } h_{FE}$$

Each stability factor is obtained while maintaining the other temperature-dependent parameters constant. For increasing temperature, S_1 and S_3 will be positive while S_2 will be a negative quantity. The smaller the absolute value of each S, the less effect each term will have on the operating point.

The change in collector current over a given temperature range, therefore, can be expressed as the sum of the individual changes due to the three stability factors, as follows:

$$dI_C \cong \Delta I_C = \frac{\Delta I_C}{\Delta I_{CO}} \Delta I_{CO} + \frac{\Delta I_C}{\Delta V_{BE}} \Delta V_{BE} + \frac{\Delta I_C}{\Delta h_{FE}} \Delta h_{FE}$$

$\Delta I_{CO} \cong dI_{CO}$ will be positive for increasing temperature.

$\Delta V_{BE} \cong dV_{BE}$ will be negative for increasing temperature.

$\Delta h_{FE} \cong dh_{FE}$ can be positive or negative, depending on the temperature range involved and type of transistor. A corresponding change in the collector-to-emitter voltage V_{CE} can be determined from a knowledge of ΔI_C and the d-c load line.

11.9f. Relationship of Circuit Parameters to Stability Factors. In order to apply the above definitions, it is useful to relate the circuit parameters of typical transistor circuits to the stability factors as defined above. The circuit shown in Fig. 11.103 is a generalized transistor amplifier circuit with supply voltages. (This circuit will also operate with one supply voltage.) The current relationships are shown in the various branches of the circuit. The temperature-dependent I_{CO} components are separated from the controllable direct current for ease of analysis. Thus, the stability factors related to I_{CO} in any branch are simply the terms (in Fig. 11.103) which are multiplied by I_{CO}, with the appropriate sign. The various collector-current stability factors (S_1, S_2, and S_3) for this circuit are shown in Table 11.15 in terms of the circuit parameters. It is important to note that these stability factors are a function only of the

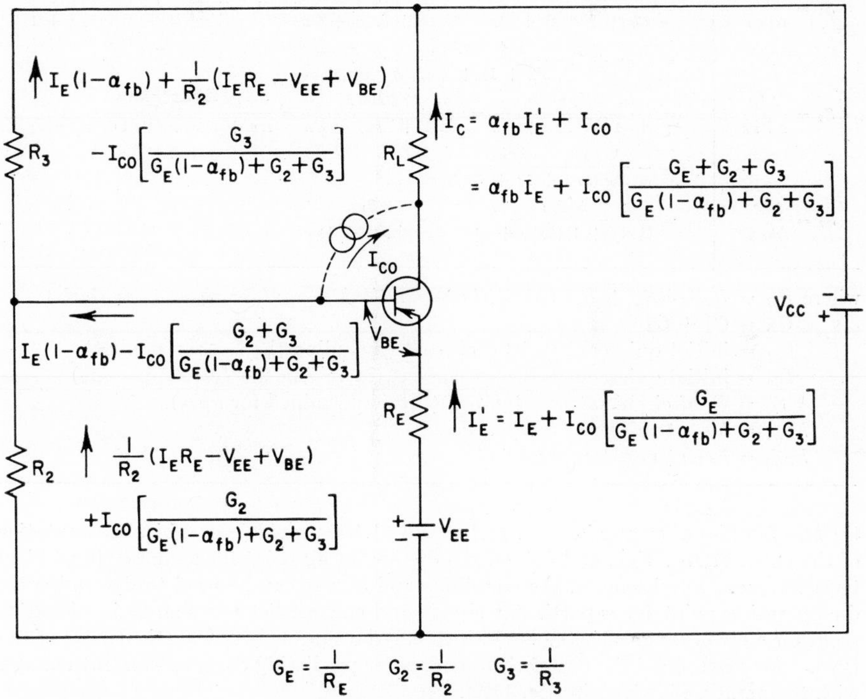

$$G_E = \frac{1}{R_E} \qquad G_2 = \frac{1}{R_2} \qquad G_3 = \frac{1}{R_3}$$

Fig. 11.103. Generalized bias circuit.

circuit parameters (R_E, R_B, etc.), the operating point (I_C), and the transistor current gain (h_{FE} or h_{FB}). The type of transistor (germanium, silicon, etc.) or the magnitude of V_{BE} or I_{CO} does not enter into these expressions.

The stability factor S_1 and $R_E S_2$ for the general circuit shown in Fig. 11.103 have been plotted in Figs. 11.104 and 11.105 versus the ratio R_B/R_E for various common-emitter d-c gains h_{FE}. S_1 can be considered to be the effective d-c gain of the circuit after feedback, since the collector current is

$$I_c \cong S_1 I_{CO} + \frac{V_{CC} + V_{EE} - V_{BE}}{R_3}(S_1 - 1)$$

For the same degree of stabilization, more d-c degeneration is required for the higher gain units, as can be noted in Figs. 11.104 and 11.105.

From Table 11.15 it can be seen that S_3, which represents the effect of a change in h_{FE} on the collector current, is directly proportional to S_1 (approximately).† Thus,

† For a more exact analysis S_1 should be determined using the current gain h_{FE2} which results when the transistor is operated at a new temperature. This factor is designated as S'_1 in Table 11.15.

TABLE 11.15. COLLECTOR-CURRENT STABILITY FACTORS FOR FIG. 11.103

Stability factors	Relationship to circuit parameters
$S_1 = \dfrac{\Delta I_C}{\Delta I_{CO}}$	$= \dfrac{R_E + R_B}{R_B(1 + h_{FB}) + R_E} = \dfrac{G_E + G_B}{G_E(1 + h_{FB}) + G_B} = (h_{FE} + 1)\dfrac{R_E + R_B}{R_B + R_E(h_{FE} + 1)}$ $= (h_{FE} + 1)\dfrac{1 + R_B/R_E}{(h_{FE} + 1) + R_B/R_E}$
$S_2 = \dfrac{\Delta I_C}{\Delta V_{BE}}$	$= \dfrac{h_{FB}}{R_B(1 + h_{FB}) + R_E} = \dfrac{h_{FB}G_E G_B}{G_E(1 + h_{FB}) + G_B} = \dfrac{-h_{FE}}{R_B + R_E(h_{FE} + 1)}$ $= -\dfrac{1}{R_E}\dfrac{h_{FE}}{(h_{FE} + 1) + R_B/R_E}$
$S_3 = \dfrac{\Delta I_C}{\Delta h_{FE}}$	$= \dfrac{S_1' I_{E1}}{(h_{FE1} + 1)(h_{FE2} + 1)} \cong \dfrac{I_{C1} S_1}{h_{FE1}(h_{FE2} + 1)}$

where $R_B = R_2 R_3/(R_2 + R_3)$ *(parallel combination)* $+ r_{bb'}$ *(for rigorous analysis)*
$G_B = G_2 + G_3$
$I_{E1} =$ initial quiescent emitter current (including the I_{CO} component)
$I_{C1} =$ initial quiescent collector current (including the I_{CO} component)
$S_1' = S_1$ of circuit at new temperature (determined for h_{FE2})
$h_{FE1} = h_{FE}$ at reference temperature
$h_{FE2} = h_{FE}$ at new temperature

the two families of curves in Figs. 11.104 and 11.105 provide a graphical presentation of the effect of I_{CO}, V_{BE}, and h_{FE} on the d-c operating point for a change in ambient temperature. Furthermore, the equations and curves can be used to determine the d-c operating point for a particular circuit and can predict the change in operating point for a given range of beta (h_{FE}) which may be expected for a particular transistor type. An example of the use of these curves for predicting collector-current changes with temperature is given in Sec. 11.9i.

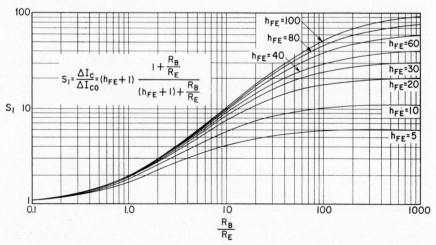

FIG. 11.104. Stability factor S_1 versus R_B/R_E.

For S_1 to be small, it is necessary that the ratio R_B/R_E be small. The same condition is necessary in order to minimize S_3. This can be accomplished by increasing R_E and decreasing R_B (the parallel combination of R_2 and R_3). In practice, a lower limit for R_B will arise, since this resistance shunts the a-c input impedance, and

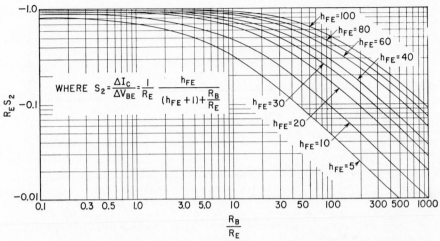

FIG. 11.105. $R_E S_2$ vs. R_B/R_E, where $S_2 = \Delta I_C/\Delta V_{BE} = (1/R_E)\{h_{FE}/[(h_{FE}+1)+(R_B/R_E)]\}$.

available signal power will be lost if R_2 and/or R_3 become too small. For an amplifier with a transformer input, this restriction need not apply, since the a-c impedance of the transformer may be much higher than the d-c resistance. In all cases, however, the internal base resistance $r_{bb'}$ is in series with R_B and sets a lower limit on the effective R_B. For a rigorous analysis, the effect of $r_{bb'}$ and any external resistances in the base lead must be taken into account.

In order to minimize S_2, the stability factor related to V_{BE}, R_B should be large. Again, the choice of a large emitter resistor R_E tends to minimize V_{BE} changes.

In order to minimize the over-all change in collector current (caused by changes in I_{CO}, V_{BE}, and h_{FE}), the operating temperature range, the type of transistor (silicon or germanium), and the relative I_{CO} and h_{FE} must be carefully considered before determining the size of R_B. A compromise usually will be necessary for the selection of R_B. In all cases, it is desirable to employ as large an emitter resistance as is practical. In practice, for the design

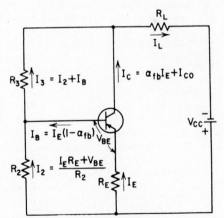

FIG. 11.106. Collector-to-base feedback bias.

of circuits which must operate over a wide temperature range, the ratio R_B/R_E generally will lie between 1 and 5.

Another d-c bias circuit often used is shown in Fig. 11.106. This circuit obtains forward base-emitter bias by means of the collector-to-base feedback resistor. This circuit is degenerative for alternating as well as direct current. If it is desired, the signal degeneration can be reduced and the a-c gain increased by splitting R_3 into two resistors and connecting their junction to ground through a bypass capacitor.

The current relationships for the circuit are shown in the various branches. The collector-current stability factors (S_1, S_2, and S_3) for this circuit are shown in Table 11.16 in terms of the circuit parameters.

From the equations given in Table 11.16, it can be seen that all the stability factors will be minimized when R_E is large. Although it is not too obvious from the equations, as in the previous circuit, S_1 and S_3 are minimized when R_2 and R_3 are reduced while S_3 is minimized when R_2 and R_3 are large. Again, compromise values of R_2 and R_3 must be chosen. In general, for germanium transistors, I_{CO} effects will predominate

TABLE 11.16. COLLECTOR-CURRENT STABILITY FACTORS FOR FIG. 11.106

Stability factors	Relationship to circuit parameters
$S_1 = \dfrac{\Delta I_C}{\Delta I_{CO}}$	$\dfrac{1}{1 + \dfrac{h_{FB}R_2R_3}{R_ER_2 + (R_E + R_2)(R_L + R_3)}}$ $= \dfrac{(h_{FE} + 1)R_ER_2 + (R_E + R_2)(R_L + R_3)}{(h_{FE} + 1)R_ER_2 + (R_E + R_2)(R_L + R_3) - h_{FE}R_2R_3}$
$S_2 = \dfrac{\Delta I_C}{\Delta V_{BE}}$	$\dfrac{1}{R_E} \dfrac{h_{FB}}{1 + (1 + h_{FB})\dfrac{R_2}{R_E}\dfrac{1 + R_L/R_3(1 + h_{FB})}{1 + (R_2 + R_L)/R_3}}$
$S_3 = \dfrac{\Delta I_C}{\Delta h_{FE}}$	$\dfrac{S_1'I_{E1}}{(h_{FE} + 1)(h_{FE2} + 1)} \cong \dfrac{S_1 I_{C1}}{h_{FE1}(h_{FE2} + 1)}$

where S_1', I_{E1}, I_{C1}, h_{FE1}, and h_{FE2} are as defined for Table 11.15.

over V_{BE} effects at room temperature and above, and these resistors normally will be chosen as small as possible. For silicon, V_{BE} effects will predominate, except possibly at very high temperatures, and R_2 and R_3 should be slightly larger for silicon transistors. For this type of bias circuit to provide effective stabilization, it is important that the load resistance R_L be relatively large and that a large percentage of the supply voltage be dropped across R_L.

The collector current for this circuit will be $I_C = [(V_{CC} - V_{BE})(S_1 - 1)/R_3] + S_1 I_{CO}$, where S_1 now is given in Table 11.16. For this circuit, S_1 represents the effective d-c gain after feedback. For the same operating-point stability, the circuit in Fig. 11.106 usually allows the use of lower values of emitter resistance and larger values of base resistances than would be the case for Fig. 11.103. In general, there is no advantage in using the feedback circuit over the circuit shown in Fig. 11.103, and in practice the latter circuit (without V_{EE}) is more commonly used.

11.9g. Effect of R_E on Operating Point. As shown in Sec. 11.9f, the use of a large emitter resistor will generally increase the d-c stability of circuits which must operate over a wide temperature range and/or use transistors having a wide range of beta. R_E is normally bypassed by a capacitor in order to prevent the loss of a-c gain due to degeneration. From the stability expressions, it can be seen that for all cases, the larger the value of R_E, the more stable will be the d-c operating point. Increasing R_E, however, will lower the effective d-c gain.

The value of the emitter resistor will generally be limited by the available d-c supply voltage or voltages, since a d-c voltage drop $I_E R_E$ appears across this resistor. An additional restriction on the magnitude of R_E may be the power-supply drain, since d-c input power correspondingly is lost in this resistor. It should be noted that for the same degree of stabilization, the d-c input power loss will always be lower for the two-power supply circuit shown in Fig. 11.103 than for an equivalent one-power supply circuit.[26]

Since the voltage drop across R_E tends to reverse-bias the base-emitter junction of the transistor, a compensating forward bias is required to obtain the desired operating point. In Fig. 11.103, this forward bias can be obtained by the use of the additional power supply V_{EE} and/or from the voltage divider network of R_3 and R_2. In Fig. 11.106, forward bias is obtained through resistor R_3.

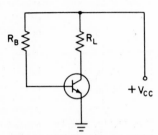

FIG. 11.107. Constant-current bias.

Where the transistor is required to operate over a wide temperature range, a reverse base-current bias may be required to obtain the proper operating point. This will be necessary when the I_{co} component is larger than the desired I_C because of elevated temperatures or other reasons. As an example, the transistor of Fig. 11.23 requires a reverse base bias current in order to obtain a collector current of less than 5 ma at $+55°$C. This reverse current can be obtained for an emitter-biased transistor, as shown in Figs. 11.103 and 11.106, whereas circuits without emitter resistors such as those shown in Figs. 11.107 and 11.110 can supply forward bias only. Thus, the use of an emitter resistor is to be preferred for operation over extremely wide temperature ranges or wherever large amounts of stabilization are needed.

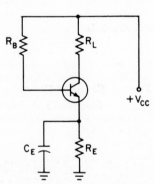

FIG. 11.108. Series stabilization.

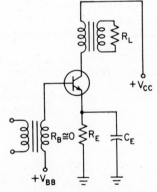

FIG. 11.109. Series stabilization for transformer-coupled stage.

11.9h. Simplified Bias Circuits. From Figs. 11.103 and 11.106, it can be seen that by open-circuiting or short-circuiting some of the resistors or by employing only one d-c power supply, various bias circuits can be obtained. Some of these permutations are shown in Figs. 11.107 to 11.110. The stability factors for these circuits can be obtained by the appropriate substitutions in the equations presented in Tables 11.15 and 11.16. In some cases where variations in transistor parameters or temperature are not severe, a simple bias circuit may be satisfactory.

Figure 11.107 shows a transistor which has a constant base current bias. Since the input resistance of the transistor is low, the base-to-emitter voltage can be neglected compared with the drop across R_B, and the base current, therefore, is $I_B = V_{CC}/R_B$. $I_C = (h_{FE} + 1)I_{CO} + h_{FE}I_B \cong h_{FE}(V_{CC}/R_B + I_{CO})$ is the corresponding collector current.   In general, an operating point determined by a fixed current bias is not desirable.   The collector current is likely to change excessively with a change in transistors or temperature.   Table 11.15 shows that the stability factor S_1 for this circuit will approach $h_{FE} + 1$, resulting in large changes of current with temperature due to I_{CO}.   Similarly, S_3 will be large, so that if the current gain changes (owing to temperature or a substitution of transistors), a correspondingly large change in collector current will result.   On the other hand, for this type of bias, the effects of V_{BE} will be minimized.

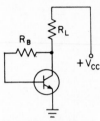

FIG. 11.110. Simple shunt stabilization.

The effects of temperature on this circuit can be minimized by adding a series emitter resistor as shown in Fig. 11.108.   As previously described, performance of this circuit with respect to S_1 and S_3 is improved, since the ratio of R_B to R_E is decreased.   However, even with an emitter resistor, this circuit cannot produce a reverse bias, since there is no d-c feedback path back to the base.   Therefore, this circuit will not perform satisfactorily if a reverse bias is required at high temperatures.

In the transformer-coupled stage shown in Fig. 11.109, the transistor essentially operates with a constant base-to-emitter voltage bias. V_{BB} provides the necessary forward-bias voltage required to overcome the reverse bias caused by the voltage drop across R_E.   It should be noted that R_B can never be zero even with a lossless transformer, since the internal base resistance $r_{bb'}$ is always present, as shown in Fig. 11.101.   This resistor must be added to the external R_B for a complete analysis. For this type of circuit, although changes in collector current due to I_{CO} and h_{FE} are minimized, the collector current will change rapidly, since V_{BE} changes are directly reflected to the collector circuit.   The addition of a large emitter resistor R_E in the circuit, however, will help to "swamp out" the V_{BE} changes due to temperature and reduce S_2.   The collector current which flows in this circuit is

$$
\begin{aligned}
I_C &= \frac{V_{BB} - V_{BE} - I_B R_E}{R_E} \\
&= \frac{V_{BB} + I_{CO}R_E(1 + 1/h_{FE}) - V_{BE}}{(1 + 1/h_{FE})R_E} \qquad \begin{matrix}(\text{if } h_{FE} \gg 1) \\ (I_{CO} \text{ small})\end{matrix} \\
&\cong \frac{V_{BB} - V_{BE}}{R_E}
\end{aligned}
$$

The circuit shown in Fig. 11.110 uses straight shunt feedback and is a simplification of Fig. 11.106.   In this case, the forward bias is obtained by connecting R_3 to the collector rather than to the supply voltage.   The base current is

$$
I_B = \frac{V_{CC} - V_{BE} - I_C R_L}{R_3 + R_L}
$$

and the collector current is $I_C \cong \dfrac{I_{CO} + V_{CC}/(R_3 + R_L)}{(1/h_{FE}) + R_L/(R_3 + R_L)}$.   Again, the temperature range of operation will be limited to those temperatures where forward bias only is required.

11.9i. Application of Stability Factors.   As previously discussed, the circuit stability factors S_1, S_2, and S_3 can be used to predict the operating-point changes with temperature.   The collector current can be calculated at various temperatures for a given circuit configuration when the parameters of the transistor are known. Figure 11.111 shows a circuit for which the transistor parameters are given in the following tables for typical germanium and silicon units. Each transistor has the same current gain

GERMANIUM TRANSISTOR PARAMETERS

Temp, °C	−55	+25	+55
h_{FE}	25	40	50
I_{CO}, μa	0.01	3	24
V_{BE}, volts†	−0.03	+0.15	+0.08

† Decreases about 2.3 mv/°C.

SILICON TRANSISTOR PARAMETERS

Temp, °C	−55	+25	+100
h_{FE}	18	40	70
I_{CO}, μa	....	0.005	1.0
V_{BE}, volts†	+0.45	+0.65	+0.84

† Decreases about 2.5 mv/°C.

(40) at room temperature. However, the performance of the circuit with temperature will depend on whether the silicon or germanium transistor is used. The operating-temperature ranges were made large in order to emphasize the effects of each stability factor on the over-all collector-current change. At room temperatures, the circuit resistances were chosen to produce a collector current of about 2 ma.

For the circuit in Fig. 11.111, the ratio R_B/R_E is equal to 1.65. From Fig. 11.104, S_1 can be determined for a transistor with a common-emitter d-c gain h_{FE} of 40. In this case, S_1 is equal to 2.55. Similarly, $R_E S_2$ can be determined from Fig. 11.105 to be equal to −0.94. Since $R_E = 4,700$ ohms, S_2 will be equal to −0.2 millimho. S_1 and S_2 are valid for either the germanium or silicon transistor operating in the given circuit.

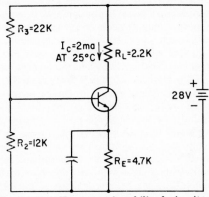

FIG. 11.111. Example of stabilized circuit.

S_3 must be determined individually for each transistor at each new temperature. For the germanium transistor, S_3 at −55°C can be calculated as follows:

$$S_3 = \frac{I_C S_1'}{h_{FE1}(h_{FE2} + 1)} = \frac{(2 \times 10^{-3})(2.5)}{40 \times 26} = 4.8 \times 10^{-3} \text{ ma}$$

Similarly, S_3 at +55°C will be equal to 2.5×10^{-3} ma. For the silicon transistor, S_3 will be 6.30×10^{-3} ma at −55°C and 1.86×10^{-3} ma at +100°C.

The change in collector current can now be determined for each transistor over its operating-temperature range. For the germanium transistor at +55°C,

$$\Delta I_C = S_1 \Delta I_{CO} + S_2 \Delta V_{BE} + S_3 \Delta h_{FE}$$
$$\Delta I_C \text{ (in ma)} = (2.55)(21 \times 10^{-3}) + (-0.2)(-0.07) + (2.5 \times 10^{-3})(10)$$
$$= 0.0535 \text{ ma} + 0.014 \text{ ma} + 0.025 \text{ ma}$$
$$\Delta I_C \cong +0.0925 \text{ ma}$$

Similarly, at $-55°C$,

$$\Delta I_C \text{ (in ma)} = (2.55)(-3 \times 10^{-3}) + (-0.2 \times 10^{-3})(0.18) + (4.8 \times 10^{-3})(-15)$$
$$= -0.0076 - 0.036 - 0.072$$
$$\Delta I_C \cong -0.11 \text{ ma}$$

Therefore, for the germanium transistor, the collector current will be about 2.09 ma at $+55°C$ and 1.89 ma at $-55°C$.

For the silicon transistor, the various components of ΔI_C will be as follows:

$$\Delta I_C \,(+100°C) \cong 0.001 \text{ ma} + 0.038 \text{ ma} + 0.0558 \text{ ma} = +0.09 \text{ ma}$$
$$\Delta I_C \,(-55°C) \cong 0 - 0.04 \text{ ma} - 0.139 \text{ ma} = -0.18 \text{ ma}$$

Thus, for the silicon transistor, the collector current will be about 2.09 ma at 100°C and 1.82 ma at $-55°C$.

Although the circuit of Fig. 11.111 is highly stabilized, it can be seen that the changes in h_{FE} and V_{BE} with temperature are quite influential in changing the collector current. In silicon transistors, the change in collector current will depend more upon the change in h_{FE} and V_{BE} than upon I_{CO}.

In order to stabilize the d-c operating point properly, the tolerance of bias resistors and supply voltages must be taken into account, in addition to the range of beta which is specified for the transistor.

11.9j. Temperature Compensation. For most applications, adequate biasing of transistors can be obtained by the use of the stabilization techniques previously described. These techniques work particularly well for low-level class A stages. Where supply power is at a premium, however, compensation techniques are generally employed. For example, an appreciable loss of power would result in a power amplifier operating at a high emitter current if an emitter resistor were used for bias stabilization. In addition, an emitter resistor in a class B amplifier could not be bypassed for a-c signal flow, since the average collector and emitter currents vary with the signal. (Thus, a class B amplifier cannot employ a constant-current bias.)

For many low-frequency amplifiers, it is advantageous to employ compensation techniques which make use of nonlinear circuit elements in order to maintain a constant operating point. Changes in the operating point of a transistor with temperature can often be compensated by the use of another temperature-dependent circuit element such as a thermistor, diode, transistor, etc., to supply a base-to-emitter voltage which will decrease with increasing temperature. As discussed in Sec. 11.9c, the base-to-emitter voltage V_{BE} should decrease about 2 to 2.5 mv/°C, depending on the transistor employed, in order to minimize the change in collector current which is a function of V_{BE}. Ideal compensation is equivalent to making the stability factor S_2 (Sec. 11.9e) equal to zero; i.e., the collector current will be independent of changes in V_{BE}. The bias schemes previously described would all have less operating-point variation with temperature if such a technique were used to bias the transistor.

Typical examples of circuits employing temperature-compensating devices are shown in Figs. 11.112 and 11.113. The first circuit employs a forward-biased diode for compensation. The resistance of the diode decreases with increasing temperature and therefore provides a decreasing voltage across the emitter-to-base junction. In some cases it is possible to obtain a diode which has the same properties as the base-to-emitter junction of the transistor. In this event, the compensation is quite good. In addition to providing a low d-c resistance path of only 5 or 10 ohms, thus improving (lowering) the stability factors S_1 and S_3, the diode also provides the exact base-emitter bias voltage required by the transistor, so that S_2 essentially becomes zero.

Figure 11.113 shows a class B amplifier employing thermistor compensation. The resistance of the thermistor R_2 also will decrease with increasing temperature, thus compensating the base-to-emitter voltage against temperature changes.   A thermistor, however, seldom can provide compensation as good as that obtained from a properly selected forward-biased diode.[23]   The use of such a diode is particularly good in a class B amplifier (in place of the thermistor), since it will present a very low dynamic impedance and thereby minimize signal loss.

Depending upon the particular voltage drop versus temperature characteristic desired, various thermistor networks can be employed.   Since both germanium and silicon transistors have a lower temperature coefficient than commercially available thermistors, one or more resistors are normally used in conjunction with the compensation network.   The simplest network usually is a thermistor in parallel with a

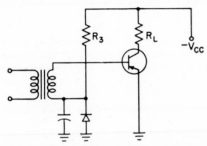

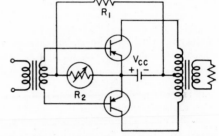

Fig. 11.112. Temperature compensation using forward-biased diode.

Fig. 11.113. Class B amplifier with thermistor compensation.

resistor.   This will normally result in tracking of the desired voltage drop versus temperature at only a few points.[23]   Better tracking can be obtained if the designer is willing to use more elaborate compensation networks.†

In the case of power transistors, it is highly desirable to have the thermistor, diode, or other temperature-sensitive element coupled directly to the collector junction through a path with negligible thermal drop.   Thus, the element would more closely compensate for junction temperature rather than ambient temperature.   When the dissipation is high, the junction temperature will be greater than the ambient temperature, and since the collector current is a function of junction temperature, improved compensation will result.

11.9k. Thermal Runaway.   As pointed out in the preceding paragraphs, the collector current of a transistor will usually increase when the temperature is raised. Thus a transistor operating at high ambient temperatures and/or high dissipation will draw more collector current as the temperature of the collector junction rises. This increase in collector current causes a corresponding increase in collector junction temperature, and under certain conditions the process becomes cumulative and continues until the transistor is destroyed.   This condition is known as thermal runaway.

The circuit thermal stability is dependent upon the thermal properties of the transistor and associated mounting (such as type of heat sink, type and location of temperature-compensating elements, and stabilization), ambient temperature, the electrical properties of the transistor (current-amplification factor I_{co} and base lead resistance $r_{bb'}$), and the circuit properties (circuit resistances and operating point).[27]   Safeguards against thermal runaway are d-c feedback (stabilization), temperature compensation, and effective means of cooling the collector junction.

† Recently silicon resistors have become available which have a positive temperature coefficient of about $+0.7\%/°C$ over a temperature range of $-60°$ to $+150°C$.   When used with silicon transistor circuits, these resistors can provide almost perfect compensation of the operating point.

Not all circuits need be stabilized against thermal runaway. Many R-C-coupled circuits limit the dissipation to a low value under any condition. Such a circuit might have considerable variation in operating point with temperature as manifested by large stability factors. In such a circuit, as the temperature rises, the collector voltage will drop until in the limit it is zero and the stage is inoperative. For this condition the transistor will not be damaged. However, in circuits which employ transformer coupling where there is little or no effective d-c resistance in series with the collector or in power amplifiers where there may not be any appreciable d-c resistance in the emitter or collector leads, thermal runaway can easily occur unless precautions are taken to maintain a constant operating point. For example, unless precautions are taken, it is possible that a silicon transistor which is operating at a low dissipation at $-55°C$ will run away when the ambient temperature is raised to 30°C.

A number of ways to analyze thermal runaway have been devised. These include graphical representations as well as analytical formulations of stability factors. Most of the analytical techniques, however, consider only instability caused by I_{CO}. Actually, thermal runaway not only is due to the increase of I_{CO} with temperature but may also be caused by the change in input resistance and current gain with temperature, as previously discussed.

It is quite complicated to calculate the allowable power dissipation and/or maximum ambient temperature at which a transistor *in a circuit* would become thermally unstable, since a knowledge of all the factors which influence the thermal stability is required. It is possible, however, to determine experimentally the maximum allowable power dissipation and/or ambient temperature and, at the same time, gain some insight into the effect of stabilization and compensation upon the thermal stability of the transistor in the circuit.

The power dissipated at a transistor junction is $P_C = (T_J - T_A)/\theta_T$ (Sec. 11.4c), where θ_T is the total thermal resistance from junction to air. The rate of change of power dissipation P_C with junction temperature T_J is $dP_C/dT_J = 1/\theta_T$. In any thermal system, the conditions for thermal stability are such that the system must be capable of dissipating more heat than is generated. Thus, $dP_C/dT_J \leq 1/\theta_T$; i.e., the heat generated in the transistor must be less than the thermal conductivity $1/\theta_T$ from junction to air.

Curve A of Fig. 11.114 is a plot of the heat generated at the junction (of a transistor in a power-output stage under quiescent conditions, for example) versus the junction temperature. The junction temperature can be obtained from a knowledge of θ_T and P_C as discussed in Sec. 11.4c. This curve is a property of the circuit and its physical environment. It should be obtained with the transistor operating in its circuit with its equivalent heat sink. The heat generated is equivalent to the transistor dissipation in watts and is dependent upon the voltages and currents in the transistor. Since the transistor collector current is temperature sensitive, the dissipation will be dependent upon the junction temperature and on the circuit. The slope of curve A is dP_C/dT_J.

Curve B represents the power-dissipation capability (rate of heat flow) of the equivalent thermal circuit as a function of the junction temperature of the transistor. The slope can be seen to be $1/\theta_T$, which corresponds to the thermal conductivity of the total thermal circuit from transistor junction to ambient air.

With no voltages applied to the transistor, the unit dissipates no power and thus the junction temperature is the same as the ambient. In Fig. 11.114, this condition corresponds to the point $T_{ambient}$. When voltages are applied to the circuit, the heat generated by the transistor (in the form of dissipation) is P_1. This amount of internal heat generation in the transistor requires that the junction temperature increase to T_1 (for the cooling facility with a thermal conductance of $1/\theta_T$) in order to permit thermal equilibrium. Since the junction temperature has now been increased, the total power generated by the transistor must increase to P_2. In this manner, the junction temperature and resultant power generation increase until a stable condition is reached at point 1, where the power-generation and thermal-conductance curves intersect, resulting in junction temperature T_2.

It is now possible to predict the effect on the transistor of changing the ambient temperature. If the ambient temperature were increased, curve B would be translated to the right, resulting in a higher junction temperature, since the intersection of curve A would be to the right of point 1. If the ambient temperature increased to T_3 (curve B_1), the junction temperature would be T_5. At values of ambient

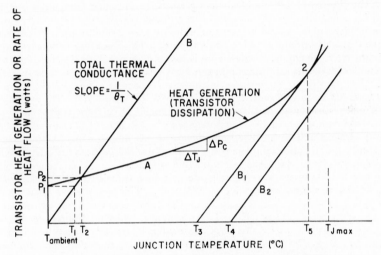

Fig. 11.114. Graphical representation of thermal stability.

temperature below T_3, for this particular thermal conductance, the transistor circuit would always meet the thermal stability criterion; i.e., $dP_C/dT_J < 1/\theta_T$ and is therefore a thermally stable circuit. At ambient temperature T_3, curve B_1 is tangent to curve A at point 2, where $dP_C/dT_J = 1/\theta_T$. Under these conditions, the circuit is conditionally stable, since a small incremental increase in junction temperature will cause an unstable condition. A further rise in the ambient temperature (e.g., ambient temperature T_4) will cause the thermal-conductance curve B_2 to fall below the power-generation curve. Under these conditions, the transistor junction temperature cannot stabilize. The power generated within the transistor continues to increase in search of a stable condition until the junction is destroyed. This is a graphic representation of thermal runaway.

From this representation, the effects of temperature stabilization and/or compensation can be determined. Also, the effect of changing the thermal conductance can be determined. If the cooling facility is changed (for instance, a better heat sink is used), the junction will run cooler for a given ambient temperature, since the slope, curve B, will be increased. If the circuit is made more stable, the curve A will tend to flatten out and, for a given heat sink and ambient temperature, the stable junction temperature will be at a lower value. If it were possible to stabilize the transistor perfectly, curve A would be a straight line with zero slope. Under such a condition, the maximum ambient temperature would be limited only by the maximum allowable junction temperature, since the circuit could exhibit no thermal regeneration. Either by improving the effective heat sink for the transistor or by improving the circuit stabilization or compensation, it is possible to operate the transistor at a higher power dissipation and/or ambient temperature. For the same power-dissipation capability, the circuit designer has a choice of increasing the thermal conductivity of the associated heat sink or improving the circuit stability. Which of these choices is made depends on the relative cost and/or complexity of each.

Curve A in Fig. 11.114 was presumed to have been plotted for a transistor operating in a circuit at a given a-c signal level. This transistor dissipation curve may change for a circuit operating at a different signal level. As an example, the conditions of maximum power dissipation will be different for class A and class B amplifiers as previously discussed. For an ideal class B amplifier with sine-wave input, maximum dissipation occurs at about 40 per cent of the maximum power output, while maximum dissipation for a class A amplifier occurs under quiescent conditions. It is important that the thermal-stability criterion be met for all conditions of power dissipation that the circuit may encounter. Unless care is taken, it is possible that a circuit may be stable under quiescent conditions and run away when the circuit is operating, or vice versa.

11.9l. Stabilization of Transistor A-C Gain with Temperature.[28]   The a-c gain of a small-signal transistor amplifier may vary as a result of changes in the temperature-sensitive a-c parameters of the transistor (described in Sec. 11.1b) as well as changes in the d-c operating point. The temperature effects due to a shift in d-c operating point can be greatly reduced if the transistor is stabilized properly with the use of the techniques previously described in Secs. 11.9f to 11.9i.

The effects of temperature upon the a-c gain of a transistor circuit generally can be minimized by the use of negative a-c feedback. This negative feedback may take the form of an unbypassed emitter resistance, collector-to-base feedback, or feedback around more than one stage (Sec. 11.8). In some cases, temperature-sensitive elements can be employed in the feedback loop.

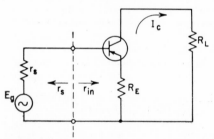

In addition to feedback, however, changes in the a-c gain can be greatly minimized by the proper selection of an a-c source resistance. If the d-c operating point is maintained constant, this optimum source resistance varies quite slowly with temperature.

Fig. 11.115. A-c representation of common-emitter circuit.

Figure 11.115 is the a-c circuit for a common-emitter amplifier which employs an unbypassed external emitter resistance R_E. The gain of this stage is directly proportional to the effective transconductance $g_m' = I_c/E_g$, where I_c is the small-signal collector current and E_g is the a-c generator voltage, as shown in Fig. 11.115. The effective transconductance g_m' (and therefore the a-c gain) can be maintained relatively constant with temperature by the selection of an a-c source resistance such that $r_S \cong r_{b'e}/2.2 - R_E$, where $r_{b'e}$ is the hybrid-pi internal base-to-emitter resistance as shown in Fig. 11.22. Using this value of a-c source resistance r_S, it is possible to achieve excellent a-c gain stability over an extremely wide temperature range when the transistor is d-c stabilized properly. In general, if r_S is lower than $r_{b'e}/2.2 - R_E$, the gain stability will still remain quite good.

Although the current gain can be reduced by driving the circuit from a low impedance, this technique is generally more advantageous than employing negative feedback. In some circuits, r_S can be made part of the d-c bias network. Since r_S will generally be low, the d-c stability will also be increased.

11.10. Noise. *11.10a. Noise Factor.* In a low-level circuit, important questions are: What signal-to-noise ratio is being realized? What is the best that can be obtained with practical components? How close are these values to those obtainable with an ideal circuit? In general, one wants this type of information without specifying the magnitude or the type of signal which will be applied to the circuit. But to talk about the signal-to-noise ratio of an amplifier, one must specify a signal. Thus signal-to-noise ratio is not necessarily the best quantity to use when comparing different amplifying devices.

It is often useful to compare an amplifier with an equivalent ideal (noiseless) amplifier. This ideal amplifier has the same input impedance, gain, output impedance, etc., as the actual amplifier. It differs in only one respect: it does not add any noise to the signal. Noise factor, or noise figure, is a quantity which compares the performance of an actual amplifier with an ideal or noiseless amplifier. The ideal amplifier is the reference and has an NF of zero decibels. The ratio of the noise power output of the actual amplifier to the noise power output of the ideal amplifier is the NF of the actual amplifier. Noise factor may be given as the numerical ratio of these two noise powers, but it is customarily expressed in decibels.

Noise factor may be defined as the ratio of the available signal-to-noise ratio at the source to the available signal-to-noise ratio at the amplifier output. An equivalent definition is that noise factor is the ratio of the total noise power at the output of the amplifier to the noise output power which is due to the thermal noise in the source impedance.

An NF measurement requires two operations:

1. Measuring the total noise at the output of the amplifier
2. Calculating how much of this noise is due to thermal noise in the source

The determination of thermal noise due to the source requires a gain measurement and sometimes a bandwidth measurement. Noise factor, per se, is meaningless unless the source resistance used for the measurement is known. Thus one speaks of an amplifier having a given NF when used with a specific source impedance.

11.10b. Single-frequency Method. In the single-frequency method of NF measurement, a sine-wave oscillator or signal generator is connected to the amplifier input through a resistance R_g, as shown in Fig. 11.116. R_g is the source resistance for which the amplifier NF is being measured. In practice, the oscillator is not connected directly to the amplifier being measured but rather is connected through a resistive attenuator such that it is equivalent to a voltage generator V_g in series with R_g. These techniques are

FIG. 11.116. Measurement of noise factor, single-frequency method.

necessary for convenience in order to measure accurately and apply V_g, which may be less than a microvolt.

The open-circuit thermal noise voltage of the source resistance R_g is

$$V_T = \sqrt{4kTBR_g} \qquad \text{volts rms}$$

where k = Boltzmann's constant = 1.38×10^{-23} joule/°K
T = temperature, °K
B = equivalent noise bandwidth, cps
R_g = source resistance, ohms

At room temperature (27°C) this reduces to

$$V_T = \sqrt{1.6 \times 10^{-20} BR_g} \qquad \text{volts rms}$$

The component of the output voltage due to thermal noise in the source is $A V_T$, where A is the gain factor that relates output voltage to open-circuit source voltage. Likewise the component of the output voltage that is due to the signal generator is $A V_g$. Since NF is the ratio of the total noise power at the output of the amplifier to that component of the noise output power which is due to the thermal noise in the source resistance, the noise figure is

$$\text{NF} = \left(\frac{V_0}{A V_T}\right)^2$$

where V_0 is the total noise voltage due to thermal noise in the source plus that added by the amplifier, actually measured at the amplifier output. This measurement is taken with the signal generator turned off, the amplifier being connected to the source resistance R_g. Next the signal generator is turned on and an open-circuit sine-wave voltage V_g is applied to the input of the amplifier through the source resistance R_g such that the amplifier power output is doubled. When the amplifier power output is doubled by applying V_g to the amplifier input,

$$A V_g = V_0$$

and
$$\text{NF} = \left(\frac{A V_g}{A V_T}\right)^2 = \frac{V_g^2}{1.6 \times 10^{-20} B R_g}$$

The amplifier power output is doubled when the rms output voltage is increased 3 db. Thus in the above measurement a sine-wave signal is applied to the amplifier input such that the amplifier output meter reads 3 db higher than it did on noise alone. Often this measurement is made by switching a 3-db pad into the amplifier circuit and then applying the signal to the input such that the output meter returns to its original reading. This method has the advantage of eliminating some meter errors.

The 3-db increase must be measured with an rms meter. Generally it is convenient to use a meter that only approximates an rms reading. Such a meter is usually in error when reading a voltage which is of some other waveform than that for which the meter was calibrated. Certain of these measurement errors can be reduced if the gain measurement is made with a sine-wave output signal. This is accomplished by increasing the signal generator voltage until the amplifier output is much larger than the amplifier noise output. For example, if $A V_g$ is adjusted to be m times larger than V_0, where m may be about 10,

$$A V_g = m V_0$$

and
$$\text{NF} = \left(\frac{V_0}{A V_T}\right)^2 = \left(\frac{V_g}{m V_T}\right)^2 = \frac{V_g^2}{1.6 \times 10^{-20} m^2 B R_g}$$

One disadvantage of the single-frequency method of noise measurement is that an accurate determination of equivalent noise bandwidth is necessary. The noise bandwidth is actually a power bandwidth. It can be obtained by taking the frequency response (i.e., output voltage as a function of input voltage) of the transistor being measured plus the measuring system. This ratio of output voltage divided by input voltage is then squared and plotted on a linear-frequency scale. The area under the curve is obtained with a planimeter or some similar method, and a rectangle of equal area is drawn representing a constant gain up to some point and then a sharp cutoff, as in Fig. 11.117. This is the noise bandwidth. As an example, for a system which falls off at 6 db/octave, the equivalent noise bandwidth is 1.57 times the 3-db bandwidth. It is noted that some noise-figure measurements are made narrow band, for example, a few cycles bandwidth in the vicinity of 1,000 cycles, while other noise-figure measurements are made wideband, for example, over the whole audio bandwidth such as 30 to 15,000 cycles.

The single-frequency method of noise-figure measurement suffers from another deficiency when used for wideband measurements. If the noise-test setup is calibrated with one transistor and others are measured that have different frequency responses, the bandwidth calibration is in error. This error may be quite serious in low-noise transistors, since the noise-frequency spectrum is quite flat in this case

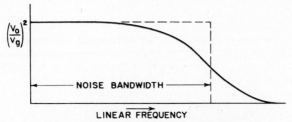

FIG. 11.117. Equivalent noise bandwidth.

and on a linear-frequency scale the high end of the spectrum carries considerable weight.

11.10c. Noise-diode Method. The noise-diode method of measuring NF effectively uses a known white-noise voltage instead of a sine wave to measure the gain of the system. As a result explicit information on bandwidth is not required.

A noise diode operates with temperature-limited emission. The alternating noise current bears a precise relationship to the direct diode current. In the arrangement shown in Fig. 11.118, the alternating noise current is $I_n = \sqrt{3.2 \times 10^{-19} I_D B}$, where I_D is the direct current and B is the bandwidth in cycles. By Thévenin's theorem this is equivalent to a voltage generator V_n in series with the source resistance R_g. Actually to be complete, another generator V_T representing the thermal noise generated in

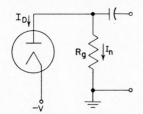

FIG. 11.118. Noise diode and load.

FIG. 11.119. Equivalent circuit of Fig. 11.118.

the source resistance R_g should be added, as shown in Fig. 11.119. The characteristics of a noise diode that make it especially useful for noise measurements are as follows: (1) It is a convenient accurate source of calibrated low currents. (2) It has the same noise-frequency spectrum as thermal noise, and hence measuring techniques are simplified.

To measure the NF of a transistor or transistor amplifier, R_g is adjusted to the desired value and the combination of R_g and the noise diode is connected to the transistor. A reading V_0 of the output voltage (any convenient amount of gain) is taken with the noise-diode direct current zero. This reading is proportional to the thermal noise contributed by R_g plus the noise added by the amplifier. The thermal noise contributed by R_g is known from theoretical considerations to be $V_T = \sqrt{4kTBR_g}$, but since the gain factor of the amplifier A is unknown, the NF of the transistor cannot be determined. The noise diode is then used as a calibrated white-noise signal generator to determine the gain factor of the amplifier. The direct current of the noise diode is increased by adjusting the filament voltage until the amplifier output power is doubled. The output voltage is now 3 db, or 1.4 times greater than V_0, the output voltage due to thermal noise in the source plus amplifier noise. Under these conditions,

$$\sqrt{(AV_n)^2 + (V_0)^2} = 1.4V_0$$

or

$$AV_n = V_0$$

The NF is the ratio of total noise power at the output of the amplifier to that component of the noise output power due to thermal noise in the source.

$$NF = \left(\frac{V_0}{AV_T}\right)^2$$

This reduces to

$$NF = \left(\frac{AV_n}{AV_T}\right)^2 = \frac{3.2 \times 10^{-19} I_D B R_g^2}{1.6 \times 10^{-20} B R_g} = 20 I_D R_g$$

Since both voltages measured with the output meter are of similar character, i.e., white noise—especially in the case of low-noise transistors—this type of measurement is relatively independent of the type of output meter used. Commonly a 3-db pad is used in this measurement, and hence the output meter need be only an indicator of level and needs no calibration whatsoever.

Care should be taken in using a noise diode, particularly for low-frequency measurements, to ensure that the flicker noise of the diode does not give rise to a measurement error. A diode can usually be selected which has a low-flicker noise component at low frequencies.

In general, for noise measurements, precautions also should be taken to ensure that external noise sources, such as excess noise in carbon resistors or microphonics in electrolytic capacitors, are minimized. Care should also be taken to ensure that hum is not present in the measurement apparatus. Shielding and shock mounting are important considerations when making low-level measurements.

11.10d. General Considerations. Before discussing the application of junction transistors in low-noise amplifiers, it is desirable to discuss the noise sources which predominate in the transistor.

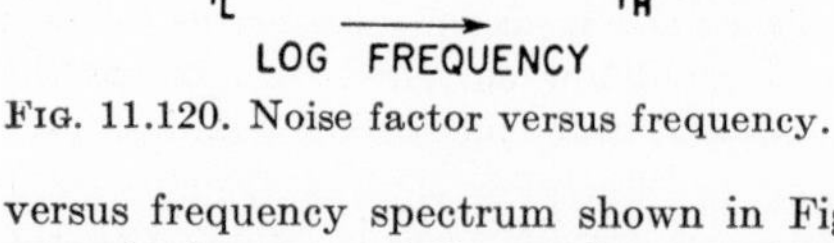

FIG. 11.120. Noise factor versus frequency.

There are two types of noise spectra present in junction devices. These are white noise, which has a flat frequency spectrum, and low-frequency flicker noise, which is frequency dependent, the noise power being approximately inversely proportional to the frequency. Flicker noise, therefore, follows the "1/f law." Their combination results in the NF versus frequency spectrum shown in Fig. 11.120. Noise factor rises at higher frequencies because of the predominance of noise attributed to the collector junction.

White noise consists of thermal (or Johnson) noise and shot noise. The noise powers arising from these terms are independent of frequency, at least for the frequencies here involved, and are directly proportional to the noise bandwidth of the circuit. As previously discussed,

$$\overline{V_T^2} = 4kTBR_g$$

or the thermal-noise component, while the shot-noise component is

$$\overline{I_n^2} = 2qI_D B$$

where q = electronic charge = 1.6×10^{-19} coulomb

I_D = equivalent direct saturated diode current

Shot noise always is present owing to the corpuscular nature of current flow† and together with thermal noise establishes a lower limit on noise performance.

The shot-noise components in a junction transistor may be attributed to two correlated generators,[29] one at the emitter and one at the collector. An independent thermal-noise generator in the base lead accounts for the noise arising from the base resistance. The transistor equivalent circuit for the white-noise components is represented by Fig. 11.121.

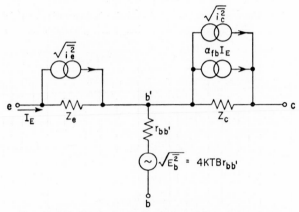

Fig. 11.121. Equivalent circuit for white-noise sources.

When dealing with low-noise circuits, the assumption that the emitter and collector noise generators are independent does not introduce a large error and leads to simplified expressions for the shot-noise generators[29] of germanium transistors†† of

$$\overline{i_e^2} = 2qI_E B$$

and
$$\overline{i_c^2} = 2qB[I_E(\alpha_0 - |\alpha_{fb}|^2) + I_{co}]$$

$$= 2qB\left[I_c\left(1 - \frac{|\alpha_{fb}|^2}{\alpha_0}\right) + \frac{|\alpha_{fb}|^2}{\alpha_0} I_{co} \right]$$

where I_E is the direct emitter current, I_c is the direct collector current, I_{co} is the reverse collector-to-base current with the emitter open-circuited, and α_{fb} is the short-circuit common-base current gain h_{fb}. α is the low frequency α_{fb} (or h_{fbo}).

An approximate expression for the NF of the common-base and common-emitter connections may be obtained from the equivalent circuit shown in Fig. 11.121.[31]

† With silicon junction devices, considerable recombination and generation of carriers occur in the depletion region compared with germanium devices. This additional recombination current leads to a higher theoretical value of shot noise for silicon transistors[30] at low current densities compared with germanium units.

†† For silicon transistors, a more accurate expression[38] for the collector shot noise generator is $I_E\left(H_{FB} + |h_{fb}|^2 - \dfrac{2|h_{fb}|^2 H_{FB}}{h_{fbo}} \right)$ where H_{FB} is the large signal common-base current gain defined on page 12-23.

Operating from a source resistance of R_g, the NF is

$$F = 1 + \frac{r_{ob'}}{R_g} + \frac{r_e}{2R_g} + \frac{(1 - \alpha_0)[R_g + r_{bb'} + r_e]^2 \left[1 + \left(\dfrac{f}{\sqrt{1 - \alpha_0 f_{ab}}} \right)^2 \right]}{2\alpha_0 r_e R_g}$$

The last term is the contribution of shot noise from the collector junction. This term increases with frequency and causes the NF to rise at about a 6 db/octave slope above f_H (Fig. 11.120). The upper noise corner frequency, f_H, may be obtained from the previous expression for NF by equating the four frequency-independent terms with the frequency-dependent term.[39] The result is

$$f_H = f_{ab} \sqrt{\alpha_0 r_e \frac{(2R_g + 2r_{bb'} + r_e)}{(R_g + r_e + r_{bb'})} + (1 - \alpha_0)}$$

In order to reduce the contributions of shot noise in low-noise transistor amplifiers, it is important to use high-gain transistors, i.e., having small values of $1 - \alpha_0$, with

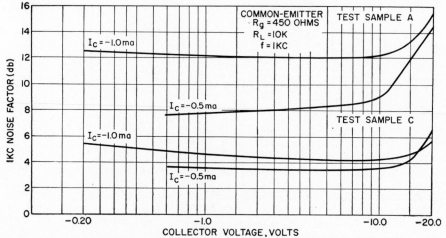

Fig. 11.122. Noise factor versus collector voltage.

high cutoff frequencies f_{ab}. This also leads to good noise figures at higher frequencies. For reduced contributions from the base-circuit noise generator, $r_{bb'}$ should be small. These requirements are similar to those of a transistor selected for high-gain wideband amplification.

Although the $1/f$ or flicker-noise components cannot be formulated exactly, they are attributable to surface phenomena of the device.[32] By careful surface treatment, it is possible to minimize the noise from these sources. The flicker components arise from two independent sources—$1/f$ surface noise and $1/f$ leakage noise. The surface noise has been associated with correlated generation of hole-electron pairs in the device which appears to modulate the series resistances of the junctions. Leakage noise is associated with the leakage resistance across a junction. This noise results from a breakdown of the electric field at the junction and is important only for reverse-biased diodes (collector junction), while surface noise is associated with both junctions.

The leakage-noise component is strongly dependent on the leakage current and can be minimized by selecting transistors with low leakage currents. Since the leakage current increases proportionally with collector voltage, the associated noise can be reduced by operating at low collector voltages. Leakage noise was one of the main causes of the high NF's measured in early transistors, and large reductions in noise resulted when the transistors were operated at low collector voltages. For most modern low-noise t ansistors, however, leakage noise is not excessive and NF is essentially independent of the collector voltage (Fig. 11.122).

The surface-noise component is very dependent on the emitter current and can be minimized by operating at low currents. Units which are designed for low-noise operation should have small flicker-noise components. This means that the frequency f_L (Fig. 11.120), at which the noise will be predominantly thermal and shot, can be quite low. For selected units, f_L can be below a few hundred cycles with the use of low emitter currents.

11.10e. Requirements for Low-noise Operation. The question now arises as to what is the best configuration, operating point, and source impedance to use in a low-noise transistor amplifier. Below the alpha-cutoff frequency it can be shown that the NF will be approximately the same for all three configurations operating from the same

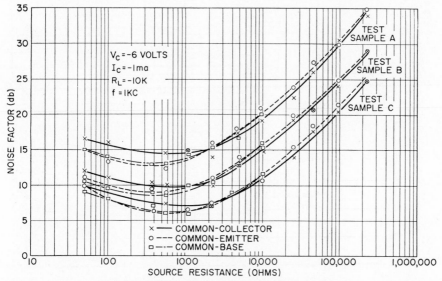

Fig. 11.123. Noise factor versus source resistance.

source impedance, irrespective of the differences in input impedance for these connections[33] (Fig. 11.123). The use of feedback, per se, has very little effect on the NF of an input stage. As long as sufficient gain can be achieved in the first stage of a low-noise amplifier, the noise contributions from succeeding stages can be neglected. Since the source impedance yielding the minimum NF is approximately the same as that which provides maximum common-emitter gain, the common-emitter configuration usually is preferable.

When plotted as a function of source resistance, the NF will have a broad minimum. Under the operating conditions shown in Fig. 11.124, the optimum source resistance for a transistor audio amplifier will be in the neighborhood of 500 to 1,000 ohms. When the $1/f$ flicker-noise components are small, the optimum source impedance will be independent of whether a narrow-band 1,000-cycle measurement or a wideband measurement is made. If the transistors measured in Fig. 11.124 had only white-noise sources, the narrow-band and wideband curves would be coincident.

Noise figure is relatively independent of collector voltage below about 5 to 10 volts in a good transistor. With a collector voltage higher than this, the NF may rise sharply with a further increase in collector voltage as is shown in Fig. 11.122. This sharp rise can be attributed to the effect of $1/f$ leakage noise becoming an important factor, as discussed in Sec. 11.10d. Low-noise units, therefore, should have low leakage currents in order to minimize the effect of collector voltage on NF.

As discussed in Sec. 11.10d, 1/f surface noise can be minimized by operating the transistor at low currents.   Similarly, the shot-noise components can be reduced by lowering the emitter current.   The result is that the NF decreases with decreasing current as shown in Fig. 11.125.   Fonger[34] has shown theoretically that for a transistor dominated by white noise, the optimum source resistance is 3,000 ohms with

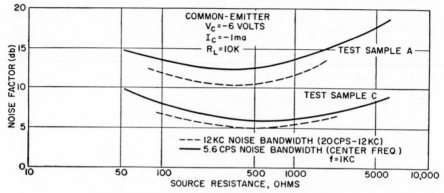

FIG. 11.124. Noise factor versus source resistance.

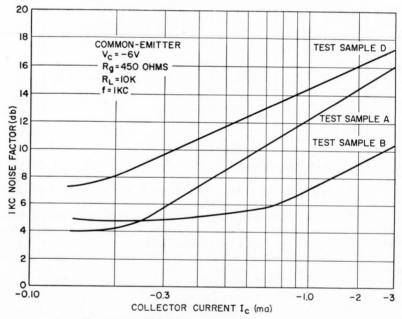

FIG. 11.125. Noise factor versus collector current.

the optimum emitter current being 100 μa, while for a transistor dominated by 1/f surface noise, the optimum source resistance is 1,000 ohms with an optimum emitter current of 30 μa.   Under these operating conditions NF's in the order of 1 to 2 db are obtainable.

Usually, however, an emitter current of 100 to 200 μa is a practical lower limit, since the current gain generally falls off at lower currents and therefore the relative contributions of the output noise sources will increase, resulting in an increase in NF at extremely low emitter currents. In addition, it is difficult to stabilize the emitter current at extremely low values. If the current is not well stabilized, the noise may vary with temperature. (The noise also may vary with temperature when the leakage noise is prominent.[35])

It should be noted that the optimum source impedance is somewhat a function of emitter current. As emitter current is decreased, the optimum source impedance will increase slightly. When it is necessary to operate from a high source impedance,

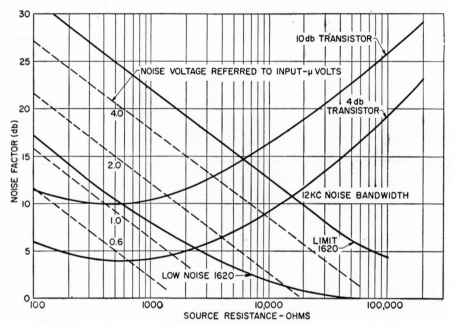

Fig. 11.126. Comparison of transistor and tube noise characteristics. Noise factor versus source resistance.

best noise performance ideally can be obtained at extremely low emitter currents. In general, the NF measured with a high source impedance will be greater than the minimum NF obtainable for a transistor operated from an optimum source resistance of about 1,000 ohms.

In case of tubes used at audio frequencies, high source impedances are required to obtain low noise figures. For this reason input transformers are generally used with tubes when the source impedance is low. As shown in Fig. 11.126, very low noise figures can be obtained with low-noise vacuum tubes if the source impedance is high. However, if the source impedance is low, as in a tape playback head when an input transformer is not used, low-noise junction transistors will outperform vacuum tubes. Additionally, hum and microphonic noise will not be present in low-noise transistor amplifiers. With present technology, low-noise transistors are available with NF's of 4 db or less.

11.10f. Noise Performance with a Reactive Source. If the source impedance is not a pure resistance, the noise performance of a circuit will be a function of frequency. When an amplifier is driven from a complex impedance, it is generally more convenient to express the performance of the circuit in terms of signal-to-noise ratio at the output rather than in terms of noise figure.   If the source impedance is a pure reactance, the concept of noise figure is meaningless.

To determine the output signal-to-noise ratio of an amplifier driven from a reactive source, a knowledge of the source voltage at various frequencies, as well as the amplifier frequency response, will be required.   The total noise power at the output depends upon the properties of the first-stage transistor (provided that sufficient gain is available so that second-stage noise is negligible) and the frequency response of the amplifier, in addition to the amplified resistive noises in the system.   Since the signal output is frequency-dependent, spot signal-to-noise measurements can be made at various frequencies.

If low-noise transistors are used (those having only white-noise sources) in the input stage, the analysis of Middlebrook[36] can be used to determine the optimum source

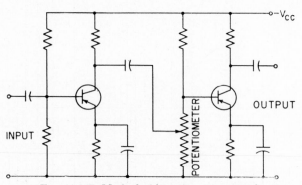

Fig. 11.127. Method of inserting gain control.

reactance to give the best signal-to-noise ratio for the amplifier.   When this analysis is used, the amplifier gain characteristics and frequency response (including equalization), as well as the first-stage transistor noise properties, will determine the optimum reactance.

For an amplifier driven from an inductive source, such as a tape head, the source inductance which will give the best over-all signal-to-noise ratio generally will have a rather broad optimum value.   In the vicinity of the optimum inductance, a change of 10 to 1 in inductance may not change the output signal-to-noise ratio by more than a few decibels.   For many audio circuits, the optimum source inductance generally will be between 50 and 500 mh, the exact value depending upon the factors previously discussed.

11.11. Miscellaneous Circuits.   *11.11a. Gain Controls.*   In transistor amplifiers it is often convenient to use the volume control in a manner that is the reverse of that commonly used in vacuum-tube amplifiers.   As shown in Fig. 11.127, the movable element of the potentiometer is connected to the preceding stage.   Thus when the gain is changed, the d-c resistance from base to ground is maintained constant and there is no change in bias of the stage.   Since the output resistance of the preceding stage is generally much higher than either the resistance of the potentiometer or the transistor input, the frequency response of the two stages is practically independent of the gain-control setting.   In the case of a transistor, as with pentode tubes, the maximum input signal that can be handled by a stage without distortion is almost independent of the collector load.   Thus the gain-control circuit shown in Fig. 11.127 is a low-distortion circuit.   Other gain-control circuits use a volume control connected in the usual fashion, a shunt variable resistor to ground, a series variable resistor, or a variable resistor in a feedback circuit.

11.11b. Automatic Gain Control. It is necessary to have a variable-gain stage in certain types of amplifiers such as limiters or compressors. One can change the gain of a transistor amplifier stage by changing the collector voltage or by changing the base current. All the *h* parameters change with operating point as can be seen from Figs. 11.15 and 11.16. However, h_{fe} changes very little, while h_{re} and h_{oe} have little effect on the gain of the stage. The factor that gives the best gain-control characteristic is the variation of h_{ie} with change in base-current bias. If a common-emitter stage is

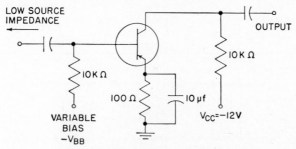

FIG. 11.128. Variable-gain stage.

operated from a low-impedance source, the input or base current is inversely proportional to the input resistance of the stage. The input resistance is primarily a function of h_{ie} which can be controlled by base bias. Thus the stage shown in Fig. 11.128 can vary the gain by 20 db. The control characteristic is shown in Fig. 11.129.

As is the case with vacuum-tube variable-gain stages, a change in the d-c operating point of the stage is necessary. If the gain is changed rapidly, components of this control current are introduced into the signal channel. These control currents or the "thump" can be reduced from 20 to 30 db by operating balanced variable-gain stages.

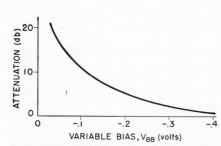

FIG. 11.129. Control characteristic for stage in Fig. 11.128.

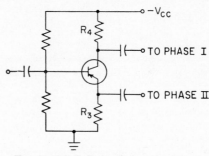

FIG. 11.130. Split-load phase inverter.

With the increasing availability of tetrodes, field-effect transistors, and other new types of semiconductor devices, improved methods of gain reduction may be possible.

11.11c. Phase Inverters. The split-load phase inverter shown in Fig. 11.130 will furnish a balanced push-pull signal if the loads are equal. It has a slight unbalance in output voltage because the emitter current is equal to the collector current plus the base current. However, this can be corrected by making R_4 slightly larger than R_3. If the phase inverter is to drive a class B stage, the drive is unequal because the input impedance of a class B stage varies considerably from one half cycle to the next. A change in loading on phase I affects only phase I, while a change in loading on phase II affects both outputs, since the loading on phase II is part of the emitter feedback circuit. Solutions to this problem are to make the driving impedance of the class B stage constant, make R_3 and R_4 smaller, or add resistances in series with the two connections to the class B stage and thereby decouple it.

The common-emitter phase inverter is shown in Fig. 11.131. The signal input to the base of the first transistor causes emitter current to flow in R_1. The voltage developed across this resistor drives the second transistor in the opposite phase. As a

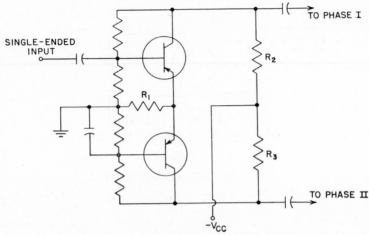

Fig. 11.131. Common-emitter phase inverter.

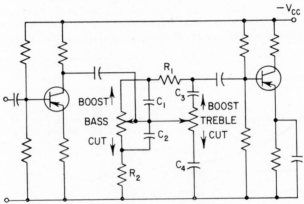

Fig. 11.132. Tone-control circuit.

result, the emitter current of the second transistor tends to cancel the voltage developed across R_1 by the emitter current of the first transistor. Since the gain of the second transistor is large, the emitter current of the first transistor need be only slightly larger than that of the second in order to develop sufficient voltage to obtain a phase-inverted signal almost equal to the direct signal. As in the case of the split-load phase inverter, special precautions must be taken when driving a class B stage.

11.11d. Tone Controls. Tone controls are often used in low-frequency amplifiers to provide frequency-selective amplification in a manually controllable manner. Normally, resistance-capacitance networks are employed to obtain the desired characteristics, although inductive networks can be used. Tone controls can be obtained by incorporating frequency-selective circuits in feedback loops or in the coupling networks of an amplifier. In general, tone controls are employed in coupling networks, since their performance is less dependent upon the transistor parameters. In most cases, the insertion of tone controls will result in a loss in over-all amplifier gain which must be made up by an additional stage of amplification. It is important that the tone controls be incorporated at a point in the amplifier which operates at a high enough signal level so as not to introduce a significant contribution to the over-all noise of the amplifier.

One type of tone control is shown in Fig. 11.132.[37] This circuit results in frequency-selective current division which allows independent control of both bass and treble "boost" and "cut." The network on the left provides a "low-frequency" (bass) control, and the series network on the right provides a "high-frequency" (treble) control. The time constants R_1C_1 and R_2C_2 are generally made equal in order to obtain a flat amplification position for the bass network. Similarly, R_1C_3 and R_2C_4 are generally made equal in order to obtain a flat position for the treble network. In a properly designed circuit, as much as 15 db "boost" and "cut" may be obtained at the extreme settings of the controls.

REFERENCES

1. Guillemin, E. A.: "Communication Networks," vol. 2, p. 134, John Wiley & Sons, Inc., New York, 1935.
2. Giacoletto, L. J.: Terminology and Equations for Linear Active Four-terminal Networks Including Transistors, *RCA Rev.*, vol. 14, no. 1, pp. 28–45, March, 1953.
3. Giacoletto, L. J.: Equipments for Measuring Junction Transistor Admittance Parameters for a Wide Range of Frequencies, *RCA Rev.*, vol. 14, no. 2, pp. 269–296, June, 1953.
4. Giacoletto, L. J.: Study of P-N-P Alloy Junction Transistor from D-C through Medium Frequencies, *RCA Rev.*, vol. 15, no. 5, pp. 506–562, December, 1954.
5. Standards on Transducers: Definitions of Terms, 1951, *Proc. IRE*, vol. 39, no. 8, pp. 897–899, August, 1951.
6. Terman, F. E.: "Radio Engineers' Handbook," p. 354, McGraw-Hill Book Company, Inc., New York, 1943.
7. Bruun, G.: Common-emitter Transistor Video Amplifiers, *Proc. IRE*, vol. 44, no. 11, pp. 1561–1572, November, 1956.
8. Gates, R. F., and R. A. Johnson: The Measurement of Thermal Resistance, *Semiconductor Prod.*, vol. 2, no. 7, pp. 21–26, July, 1959.
9. Hangstefer, J. B., and L. H. Dixon, Jr.: How to Design for Transistor Reliability I, *Electronic Equipment Eng.*, pp. 91–94, March, 1959.
10. Schauwecker, H. E.: Understanding Transistor Voltage Breakdown, *Electronic Design*, pp. 28–31, July 22, 1959.
11. Reich, H. J.: "Theory and Application of Electron Tubes," chap. 8, McGraw-Hill Book Company, Inc., New York, 1944.
12. Reich, H. J.: "Theory and Application of Electron Tubes," chap. 9, McGraw-Hill Book Company, Inc., New York, 1944.
13. Terman, F. E.: "Radio Engineers' Handbook," p. 384, McGraw-Hill Book Company, Inc., New York, 1943.
14. Baker, L.: "Design of Class B Amplifiers Using Imperfect Devices," Master's Thesis, Moore School of Electrical Engineering, University of Pennsylvania, 1959.
15. Jones, D. D., and R. A. Hilbourne: "Transistor A.F. Amplifiers," chap. 4, Philosophical Library, Inc., New York, 1957.
16. Aronson, A.: Transistor Audio Amplifiers, in "Transistors I," pp. 515–535, RCA Laboratories, Princeton, N.J., 1956.
17. Herscher, M. B.: Designing Transistor A-F Power Amplifiers, *Electronics*, vol. 31, no. 15, pp. 96–99, Apr. 11, 1958.
18. Sziklai, G. C.: Symmetrical Properties of Transistors and Their Applications, *Proc. IRE*, vol. 41, no. 6, pp. 717–724, June, 1953.
19. Lohman, R. D.: Complementary Symmetry Transistor Circuits, *Electronics*, vol. 26, no. 9, pp. 140–143, September, 1953.
20. Lin, H. C.: Quasi-complementary Transistor Amplifier, *Electronics*, pp. 173–175, September, 1956.
21. Terman, F. E.: "Radio Engineers' Handbook," p. 226, McGraw-Hill Book Company, Inc., New York, 1943.

22. Bode, H. W.: "Network Analysis and Feedback Amplifier Design," p. 31, D. Van Nostrand Company, Inc., Princeton, N.J., 1945.
23. Lin, H. C., and A. A. Barco: Temperature Effects in Circuits Using Junction Transistors, in "Transistors I," pp. 369–402, RCA Laboratories, Princeton, N.J., 1956.
24. Shea, R. F. (ed.): "Principles of Transistor Circuits," John Wiley & Sons, Inc., New York, 1953.
25. Hall, D. B.: Biasing Network Design for Silicon Tetrode Transistors, *Elec. Design News*, April, 1959.
26. Shea, R. F.: Transistor Operation: Stabilization of Operating Points, *Proc. IRE*, vol. 40, pp. 1435–1437, November, 1952.
27. Lin, H. C.: Thermal Stability of Junction Transistors and Its Effect on Maximum Power Dissipation, *Trans. IRE*, Professional Group on Circuit Theory, vol. CT-4, no. 3, pp. 202–210, September, 1957.
28. Schmeltzer, R. A.: Stabilization of Transistor Gain over Wide Temperature Ranges, *RCA Rev.*, vol. 20, no. 2, pp. 284–292, June, 1959.
29. Van der Ziel, A.: Noise in Junction Transistors, *Proc. IRE*, vol. 46, no. 6, pp. 1019–1038, June, 1958.
30. Schneider, B., and M. J. O. Strutt: Theory and Experiments on Shot Noise in Silicon P-N Junction Diodes and Transistors, *Proc. IRE*, vol. 47, no. 4, pp. 546–554, April, 1959.
31. Nielsen, E. G.: Behavior of Noise Figure in Junction Transistors, *Proc. IRE*, vol. 45, no. 7, pp. 957–963, July, 1957.
32. Giacoletto, L. J.: The Noise Factor of Junction Transistors, in "Transistors I," pp. 296–308, RCA Laboratories, Princeton, N.J., 1956.
33. Bargellini, P. L., and M. B. Herscher: Investigations of Noise in Audio Frequency Amplifiers Using Junction Transistors, *Proc. IRE*, vol. 43, no. 2, pp. 217–226, February, 1955.
34. Fonger, W. H.: Noise in Transistors, in "Noise in Electron Devices," pp. 344–406, Technology Press, MIT, Cambridge, Mass., 1959.
35. Fonger, W. H.: A Determination of 1/F Noise Sources in Semiconductor Diodes and Triodes, in "Transistors I," pp. 239–295, RCA Laboratories, Princeton, N.J., 1956.
36. Middlebrook, R. D.: Optimum Noise Performance of Transistor Input Circuits, *Semiconductor Prod.*, vol. 1, no. 4, pp. 14–20, July–August, 1958.
37. Lo, A. W., R. O. Endres, J. Zawels, F. D. Waldhauer, and C. C. Cheng: "Transistor Electronics," pp. 187–189, Prentice-Hall, Inc., Englewood Cliffs, N.J., 1955.
38. Chenette, E. R.: Frequency Dependence of the Noise and Current Amplification Factor of Silicon Transistors, *Proc. IRE*, vol. 48, no. 1, pp. 111–112, January, 1960.
39. Cooke, H. F.: Transistor Upper Noise Corner Frequency, *Proc. IRE*, vol. 49, no. 3, p. 648, March, 1961.

Section 12

HIGH-FREQUENCY AND VIDEO AMPLIFICATION

James B. Angell

Philco Corporation, Philadelphia, Pa.†

† Now at Stanford University, Stanford, Calif.

Video Amplifiers

Bandpass Amplifiers

  The high-frequency capabilities of transistors are determined by various physical phenomena which usually are not important at low frequencies.   The most significant of the high-frequency factors generally include (1) the depletion-layer capacitances, (2) the transit time of the useful charge carriers through the active transistor regions, (3) series impedances in the connections to the active transistor regions, and (4) capacitances in the enclosing structure.   These factors frequently demand sophisticated circuit techniques for minimizing their effects and optimizing transistor performance.

  This section will treat the application of transistors to bandpass and video amplifiers by first relating the various important phenomena to useful high-frequency equivalent-circuit representations of the transistor.   Next, suitable circuits for the respective applications will be described, together with their expected performance.

TRANSISTOR HIGH-FREQUENCY PARAMETERS

  12.1. Transit Time.   There is a finite time delay between an incremental change in injected minority-carrier current from the emitter of a transistor and the corresponding change in collector current.   This delay results primarily from the time required for carriers to traverse the base region.   However, in some transistor structures the finite time which carriers take to move through the collector depletion layer also contributes to the time delay; this contribution is particularly important in certain modern high-frequency transistor structures in which the base transit times have been reduced to impressively small values.

  In addition to the above time delays, there is also dispersion in the transit times of individual carriers, particularly in the transit through the base. This dispersion gives rise to a decrease in current gain as frequency increases.

12.1a. Base Transit Time. The transit time through the base and the dispersion thereof can be accounted for in the base transport factor β. This factor is defined as the ratio of the hole current I_{pc} (in a PNP transistor) passing from the base region into the collector depletion layer to the injected hole current I_{pe} entering the base region from the emitter, with the internal collector-to-base voltage held constant. Thus,

$$\beta = \frac{I_{pc}}{I_{pe}}\bigg|_{V_{c'b'}=0} \tag{12.1}$$

For a homogeneous-base transistor with parallel junctions, the frequency dependence of the base transport factor is given by[1]

$$\beta = \text{sech} \left[\left(\frac{W}{L_B}\right) + j\omega \frac{W^2}{D_B} \right]^{\frac{1}{2}}$$
$$\approx \beta_0 \, \text{sech} \, (j\omega t_D)^{\frac{1}{2}} \tag{12.2}$$

where t_D is the minority-carrier diffusion time across the base region (compare Sec. 4.5a). A useful approximation for this expression is

$$\beta = \beta_0 \frac{e^{-j0.22(f/f_\beta)}}{1 + j(f/f_\beta)} \tag{12.3}$$

where f_β is the frequency where $|\beta| = \beta_0/\sqrt{2}$. In certain cases where rough computational accuracy suffices, the transport factor can be approximated by

$$\beta = \frac{\beta_0}{1 + j(f/f_\beta)} \tag{12.4}$$

Figure 12.1 contains two sets of plots comparing Eqs. (12.2), (12.3), and (12.4). The plots of amplitude versus normalized frequency in Fig. 12.1a show that the magnitudes given by the three expressions are indistinguishable for $f < 2f_\beta$. The polar plots in Fig. 12.1b show that the phase of β given by Eqs. (12.2) and (12.3) agrees adequately over the entire range whereas the phase given by Eq. (12.4) is consistently low by 22 per cent. In many computations of circuit performance, the only significant factors containing β are of the form $1 - \beta$; Fig. 12.1b shows that the use of Eq. (12.4) would lead to errors of 22 per cent in these factors.

In a graded-base transistor, the impurity distribution within the base region provides a built-in electric field which, in most cases, decreases the transit time from emitter to collector for a given base width.[2] In these cases, the percentage reduction in the dispersion of transit times is even greater than the percentage reduction in average transit time. Therefore, the cutoff frequency f_β is increased in the graded-base transistor even more than the frequency corresponding to any given phase lag of β. Conversely, the phase lag for any given amplitude ratio $|\beta|/\beta_0$ is greater in a graded-base transistor than in a homogeneous-base transistor. This additional phase lag in β can be included mathematically, to a good approximation, by modifying Eq. (12.3) to the form[3]

$$\beta \approx \beta_0 \frac{e^{-j\nu(f/f_\beta)}}{1 + j(f/f_\beta)} \tag{12.5}$$

where ν is a constant usually bounded by $0.4 < \nu < 1.2$ for graded-base transistors. The validity of Eq. (12.5) as a reasonable approximation to more exact and far more complex expressions is shown by Fig. 12.2, where Eq. (12.5) is compared with a more exact representation for β for various values of the excess phase factor ν.

The excess phase factor ν can be directly related to the potential difference ΔV between the emitter side and the collector side of the base region that results from

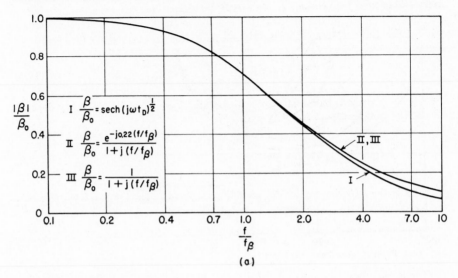

(a)

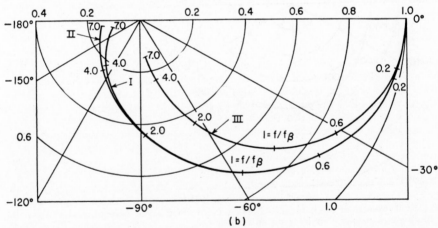

(b)

Fig. 12.1. (a) Normalized magnitude of base transport factor vs. frequency. (b) Polar plot of base transport factor.

the impurity density gradient in the base. To a good approximation, this factor is given by[4]

$$\nu = 0.22 + 0.098 \frac{q}{kT} \Delta V \qquad \text{radians} \qquad (12.6)$$

An example of the excess phase which may be encountered in the common-base forward current-transfer ratio of a high-frequency graded-base transistor is shown in Fig. 12.3, together with an appropriate plot of Eq. (12.5).[5]

It is possible to account for the finite carrier transit time through the base on the basis of charge stored in the base.[6] With this approach a mean transit time T_m can be defined as the ratio of minority-carrier charge stored in the base region to the emitter current.[7] This concept is useful in deriving certain equivalent-circuit representations which contain no frequency-dependent generators.†

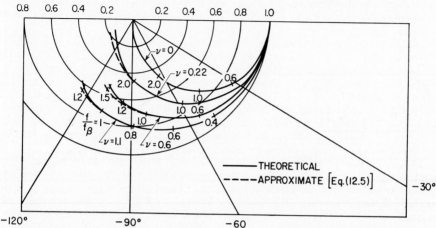

FIG. 12.2. Polar plots of base transport factor. (*Courtesy of Electronic and Radio Engineer.*)

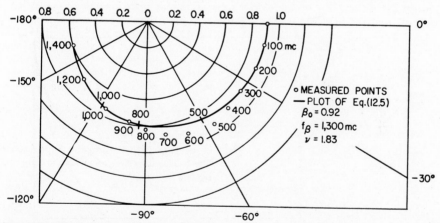

FIG. 12.3. Measured common-base short-circuit forward current-transfer ratio, $-h_{fb}$, for experimental coaxial microalloy diffused transistor.

12.1b. Depletion-layer Transit Time. A charge carrier entering the collector depletion layer from the base moves away from the base with roughly constant velocity (the terminal velocity of that carrier type in the semiconductor) because of the high electric field within the depletion layer. This motion gives rise to a current pulse of constant amplitude in the collector, which persists for the time T that the charge carrier takes to traverse the depletion layer.

† The stored-charge method of analysis also leads to the interesting conclusion that minimum transit time and maximum cutoff frequency f_β, for a given minimum β_0 and a given minimum collector reach-through voltage, are obtained with a base impurity distribution that provides a retarding electric field.[7]

For the intrinsic transistor (neglecting the current through C_c) without avalanche, one can write[8]

$$\frac{I_c}{I_{pc}} = \frac{1 - e^{-j\omega T}}{j\omega T} \tag{12.7}$$

to account for the finite transit time through the collector depletion layer. This relation should be combined with Eq. (12.5) or one of its simplified forms to relate collector current to injected current from the emitter.

It is only recently that transistor structures have been improved to the point where barrier transit time is important. In homogeneous-base structures, the base region is normally so thick and the diffusion velocity so slow that barrier transit time is negligible. However, graded-base structures can be built with base thicknesses less than 0.05×10^{-3} in. and with sufficient built-in electric field to give a drift velocity more than one-tenth terminal velocity.[9,10] In addition, certain of these structures employ a high-resistivity collector body to reduce C_c, which results in a depletion layer many times thicker than the base region. In some of these cases the barrier transit time may actually exceed the base transit time.

12.2. Depletion-layer Transition Capacitances. Both the emitter transition capacitance C_{Te} and the collector transition capacitance C_{Tc} or C_c are important factors in high-frequency transistor operation. These capacitances are not basic to the amplifying properties of a transistor in that they have no direct relation to minority-carrier flow in the base region. Nevertheless, they cannot be completely circumvented by either device designers or circuit designers.

12.2a. Emitter Transition Capacitance. This capacitance C_{Te} affects high-frequency performance in two principal ways: It lowers input impedance and it robs current from the injecting emitter. Mathematically, these effects can be approximated rather simply, with precision adequate for most circuit computations.

The emitter-to-base diffusion admittance, y_{pe} in a PNP transistor, can normally be approximated by a conductance

$$g_{pe} = \frac{1}{r_e'} \approx \frac{qI_E}{kT} = \frac{I_E}{0.027} \tag{12.8}$$

in parallel with a diffusion capacitance C_{De}. The diffusion capacitance is given by the approximation

$$C_{De} = \frac{M}{2\pi f_T r_e'} \tag{12.9}$$

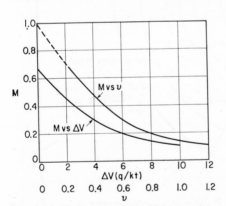

Fig. 12.4. Multiplying factor M for emitter transition capacitance of graded-base transistors versus excess phase factor ν and emitter-to-collector potential difference due to drift field.

where M is a constant depending on the built-in field resulting from the doping gradient.[4] M is given in Fig. 12.4 as a function of the built-in potential difference and the excess phase factor. The characteristic frequency f_T is that at which $|h_{fe}| = 1$, or Re $(\alpha) \approx \frac{1}{2}$. The total emitter-to-base admittance is then

$$y_{e'b'} = \frac{1}{r_e'} + j\omega(C_{De} + C_{Te}) \tag{12.10}$$

and the fraction of the emitter current which appears as useful injected current (neglecting injection from the base into the emitter) is

$$\frac{I_{pe}}{I_e} = \left| \frac{1 + j\omega r_e' C_{De}}{1 + j\omega r_e' (C_{De} + C_{Te})} \right| \tag{12.11}$$

The emitter transition capacitance is generally much larger than the collector capacitance, even though the emitter is smaller. For amplifier service, the emitter is forward-biased, yielding a narrow depletion layer and a large capacitance. Second, in graded-base transistors, the resistivities of both the emitter region and the base region adjacent to the emitter are very low and the capacitance per unit area correspondingly great.

C_{Te} is relatively independent of forward emitter current, because the junction voltage varies only slightly with forward current. The other components of the emitter conductance vary directly with emitter current. Therefore, the emitter transition capacitance is particularly important at low bias currents, and its effect

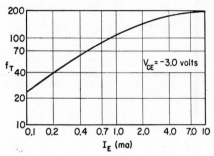

FIG. 12.5. f_T versus I_E for 2N501A.

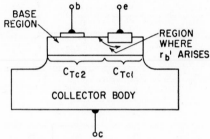

FIG. 12.6. Cross-section sketch of a diffused-base (mesa) transistor.

can be decreased by increasing the current through the transistor. In modern high-frequency transistors, which are useful up to and within the ultra-high-frequency spectrum, bias currents of at least 1 to 2 ma are needed to overcome most of the handicap wrought by C_{Te}, which is of the order of 5 to 20 pf in such transistors.

The plot of f_T in megacycles versus bias point shown in Fig. 12.5 illustrates the effect of C_{Te} at low currents.

12.2b. Collector Transition Capacitance. This capacitance, usually called simply "collector capacitance" and designated by C_{Tc} or C_c, contributes both to the output admittance and to the feedback from output to input at high frequencies. Although it is generally much smaller than C_{Te}, it can affect performance just as much, because the impedance level of the collector junction and its associated circuitry is much higher than that of the emitter.

The principal difficulty which the circuit engineer has in dealing with collector capacitance stems from the fact that it is not available via direct external connections. Consequently, it cannot be tuned out with an inductance but must be compensated in a less direct manner.

The collector capacitance is distributed over the entire area of the collector junction. Fortunately, for the large number of transistors having a geometry exemplified by alloy-junction units, it is generally possible to treat the collector capacitance as a single lumped capacitance between the base and collector terminals of the intrinsic transistor (b' and c', respectively). However, there are two geometries, both important in the high-frequency area, where this approximation does not suffice.[11] First is the diffused-base (mesa) structure, illustrated in cross section in Fig. 12.6. In this case, only that portion C_{Tc1} of the entire junction capacitance contributes to the internal, inaccessible feedback; with the transistor base grounded, only the high-frequency current flowing through this portion of the capacitance will affect the emitter potential. The remainder of the capacitance C_{Tc2} appears as a capacitance directly accessible to the base terminal, as shown in the equivalent-circuit model in Fig. 12.7.[12] The second important exception is the high-frequency tetrode transistor, which is usually formed from the grown-junction geometry, as sketched in Fig. 12.8. In this structure the high-frequency current flowing through the collector capacitance encounters an impedance to flow within the base, stemming from the thinness, resistivity, and relatively large extent of the base region. Thus, the base side of the

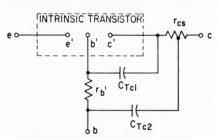

FIG. 12.7. Equivalent-circuit model of a diffused-base transistor.

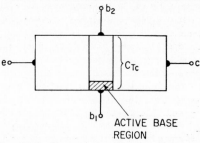

FIG. 12.8. Cross-section sketch of a grown tetrode transistor.

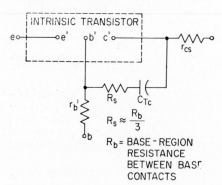

FIG. 12.9. Equivalent-circuit model of a tetrode transistor.

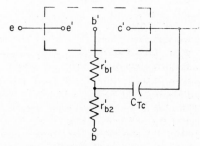

FIG. 12.10. Equivalent-circuit model of an alloy-junction transistor.

collector depletion layer is not an equipotential surface. The distributed nature of this phenomenon can be approximated in the circuit model shown in Fig. 12.9 by forcing the current that flows through the collector capacitance to flow also through a resistance $R_s = R_b/3$, where R_b is the ohmic resistance between base terminals.

12.3. Lead Impedance. In a practical transistor structure the three or more current paths from the active region to the external connections include both semiconductor regions and leads of finite length. Hence, both series resistance and inductance may be present in significant quantity.

12.3a. Base Resistance. Usually the most important series impedance is the base resistance, sometimes called the base spreading resistance, which is designated r_b' or r_{bs}. The only high-frequency structure in which it is of other than primary importance is the tetrode transistor, which was developed specifically to minimize r_b'. In other structures it usually lies in the range from 5 to 500 ohms.

Base spreading resistance arises primarily from the comparatively long semiconductor path between the active transistor region and the ohmic base contact. Frequently this region is very thin, as in surface-barrier transistors. Occasionally the radial flow of base current from the central regions of the active transistor structure to the periphery of the active base region gives rise to a significant voltage drop, which must be accounted for by additional base resistance. An equivalent-circuit model for an alloy-junction transistor may require the use of two components of base resistance, as shown in Fig. 12.10. In this structure the (majority of the) current flowing through the collector capacitance passes only through the resistance r'_{b2}, whereas the base current arising within the active region flows also through r'_{b1}. This separation of the base region into two parts emphasizes the fact that in these structures the collector region is on the average closer to the base contact than is the emitter region.

12.3b. Collector Body Resistance. The collector body resistance, sometimes called collector spreading resistance and designated r'_c or r_{cs}, arises from the finite resistivity of the collector region between the collector depletion layer and the ohmic connection to the collector region. In transistors possessing the geometry of alloy-junction transistors, this resistance is completely negligible for all high-frequency service. However, in grown-junction and diffused-base (mesa) structures it is often important. Its value may reach as high as 200 ohms in certain structures. This resistance is extrinsic to the active transistor region, so that all the collector current, including that component which flows through C_{Tc}, gives rise to losses in r'_c. In small-signal amplifier service, it is only the losses associated with the reactive currents through C_{Tc} that make r'_c important, because r'_c is always low compared with the output impedance of the intrinsic transistor.

12.3c. Emitter Body Resistance. The series resistance r_{es} in the emitter lead is usually negligibly low, because the emitter regions of most transistors possess very low resistivities. Furthermore, all present high-frequency transistors other than grown-junction structures have extremely thin emitter regions.

12.3d. Lead Inductance. Lead inductance will generally exist in all three or more leads to a transistor and is the result of two principal contributors. First is the finite lead length from the external circuit connection up through the transistor header. Second, the length of extremely fine whisker wire used in making one or more connections from the header to the transistor structure may add appreciable inductance. Generally, transistors possessing the alloy-junction geometry usually have the greatest inductance in the emitter and collector leads, while diffused-base (mesa) structures have a large emitter and base inductance.

From a circuit designer's standpoint, the emitter lead inductance is generally most important because of the feedback it causes in the widely used common-emitter connection. For example, a 125-mil length of 25-mil lead wire has an inductance of 2 nanohenrys, giving a reactance of 6 ohms at 500 mc and resonating with a typical graded-base input capacitance of 30 pf at 650 mc. The collector lead inductance is generally of negligible importance, because the collector circuit has a much higher impedance level than the others.

12.4. Equivalent-circuit Representations. Many small-signal equivalent-circuit representations have been proposed for describing the frequency dependence of transistor characteristics. The principal value of such representations is usually to the circuit designer, whose computations and design problems may be greatly simplified by a well-chosen circuit representation. Occasionally these representations are of value to the device designer in that they assist him in deriving figures of merit and optimum transistor designs for certain types of intended service. Only the simple representations find much use, because the complicated forms usually add much more complexity to the computations than accuracy to the answers.

Various viewpoints of transistor operation have been used as a basis for deriving equivalent-circuit representations. Historically, the flow of minority carriers in the base and the influence of emitter and collector voltages on this flow have been used most widely for deriving circuit models. However, the alternative viewpoint, in which the stored minority-carrier charge in the base is considered as the fundamental variable,[6] leads directly to the equivalent-circuit representation that generally is most easily applied to high-frequency circuit analysis.[13] The most used representations can be closely interrelated in the manner described in succeeding paragraphs, so that the choice of which to use in a given case is largely based on analytical or conceptual convenience.

The derivation and meaning of the most widely used equivalent-circuit representations are most readily presented by considering first the representations for the

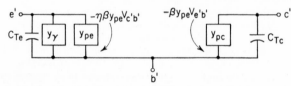

Fig. 12.11. Admittance representation of the intrinsic transistor.

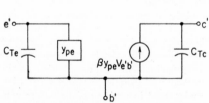

Fig. 12.12. High-frequency approximation of the admittance representation of the intrinsic transistor.

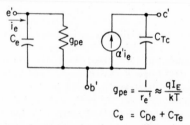

Fig. 12.13. High-frequency hybrid representation of the intrinsic transistor.

intrinsic transistor, consisting of the active base region and the emitter and collector junctions. The extrinsic parameters, such as the series lead impedances and the interlead capacitances, can be added, when significant, to any of the intrinsic transistor representations.

12.4a. The Intrinsic Transistor. If the emitter and collector currents of the intrinsic transistor are considered to be functions of both the emitter-to-base voltage and the collector-to-base voltage, an admittance representation, such as is shown in Fig. 12.11, is suggested.[11] A simplification of Fig. 12.11 that is useful for high-frequency computations is shown in Fig. 12.12. In this approximation, the feedback and output conductance resulting from space-charge widening and the injection from the base into the emitter have been deleted; these quantities are usually relatively unimportant at high frequencies.

A widely used variation of Fig. 12.12 is shown in Fig. 12.13, wherein the transadmittance generator of Fig. 12.12 is replaced by a current transfer generator $\alpha' I_e$. The current transfer ratio α' may differ from the terminal short-circuit forward-current transfer ratio α of the transistor because of the effects of extrinsic parameters, particularly base-lead and collector-lead impedance and capacitances to the emitter. The frequency dependence of α' includes not only the contributions from transit time but also the effects of the emitter transition capacitance and emitter injection efficiency. Fortunately, in most cases a highly satisfactory approximation for α' is obtained by representing it with an expression of the form of Eq. (12.5).

A third form of representation for the intrinsic transistor is the pi equivalent circuit, shown in Fig. 12.14. This representation is generally used with the emitter as the common element to input and output.† For those rough computations where one can approximate α' by

$$\alpha' = \alpha'_0 \frac{1}{1 + jf/f_{\alpha'}} \tag{12.4a}$$

the common-emitter pi equivalent representation for the intrinsic transistor reduces to the simple form shown in Fig. 12.15a. In this representation, none of the element

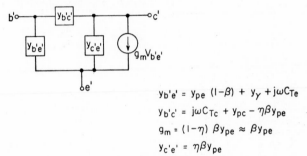

$$y_{b'e'} = y_{pe} (1-\beta) + y_y + j\omega C_{Te}$$
$$y_{b'c'} = j\omega C_{Tc} + y_{pc} - \eta\beta y_{pe}$$
$$g_m = (1-\eta) \beta y_{pe} \approx \beta y_{pe}$$
$$y_{c'e'} = \eta\beta y_{pe}$$

FIG. 12.14. Common-emitter pi representation of the intrinsic transistor.

values vary with frequency; the frequency variation of the forward transfer function is contained in the frequency dependence of the voltage on which the transconductance generator depends. The validity of the simplified representation is particularly apparent from the stored-charge analysis, since the capacitance in the equivalent circuit represents the ability of the base to store minority carriers. The simplified representation shown in Fig. 12.15a is probably the most useful and widely used equivalent circuit for the intrinsic transistor because of its simplicity and reasonably good accuracy.

For transistors in which the excess phase factor ν of β is important, the common-emitter high-frequency pi representation must be complicated slightly. The equivalent-circuit representation shown in Fig. 12.15b includes the first-order effects of excess phase on both input impedance and the transconductance. Frequently the resistance r_ν in series with C_ν can be neglected, in which case Fig. 12.15b reduces to Fig. 12.15a with the modifications that $C_{b'e'} = (1 + \nu)g_{pe}/2\pi f'_\alpha \approx g_{pe}/2\pi f_T$ and $g_m = (\alpha_0/r_e)e^{-j\nu f/f_\alpha}$.

12.4b. The Complete Transistor. The simplest transistor equivalent-circuit representations which characterize a transistor moderately well at high frequencies are obtained by adding base spreading resistance r'_b in the base lead of Figs. 12.13 and 12.15a, giving the results shown in Figs. 12.16 and 12.17, respectively. Figure 12.16 is frequently the simpler of these two for analysis of common-base amplifiers or for

---

† This form of representation was originally proposed by L. J. Giacoletto and H. Johnson in their paper "Considerations of Admittance Representation of Junction Transistors" given at the Transistor Standardization Forum, AIEE Summer Meeting, Atlantic City, N.J., June 17, 1953, and, after the addition of r'_b, is often called the "Giacoletto hybrid-pi equivalent circuit."

computing performance of transistors with considerable excess phase shift ($\nu > 0.2$). Figure 12.17 is the more useful representation for computing common-emitter performance, particularly of video (base-band) amplifiers, in which capacitive feedback is almost negligible.

Various additions to these equivalent-circuit representations are required in certain specific cases. The following examples are the most widely encountered additions.

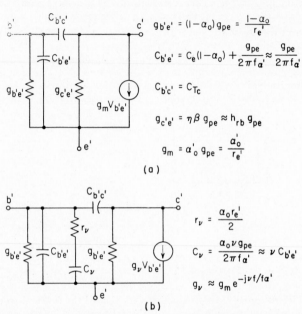

(a)

(b)

Fig. 12.15. Lumped-parameter common-emitter pi representations of the intrinsic transistor. (a) Minimum-phase transistor. (b) Transistor with excess phase.

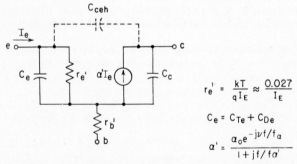

Fig. 12.16. Simplified representation of complete transistor.

1. Series spreading resistance in the collector r_{cs} must be added to the equivalent circuits for diffused-base (mesa) transistors and grown-junction transistors in order to include the significant resistance of the collector body (see Fig. 12.7).

2. Collector-to-base interlead capacitance C_{cbh} must be added to the equivalent circuits of most graded-base transistors, because the internal collector depletion-layer capacitance C_{Tc} of these transistors is so small that the header capacitance is frequently

the major contributor to C_{ob}.   Usually the inactive depletion-layer capacitance, C_{Tc2} in Fig. 12.7, can be lumped into C_{cbh} without serious loss of computational accuracy.

3. The base-lead impedance of grown-junction transistors, particularly triodes, must generally include a capacitance in parallel with r_b' in order to account for the distributed nature of the base resistance of these structures throughout the active transistor region.[14]   In most other transistor geometries, there is sufficient base spreading resistance extrinsic to the active transistor regions that the addition of this capacitance is not required for accurate representation.

4. The base spreading resistance r_b' of transistors made on a base wafer, such as the alloy-junction and surface-barrier types, must frequently be split into two components, r_{b1}' and r_{b2}', as shown in Fig. 12.10, to show that the majority of the current through C_c flows through less of the extrinsic base material than does the base current to the active transistor region.

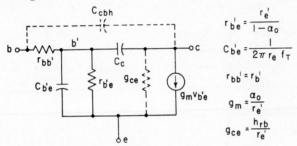

$$r_{b'e}' = \frac{r_e'}{1-\alpha_0}$$

$$C_{b'e}' = \frac{1}{2\pi r_e f_T}$$

$$r_{bb'}' = r_b'$$

$$g_m = \frac{\alpha_0}{r_e'}$$

$$g_{ce} = \frac{h_{rb}}{r_e'}$$

Fig. 12.17. Simplified hybrid-pi transistor representation.

12.5. High-frequency Figures of Merit.   There are two high-frequency figures of merit which have received wide acceptance and usage for describing the high-frequency performance capabilities of transistors.   These are f_T, the frequency at which $|h_{fe}| = 1$, and f_{max}, the maximum frequency of oscillation.   Both these quantities are usually complicated functions of many of the transistor high-frequency parameters discussed in the preceding sections of this chapter.

12.5a. The Characteristic Frequency f_T.   This is defined as that frequency for which the common-emitter, short-circuit, forward-current transfer ratio h_{fe} equals 1. Because $h_{fe} \approx \alpha/(1 - \alpha)$, this characteristic frequency is also the frequency at which Re $(\alpha) = 0.5$.†

The frequency f_T is related to the alpha-cutoff frequency f_α, which is the frequency at which $|\alpha| = 0.707\alpha_0$.   For an idealized transistor in which $\alpha = \alpha_0/(1 + jf/f_\alpha)$, f_T is given by

$$f_T = f_\alpha \sqrt{2\alpha_0 - 1} \approx f_\alpha \qquad (12.12)$$

† The approximation $h_{fe} = \alpha/(1 - \alpha)$ is usually extremely good at low frequencies but becomes poorer as frequency increases.   The exact expression for h_{fe} in terms of the common-base h parameters is

$$-h_{fe} = \frac{h_{fb} + h_{ib}h_{ob}/(1 - h_{rb})}{1 + h_{fb} + h_{ib}h_{ob}/(1 - h_r)} \qquad h_{fb} = -\alpha$$

in which the right-hand quotient in both numerator and denominator is completely negligible at low frequencies.   However, this factor increases with increasing frequency, because $h_{ob} \approx j\omega C_{ob}$.   Fortunately, the magnitude of this factor never exceeds $C_{ob}/(C_{De} + C_{Te})$, which is seldom greater than 0.1 in high-frequency transistors.   It reaches this limit at a frequency of f_T or greater, below which it is proportional to frequency.   Therefore, the factor in question is, in practice, never more than 20 per cent of h_{fb} or $1 + h_{fb}$ and is generally much less, so that the approximation calling f_T that frequency where Re $(\alpha) = 0.5$ is analytically useful.

When α can be represented by a single pole with an excess phase factor

$$\alpha = \alpha_0 \frac{e^{-j\nu(f/f_\alpha)}}{1 + j(f/f_\alpha)} \qquad (12.13)$$

the alpha-cutoff frequency f_α is related to f_T by the curves shown in Fig. 12.18.

The usefulness of f_T as a performance figure of merit stems both from the ease with which it can be measured and from the direct manner in which it relates to certain types of transistor performance. Both these advantages result from the observed (and theoretically predicted) fact that the magnitude of h_{fe} varies inversely with frequency at high frequencies, as shown in Fig. 12.19. Because of this well-behaved dependence, f_T can be computed simply by measuring h_{fe} at a fixed frequency near f_T and then multiplying the measured magnitude of h_{fe} by the frequency of measurement. Likewise, f_T equals the product of the current gain of a common-emitter stage

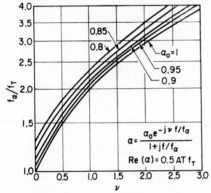

FIG. 12.18. The influence of excess phase on f_α/f_T.

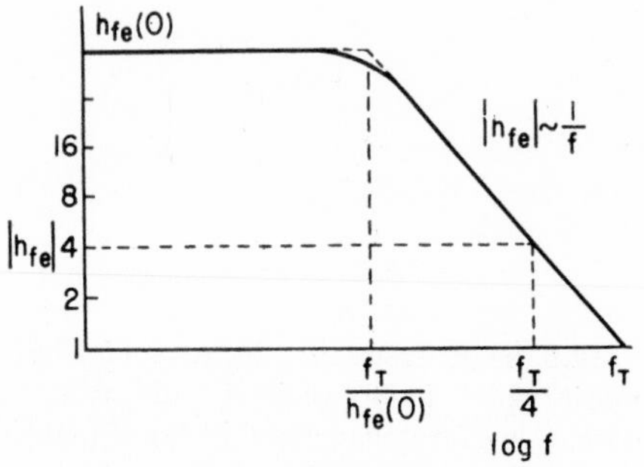

FIG. 12.19. Common-emitter current gain versus frequency.

with a small load impedance times the half-power bandwidth of the current gain, thus providing a very useful indication of video-amplifier performance.

The phase lag in α at f_T lies between 45 and 60°, corresponding to ν in Eq. (12.13) of 0 and ∞, respectively. Because phase shift in α limits high-frequency transistor performance just as much as does a magnitude reduction, f_T provides a far better rough indication of high-frequency transistor capability than does f_α, which formerly was thought to be a valuable transistor figure of merit.

12.5b. The Maximum Frequency of Oscillation, $f_{\max}$, of a transistor is the highest frequency at which the transistor can be made to oscillate under the most favorable conditions. The value of $f_{\max}$ is theoretically independent of circuit configuration. However, in order to achieve the true transistor $f_{\max}$, high-frequency losses in the circuitry must be negligibly small, the circuit must present the proper impedances to the input and output of the transistor, and the attenuation and phase shift in any circuit feedback path from output to input must be adjusted to their optimum values with the use of lossless circuitry. The $f_{\max}$ is strongly dependent on transistor operating point, generally increasing with increases in collector voltage and maximizing for emitter currents which are above the range where C_{Te} is important and below the range where current densities are so high as to reduce β.

The $f_{\max}$ of any transistor at a certain operating point is the upper boundary of the frequency range over which the transistor is an active device (at that operating point). At frequencies higher than $f_{\max}$, the transistor cannot provide useful gain, since any device with power gain can be made to oscillate by feeding all the available output power back to the input with the proper phase. Conversely, if the transistor can oscillate at a given frequency, it can provide gain at that frequency with suitable circuitry. Therefore, f_{max} is the frequency at which the maximum available power gain is 1.

The direct measurement of f_{max} is bound to provide a conservative indication of transistor capability, since circuit losses and maladjustment can only reduce the measured maximum oscillation frequency. However, experience has shown that a high-Q circuit with a feedback path having adjustable phase and attenuation will readily yield measured values within 5 per cent of the true f_{max}. A lumped-constant circuit suitable for measuring f_{max} below 200 mc is shown in Fig. 12.20.

For most transistor structures, the useful high-frequency power gain† varies inversely with the square of frequency (-6 db/octave). For such structures, f_{max} provides a good indication of the gain to be expected at any lower frequency (in the high-frequency region). The principal exceptions to this convenient empirical law are found with transistors having:

1. Large collector body resistance, which causes the useful power gain to vary more rapidly with frequency than -6 db/octave

2. Very low extrinsic base resistance and a significantly distributed active region (see 3 of Sec. 12.4b), for which the high-frequency gain varies more slowly

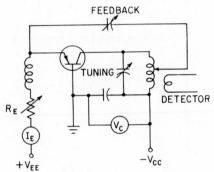

FIG. 12.20. Schematic of f_{max} test set.

than -6 db/octave (because the base-lead impedance in effect decreases with increasing frequency)

In the first of these two cases, useful power gain at frequency f is greater than $(f_{max}/f)^2$, whereas in the second case gain computed on this basis from a measured f_{max} would be optimistically high.

Exact expressions for the maximum frequency of oscillation can be obtained in terms of the elements of the equivalent-circuit representations introduced in Sec. 12.4. However, such expressions are uselessly complex for all but the simplest representations. On the basis of Fig. 12.16, assuming that $\nu = 0$, one finds

$$\frac{\alpha_0 f_\alpha}{8\pi r_b' C_c(1 + 2\pi r_e' C_c f_\alpha)} < f_{max}^2 < \frac{\alpha_0 f_\alpha}{8\pi r_b' C_c} \tag{12.14}$$

or

$$f_{max} \approx \sqrt{\frac{\alpha_0 f_\alpha}{8\pi r_b' C_c}} \tag{12.15}$$

A first-order approximation for f_{max} with finite ν, which is adequate for $\nu < 1$, gives

$$f_{max} \approx \sqrt{\frac{\alpha_0 f_\alpha}{8\pi r_b' C_c(1 + \nu)}} \tag{12.16}$$

or

$$f_{max} \approx \sqrt{\frac{\alpha_0 f_T}{8\pi r_b' C_c}} \tag{12.17}$$

† The term "useful" gain is considered in Sec. 12.19 and possesses no rigorous definition, because the requirements of different applications may impose vastly different criteria for optimization.

A comparable approximation based on Fig. 12.17 yields

$$f_{max} \approx \frac{1}{4\pi} \sqrt{\frac{g_m}{r_{bb'} C_{b'e} C_c}} \qquad (12.18)$$

12.6. High-frequency Impedance Levels. The impedance levels at the input and output of transistors operating at high frequencies usually can be ascertained from simplified transistor equivalent-circuit representations, such as those of Figs. 12.16 and 12.17, to an accuracy sufficient for the majority of amplifier design procedures. Such representations show clearly how the impedance levels vary with frequency and

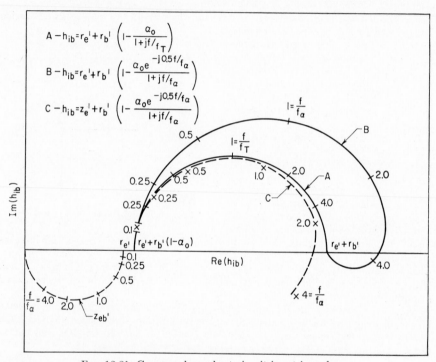

Fig. 12.21. Common-base short-circuit input impedance.

will suggest both the magnitude and phase of the input and output circuit impedances needed to provide the desired results.

Frequently there is significant interaction between the input and output circuits in a tuned high-frequency amplifier stage, which results from the internal feedback within the transistor. In such cases, the appropriate impedance levels can be determined by suitably terminating (short-circuiting or open-circuiting) the output or input when the input impedance or output impedance, respectively, is being determined. The validity of this procedure is related to the need for neutralizing the feedback of any amplifier stage having substantial interaction: When the stage is neutralized, the input and output impedances are independent of the opposite termination, so that a short-circuit or open-circuit impedance determination is as good as any other.

12.6a. Input Impedance. Transistor input impedance generally is most usefully determined with the output short-circuited. In those cases where internal feedback is negligibly small, the load impedance is generally small compared with the transistor output impedance. All widely used neutralizing schemes derive their feedback signal from the output voltage (rather than the output current); hence, the output voltage of a neutralized amplifier should be zero for computing independently the contributions of the transistor and the neutralizing circuit to input impedance.

For a common-base connection, Fig. 12.16 suggests that the short-circuit input impedance is

$$h_{ib} = z_{eb'} + r_b'(1 - \alpha') \quad (12.19)$$

The simplest approximation to Eq. (12.19) is

$$h_{ib} = r_e' + r_b'\left(1 - \frac{\alpha_0}{1 + jf/f_T}\right) \quad (12.20)$$

which is plotted as curve A in Fig. 12.21. Obviously, the common-base input impedance is inductive. In curve B of Fig. 12.21, a somewhat more typical representation for α' [Eq. (12.13) with $\nu = 0.5$] is included. In curve C, a first-order frequency dependence for $z_{eb'}$ has been added; usually, the capacitive reactance of $z_{eb'}$ is not sufficient to cancel the inductive reactance resulting from the phase lag in α. These curves are typical of the input impedance measured for transistors intended for service up to 50 mc.

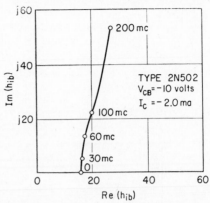

FIG. 12.22. Measured common-base short-circuit input impedance showing effect of lead inductance.

Transistors for higher frequencies have such low base spreading resistance r_b' and emitter impedance that lead inductance becomes very important. Emitter lead inductance merely adds to the inductive input impedance, whereas base lead inductance contributes both an inductive reactance and a negative resistive component which increases with frequency. The measured plot of Fig. 12.22, taken on a 2N502, shows the effect of these inductances.

The maximum phase angle of h_{ib} is not great. For curve A of Fig. 12.21, the maximum phase angle is given by

$$\csc^{-1}\left[\frac{2(r_e' + r_b')}{\alpha_0 r_b'} - 1\right] \approx \csc^{-1}\left(1 + \frac{2r_e'}{r_b'}\right)$$

Based on this relation, the maximum Q (ratio of reactance to resistance) of the common-base input impedance is given by

$$Q_{\max} = \frac{\alpha_0 r_b'}{2r_e'\sqrt{\left(1 + \frac{r_b'}{r_e'}\right)\left[1 + \frac{r_b'(1 - \alpha_0)}{r_e'}\right]}} < \frac{\alpha_0 r_b'}{2r_e'}$$

which shows that this input impedance has a low Q and is compatible with broadband circuitry.

For a common-emitter connection, Fig. 12.17 provides the simplest basis for visualizing and computing the input impedance. The first-order approximation to the short-circuit input impedance is

$$h_{ie} \approx r_{bb'} + \frac{r_{b'e}}{1 + j\omega C_{b'e}r_{b'e}} \quad (12.21)$$

which is plotted in Fig. 12.23.   This plot shows that the impedance approaches r_{bb}'
at very high frequencies and has a capacitive reactance.   The maximum phase angle
of this impedance is given by

$$\csc^{-1}\left(1 + \frac{2r_{bb'}}{r_{b'e}}\right)$$

Therefore, the maximum Q of the common-emitter input impedance h_{ie} is

$$Q_{max} = \frac{r_{b'e}}{2r_{bb'}\sqrt{1 + \dfrac{r_{b'e}}{r_{bb'}}}} < \frac{r_{b'e}}{2r_{bb'}} \approx \frac{r_e'}{2r_b'(1 - \alpha_0)}$$

which, for this simple model, is usually greater than the maximum Q of the common-
base input impedance.

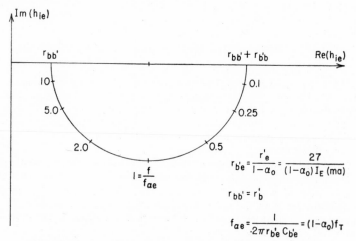

$$r_{b'e} = \frac{r_e'}{1-\alpha_0} = \frac{27}{(1-\alpha_0)\,I_E\,(ma)}$$

$$r_{bb'} = r_b'$$

$$f_{ae} = \frac{1}{2\pi\,r_{b'e}\,C_{b'e}} = (1-\alpha_0)f_T$$

FIG. 12.23. Common-emitter short-circuit input impedance.

Two factors frequently encountered in practice, particularly in high-frequency
transistors, tend to modify the simple frequency dependence of h_{ie} shown in Fig. 12.23.
The more important of these factors is lead inductance from the active transistor
region to the external terminals.   Base lead inductance reduces the magnitude of the
capacitive reactance of h_{ie} at high frequency, thereby decreasing the phase angle.
Emitter lead inductance contributes to h_{ie} both an inductive reactance and a positive
resistive component which varies with the square of frequency; these contributions
likewise reduce the phase angle of h_{ie} at high frequencies.   The second factor is the
complicated dependence of the intrinsic base-to-emitter impedance $z_{b'e}$ on frequency
in actual transistor structures, particularly graded-base transistors; this impedance
cannot be accurately described by a single-pole R-C circuit, in all cases.   Figure 12.24
shows plots of h_{ie} versus frequency measured on typical samples of two high-frequency
transistor types widely used for amplifier service.

12.6b. Output Impedance.   Transistor high-frequency output impedance may be
desired with either an open-circuited or a short-circuited input.†   The open-circuit

† Output impedance has also been measured for finite known input terminations because
of the practical difficulty of providing a short circuit or an open circuit at high frequency.
Such measurements are not directly applicable to impedance calculations of neutralized
amplifiers, although they provide an indication of the output impedance of certain unneutralized amplifiers.

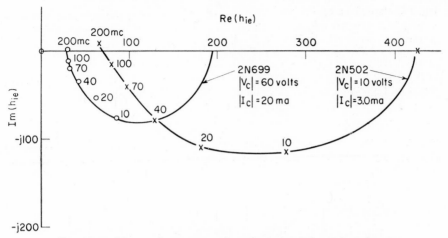

FIG. 12.24. Measured common-emitter short-circuit input impedance.

output impedance is of particular use with amplifiers employing bridge, or *h*-type, neutralization, whereas the short-circuit value is most useful for computing output impedance of amplifiers with admittance, or *y*-type, neutralization. The open-circuit common-base output impedance is generally much higher than the open-circuit common-emitter output impedance, whereas the short-circuit impedances are obviously equal for both connections.

The short-circuit output impedance can be estimated from the hybrid-pi equivalent-circuit representation of Fig. 12.17, giving the result

$$\frac{1}{z_{oes}} \triangleq y_{ob} = y_{oe} = j\omega C_c \frac{1 + g_m R + j\omega C_{b'e} R}{1 + j\omega(C_c + C_{b'e})R} + g_{ce} + j\omega C_{cbh} \qquad (12.22)$$

where

$$\frac{1}{R} \triangleq \frac{1}{r_{bb'}} + \frac{1}{r_{b'e}} \approx \frac{1}{r_{bb'}}$$

A plot of the magnitude of this impedance versus frequency is shown in Fig. 12.25.

The impedance given by Eq. (12.22) can be obtained from the circuit shown in Fig. 12.26. For a short-circuit output impedance representation, the elements of

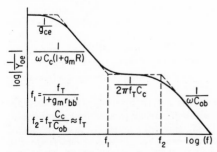

FIG. 12.25. Magnitude of short-circuit output impedance versus frequency.

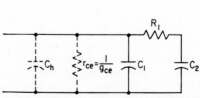

FIG. 12.26. Two-terminal representation for common-emitter output impedance.

Fig. 12.26 are given by

$$\frac{1}{C_1} = \frac{1}{C_c} + \frac{1}{C_{b'e}} \approx \frac{1}{C_c} \qquad C_h = C_{cbh}$$

$$C_2 = C_c(1 + g_m R) - C_1 \approx g_m r_{bb'} C_c = C_c \frac{r_b'}{r_e'} \qquad (12.23)$$

$$R_1 = \frac{C_c + C_{b'e}}{C_2} R \approx \frac{C_{b'e} r_{bb'}}{C_2} \approx \frac{C_{b'e} r_e'}{C_c} \approx \frac{1}{2\pi f_T C_c}$$

The shunt resistance r_{ce} shown dashed in Fig. 12.26 is the result of such phenomena as depletion-layer widening and leakage, which are important at low frequencies and

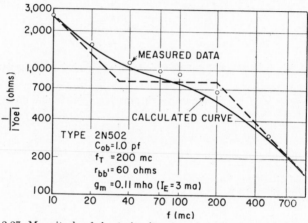

Fig. 12.27. Magnitude of short-circuit output impedance versus frequency.

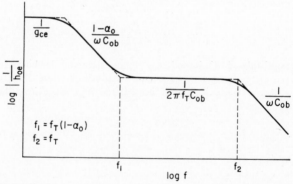

Fig. 12.28. Magnitude of open-circuit common-emitter output impedance versus frequency.

which provide the lower boundary to the frequency range over which the high-frequency representations given here are applicable. In most amplifier applications this shunt resistance is negligible. Figure 12.27 shows the comparison of measured and calculated values of short-circuit output impedance for a modern high-frequency transistor. The degree of agreement illustrates the value of the simplified representations described herein.

The open-circuit common-emitter output impedance can be similarly obtained from Fig. 12.17 as

$$\frac{1}{z_{oc}} \triangleq h_{oe} = j\omega C_{ob} \frac{1 + g_m r_{b'e} + j\omega C_{b'e} r_{b'e}}{1 + j\omega(C_{ob} + C_{b'e})r_{b'e}} + g_{ce} \tag{12.24}$$

This impedance has much the same form as Eq. (12.22), although the characteristic frequencies are separated more widely. In this expression the entire collector-to-base capacitance C_{ob} is used because the reactive currents through both the header capacitance C_{cbh} and the junction capacitance C_c contribute to the feedback which determines the output impedance. A plot of the magnitude of this impedance versus frequency is shown in Fig. 12.28. Figure 12.26 is likewise applicable to the open-circuit common-emitter output impedance, with the following values:

$$\frac{1}{C_1} = \frac{1}{C_{ob}} + \frac{1}{C_{b'e}} \approx \frac{1}{C_{ob}}$$
$$C_2 = C_{ob}(1 + g_m r_{b'e}) - C_1 \approx C_{ob} h_{fe}(0) \tag{12.25}$$
$$R_1 = \frac{(C_{ob} + C_{b'e})r_{b'e}}{C_2} \approx \frac{C_{b'e}}{C_{ob}} \frac{r_{b'e}}{h_{fe}(0)} \approx \frac{1}{2\pi f_T C_{ob}}$$

This impedance is not readily measured because of the difficulty of presenting the transistor input with a source of negligibly high impedance at high frequencies. For these same reasons, it is seldom needed in circuit computations.

The open-circuit common-base output impedance can be visualized with the aid of Fig. 12.16. If header capacitances were negligible, the high-frequency output impedance would be simply

$$z_{ob} = \frac{1}{h_{ob}} = r_b' + \frac{1}{j\omega C_c}$$

This impedance has a large magnitude and a high Q; consequently header capacitances may alter it appreciably. The collector-to-base capacitance and the collector-to-can capacitance

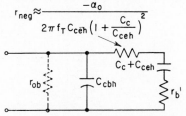

FIG. 12.29. Two-terminal representation for open-circuit common-base output impedance. Expression for r_{neg} is valid if f is less than $f_T/3$.

of the header appear in parallel with the above output impedance. More important, any collector-to-emitter capacitance introduces feedback into the open-circuited emitter; this feedback is reactive at low frequencies but becomes regenerative at high frequencies. The regenerative feedback can be represented by a negative resistance, whose value is almost independent of frequency, in series with the output impedance. Finally, because the output impedance is high, it is often necessary to include the low-frequency output resistance r_{ob} in shunt with the intrinsic output impedance. These various elements are combined into the equivalent circuit for the common-base output impedance shown in Fig. 12.29.

The combination of high output-impedance level and regeneration from collector-to-emitter feedback makes it difficult to measure and use this transistor connection; consequently, h-type neutralization of common-base stages has only very limited use.

12.7. Dependence of High-frequency Properties on Bias Point. Both emitter current and collector-junction voltage govern transistor high-frequency properties. Although the dependence of these properties on operating point differs greatly among various transistor types, it is still possible to see qualitatively how the properties should vary with operating point. Detailed data on any given type are frequently supplied by the manufacturer.

12.7a. Emitter-current Effects. The principal effect of an increase in emitter current is a decrease in the importance of emitter transition capacitance C_{Te}, as discussed in Sec. 12.2a. The effect of this capacitance is roughly halved for each doubling of emitter current. Therefore, the high-frequency gain of a transistor increases proportionately with emitter current at low current levels, where C_{Te} has great influence. Figure 12.5 illustrates this effect.

Transistor input and output impedance levels vary inversely with emitter current and are frequently inversely proportional to the emitter current over wide current ranges. Therefore, at low currents header and wiring capacitances are of major importance, while at high currents the header and wiring inductances may limit performance.

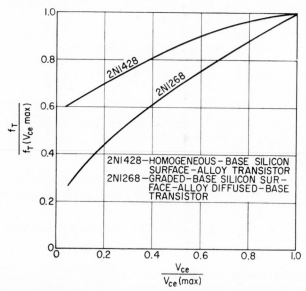

FIG. 12.30. High-frequency current gain versus collector voltage.

Other emitter-current effects are important primarily at high currents. High current densities may establish a sufficiently large minority-carrier density in the base region to swamp out the impurity-ion density therein, thus obliterating much of the accelerating field in a graded-base transistor. In this current range, transit time increases with emitter current. Furthermore, minority-carrier mobility decreases at high current densities. These two effects cause high-frequency gain to decrease with increasing emitter current at high current levels. Finally, it is frequently found that base spreading resistance r_b' decreases with increasing current through the transistor at high current levels; this decreased resistance may be produced both by conductivity modulation of the base region and by the tendency of the active transistor region to crowd toward the periphery of the emitter at high currents. This latter tendency is a result of the voltage drop associated with the transverse majority-carrier current within the base, which is in such a direction as to bias off the central regions of the transistor.

12.7b. Collector-voltage Effects. The collector voltage affects both the transit time through the base region and the collector transition capacitance C_{Tc}. Because the collector depletion layer widens as collector voltage increases, the base width must decrease. The exact dependence of base width on collector voltage is a complicated function of impurity distributions in both the base and collector regions. Therefore, although one can say that the transit time (or the charge stored in the base region for a given current) always decreases with increasing collector bias, the exact form of the dependence cannot be specified. For homogeneous-base transistors, the characteristic frequency f_T increases at a relatively constant rate with collector voltage, seldom varying by more than 2 to 1 or 3 to 1 over the collector-voltage range from zero to maximum bias. On the other hand, graded-base transistors, particularly those with a wide region of high resistivity at the collector side of the base, may exhibit an extremely wide change in f_T as collector voltage ranges from zero to maximum. The change with collector voltage is very rapid at low voltages, because the collector depletion layer is then pushing through the high-resistivity portion of the base, but slows down at higher voltage as the depletion layer reaches through to the lower-resistivity region of the base near the emitter. The dependence of f_T on collector bias for these two different classes of transistor is illustrated by the curves in Fig. 12.30.

The collector capacitance decreases with increasing collector voltage. In homogeneous-base transistors, the capacitance varies as $V_{CB}^{-\frac{1}{2}}$ or $V_{CB}^{-\frac{1}{3}}$, whereas in graded-base transistors, the capacitance varies as $V_{CB}^{-\frac{1}{2}}$ at low voltages but varies very little at high voltages.

12.8. Noise Figure. The excess noise in a transistor operating at high frequencies is produced both by thermal noise in the extrinsic lead resistances, particularly the base resistance r_b', and by shot noise from charge carriers entering and leaving the base. Both these contributors are amenable to mathematical description, with the result that high-frequency transistor noise figure usually can be predicted from simple models with satisfactory accuracy.[15,16]

For the simplified transistor equivalent-circuit representation given by Fig. 12.16, the noise figure for the common-base or common-emitter connection† is approximated by

$$F_b = F_e = 1 + \frac{r_b' + (r_e'/2)}{R_g} + \frac{(1 + H_{FB})[1 + (f/\sqrt{1 + H_{FB}}f_T)^2](R_g + r_b' + r_e')^2}{(-)2H_{FB}r_e'R_g}$$

(12.26)

where R_g is the real part of the source impedance. This expression is an extension of a result given by Nielsen.[15] In Eq. (12.26), the large-signal value of the common-base forward-current transfer ratio,‡ given by

$$-H_{FB} = \frac{|I_C| - |I_{CO}|}{|I_E|}$$

has been introduced in place of the small-signal quantity h_{fb}, and the characteristic

---

† The results presented here for both noise figure and source impedances are roughly applicable to the common-collector connection, as well as the common-base and common-emitter connections, at any frequency where a common-collector stage has gain.[15] However, since the gain of the common-collector stage is never greater than its ratio of input impedance to output impedance and is so low that the stage must generally be followed by another low-noise stage, no advantages in low-noise performance are ever provided by the common-collector connection compared with using the same transistor in the common-emitter connection. Consequently, the common-collector connection is completely disregarded in this section.

‡ It should be noted that H_{FB} and $h_{fb} = -\alpha_0$ are negative, since they are defined in terms of currents entering the transistor. For transistors with $\alpha < 1$, the common-emitter forward-current transfer ratios H_{FE} and h_{fe} are positive.

frequency f_T has been used in place of the alpha-cutoff frequency.† The use of H_{FB} in place of h_{fb} makes no difference for germanium transistors, for which the two quantities are nearly equal at currents normally used for low-noise amplification. However, for silicon transistors biased at low currents, both theory and experiment suggest that closer results are obtained with the large-signal quantity, which may be significantly smaller than h_{fb} at low bias currents.[17] The use of f_T is based on the fact that this quantity relates directly to the loss of correlation between emitter and collector currents at high frequencies; it is this loss of correlation that causes much of the increase in noise figure with increasing frequency.

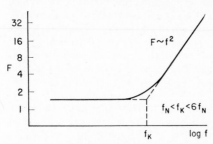

FIG. 12.31. High-frequency noise figure versus frequency.

The frequency dependence of noise figure at high frequencies is illustrated in Fig. 12.31. Below the corner frequency the noise figure is independent of frequency (provided low-frequency flicker noise is absent, as is generally the case above the audio-frequency range). Above the corner frequency, the noise figure increases as the square of frequency. The exact shape of the curve in the vicinity of the corner is not well defined and is not the same for all transistors. The corner frequency itself is not simply related to transistor parameters, although it is greater than $f_N = \sqrt{1 + H_{FB} f_T}$ and generally less than $6f_N$.

12.8a. Midband Noise Figure. The midband frequency range, over which the noise figure is nearly constant, is an extremely useful one and covers a large number of transistor low-noise applications. This range extends at least up to the frequency f_N, which is generally of the order of $0.1f_{max}$. In this range, the noise figure is

$$F = 1 + \frac{r_b' + (r_e'/2)}{R_g} + \frac{(R_g + r_b' + r_e')^2}{2H_{FE}r_e'R_g} \tag{12.27}$$

where

$$H_{FE} \triangleq \frac{I_C - I_{CO}}{I_B + I_{CO}} = \frac{-H_{FB}}{1 + H_{FB}} \approx \frac{I_C}{I_B}$$

This expression gives a value that generally agrees with observed midband noise figures within 1 db, except for transistors possessing significant feedback from depletion-layer widening, for which the noise figure is 1 to 3 db higher than that predicted by Eq. (12.27).

The source resistance which minimizes the midband noise figure is

$$R_g(\text{opt}) = (r_b' + r_e') \sqrt{1 + H_{FE} \frac{1 + (2r_b'/r_e')}{[1 + (r_b'/r_e')]^2}}$$

$$= r_e' \sqrt{H_{FE}} \sqrt{\frac{[1 + (r_b'/r_e')]^2}{-H_{FB}} - \left(\frac{r_b'}{r_e'}\right)^2} \tag{12.28}$$

or

$$R_g(\text{opt}) \approx r_e' \sqrt{H_{FE}} \sqrt{1 + \frac{2r_b'}{r_e'}} \tag{12.29}$$

The curves of Fig. 12.32 are based on Eq. (12.28).

It should be noted that the optimum source resistance for minimum noise is the same

† The author acknowledges with gratitude the many suggestions regarding the practical prediction of noise figure furnished by his colleague William C. Follmer.

for the common-emitter and common-base connections.   It can be shown that the resistance given by Eq. (12.28) is, in all cases, within a factor of 1.42 of the source resistance for maximum gain of the common-emitter connection.   Therefore, minimum noise and high gain are compatible in the common-emitter connection.   However, since the source resistance for maximum gain of the common-base connection is lower than that for the common-emitter connection by the multiplicative factor $\sqrt{(1 - \alpha_0)}$, high gain and low noise figure are not achieved together in the common-base connection.   Consequently, the common-emitter connection is almost invariably used for low-noise amplification.

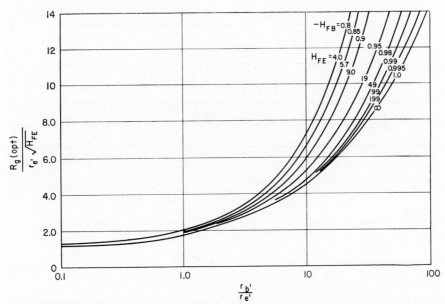

FIG. 12.32. Source resistance for minimum midband noise figure in a common-base or a common-emitter stage.

When the optimum source resistance, given by Eq. (12.28), is used, the midband noise figure becomes[16]

$$F_{\min} = \frac{[1 + (1 + H_{FB})(r_b'/r_e')] + \sqrt{[1 + (1 + H_{FB})(r_b'/r_e')]^2 + H_{FB}}}{-H_{FB}} \quad (12.30)$$

for the common-emitter or common-base connection.   The curves of Fig. 12.33 are based on this relationship.   These data show the importance of having high current gain and low base spreading resistance in low-noise transistors.   Since the emitter resistance r_e' is inversely proportional to emitter current, it can also be seen that low-noise stages should be operated with low emitter currents.

The noise figure does not deteriorate rapidly as the source resistance varies from its optimum value.   Nielsen[15] has shown that the worst possible deterioration is given by

$$\frac{F}{F_{\min}} \leq \frac{1 + \frac{1}{2}[(R_g/R_g(\text{opt})) + (R_g(\text{opt})/R_g)]}{2} \quad (12.31)$$

Therefore, with the source resistance in error by a factor of 2, the noise figure has increased no more than 0.5 db, or with a source resistance error ratio of 4, the noise figure is within 2 db of its minimum value.

12.8b. High-frequency Noise Figure. At frequencies beyond the midband range considered in the preceding section, the noise figure increases with increasing frequency at a rate that approaches 6 db/octave well above the corner frequency. It is the purpose of this section to show how noise figure depends on the frequency, the principal transistor parameters, and the circuit conditions in order to provide a useful basis both for the design of low-noise, high-frequency amplifiers and for the selection of transistors for such service.

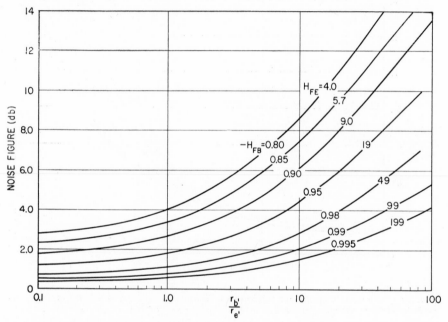

Fig. 12.33. Midband noise figure of common-emitter or common-base stage with optimum source impedance.

The precise determination of the influence on noise figure of all the major high-frequency limitations of transistor performance, which include emitter transition capacitance, transit time and the dispersion thereof, and header parasitics, is hopelessly complicated. However, the simplified procedures described herein will usually yield noise figures within 1 or 2 db of carefully measured values and will yield source resistance values with compatible accuracy.

12.8c. The Corner Frequency. The upper limit of the midband frequency range, over which the noise figure is independent of frequency, may be defined as that frequency where the minimum noise figure is twice (3 db greater than) its midband value. Such a definition agrees closely with the corner frequency as shown in Fig. 12.31, wherein the straight-line extrapolation of the high-frequency portion of the noise-figure-versus-frequency curve down to the midband noise-figure value defines the corner frequency. With the corner frequency defined by the 3-db increase with frequency, the curve of Fig. 12.34 shows its value in terms of transistor parameters. This curve is based on noise figure as given by Eq. (12.26).

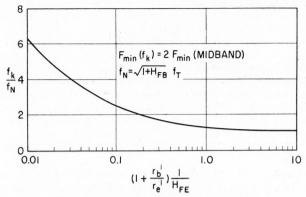

FIG. 12.34. Corner frequency for noise.

12.8d. Optimum Source Resistance. The source resistance Re (Z_g) which minimizes the high-frequency noise figure, as given by Eq. (12.26), is

$$R_g(\text{opt}) = (r_b' + r_e') \sqrt{1 + \frac{H_{FE}}{1 + (f/f_N)^2} \frac{1 + (2r_b'/r_e')}{[1 + (r_b'/r_e')]^2}} \qquad (12.32)$$

The curves of Fig. 12.32 can be used for evaluating this expression if the quantity

$$H_{FE}' \triangleq \frac{H_{FE}}{1 + (f/f_N)^2}$$

is used in place of H_{FE} both in entering the appropriate curve and in the normalizing factor on the vertical axis. This expression shows that the optimum source resistance decreases in inverse proportion to frequency above the frequency f_N but does not go below a high-frequency asymptote $r_b' + r_e'$. This result is not strictly accurate, because the derivation of Eq. (12.26) ignores any junction capacitance or diffusion capacitance in the emitter impedance z_e'. This limitation can be avoided by merely changing the high-frequency limit to r_b'. Figure 12.35 depicts the frequency dependence of optimum source resistance, as described here.

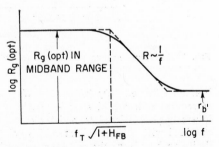

FIG. 12.35. Optimum source resistance for minimum noise figure as a function of frequency.

12.8e. Minimum Noise Figure versus Frequency. The lowest noise figure for a given frequency and given parameters can be determined by substituting the value from Eq. (12.32) into Eq. (12.26), which gives

$$F_{\min} = 1 + \left(1 + \frac{r_b'}{r_e'}\right) \frac{1 + (f/f_N)^2}{H_{FE}} \left[1 + \sqrt{1 + \frac{\alpha_0}{(1 + r_b'/r_e')\dfrac{1 + (f/f_N)^2}{H_{FE}}} \times \frac{1 + (2r_b'/r_e')}{1 + \dfrac{r_b'}{r_e'}}}\right] \qquad (12.33)$$

This expression can be evaluated from Fig. 12.36 to an accuracy of better than 0.3 db.

This figure is obtained by setting

$$\frac{1 + (2r_b'/r_e')}{1 + (r_b'/r_e')} = 1.4$$

since this factor always lies between 1 and 2.

The derivation of Eq. (12.33) ignores the effects of junction capacitance or diffusion capacitance across r_e'. More complete analyses[18] of noise figure at high frequencies show that this effect is not important at frequencies below $0.5f_T$. Experimental tests above this limit have shown that the presence of this capacitance can introduce a difference between observed and computed noise figures of no more than 1 or 2 db and that the observed values are sometimes lower and sometimes higher than the corresponding computed values.

12.8f. Biasing for Minimum Noise Figure. In the midband frequency range, it is evident from Eq. (12.30) that the quantity $(1 + H_{FB})r_b'/r_e'$ should be minimized for

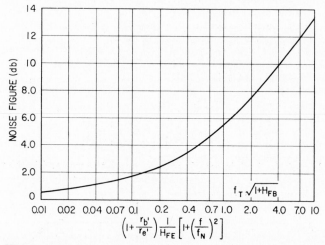

Fig. 12.36. High-frequency noise figure of common-emitter or common-base stage with optimum source impedance.

best noise figure. The factor $(1 + H_{FB})$ decreases slightly with increasing magnitude of reverse collector bias, r_b' is relatively independent of operating point, and r_e' is inversely proportional to emitter current. Therefore, low midband noise figure is obtained with a large collector bias voltage and a small emitter current. Practical limits on how large the collector bias voltage can be made are imposed by the low-frequency flicker noise, which increases with bias voltage, and increased leakage current I_{co}, which contributes shot noise. There is a minimum limit to the emitter current which is determined by the decreases in current gain, matched power gain, and the frequency response with decreasing current in the low-current range. For most germanium transistors intended for low-noise midband amplification, it is suitable to use emitter currents of 0.2 to 1 ma, with collector bias voltages of 3 to 10 volts. For silicon transistors, somewhat larger emitter currents are required because of the dependence of $1 + H_{FB}$ on emitter current.

In the high-frequency range, it is found that the lowest noise figure is obtained when the transistor is biased at higher emitter currents than are best for the midband range. The principal reason is the effect of emitter junction capacitance C_{Te} on high-frequency current gain (see Fig. 12.5); as the bias current increases, f_T and f_N increase and the noise figure decreases [see Eq. (12.33)]. Increasing the collector bias voltage also increases the high-frequency current gain because of reduced base width. Therefore, one can say that the optimum bias current for lowest noise figure increases with increasing frequency and that noise figure improves more rapidly with increasing collector bias voltage in the high-frequency range than in the midband frequency range. In practice, it is usually found that minimum noise figure at high frequencies is obtained at roughly the same bias conditions that give maximum matched common-emitter gain.

12.9. Temperature Dependence at High Frequency. The parameters which govern transistor high-frequency performance do not vary rapidly with temperature change. Consequently, the performance of high-frequency transistor amplifiers need not vary greatly with temperature. Indeed, it is frequently found that the dependence of high-frequency parameters on operating point will contribute more to performance changes with temperature, as a result of the shift of operating point with temperature, than will the changes in high-frequency parameters. Therefore, care must be taken in the design of bias circuits of high-frequency amplifiers intended for operation over wide temperature ranges in order to ensure that the operating point will be sufficiently stable to minimize detuning and change of gain with temperature.

The base transit time (or charge stored in the base per unit emitter current) tends to increase with increasing temperature because minority-carrier mobility varies inversely with temperature. Therefore, f_T can be raised by cooling a transistor, although the improvement is generally less than 50 per cent for a 100°C reduction.

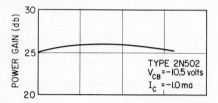
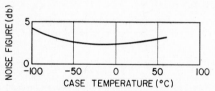

FIG. 12.37. Matched 30-mc gain and noise figure versus temperature, type 2N502.

The base spreading resistance increases with increasing temperature because majority-carrier mobility varies inversely with temperature. This effect is more pronounced in homogeneous-base transistors than in graded-base structures. In the former types, r_b' will typically increase by 50 to 100 per cent for a 100°C temperature rise, while in graded-base structures, the corresponding increase is 10 to 30 per cent.

The collector capacitance is practically independent of temperature.

Because of the dependence of transit time and base spreading resistance on temperature, it is found that high-frequency gain decreases with increasing temperature. For both germanium and silicon transistors, gain at 80°C is typically 2 to 3 db lower than at room temperature while gain at −40°C is generally 1 to 3 db higher than at room temperature. The increase in gain at low temperatures may not be realized in a fixed circuit because the transistor impedance levels likewise change with temperature and may create gain-robbing mismatches. If constancy of gain is desired over the widest possible temperature range, it is apparent that the circuit impedance levels and tuning should be optimized for the maximum temperature.

High-frequency noise figure is at a minimum at roughly −20°C for germanium transistors and at room temperature for silicon transistors. At higher temperatures, the noise figure increases because of the lower cutoff frequency and the higher r_b'. At lower temperatures, the noise figure increases because of the reduced current gain H_{FE}.

Typical measurements of high-frequency gain and noise figure versus temperature are shown in Fig. 12.37.   These data were taken with the circuit optimized at each measurement; hence, the gain curve can be used as an illustration of the variation of f_{max} with temperature.

VIDEO AMPLIFIERS

A video amplifier is considered here as a wideband amplifier whose passband extends from a low frequency, typically in the audio-frequency range, up to an upper limit many times higher than the low-frequency limit.   Such amplifiers are sometimes called base-band amplifiers.   The upper frequency limit may be no more than 100 kc or as great as many hundreds of megacycles per second.   Because such amplifiers cover a frequency range of many octaves, impedance matching between stages is seldom feasible.   The load impedance of a video amplifier is usually low in order to provide the d-c bias and to minimize capacitive bandwidth limiting.   The perform-

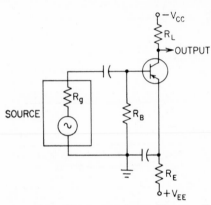

ance of a video amplifier is usually described in terms of its midband power gain or current (voltage) amplification and its half-power bandwidth.

In the following paragraphs, various transistor video-amplifier circuits will be described, together with their performance figures of merit and with techniques for trading gain and bandwidth.

12.10. Single-stage Video Amplifiers. Power amplification with a single stage can be achieved with any of the three normal transistor connections, although the common-emitter connection is generally most useful for transistors having α_0 less than 1.

FIG. 12.38. Common-emitter video-amplifier stage.

12.10a.   Common   Emitter.   Figure 12.38 shows the circuit of a single-stage common-emitter amplifier having a load resistance R_L.[†]   The biasing resistors R_B and R_E are selected on the basis of compromise between operating-point stability and loss of gain or d-c supply power.   In general, in order to minimize the effects on operating point of changes in I_{CO} and h_{FB} due to aging, temperature change, and variations among transistors, it is desirable to have as low a d-c resistance as possible in the base and collector circuits and a high d-c resistance in the emitter circuit.[19]   Except for special cases, the effects of biasing resistors on gain will be ignored here.

The low-frequency current amplification of the single-stage common-emitter amplifier, determined on the basis of the equivalent-circuit representation in Fig. 12.17, is[‡]

$$A_i = \frac{i_L}{i_b} = h_{fe} = g_m r_{b'e} = \frac{\alpha_0}{1 - \alpha_0} \tag{12.34}$$

† While the circuits in the remainder of this section will show PNP transistors, complementary types with suitable high-frequency properties could be used equally well, with appropriate changes in transistor bias supplies.

‡ For both video and high-frequency tuned amplifiers it is convenient to define current (voltage) amplification or power gain as the ratio of load current (voltage) or power to the current (voltage) or power into the transistor input.   Gain expressions become unnecessarily complicated and obscure if the ratio of the load current (voltage) or power to source current (voltage) or available power is used.   (The ratio of load power to available source power is sometimes called transducer gain.)   It is more straightforward to separate the input-matching problem from transistor-gain consideration.

The input resistance at low frequencies is

$$R_i = h_{ie} = r_{bb'} + r_{b'e} = r_b' + \frac{r_e'}{1 - \alpha_0} \qquad (12.35)$$

which is typically of the order of 1,000 to 3,000 ohms for a bias current of $I_E = 1\,\text{ma}$. Hence, the low-frequency power gain is

$$G = \frac{R_L}{h_{ie}} h_{fe}^2 = \frac{R_L}{r_{bb'} + r_{b'e}} (g_m r_{b'e})^2$$

$$= \frac{R_L}{r_b' + \dfrac{r_e'}{1 - \alpha_0}} \left(\frac{\alpha_0}{1 - \alpha_0}\right)^2 \qquad (12.36)$$

The half-power bandwidth of the current amplification is given by[20]

$$f_i \approx \frac{1}{2\pi r_{b'e}[C_{b'e} + C_c(1 + g_m R_L)]}$$

$$\approx \frac{1 - \alpha_0}{1/f_T + 2\pi C_c R_L} \qquad (12.37)$$

In many cases, the contribution of collector capacitance to the bandwidth is negligible, in which case the bandwidth becomes

$$f_i = (1 - \alpha_0)f_T \qquad (12.38)$$

In these cases, the product of current amplification and bandwidth (analogous to the vacuum-tube video gain-bandwidth product) for a single-stage amplifier is

$$A_i f_i = \alpha_0 f_T \approx f_T \qquad (12.39)$$

In cases where the effects of collector capacitance are significant, the current amplification–bandwidth product can be given as

$$A_i f_i = \frac{\alpha_0 f_T}{1 + (R_L/X_o)} \qquad (12.40)$$

where X_c is the reactance of C_c at the frequency f_T.

In many transistors designed for high-frequency or wideband use, particularly graded-base transistors, the collector depletion-layer capacitance is extremely small, being well under 1 pf. In these transistors, the base-lead-to-collector-lead capacitance C_{cbh} may contribute much of the feedback in a common-emitter stage. Although the header capacitance is not precisely in parallel with C_c, its effect can be included with adequate accuracy by modifying Eqs. (12.37) and (12.40) to read

$$f_i \approx \frac{1 - \alpha_0}{(1/f_T) + 2\pi C_{ob} R_L} \qquad (12.37a)$$

$$A_i f_i = \frac{\alpha_0 f_T}{1 + 2\pi f_T C_{ob} R_L} \qquad (12.40a)$$

where C_{ob} is the common-base output capacitance with I_E and i_e both zero.

The bandwidth of a single-stage common-emitter video amplifier connected to a source of finite resistance will be somewhat larger than the bandwidth of the current amplification, as given by Eq. (12.37), because the transistor input impedance decreases with increasing frequency. This increased bandwidth is seldom more than twice f_i, because in most practical cases $R_g + r_{bb'} > r_{b'e}$.

With optimum source and load resistances, it is possible to exceed the gain-bandwidth product implied by Eq. (12.40), provided the header capacitances are not controlling the output capacitance. Here it is convenient to speak of the product of half-power bandwidth times the square root of the transducer power gain $f_i \sqrt{G_{\scriptscriptstyle 0}}$, which would be the amplification-bandwidth product if both input and output were transformed to the same impedance level by ideal transformers. With optimum loading on transistor input and output, this product is[20]

$$f_i \sqrt{G_t} \, (\text{max}) \approx \sqrt{\frac{\alpha_0 f_T}{8\pi r_b' C_c}} = \frac{1}{4\pi} \sqrt{\frac{g_m}{r_{bb'} C_{b'e} C_c}} \approx f_{\text{max}} \tag{12.41}$$

which is obtained with

$$R_g = r_b'$$

$$R_L = \frac{1}{2\pi f_T C_c} \tag{12.42}$$

The optimum load resistance is typically in the range from 500 to 4,000 ohms. Therefore, the presence of only 1 or 2 pf of stray plus header capacitance may make it impossible to achieve a gain-bandwidth product equaling f_{max} with high-performance transistors.

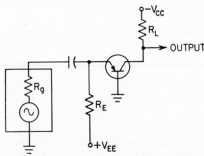

FIG. 12.39. Common-base video-amplifier stage.

12.10b. Common Base. A single-stage common-base amplifier, such as the one in Fig. 12.39, can be used in cases where an amplifying transducer is needed between a small source impedance and a large load impedance. This stage provides no current amplification but can give a large voltage amplification. For this stage, the low-frequency voltage amplification is approximately

$$A_v \approx \frac{R_L}{h_{ib}} h_{fb} = \frac{R_L \alpha_0}{r_e' + r_b'(1 - \alpha_0)} \tag{12.43}$$

which is the same expression as for the voltage amplification of the common-emitter stage. However, the common-base stage can give more voltage amplification because a larger load resistance can be used.

For the common-base stage, the bandwidth of the current amplification (whose low-frequency value is approximately α_0) is

$$f_i \approx \frac{1}{(1/f_\alpha) + 2\pi R_L C_{ob}} \tag{12.44}$$

Hence the current amplification–bandwidth product is approximately the same as for the common-emitter stage.

Because of the wide bandwidth of the current amplification of the common-base stage, this configuration is useful in high-level output stages of cascaded video amplifiers. It should be driven from a source whose internal impedance is high compared with h_{ib}, because h_{ib} starts increasing with frequency at a frequency $(1 - \alpha_0)f_T$.

A common-collector stage has a voltage amplification slightly less than 1 and a current amplification of $1/(1 - \alpha_0)$. The bandwidth of the current amplification is given by Eq. (12.38). Because of its limited gain and bandwidth, the common-collector stage finds little application as a video amplifier.

12.11. Multistage Video Amplifiers. The bandwidths normally associated with video amplifiers are sufficiently wide that impedance matching between stages is seldom employed. Consequently, video signals in a multistage amplifier are usually coupled directly from the output of one stage to the input of the next.† There are only six unique combinations of the three basic transistor connections for any two adjacent stages of an iterated cascade of video-amplifier stages. A cascade employing all three connections offers no advantage as far as gain or bandwidth is concerned and need not be considered. For transistors with $\alpha_0 < 1$, any connection can be used for either of the two adjacent stages.

Table 12.1 shows the approximate iterative amplification‡ and 3-db bandwidth to be expected from various two-stage combinations in which capacitive feedback is neglected ($C_{ob} = 0$).

TABLE 12.1. APPROXIMATE PERFORMANCE OF TWO-STAGE VIDEO AMPLIFIERS

Circuit	Two-stage voltage amplification	Two-stage half-power bandwidth	Amplification-band-width product per stage
CE-CE	$\left(\dfrac{\alpha_0}{1 - \alpha_0}\right)^2$	$0.64 f_T(1 - \alpha_0)$	$\alpha_0 f_T$
CB-CB	α_0^2	$0.64 f_\alpha$	$\alpha_0 f_\alpha$
CC-CC	1		
CB-CC	$\dfrac{\alpha_0}{1 - \alpha_0}$	$f_T(1 - \alpha_0)$	$1.56 f_T \sqrt{\alpha_0(1 - \alpha_0)}$
CB-CE	$\dfrac{\alpha_0^2}{1 - \alpha_0}$	$f_T(1 - \alpha_0)$	$1.56 f_T \alpha_0 \sqrt{(1 - \alpha_0)}$
CE-CC	$\dfrac{K\alpha_0}{(1 - \alpha_0)^2}\,(K < 1)$	$0.64 f_T(1 - \alpha_0)$	$f_T \sqrt{K\alpha_0}$

The common-emitter cascade provides the greatest amplification-bandwidth product with useful amplification for transistors with $\alpha_0 < 1$. Slightly less amplification and amplification-bandwidth product are obtained with alternate common-emitter and common-collector stages; however, this configuration may be useful for inverting the output which would be provided by the common-emitter cascade. The reduction in amplification and amplification-bandwidth product with alternate common-emitter and common-collector stages is caused by the high common-collector input impedance, which is not negligibly low compared with the common-emitter output impedance. This alternating configuration has the further disadvantage that the interstage between a common-emitter driver and its common-collector load is at a high impedance level, with the result that biasing resistors and stray capacitance may cause appreciable loss of gain and bandwidth.

The factor 1.56 appearing in the amplification-bandwidth products for the common-base–common-collector and common-base–common-emitter amplifiers exists because only one of the stages in each case contributes to the bandwidth limiting.

The bandwidth of the common-collector cascade cannot be specified for the general case. The voltage amplification of a single stage is just slightly less than 1, and with a

† Recent developments in wideband pulse transformers, employing transmission-line-type winding techniques, have made possible impedance optimization over bandwidths as wide as 1 Gc. However, the low-frequency response characteristics of these wideband transformers limit their use to pulse amplifiers. Such transformers are described by C. L. Ruthroff, Some Broad-band Transformers, *Proc. IRE*, vol. 47, pp. 1337–1342, August, 1959.

‡ Iterative amplification is the amplification of the circuit in an iterated cascade, that is, when driven from and driving like circuits as part of an infinite cascade.

low-impedance source the half-power bandwidth may become very large. The substantial current amplification of the common-collector stage could be useful in circuits between a high-impedance source and a low-impedance load, although in this case its bandwidth equals that of the common-emitter stage.

The effect of capacitive feedback on bandwidth of the common-emitter cascade can be determined with the aid of Eq. (12.40a), where R_L is now the input impedance of the following stage in parallel with the interstage biasing resistors.

The loss of low-frequency amplification due to the biasing resistors in a common-emitter cascade circuit, such as the one in Fig. 12.40, can be readily determined. The low-frequency input resistance of any stage is given by Eq. (12.35). The low-frequency output resistance of the preceding stage is nearly infinite. Hence, the division of signal current, from the preceding transistor, between the biasing resistors and the transistor input is proportional to their conductance values. The loss of signal into the biasing resistors can be minimized by raising the supply voltage and raising the values of the resistors. For a given supply voltage, this loss of signal cannot in general be decreased appreciably by raising the values of the biasing resistors,

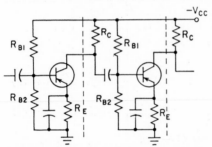

FIG. 12.40. Common-emitter video-amplifier cascade.

because raising the resistor values lowers the bias current and correspondingly raises the input impedance in the same proportion. To a certain extent, interstage loading widens the bandwidth of the amplifier, as described in Sec. 12.12, so that the amplification-bandwidth product is not altered so much by the biasing resistors as is the low-frequency gain.

The low-frequency response of video amplifiers is governed by the values of the coupling and bypass capacitors. The collector-to-base coupling capacitor should be sufficiently large that its reactance is low, at all frequencies of interest, compared with the sum of the transistor input and output incremental impedances (including the biasing resistors). Care should be taken that the signal voltage drop across this coupling capacitor is kept low enough to prevent distortion due to excessive collector-voltage swing in high-level applications. In high-level stages, the capacitive reactance should be low compared with the transistor input impedance. The emitter bypass capacitor must have a reactance which is low compared with the impedance looking into the emitter $[r_e' + r_b'(1 - \alpha_0)]$.

When low-noise video amplification is required, the common-emitter connection is most suitable for the input stage because the source impedance it demands for highest gain is close to the optimum source impedance for minimum noise. The over-all noise figure of a wideband video amplifier is nearly equal to the noise figure of the transistor in the midband frequency range (see Sec. 12.8a). The low-frequency cutoff of the later stages of the amplifier should be at as high a frequency as the signal passband permits in order to minimize the contribution of semiconductor $(1/f)$ noise from the first stage. With most designs of video amplifiers having bandwidths wider than 100 kc, this contribution is negligible.

12.12. Gain-Bandwidth Trade. A video amplifier consisting of one or more common-emitter stages in cascade generally has a specific gain and bandwidth per stage that is governed by the current gain h_{fe} and gain-bandwidth product f_T of the transistors. The bandwidth is not governed only by capacitances which are directly accessible at the device terminals and therefore is not directly proportional to interstage node conductance. This condition is in contrast to the vacuum-tube video amplifier, in which amplification and bandwidth can be linearly traded by varying the interstage load resistor. However, combinations of feedback and loading can be employed in transistor amplifiers for trading gain and bandwidth without serious sacrifice of gain-bandwidth product.[20]

The transistor equivalent-circuit model shown in Fig. 12.17 is of great use in evaluating various schemes for trading gain and bandwidth. Bruun has shown[20] that the major effects of collector-to-base capacitance can be included by modifying this circuit model to the form shown in Fig. 12.41. The multistage bandwidths computed on the basis of Fig. 12.41 will be slightly smaller than they should be, because the input capacitance due to feedback (Miller effect) is assumed constant in Fig. 12.41, whereas in reality this capacitance decreases with increasing frequency owing to the frequency dependence of the load impedance.

Consider the video-amplifier stage shown in Fig. 12.42, which includes both an input shunting resistor R_s and an emitter feedback impedance Z_e. The shunt resis-

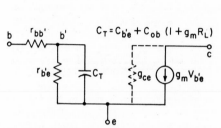

Fig. 12.41. Common-emitter representation for video amplification.

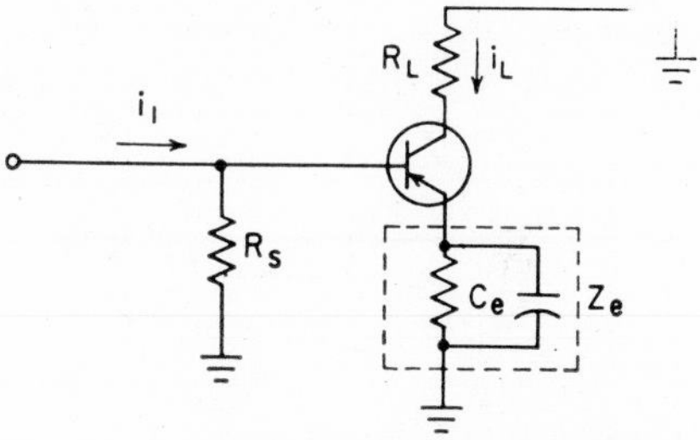

Fig. 12.42. A-c circuit of video amplifier with input loading and emitter degeneration.

tor could be either the generator impedance, if this is a one-stage amplifier, or the interstage loading, including the bias resistors, if we are considering one stage of a cascade. Using the transistor parameters shown in Fig. 12.41, the current amplification of this stage is

$$\frac{I_L}{I_1} = \frac{1}{\dfrac{Z_e + (1/g_m)}{R_s} + \dfrac{1 + j\omega C_T r_{b'e}}{g_m r_{b'e}}\left(1 + \dfrac{r_{bb'} + Z_e}{R_s}\right)} \tag{12.45}$$

If there is no interstage loading ($R_s = \infty$), the emitter feedback impedance will not affect the current amplification and cannot be used for trading gain and bandwidth. However, with interstage loading and with resistive emitter degeneration ($Z_e = R_e + j0$), the low-frequency current amplification is

$$A_i = \frac{I_L}{I_1}(0) = \frac{g_m R_s r_{b'e}}{r_{bb'} + r_{b'e} + R_s + R_e(1 + g_m r_{b'e})} = \frac{\alpha_0}{(1 - \alpha_0)[1 + (r_{bb'}r_{b'e}/R_s)] + (R_e/R_s)} \tag{12.46}$$

and the half-power bandwidth of the current amplification is

$$f_i = \frac{r_{bb'} + r_{b'e} + R_s + R_e(1 + g_m r_{b'e})}{2\pi r_{b'e} C_T (r_{bb'} + R_s + R_e)} \tag{12.47}$$

Therefore, the current amplification–bandwidth product is

$$A_i f_i = \frac{g_m}{2\pi C_T[1 + (r_{bb'} + R_e)/R_s]}$$

$$\approx \frac{\alpha_0 f_T}{1 + (r_{bb'} + R_e)/R_s} \tag{12.48}$$

These relations show that added emitter resistance is effective for trading amplification and bandwidth for the range $R_s(1 - \alpha_0) < R_e < R_s$. They also show that the interstage loading resistance R_s should be large compared with the base spreading resistance $r_{bb'} = r_b'$.

An interesting possibility for the electronic trade of gain and bandwidth was proposed by Bruun,[20] based on the recognition of the fact that both g_m and C_T in Fig. 12.41 are more or less proportional to emitter current. To the extent that these proportionalities are true, the amplification-bandwidth product, as given by Eq. (12.48), is unaffected by changes in bias current. The low-frequency amplification, as given by the second equality of Eq. (12.46), varies inversely with $r_{b'e}$ (provided $r_{b'e} > R_s$ and $R_e = 0$), which in turn varies inversely with bias current. The limitations on this technique are set at one extreme (high currents) by the need for having

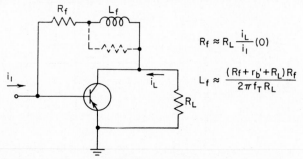

$$R_f \approx R_L \frac{i_L}{i_I}(0)$$

$$L_f \approx \frac{(R_f + r_b' + R_L)R_f}{2\pi f_T R_L}$$

FIG. 12.43. A-c circuit of video-amplifier stage with collector-to-base feedback.

$r_{b'e} > r_{bb'}$ and at the low-current extreme by the contribution to C_T of the emitter depletion-layer capacitance C_{Te}, which varies only slightly with emitter current. The latter limitation is particularly important with graded-base transistors, which have large C_{Te}. The fact that gain and bandwidth may be affected by bias current changes suggests that care must be taken to hold the bias current constant in video amplifiers not employing feedback.

Interstage loading alone can be employed for trading gain and bandwidth (as in vacuum-tube amplifiers) with transistors having low base spreading resistance.[21] It can be seen from Eqs. (12.46) and (12.48) that, even with $R_e = 0$, the current amplification can be traded for bandwidth without loss of current amplification–bandwidth product in the range $r_{bb'} < R_s < r_{b'e}$.

Feedback from output to input of a common-emitter video stage, obtained by connecting a resistive feedback path from collector to base, can be used for trading gain and bandwidth to a limited extent. In this case the resistance R_f of the feedback path at signal frequencies should be in the range $R_L < R_f < R_L/(1 - \alpha_0)$. This technique is not efficient for obtaining very wide bandwidths, because the feedback resistance becomes so low that it substantially loads both the input and output circuits, thereby reducing the amplification-bandwidth product. However, if an inductance L_f is connected in series with the feedback resistance R_f, the gain-bandwidth product can be restored to its value without feedback.[22] The inductance tends to remove the feedback resistance from the circuit at frequencies above $(1 - \alpha_0)f_T$, thereby eliminating its effect on the high-frequency current amplification. The circuit shown in Fig. 12.43 shows this feedback principle together with an approximate expression for determining the value of the inductance. The resistor in shunt with the inductor serves to limit the Q of the resonant circuit formed by the inductor and the collector-to-base capacitance of the transistors.

Degenerative feedback around two stages affords the possibility of very large increases in bandwidth without loss of amplification-bandwidth product. Two such feedback schemes are shown in Fig. 12.44. The first circuit is satisfactory where moderately wide bandwidths, perhaps up to $0.1f_T$, are desired. However, for bandwidths approaching f_T (assuming the same characteristic frequency for both transistors), a feedback ratio approaching 1 is required, implying that the emitter resistance R_{e1} is large and the feedback resistance R_{f1} is small. In this condition, substantial amounts of the available input power and output power are lost in these resistances because of their loading on both the input and output circuits. This loading stems from the fact that the current feedback is returned from a high-impedance point and is applied, in effect, only around the current amplification of the second common-emitter stage.

The second feedback circuit shown in Fig. 12.44 obtains the feedback from a low-impedance point and returns it to a point of somewhat higher impedance, around the

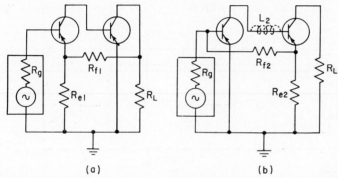

(a)   (b)

FIG. 12.44. A-c circuits of two-stage video amplifiers with feedback for trading current amplification and bandwidth.

current amplification of both transistors. As a result, substantial increases in bandwidth (up to $0.5f_T$) can be obtained while maintaining a constant amplification-bandwidth product.[23] The input and output impedances of this circuit are such that two or more feedback pairs can be directly cascaded without loss of performance and that equal source and load resistances of 500 to 1,000 ohms provide optimum performance with 1-ma transistor bias currents. Because the feedback in this circuit is obtained across a resistance which is, in effect, in series with the load, variations in load impedance do not affect the feedback. Furthermore, because the degenerative loop gain is high, this circuit provides performance which is relatively insensitive to variations in transistor parameters. In many cases, the bandwidth of this circuit can be almost doubled by a series interstage inductance, as discussed in Sec. 12.13.

12.13. High-frequency Peaking. The high-frequency cutoff of video amplifiers can be extended by a ratio of approximately 2 through the addition of appropriate reactive elements. This bandwidth extension is usually obtained at the expense of a more rapid attenuation with frequency and poorer phase linearity beyond the cutoff frequency.

One technique for high-frequency peaking, proposed by Bruun,[20] consists of the addition of a capacitor C_e in shunt with the emitter resistor R_e of a video-amplifier stage with emitter degeneration (Fig. 12.42). The value of the capacitance is adjusted so as to decrease the degeneration, through its shunting effect, in the frequency range where the transistor gain begins to fall with increasing frequency. The required capacitance is $C_e \approx 1/15f_T R_e$.

A second peaking scheme, which accomplishes roughly the same improvement as the emitter capacitor, is to add an inductance L_1 in series with the input shunting resistor R_s of a video amplifier with loading (Fig. 12.42). If the loading is contributed by more than one resistor, as, for example, the collector bias resistor of the driving stage plus the base bias resistor, the inductances in series with each should be adjusted to provide the same time constants L/R. The inductance is adjusted so as to remove the loading in the frequency range where the transistor gain begins to fall. The required inductance is $L_1 \approx R_s/15f_T$.

A third peaking circuit is obtained by adding series interstage inductance L_2 in the base lead of the second transistor of a feedback pair, as shown in Fig. 12.44.[23]

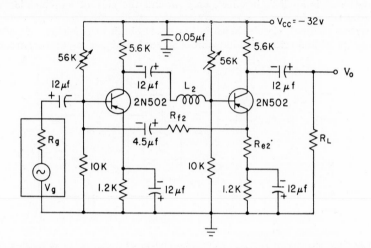

$R_G = R_L$	R_{e2}	R_{f2}	$\dfrac{V_o}{V_g}$	3 – db BW	$G_V \times$ BW PER STAGE $1.56 \times (3\text{-db BW}) \times \sqrt{\dfrac{2\,V_o}{V_g}}$
50	0	∞	150	4.5mc	121 mc
	16.5 ohms	1,500 ohms	45	13	191
	30	430	10.4	48	340
300	0	∞	437	3.3	152
	10	1,300	74	18	340
	22	600	19.9	38	375

Fig. 12.45. Video-amplifier feedback pair. (*Courtesy of Lansdale Tube Company.*)

This inductance increases the bandwidth by forming a resonant impedance-matching network, with transistor input and output capacitances, at frequencies near the amplifier cutoff frequency. The optimum inductance for this service cannot be easily computed because of the many variables on which it depends. However, experience has shown that its reactance at the cutoff frequency of the unpeaked amplifier should be of the order of magnitude of the transistor input impedance h_{ie}. The schematic of a complete video-amplifier feedback pair is shown in Fig. 12.45, together with performance data.

12.14. High-level Video Amplifiers. Video amplifiers are frequently needed for furnishing large peak-to-peak voltage swings with bandwidths of many megacycles for such applications as driving the grid or deflection plates of cathode-ray tubes. The maximum output which can be obtained may be limited by the maximum voltage rating of the transistor or by the useful range of currents over which the transistor provides high-frequency performance.

For amplifiers with very wide bandwidths (greater than 25 mc), the unavoidable wiring capacitance and the transistor output capacitance will force the use of a small load resistance. In these cases the current swing will limit the maximum voltage output. Paralleling output transistors will increase the peak-to-peak load voltage in

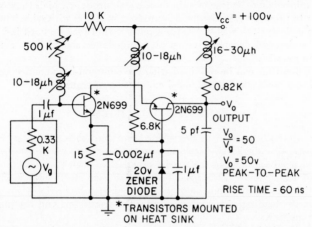

FIG. 12.46. High-level video amplifier. (*Courtesy of Fairchild Semiconductor Corporation.*

those cases where the majority of the output-circuit capacitance is due to the load and wiring and not to the transistors.

For bandwidths less than 5 mc, the limited voltage range of the transistor usually sets the maximum output level. In these cases, it becomes advantageous to use the common-base output circuit, since the characteristics with a common-base connection generally tolerate a larger magnitude of collector voltage before distortion of the collector-characteristic curves is encountered. A further advantage of the common-base connection is the wide bandwidth of its current amplification, which means that its collector voltage can be swung closer to zero without transient distortion than in the common-emitter connection. The required conditions are particularly well met if the common-base output stage is driven from a relatively high-impedance source, such as the output of a common-emitter stage. A practical circuit providing a peak-to-peak swing of 50 volts and a rise time of 60 nanoseconds is shown in Fig. 12.46.

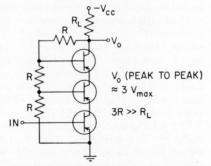

FIG. 12.47. Stacked video amplifier for large output voltage.

If a voltage swing greater than the transistor rated voltage is desired, it is possible to connect transistors in a stack employing signal feedback to ensure that all transistors share the output voltage equally. One such configuration is shown in Fig. 12.47. Employing n similar transistors in such a circuit will provide an output voltage capability of n times the maximum voltage rating of each transistor.

12.15. Summary of Video-amplifier Design Procedures. The following list summarizes the video-amplifier design factors described in the preceding sections.

1. The common-emitter connection is almost universally used.

2. The amplification-bandwidth product per stage is close to f_T.

3. Low-frequency gain per stage is controlled by h_{fe} but can be stabilized by collector-to-emitter feedback, by loading plus emitter degeneration, or by feedback around two stages.

4. The base-bias and collector-bias resistors can be included in the interstage loading, thereby minimizing the loss of gain-bandwidth product which they cause.

5. In order to preserve gain-bandwidth product in stages with wide bandwidth and low gain, the collector-to-emitter feedback path should include both inductance and resistance in series and degenerative emitter impedance should have resistance and capacitance in parallel.

6. High-level output can be obtained with the common-base connection driven by a high-impedance source or by a stacked connection of transistors.

BANDPASS AMPLIFIERS

It is the aim of this section to describe various methods for using transistors in tuned amplifiers, to indicate the performance to be expected from such circuits, and to consider the need and reasons for special precautions which should accompany this application of transistors. This need for special care stems principally from the feedback, which usually becomes more pronounced with increasing frequency, within the transistor, the loading of tuned circuits by the transistor, and the limited usable gain of the transistor.

The feedback within the transistor causes input-output interaction or circuit instability, thereby demanding unilateralization or deliberate mismatch in the great majority of high-frequency tuned-circuit applications. The phenomenon of tuned-circuit loading is usually most prevalent in narrow-band applications, such as a-m radio-amplifier circuits. The limited usable gain, on the other hand, is most serious in higher frequency applications, such as radar and television tuned amplifiers, where wideband amplification is frequently the goal.

In the following paragraphs, a general discussion of high-frequency circuits will precede detailed consideration of unilateralized amplifiers, nonunilateralized amplifiers, tuned circuit losses, and performance.

12.16. High-frequency Circuits. High-frequency transistor amplifiers can be constructed using emitter, base, or collector as the common element to input and output circuits. The majority of requirements, including greatest possible gain, is usually best satisfied by the common-emitter connection, although the common-base connection is more suitable in certain special cases. In general, some form of impedance matching is required or desirable because of the substantial increase of gain which thus can be obtained and because of the relative ease (compared, for example, with video amplifiers) with which it can be applied.

The principal advantages of the common-emitter connection are its high gain, its easily matched impedance levels, and the wide bandwidth (low Q) of its input and output impedances. It will provide gain without interstage impedance transformation. In many cases it has a sufficiently high matched gain that it can be mismatched sufficiently to eliminate the need for unilateralization and still provide substantial gain.

The common-base stage can be used to take advantage of any of a variety of unique features. One such use is with transistors having very low collector-to-emitter feedback, which eliminate any need for unilateralization. Junction tetrode transistors,[24] which have very low base spreading resistance, and many graded-base transistors, particularly those in coaxial[5] or shielded packages which eliminate the header capacitance between collector and emitter leads, are suited for this application. When a common-base stage is deliberately mismatched by making the source impedance high compared with the transistor input impedance and the load impedance low compared with the transistor output impedance, a very constant stage gain can be obtained, particularly for transistors having $\alpha_0 < 1$. In this mode of operation, the only transistor parameter of importance is its common-base current transfer ratio h_{fb} to which the stage amplification is directly proportional. This quantity does not vary appreciably from transistor to transistor, with temperature (except, with some transistors, at very low temperatures), or with aging.

Other applications of the common-base circuit include point-contact transistors and other types having $\alpha_0 > 1$. With such transistors, it is found that the common-base connection is almost universally needed, since a low base-lead impedance is imperative to prevent r-f instability and possible oscillation. The common-base connection lends itself conveniently to broadband unilateralization, as described in Sec. 12.18. Finally, the common-base connection is the most convenient to bias for a stable operating point, since low d-c resistance in the base lead and high d-c resistance in the emitter lead are needed to ensure this stability.

The common-base stage gives power gain principally, and often entirely, by the transfer of signal current from a low-impedance input to a high-impedance output. Therefore impedance matching between stages is imperative. With transistors having $\alpha_0 < 1$, the power gain of a common-base stage is less than the ratio of source conductance G_s to load conductance G_L; therefore the resonant load impedance must be high, implying a narrow bandwidth and critical tuning.

The principal differences between the common-base and the common-emitter connection all involve the factor $1 - \alpha$, since $h_{ib} \approx (1 - \alpha)h_{ie}$, $h_{ob} \approx (1 - \alpha)h_{oe}$, and $(-\alpha) = h_{fb} \approx (1 - \alpha)h_{fe}$. This factor is much less than 1 at low frequencies but becomes comparable to 1 at frequencies near and above the characteristic frequency f_T. Therefore, near the upper end of the frequency range where a transistor can be used, the choice of connection depends not on gain or impedance level but merely on the phase relationships which are desired and on the ease with which it can be unilateralized.

12.17. Interstages. The circuitry between amplifier stages and at the amplifier input and output must meet three requirements. First, it must present the proper impedance levels to the transistors. Second, this circuitry must provide the frequency selectivity. Finally, it must provide the d-c paths for the transistor biases. In addition, if the amplifier stages require unilateralization, the interstages must be considered as part of the external feedback paths which cancel out the internal feedback within the transistors.

Various interstage coupling networks for providing an impedance transformation between the output of one transistor and the input of the next are shown in Fig. 12.48. The first interstage shown is a tapped single-tuned circuit, in which the impedance transformation results from tapping of the coil. The second circuit uses capacitive voltage division within a single-tuned circuit and is almost the equivalent of the tapped coil. Either single-tuned or double-tuned action can be achieved using the third interstage circuit, depending on the degree of coupling between windings of the transformer. This configuration is widely used in unilateralized amplifiers, because the needed inversion of the signal can be achieved with the transformer windings. The series circuit shown as the fourth interstage provides a form of impedance matching without the use of impedance-dividing circuits. This interstage makes use of the fact that, in a high-Q circuit, a small resistance R_1 in series with a capacitance whose reactance at a given frequency is X_c is equivalent, over a narrow band of frequencies, to a resistance X_c^2/R_1 in shunt with the capacitance.

The biasing arrangements shown in Fig. 12.48 are particularly well suited for the common-base connection, because they provide the high d-c resistance in the emitter circuit and the low d-c resistance in the base circuit needed for a stable operating point. They also provide a low d-c resistance in the collector circuit, which minimizes the change of collector voltage with emitter current. For the common-emitter connection, the same impedance transforming techniques can be employed, although different biasing arrangements are optimum. Figure 12.49 shows two widely used interstages for the common-emitter connection. The first circuit, with the base connected to d-c ground, provides as good operating point stability as the circuits of

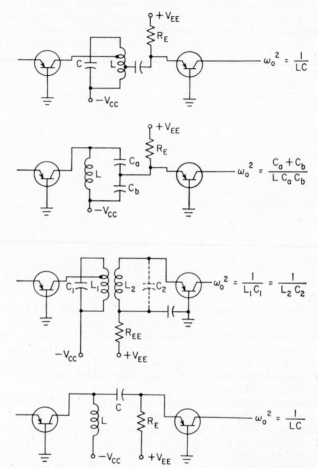

FIG. 12.48. Impedance-transforming interstages for common-base bandpass amplifiers.

Fig. 12.48 but requires the use of two power supplies. In the second circuit, the base supply potential V_{BB} can be obtained from the collector voltage supply via a low-impedance voltage divider; this circuit is also adaptable to electronic gain control when the gain-control bias is applied as the base supply potential.

12.18. Unilateralization (Neutralization). Circuit techniques for canceling the effects of the undesired internal feedback arising within the transistor will be described in this section. The conditions which govern whether or not such techniques are required will be considered in subsequent sections.

A unilateral amplifier stage is one in which the reverse transfer ($h_r = h_{12}$, $y_r = y_{12}$, and $z_r = z_{12}$) is zero. A nonunilateral stage can be completely unilateralized at a given frequency by the addition of feedback from output to input of appropriate amplitude and phase to cancel the internal feedback.† This technique of unilateralization by means of output-to-input feedback is called neutralization.[25,26]

Neutralization can be achieved by many forms of feedback. It is possible to have the neutralizing path either in series or in shunt with the transistor input and independently either in series or in shunt with the output.[25] However, the so-called admittance neutralization, with which the neutralizing path is in shunt with both the input and the output, is most widely used. The term admittance, or y-type, neutralization is applied here because the reverse transfer admittance of the neutralizing

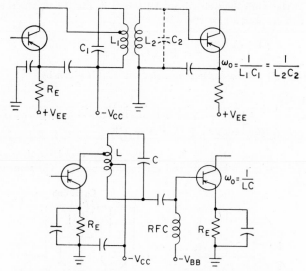

Fig. 12.49. Common-emitter tuned-amplifier interstages.

path Y_{rn} adds directly to the reverse transfer admittance y_r of the amplifier; hence for unilateralization, $Y_{rn} = -y_r$. A second technique, called bridge, or h-type, neutralization, has also been used, particularly for common-base amplifiers. With this circuit the neutralizing network is connected in shunt with the output and in series with the input of the amplifier.

In common-emitter amplifiers, the principal cause of internal feedback within the transistor is the collector-to-base capacitance $C_{ob} = C_c + C_{cbh}$. Based on the equivalent-circuit model of Fig. 12.17, the reverse transfer admittance is

$$y_{re} = j\omega C_{cbh} + j\omega C_c \frac{1}{1 + r_{bb'}[(1/z_{b'e}) + j\omega C_c]} \approx j\omega(C_{cbh} + C_c) \approx j\omega C_{ob} \quad (12.49)$$

Therefore the neutralizing admittance to be tied in shunt with both input and output is

$$Y_{ne} = -y_{re} \approx -j\omega C_{ob} \quad (12.50)$$

Equation (12.50) shows that admittance neutralization of a common-emitter stage can be effected with one capacitor and a 180° phase inversion. The two circuits of Fig. 12.50 show how transformers can be applied to this end. It should be noted that the transformer windings should be tightly coupled in order to preserve the desired phase

† A nonunilateral stage could also be unilateralized by connecting it in cascade with a unilateral isolator; however, such nonreciprocal devices have not yet been proved practical in the frequency ranges at which transistors are applied.

in the neutralizing feedback path.   If a double-tuned interstage is desired, a separate winding, tightly coupled to the primary, or another tap on the primary must be provided for the neutralizing path.

The transistor parameter which should be controlled for designability of neutralized common-emitter amplifiers is C_{ob}, which is easily measured.   Fortunately, this parameter does not vary rapidly with transistor operating point, particularly with graded-base transistors, where a large part of C_{ob} may be contributed by the header.

In common-base amplifiers, the internal feedback within the transistor is caused by both the collector-to-emitter header capacitance C_{ceh} and the collector capacitance. On the basis of the equivalent-circuit model shown in Fig. 12.16, the reverse transfer admittance of the common-base stage is

$$y_{rb} = j\omega C_c \frac{1}{1 - \alpha + z_e'[(1/r_b') + j\omega C_c]} + j\omega C_{ceh} \tag{12.51}$$

and the open-circuit reverse-voltage-transfer ratio h_{rb} is given by

$$\frac{1}{h_{rb}} = 1 + \frac{1}{j\omega[C_c r_b' + C_{ceh} z_e' + C_{ceh} r_b'(1 - \alpha)] - (\omega C_c r_b')(\omega C_{ceh} z_e')}$$

or $$h_{rb} \approx j\omega[C_c r_b' + C_{ceh} z_e' + C_{ceh} r_b'(1 - \alpha)] \tag{12.52}$$

Equation (12.51) shows that y_{rb} is generally complex and requires a neutralizing admittance $Y_{nb} = -y_{rb}$ having both real and reactive parts.   The same two neutraliz-

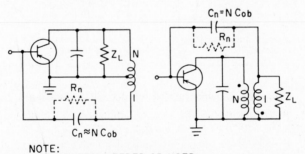

NOTE:
R_n SELDOM NEEDED OR USED

FIG. 12.50. A-c circuits of neutralized common-emitter stages.

ing schemes shown for the common-emitter connection in Fig. 12.50 can be applied to the common-base stage, provided the neutralizing path contains both capacitance and resistance either in series or in parallel.

Equation (12.52) shows that h_{rb} is largely reactive, particularly in those transistors for which $C_{ceh} \ll C_c$.   Furthermore, the reverse-voltage-transfer ratio is roughly proportional to frequency.   When these conditions hold, the broadband neutralizing scheme shown in Fig. 12.51 can be applied.   This circuit is a form of h-type neutralization, in which the neutralizing circuit forms a balanced bridge with the internal collector capacitance and base spreading resistance.   Neutralization of small amounts of in-phase feedback can be achieved with this circuit through the addition of resistance in shunt with C_n or capacitance in shunt with R_n.   An appreciable disadvantage of this circuit is that either the input or the output must be ungrounded.

Care must be taken to avoid overneutralizing a tuned transistor amplifier, because overneutralization causes the same undesirable effects as does the internal feedback. The tolerances on the precision of neutralization are considered in the following sections.

12.18a. Imperfect Neutralization. It is not necessary that the cancellation of the internal feedback within a transistor be complete in order to achieve the desired freedom from input-output interaction and from instability in a tuned amplifier. In this section the limits of misneutralization will be determined, in terms of the pertinent transistor and circuit parameters, for the widely used common-emitter stage.†

A neutralized common-emitter amplifier can be represented by the equivalent circuit shown in Fig. 12.52. The feedback capacitor C includes both the transistor capacitance C_{ob} and the neutralizing capacitance C_n and may be either positive or negative, depending on whether the stage is underneutralized or overneutralized. The effect on neutralization of the base spreading resistance r_b' between C_c and C_n can almost always be neglected. The input and output circuits include con-

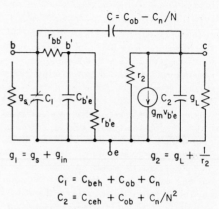

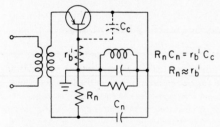

FIG. 12.51. Broadband bridge neutralization of a common-base stage.

FIG. 12.52. Equivalent circuit representation for a nominally neutralized common-emitter stage.

tributions, both to conductance and to capacitance, from the transistor. The feedback through C contributes an admittance to the input terminals which may have a negative conductive component with certain output impedances. The maximum value of this negative conductance is

$$-g = \frac{g_m \omega C}{2g_2}$$

which occurs at a 45° phase angle of the load impedance. If this negative conductance exceeds g_1, the amplifier will be unstable. Hence, the minimum feedback capacitance $C = C_{ob} - C_n/N$ which will cause instability is[27]

$$C_{osc} = \frac{2g_1 g_2}{\omega g_m} \qquad (12.53)$$

If the stage is conjugately matched, in order to provide the maximum available gain, $g_1 = 2g_{in}$ and $g_2 = 2g_{out}$, where g_{in} and g_{out} are the input and output conductances of the neutralized transistor ($C = 0$). Therefore,

$$C_{osc,min} = \frac{8g_{in}g_{out}}{\omega g_m} \qquad (12.54)$$

† The author is indebted to Joseph C. Tellier for his many contributions, including Fig. 12.53, to this section. Detailed discussions of many of the topics described herein can be found in reference 27.

Since the maximum available power gain is given by

$$G_{mi}^{mo} = \frac{g_m^2}{4g_{in}g_{out}}$$

the maximum feedback capacitance which can be tolerated without instability is

$$C_{osc,min} = \frac{4}{\omega}\sqrt{\frac{g_{in}g_{out}}{G_{mi}^{mo}}} \tag{12.55}$$

It is apparent from Eq. (12.53) that an amplifier stage can be made more tolerant of feedback-capacitance variations by increasing g_1 and g_2. In a single-stage circuit, this loading can be accomplished by decreasing the source and load resistances. In a multistage amplifier, this loading can be accomplished only by the addition of shunt resistance to the interstages or by mismatching so as to increase coil losses. With most transistors, both the input conductance and the output conductance are roughly proportional to emitter current whereas the feedback current is almost independent of bias current. Therefore, it is possible to improve stability without sacrifice of gain by increasing the transistor bias current.

Feedback capacitances too small to give oscillation may nevertheless cause apparent detuning and narrowing (skewing) of synchronously tuned stages. The apparent detuning is a result of the negative conductance due to feedback on one side of the resonant frequency, which appears as a positive conductance of the same magnitude on the other side of the resonant frequency. If the stage is underneutralized ($C > 0$), the apparent resonant frequency is lower than the actual resonance, whereas overneutralization raises the apparent resonant frequency. The curves of Fig. 12.53 show the effects of underneutralization on a stage with synchronously tuned input and output of equal Q's. It can be seen that small amounts of misneutralization cause frequency shift without much bandwidth change. This change is not serious in practice, because it would be counteracted during amplifier alignment by raising the resonant frequency of the tuned circuits. It is found that misneutralization of $C/C_{osc} = 0.4$ is the limit that can be tolerated in practical amplifiers without severe interaction of input tuning and output tuning in fixed-gain stages. In gain-controlled stages, $C/C_{osc} = 0.2$ is the maximum misneutralization that can be employed without significant shift of center frequency with gain change.

12.18b. Fixed Neutralization. Because a certain amount of misneutralization can be tolerated without instability or noticeable skewing, it is possible in many cases to design reproducible transistor amplifiers using a fixed value of neutralizing capacitance. The first step is to select a value for the neutralizing capacitance C_n which will provide optimum neutralization of the design center value of feedback capacitance C_{ob}. The following procedure will then ensure stable operation of the common-emitter stage, despite variations in C_n and C_{ob}.

The maximum feedback capacitance C which exists in this nominally neutralized stage is equal to the sum $\Delta C_{ob} + \Delta C_n/N$, where the tolerance values are defined as $\Delta C_{ob} = \frac{1}{2}(C_{ob,max} - C_{ob,min})$. In a fixed-gain stage, the feedback capacitance required for oscillation is then

$$C_{o,c} = \frac{C}{0.4} = 2.5\left(\Delta C_{ob} + \frac{\Delta C_n}{N}\right) \tag{12.56}$$

This case will be considered further; however, it should be realized that for a variable-gain stage, the equivalent relation would be $C_{osc} = 5C$.

Using Eq. (12.53), the product g_1g_2 of the conductances of the input and output circuits can be determined,

$$g_1 g_2 = \frac{g_m \omega C_{osc}}{2} = 1.25 g_m \omega C \qquad (12.57)$$

where $g_m \approx I_E(\text{ma})/27$. If this product is less than $4g_{in}g_{out}$, the transistor may be conjugately matched, and full use made of its maximum available gain. The conductances g_{in} and g_{out} (for the neutralized transistor) are equal to the real parts of the short-circuit input and output admittances, as determined from Sec. 12.6a. However, if the value of Eq. (12.57) is greater than $4g_{in}g_{out}$ (as is usually the case), additional

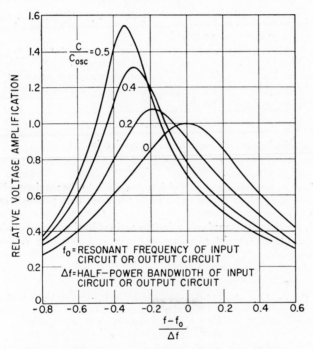

FIG. 12.53. Tuning asymmetry due to misneutralization.

loading is required. It is usually optimum to equalize the loading between the input and the output, by making

$$\frac{g_{in}}{g_1} = \frac{g_{out}}{g_2} \qquad (12.58)$$

Simultaneously satisfying Eqs. (12.57) and (12.58) leads to a design which meets the desired stability and skewing requirements. Examination of these relations shows the advantage of increasing emitter current, because g_m, g_{in}, and g_{out} are all roughly proportional to emitter current.

If the source and load for the amplifier are nonregenerative, it is possible to achieve the desired loading by mismatch. In this case, the mismatch loss at the input and output are given by

$$\frac{P_i}{P_s} = \frac{P_L}{P_o} = 4\left(1 - \frac{g_{in}}{g_1}\right)\frac{g_{in}}{g_1} = 4\left(1 - \frac{g_{out}}{g_2}\right)\frac{g_{out}}{g_2} \qquad (12.59)$$

However, in an interstage of a multistage amplifier, it is not possible to achieve stability by mismatch, since the improvement in the stability of one stage is achieved at the expense of poorer stability in the other.   In this case, it is desirable to maintain equal loading by both transistors connected to an interstage and obtain the stability by either coil losses or added conductance.   Therefore, the interstage loss required for a certain degree of stability is much greater than the mismatch loss given by Eq. (12.59).   For equal loading of an interstage by both transistors, the interstage loss is given by

$$\frac{P_{\text{in}}}{P_{\text{avail}}} = 4\left(\frac{g_{\text{in}}}{g_1}\right)^2 \tag{12.60}$$

where P_{in} is the power delivered into the second transistor, and P_{avail} is the available power from the output of the first transistor.

12.18c. Unneutralized Stages.   An unneutralized amplifier can be treated as a special case of misneutralization in which the neutralizing capacitor is identically zero. The maximum feedback capacitance C in a common-emitter amplifier is then the maximum collector-to-base capacitance $C_{ob,\text{max}}$.   The product of the input and output conductances for a fixed-gain stage is

$$g_1 g_2 = 1.25 g_m \omega C_{ob,\text{max}} \tag{12.61}$$

For a gain-controlled stage, the equivalent expression is

$$g_1 g_2 = 2.5 g_m \omega C_{ob,\text{max}} \tag{12.62}$$

where g_m is given its maximum value, which corresponds to the maximum bias current. The analysis for the desired source and load impedances then proceeds exactly as in Sec. 12.18*b*.

It can be shown that the transducer gain (the ratio of load power to available source power) of the stabilized transistor (with $g_s = g_{\text{in}}$, $g_L = g_{\text{out}}$) can be written

$$\frac{P_L}{P_s} = \frac{g_m^2}{g_1 g_2}\frac{2g_s}{g_1}\frac{2g_L}{g_2} = \frac{g_m^2}{g_1 g_2}\frac{2g_{\text{in}}}{g_1}\frac{2g_{\text{out}}}{g_2} \tag{12.63}$$

Substituting the product of conductances given by Eq. (12.61) yields the expression

$$\frac{P_L}{P_s} = \frac{g_m}{1.25\omega C_{ob}}\frac{2g_{\text{in}}}{g_1}\frac{2g_{\text{out}}}{g_2} \tag{12.64}$$

which shows that the figure of merit for unneutralized amplification is g_m/C_{ob}. Because the factors $2g_{\text{in}}/g_1$ and $2g_{\text{out}}/g_2$ are never greater than 1 (they are typically 0.2 to 0.5), the maximum unneutralized gain is bounded by

$$\frac{P_L}{P_s} < \frac{g_m}{1.25\omega C_{ob}} \tag{12.65}$$

For a transistor with $C_{ob} = 3$ pf and $g_m = 0.037$ mho ($I_E = 1$ ma) the maximum usable unneutralized gain at 455 kc would be slightly less than 3,500 (35 db).

12.19. Gain of Tuned Amplifiers.   The gain of a tuned transistor amplifier is governed both by various transistor parameters and by certain properties of associated components.   Since transistors have limited power gain, losses in the coupling, selective, and neutralizing circuits must be included.   As a general rule, circuit losses are most important in narrow-band circuits, while transistor limitations are most pronounced in wideband circuits, particularly at high frequencies.

The power gain

$$G = \frac{R_L}{r_{\text{in}}}\left(\frac{i_L}{i_{\text{in}}}\right)^2 \tag{12.66}$$

of an amplifier is the ratio of power delivered to the desired load to power delivered to the transistor input. Here R_L and r_{in} are the real parts of the load and transistor input impedances, respectively, and i_L and i_{in} are the signal currents through the load and input. This gain must include both the transistor gain and the losses in the associated circuits. This definition of gain implies that any losses due to dissipation and mismatch in the input circuit are included in the gain of the preceding stage.

Because transistors are bilateral elements, particularly at high frequency, the computation of transistor gain is involved. Fortunately, useful theoretical aids are available which lead to simple methods for predicting transistor gain. One useful theoretical quantity is the unilateral power gain, which is defined as the gain of an active circuit neutralized by means of a lossless network so that the reverse transfer function (z_r, y_r, or h_r) is zero.[28] The unilateral power gain U is given by

$$U = \frac{|z_f - z_r|^2}{4(r_i r_o - r_f r_r)} = \frac{|y_f - y_r|^2}{4(g_i g_o - g_f g_r)}$$

$$= \frac{|h_f + h_r|^2}{4[\text{Re}\,(h_i)\,\text{Re}\,(h_o) + \text{Im}\,(h_f)\,\text{Im}\,(h_r)]} \tag{12.67}$$

where r_j is the real part of the open-circuit impedance z_j of the active network and g_j is the real part of the short-circuit admittance y_j. This gain is the same for common-base, common-emitter, and common-collector connections and represents a single very useful figure of merit for the transistor. In those rare cases where the reverse transfer within the transistor is negligible, the unilateral power gain becomes

$$U = \frac{|z_f|^2}{4 r_i r_o} = \frac{|y_f|^2}{4 g_i g_o} = \frac{|h_f|^2}{4\,\text{Re}\,(h_i)\,\text{Re}\,(h_o)} \tag{12.68}$$

Comparison of Eqs. (12.68) and (12.65) will indicate the validity of neglecting the reverse transfer in a common-emitter stage.

A somewhat equivalent expression to Eq. (12.67) was derived by Linvill,[29] who showed that the maximum available gain of a two-port active element that is unconditionally stable (for all passive source and load impedances) is within 3 db of

$$\frac{P_L}{P_s} = \frac{|h_f|^2}{4\,\text{Re}\,(h_i)\,\text{Re}\,(h_o) - 2\,\text{Re}\,(h_f h_r)} \tag{12.69}$$

The exact evaluation of Eqs. (12.67) and (12.69) from equivalent-circuit models is uselessly tedious. The main value of these relationships is in the design of circuits based on transistor parameter measurements, as those made with a transadmittance meter. Nevertheless, they do provide analytical confirmation of the widely observed fact that the unilateral power gain at high frequencies varies inversely with the square of frequency (-6 db/octave). For example, the hybrid parameters for a common-emitter connection of the equivalent-circuit model of Fig. 12.17 are

$$h_f = (g_m - j\omega C_c)\frac{r_{b'e}}{1 + j\omega(C_{b'e} + C_c)r_{b'e}}$$

$$h_i = r_{bb'} + \frac{r_{b'e}}{1 + j\omega(C_{b'e} + C_c)r_{b'e}}$$

$$h_o = \frac{j\omega C_c[1 + (g_m + j\omega C_{b'e})r_{b'e}]}{1 + j\omega(C_{b'e} + C_c)r_{b'e}} + g_{ce}$$

$$h_r = \frac{j\omega C_{b'e}r_{b'e}}{1 + j\omega(C_{b'e} + C_c)r_{b'e}}$$

$$\tag{12.70}$$

In the frequency range where $\omega(C_{b'c} + C_c)r_{b'e} \gg 1$, which is the range where h_{fe} varies inversely with frequency, the unilateral power gain is approximated by

$$U \approx \frac{g_m}{4r_{bb'}C_{b'e}C_c\omega^2} = \frac{\alpha_0 f_T}{8\pi r_b' C_c f^2} \tag{12.71}$$

in which the additional assumptions that $C_{b'e} \gg C_c$, $g_m \gg 1/r_{b'e}$, and $g_{ce} \ll g_m C_c/C_{b'e}$ have been used. In addition to showing that high-frequency power gain varies inversely with the square of frequency, Eq. (12.71) also shows that the frequency corresponding to $U = 1$, which is the maximum frequency of oscillation, is

$$f_{max} = \sqrt{\frac{\alpha_0 f_T}{8\pi r_b' C_c}} \tag{12.17}$$

Figure 12.54 summarizes the frequency dependence of high-frequency transistor gain and can generally be used in place of more rigorous computations once the matched, neutralized gain is known at one high frequency. If the gain predicted from Fig. 12.54 does not exceed the gain limit predicted by Eq. (12.65), a common-emitter stage need not be neutralized for obtaining maximum available gain without regeneration. Otherwise, either neutralization or gain sacrifice through mismatch must be employed.

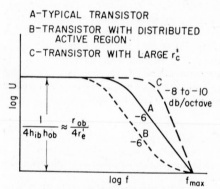

A-TYPICAL TRANSISTOR

B-TRANSISTOR WITH DISTRIBUTED ACTIVE REGION

C-TRANSISTOR WITH LARGE r_c'

FIG. 12.54. Unilateral gain versus frequency.

The only significant violations of the -6 db/octave law implied by Fig. 12.54 are provided by transistors with large collector body resistance or with a significantly distributed active region, as discussed in Sec. 12.5b. Certain "mesa" and grown-junction transistors possess such characteristics. The frequency dependence of the gain of these exceptions is illustrated by the dashed curves in Fig. 12.54.

The maximum useful gain which can be obtained from a transistor at high frequencies can now be described. If complete neutralization can be provided, the maximum useful gain is close to the unilateral power gain. Even though higher gain than the unilateral power gain can be obtained in some cases with dissipative neutralization, the higher gain is obtained at the price of gain stability and is of questionable usefulness. In order to provide complete neutralization, it is necessary to measure the reverse transfer through the stage during adjustment of the neutralizing circuits, which measurement is seldom practical in a multistage amplifier. In these cases, fixed neutralization can be employed but the maximum useful gain per common-emitter stage cannot exceed

$$G_{max} \leqq \frac{g_m}{1.25\omega(\Delta C_{ob} + \Delta C_n/N)} \tag{12.72}$$

Finally, in an unneutralized common-emitter amplifier, the maximum useful gain cannot exceed the limit imposed by Eq. (12.65).

12.20. Input and Output Impedance. The input and output impedances of a neutralized amplifier are conveniently determined quantities because they are independent of the load or source impedance. It is merely necessary to combine the appropriate impedance of the transistor itself, having any suitable termination, with the contribution from the neutralizing circuit. The transistor impedances were derived in Sec. 12.6.

The impedance levels of an amplifier with imperfect or no neutralization cannot be specified exactly. However, the results for the neutralized amplifier are a good guide, because the only amplifiers of practical interest are those in which the interaction between input and output is almost negligible. Therefore, one can use the impedance levels of the neutralized transistor (with appropriate changes in the contribution from the neutralizing circuit) as the impedance levels of a stage with imperfect or no neutralization.

Input impedance is readily computed for a short-circuited output, since almost all neutralizing circuits are connected in parallel with the transistor output. For the admittance-neutralized common-emitter stage, the neutralizing capacitor $C_n = NC_{ob}$ appears in parallel with the transistor short-circuit input impedance, as given by Eq. (12.21). For an admittance-neutralized common-base stage, the input impedance is given by the transistor impedance h_{ib}, as given by Eq. (12.19), in parallel with the neutralizing impedance $1/Ny_{rb}$, with y_{rb} given by Eq. (12.51). For bridge, or h-type, neutralization of a common-base stage, the input impedance consists of the transistor impedance h_{ib} in series with the neutralizing resistance and capacitance in parallel. With the most efficient impedance level in the bridge-neutralizing circuit, $R_n = r'_b$, so that the input impedance becomes

$$z_{\text{in}} \text{ (bridge neut)} = h_{ib} + \frac{R_n}{1 + j\omega C_n R_n} \approx z_{eb'} + r'_b(2 - \alpha') \qquad (12.73)$$

Output impedance levels can be determined similarly. For an admittance-neutralized common-emitter stage, the output admittance consists of the transistor output admittance y_{oe} plus the admittance of the neutralizing circuit referred to the impedance level of the collector, $j\omega C_n/N^2$. The output impedance of an admittance-neutralized common-base stage is of the same order as that of the common-emitter stage because $y_{ob} = y_{oe}$. However, the resistance in the common-base neutralizing path will somewhat increase the output conductance of this connection. Finally, for the common-base bridge-neutralized stage, the output impedance consists of the parallel combination of the open-circuit transistor output impedance, given by the circuit of Fig. 12.29, and the neutralizing components in series, $R_n + (1/j\omega C_n)$.

12.21. Interstage Losses. Parasitic losses in interstage tuning elements may significantly reduce the gain which can be obtained from a tuned transistor stage, particularly in cases where the unloaded bandwidth of the tuning elements is comparable to the over-all bandwidth. Fortunately, in many cases the interstage losses can be used to provide part or all of the interstage loading needed for stability of unneutralized or fixed-neutralized amplifiers (see Secs. 12.18b and 12.18c). However, when one desires the maximum possible gain or the best noise figure, the losses in tuning elements become highly undesirable and must be minimized. In this section it will be shown that the minimum interstage losses are related directly to the ratio of loaded Q to unloaded Q of the tuning elements.

Transistor input impedance at high frequencies is normally complex but of low Q (Sec. 12.6), with the result that it can be adequately represented, for narrow-band amplifiers, by a constant resistance. The reactive component may produce detuning but has negligible effect on circuit Q. The output impedance can be represented by a constant resistance and capacitance in parallel for a narrow bandwidth.

A single-tuned circuit with transistor driver and load can be represented by the circuit of Fig. 12.55. In this figure the tuned circuit is represented by inductance L_x and capacitance C_x in parallel with g_x, which represents the losses in these and other auxiliary elements. The transistor output impedance is represented by g_t and capacitance C_t across the tuned circuit. This representation is satisfactory for any high-Q circuit if the appropriate impedance transformations (to account for inductive or capacitive tapping into the tuned circuit) are included. The load conductance g_L is likewise a conductance across the whole tank circuit and may include an impedance transformation or a series-parallel transformation in the case of the series-tuned circuit of Fig. 12.48. The normalized power gain of this circuit is

$$\frac{G}{G_{mo}} = \left(1 - \frac{Q_L}{Q_U}\right)^2 \frac{4g_t g_L}{(g_t + g_L)^2} \tag{12.74}$$

where

$$Q_U = \frac{1}{\omega_0 L g_x}$$

is the unloaded Q of the coil (losses due to biasing resistors, etc., are included in Q_U) and

$$Q_L = \frac{f_0}{\Delta f} = \frac{1}{\omega_0 L(g_t + g_x + g_L)}$$

is the loaded Q of the interstage. G_{mo} is the gain if all the available power from the driver transistor is transferred to the load. The first factor in Eq. (12.74) represents

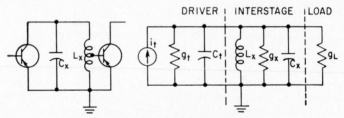

DRIVER ┆ INTERSTAGE ┆LOAD

FIG. 12.55. Single-tuned interstage.

the losses due to coil dissipation, whereas the second factor is the mismatch function. This equation shows that the power gain decreases as the loaded Q of the tuned circuit approaches the unloaded Q. It also shows that maximum gain for any given ratio of Q_L/Q_U is obtained by matching the load impedance to the transistor output impedance ($g_t = g_L$) without regard to the coil dissipation. This condition is met when

$$C_x + C_t = \frac{2g_t}{\omega_0[(1/Q_L) - (1/Q_U)]} \tag{12.75}$$

from which the optimum value of externally added capacitance C_x (referred to the same impedance level as C_t) can be found. In some cases, particularly wideband amplifiers, this value of externally added capacitance could become negative. However, coil losses are not important in wideband amplifiers.

Doubled-tuned circuits can be represented by Fig. 12.56, where the appropriate impedance and series-parallel transformations have been included. The normalized power gain of this circuit, the ratio of load power to available power from the driver transistor, is

$$\frac{G}{G_{mo}} = \left(\frac{2P}{1 + P^2}\right)^2 \left(1 - \frac{Q_{Lp}}{Q_{Up}}\right)\left(1 - \frac{Q_{Ls}}{Q_{Us}}\right) \tag{12.76}$$

where $P = k/k_c$ is the ratio of coefficient of coupling to critical coupling,

$$Q_{Lp} = \frac{1}{\omega_0 L_p(g_p + g_t)} \qquad Q_{Ls} = \frac{1}{\omega_0 L_s(g_s + g_L)} \tag{12.77}$$

are the loaded Q's of the primary and secondary, respectively, and

$$Q_{Up} = \frac{1}{\omega_0 L_p g_p} \qquad Q_{Us} = \frac{1}{\omega_0 L_s g_s} \tag{12.78}$$

are the unloaded coil Q's. For critical coupling, Eq. (12.76) becomes

$$\frac{G}{G_{mo}} = \left(1 - \frac{Q_{Lp}}{Q_{Up}}\right)\left(1 - \frac{Q_{Ls}}{Q_{Us}}\right) \tag{12.79}$$

To the extent that the transistor input and output representations are valid, Eqs. (12.74), (12.75), and (12.79) are valid even in a broadband case, provided that for

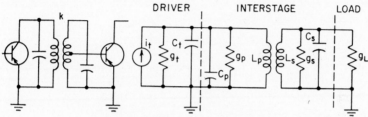

FIG. 12.56. Double-tuned interstage.

the double-tuned case the Q's are defined in Eqs. (12.77) and (12.78) on the basis of a frequency

$$\omega_0 = \sqrt{\frac{1}{LC}} \sqrt{\frac{1}{1 - k^2}}$$

There are cases where it may be desirable to violate the conditions indicated by Eqs. (12.74) and (12.76) in order to improve stability or to render the amplifier bandwidth and center frequency independent of transistor characteristics. For example, if the driver transistor were to be gain-controlled, its output impedance would vary with gain change; in this case the driver would be coupled more lightly than the load ($g_t \ll g_L$). Although such compromises can be prescribed only for specific cases, the

FIG. 12.57. Narrow-band transistor amplifier with separate gain and selectivity sections.

gain expressions given here can serve equally well for optimum and compromise conditions.

Because of the importance of interstage losses in narrow-band amplifiers, it is frequently desirable to separate the gain and selectivity functions, as indicated in Fig. 12.57. Highly selective crystal, ceramic, or multisection mechanical filters make this approach extremely attractive. The amplifier interstage bandwidths are made sufficiently broad that coil losses in them are negligible. An additional advantage of this approach is that the interstages need not be precisely tuned and that tuning variations with gain control are unimportant. The preamplifier preceding the filter must have sufficient gain that the signal level at the output of the filter (which may have appreciable attenuation at band center) is well above the noise level of the postamplifier. On the other hand, the gain of the preamplifier must not be so great that noise or signals outside the passband of the filter could cause overload in the output stage of the preamplifier.

12.22. Bandwidth of Tuned Amplifiers.   There are two distinct limitations to the freedom of control that one has over the bandwidth of a tuned transistor amplifier. First is the limitation on the degree to which the bandwidth of an amplifier can be narrowed before the loss of gain, due to coil losses, becomes excessive.   This question is almost independent of transistor characteristics and is concerned entirely with interstage losses, as discussed in Sec. 12.21.   These narrow-band limitations are summarized by Eq. (12.74) for the single-tuned interstage and by Eq. (12.76) for the double-tuned interstage.†   The second bandwidth limitation is imposed on wideband amplifiers either directly or indirectly by the transistor characteristics.   These points are illustrated by Fig. 12.58.

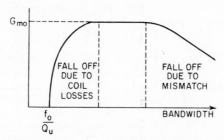

FIG. 12.58. Transistor bandpass amplifier gain versus bandwidth.

As with vacuum-tube amplifiers, the widest bandwidth for a given gain is obtained with the minimum possible total shunt capacitance across the tuned circuit.   The transistor input and output susceptances provide an irreducible minimum of capacitance, thereby limiting the maximum bandwidth.   Additional limitations are imposed in some cases by the need for equalizing the fall off of gain with frequency or by the need for added capacitance to stabilize the center frequency.

The bridge-neutralized common-base amplifier has the narrowest bandwidth and provides the most easily visualized bandwidth limitation.   In this connection, the Q of the output circuit is high and hence provides the bandwidth limitation.   To the extent that the header capacitances are negligible, Fig. 12.29 shows that the Q of the transistor output impedance is

$$Q_t = \frac{1}{2\pi f_0 C_c r_b'} \tag{12.80}$$

With a matched load, the loaded Q is half that given by Eq. (12.80), or

$$\Delta f = \frac{2f_0}{Q_t} = 4\pi f_0^2 C_c r_b' \tag{12.81}$$

Combining this expression with Eq. (12.71) for the unilateral gain gives a matched-load, amplification-bandwidth product of

$$\sqrt{U}\, \Delta f \approx \frac{f_T}{f_{max}} \frac{f_0}{2} \tag{12.82}$$

† The half-power bandwidth of a transitionally coupled double-tuned circuit varies between $\sqrt{2}\,f_0/Q_L$ for $Q_L = Q_{Lp} = Q_{Ls}$ and $f_0/\sqrt{2}\,Q_L$ for $Q_L = Q_{Lp}$ with $Q_{Ls} \gg Q_{Lp}$ or $Q_L = Q_{Ls}$ with $Q_{Lp} \gg Q_{Ls}$.   With critical coupling, the bandwidths are comparable when Q_{Lp} and Q_{Ls} are of the same order of magnitude.

which shows that this performance figure is proportional to center frequency. The matched power-gain–bandwidth product is simply

$$U \, \Delta f \approx \frac{f_T}{2}$$

For admittance neutralization of common-emitter or common-base stages, the Q of the transistor output impedance is appreciably lower than that of the bridge-neutralized stage. Therefore, broader bandwidths can be obtained with this circuit. Figure 12.26 and Eqs. (12.23) yield the result that the short-circuit output admittance (either common-base or common-emitter) has a Q (the ratio of conductance to susceptance at frequency f_0) given by

$$Q_t = \frac{f_0}{f_T} + \frac{f_T}{f_0} \left[\left(\frac{r_e'}{r_b'} \right)^2 + \frac{r_e'}{r_b'} \right] \tag{12.83}$$

This expression confirms the widely observed fact that, in the range $0.1f_{max} < f_0 < f_{max}$, the output Q with the input short-circuited usually lies between 1 and 5 and increases with decreasing frequency.

The short-circuit input impedance of a transistor, which approximates closely the input impedance of an admittance-neutralized stage, likewise has a low Q. The maximum phase angle of the input impedance, from Eqs. (12.20) and (12.21) and Figs. 12.21 and 12.23, is seldom greater than 75°, implying a maximum input Q of 4, and is usually much lower than this limit.

It should be realized that the input and output impedances are not equivalent to simple parallel combinations of a single fixed resistance and a single fixed capacitance, so that half-power bandwidths cannot be predicted precisely by the quotient f_0/Q. Nevertheless, the preceding two paragraphs should serve to indicate that the transistor itself can be a wideband device. Equation (12.83) shows that the bandwidth of the output admittance of a matched, admittance-neutralized stage tends to vary as the square of center frequency for frequencies below $0.2f_T$ and as the first power of frequency for frequencies near f_T. Therefore, for frequencies well below f_T (and hence f_{max}), the amplification-bandwidth product is proportional to center frequency, whereas near f_T the product is independent of center frequency. For example a transistor with $r_e' = r_b'/4$ would have an amplification-bandwidth product of $0.6f_{max}$ at a frequency $f_0 = 0.1f_{max}$, and a product of $1.5f_{max}$ at $f_0 = 0.3f_{max}$.

It is fortunate that the transistor has a large inherent amplification-bandwidth capability, because in practice it is seldom possible to make full use of it. Both the input and output susceptance of a transistor vary with operating bias and from unit to unit, so that it is generally desirable to add capacitance to tuned circuits within transistor amplifiers in order to desensitize the center frequency to these changes. The loss of amplification-bandwidth product is directly proportional to the amount of desensitizing. The need for additional tuning capacitance is particularly pressing in gain-controlled stages, where the bias current is deliberately changed over wide ranges. In wideband service, it is typical to add capacitance equal to 1.5 to 4 times the transistor susceptance, thereby reducing the amplification-bandwidth product to 0.4 to 0.2 times its maximum matched value.

The foregoing considerations apply for a matched load with a single-tuned interstage. It is possible to increase the amplification-bandwidth product at any frequency by mismatching the load, making its conductance larger than that required for match. This procedure is entirely compatible with the technique of mismatching to reduce the need for neutralization, as discussed in Secs. 12.18b and 12.18c. If the interstage conductance g_x (of Fig. 12.55) is neglected, the gain, bandwidth, and amplification-bandwidth product vary as follows:

$$\frac{G}{G_{mo}} = \frac{4g_L g_t}{[1 + (g_L/g_t)]^2}$$

$$\frac{\Delta f}{\Delta f_{mo}} = \frac{1 + (g_L/g_t)}{2} \tag{12.84}$$

$$\frac{\sqrt{G}\,\Delta f}{\sqrt{G_{mo}}\,\Delta f_{mo}} = \sqrt{\frac{g_L}{g_t}}$$

Curves showing these functions are given in Fig. 12.59. It can be seen that the amplification-bandwidth product which is lost through the necessary addition of tuning capacitance can be recovered in large part through mismatch. To use interstage

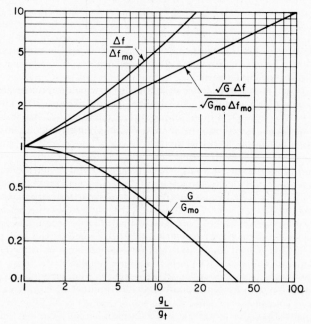

Fig. 12.59. Gain and bandwidth versus load mismatch.

loading is not so efficient a method of increasing bandwidth as is the use of load mismatch; however, it may be required for interstages in multistage amplifiers, as discussed in Secs. 12.18b and 12.18c. With equal coupling of both transistors to an interstage ($g_t = g_L$), the gain and bandwidth vary with interstage loading as follows:

$$\frac{G}{G_{mo}} = \frac{1}{[1 + (g_x/2g_t)]^2}$$

$$\frac{\Delta f}{\Delta f_{mo}} = 1 + \frac{g_x}{2g_t} \tag{12.85}$$

It can be seen that the amplification-bandwidth product in this case is unaffected by the loading.

12.23. Gain Control of Tuned Amplifiers. The gain of a transistor tuned amplifier stage can be varied by changing the quiescent operating point of the transistor. A change in operating point does not vary the maximum available gain of the transistor to a great extent. However, the input and output impedances of transistors are approximately inversely proportional to emitter current. Consequently, gain control is effected by designing the input and output circuits such that the mismatch varies with transistor bias. The circuits shown in Fig. 12.49 are two examples of how gain-controlled stages could be connected. Usually the gain-control bias is applied to the base, although the emitter can be used with a low-impedance bias supply.

A compromise is necessary between ease of gain control and operating-point stability. For good stability it is desirable to have a large d-c resistance in the emitter circuit. However, the larger this resistance, the larger the range over which the variable bias voltage must be changed to produce a given change in gain. Good stability also requires a low-impedance bias supply for base control. Consequently, operating-point stability is achieved at the direct expense of control power.

Because gain variations are achieved by mismatch at both input and output, both the bandwidth and center frequency may be affected by a change in operating point. Again a compromise is required, this time between constancy of center frequency or bandwidth and maximum stage gain. When the stage gain is reduced appreciably, the interstage loading due to the transistor input and output impedance is negligible. If stable center frequency and bandwidth are required, it is necessary to ensure that even for maximum gain the loading on input and output circuits by the transistor be small. Hence, even at maximum gain a gain-controlled stage should be mismatched with $g_s > g_{in}$ and $g_L > g_{out}$ for greatest constancy of selectivity. This condition is compatible with the requirements for noncritical neutralization, as discussed in Secs. 12.18b and 12.18c. With this mismatch condition, the power gain varies directly with the square of bias current.

The amount of gain variation that can be achieved by bias control depends on the degree of neutralization. If no neutralization is employed, the gain cannot be reduced much below 1 because of the capacitive coupling from the low-impedance input to the higher-impedance output. In many cases, such as broadcast-band intermediate-frequency amplifiers, this minimum limit is adequate, because the maximum gain per stage may be 30 db or more. However, for higher frequencies and wider bandwidths or for a wider range of gain control, neutralization is required and should be adjusted for best balance with the transistor in a low-gain condition.

Overloading in a gain-controlled stage is frequently a serious problem. The maximum signal input demands the smallest stage gain in an automatic-gain-control system. Gain is reduced by reducing bias current, and hence bias power. Therefore, a gain-controlled stage is required to handle maximum signal just when it is least able to do so. For this reason, gain control must be applied to the early stages in an amplifying cascade. If overload is still serious, it is necessary to resort to other gain-control techniques for the strong-signal condition. A semiconductor diode, used as a variable-conductance shunt across the input, can be used as a very efficient gain-reducing element by biasing it in the forward direction to reduce gain. With this element, maximum signals accompany maximum bias current and greatest immunity to overload.

With tetrode transistor amplifiers, it is possible to achieve gain control by varying the bias of the second base (b_2 of Fig. 12.8). This technique nicely circumvents the overload problem because the emitter current and collector voltage are unchanged. However, it provides a more limited range of gain change than that obtained with the emitter-current control.

The possibility exists of gain control by varying the collector bias voltage. This mode of operation can be attained by providing a large d-c resistance in the collector-supply circuit. This technique is less used than emitter-current variation, because it is more apt to cause difficulty with misneutralization and with large-signal overload.

12.24. High-level Tuned Amplifiers. The techniques described in this section are applicable when one is interested in obtaining as much high-frequency power as possible from a transistor amplifier. This maximum power decreases with increasing frequency, both because transistors have lower gain and efficiency as the frequency is raised and because the active regions of transistors optimized for high-frequency service are physically smaller than their lower-frequency counterparts, thereby being limited to smaller dissipations. As of the time of writing, power outputs per transistor of 5 watts at 30 mc, 1 watt at 70 mc, 0.4 watt at 200 mc, and 0.1 watt at 500 mc can be obtained with reasonable gains.

The optimum transistor for a high-level application may have substantially different characteristics from the most suitable transistor for small-signal operation at the same frequency. In the latter case, the principal requirement is that the transistor have a high f_{max} at some operating point. For large-signal amplification, it is necessary that the transistor have suitably good high-frequency performance over a wide range of operating currents and voltages. For high efficiencies, it is particularly important that the transistor have good frequency response at low voltages and high currents. To meet this condition in a transistor generally demands some sacrifice of small-signal frequency response, brought about by relatively large emitter and collector transition capacitances.

Class A operation is achieved by biasing the transistor with a quiescent collector voltage slightly more than half the maximum voltage rating of the transistor connection being used. With this bias voltage, the instantaneous collector voltage can swing up to its maximum rating at low currents and down to a few volts at high currents. The quiescent bias current would normally be as large as is compatible with the maximum dissipation rating of the transistor; for intermittent signals, $V_C I_C \leq P_{max}$, or for continuous signals, $V_C I_C \leq K P_{max}$, where $1 < K < 2$. In the latter case, suitable precautions must be made for reducing the bias power if the signal input is interrupted. The resonant load impedance is typically $R_L = V_C/I_C$. The class A amplifier is normally used only for high-level applications requiring a high degree of linearity (such as the transmission of amplitude-modulated signals) and for those applications where the frequency of operation is sufficiently close to f_{max} that too little signal input power is available for class B operation.

Class AB, class B, or class C operation leads to greater efficiency than class A operation for frequencies well below f_{max}. As a general rule, the smaller the ratio f/f_{max}, the smaller can be the conduction angle. In a typical optimized application, class B operation is most suitable at $f = f_{max}/4$ and provides an efficiency (signal power output divided by direct current plus signal power input) of 30 to 60 per cent and a gain of 8 to 10 db. The quiescent collector voltage is set at half the collector diode-breakdown voltage (which may be slightly higher than in the class A application, because the transistor is now cut off when the maximum collector voltage is present). The load impedance is set so that the collector voltage reaches zero at the maximum instantaneous current. A significant advantage of class B and class C operation is that the zero-signal power consumption and dissipation are small, so that maximum power outputs can often exceed the transistor dissipation.

Neutralization is needed less often in high-level amplifiers than in small-signal amplifiers of the same frequency ranges. There are at least three reasons for this fortunate condition. First, load conductances are generally larger than the transistor output conductance in high-level applications, thereby reducing the power gain and internal feedback. Second, high-level gain is a weighted average of the gains along the load line over which the transistor operates and is much smaller than the maximum gain. Third, high-level stages are normally operated at higher bias currents than are small-signal amplifiers; Eq. (12.65) emphasizes the desirable effect on neutralization which results from the correspondingly larger transconductance.

Push-pull and parallel operation of transistors can be employed for increasing power output beyond that obtainable with a single unit. Unless the greater linearity of the push-pull arrangement is desirable, there seems to be no advantage to push-pull over parallel operation. The latter can be effected by tying the collectors directly together. If a common-base configuration is employed, the bases also can be tied directly together. The emitters should be supplied from separate d-c supplies (in order to ensure equal distribution of the current, regardless of variations in emitter-to-base resistance from unit to unit). Similarly, a small a-c impedance may be needed in each input lead in order to ensure equitable distribution of the signal current. In

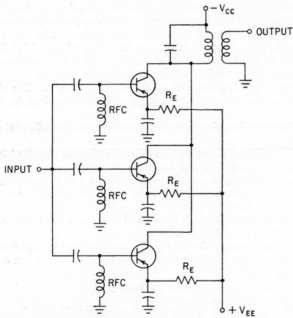

FIG. 12.60. Parallel operation of transistors.

some cases, a small resistance (a few ohms) should be added in each emitter lead so as to prevent parasitic oscillations. A possible parallel circuit arrangement is shown in Fig. 12.60.

12.25. Ultra-high-frequency Applications. There is a limited number of developmental transistor types which are suitable for certain ultra-high-frequency applications. Although there has been little engineering effort applied to the practical application of these devices, sufficient experimental work has been performed to emphasize the major problems, which are outlined as follows.

Lumped-constant tuned circuits cannot be used with transistors in the ultra-high-frequency range. The maximum frequency at which lumped-constant circuits appear feasible is 300 to 400 mc. Above this limit, it is necessary to use distributed or self-contained resonant structures for matching transistor input and output impedances. Among the more convenient circuit techniques that have been employed are the following:

1. Coaxial-line matching circuits, which are particularly convenient for matching transistor input circuits, where impedance levels of 20 to 100 ohms are typical.

2. Spiral delay-line resonators, which provide a small resonant structure with an

unloaded Q of 500 or more, make a convenient resonant output circuit for the frequency range from 300 to 1,500 mc.[31]   These elements can be considered as a shielded inductor in which the shielding provides a distributed resonating capacitance.   Alternatively they can be considered as a shortened coaxial resonator in which the inductance of the center conductor is increased by forming this conductor in the form of a helix.

3. Coaxial cavities provide a convenient output resonator for frequencies above 1 Gc.   The center conductor may be isolated, for low frequency, from the outer conductor by means of a capacitive short circuit at the end of the cavity, thereby providing a convenient path for d-c bias.

The application of unilateralizing feedback (neutralization) to ultra-high-frequency amplifiers is generally highly inconvenient.   Therefore, it is generally necessary to design ultra-high-frequency amplifiers without neutralization, in accordance with the techniques described in Sec. 12.18c.   The minimizing of capacitive feedback from output to input is highly important in these amplifiers.   Consequently, there is considerable interest in coaxially mounted transistors.[5]

12.26. Summary of Tuned-amplifier Design Procedures.   The following list summarizes the major tuned-amplifier design factors described in the preceding sections.

1. The maximum useful gain per stage will not exceed the unilateral gain, which is approximated by $(f_{max}/f_0)^2$.

2. If this gain can be achieved without neutralization, as described in Sec. 12.18c, the amplifier can be conjugately matched at input and output.

3. When the unilateral gain exceeds the maximum usable unneutralized gain, as given by Eq. (12.65), the amplifier must be either neutralized or mismatched, as described in Secs. 12.18b and 12.18c.

4. In narrow-band amplifiers, coil losses are important and are governed primarily by the ratio of loaded to unloaded Q.

5. Transistors can be conveniently paralleled for increasing high-frequency power output by providing separate emitter current bias supplies for each transistor.

REFERENCES

1. Pritchard, R. L.: Frequency Variations of Current-amplification Factor for Junction Transistors, *Proc. IRE*, vol. 40, pp. 1476–1481, November, 1952.
2. Krömer, H.: The Drift Transistor, in "Transistors I," pp. 202–220, RCA Laboratories, Princeton, N.J., 1956.
3. Thomas, D. E., and J. L. Moll: Junction Transistor Short-circuit Current Gain and Phase Determination, *Proc. IRE*, vol. 46, pp. 1177–1184, June, 1958.
4. te Winkel, J.: Drift Transistor—Simplified Electrical Characterization, *Electronic and Radio Eng.*, vol. 36, pp. 280–288, August, 1959.
5. McCotter, J. D., M. Walker, and M. Fortini: A Coaxially Packed MADT for Microwave Applications, presented at 1959 IRE Electron Devices Meeting, Washington, D.C., October, 1959.
6. Beaufoy, R., and J. J. Sparkes: The Junction Transistor as a Charge-controlled Device, *J. ATE*, vol. 13, pp. 310–317, April, 1957, and *Proc. IRE*, vol. 45, pp. 1740–1741, December, 1957.
7. Varnerin, L. J.: Stored Charge Method of Transistor Base Transit Analysis, *Proc. IRE*, vol. 47, pp. 523–527, April, 1959.
8. Early, J. M.: PNIP and NPIN Junction Transistor Triodes, *Bell System Tech. J.*, vol. 33, pp. 517–533, May, 1954.
9. Lee, C. A.: A High Frequency Diffused Base Germanium Transistor, *Bell System Tech. J.*, vol. 35, pp. 23–34, January 1956.
10. Thornton, C. G., and J. B. Angell: Technology of Micro-alloy Diffused Transistors, *Proc. IRE*, vol. 46, pp. 1166–1176, June, 1958.
11. Pritchard, R. L., J. B. Angell, R. B. Adler, J. M. Early, and W. M. Webster: Transistor Internal Parameters for Small-signal Representation, *Proc. IRE*, vol. 49, pp. 725–738, April, 1961.

12. Nelson, J. T., J. E. Iwersen, and F. Keywell: A Five-watt Ten-megacycle Transistor, *Proc. IRE*, vol. 46, pp. 1209–1215, June, 1958.
13. Mueller, C. W., and J. I. Pankove: A P-N-P Triode Alloy-junction Transistor for Radio-frequency Amplification, *RCA Rev.*, vol. 14, pp. 586–599, December, 1953, and *Proc. IRE*, vol. 42, pp. 386–391, February, 1954.
14. Pritchard, R. L.: Two-dimensional Current Flow in Junction Transistors at High Frequencies, *Proc. IRE*, vol. 46, pp. 1152–1160, June, 1958.
15. Nielsen, E. G.: Behavior of Noise Figure in Junction Transistors, *Proc. IRE*, vol. 45, pp. 957–963, July, 1957.
16. van der Ziel, A.: Theory of Shot Noise in Junction Diodes and Junction Transistors, *Proc. IRE*, vol. 43, pp. 1639–1646, November, 1955.
17. Chenette, E. R.: Frequency Dependence of the Noise and the Current Amplification Factor of Silicon Transistors, *Proc. IRE*, vol. 48, pp. 111–112, January, 1960.
18. Guggenbuehl, W., and M. J. O. Strutt: Theory and Experiments on Shot Noise in Semiconductor Junction Diodes and Transistors, *Proc. IRE*, vol. 45, pp. 839–854, June, 1957.
19. Shea, R. F.: Transistor Operation: Stabilization of Operating Points, *Proc. IRE*, vol. 40, pp. 1435–1437, November, 1952.
20. Bruun, Georg: Common-emitter Transistor Video Amplifiers, *Proc. IRE*, vol. 44, pp. 1561–1572, November, 1956.
21. Prugh, Thomas A.: Amplification-Bandwidth Exchange in Transistor Video Amplifiers, *Proc. IRE*, vol. 45, pp. 694–695, May, 1957.
22. Ballentine, W. E., and F. H. Blecher: Broadband Transistor Video Amplifiers, in "Digest of Technical Papers," pp. 42–43, 1959 Solid-state Circuits Conference, University of Pennsylvania, Feb. 12–13, 1959.
23. Steggerda, C. S.: A Study of Gain and Bandwidth in Transistor Video Amplifiers, M.Sc. Thesis, Department of Electrical Engineering, MIT, June, 1954, and published as *Philco Rept.* 242 by the Research Division, Philco Corp., Philadelphia, August, 1957.
24. Wallace, Jr., R. L., L. G. Shimpf, and E. Dickten: A Junction Transistor Tetrode for High-frequency Use, *Proc. IRE*, vol. 40, pp. 1395–1400, November, 1952.
25. Stern, A. P., C. A. Aldridge, and W. F. Chow: Internal Feedback and Neutralization of Transistor Amplifiers, *Proc. IRE*, vol. 43, pp. 838–847, July, 1955.
26. Cheng, C. C.: Neutralization and Unilateralization, *IRE Trans. on Circuit Theory*, vol. CT-2, pp. 138–145, June, 1955.
27. Holmes, David D., and T. O. Stanley: Stability Considerations in Transistor Intermediate-frequency Amplifiers, in "Transistors I," pp. 403–421, RCA Laboratories, Princeton, N.J., March, 1956.
28. Mason, S. J.: Power Gain in Feedback Amplifiers, *IRE Trans. on Circuit Theory*, vol. CT-1, no. 2, p. 20, June, 1954.
29. Linvill, J. G.: The Relationship of Transistor Parameters to Amplifier Performance, presented at the IRE–AIEE–University of Pennsylvania Conference on Transistor Circuits, Philadelphia, Feb. 17, 1955.
30. Chow, W. F., and A. P. Stern: Automatic Gain Control of Transistor Amplifiers, *Proc. IRE*, vol. 43, pp. 1119–1127, September, 1955.
31. "Reference Data for Radio Engineers," 4th ed., chap. 20, pp. 600–603, International Telephone and Telegraph Corp., New York, 1956.

Section 13

D–C AMPLIFIERS

G. B. B. Chaplin

The Plessey Company, Ltd., Roke Manor, Near Romsey, Hampshire, England

13.1. Introduction. The term "d-c amplifier" is variously defined as either a directly coupled or direct-current amplifier. The former definition, however, would exclude the very important class of modulated systems, and the latter would imply an amplifier having zero bandwidth. Nevertheless, in accordance with common usage, the term d-c amplifier will be used to describe any amplifier which will respond to unidirectional signals and the term directly coupled will be reserved for amplifiers having no reactive couplings.

Many of the problems associated with the design of a-c amplifiers, for example output power, noise, and stability, may also apply to certain d-c amplifiers, but the present chapter is concerned mainly with those problems peculiar to the extension of the response to very low frequencies. In particular, it is concerned with the measurement of small signals, the limit of sensitivity of the amplifier being set by the spurious output signals which occur for no input. These spurious signals may be an extension of thermal noise into the very low frequency region, being random in both time and amplitude, or they may represent a gradual drift of operating point. In either case it is convenient to divide the output signal by the gain of the amplifier to give an effective input signal (noise or drift) which can now be specified without referring to the gain of the amplifier.

Although each stage of the amplifier will contribute to the noise and drift, the effect at the output will depend on the intervening amplification. Thus, for reasonably large stage gains, little accuracy will be lost if all the noise and drift is assumed to originate in the input stage.

13.1a. Noise. For white noise the power per unit bandwidth is independent of frequency and so the contribution at low frequencies is small. On the other hand there is normally present in transistors a component of noise in which the noise power per unit bandwidth increases as the frequency is decreased. This excess, or $1/f$, noise

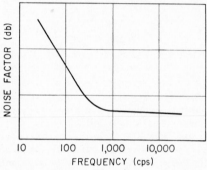

FIG. 13.1. Excess noise at low frequencies.

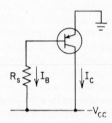

FIG. 13.2. Common-emitter stage.

becomes important below a few hundred cycles per second and follows the $1/f$ law down to less than 1 cps, as illustrated in Fig. 13.1.

The effective input noise of the amplifier will thus depend both on its bandwidth and on the frequency about which the bandwidth is centered.

13.1b. Drift. Superimposed on the random noise, and in most cases greatly exceeding it in magnitude, there will be a drift of operating point. Some of this drift may be due to change in characteristics as the transistor ages, but in normal circumstances the biggest source of drift will be that due to change of ambient temperature.

The rest of this chapter is concerned largely with the effect of changes of ambient temperature on the drift and is in two main sections dealing, in turn, with directly coupled and modulated systems.

13.2. Directly Coupled Amplifiers. *13.2a. Common-emitter Stage.* Consider the common-emitter stage of Fig. 13.2 which has a current I_B extracted from the base. The collector current I_C will be equal to $\alpha_{FE}(I_B + I_{CO})$, where α_{FE} is the large-signal base-to-collector current gain for the particular value of I_C.

A change of ambient temperature will have three main effects: (1) The leakage current will change by an amount ΔI_{CO}, (2) the current gain α_{FE} will change by $\Delta\alpha_{FE}$, and (3) the base-to-emitter voltage will change by an amount ΔV_{EB}, causing a change of base current of $\Delta V_{EB}/R_s$, where R_s is the source resistance.

To prevent any change of output current, an input current must be supplied to the base consisting of (1) $\Delta I_{CO}/\alpha_{FB}$ to compensate for change of I_{CO}, (2) $(\Delta\alpha_{FE}/\alpha_{FE} + \Delta\alpha_{FE})(I_B + I_{CO})$ to compensate for change of α_{FE}, and (3) $\Delta V_{EB}/R_s$ to compensate for change of V_{EB}.

All three changes have the same sign, and so the total compensating current required is

$$\frac{\Delta I_{CO}}{\alpha_{FE}} + \frac{\Delta \alpha_{FE}}{\alpha_{FE} + \Delta \alpha_{FE}}(I_B + I_{CO}) + \frac{\Delta V_{EB}}{R_s}$$

which, by definition, is the magnitude of the drift.

The relative importance of these three sources of drift will depend on the characteristics of the transistor and the magnitude of the biasing current and the source resistance, all of which will now be examined in more detail.

LEAKAGE CURRENT I_{CO}. The variation of leakage current with temperature will depend on its value at a standard reference temperature (normally 25°C) and the range of junction temperature under consideration. The leakage current of a medium-frequency germanium transistor is usually

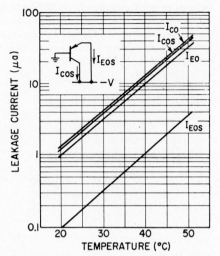

FIG. 13.3. Leakage current versus temperature for germanium transistor type OC71.

a few microamperes at 25°C, although that of low-frequency types may be many tens of microamperes. On the other hand, a carefully made silicon transistor can have a leakage current 4 decades smaller, a typical value being a few times 10^{-9} amp.

The relationship between leakage current and temperature is exponential, the leakage current doubling for approximately each 7°C rise in temperature. Figure 13.3 shows the effect plotted on a logarithmic current scale for a low-frequency germanium transistor type OC71 and includes other leakage currents whose significance will be discussed later on.

The range of temperature to which equipments operating under laboratory conditions are usually exposed is approximately 20 to 50°C. Thus, in this 30°C range the

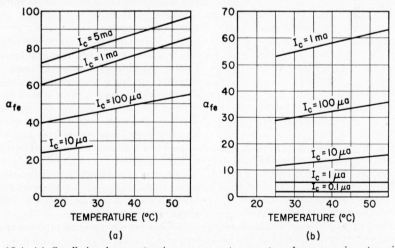

FIG. 13.4. (a) Small-signal current gain α_{fe} versus temperature for germanium transistor type OC71. (b) Small-signal current gain α_{fe} versus temperature for silicon transistor type OC201.

leakage current will double itself five times, representing a total factor of 32. Since this factor is large compared with unity, the drift can be assumed to be the value of leakage current at the highest temperature.

GAIN α_{fe}. Figure 13.4a shows the variation of small-signal base-to-collector current gain α_{fe} with temperature for a low-frequency germanium transistor at constant collector current. It can be seen that α_{fe} increases approximately linearly with temperature and that the magnitude of the increase is not greatly affected by the biasing current I_C.

The magnitude of the drift associated with the change of α_{fe} has already been shown to be $(\Delta\alpha_{fe}/\alpha_{fe} + \Delta\alpha_{fe})(I_B + I_{CO})$, and it is instructive to assess the effect of bias current on this drift. Reducing I_C from 5 ma to 100 μa reduces α_{fe} to about half its initial value and leaves $\Delta\alpha_{fe}$ almost unchanged. The result is, therefore, a small increase in $\Delta\alpha_{fe}/(\alpha_{fe} + \Delta\alpha_{fe})$, but this increase is far outweighed by the decrease in I_B occasioned by the hundredfold decrease in I_C.

It therefore seems to be desirable to reduce the biasing current as far as possible in order to reduce the drift from this cause. However, there is little point in reducing the biasing current below several times I_{CO}, since the drift of I_{CO} would then predominate.

The situation is no better in the case of the silicon transistor shown in Fig. 13.4b. Below a collector current of about 10 μa, the gain is too small to be of use, and so it is not possible to take advantage of the low leakage current.

The lowest practical operating current can be deduced from Fig. 13.5a and b, which shows the relationship between I_B and I_C at currents of a few microamperes for the germanium and silicon transistors, respectively. The curves plotted for the two temperatures 20 and 50°C and the total current drift between these two temperatures can be seen at a glance for any given value of I_C.

The small-signal current gain is given by the slope of the curves, and in the case of germanium (Fig. 13.5a) the current gain is maintained at a reasonable value right

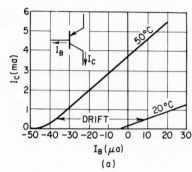

(a)

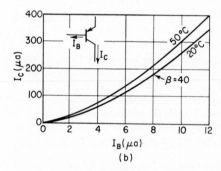

(b)

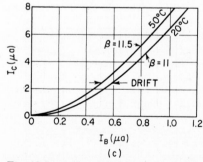

(c)

FIG. 13.5. (a) I_C versus I_B at 20 and 50°C for germanium transistor type OC71. (b) I_C versus I_B at 20 and 50°C for silicon transistor type OC201. (c) Enlargement of (b) near origin.

down to leakage current. On the other hand, the small-signal gain of the silicon transistor (Fig. 13.5b and c) falls below 10 at a collector current of about 5 μa, which is many decades greater than the leakage current. In both cases, therefore, the minimum bias current is a few microamperes, although the silicon transistor is preferable, since the component of drift due to leakage current is negligible. Although the limitations imposed by the fall of current gain at low current appears to be a funda-mental property of silicon transistors, a way out of the difficulty is discussed in Sec. 4.

EMITTER-BASE VOLTAGE. The third component of current drift is that due to the change of V_{EB} with temperature. For a constant collector current this voltage decreases by about 2.5 mv for each degree centigrade increase in temperature and so causes the base current to increase by an amount $\Delta V_{EB}/R_s$. The relative importance of this source of drift thus depends on the source impedance. For germanium tran-sistors this drift is negligible for values of R_s of several thousand ohms.

13.2b. Drift-compensated Stage. The drift of the circuit of Fig. 13.2 could be reduced to zero if a current equal and opposite to the total drift could be supplied automatically to the input by a circuit element having a resistance varying appro-priately with temperature. Exact compensation is not possible, but an improvement of 1 or 2 decades is readily realizable. For accurate compensation throughout the required temperature range, the compensating element should follow closely a par-ticular resistance/temperature law and possess a similar thermal time constant to the

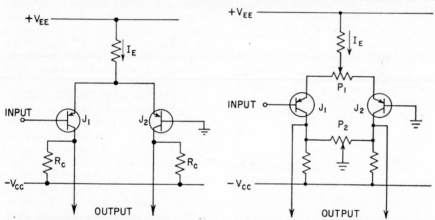

FIG. 13.6. Balanced amplifier.   FIG. 13.7. Balancing adjustments.

transistor. Thermistors and semiconductor diodes have been used for this purpose, but perhaps the most obvious choice is another similar transistor. The use of a transistor for the purpose provides the correct thermal time constant. A suitable balanced circuit in which J_2 is the compensating transistor is shown in Fig. 13.6.

Both the absolute value of V_{EB} and the variation with temperature are fairly consistent among transistors, and a factor of about 10 improvement can be expected without resorting to adjustment. On the other hand the drifts due to leakage current and gain are much less reproducible, and balancing is effective only if the transistors are carefully selected or if a balancing control is used.

To make the compensation worthwhile it is essential to use matched transistors and to adjust two or more component values. In Fig. 13.7 the potentiometer P_1 controls the division of emitter current between J_1 and J_2 and is adjusted for zero differential output voltage at the lower temperature while P_2 controls the relative voltage gains of J_1 and J_2 and is adjusted for zero differential output at the higher temperature. These controls are interdependent, and so it is necessary to go through several tem-perature cycles when adjusting the amplifier. Two or three temperature cycles are sufficient to reduce the input drift to 1 or 2 mv over the temperature range 20 to 50°C, but a greater reduction is possible if the process is repeated.

A limit to the reduction of drift by balancing is set by the change of transistor char-acteristics with time and also by the self-heating of the transistors due to internal power dissipation.   The latter effect usually predominates and can result in a recovery time of many minutes following a transient overload at the input.

For these reasons, together with the tedious balancing procedure, it is preferable to use some other system if lower drifts are required.

If the d-c signal can be converted by a modulator to an a-c signal of proportional amplitude, it can be amplified in an a-c amplifier and then demodulated to form an amplified version of the original d-c signal.   Providing the a-c gain is sufficiently large, drift originating in the demodulator can be neglected, and so only the modulator need be considered when estimating the drift.   It is therefore necessary to examine various ways of using transistors to perform the function of modulation and to see what reduction in drift can be achieved over the direct-coupled system.

13.3. Modulated Amplifiers—Current Modulator.   If the source of direct current to be amplified has a high resistance, such as an ionization chamber, a modulator having a relatively large voltage drift can be tolerated, provided that the current drift is sufficiently small.   The current from an ionization chamber is unidirectional, and so a modulator which responds to current of only one polarity is adequate.

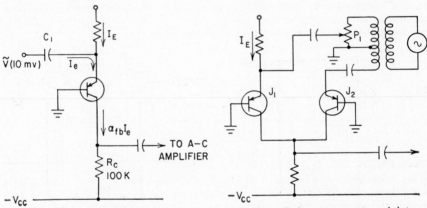

FIG. 13.8. Current modulator.   FIG. 13.9. Balanced current modulator.

A simple modulator which meets these requirements is shown in Fig. 13.8.   It consists of a common-base transistor with a collector load R_c.   A direct input current I_E is fed into the emitter.   If a small alternating voltage V, of a few millivolts amplitude, is applied to the emitter through a capacitor C_1, the alternating component of the emitter current I_e is equal to V/r_e [if $r_e \gg r_b/(1 - \alpha_{fb})$], which is increasingly true as $I_E \to 0$.   The emitter resistance r_e is inversely proportional to $(I_E + I_{EOS})$, where I_{EOS} is the simultaneous emitter leakage current measured when both collector and emitter are simultaneously negative with respect to the base.   Thus, if $I_E \gg I_{EOS}$ and V is held constant, I_e is directly proportional to I_E.   The resulting alternating component of collector voltage is $\alpha_{fb}I_e R_c$, which can then be amplified by an a-c amplifier and demodulated by a rectifying system.

When the input current I_E is zero, I_{EOS} can no longer be neglected and there remains a residual alternating output voltage at the collector directly proportional to I_{EOS}. The magnitude and temperature dependence of I_{EOS} in relation to the other transistor leakage currents are shown in Fig. 13.3.   Now, I_{EOS} is the smallest of these currents, being approximately equal to $I_{co}/10$ (see Sec. 13.8, Appendix) for the OC71 transistor, and so the drift of I_{EOS} through a given range of temperature is only one-tenth that of I_{co}.   Typically, between 20 and 50°C, I_{EOS} increases from 10^{-7} to 3.8×10^{-6} amp for a type OC71 transistor, resulting in a drift of only 3.7×10^{-6} amp for the modulator of Fig. 13.8. This is to be compared with about 40×10^{-6} amp for the direct-coupled amplifier of Fig. 13.2.

If the residual error signal is balanced against a similar temperature-dependent signal from another transistor, a further reduction in drift is possible. The circuit arrangement is shown in Fig. 13.9, in which J_1 is the modulator and J_2 provides the canceling signal. The alternating carrier voltage is inverted and applied to the emitter of J_2, which is arranged to have no direct current, so that the alternating current at the collector of J_2 is a function of I_{EOS} only. The output at the collector of J_2 is thus in antiphase to the output of the collector of J_1, and cancellation takes place in the common-collector load. The relative magnitudes of the carrier voltages applied to J_1 and J_2 are governed by P_1, which is adjusted for zero output voltage when I_E is zero. A reduction in drift of between 10 and 100 times is typical when this type of cancellation is used.

In the case of the silicon transistor, the sensitivity is limited by the fall off of current gain as the signal current is reduced, although emitter-to-collector current gain substantially less than unity can be tolerated.

13.4. Modulated Amplifiers—Chopper Amplifier. If both the current and voltage drifts are required to be small and both polarities of output voltage are required, the modulator and demodulator may consist of switches, known as choppers, operated synchronously. A basic system is shown in Fig. 13.10.

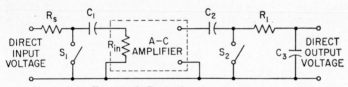

FIG. 13.10. Basic chopper system.

Switches S_1 and S_2 are periodically opened and closed synchronously. When they are closed, the capacitors C_1 and C_2 are allowed sufficient time for their charges to reach equilibrium, after which the switches are opened. If there is no d-c input signal, opening the switches will have no effect on the a-c amplifier output voltage. However, if a d-c input signal V_1 is present at the d-c input terminal, a step of current $V_1/(R_s + R_i)$ will be applied to the a-c amplifier when S_1 is opened, producing an output voltage $ZV_1/(R_s + R_i)$ at S_2, where Z is the amplifier transfer impedance. While closed, S_2 clamps the right-hand terminal of C_2 to zero potential so that the opening of S_2 allows the voltage on it to change from zero potential by a voltage $ZV_1/(R_s + R_i)$. This step of voltage is then smoothed by R_1 and C_3 to produce a direct output voltage which is an amplified version of the d-c input signal.

If the switches are operated sufficiently rapidly, the drift which occurs when they are open will be negligible.

Mechanical vibrators, magnetic modulators, etc., can be used for the synchronous switches, but only the use of the transistor for this function will be discussed. Furthermore, it is only necessary to consider the operation of S_1, since any drift originating in S_2 is reduced by a factor of the gain of the a-c amplifier when referred to the input.

13.4a. The Transistor as a Switch. The collector-emitter impedance of a transistor depends on the relative magnitudes of the base and collector currents as can be seen from the collector characteristic of a common-emitter transistor shown in Fig. 13.11. If the base current I_B is large compared with I_C/α_{FE}, as at A, the collector impedance is only about 20 ohms. On the other hand, if the base voltage is positive with respect to the emitter, as at B, then $I_B \simeq -I_{CO}$ and the collector impedance is increased to 1 megohm or more. This large ratio of collector impedances enables the transistor to be used as a switch.

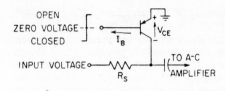

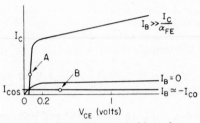

Fig. 13.11. Transistor switching characteristics.

13.4b. Errors in a Transistor Chopper. Ideally, a switch should have zero impedance and no internal voltage when closed and infinite impedance and no leakage current when open. Although a transistor switch is defective in these respects, the resulting errors can be reduced sufficiently to allow the function of S_1 in Fig. 13.10 to be performed by a transistor chopper.

The current interrupted by S_1 will be small if the a-c amplifier gain is to be large, and in analyzing the performance of the chopper, it is legitimate to assume that the input current is almost zero. The closed condition of the chopper represented by point A in Fig. 13.11 can thus be moved down the curve to the zero current axis. An enlargement of this part of the characteristic is given in Fig. 13.12a, which shows a voltage error V_{CE} of about 12 mv at the new point A when the switch is closed and a current error I_{cos}, which is slightly less than I_{co}, when the switch is open. These errors would be fed into the a-c amplifier as unwanted input signals, and although

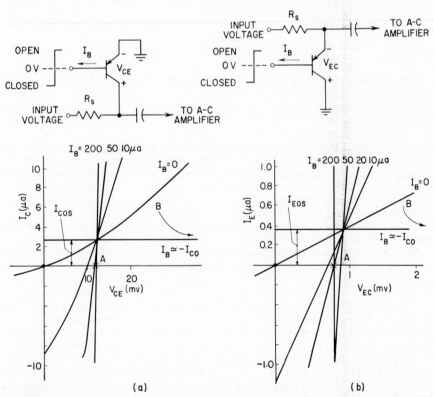

Fig. 13.12. Enlarged characteristics near origin for type OC71 transistor: (*a*) transistor normally connected and (*b*) transistor reversed.

they could be "backed off," their variation with temperature would give rise to a considerable drift.   Between 20 and 50°C the current drift would be typically 40 μa and the voltage drift 2 mv.

When the emitter and collector connections are reversed,[1–4] a substantial improvement in performance is obtained, as shown by the output characteristics of the reversed transistor (Fig. 13.12*b*).   The voltage error V_{EC} is now only 1 mv, and the current error is reduced to I_{EOS}.   Since the drift of the voltage error is approximately proportional to its magnitude, reversal of the transistor reduces the voltage drift by a factor of approximately 20 to 100 μv.

The voltage error V_{EC} for the reversed-transistor switch is plotted against temperature in Fig. 13.13 for various values of I_B and with zero emitter current.   The drift of V_{EC} with temperature can be of either sign, depending on the base current, and it is possible to choose an optimum value of base current for a particular transistor which gives a voltage drift of only a few microvolts between 20 and 50°C.   The optimum value of I_B varies among transistors of the same type, but there is an average value

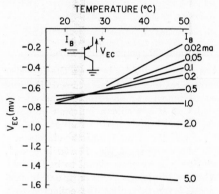

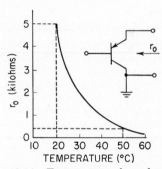

FIG. 13.13. Dependence of chopper voltage error on temperature and base current for type OC71 transistor.

FIG. 13.14.   Temperature dependence of chopper open impedance r_o for type OC71 transistor.

that can usually be chosen for any one type of transistor which results in a maximum voltage drift of about 100 μv.   For example, type OC71 has an optimum base current of about 1 ma, whereas types OC72 and SB100 require 6 ma and 100 μa, respectively, for least drift.

By individual adjustment of the base current, the drift can be reduced to a few microvolts.

13.4c. Reduction of Current Error.   The reduced current error I_{ESIM} after reversal of the transistor is still excessive for many applications.   However, this error can be considerably reduced by modifying the open condition of the chopper.[5,6]   If the base is not taken positive with respect to the other electrodes when the switch is open but instead is returned through a resistance to zero potential, the potential difference which causes leakage currents to flow is removed and the leakage currents vanish.

The open condition of the switch is now represented by the curve $I_B = 0$ in Fig. 13.12*b* which passes through the origin.   In fact, if no signal current is present, there is no current flowing in any electrode, since all are at zero potential.   There is, therefore, no error current.

The price paid for eliminating the leakage current is a reduction in the open impedance r_o of the chopper which falls to about 5 kilohms at 20°C, but the chopper still exhibits a useful ratio of impedance between being open and closed.   The open impedance r_o is, however, a function of temperature.   As the temperature rises, so r_o falls, as shown in Fig. 13.14, and the gain of the d-c amplifier will be reduced owing to the shunting effect of the chopper across the input terminals. Nevertheless, if the input impedance R_i of the a-c amplifier is small compared with r_o, most of the signal current will flow into the amplifier and the loss in gain will be negligible.

A complete chopper circuit is shown in Fig. 13.15a. When the chopping waveform is positive with respect to zero potential, the diode D is cut off and the resistors R_2 and R_1 hold the base almost at zero potential. R_1 is made much greater than R_2, so that only a fraction $R_2/(R_1 + R_2)$ of the reverse leakage current of the diode flows

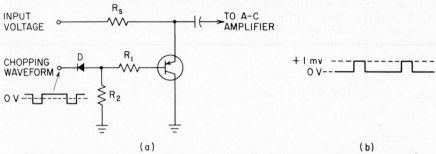

(a)   (b)

Fig. 13.15. Input chopper: (a) complete circuit and (b) compensating waveform.

into the base of the transistor. This small base current divides between the collector and emitter in the ratio of $I_{COS}:I_{EOS}$, typically a ratio of 10:1. If $R_1 = 10R_2$, only one one-hundredth of the diode leakage current appears as an error current at the transistor emitter when the chopper is opened. If D is a silicon junction diode, it can be chosen to have a maximum leakage current of less than 10^{-8} amp at $+50°C$, resulting in a drift of less than 10^{-10} amp at the emitter of the transistor chopper.

13.4d. Balancing the Voltage Error. When the chopper of Fig. 13.15a is closed, the emitter potential V_{EC} falls to -1 mv, causing a 1-mv error signal to be fed into

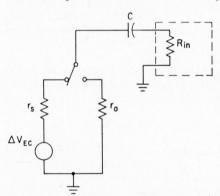

Fig. 13.16. Equivalent circuit of input chopper of Fig. 13.15.

the a-c amplifier. This error can be prevented by returning the collector to a potential of about $+1$ mv, which is adjusted for zero a-c output voltage. However, when the chopper is open the collector is positive with respect to the emitter by 1 mv, causing a small error current to flow into R_s. If the zero-setting voltage is applied to the collector only during the clamped period and the inverse phase of the chopping waveform used (Fig. 13.15b), this error is removed.

The main source of drift is now the actual variation of the error voltage with temperature ΔV_{EC}. Although ΔV_{EC} is a voltage drift, it can be resolved conveniently into an equivalent current drift as shown by the equivalent circuit of Fig. 13.16. When the chopper is closed, the switch is connected to r_s, the closed impedance of the chopper, and the coupling capacitor is charged up to ΔV_{EC} through $r_s + R_i$, both of which have relatively low values. When the chopper opens, the switch is connected to r_o, so that the capacitor attempts to discharge through $r_o + R_i$. However, r_o is normally large compared with r_z and R_i, and the discharge current remains fairly constant during the open period at its initial value of $\Delta V_{EC}/(r_o + R_i)$, which is practically equal to $\Delta V_{EC}/r_o$.

If the chopper of Fig. 13.15a is set for zero voltage error at $+20°C$ by adjusting the amplitude of the collector waveform (Fig. 13.15b) to produce zero a-c output for zero d-c input, the current drift at $+50°C$ will be $\Delta V_{EC}/r_o$, where r_o is measured at $50°C$ (Fig. 13.14). The minimum value of r_o at $50°C$ for the type OC71 transistor is 300 ohms, and so if $\Delta V_{EC} = 100\ \mu v$, the maximum current drift is $100\ \mu v/300$ ohms, or 3×10^{-7} amp.

This current drift is reduced by setting the voltage error to zero at $+50°C$, for then the value of r_o at the lower temperature must be used in computing the drift at $20°C$. The three curves in Fig. 13.17 show the drift when the chopper is set to zero at 20, 35, and 50°C, using values of r_o taken from Fig. 13.14 and assuming ΔV_{EC} to be $100\ \mu v$ and a linear function of temperature.

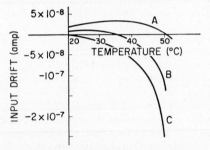

FIG. 13.17. Theoretical drift curves for type OC71 transistor chopper set to zero at 50°C for A, 35°C for B, and 20°C for C.

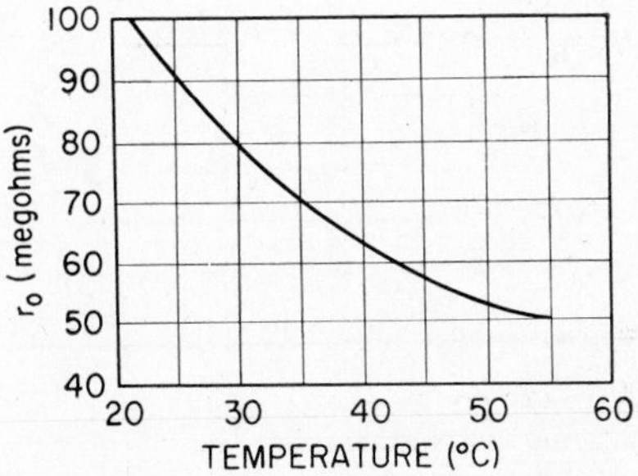

FIG. 13.18. Collector-emitter impedance r_o versus temperature for silicon transistor type OC201.

For a germanium audio-frequency transistor, such as type OC71 transistor, a drift of 3×10^{-8} amp is typical when the zero is set at 50°C. This is a factor of 10 smaller than the drift obtained when the same transistor type is used in the basic chopper circuit, where the drift is due to I_{ESIM}. The use of a medium-frequency transistor, such as the type OC45, yields a fivefold increase in r_o, giving a corresponding reduction in chopper drift. A high-frequency transistor such as the type SB100 shows a further reduction in I_{co}, giving a higher value of r_o, and since the chopper voltage drift remains the same, the chopper current drift is further reduced.

If the SB100 has a base drive current of $100\ \mu a$, the drift should be less than 5×10^{-9} amp.

In the case of silicon, the voltage drift is similar to that for germanium ($100\ \mu v$) but the current drift can be much smaller. For example, for the OC201 transistor, r_o is typically greater than 100 megohms at 20°C (Fig. 13.18), resulting in a current drift less than 10^{-11} amp.

Another version of Fig. 13.15a in which the small balancing voltage is supplied directly by the input chopping waveform is shown in Fig. 13.19. As the variable resistor R is decreased in value, the amplitude of the inverted chopping waveform at the collector increases.[7]

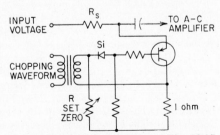

FIG. 13.19. Modified version of Fig. 13.15.

13.4e. *Effect of Transients.* Because of carrier storage and interelectrode capacity between base and emitter, a differentiated version of the base driving waveform will appear directly on the output and be superimposed on the signal. For low-frequency transistors, carrier storage is responsible for most of this transient, but in the case of high-frequency transistors, the base-to-emitter capacity plays a large part. Figure 13.20b shows typical transients for the Philco type 2N496 which is a silicon transistor having a cutoff frequency of 25 mc/sec. The chopper circuit (Fig. 13.20a)

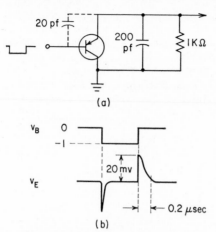

(a)

(b)

Fig. 13.20. (a) Transient equivalent circuit. (b) Transient waveforms.

shows a base-to-emitter capacitance of 20 pf, and the transistor is working into a load consisting of a 1-kilohm resistor and a 200-pf capacitor which simulate the input circuit of a possible transistor a-c amplifier. Considering the switch-off transient, the 1-volt positive edge on the base is attenuated by the ratio of the capacitors and produces a 100-mv positive spike on the emitter which decays with a 0.2-μsec time constant. On the other hand, the negative spike which occurs during switch-on is much narrower, since the transistor impedance is rapidly decreasing. The transistor thus chops its own negative transient and makes the duration negligible compared with that occurring at switch-off. The switch-off transient can easily be computed for different load circuits, the basic problem being that an unwanted charge of about 20 $\mu\mu$coulombs appears on the emitter whenever the transistor switches off.

13.4f. Chopping-frequency Limitations. Since the ultimate bandwidth of the demodulated output signal is limited to some fraction of the chopping frequency, it is obviously desirable to have as high a chopping frequency as possible. There is, however, a limit to this frequency which is determined both by the charge in the transients and by the value of the input current to be measured. Although the transient charge could in theory be backed off, it varies quite rapidly with temperature and so constitutes a drift. In general the limit is approached when the transient charge is approximately equal to the signal charge in 1 cycle of chopping waveform. In the case of the Philco SB100 germanium transistor, the transient charge is about 5 $\mu\mu$coulombs and the lowest input current which can be measured about 10^{-8} amp, and so the charges will be equal for a chopping period of $(5 \times 10^{-12})/10^{-8} = \frac{1}{2}$ msec, or a chopping frequency of 1 kc/sec.

The situation, however, is more serious in the case of the silicon transistor, since the base-emitter capacity is higher (20 pf) and the current which can be measured lower (10^{-10} amp) or less. Under these conditions the maximum chopping frequency becomes only a few cycles per second, a rather unrealistic figure.

13.4g. Double Chopper System. The restriction on chopping frequency imposed by the transients can fortunately be reduced by taking advantage of their transient nature. Thus if the time constant of decay of the charge can be made relatively short, it is possible to arrange that the demodulator ignores the transient and waits until the waveform has settled down to the correct input level.[8]

If the transient is to be kept short, its amplitude will then be a good fraction of a volt, and since the full-scale input signal may only be a few microvolts, the transient will overload the amplifier by a very large factor. Amplifier saturation and the attendant long recovery time can be prevented by using a double chopping system as illustrated in Fig. 13.21. This circuit allows a much higher chopping frequency than normal to be used by including a second chopper partway through the a-c amplifier to clamp the transients produced by the input chopper. The waveform generated in the first chopper, which operates at 25 kc/sec, is amplified a hundred times in the wideband amplifier, and the transients are then removed by the second chopper, which operates at twice the frequency, 50 kc/sec. Transients generated in this second chopper occur twice in every cycle of the input chopper and are therefore filtered out in the following narrow-band amplifier, tuned to the fundamental, and the 25-kc/sec demodulator. Thus each transient produced by the input chopper is effectively replaced by a pair of transients which are attenuated by a factor of 100 in relation to the original transients and are then arranged to cancel in the demodulator.

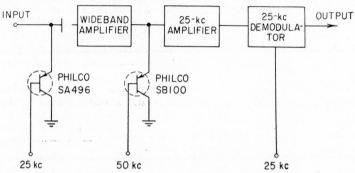

Fig. 13.21. Double chopper system.

The high chopping frequency enables a final bandwidth of several kilocycles per second to be obtained, but with such a bandwidth the amount of thermal noise is greater than the drift. Thus, using a Philco type SA496 silicon transistor as the first chopper and limiting the bandwidth to 1 kc/sec the performance is approximately as follows:

$$\left.\begin{array}{l} \text{Thermal noise}\dots\dots\dots 2 \times 10^{-10} \text{ amp} \\ \text{Current drift}\dots\dots\dots\dots 10^{-10} \text{ amp} \\ \text{Voltage drift}\dots\dots\dots\dots 100 \ \mu\text{v} \end{array}\right\} 20 \text{ to } 50°\text{C}$$

13.5. A Pulsed Silicon Transistor Current Amplifier. The reduction of current gain in a silicon transistor, when the biasing current is small, prevents the exploitation of the low leakage current of these transistors in simple direct-coupled systems such as those of Figs. 13.2 and 13.6. Nevertheless the difficulty can be overcome by a simple modification suggested by Cooke-Yarborough.[9]

If the low input current is integrated for a certain time, for example in a capacitor, and then released into the transistor in the form of a short pulse of fairly high current, the current gain of the transistor will assume its normal high value consistent with the amplitude of the current pulse. Thus if a current of 10^{-9} amp is integrated for 1 msec and then injected into the base as a 1-μsec pulse, the pulse current will be 1 μa and the collector current of the transistor plotted in Fig. 13.5c will be 7 μa.

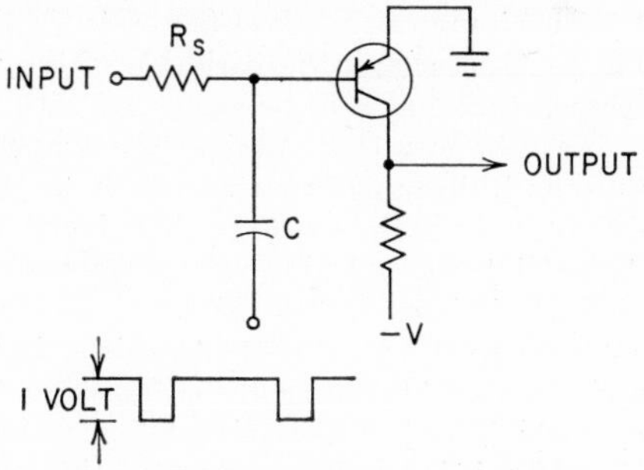

Fig. 13.22. Pulsed current amplifier.

The pulsing of the current can be achieved by applying pulses to the base via a capacitor, as shown in Fig. 13.22. The pulse amplitude should be sufficient to ensure that the transistor does not conduct between pulses, 1 volt being ample. Thus if the peak base current during the negative pulse is 1 μa, the base-to-emitter potential required to produce this current will be about -0.5 volt, and so a pulse amplitude of 1 volt will cause the base to be taken to $+0.5$ volt in between pulses.

Although the collector current is in the form of pulses, the mean current will be equal to the input current multiplied by the effective current gain of the transistor at the peak current and so requires no demodulation. In the present example in which the input current is 10^{-9} amp, the output current would be just under 10^{-8} amp and so further similar pulsing stages would be necessary to raise the mean current to 10^{-6} amp and so allow the subsequent stages to be conventional.

The limit to the narrowness of pulse which can be used is governed by the transit time of the transistor. In general the pulse should not be shorter than a few transit times, otherwise the effective emitter injection efficiency will be impaired. Thus a transistor having a cutoff frequency of 10 mc/sec would require a pulse duration of about 100 mμsec.

The lower limit on pulse repetition frequency (prf) is set only by output bandwidth considerations and so a very large mark-space ratio is allowable. Thus 100-mμsec

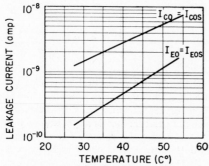

FIG. 13.23. Leakage current versus temperature for silicon transistor type OC201.

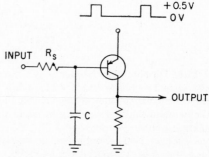

FIG. 13.24. Alternative arrangement of Fig. 13.22 allowing leakage current to be reduced.

pulses at a prf of only 1,000 would yield a mark-space ratio of 10^4 and enable a transistor requiring a pulse current of 1 μa to operate with an input current of only 10^{-10} amp. With an input current of this magnitude, the leakage current of the silicon transistor becomes important and, in fact, sets the limit on the maximum sensitivity attainable. Figure 13.23 shows the variation of the leakage currents of a silicon transistor with temperature and is to be compared with that for a germanium unit (Fig. 13.3).

It can be seen that although the temperature variation is like that for Ge, the simultaneous leakage currents are equal to those measured separately. This result is a consequence of the current gain being almost zero [see expressions (13.6) and (13.7) in Appendix], so that the leakage currents of the emitter and collector junctions are virtually independent.

The base potential of the transistor in Fig. 13.22 is positive to that of both emitter and collector between pulses, and so the drift will be equal to the combined leakage currents ($I_{CO} + I_{EO}$), which is approximately 5×10^{-9} amp between 20 and 50°C. However, it is possible to arrange that all electrode potentials are within a few millivolts of each other between pulses, and under these conditions a substantial reduction in drift is possible, the situation being analogous to that of the chopper in Fig. 13.15a, where all electrodes are at zero potential in the "off" state. A possible circuit is shown in Fig. 13.24. In this circuit the pulses are positive and are applied to the emitter. The upper level of the pulse is adjusted so that the base is almost at zero potential. Since the lower level of the pulse waveform is at zero potential, there will be no appreciable difference between base and emitter potentials in between pulses.

Likewise, if the collector is returned to zero potential, there will be no significant collector-to-base potential, and so the leakage currents will be greatly reduced. Typically, a transistor having a leakage current of 10^{-9} amp will have a drift as low as 10^{-11} amp in this circuit.

Stages can be directly cascaded as shown in Fig. 13.25. As in the case of Fig. 13.24, the emitter pulse amplitude can be adjusted virtually to eliminate leakage current. To compensate for the variation of V_{EB} with temperature, however, an equal and opposite variation should be impressed on the pulse amplitude, and this can be

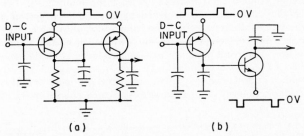

FIG. 13.25. Cascaded stages: (*a*) PNP transistors and (*b*) complementary transistors.

achieved by limiting the pulse amplitude with a silicon diode. The main application of this pulsing system is to fairly high impedance sources of single polarity.

13.6. Output Demodulator. Having converted the input signal from direct to alternating current in the input modulator or chopper, it is necessary to amplify it and then demodulate to provide the amplified direct current. The drift introduced by the demodulation is normally no problem, since it is divided by the intervening gain of the amplifier when referring it to the input. The main problem that arises is that the simple output chopper and integrator normally used result in the flow of fairly large currents. A basic circuit of this type is shown in Fig. 13.26.

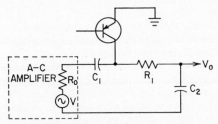

FIG. 13.26. Output chopper circuit.

The a-c signal is supplied from the amplifier output impedance R_o to the chopper transistor through a capacitor C_1. The demodulated output signal appearing across the chopper is then integrated by R_1 and C_2 to provide a smoothed d-c output.

When the chopper is clamped, the output capacitor C_2 discharges through R_1 and the lost charge must be replaced during the unclamped period by the discharge of C_1 if equilibrium is to be maintained. The resulting charge lost by C_1 is then replaced when the chopper is next clamped, and to do this a large current must flow from the a-c amplifier. This current, which represents a waste of power, can be eliminated by a more complex demodulator, but another solution is to demodulate at a lower signal level as described by Hutcheon.[7] In this system (Fig. 13.27) the output chopper s_2 is followed by a directly coupled amplifier having a gain of about 1,000, so that its full-scale input voltage is several millivolts. This voltage is low enough to reduce greatly the current flowing in the output chopper but high enough to prevent the directly coupled amplifier from adding drift to the system. If this amplifier has a phase reversal, the integrating capacitor can be connected across it, as shown, to form a feedback integrator. Over-all negative feedback can be placed across the whole system.

13.7. Choice of D-C Amplifier. The selection of the best type of d-c amplifier for a particular purpose will depend primarily on the sensitivity and bandwidth required. If the application can tolerate a low sensitivity, then the direct-coupled amplifier offers a simple solution with the advantage of large bandwidth. At the opposite extreme the highest sensitivity is achieved by a modulated system. Not only is the drift reduced but the excess $(1/f)$ noise is removed, allowing a greater bandwidth than would otherwise be the case. The double chopper system probably offers the best combination of current and voltage sensitivity and of bandwidth, but the pulsed amplifier of Sec. 13.5 is equally sensitive as far as current is concerned and more straight-forward. This latter amplifier, however, is not, strictly speaking, a modulated system because it requires no demodulator at the output. Consequently,

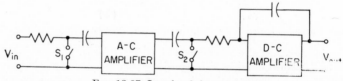

FIG. 13.27. Low-level demodulator.

the excess noise is not eliminated, although the total noise is reduced because the bias current is smaller.

A system commonly adopted for thermionic valve amplifiers is to use a directly coupled amplifier to provide adequate bandwidth, together with a mechanical chopper amplifier to reduce the drift. The same procedure can be adopted for transistors, but if a transistor chopper is used in place of the mechanical chopper, the bandwidth of the chopper amplifier can be greatly increased. Not only may it then be possible to dispense with the directly coupled amplifier altogether, but the resulting wideband chopper amplifier will have less noise than the initial combined amplifiers because the directly coupled amplifier includes excess noise.

The scope of this chapter has been limited to transistor systems, although other semiconductor devices can be used. For example, the Hall-effect multiplier can be used as a modulator in which one input is the d-c signal and the other the modulating waveform. However, a large number of turns are required on the specimen to approach the sensitivity of a silicon transistor chopper, and the resulting bandwidth is small. A sensitive modulator can also be made using silicon diodes.[10] Another, and very useful, chopping device is the photoconductor. The chopping waveform is a flashing light, and the ensuing change of resistance is used to modulate the d-c signal. Very large ratios of resistance between the two states can be obtainable, resulting in high efficiency, but the transition from low to high resistance is relatively slow, and with present materials (cadmium sulfide or selenide) the chopping frequency must be restricted to a few tens of cycles per second. Nevertheless, drifts of less than 1 μv and 10^{-12} amp are possible in the room-temperature range, and there are plenty of applications which can accept the low bandwidth.

13.8. Appendix. The electrode potentials and currents of an idealized junction transistor can be described by the equations[11]

$$I_E + \alpha_{RB}I_C = I_{EO}(e^{qV_E/kT} - 1) \tag{13.1}$$
$$I_E + \alpha_{FB}I_E = I_{CO}(e^{qV_C/kT} - 1) \tag{13.2}$$

where I_E and I_C are the currents flowing into the transistor and V_E and V_C are the potential difference across the junctions at the emitter and collector, respectively.

The leakage currents are related to each other[11] by ratio α_{FB} and α_{RB}:

$$I_{EO} = \frac{\alpha_{RB}}{\alpha_{FB}} I_{CO} \qquad (13.3)$$

13.8a. Simultaneous Leakage Currents. When the collector and emitter junctions are simultaneously biased in the reverse direction, the resulting leakage currents are designated I_{EOS} and I_{COS}. The condition for this test is that V_E and V_C are both large and negative, so that Eqs. (13.1) and (13.2) reduce to

$$I_E + \alpha_{RB}I_C = -I_{EO} \qquad (13.4)$$
$$I_C + \alpha_{FB}I_E = -I_{CO} \qquad (13.5)$$

The currents flowing out of the emitter and collector are therefore

$$I_{EOS} = -I_E = I_{EO} \frac{1 - \alpha_{FB}}{1 - \alpha_{FB}\alpha_{RB}} \qquad (13.6)$$

$$I_{COS} = -I_C = I_{CO} \frac{1 - \alpha_{FB}}{1 - \alpha_{FB}\alpha_{RB}} \qquad (13.7)$$

In terms of I_{CO}, I_{EOS} is given by

$$I_{EOS} = I_{CO} \frac{\alpha_{RB}}{\alpha_{FB}} \frac{1 - \alpha_{FB}}{1 - \alpha_{FB}\alpha_{RB}} \qquad (13.6a)$$

Typical values for α_{FB} and α_{RB} are 0.96 and 0.7, respectively, so that

$$I_{EO} = 0.73 I_{CO}$$
$$I_{EOS} = 0.12 I_{EO} = 0.087 I_{CO}$$
$$I_{COS} = 0.915 I_{CO}$$

The value of I_{CO} is approximately doubled for a rise in temperature of 7°C, and since α_{FB} and α_{RB} are almost unaffected by temperature, the other leakage currents obey the same law as I_{CO}. This is illustrated by the parallel curves in Fig. 13.3.

13.8b. Open-circuit Chopper Impedance r_o. The collector-emitter potential is obtained from Eqs. (13.1) and (13.2) by adding V_E and V_C in the correct sense. Thus

$$V_{EC} = V_E - V_C$$
$$V_{EC} = \frac{kT}{q} \ln \left(\frac{I_E + \alpha_{RB}I_C + I_{EO}I_{CO}}{I_C + \alpha_{FB}I_E + I_{CO}I_{EO}} \right) \qquad (13.8)$$

I_B is given by the sum of I_E and I_C.

Hence,

$$V_{EC} = \frac{kT}{q} \ln \left(\frac{I_E(1 - \alpha_{RB}) + \alpha_{RB}I_B + I_{EO}I_{CO}}{I_E(\alpha_{FB} - 1) + I_B + I_{CO}I_{EO}} \right) \qquad (13.9)$$

The impedance between the emitter and collector for a fixed base current is obtained by differentiating Eq. (13.9):

$$Z_{EC} = \frac{kT}{q} \left(\frac{1 - \alpha_{RB}}{I_E(1 - \alpha_{RB}) + \alpha_{RB}I_B + I_{EO}} + \frac{1 - \alpha_{FB}}{I_E(\alpha_{FB} - 1) + I_B + I_{CO}} \right) \qquad (13.10)$$

The open-circuit impedance of the chopper is obtained by inserting the appropriate condition $I_B = 0$. Also, since low-signal currents are contemplated, we can write $I_E = 0$. Hence,

$$r_o = \frac{kT}{q}\left(\frac{1 - \alpha_{RB}}{I_{EO}} + \frac{1 - \alpha_{FB}}{I_{CO}}\right) \tag{13.11}$$

$$r_o = \frac{kT}{qI_{CO}}\left(1 + \frac{\alpha_{FB}}{\alpha_{RB}} - 2\alpha_{FB}\right) \tag{13.11a}$$

r_o is thus shown to be inversely proportional to I_{CO}, and a rise in temperature of $7°C$ results in a halving of r_o, as shown by Figs. 13.14 and 13.18.

With the values of α_{FB} and α_{RB} assumed above and $I_{CO} = 2$ μa, then, since $kT/q = 25$ mv at room temperature, Eq. (13.11a) predicts that $r_o = 5$ kilohms at room temperature for the low-frequency germanium transistor of Fig. 13.14.

REFERENCES

1. Blecher, F. H.: Transistor Circuits for Analogue and Digital Systems, *Bell System Tech. J.*, vol. 35, p. 295, 1956.
2. Bright, R. L., and A. P. Kruper: Transistor Chopper for Stable D.C. Amplifiers, *Electronics*, April, 1955, p. 135.
3. Hillbourne, R. A.: "D.C. Amplifiers and Associated Circuits," Brooklyn Polytechnic Lectures on Special Applications of Transistor Circuits, 1955–1956.
4. Burton, P. L.: An All Transistor D.C. Chopper Amplifier, *English Elec. Rept.* LEL.t.054.
5. Chaplin, G. B. B., and A. R. Owens: Some Transistor Input Stages for High-gain D.C. Amplifiers, *Proc. Inst. Elec. Engrs.*, vol. 105, part B, no. 21, May, 1958.
6. Chaplin, G. B. B., and A. R. Owens: A Transistor High-gain Chopper-type D.C. Amplifier, *Proc. Inst. Elec. Engrs.*, vol. 105, part B, no. 21, May, 1958.
7. Hutcheon, I. C.: A Low-drift Transistor Chopper-type D.C. Amplifier with High Gain and Large Dynamic Range, *Proc. Inst. Elec. Engrs.*, vol. 107, part B, to be published in 1960.
8. To be published.
9. Cooke-Yarborough, E. H.: The Pulsed Direct Current Amplifier, A Method of Operating Transistors at Very Low Currents, *United Kingdom Atomic Energy Authority Rept.* HL.59/7781(S.C.9).
10. Moody, N. F.: A Silicon Diode Modulator of 10^{-8} A. Sensitivity for Use in Junction Transistor D.C. Amplifiers, *Electronic Eng.*, vol. 28, pp. 94–100, March, 1956.
11. Ebers, J. J., and J. L. Moll: Large Signal Behaviour of Junction Transistors, *Proc. IRE*, vol. 42, p. 1761, 1954.

Section 14

TRANSISTOR OSCILLATORS

D. F. PAGE

Department of Electrical Engineering,
Imperial College of Science and Technology,
University of London, London, England.

Sinusoidal Oscillators

Nonsinusoidal Oscillators

The electronic conversion of d-c to a-c power requires an active device with feedback arranged to return a-c power from output to input.   If the active device has a power gain sufficiently greater than unity to supply the feedback losses, the system oscillates and a-c power is available for use in a load.   Such an oscillator is illustrated in Fig. 14.1, where the load power

$$P_o = (K - 1)P_i - P_F \qquad (14.1)$$

is positive if the power gain K is sufficiently greater than unity.   The transistor is an active device and can be used as an oscillator at conversion frequencies up to a frequency f_{max}, above which its available power gain drops below unity.   This maximum

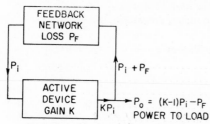

Fig. 14.1. Basic oscillator circuit.

frequency has risen steadily with the development of transistor technology, being of the order of 100 mc/sec for the best available uniform-base transistors, while for the most recent graded-base devices f_{max} is in the kilomegacycle region.   Similarly, the output power available from transistor oscillators at high frequencies has been steadily increased, mainly by the use of silicon to produce high-frequency transistors capable of increased power dissipation.

The nature of the output waveform is determined by the design of the load and feedback network surrounding the transistor.   If this external network is such that the loop gain of the system is greater than unity over only a narrow band of frequencies, the output waveform is sinusoidal.   If on the other hand this loop gain exceeds unity over a broad band of frequencies, the resulting oscillations are nonsinusoidal.   Oscillator design reduces, therefore, to the design of these external feedback and load elements so that the circuit exhibits:

1. The required output waveform at the required frequency and amplitude for the range of transistor parameters to be expected when manufacturing tolerances are considered.

2. The required stability of the frequency and amplitude of this output waveform when the transistor parameters change with changes of temperature and d-c bias levels.

Transistor oscillators can be constructed in a wide variety of feedback arrangements which can be grouped into a few basic classes.   In this section, these main classes of circuits are evaluated and a unified approach is presented for the design of practical oscillator arrangements at all useful frequencies.   Particular attention is paid to the use of the junction triode, as this is currently the most highly developed of the transistor structures.   The PNP transistor is used in the illustrations, although the design principles are equally valid for NPN transistors with appropriate reversal of bias potentials.   The general design principles are also valid for any active device and are applied here to the use of devices exhibiting a charge multiplication mechanism, such as the junction transistor in avalanche, double-base diodes, and the now obsolete point-contact transistor.   All these devices are useful for obtaining oscillators with nonsinusoidal waveforms, as is discussed in the second part of this section.   The first part of the section deals with the use of the junction transistor in oscillator circuits producing near-sinusoidal waveforms.

SINUSOIDAL OSCILLATORS†

The most widely used sinusoidal oscillators make use of resonant L-C circuits to define the oscillation frequency, and a variety of such tuned arrangements can be constructed using transistors. In selecting a circuit appropriate for a particular application, the designer must choose:

1. The type of transistor
2. The transistor configuration (whether common-base, etc.)
3. Between shunt tuning and series tuning
4. The type of feedback (whether using a transformer or lumped or distributed feedback without a transformer)
5. Between class A operation for good frequency stability and low harmonic content, class C operation for high power conversion efficiency, or some compromise operating condition intermediate between these

This section begins with a brief discussion of the more common one-transistor oscillator arrangements for which the relative advantages are simply stated. The justification for these comparisons then follows in subsequent discussions dealing with the detailed design of specific oscillator conditions. The use of R-C elements rather than L-C elements to define the oscillation frequency is also considered in a discussion of the transistor phase-shift oscillator.

14.1. Circuits Using One Transistor. *14.1a. Common-base Circuits.* In Fig. 14.2 are shown some shunt-tuned oscillator circuits using the common-base transistor connection, including (*a*) the transformer-coupled feedback arrangement, (*b*) the Hartley arrangement, and (*c*) the Colpitts arrangement. For convenient comparison, the load conductance G_L in each case is shown connected from collector to base, although it can, of course, be referred to any other convenient transformer winding. In each circuit is shown a feedback resistance R_F which, though required to be small for class C operation, is usefully given a value of a few tens or hundreds of ohms when it is desirable to reduce the effective emitter nonlinearity for class A operation. The d-c blocking capacitors C_F in (*b*) and $C_1 + C_2 = C_F$ in (*c*) are designed to have negligible reactances for oscillation at low frequencies. At high oscillation frequencies, however, the transistor introduces a significant phase lag in the current flow around the feedback loop, and C_F can be chosen to produce a compensating phase advance in the loop.

With the exception of the resonant circuit, the remaining elements in the circuits of Fig. 14.2 relate to the biasing of the transistor and play no part in the a-c circuit. It is shown in a later analysis that the various circuits of Fig. 14.2 are equivalent from an a-c point of view when they have identical values for C_F, R_F, G_L, the turns ratio $T = N_2/N_1$, and the tuned-circuit elements. Thus in the later discussions concerning the design of these elements for given a-c circuit conditions, only one circuit form need be considered. For simplicity in the analyses, the transformer feedback form is chosen, from which the corresponding elements for the Hartley and Colpitts feedback can be found from the circuit equivalences indicated in Fig. 14.2.

14.1b. Bias Arrangements. The most efficient bias arrangement uses a single battery to define collector voltage and to define base current through a large resistor;

† Much of this material is taken from the author's doctoral thesis for the University of London. The research was carried out under the direction of Dr. A. R. Boothroyd in the Department of Electrical Engineering of the Imperial College of Science and Technology, London, England, and was sponsored in part by the Department of Scientific and Industrial Research of the United Kingdom and by the Signals Research and Development Establishment (Ministry of Supply).

the resulting bias conditions are dependent upon the transistor parameters α_{fb0} and I_{co}. With a much greater loss of d-c power in bias resistors, oscillator bias conditions can be made relatively independent of transistor parameters if the emitter current rather than the base current is defined, using two batteries (Fig. 14.2a, b) or using one battery (Fig. 14.2c). For any given a-c oscillator arrangement, a choice of

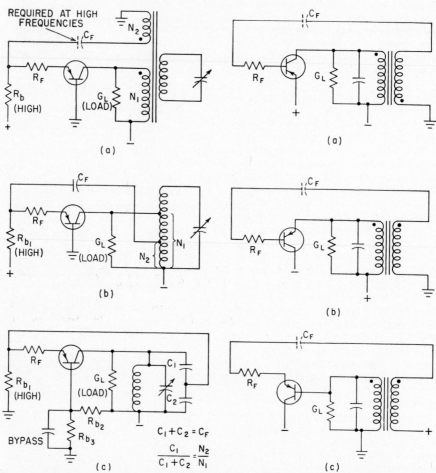

FIG. 14.2. Common-base oscillator arrangements with biasing: (a) transformer-coupled, (b) Hartley type, and (c) Colpitts type.

FIG. 14.3. Transformer feedback circuits using (a) common-emitter configuration, (b) common-collector configurations with base feedback, and (c) common-collector configuration with emitter feedback.

several bias arrangements is possible; the main choice, however, lies between the definition of emitter current and the definition of base current. This choice is assumed to have been made in the following discussions, where, for simplicity, bias elements are omitted in the illustrations.

14.1c. Common-emitter Circuits. In Fig. 14.3a is shown the transformer feedback circuit using a transistor in the common-emitter connection. Equivalent feedback without a transformer can be found with feedback relationships similar to those for the common-base circuits of Fig. 14.2. It will be seen subsequently that the performance of the common-emitter circuit is comparable to that of the common-base circuit at low frequencies where reactive phase shifts in the transistor are negligible. At higher frequencies where the transistor current gain becomes reactive, the common-emitter circuit exhibits a relatively poor frequency stability and is much more critical to adjust for given a-c operating conditions than is the common-base circuit. However, at still higher frequencies where the common-emitter transistor connection exhibits a phase shift approaching 180° in its current transfer ratio, it is the common-base connection which exhibits the poorest stability of performance. It will therefore be evident from later discussions that the common-emitter connection is to be preferred when the transistor is required to be used as an oscillator at these very high frequencies while at lower frequencies the common-base connection is preferable.

14.1d. Common-collector Circuits. Common-collector versions of the transformer feedback oscillator circuit are shown at (*b*) and (*c*) of Fig. 14.3. It will be found in Sec. 14.2*d* that with an appropriate relation between transformer turns ratios the base-feedback circuit (*b*) is equivalent to the common-emitter circuit (*a*), suffering the same low- and medium-frequency limitations. On the other hand, the emitter-feedback circuit (*c*) is equivalent to the common-base circuit.

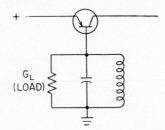

14.1e. Circuits with No External Feedback. The preceding circuits assume feedback applied externally to determine the oscillation conditions. However, within a transistor there exists some feedback to which the external feedback is added. In a junction transistor, internal feedback is not usually sufficient to sustain oscillation; external feedback must be used.

FIG. 14.4. Two-terminal oscillator using a point-contact transistor with no external feedback.

However, if the device possesses a charge multiplication mechanism, as did the now obsolete point-contact transistor, external feedback is not necessary to maintain oscillation. As a result, the point-contact transistor was used in a variety of two-terminal oscillator arrangements,[1] the simplest of which had the basic form shown in Fig. 14.4.

14.1f. Choice of the Junction Transistor with External Feedback. The junction transistor has no charge multiplication mechanism when biased normally to avoid avalanche multiplication, so that it requires external feedback when connected as an oscillator. By comparison, the two-terminal oscillator using a point-contact transistor might appear to be preferable for its relative simplicity. However, it is found that the characteristics (frequency and available power) of such two-terminal oscillators are critically dependent upon the device parameters, and it is desirable to use additional feedback applied externally to define the oscillator performance. Having thus found the application of external feedback to be necessary or desirable for all types of transistors, one prefers the junction triode for its relatively well-defined and reproducible parameters and for its higher frequency and power-handling capabilities. For this reason, the following design discussions are concerned with oscillators using junction transistors with external feedback.

14.1g. Series-tuned Circuits. So far, the circuit examples have used parallel-tuned L-C circuits to restrict the bandwidth of the feedback loop and so to define the oscillation frequency. However, the reader will see that series-tuned L-C circuits could equally well be used. For example, a series-tuned circuit could replace C_F in each of the preceding circuits, or the series-tuned circuit could be placed in series with the grounded transistor terminal. The design of the equilibrium conditions for such arrangements is unchanged provided the series-tuned circuit is relatively lossless while the load remains shunted across the transistor output terminals with feedback taken proportional to load voltage.

However, fundamentally different circuits arise if the load is put in series with a series-tuned circuit and if the feedback is taken proportional to load current. Some simplified versions of such arrangements have been proposed,[2,3] examples of which are shown in Fig. 14.5. In these circuits, the L and C elements are approximately

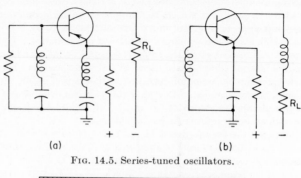

FIG. 14.5. Series-tuned oscillators.

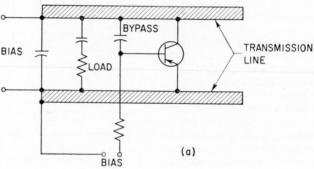

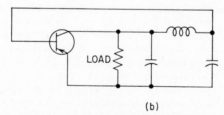

FIG. 14.6. Oscillator with (a) distributed feedback and (b) equivalent lumped feedback.

series-resonant while the output power is taken at the load R_L. An analysis of such circuits results in equilibrium design conditions which are analogous to those for shunt-tuned oscillators.[4] The maximum oscillation frequency and the available power at any lower frequency are the same whether shunt- or series-tuned loads are used. However, with given circuit components and with the nonlinearities associated with the transistor, it appears to be more difficult to maintain a sinusoidal operating current than to maintain a sinusoidal collector-base voltage or collector-emitter voltage. As a result, the previously discussed shunt-loaded oscillators are found to develop a more nearly sinusoidal load waveform than do their dual circuits using series-tuned loads. For this reason, only shunt-loaded circuits will be considered in these design discussions. However, if further investigation should prove series-tuned circuits to be desirable, the appropriate design procedures are analogous to those presented here for the shunt-tuned oscillator.

14.1h. Circuits with Distributed Feedback. For oscillations at ultra-high and very high frequencies, it is convenient to abandon the use of transformers and lumped L and C elements in the feedback network and, instead, to use distributed feedback in the form of transmission lines. One such arrangement which has been used[5] is shown in Fig. 14.6 at (*a*), with the equivalent lumped circuit indicated at (*b*). The required tapping points on the transmission line are usually found experimentally. However, they can be predicted from the following analyses, which permit the design of the equivalent lumped feedback network (*b*).

14.2. Unified Approach to Oscillator Design. Let us now establish a basic analysis which can be used for the design of feedback for all tuned oscillator arrangements. We also require this analysis to be valid at all frequencies, so that the maximum possible oscillation frequency f_{max} can be defined and so that oscillation conditions can be designed at any useful frequency below f_{max}. In this regard, one must note that useful oscillator power can be obtained at frequencies sufficiently close to f_{max} that the transistor parameters are highly reactive. For this reason, conventional mesh analysis leads to large and difficult determinants; instead, the terminal admittance method of analysis is used here because it is found to provide the necessary simplification of concepts and analysis.[4]

As previously explained in Secs. 14.1*f* and 14.1*g*, these design analyses are to be carried out for junction transistor oscillators using external feedback with shunt-tuned loading. However, exactly similar methods can be used for oscillators with series-tuned loading.

14.2a. The Oscillation Condition. The basic shunt-tuned triode oscillator with feedback is illustrated in Fig. 14.7. Oscillations occur at the frequency for which the total terminal admittance Y_T vanishes:

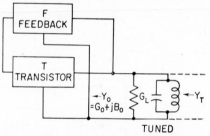

FIG. 14.7. Basic shunt-tuned triode feedback oscillator.

$$Y_T = G_T + B_T = 0 \qquad (14.2)$$

so that $$G_T = 0 \quad \text{and} \quad B_T = 0$$

It will be observed that this condition is equivalent to setting the over-all circuit determinant to zero. For the existence of oscillations, this condition requires the output conductance G_o to be negative with a magnitude exceeding G_L when the circuit is switched on. As oscillations build up, nonlinearities in the transistor reduce the effective negative value of G_o until, at the limiting oscillation amplitude, $G_o = -G_L$. The real frequency at which this limiting of oscillations takes place is that at which the susceptance B_T is zero.

14.2b. Transformer Feedback. The feedback network F in Fig. 14.7 performs two functions. It provides an impedance transformation to match the output of the transistor to its input, while at the same time it provides the compensating phase shift required in the feedback loop to cancel any phase shift introduced by the transistor. The transformer feedback network of Fig. 14.8*a* performs these functions and can be used to represent the externally applied feedback in all tuned oscillators of practical interest. Of the practical oscillator arrangements in Figs. 14.2 and 14.3, the transformer-coupled feedback and the tapped inductance Hartley-type feedback can be represented directly in the form of Fig. 14.8a. Furthermore, it is useful to note that the elements of the equivalent circuit for a practical transformer can be included in the feedback elements of Fig. 14.8a. Thus, B_L is the resultant susceptance of a tuned L-C circuit in which is included the transformer magnetizing inductance, while the feedback impedance Z_F includes the transformer leakage inductance and winding resistance.

14.2c. Feedback without Transformers. It is often convenient, especially at high frequencies, to avoid the use of a transformer in the feedback network. The most

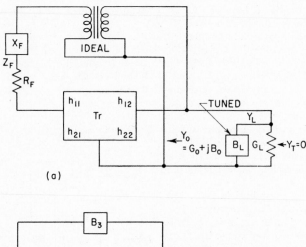

(a)

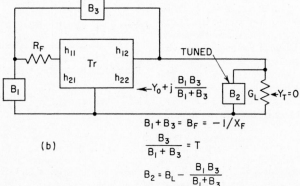

(b)

$$B_1 + B_3 = B_F = -1/X_F$$

$$\frac{B_3}{B_1 + B_3} = T$$

$$B_2 = B_L - \frac{B_1 B_3}{B_1 + B_3}$$

Fig. 14.8. Oscillator equivalent circuits with (a) transformer feedback and (b) equivalent pi feedback.

common alternative feedback form is the pi network, shown in Fig. 14.8b, which will be recognized as a general form of the feedback used in the Colpitts-type oscillator of Fig. 14.2c. Another alternative feedback form is the distributed feedback used in the ultra-high-frequency oscillator illustrated in Fig. 14.6, which can be represented by a lumped equivalent circuit in the pi or transformer forms of Fig. 14.8. Regardless of the feedback form to be used, it is usually convenient to carry out the initial design of feedback in the transformer form; the appropriate network transformations can then be used to obtain the element values of any desired alternative feedback arrangement.

A real transformer ratio T is assumed in the following analyses, and this imposes certain restrictions on the distribution of losses in such alternative feedback networks. Thus, in the pi network of Fig. 14.8b, B_1 and B_3 are required to have similar phase angles if the losses associated with these elements are appreciable. Fortunately, in practical circuits these losses are small and the restriction is unimportant. If the feedback is to be distributed, it should be noted that the restriction requires the equivalent transmission line to be approximately lossless.

14.2d. Equilibrium of Oscillations—h-parameter Analysis. The output admittance Y_o which is presented to the load admittance Y_L in Fig. 14.8a can be expanded in terms of the transistor h parameters. Thus

$$Y_o = h_{22} - Y_n \tag{14.3}$$

The transistor output admittance without feedback is therefore modified by a term Y_n arising from the presence of feedback. A circuit analysis shows this additional term to have the value

$$Y_n = \frac{(h_{12} - T)(h_{21} + T)}{Z_F + h_{11}} \tag{14.4}$$

Applying the equilibrium condition $Y_L + Y_o = 0$, we can thus write

$$Y_L + h_{22} = \frac{(h_{12} - T)(h_{21} + T)}{Z_F + h_{11}} \tag{14.5}$$

When h_{12} is neglected, a valid neglect for all practical frequencies and feedback arrangements, Eq. (14.5) yields the following equalities:

$$G_L + \text{Re}\,(h_{22}) = \frac{T[kx_2 - (T - r_2)]}{R'(1 + k^2)} \tag{14.6}$$

$$B_L + \text{Im}\,(h_{22}) = \frac{T[x_2 + k(T - r_2)]}{R'(1 + k^2)} \tag{14.7}$$

where
$$R' = R_F + \text{Re}\,(h_{11}) \qquad k = \frac{X_F + \text{Im}\,(h_{11})}{R'} \tag{14.8}$$

$$-h_{21} = r_2 + jx_2$$

These relationships express the circuit conditions which must exist at the oscillation frequency for equilibrium of oscillations. They thus form a basis for the design of the feedback and load for any required a-c conditions at equilibrium of oscillations. It remains to substitute physical transistor parameters for the h parameters. However, before discussing the appropriate equivalent circuit for the junction transistor, let us classify the transistor configurations which are of interest.

14.2e. Transistor Configurations. Of the six possible transistor configurations, only the four listed in Table 14.1 need be considered for use in practical shunt-tuned oscillator circuits. (The two remaining possible configurations have unsuitable terminal impedances which lead to impractical values for the tuned-circuit and feedback elements.) Now the four configurations of Table 14.1 are further reduced to two basic groups for oscillator analysis:

1. A and D, in which current is fed back to the emitter proportional to the collector-base load voltage
2. B and C, in which current is fed back to the base proportional to the collector-emitter load voltage

Thus, it is found that a design of oscillator feedback for the common-base configuration A can be applied for configuration D with the following relationship between transformer turns ratios:

$$T_D = 1 - T_A \tag{14.9}$$

Similarly, a feedback design for the common-emitter configuration B is also a design for configuration C with the substitution

$$T_C = 1 - T_B \tag{14.10}$$

TABLE 14.1. THE FOUR TRANSISTOR CONFIGURATIONS FOR OSCILLATOR USE

Configuration	Load connected	Feedback to	Common terminal	Example circuit
A	Collector-base	Emitter	Base	Fig. 14.2
B	Collector-emitter	Base	Emitter	Fig. 14.3a
C	Emitter-collector	Base	Collector	Fig. 14.3b
D	Base-collector	Emitter	Collector	Fig. 14.3c

14.2f. The Junction Transistor Equivalent Circuit. The equivalent circuit of Fig. 14.9 is a good approximation for most presently available uniform-base and graded-base junction transistors. An exception is the grown transistor, for which $r_{bb'}$ is

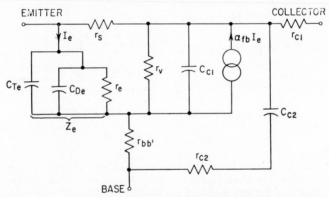

FIG. 14.9. Approximate equivalent circuit for the junction transistor.

complex; however, though the following oscillator theory is based on this equivalent circuit, it can be applied for the grown-junction transistor when $r_{bb'}$ is given the necessary complex value.

The base-width modulation parameters r_v and r_s introduce feedback within the transistor; however, since this internal feedback is always small compared with that applied externally in an oscillator circuit, these parameters can be neglected for oscillator analysis. Of the remaining parameters, r_{c_1}, r_{c_2}, and C_{c_2} are only necessary for a complete representation of diffused junction devices constructed in the mesa form. Even for these transistors, however, it is found that r_{c_1} and r_{c_2} can be neglected for oscillator design purposes, the resulting errors being significant only at frequencies immediately approaching f_{max}. As a result, the simplified high-frequency equivalent circuit of Fig. 14.10a can be used for oscillator analysis at all useful frequencies.

Of the reactive parameters which represent phase shift in the transistor at high frequencies, it is found that the low impedance Z_e and the low capacitances C_{c_1} and C_{c_2} can be lumped with the external feedback and load elements. The current gain α_{fb} remains, therefore, as the most important reactive parameter. A frequency locus for α_{fb} plotted in real and imaginary parts

$$\alpha_{fb} = m - jn \tag{14.11}$$

is shown in Fig. 14.11a for a typical graded-base transistor. The locus for uniform-base transistors will remain substantially the same shape for all such transistors, and in order to obtain the phase angle $\varphi\alpha_{fb}$ at any frequency it is necessary simply to calibrate the locus for the particular transistor by measuring the modulus $[\alpha_{fb}]$ at a single frequency, usually $f_{\alpha fb}$. For graded-base transistors, however, no fixed locus is generally applicable because each transistor has a somewhat different drift field in the base region. Furthermore, the shape of the α_{fb} locus for these transistors is dependent at high frequencies on the relatively ill-defined emitter depletion-layer capacitance C_{Te}. For graded-base transistors, therefore, the complete α_{fb} locus must be plotted for each transistor type and, often, for each transistor. A commonly used comparison for these transistors is the frequency f_T at which m is one-half of its low-frequency value.

As the common-emitter configuration is also to be considered for oscillator use, it is useful to note the appropriate conversion from the common-base equivalent circuit of Fig. 14.10a to the common-emitter circuit of Fig. 14.10b. The current gain

$$\alpha_{fe} = \frac{\alpha_{fb}}{1 - \alpha_{fb}} = u - jq \tag{14.12}$$

has now become the most significant reactive parameter, a frequency locus of which is drawn in Fig. 14.11b for the same graded-base transistor for which α_{fb}

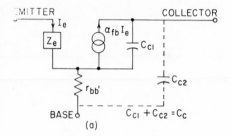

(a)

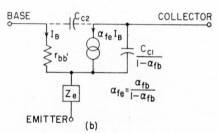

(b)

FIG. 14.10. Simplified equivalent circuits appropriate for oscillator design (a) for common-base connection, (b) for common-emitter connection.

is plotted in (a) of the same figure. For comparison, certain frequencies are marked on each plot to indicate the relative rates of change of α_{fb} and α_{fe} in magnitude and phase as the frequency is increased. It will be noted that α_{fe} changes most rapidly up to a frequency approximating f_T, above which α_{fb} changes most rapidly up to the higher frequency f, where

$$\varphi\alpha_{fb} = \varphi\alpha_{fe} = 180°$$

The imaginary components n and q approach zero at low frequencies, where α_{fb} and α_{fe} have their real low-frequency values α_{fb0} and α_{fe0}, respectively.

14.2g. Maximum Oscillation Frequency. The frequency f_{max} is the same for all configurations of the transistor[6] and usually occurs for angles $\varphi\alpha_{fb}$ between 60 and 180°; however, for certain graded-base transistors $\varphi\alpha_{fb}$ may exceed 180° at f_{max}. This frequency must be known if a transistor is to be evaluated for use as an oscillator at high frequencies. When not available from the manufacturer's data sheets, f_{max} can be estimated from the following expression:[7]

$$f_{max} = \frac{|\alpha_{fb}|^2}{8\pi n r_{bb'} C_{c_1}} \qquad (14.13)$$

This is a geometric solution for f_{max} requiring the α_{fb} locus to be investigated over a range of frequencies until it is satisfied. It assumes a high emitter bias current so

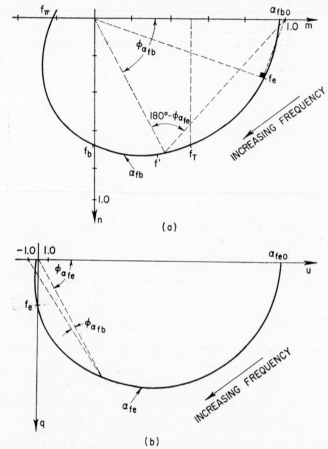

Fig. 14.11. Frequency loci of the complex current gains α_{fb} and α_{fe}.

that r_e is unimportant. Furthermore, it assumes the collector losses r_{c1} and r_{c2} to be negligible, so that the resulting value for f_{max} is somewhat optimistic for certain graded-base transistors. It is also assumed that n is not very small at f_{max}.

For uniform-base transistors, the following oversimplified expression has been used for α_{fb}:

$$\alpha_{fb} = \frac{\alpha_{fb0}}{1 + jf/f_{\alpha_{fb}}} \qquad (14.14)$$

which with (14.13) leads to

$$f_{\max}^2 = \frac{\alpha_{fb0} f_{\alpha fb}}{8\pi n r_{bb'} C_{e_1}} \tag{14.15}$$

This gives a value of $f_{\max}$ for uniform-base transistors which is approximately 9 per cent higher than the true value. For graded-base devices, however, α_{fb} cannot be approximated by (14.14) and $f_{\max}$ must be estimated by means of the geometric expression (14.13).

14.2h. Design Expressions for Small-signal Equilibrium. Having chosen an appropriate equivalent circuit for the transistor, we are in a position to express the design relationships (14.6) and (14.7) in terms of the physical transistor parameters. For this purpose, the h parameters listed in Table 14.2 can be used for all frequencies of practical interest, that is, for all frequencies except those immediately approaching

TABLE 14.2. JUNCTION TRANSISTOR h PARAMETERS

	Common-base	Common-emitter
h_{11}	$h_{11b} = Z_e + r_{bb'}(1 - \alpha_{fb})$	$h_{11e} = \dfrac{Z_e}{1 - \alpha_{fb}} + r_{bb'}$
h_{21}	$h_{21b} = -\alpha_{fb}$	$h_{21e} = \alpha_{fe} = \dfrac{\alpha_{fb}}{1 - \alpha_{fb}}$
h_{22}	$h_{22b} = j\omega C_c$	$h_{22e} = \dfrac{j\omega C_{c_1}}{1 - \alpha_{fb}}$
h_{12}	$\ll 1.0$	$\ll 1.0$

TABLE 14.3. TRANSISTOR OSCILLATOR LOAD FOR EQUILIBRIUM

	Configuration A	Configuration B
$G_L + \operatorname{Re}(h_{22})$	$\dfrac{(m - k_b n - T_A)T_A}{R_b'(1 + k_b^2)}$	$\dfrac{(k_e q - u - T_B)T_B}{R_e'(1 + k_e^2)}$
$B_L + \operatorname{Im}(h_{22})$	$\dfrac{[k_b(T_A - m) - n]T_A}{R_b'(1 + k_b^2)}$	$\dfrac{[k_e(T_B + u) + q]T_B}{R_e'(1 + k_e^2)}$
	where	
	$R_b' = R_F + \operatorname{Re}(h_{11b})$	$R_e' = R_F + \operatorname{Re}(h_{11e})$
	$k_b = \dfrac{X_F + \operatorname{Im}(h_{11b})}{R_b'}$	$k_e = \dfrac{X_F + \operatorname{Im}(h_{11e})}{R_e'}$

$f_{\max}$. Substituting these into (14.6) and (14.7) one obtains the relationships listed in Table 14.3; these express the load admittance required to permit oscillations to start with any given feedback conditions. Similar expressions apply for configurations C and D with the substitutions (14.9) and (14.10).

14.2i. Maximum Potential Instability. The maximum oscillation frequency $f_{\max}$ has been defined in Sec. 14.2g. At frequencies below $f_{\max}$ a further boundary on available oscillator performance can be defined as the condition of maximum instability in which feedback is optimized to allow the maximum possible load conductance.[7] This optimum feedback and maximum load are given in Table 14.4 and are seen to depend only upon the short-circuit input resistance (including R_F) and current gain

TABLE 14.4. FEEDBACK AND LOAD FOR MAXIMUM INSTABILITY

	Configuration A	Configuration B
T^o	$\dfrac{\lvert \alpha_{fb} \rvert^2}{2m}$	$-\dfrac{\lvert \alpha_{fe} \rvert^2}{2u}$
k^o	$\dfrac{-n}{m}$	$\dfrac{-q}{u}$
$G_L^o + \mathrm{Re}\,(h_{22})$	$\dfrac{\lvert \alpha_{fb} \rvert^2}{4R_b'}$	$\dfrac{\lvert \alpha_{fe} \rvert^2}{4R_e'}$
$B_L^o + \mathrm{Im}\,(h_{22})$	$\dfrac{-n}{m}\dfrac{\lvert \alpha_{fb} \rvert^2}{4R_b'}$	$\dfrac{-q}{u}\dfrac{\lvert \alpha_{fe} \rvert^2}{4R_e'}$

TABLE 14.5. FEEDBACK PRODUCING MAXIMUM INSTABILITY
AT FREQUENCIES LESS THAN f'

Configuration	F

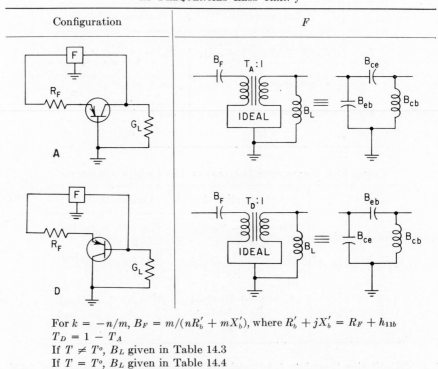

For $k = -n/m$, $B_F = m/(nR_b' + mX_b')$, where $R_b' + jX_b' = R_F + h_{11b}$
$T_D = 1 - T_A$
If $T \neq T^o$, B_L given in Table 14.3
If $T = T^o$, B_L given in Table 14.4
B_{eb}, B_{cb}, B_{ce} calculated as in Fig. 14.8

of the transistor; furthermore, Re (h_{22}) is negligible except at frequencies immediately approaching $f_{\max}$. As an example, a plot of G_L^o with frequency is given in Fig. 14.12 for a typical graded-base transistor. The corresponding frequency variation of the optimum turns ratio T_A^o for this transistor in configuration A is plotted in Fig. 14.13. This shows T_A^o to increase with increasing frequency from its low-frequency value of $\alpha_{fb0}/2$ to a very high value when $\varphi_{\alpha_{fb}}$ is in the region of 90°; at higher frequencies, T_A^o has a decreasing negative value. A similar frequency variation occurs for T_B^o, which has a low-frequency value of $-\alpha_{fe0}/2$; high-frequency values of T_B^o for this transistor are shown dashed in Fig. 14.13. At a frequency f', somewhat less than f_b where $\varphi_{\alpha_{fb}} = 90°$, the optimum turns ratios T_A^o and T_B^o are equal with values of unity.

Feedback circuits which can be used to achieve maximum instability are illustrated in Tables 14.5 and 14.6. For oscillators at frequencies lower than f', configurations A and D are chosen for their relative stability of performance resulting from the relatively slow change with frequency of α_{fb} compared with α_{fe} at these frequencies (Fig. 14.11). On the other hand, configurations B and C are preferred for frequencies higher than f' because of the relatively slow rate of change with frequency of α_{fe} compared with that of α in this higher-frequency region.

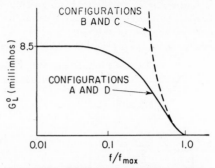

FIG. 14.12. Maximum possible oscillator load for a typical graded-base transistor.

14.3. Design of Limiting Conditions. Having considered the conditions required for oscillations to start, we must modify the results of these small-signal analyses to include the circuit nonlinearities which cause the limiting of oscillations. For example, in the design of power oscillators it is required to achieve a high conversion efficiency from the d-c bias power supplied to the a-c power available in the load. Or conversion efficiency may be less important, while the major requirements may be a low harmonic content or good frequency stability. Let us first consider the nonlinear mechanisms.

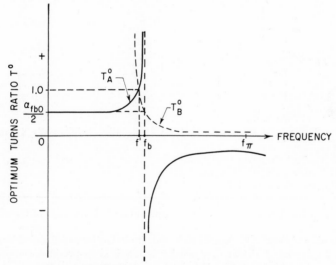

FIG. 14.13. Typical variation of T^o with frequency.

If the oscillator load conductance is chosen exactly equal to the value given by the previous small-signal design expressions of Table 14.3 or 14.4, oscillations will not rise in the circuit. If the load is decreased from this value, however, oscillations rise and energy is stored in the circuit until transistor nonlinearities reduce the regeneration sufficiently to produce amplitude equilibrium. The nonlinearities result from modulation of the d-c bias supply levels by the alternating voltage and current excursions in the circuit. In practical oscillator applications it is usually necessary that these excursions be large; for example, if the d-c to a-c conversion efficiency is to be high, the a-c excursions must be comparable to the d-c supply levels. Of the many nonlinear mechanisms in the transistor, the two major effects occur when the emitter-base diode opens (cutoff) and when the collector-base diode closes (saturation or bottoming). Of the remaining nonlinear mechanisms, the greatest is the modulation of the base transport mechanism due to the effects of high-level carrier injection and modulation of the effective base width. However, these remaining effects can be neglected in a first-order oscillator design and, instead, can be included afterward as

TABLE 14.6. FEEDBACK PRODUCING MAXIMUM INSTABILITY
AT FREQUENCIES BETWEEN f' AND f_π

Configuration	F

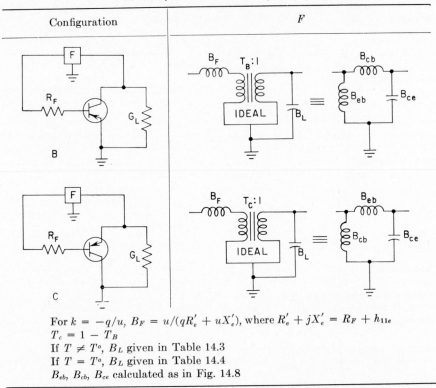

For $k = -q/u$, $B_F = u/(qR'_e + uX'_e)$, where $R'_e + jX'_e = R_F + h_{11e}$
$T_c = 1 - T_B$
If $T \neq T^\circ$, B_L given in Table 14.3
If $T = T^\circ$, B_L given in Table 14.4
B_{eb}, B_{cb}, B_{ce} calculated as in Fig. 14.8

second-order refinements which depend to some extent on the type of transistor to be used.

If the load is chosen only slightly less than its value for small-signal equilibrium, only a small degree of circuit nonlinearity is required to produce amplitude equilibrium; as a result, little energy exists in the circuit at harmonic frequencies, and the oscillator currents and voltages appear sinusoidal. This is the class A or near class A condition used when it is required to achieve good frequency stability with a good output waveform. On the other hand, if the load is chosen appreciably less than its value for small-signal equilibrium, a high degree of circuit nonlinearity is necessary to produce amplitude equilibrium. This is the condition in a class C power oscillator in which the operating current is designed to be nonsinusoidal for high d-c to a-c conversion efficiency.

14.3a. Class A Oscillation. With the load conductance chosen only slightly less than the value given by Table 14.3, a near class A oscillation state can be considered with the following idealizations:

1. Excursions of emitter current I_e take place to an amplitude approximating the direct emitter bias current I_E. At higher amplitudes cutoff occurs over part of the cycle, which causes the average value of Re (h_{11}) to increase sharply, decreasing the effective negative output conductance and limiting the oscillation amplitude.

2. Excursions of collector voltage V_{cb} occur up to the d-c collector-base bias voltage V_C. At higher excursions the collector bottoms over part of the cycle, severely damping the oscillator and limiting the oscillation amplitude.

3. The parameters α_{fb}, C_c, and h_{11} retain their small-signal values for the excursions of emitter current and collector voltage under discussion.

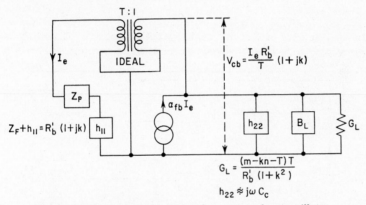

Fig. 14.14. Equivalent circuit for the common-base oscillator.

The oscillator conversion efficiency is highest when both cutoff and bottoming operate simultaneously to limit oscillation; on the other hand, the efficiency is reduced if limiting is caused by only one nonlinearity.

The relative importance of these nonlinearities can be studied in terms of the alternating currents and a-c voltages existing in a common-base oscillator, the equivalent circuit for which is shown in Fig. 14.14 using the transistor parameter simplifications discussed previously. With Re (h_{22}) neglected for all useful frequencies and with the load conductance given its value for circuit equilibrium from Table 14.3,

$$G_L = \frac{(m - kn - T)T}{R_b'(1 + k^2)} \tag{14.16}$$

the load voltage and power can be written in terms of the alternating emitter current I_e and the a-c collector-base voltage V_{cb}:

$$V_{cb} = \frac{I_e R_b'}{T}(1 + jk) \tag{14.17}$$

$$P_L = V_{cb}I_e \frac{(m - kn - T)}{\sqrt{1 + k^2}} \tag{14.18}$$

Now if the feedback is optimized for maximum instability (see Table 14.4) and with Re (h_{22}) neglected for all useful frequencies, the load conductance, voltage, and power are given by

$$G_L^o = \frac{|\alpha_{fb}|^2}{4R_b'} \qquad V_{cb} = \frac{2I_eR_b'}{|\alpha_{fb}|} \qquad P_L = I_e^2R_b' \qquad (14.19)$$

The resulting class A oscillations limit at the emitter, so that with the approximation $I_e = I_E/\sqrt{2}$, the load voltage and power are given by

$$V_{cb} = \frac{\sqrt{2}I_ER_b'}{|\alpha_{fb}|} \qquad P_L = \frac{I_E^2R_b'}{2} \qquad (14.20)$$

Typical low-frequency values for V_{cb} and P_L are 0.14 volt and 0.1 milliwatt if $I_E = 1$ ma and $R_b' = 100$ ohms; thus, such oscillation is found to be extremely inefficient when the collector bias voltage V_C is given its usual value of several volts.

If, however, a resistive load R_c is now put in series with the collector as shown in Fig. 14.15a, the circuit is not significantly disturbed provided R_c has a value somewhat less than the reactance of C_c. With this restriction and with G_L and the feedback optimized as above, R_c may be given any value up to $V_C/2\alpha_{fb0}I_E$ at which it will

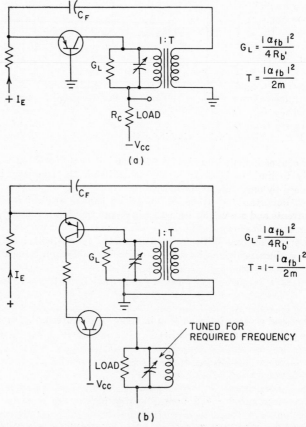

FIG. 14.15. Shunt-tuned oscillator (a) using series collector loading, (b) using configuration Ϙ with a second transistor as the series collector load.

dissipate the remaining available a-c collector power

$$P_s = \frac{|\alpha_{fb}| I_E V_C}{2} - \frac{I_E^2 R_b'}{2} \qquad (14.21)$$

Neglecting the small component $I_E^2 R_b'/2$ dissipated at G_L, the resulting class A collector efficiency can be written as

$$\rho_c = \frac{|\alpha_{fb}|}{2\alpha_{fb0}} (100)\% \qquad (14.22)$$

which has a value of 50 per cent at low frequencies. In practice, the available efficiency is somewhat reduced from this value by the adverse effects on α_{fb} of the base-width modulation and high injection levels which occur during the cycle; these effects are most pronounced with graded-base transistors.

A significant advantage of this series collector load arrangement lies in the fact that the feedback and frequency definition are almost independent of variations in the load R_c provided the frequency is sufficiently low that the reactance of C_c is high compared with R_c. In order to maintain a low value for the short-circuit input resistance R_b', no series emitter resistance should be used and the emitter bias current I_E should be high. A high value for I_E also lowers the necessary load resistance R_c, permitting the circuit advantages to be achieved to higher frequencies. For many applications, the load R_c can be the input of a common-base amplifier as shown in Fig. 14.15b; the collector load of this second transistor can be tuned for reduced harmonic distortion of the output waveform. At high frequencies where C_c becomes important, R_c introduces a value for Re (h_{22}) which reduces the required value of G_L^o.

If the more conventional technique of loading by means of G_L (with R_c omitted) is used, the full load power [Eq. (14.21)] can be dissipated in G_L with the maximum available efficiency [Eq. (14.22)]. This requires the feedback turns ratio and the load to be reduced, from their values T_A^o and G_L^o for maximum instability, to

$$T_A = \frac{I_E R_b'}{V_C} \frac{|\alpha_{fb}|}{m} = \frac{2 I_E R_b'}{V_C} T_A^o$$

$$G_L = \frac{I_E}{V_C} \left\{ |\alpha_{fb}| - \frac{I_E}{V_C} R_b' \right\} \qquad (14.23)$$

However, feedback is now dependent upon the load, which must remain constant if class A conditions are to be maintained.

Regardless of the loading technique, the available oscillator power is reduced at high frequencies where $|\alpha_{fb}|$ is reduced. At sufficiently high frequencies, efficiency is further reduced by the inevitable losses associated with tuned-circuit and feedback elements until at a frequency approaching f_{max} the useful output power becomes insignificant.

To ensure that oscillations will start and build up to the required amplitude, it is necessary to choose a value of G_L somewhat less than the small-signal equilibrium value. The class A condition is therefore an idealization which can be only approximated in a practical oscillator. Furthermore, it should be noted that G_L as used here includes the equivalent loss conductance associated with the tuned circuit, so that the true load conductance must be reduced accordingly.

14.3b. Class C Oscillation. If G_L is chosen much less than its class A value, the emitter is driven into cutoff during an appreciable part of the cycle and the emitter current flows in pulses. This class C condition produces the high collector efficiencies required when the a-c power to be derived from the oscillator is comparable to the maximum permissible collector dissipation of the transistor. As a guide to the design of class C conditions, the preceding class A analysis can be extended with the following idealizations:

1. I_e has a pulse wave shape consisting of a fundamental component I_F together with harmonic frequency components.

2. The frequency components of I_e are modified individually by the current ratio α_{fb}, so that in the collector current $\alpha_{fb}I_e$ the fundamental component is $\alpha_{fb}I_F$.

3. Of the frequency components of $\alpha_{fb}I_e$, only $\alpha_{fb}I_F$ contributes significantly to feedback; that is, the tuned-circuit voltage is assumed to remain sinusoidal. The permissible class C shunt load conductance is therefore related as follows to the class A conductance permitted with the same feedback elements:

$$G_L^C = \frac{i_F}{i_E}\,G_L^A \qquad (14.24)$$

where i_F is the amplitude of I_F and i_E is the amplitude of the sinusoidal emitter current that would flow if the emitter were linear with its small-signal impedance over the full oscillation cycle.

4. During the "active" part of the cycle, the transistor parameters have effective values approximating the small-signal values at start of oscillations.

This last assumption is found to break down at high frequencies where it is necessary to choose an effective complex value for α_{fb} which includes the very significant effects in the base region of high injection level and dispersion associated with the class C current pulses. At lower frequencies, however, where $\varphi_{\alpha_{fb}}$ is not greater than a few degrees, values for R_b', C_c, and α_{fb} estimated from small-signal measurements are found to suffice for approximate class C design.

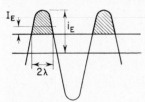

FIG. 14.16. Part-sinusoidal emitter current assumed for class C oscillator design.

With the emitter current pulse assumed to be a part sinusoid as shown in Fig. 14.16, the ratio i_F/i_E can be written as

$$\frac{i_F}{i_E} = \frac{\lambda}{\pi}\left(1 - \frac{\sin 2\lambda}{2\lambda}\right) \qquad (14.25)$$

so that the required load conductance can be calculated from (14.24) when the flow angle 2λ has been chosen. The average value

$$I_E = \frac{\lambda}{\pi}\left(\frac{\sin \lambda}{\lambda} - \cos \lambda\right)i_E \qquad (14.26)$$

is fixed by the direct emitter-current bias supply. Meanwhile, with I_E replaced by i_E in expressions (14.23), the necessary feedback turns ratio can be calculated when V_c, I_E, and 2λ are specified. The angle 2λ can be chosen for the required collector efficiency from the relation

$$\rho_c = \frac{|\alpha_{fb}|}{2\alpha_{jb0}}\frac{1 - (\sin 2\lambda/2\lambda)}{(\sin \lambda/\lambda) - \cos \lambda} \qquad (14.27)$$

In practice, this procedure is found to lead to a good circuit approximation which, if necessary, can be modified experimentally to achieve the desired results.

A class C oscillator can be used to deliver power at a harmonic frequency with the circuit of Fig. 14.15b, in which the load of the second transistor is tuned to the required frequency.

In the provision of d-c bias to a class C oscillator, care must be taken in the use of feedback and d-c blocking capacitors in the emitter circuit. These must charge during build-up of oscillations in order to produce the necessary emitter self-bias for the required angle of flow. However, if the discharge time constants of these capacitors is long compared with the dynamic time constant of the oscillator, squegging will result. The transient conditions in a transistor oscillator are discussed in Sec. 14.6.

14.3c. Multiple Oscillations. Some care is necessary in the choice of feedback at high frequencies to avoid simultaneous oscillation at more than one frequency. In a common-base class C oscillator, for example, the circuit waveform may be found to be the sum of the required sinusoid and another sinusoid at a higher harmonic frequency. An investigation[4] shows this to be due to the simultaneous feedback of current to the emitter when the circuit is redrawn with the transistor considered to be in the common-emitter connection. However, this higher frequency instability is readily eliminated by choosing a high C/L ratio in the common-base load or by using a series-tuned circuit for C_F. This unwanted oscillation cannot occur if the common-base circuit is loaded to a near class A condition.

In the same way, feedback designed to produce common-emitter oscillations is often found to produce simultaneous common-base oscillations at a lower subharmonic frequency. For example, if pi feedback is chosen to produce common-emitter oscillations at 20 mc/sec with a 2N247 transistor for which f_T is approximately 25 mc/sec, simultaneous oscillations are likely to occur at 4 or 5 mc/sec. Unless crystal control is used on such common-emitter oscillators, simultaneous subharmonic oscillation is difficult to avoid, even with class A loading.

14.4. Oscillator Stability. *14.4a. Amplitude Stability.* The oscillation amplitude is proportional to the direct emitter bias current I_E if limiting is due to cutoff, while it is proportional to the d-c collector voltage V_C if limiting is due to bottoming. Fortunately, the usual stability of supply voltage levels provides a sufficient degree of amplitude stability for most applications. Changes in the load G_L are a further source of amplitude instability when limiting occurs owing to emitter cutoff.

14.4b. Frequency Stability. The factors determining the stability of oscillation frequency can be understood from a study of the terminal susceptance B_T (see Fig. 14.7), which for a common-base oscillator has the value

$$B_T = B_L + \text{Im}\,(h_{22}) - B_n \qquad (14.28)$$

where

$$\text{Im}\,(h_{22}) = \omega C_c$$

$$B_n = \frac{kT(T - m) - nT}{R_b'\,(1 + k^2)}$$

Oscillations occur at the angular frequency ω_0 for which $B_T = 0$ and for which the slope $\partial B_T/\partial \omega$ has a positive value.[8] Now this slope also determines the frequency stability;[4] the higher is $\partial B_T/\partial \omega$, the more stable is ω_0 when changes of bias levels or of temperature tend to modify the transistor parameters or the tuned-circuit and feedback elements.

For a stable frequency, therefore, one designs the highest possible slope $\partial B_T/\partial \omega$ in the load susceptance; for example, this slope can be made high with a high C/L ratio or with the tuned-circuit arrangement suggested by Clapp.[9] If B_L includes a crystal, a very high slope is obtained.

Having observed the requirements on the load susceptance for good frequency stability, let us examine the remaining three terms included in B_T. From (14.28), these are

$$\omega C_c \qquad \frac{nT}{R_b'(1 + k^2)} \qquad \frac{-k(T - m)}{R_b'(1 + k^2)}$$

all of which are functions of bias-dependent and temperature-dependent transistor parameters. To minimize its dependence on C_c, the frequency must be sufficiently low that C_c is small compared with the tuned-circuit capacitances. The second term, containing n, introduces the significant bias dependence of frequency at high frequencies. If this source of frequency instability is to be eliminated, it is therefore necessary to choose a transistor for which n is small, that is, a transistor whose f_T is high compared with the oscillation frequency. Finally, the third term containing k introduces a dependence of frequency on bias levels, even at low frequencies. To eliminate this source of frequency instability, it is necessary to reduce k to zero by an appropriate choice of feedback reactance.

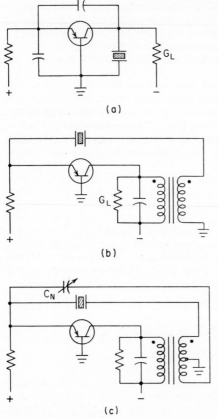

(a)

(b)

(c)

FIG. 14.17. Crystal-controlled oscillator circuits.

This requires a feedback capacitance C_F in the transformer-coupled circuits of Figs. 14.2 and 14.3, to resonate with the transformer leakage inductance. In the Colpitts type of circuit of Fig. 14.2c, a feedback inductance is required in series with the emitter to resonate with the equivalent feedback capacitance $C_1 + C_2$.

Such series tuning of the feedback loop increases the slope $\partial B_T/\partial\omega$ and thus further improves the frequency stability. This reasoning leads to the use of crystal-controlled feedback.

14.4c. Crystal-controlled Oscillators. Where high stability of frequency is required, a crystal can be used to produce a high slope $\partial B_T/\partial\omega$, as discussed above; typical circuits are shown in Fig. 14.17. In (a) the crystal operates in its shunt-resonant mode and replaces the L-C-tuned circuit. In (b) the crystal operates in its series-resonant mode and replaces the feedback reactance X_F. If possible, a high-frequency transistor is chosen such that f_T is much higher than the oscillation frequency, as discussed in the previous section. Furthermore, the emitter feedback circuits (configurations A and D) are preferred in this frequency range because of the relatively good stability of α_{fb} compared with that of α_{fe}.

When the crystal feedback circuit of Fig. 14.17b is used, care must be taken to avoid oscillation arising from feedback paths external to the crystal. At high frequencies, for example, stray interelectrode capacitances alone can introduce sufficient feedback to produce oscillation. The neutralized arrangement of Fig. 14.17c can be used to balance out the feedback due to stray emitter-collector capacitance, particularly the stray capacitance across the crystal. This technique is identical with that widely used with crystal filters. Furthermore, the crystal-controlled oscillator should be loaded to the near class A condition in order to minimize the possibility of oscillation due to other feedback paths. We might note here that the design of starting and limiting conditions is unchanged by the use of the crystal.

The series collector load arrangements of Fig. 14.15 can be used with a crystal oscillator. The circuit of Fig. 14.15b permits the extraction of power at harmonics of the crystal frequency.

When the highest available frequency stability is required from a transistor oscillator, the crystal can be put in one arm of a bridge circuit, as in the well-known Meacham vacuum-tube oscillator.[10]

14.5. Modulation of a Transistor Oscillator. The direct dependence of the oscillation amplitude upon bias levels makes it possible to obtain linear amplitude modulation by modulating the bias levels. A study of the relative merits of base, emitter, and collector modulation[11] shows the required modulation power to be least for modulation of the base current and greatest for modulation of the collector voltage. The frequency modulation which tends to occur during amplitude modulation can be minimized by simultaneously modulating both base and collector[11] or by using a crystal to define the oscillation frequency.

Frequency modulation can be achieved by modulating the current bias levels I_E or I_B, while simultaneous amplitude modulation can be reduced by designing the oscillator to limit on the collector voltage. In a more satisfactory method of frequency modulation, however, modulation is applied in series with the reverse bias of a variable-capacitance diode which forms part of the tuned-circuit capacitance.

14.6. Oscillator Transient Conditions. It is often necessary to know the rate of build-up or decay of oscillations. To avoid squegging in a class C oscillator, for example, capacitors associated with the feedback must have discharge time constants short enough to cope with the expected rate of build-up of oscillations. Or these build-up and decay rates may be required for the design of a superregenerative oscillator.

In the transient oscillator voltage

$$V_{cb} = V e^{at} \sin \omega t \qquad (14.29)$$

the dynamic time constant $1/a$ expresses the rate of build-up or decay and depends upon the negative conductance across the tuned circuit and upon the capacity of the circuit for storing energy. It can be shown[4] that for practical purposes

$$a = \frac{-G_T}{\partial B_T/\partial \omega|_{\omega=\omega_0}} \qquad (14.30)$$

where G_T and B_T are the components of the total terminal admittance Y_T (see Fig. 14.8) at the equilibrium frequency ω_0. In this calculation for configuration A or D, B_T is given by (14.28) and it is found that

$$\left.\frac{\partial(-B_n)}{\partial \omega}\right|_{\omega=\omega_0} = \frac{-T}{R_b'(1+k^2)}\left[\frac{(T-m)(1-k^2)+2kn}{1+k^2}\frac{\partial k}{\partial \omega} - k\frac{\partial m}{\partial \omega} - \frac{\partial n}{\partial \omega}\right]_{\omega=\omega_0} \qquad (14.31)$$

where for practical purposes

$$\left.\frac{\partial k}{\partial \omega}\right|_{\omega=\omega_0} = \frac{-k}{\omega_0} \qquad (14.32)$$

The slopes $\partial m/\partial \omega$ and $\partial n/\partial \omega$ can be obtained from the frequency locus of α_{fb}.

14.7. Push-Pull Circuits. Having outlined the design and limitations of the tuned oscillator using a single transistor, let us turn to circuits using more than one transistor. Certain general observations will first be made. Whether transistors are cascaded or operated in push-pull or in parallel before feedback is applied, the frequency f_{max} for the resulting oscillator is the same as that for a single transistor if identical transistors are used. If transistors are cascaded to form the amplifier to which feedback is applied, the available power is determined by the d-c collector power supplied to only the final transistor. On the other hand, the push-pull connection offers the total power available from both transistors, with no degradation of high-frequency performance. Moreover, the starting, build-up, and limiting conditions in the push-pull oscillator are readily found by extending the previously outlined design of these conditions for the single transistor.

If the push-pull connection is made in the usual way, the problem remains of preventing squegging under the class C conditions required for high efficiency. The problem is avoided, however, in the circuits of Fig. 14.18, where the transistors are used simply as switches, with the supply current or voltage remaining constant.[12] Here, the transistors each conduct for alternate 180° periods of the cycle, and while conducting, they are bottomed so that there is little collector dissipation. In (a), the collector supply current is maintained constant by L_2 and is switched alternately between transistors by the feedback voltage. The bias resistor R_b is chosen to define the base current of each transistor such that the transistor remains bottomed while conducting. The amplitude of oscillation adjusts itself so that the mean voltage at the center tap of the tuned circuit is equal to the negative d-c supply voltage; the waveform at this center tap consists of a series of half sine waves. In circuit (b), a square waveform exists on the common lead between the transistors, the harmonics being highly attenuated by the tuned circuits. These circuits have been used[12] to give over-all efficiencies greater than 80 per cent with total harmonic distortion of less than 1 per cent; also, the output voltage of circuit (a) is relatively independent of variations in the load.

These circuits have high-frequency limitations determined not only by the linear parameters of the transistors but also to some extent because of the effects of carrier storage in the base during

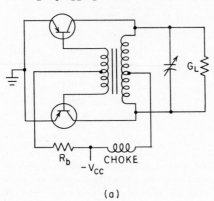

(a)

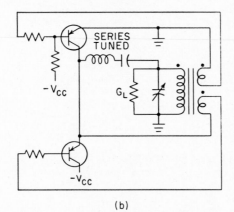

(b)

Fig. 14.18. Push-pull oscillator circuits having high efficiency and low harmonic content.

bottoming. Moreover, the use of the transistors in the bottomed state precludes the use of graded-base transistors in which a maximum collector-base bias voltage is necessary to define a narrow base region and to minimize collector capacitance.

Bottoming is avoided in the circuit of Fig. 14.19, in which a defined emitter supply current is switched between the transistors. A low harmonic distortion (less than 0.1 per cent) is claimed for the output of this oscillator,[12] while the definition of emitter current, though reducing efficiency, makes the oscillator performance independent of I_{CO}. In this and the preceding circuits of Fig. 14.18 feedback can be returned to the emitters rather than to the bases in order to minimize the dependence of oscillator performance on transistor phase shift at higher frequencies.

14.8. R-C Phase-shift Oscillators. A ladder-type R-C phase-shift network can be used in the feedback loop to define a fixed oscillation frequency at low frequencies where it is desirable to eliminate the tuned L-C circuit because of the large inductance required. It has been pointed out[13] that to obtain good frequency stability together with a circuit performance which is relatively independent of the transistor parameter α_{fe0}, the use of two transistors is desirable in the amplifier. In the circuit example of Fig. 14.20, the amplifier consists of an emitter-follower stage followed by a common-emitter stage. The terminal impedance of the frequency-determining R-C network is chosen to be much less than the amplifier input impedance and much higher than the amplifier output impedance in order to minimize the effects of variations in the amplifier. The maximum oscillation frequency for such oscillator arrangements, though much less than the frequency f_{max} available with lossless feedback, has been found[13] to be sufficiently high to more than cover the audio range of frequencies over which

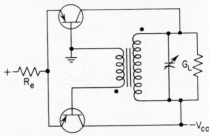

FIG. 14.19. Push-pull oscillator which is relatively independent of transistor parameters.

such oscillators are advantageous. In a typical circuit using transistors with collector capacitances of 20 pf, for example, oscillations were found possible up to 87.5 kc/sec.

In the circuit of Fig. 14.20, a third transistor is used to couple to the load. Limiting of oscillation amplitude is accomplished by a pair of diodes in order to prevent limiting on the transistor characteristics. Second- and third-harmonic distortions of approximately 1 per cent have been obtained with this circuit.[13]

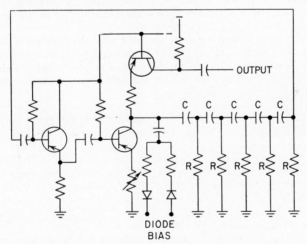

FIG. 14.20. A transistor phase-shift oscillator circuit.

NONSINUSOIDAL OSCILLATORS

If feedback exists over a sufficiently wide band of frequencies, the circuit determinant when written as a function of complex frequency is no longer characterized by the complex pair of roots determining sinusoidal oscillations. Instead, a single positive real root determines the transient condition in the circuit as it switches between one of two states in which the transistor is either fully conducting or cut off. The feedback, however, leads to a periodic switching of the circuit from one state to the other, the repetition rate being determined by the time constants associated with the charge and discharge of circuit reactances. In the resulting relaxation oscillator, the circuit waveforms are usually designed to be approximately rectangular or triangular.

External feedback is not required to achieve relaxation oscillations if a charge multiplication mechanism is present in the device, as, for example, in the old point-contact transistor or in the junction transistor operated under avalanche conditions. For the normally biased junction transistor, however, current gain must be supplied in an external feedback loop by means of a transformer as in the blocking oscillator or by means of a second transistor as in the Eccles-Jordan type multivibrator. These classes of circuits are discussed in turn.

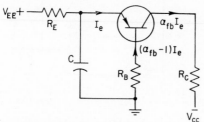

Fig. 14.21. A point-contact transistor relaxation oscillator.

14.9. One-transistor Circuits with No External Feedback. Although the point-contact transistor is no longer widely used, it is worthwhile to consider it briefly. The charge multiplication process in this transistor produces a current gain from emitter to collector which is greater than unity. As a result, the point-contact transistor can be used in several relaxation oscillator circuits, an example of which is shown in Fig. 14.21. When this circuit is switched "on" capacitor C charges through R_E until the transistor conducts and α_{fb} becomes greater than unity. At this point, C discharges rapidly into the transistor while the base is driven negatively; when the discharge of C has lowered the emitter to the negative base voltage, the transistor is cut off. The cycle is then repeated after a charge time determined by R_E and C. Narrow pulses are available across R_B or R_C, while a sawtooth voltage can be obtained across C.

A similar relaxation oscillator can be obtained with the junction transistor if it is operated at a collector bias voltage which is sufficiently high to produce avalanche multiplication of carriers in the collector depletion region.[14] In the circuit of Fig. 14.22, the capacitor C charges toward V_C through R_C when the circuit is switched "on." Meanwhile, the transistor is maintained cut off by the positive base voltage V_B, so that only the current I_{co} flows between collector and base. When the collector reaches the avalanche potential, I_{co} increases rapidly, decreasing the base potential, so that the transistor conducts. The collector current now increases very rapidly until the voltage at the collector is reduced to below the avalanche potential, when the base potential becomes positive

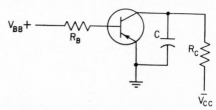

Fig. 14.22. A relaxation oscillator using a junction transistor in avalanche.

and the emitter becomes cut off. However, collector current continues to flow until all the stored charge is removed from the base, and the cycle is then repeated. A series of very short pulses is available across R_B or R_C; alternatively, a current pulse can be obtained by means of a pulse transformer in series with the emitter. With an ordinary alloy-junction transistor,[14] these pulses can be much less than 10 mμsec in duration and several tens or hundreds of milliamperes in amplitude.

14.10. Junction Transistor Blocking Oscillators.† The appropriate addition of transformer feedback to a single normally biased junction transistor produces the

---

† The author is grateful for the advice of C. A. Franklin of the Defence Research Telecommunications Establishment, Ottawa, whose research[15] contributes to much of the material in Secs. 14.10 and 14.11.

blocking oscillator, a circuit which can be used to develop relaxation oscillations similar to those discussed previously for devices with internal current multiplication. Of the many possible configurations, two basic arrangements are illustrated in Fig. 14.23. At (a), feedback is returned from collector to emitter, while feedback is from collector to base at (b). The series collector load resistance R_L could equally well be put in series with the base or emitter. Similarly, the R-C elements through which initial bias is applied can be placed in the emitter circuit to define emitter current or in the base circuit to define base current.

The transistor conducts when the circuit is switched "on," and its current increases rapidly because of the current gain around the feedback loop. The transistor quickly saturates after a rise time determined primarily by the transformer leakage inductance, by the transistor time constants associated with the depletion-layer capacitances, and by $1/f\alpha_{fb}$. The collector current then continues to increase more slowly as the current

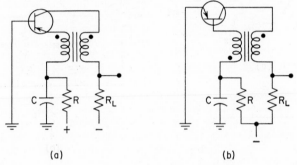

Fig. 14.23. Junction transistor blocking oscillator circuits with (a) emitter feedback and (b) base feedback.

in the transformer magnetizing inductance L_p increases linearly with time while at the same time the capacitor C is discharging into the transistor; these processes determine the pulse width for most practical purposes. The collector comes out of saturation at the end of this phase, when the collector current is α_{fb} times the emitter current for circuit (a) or is α_{fe} times the base current (neglecting I_{CO}) for circuit (b). The circuit then turns "off" rapidly and does not come "on" again until C, which was steadily discharged during the above current pulse, has recharged through R.

The pulse width is therefore approximately proportional to the magnetizing inductance L_p, while it is also proportional to C except when C is very large. With an optimum turns ratio of 2:1 for the emitter feedback circuit (a), some transformer leakage inductance inevitably exists to degrade the pulse rise time. However, circuit (a) exhibits the greater stability of pulse width, this being found to depend upon α_{fb} rather than upon α_{fe} as in circuit (b). On the other hand, a turns ratio of 1:1 can be used in circuit (b) so that a lower leakage inductance can be obtained if care is taken in winding the transformer. As a result, faster pulse edges are possible with circuit (b).

The pulse repetition rate is determined largely by R and C. However, transistor leakage currents also contribute to the recharging of C, and with R and C in the base circuit, the pulse repetition rate is found to be highly dependent upon the temperature-dependent leakage current I_{co}. When a stable repetition frequency is required, therefore, R and C should be placed in the emitter circuit.

These circuits may be synchronized or triggered with signals applied at the emitter or base. Moreover, each circuit would be found to have the same triggering sensitivity if the necessary modification of transformer turns ratio were permitted by the pulse-width and rise-time requirements.

14.11. Two-transistor Multivibrators. The multivibrator is used in such applications as square-wave generation where the required duty cycle is greater than that obtainable with the blocking oscillator. Two cross-coupled junction transistors are used, the simplest arrangement being that shown in Fig. 14.24a. In operation, this

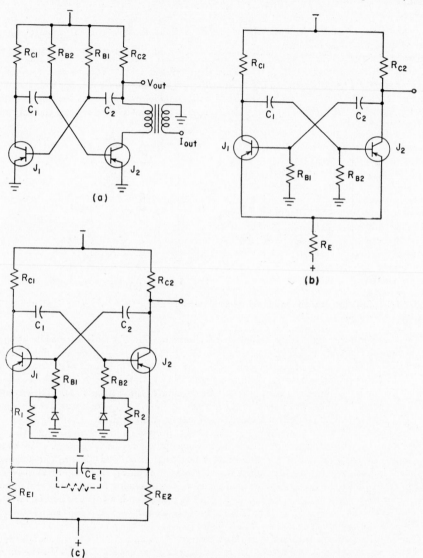

Fig. 14.24. Junction transistor multivibrator circuits.

circuit is similar to its vacuum-tube counterpart. The transistors conduct alternately with very fast regenerative transitions owing to the presence of the cross-coupling capacitors. For example, if J_1 is turning "on," its collector potential rises and a positive-voltage step is transmitted via C_1 to the base of J_2. As a result, J_2 is driven "off" and its collector voltage falls, so that a negative step is transmitted via C_2 to the base of J_1. The process is therefore regenerative, the current in J_1 limiting abruptly when the base of J_1 approaches ground potential and the base current is defined by R_{B1}. The circuit maintains this state for the time required for capacitor C_1 to charge sufficiently through R_{B2} and R_{C1} to pull the base of J_2 negative so that this transistor conducts. Another transition occurs during which J_1 is turned "off" and J_2 is turned "on" with a base current defined by R_{B2}. After a time defined by the charging of C_2 through R_{B1} and R_{C2}, the cycle is repeated. A rectangular voltage waveform can be obtained across either of the collector load resistors, or a pulse transformer can be used in series with one of the collectors, as illustrated, for driving a low-impedance load. Capacitors C_1 and C_2 can be chosen appropriately different when the duty cycle is required to be other than one-half.

In this circuit, resistors R_B are much larger than resistors R_C, which are of the order of 2 kilohms. Therefore, the timing is very dependent upon the temperature-dependent leakage current I_{CO} which flows through the base resistor R_B while the coupling capacitor is charging. A further disadvantage of this base-current defined arrangement is the dependence of collector current on the variable parameters α_{fe} and I_{CO}. Instead, it is desirable to define the collector current accurately so that R_C can be chosen either to avoid bottoming for high-frequency operation or to produce bottoming with a limited degree of base storage. The circuit shown at (b) permits this definition of collector current by means of the large resistor R_E. Also, because the resistors R_B are now greatly reduced to values somewhat less than resistors R_C, the values of the cross-coupling capacitors must be increased for the same timing. As a result, much

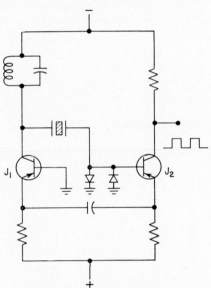

FIG. 14.25. Accurate square-wave generator.

higher charge currents flow during the timing process and the flow of I_{CO} has much less effect.

If the multivibrator is not synchronized to an external signal, circuit (b) exhibits some jitter in the timing, although this is unimportant for most applications. A serious disadvantage for free-running applications, however, is the possibility that this circuit will lock in one state if one transistor has a very high leakage current I_{CO}. This possibility is avoided in circuit (c), where the currents of each transistor are defined separately. Furthermore, as a result of the charging of capacitor C_E during the timing process, timing jitter is reduced. When slow timing rates are required, diodes can be used in the base circuits as shown, with large bias resistors R. With silicon diodes and transistors, times of many seconds are possible.

The circuit of Fig. 14.25 has been used[16] for the generation of very accurately controlled square waves and is an interesting example of the design procedures outlined above. When the circuit is switched "on," both transistors conduct with currents defined by the series emitter resistances. Transistor J_1 is connected as a crystal-controlled sinusoidal oscillator at the required repetition frequency, and when these oscillations build up to the limiting amplitude, transistor J_2 is cut off for 180° periods of the cycle. As a result, the transistors conduct alternately and an accurately defined square wave is available at the collector of J_2.

REFERENCES

1. Oser, E. A., R. O. Endres, and R. P. Moore, Jr.: Transistor Oscillators, *RCA Rev.*, September, 1952, pp. 369–385.
2. Chow, W. F., and D. A. Paynter: Series Tuned Methods in Transistor Radio Circuitry, *IRE Trans. on Circuit Theory*, vol. CT-4, pp. 174–178, September, 1957.
3. Cotes, Jr., A. J.: Matrix Analysis of Oscillators and Transistor Applications, *IRE Trans. on Circuit Theory*, vol. CT-5, pp. 181–188, September, 1958.
4. Page, D. F.: "Instability in Transistor Circuits," Ph.D. Thesis, University of London, April, 1959.
5. Nelson, J. T., J. E. Iwerson, and F. Keywell: A Five-watt Ten-megacycle Transistor, *Proc. IRE*, vol. 46, pp. 1209–1215, June, 1958.
6. Mason, S. J.: Power Gain in Feedback Amplifiers, *IRE Trans. on Circuit Theory*, vol. CT-1, pp. 20–25, June, 1954.
7. Page, D. F.: A Design Basis for Junction Transistor Oscillator Circuits, *Proc. IRE*, vol. 46, pp. 1271–1280, June, 1958.
8. Edson, W. A.: "Vacuum-tube Oscillators," p. 438, John Wiley & Sons, Inc., New York, 1953.
9. Clapp, J. K.: An Inductance-Capacitance Oscillator of Unusual Frequency Stability, *Proc. IRE*, vol. 36, pp. 356–358, 1948.
10. Hufner, W.: Frequenzstabile Oszillatoren mit Transistoren in der Tragerfrequenztechnik, *Nachrtech.*, March, 1958, pp. 117–123.
11. Lin, H. C.: Modulated Transistor Oscillators and Their Applications, in "Transistors I," p. 547, RCA Laboratories, Princeton, N.J., March, 1956.
12. Baxandall, P. J.: Transistor Sine-wave L-C Oscillators—Some General Considerations and New Developments, International Convention on Transistors and Associated Semiconductor Devices, Institution of Electrical Engineers, London, May, 1959.
13. Spence, R.: The Transistor Phase-shift Oscillator, *Ministry of Supply SRDE Rept.*, October, 1956.
14. Beale, J. R. A., W. L. Stephenson, and E. Wolfendale: A Study of High-speed Avalanche Transistors, *Proc. Inst. Elec. Engrs.*, part B, vol. 104, no. 16, paper 2367R, pp. 394–402, July, 1957.
15. Franklin, C. A.: "The Application of Transistors to Pulse Communication Systems," Ph.D. Thesis, University of London, May, 1957.
16. Moody, N. F., et al.: A Lightweight and Self-contained Airborne Navigational System, Part III, *Proc. IRE*, vol. 47, p. 784, May, 1959.

Section 15

TRANSISTOR SWITCHING CIRCUITS

J. L. WALSH†

IBM Corporation, Poughkeepsie, N.Y.

† The author wishes to acknowledge the help and suggestions of his coworkers in the IBM Product Development Laboratory, Poughkeepsie, N.Y.
‡ Adapted from original text by J. C. Logue.

In recent years the transistor has replaced the vacuum tube for most switching applications. This change has occurred because of the superior switching characteristics of the transistor, its low power requirements, and its long life. Although there are many different types of transistor switching circuits, the differences are often mainly in details rather than in broad aspects. In this section, we shall limit our discussion to those approaches which have enjoyed the most usage.

In implementing a large system, such as a digital computer, the modular or building-block concept is usually employed. A building block generally will be a single transistor circuit or a group of circuits that is capable of performing some required function. The over-all objective, then, in the design of transistor switching circuits is to develop a compatible set of building blocks that perform the required system functions and to specify simple rules for their interconnection and use. With these building blocks, the systems designer can then implement his system with little reference to circuit diagrams and little knowledge of the details of the circuit design. The multiple-input NOR block which is discussed in Sec. 15.9 is one example of a building block and is used in many present-day computers. The pyramiding or branching factor signifies the number of building blocks which can be driven from the output of one block and is an important measure of the usefulness of the block. In digital-computer systems, pyramiding factors generally must be 3 or greater if the block is to be of any use, and often a power-driver block with a pyramiding factor of 50 or more is required. The design of power drivers or building blocks with large pyramiding factors is discussed in Sec. 15.6. In a digital-computing system, the building blocks that are of particular importance are inverters, power drivers, flip-flops, and the logical circuits, such as "and," "or," and "exclusive or." In this chapter, we shall discuss different transistor switching circuits that perform the above functions.

15.1. Transistor Characteristics. Let us start by reviewing the switching characteristics of transistors (a more detailed discussion can be found in Sec. 4). Figure 15.1 is a plot of the grounded-base-collector characteristic of a PNP transistor for constant values of emitter current. Note that the plot is divided into three regions:

cutoff, active, and saturation.   The current gain α_{fb} in the active region is very close
to unity.   Generally α_{fb} will be in the range 0.93 to 1.0.   The shape of the saturation
characteristic is important.   In the active and cutoff regions, the output resistance
of the transistor will be of the order of megohms, but note that in the saturation
region the output resistance drops to a very low value.   Saturation resistances of
50 ohms or less are representative.   The transistor, then, because of its very high
"off" resistance and its very low "on" resistance more closely approaches what might
be considered an ideal switch (infinite "on" resistance, zero "off" resistance) than does
the vacuum tube.

The parameter I_{CBO}, which is also shown in Fig. 15.1, is very important in circuit
design. I_{CBO}, the collector current that flows when the emitter current is zero, is

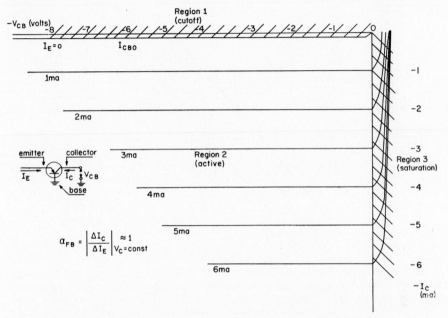

FIG. 15.1. Grounded-base collector characteristic of a PNP transistor.

very temperature-dependent.   The plots of I_{CBO} versus temperature shown in Fig.
15.2 indicate that I_{CBO} will increase by a factor of 10 for a 30°C rise in temperature.
Values of 5 μa or less are representative for germanium transistors at room temperature, while values of 0.5 μa or less are representative of silicon transistors.   As shown
in Fig. 15.2, I_{CBO} can be computed from the empirical relation

$$I_{CBO} = A 10^{\frac{T - T_{\text{measured}}}{30°C}} \tag{15.1}$$

where A is the value of I_{CBO} at T measured.   The value of I_{CBO} that is used in design,
however, is not only a function of the ambient temperature, as shown in Fig. 15.2, but
also a function of the power that is dissipated in the transistor when the circuit is on.
This power dissipated in the transistor raises the junction temperature of the transistor and increases I_{CBO}.   The thermal time constant of a switching transistor is
generally of the order of milliseconds, and since most circuits are designed to switch
in the order of microseconds or millimicroseconds, the value of I_{CBO} that must be

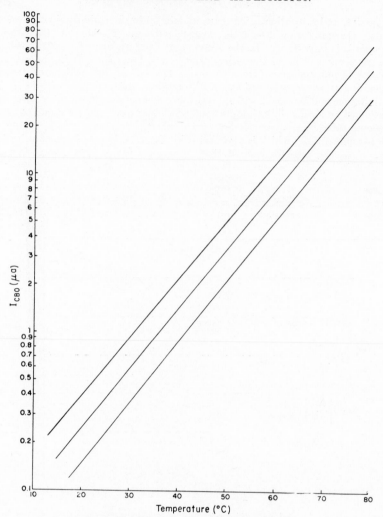

Fɪɢ. 15.2. I_{CBO} versus temperature.

designed for corresponds to the junction temperature that the transistor reaches when it is turned on and is dissipating power.

Power dissipation and junction temperature are related by the thermal resistance of the transistor, which is defined to be

$$K = \frac{°C \text{ rise in junction temperature}}{\text{milliwatts of power dissipation}} \qquad (15.2)$$

The thermal resistance or K factor is not a constant for a particular device but depends on the mounting, the presence or absence of a heat sink, and the environment of the transistor. This parameter is generally determined experimentally, and values of 0.3°C/mw are representative. To illustrate the use of Eqs. (15.1) and (15.2), consider the following typical problem: A transistor with a K factor of 0.3°C/mw, internal junction to the transistor package, dissipates 50 mw when on. The maximum value of I_{CBO} at room temperature is specified to be 5.0 μa or less. What will be the maximum value of I_{CBO} in an ambient of 50°C?

From Eq. (15.2)

$$\Delta T_j = P_d K = 50 \times 0.3 = 15°C$$

Then the total junction temperature T_j will equal

$$T_j = T_{\mathrm{amb}} + \Delta T_j$$
$$= 50°C + 15°C = 65°C$$

From Eq. (15.1)

$$\frac{5.0}{I_{CBO}(65°C)} = \frac{A 10^{2\frac{3}{30}}}{A 10^{6\frac{3}{30}}} \quad I_{CBO}(65°C) = 108 \mu a$$

Before concluding the discussion of I_{CBO}, one more important point should be made. Although Fig. 15.1 showed that I_{CBO} is relatively independent of the collector-to-base voltage, the same cannot be said of the base-to-emitter voltage. Figure 15.3

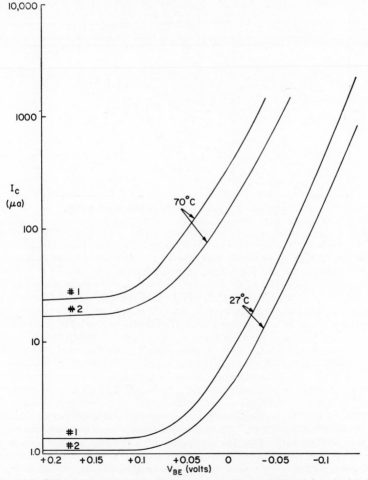

FIG. 15.3. Collector current vs. emitter base bias for two PNP alloy transistors.

shows a plot of the base-to-emitter voltage V_{BE} versus collector current I_{CBO} for two PNP alloy transistors. Note that the value of collector current for very small values of reverse base-to-emitter bias is considerably increased over the value of I_{CBO}. This increase is caused by the voltage drop $I_{CBO}R_{bb}$, which tends to forward-bias the emitter and allow conduction. In design it is necessary to reverse-bias the emitter base diode sufficiently if the transistor is to remain cut off. Plots of this type are generally considered when determining the necessary off condition for a particular transistor type.

One equivalent circuit that can be used to represent a transistor is shown in Fig. 15.4.[1] If it is assumed that the collector generator can be represented by a minimum phase-shift network, then a straightforward analysis shows that the response of the collector current depends on two principal time constants. These are ω, the small-signal angular frequency cutoff of the collector generator, and $(r_b + R_L)C_c$, the time

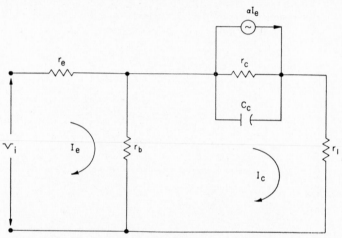

FIG. 15.4. Small-signal transistor equivalent circuit.

constant formed by the load and base resistances and the collector capacitance. By forming the ratio ω/r_bC_c, one could obtain a figure of merit which would give an indication of the relative speed of the transistor. However, this figure of merit would be very dependent on the d-c operating conditions of the transistor because $\omega_{\alpha_{fb}}$ and C_c are marked functions of the d-c operating point. Contours of constant values of $\omega_{\alpha_{fb}}$ and C_c are plotted in Fig. 15.5. Note that the contours of frequency cutoff resemble a family of rectangular hyperbolas. At a fixed value of collector voltage, the frequency cutoff is low for low values of collector current and increases as the collector current increases but then starts to fall off again after an optimum value of collector current is exceeded. The collector-capacitance contours shown in Fig. 15.5. are quite dependent on collector voltage but relatively independent of collector current. In general, the collector capacitance of a transistor will vary inversely as the half or third power of the collector voltage. An insight into why the frequency cutoff is low at low values of collector currents can be gained from the equivalent circuit[2] of Fig. 15.6. Here the frequency response of the collector generator depends on the two input capacitors C_{te} and C_s. The transition capacitance C_{te} represents the barrier capacitance of the emitter junction and varies with the emitter-base voltage in the same manner that the collector capacitance varies with the collector-base voltage. The storage capacitance C_S represents the number of carriers in the base region. At low values of emitter current, the value of emitter resistance is high ($r_e = kT/qI_e$)

and most input current goes into charging the transition capacitance. This initial charging of the transition capacitance causes the frequency response to be poor at low currents. The contours of ω and C_c shown in Fig. 15.5 indicate that the principal time constants of a large-signal transistor switching circuit can vary widely over the range of voltage and current normally covered by the path of the operating point. The

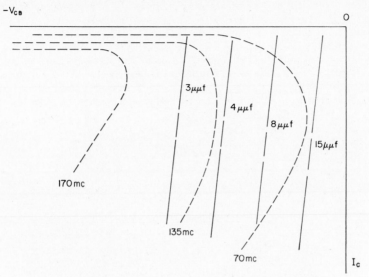

FIG. 15.5. Curve of frequency cutoff and collector capacitance.

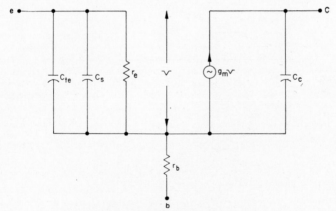

FIG. 15.6. Transistor equivalent circuit.

problem of accurate transient analysis utilizing linear equivalent circuits then is an involved boundary-value problem. Digital computers have been used to solve such problems, and the results have been reported on in the literature.[3]

15.2. Inverters. The first circuit to be discussed is the saturating inverter. As its name implies, it will invert a signal applied to its input. Only the grounded-emitter amplifier will perform this operation. In order that the inverter function properly, it must produce an output signal that is "up" when the input signal is "down" or produce a "one" signal on applying a "zero" signal to its input. For a

PNP transistor this means that the transistor must be on when the input signal is down and off when the input signal is up.

Figure 15.7 shows the collector characteristic for a PNP grounded-emitter transistor. The off, active, and saturated regions are shown, and a load line is drawn. The inverter to be discussed is called a saturating inverter because when the circuit is on, the operating point will be located on the load line within the shaded saturated region

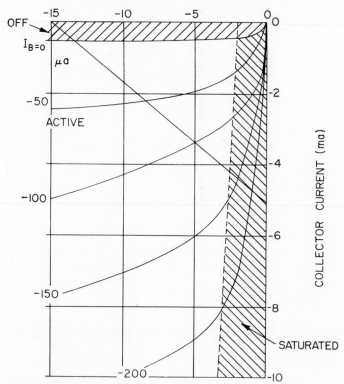

Fig. 15.7. Characteristic curves for a grounded-emitter PNP transistor.

of the collector characteristic. The operating point will enter the saturation region if the circuit design is such that $\alpha_{FE}I_B > I_C$, where

$$\alpha_{FE} = \frac{\alpha_{FB}}{1 - \alpha_{FB}}$$

Usually in circuit design, it is more desirable to specify saturation in terms of a negative value of collector-to-emitter voltage V_{CE} that will not be exceeded for the minimum specified value of α_{FE}. Note that once the operating point is in saturation, the "on" values of the collector current and the collector-to-emitter voltage V_{CE} will vary only a small amount for a large variation in input base current. The "off" operating point is located above the $I_B = 0$ curve, and the off collector current of the transistor may be taken to be I_{CBO}.

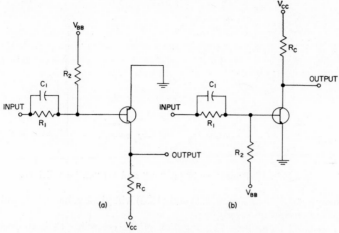

FIG. 15.8. (a) PNP and (b) NPN saturating inverters.

15.2a. D-C Requirements of Saturating Inverter. The collector characteristic and the load shown in Fig. 15.7 pretty well define for the saturating inverter the type of circuit shown in Fig. 15.8. Figure 15.8a shows the configuration for a PNP transistor, while Fig. 15.8b shows the NPN version. The calculation of the resistor values is straightforward. Let us discuss the PNP circuit of Fig. 15.8a and define the following necessary conditions:

V_U = "up" level of input voltage

V_D = "down" level of input voltage

$V_{B,\mathrm{on}}$ = voltage from base to emitter when transistor is in saturation

$I_{CBO,\max}$ = maximum value of I_{CBO} which is calculated as discussed in Sec. 15.1

$V_{B,\mathrm{off}}$ = voltage from base to emitter when transistor is off. Value would come from curve similar to those shown in Fig. 15.3. A value of $+0.2$ volt at maximum ambient temperature would be representative for PNP transistor

Referring to Fig. 15.7 and neglecting the small voltage drop in the saturated region,

$$I_C = \frac{V_{CC}}{R_C} \qquad I_B = \frac{V_{CC}}{R_C \alpha_{FE}} \tag{15.3}$$

Now refer to Fig. 15.9, which shows the inverter input network. Summing currents at the base node for the on condition (Fig. 15.9a) yields

$$\frac{V_D - V_{B,\mathrm{on}}}{R_1} = \frac{V_{BB} + V_{B,\mathrm{on}}}{R_2} + I_B$$

Substituting Eq. (15.3),

$$\frac{V_D - V_{B,\mathrm{on}}}{R_1} = \frac{V_{BB} + V_{B,\mathrm{on}}}{R_2} + \frac{V_{CC}}{R_C \alpha_{FE}} \tag{15.4}$$

For the off condition from Fig. 15.9b

$$\frac{V_{B,\mathrm{off}} + V_U}{R_1} + I_{CBO,\max} = \frac{V_{BB} - V_{B,\mathrm{off}}}{R_2} \tag{15.5}$$

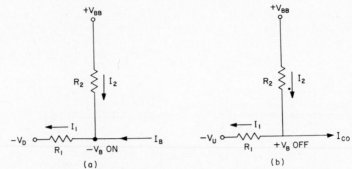

Fig. 15.9. PNP inverter in (a) "on" and (b) "off" conditions.

A simultaneous solution of Eqs. (15.4) and (15.5) will yield values of R_1 and R_2 which will satisfy the on and off conditions

15.2b. Transient Response. The function of the capacitor C_1 is to overdrive the transistor momentarily. This overdriving action is basic to the operation of saturating circuits. If the transistor is not momentarily overdriven, then the rise time of the output is quite slow. This can be seen in the following way. The response of a grounded-base transistor is given by the differential equation

$$\frac{1}{\omega_{\alpha_{FB}}}\frac{di_C}{dt} + i_C = \alpha_{FB}i_E \tag{15.6}$$

whose solution for a step function of emitter current is

$$i_C = -\alpha_{FB}I_E(1 - e^{-\omega_{\alpha_{FB}}t}) \tag{15.7}$$

For a grounded-emitter transistor we have

$$\frac{1}{\omega_{\alpha_{FE}}}\frac{di_C}{dt} + i_C = \alpha_{FE}i_B \tag{15.8}$$

and for a step function of base current

$$i_C = \alpha_{FE}I_B(1 - e^{-\omega_{\alpha_{FE}}t}) \tag{15.9}$$

where $\qquad \omega_{\alpha_{FE}} = \omega_{\alpha_{FB}}/(1 - \alpha_{FB}) \qquad$ and $\qquad \alpha_{FE} = \alpha_{FB}/(1 - \alpha_{FB})$

The initial rate of rise of i_C given by Eq. (15.7) is

$$\frac{di_C}{dt}\bigg|_{t=0} = -\alpha_{FB}\omega_{\alpha_{FB}}I_E \tag{15.10}$$

For (15.9) we have

$$\frac{di_C}{dt}\bigg|_{t=0} = \alpha_{FE}\omega_{\alpha_{FE}}I_B \tag{15.11}$$

Comparing (15.10) and (15.11) under the conditions that $I_E = I_B$ we find that the initial rate of rise is independent of whether the transistor is operated with grounded base or grounded emitter.

15.2c. Rise Time. The capacitor C_1, therefore, serves the function of supplying a large surge of current in order to overdrive the transistor and momentarily achieve the desired condition of maximum initial rate of rise ($I_E = -I_B$). This overdriving action must take place for only a short time; otherwise the transistor will be driven too far into saturation and thus be difficult to turn off. If the rise time T_R is defined as the time required for the collector current to reach 90 per cent of its final value, then

$$T_R = \frac{1}{\omega_{\alpha_{FE}}} \ln \frac{1}{1 - 0.9 I_{CM}/\alpha_{FE} I_B} \tag{15.12}$$

when a step function of current is applied to the base of the transistor. The final value of the collector current is $I_{CM} = V_{CC}/R_c$. Figure 15.10 shows Eq. (15.9) plotted as a function of time plus some additional information. The rise time T_R, the saturation time T_S, and the fall time T_F are shown in this figure.

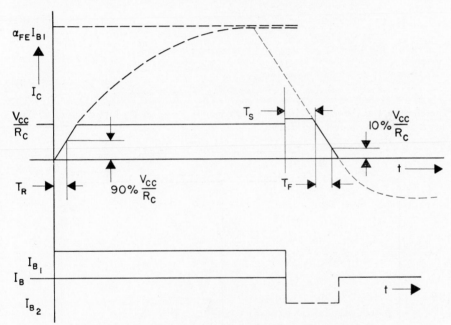

Fig. 15.10. Collector current versus time for an inverter stage.

15.2d. Storage Time. If the collector is assumed to rise to a value $\alpha_{FE} I_{B_1}$, then it must be assumed that the collector current starts from this value when the transistor is turned off. The rate at which minority carriers are cleared out of the base region is dependent on the magnitude of the final base current I_{B_2}. J. J. Ebers and J. L. Moll of the Bell Telephone Laboratories[4] have shown that the inverted current gain α_{RB} and the inverted angular frequency cutoff $\omega_{\alpha_{RB}}$ of the transistor, in part, determine the storage time T_S. The parameters $\omega_{\alpha_{RB}}$ and α_{RB} are measured with the emitter functioning as the collector and the collector functioning as the emitter. Specifying an $\omega_{\alpha_{RB}}$ and an α_{RB} leads to the simplified equivalent circuit for the transistor in saturation shown in Fig. 15.11. The differential equations for this circuit are

$$\frac{di_C}{dt} = \omega_{\alpha_{RB}} i_C = -\alpha_{FB} \omega_{\alpha_{FB}} i_E \tag{15.13}$$

$$\frac{di_E}{dt} + \omega_{\alpha_{RB}} i_E = -\alpha_{RB} \omega_{\alpha_{RB}} i_C \tag{15.14}$$

$$i_E + i_C + i_B = 0 \tag{15.15}$$

Solving these equations for i_C, it can be shown that the storage time for the grounded-emitter transistor is

$$T_S = \frac{1}{\omega_S} \ln \frac{I_{B_1} - I_{B_2}}{I_{CM}/\alpha_{FE} - I_{B_2}} \tag{15.16}$$

where

$$\omega_S = \frac{\omega_{\alpha_{FB}} \omega_{\alpha_{RB}} (1 - \alpha_{FB}\alpha_{RB})}{\omega_{\alpha_{FB}} + \omega_{\alpha_{RB}}} \tag{15.17}$$

and I_{B_1} and I_{B_2} are the initial and final values of base current. In symmetrical transistors, that is, $\alpha_{RB} = \alpha_{FB}$ and $\omega_{\alpha_{RB}} = \omega_{\alpha_{FB}}$, the time constant is

$$\frac{1}{\omega_S} \approx \frac{1}{\omega_{\alpha_{FB}}(1 - \alpha_{FB})} \tag{15.18}$$

In normal transistors $\omega_{\alpha_{FB}} \gg \omega_{\alpha_{RB}}$ and $\alpha_{FB} \gg \alpha_{RB}$; hence

$$\frac{\omega_{\alpha_{FB}} + \omega_{\alpha_{RB}}}{\omega_{\alpha_{FB}} \omega_{\alpha_{RB}} (1 - \alpha_{FB}\alpha_{RB})} \approx \frac{1}{\omega_{\alpha_{RB}}(1 - \alpha_{FB})} \tag{15.19}$$

Therefore, a transistor should have a high value of $\omega_{\alpha_{RB}}$ and a low value of α_{RB} to ensure fast recovery from saturation.

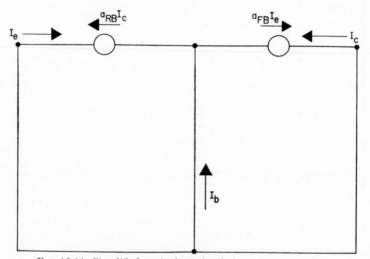

Fig. 15.11. Simplified equivalent circuit for saturated region.

15.2e. Fall Time. The fall time T_F will now be considered. As seen from Fig. 15.10, T_F is the time required for the collector current to drop to 10 per cent of its change. Upon solving the differential equation for the circuit subject to the proper boundary conditions and solving for T_F, we have

$$T_F = \frac{1}{\omega_{\alpha_{FE}}} \ln \frac{I_{CM} - \alpha_{FE}I_{B_2}}{0.1 I_{CM} - \alpha_{FE}I_{B_2}} \tag{15.20}$$

15.2f. Off-level Stabilization. As was mentioned previously, a pyramiding factor of at least 3 is required of a transistor circuit in order that it can be used with ease in a computing system. If this is the case, then an inverter may be called upon to drive at least three other inverters. This means that there will be a load of approximately $R_1/3$ connected between the collector and ground of any inverter. If this were a fixed load, there would not be too great a problem. The difficulty arises from the fact that an inverter may be required to drive anywhere from one to three other stages. The potential of the collector, when the transistor is off, will therefore be dependent on the load placed on the inverter and the value of I_{CBO}. The potential of the collector in the off condition can be well defined by the addition of a clamp diode returned to a voltage E_1, as shown in Fig. 15.12a. The load line for this circuit is shown in Fig. 15.12b. In addition to stabilizing the off level of the collector, it serves a major function of speeding up the fall time. Naturally, it cannot change the storage time.

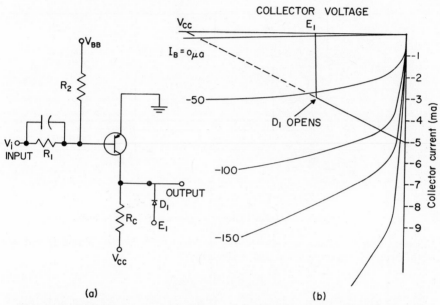

Fig. 15.12. (a) Inverter with diode clamp. (b) Effect of diode clamp on load line.

15.2g. Minority-carrier Storage. Minority-carrier storage is a problem unique to transistor switching circuits. Where the highest possible speed of operation is desired, it cannot be overlooked, since it will constitute a significant portion of the turn-off delay. As was mentioned previously, the phenomenon is dependent on the magnitude of emitter current and the length of time that it is permitted to flow while the transistor is in the saturated region. In pulse-type computer systems, the length of time that the transistor is driven into saturation is controllable. Even in this case, the problem is still present. In d-c-type computing systems, the only way to eliminate minority-carrier storage is by keeping the transistor out of the saturated region. This can be done by limiting the emitter or base current or by clamping the collector voltage out of the saturated region. Clamping the collector voltage generally is undesirable, since it merely shifts the storage problem from the transistor to the clamping diode. A significant improvement can be achieved, however, if a silicon Zener diode is used for clamping. These diodes when operated in the Zener region have excellent recovery characteristics.

15.2h. Using Nonlinear Feedback. A method for minimizing minority-carrier storage which was developed by J. Warnock of Philco will be described. This is a method that uses a diode in a feedback path as shown in Fig. 15.13. As the input is made negative, the potential of point 3 rises until the diode D_1 conducts, thus preventing any further increase of base current.   This provides a low-impedance feedback path from the collector to base of the transistor.   The value of $R_1 + R_2$ is determined in the normal way.   The value of R_2 is determined by the potential to which the collector is permitted to rise.   If the collector is prevented from becoming any more positive than about -0.5 volt, satisfactory operation is obtained.   With

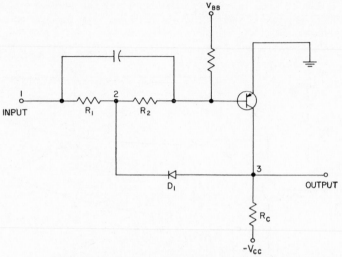

Fig. 15.13. Nonsaturating inverter using nonlinear feedback.

this circuit only a minimum value of α_{FE} need be specified.   The output impedance of the inverter, when on, is low and is given by

$$R_o \cong R_2(1 - \alpha_{FB}) \tag{15.21}$$

Since the feedback diode conducts a small current, there is no problem from hole storage in it.   Even though the transistor is in its active region, the change of I_{CBO} with temperature is not very troublesome.   Because of the degenerative feedback

$$\Delta I_C \cong \left(\frac{R_{eq}}{R_C} + 1\right) \Delta I_{CBO} \tag{15.22}$$

where

$$R_{eq} = \frac{R_1 R_2}{R_1 + R_2} \tag{15.23}$$

Another method for operating a transistor inverter out of saturation by limiting the base current is shown in Fig. 15.14.   In this circuit the collector of transistor T_1, the inverter, feeds the base of transistor T_2, a PNP emitter follower.   (The reader is referred to Sec. 15.3 for a discussion of the emitter follower.)   The output of the emitter follower is translated back up to the desired voltage level by a Zener diode, and the feedback loop to the base is completed through diode D_2.   Resistors R_e and R_b are generally large and constitute current sources.   The operation of the circuit is as follows: In the off state the input potential at D_1 is made sufficiently positive to bias the base of T_1 above ground and shut T_1 off.   Under these conditions, the collector of T_1 will drop to $V_{CC} - (I_{B2} + I_{CBO})R_c$.   This voltage level at the collector of T_1 will be shifted positive at the output by the emitter base drop in T_2 and the voltage drop in the Zener diode which is biased on by a current from R_e. Diode D_2 will be biased off. If a negative voltage step is applied at the input, diode D_1 will be cut off and transistor T_1 will turn on, base current flowing through R_b to V_{CC_1}. Under these conditions, the collector voltage of T_1 will rise and the output voltage will follow closely because of the low output impedance of the emitter follower and the low impedance of the Zener diode. The collector voltage of T_1 and the output voltage will continue to rise until diode D_2 conducts. When D_2 conducts, current will flow

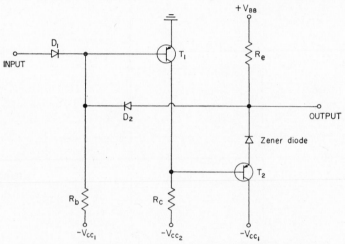

Fig. 15.14. PNP feedback inverter with emitter-follower output.

from R_e through D_2 into R_b and the base current of T_1 will be reduced. This will cause the collector voltage of T_1 to drop and D_2 will shut off, the base current will start to increase, and the cycle starts all over again. In short, diode D_2 will teeter on the edge of conduction, maintaining the collector voltage of T_1 at a determined value. Diode D_1 serves to disconnect the driving source from the base of T_1. The negative input signal therefore should be greater than the steady-state on voltage level at the base of T_1. With a capacitive load on the input, the output voltage will not be able to follow the collector-voltage rise at T_1. This will delay the feedback and cause either a large single overshoot or even a damped oscillation at the collector of T_1. This can be controlled by rising the value of R_b or lowering the value of R_e or limiting the amount of capacitive load that is driven. By suitable choice of the Zener diode voltage and V_{CC_2}, it is possible to realize different negative output levels. The emitter-follower circuit is generally operated class A, and for this reason $-V_{CC_1}$ in Fig. 15.14 would be more negative than $-V_{CC_2}$. This feedback inverter is capable of very fast switching. In a typical application, using 500-mc mesa transistors operated 2.0 volts out of saturation, rise and fall times of 5.0 mμsec were achieved for a 1.5-volt signal swing.

15.2i. Limiting the Emitter Current. In the current-switching inverter shown in Fig. 15.15, the transistor is operated out of saturation and the delay due to minority-carrier storage is eliminated. In the off condition, the input potential at point 1 is made sufficiently positive with respect to ground that all current from the constant-current source V_{EE}/R_e flows into the diode D_1. The collector potential at point 3 will then drop to $V_{CC} = I_{CBO}R_L$. To turn the transistor on, the input potential is made sufficiently negative that point 2 reaches ground potential, the diode D_1 is cut off, and all the constant current V_{EE}/R_e flows into the emitter of the transistor. The on level collector potential at point 3 can be adjusted to any desired value by suitable choice of the load resistor R_3. The on and off conditions at the input (point 1) are shown in Fig. 15.16. Defining the voltage drop across the diode D_1 as V_D, the transistor emitter-base drop as V_{EB}, and the input current as I, the following relations satisfy the on and off conditions:

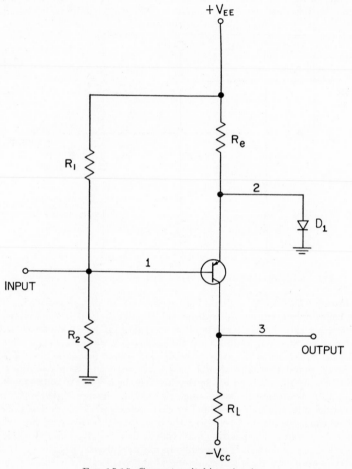

Fig. 15.15. Current-switching circuits.

On condition:

$$I = \frac{V_{EE}}{R_e}(1 - \alpha_{FB}) + \frac{V_{EE} + V_{EB}}{R_1} + \frac{V_{EB}}{R_2} \tag{15.24}$$

Off condition:

$$\frac{V_{EE} - V_D}{R_1} = I_{CBO,\text{max}} + \frac{V_D}{R_2} \tag{15.25}$$

Because the PNP current switch of Fig. 15.15 is operated out of saturation, the output on and off potentials will be negative with respect to those at the input. One current switch, then, cannot drive another unless a suitable battery or voltage-

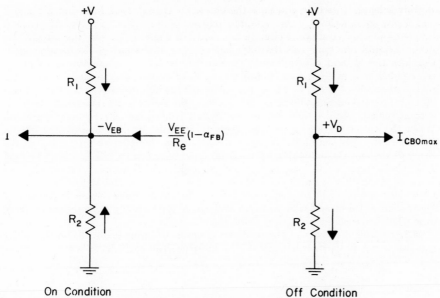

On Condition   Off Condition

Fig. 15.16. PNP current switch "on" and "off" conditions.

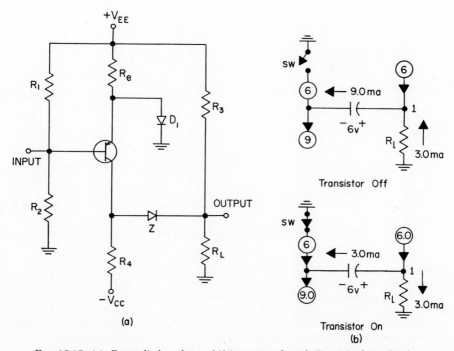

(a)

Fig. 15.17. (a) Zener diode voltage-shifting network and (b) equivalent circuits.

shifting scheme is used to translate the output level back to values that are above and below ground level. One suitable arrangement is shown in Fig. 15.17a and simple on and off equivalent circuits are shown in Fig. 15.17b. In this circuit, the Zener diode Z functions as a battery and never operates out of the Zener region. Consider the on and off equivalent circuits of Fig. 15.17b where the transistor is represented as a switch sw and a current source of 6 ma. The 9- and 6-ma current sources represent V_{CC}/R_4 and V_{EE}/R_3. When the switch sw is open, the transistor is off and the 9-ma current sink accepts 3 ma from the load R_L and 6 ma from the 6-ma current source. Under these conditions, node 1 is negative with respect to ground. When the switch sw is closed, 6 ma from the transistor will flow into the 9.0-ma current sink. The additional 3.0 ma will come from the 6.0-ma source through the Zener diode, and the remaining 3.0 ma from the 6.0-ma source will flow into the load R_L. Under these conditions, node 1 will be positive with respect to ground. The Zener diode in this example conducts either 3.0 or 9.0 ma, and the desired output potential can be realized by a suitable choice of R_L. Because of the low impedance of Zener diodes, this translating network will introduce virtually no increase in delay over what is measured with only a load R_L.

15.3. Emitter Follower. The emitter follower or grounded-collector amplifier gets its name from its vacuum-tube counterpart, the cathode follower. Emitter

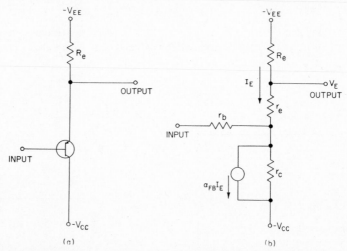

Fig. 15.18. (a) Emitter follower.   (b) Equivalent circuit for emitter follower.

followers find frequent use in computers as logical switches and as power drivers. The circuit is characterized by a voltage gain of less than unity, a slight change in the d-c level of the signal from input to output, and a low output impedance. Output impedances of 10 to 50 ohms with commercially available transistors can be obtained from emitter followers.

The operation of the emitter follower can be explained in the following way. Referring to Fig. 15.18a, we see that if the base terminal is at ground potential, the emitter will be forward-biased and the output potential will be a few tenths of a volt positive with respect to the input. If the emitter follower is driving a capacitive load and a positive step of voltage is applied at the input, the emitter-base junction will cut off momentarily. During this time, the capacitive load will be charged through R_e and the back impedance of the emitter junction. (For most transistors, the back impedance of the emitter junction can be considered much higher than R_e and hence neglected.) The output voltage will continue to rise toward $+V_{EE}$ until it rises above the input voltage. At this point the transistor will again conduct and the output voltage will be clamped to a value slightly larger than the input voltage. It is common practice to make the collector supply $-V_{CC}$ negative with respect to the most negative input signal. Also, the emitter supply $+V_{EE}$ is usually made larger than the most positive input signal, and under these conditions the emitter follower is a class A amplifier for relatively slow changes of input signal.

15.3a. Steady-state Conditions. The equivalent circuit of Fig. 15.18b can be used to obtain an expression for the output voltage V_E. Under the assumption that $r_c \gg r_b$ and r_e, we find that

$$V_E = \frac{R_e V_B}{R_e + [r_e + r_b(1 - \alpha_{FB})]} + \frac{r_e + r_b(1 - \alpha_{FB})V_{EE}}{R_e + [r_e + r_b(1 - \alpha_{FB})]} \qquad (15.26)$$

The coefficient of V_B in the first term on the right of Eq. (15.26) is the voltage gain, while the second term on the right is the shift in voltage level between input and output. It can be seen that, if the output impedance $r_e + r_b(1 - \alpha_{FB})$ of the emitter follower is made negligibly small, then the voltage gain will be unity and the shift in level negligible. When a signal is passed through several emitter followers in the

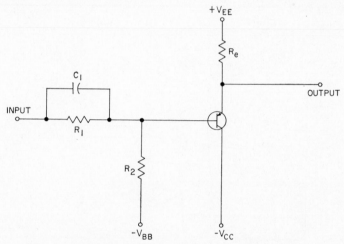

FIG. 15.19. PNP emitter follower with level restoring circuit.

performance of logical operations, the shift in level can be compensated by a level setting input divider as shown in Fig. 15.19.

The steady-state conditions in emitter followers are most easily established by graphical means. Consider the PNP emitter follower shown in Fig. 15.20a. For convenience V_{EE} is chosen to be $+6$ volts and V_{CC} is chosen to be -7.5 volts. The output voltage is referenced to V_{CC} (-7.5 volts). To define the steady-state conditions completely, we wish to obtain a plot of the output voltage versus the output current I_E for constant values of input voltage V_I and input current I_B. The curves that we desire are plotted in Fig. 15.20c, and in order to obtain these curves, we make use of the volt-ampere characteristic of the emitter base diode which is shown in Fig. 15.20b. Note that the volt-ampere characteristic in Fig. 15.20b is plotted for a constant-collector voltage of -7.5 volts, the value that we are using here. Referring to Fig. 15.20c, we plot in the first quadrant the PNP grounded-emitter characteristic curves that were shown in Fig. 15.7. The voltage axis will now start at V_{CC} (-7.5

volts) and increase out to V_{EE} (+6.0 volts).   If we make the assumption that $I_E = I_C$ (for values of $\alpha_{FE} > 20$ the error is negligible), then the current axis can be labeled I_E, the output current.   We now have a plot of output voltage versus output current for constant values of input current I_B, and all that remains is to plot curves for constant values of input voltage V_I.   We refer again to Fig. 15.20c and consider that the input-voltage curves for R_b equal zero.   When R_t equals zero,

$$V_O = V_I + V_{EB} \tag{15.27}$$

and values of V_{EB} for various values of output current are plotted in Fig. 15.20b.

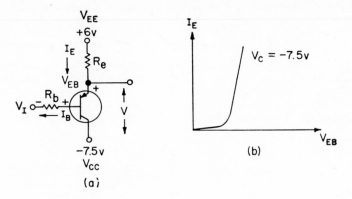

(b)

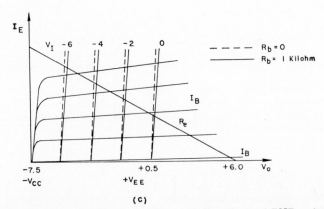

(c)

FIG. 15.20. Circuit (a) and curves (b, c) for graphical analysis of PNP emitter follower.

Therefore, the volt-ampere characteristic of Fig. 15.20b can be plotted on Fig. 15.20c as a curve of constant input voltage where, in this case, the input voltage is zero. Plots similar to Fig. 15.20b are easily made for other constant values of collector voltage, and when they are transferred to Fig. 15.20c, a family of curves of constant values of input voltage similar to those in Fig. 15.20c is obtained.   For most commercially available switching transistors, it will be found that the curves of Fig. 15.20b will differ only slightly when the collector voltage is varied, and usually negligible error results if one curve is plotted and all others are simply made parallel to it.   The dashed curves of Fig. 15.20c apply when R_b equals zero and the input voltage is applied directly to the base.   When R_b is not zero, we have

$$V_O = V_I + V_{EB} + I_B R_b \tag{15.28}$$

and the input-voltage curves must be adjusted for the voltage drop ($I_B R_b$). As shown in Fig. 15.20c, the curves for constant input voltage are displaced to the right by the additional voltage drop $I_B R_b$. Once plotted for a particular transistor being used frequently in a large system, the curves of Fig. 15.20c will be found to be a quick means for establishing steady-state conditions.

15.3b. Transient Response. When emitter followers are used in logic or in power-driver applications, trouble is almost always encountered with oscillations or with large overshoots on the output waveform. The trouble is aggravated by the capacitive load on the output. Under the right conditions, the phase shift in the load network plus the phase shift in the transistor is sufficient to make the input impedance

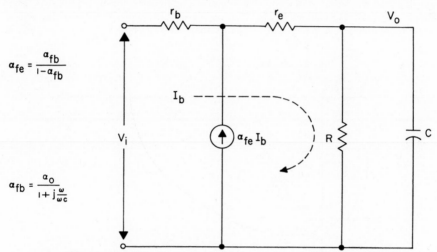

$$\alpha_{fe} = \frac{\alpha_{fb}}{1 - \alpha_{fb}}$$

$$\alpha_{fb} = \frac{\alpha_o}{1 + j\frac{\omega}{\omega_c}}$$

FIG. 15.21. Simplified equivalent circuit for input impedance calculation.

of the emitter follower have a negative real part. To see this, we make use of the simplified equivalent circuit shown in Fig. 15.21, where $\alpha_{fe} I_b$, the collector-current generator, is assumed to follow the minimum phase relation shown. The input impedance can be written as

$$\frac{V_i}{I_b} = r_b + (1 + \alpha_{fe})\left(r_e + \frac{R}{j\omega RC + 1}\right) \tag{15.29}$$

where ω is the angular frequency of the input signal. Upon substituting the relations for α_{fe} and frequency response shown in Fig. 15.21, we obtain the following expression of the form $R - jXc$:

$$z_i = r_b + \frac{[1 - \alpha_{fb} + (\omega/\omega_{\alpha_{fb}})^2]R - (\alpha_{fb}\omega^2 R^2 C/\omega_{\alpha_{fb}})}{[(1 - \alpha_{fb})^2 + (\omega/\omega_{\alpha_{fb}})^2][1 + \omega^2(RC)^2]} + \frac{[1 - \alpha_{fb} + (\omega/\omega_{\alpha_{fb}})^2]r_e}{(1 - \alpha_{fb})^2 + (\omega/\omega_{\alpha_{fb}})^2}$$

$$-j\left\{\frac{(\alpha_{fb}\omega/\omega_{\alpha_{fb}})R + [1 - \alpha_{fb} + (\omega/\omega_{\alpha_{fb}})^2]\omega R^2 C}{[(1 - \alpha_{fb})^2 + (\omega/\omega_{\alpha_{fb}})^2][1 + \omega^2(RC)^2]} + \frac{(\alpha_{fb}\omega/\omega_{\alpha_{fb}})r_e}{(1 - \alpha_{fb})^2 + (\omega/\omega_{\alpha_{fb}})^2}\right\} \tag{15.30}$$

Note that the first and second terms of the real part of Eq. (15.30) involve the base resistance and the emitter resistance and are always positive. However, the numerator of the second term can be negative if

$$1 - \alpha_{fb} + \left(\frac{\omega}{\omega_{\alpha_{fb}}}\right)^2 < \frac{\alpha_{fb}\omega^2 RC}{\omega_{\alpha_{fb}}} \tag{15.31}$$

and since the left side of Eq. (15.31) is small, this is not difficult to achieve. If the negative term is larger than the sum of the base-resistance and the emitter-resistance terms, the net input impedance will have a negative real part. Plots of emitter-follower input impedance show large values of negative resistance in the high-frequency range. A sample plot is shown in Fig. 15.22, and the input impedance is negative in the frequency range from ω_1 to ω_2. If the input of this emitter-follower circuit is connected to a line which has an inductive component, then the circuit will oscillate at a frequency determined by the line inductance and the input capacitance of the circuit providing this frequency is in the range of ω_1 to ω_2.

In general, in a large system emitter followers are required to operate under widely varying load conditions and some circuit-stabilizing means must be employed. Four simple approaches are shown in Fig. 15.23. Figure 15.23a and b represent the easiest ways to stabilize. A resistor of sufficient magnitude is added to the base (R_b in

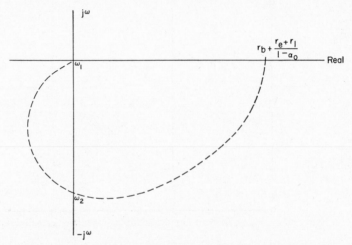

Fig. 15.22. Emitter-follower input impedance versus frequency.

Fig. 15.23a) or the emitter (R_E in Fig. 15.23b) to make the net input resistance positive at the frequency in question. The addition of a resistor to the base or the emitter has disadvantages. The circuit will be slowed down, and there will be a greater d-c level shift between input and output. In Fig. 15.23c, negative feedback is applied from the collector to the base. Although the negative-feedback network does not introduce an additional level shift, it does slow the circuit down. In Fig. 15.23d, a lossy-ferrite core is placed in series with the emitter. The core may be regarded as a resistor in parallel with a small inductance. At high frequencies, a resistor will appear in series with the emitter, but at direct current there will be no resistance and therefore no voltage shift. Of the four approaches shown, the one employing the ferrite core† is the best, particularly in higher-speed circuits where it is desirable to use small-signal swings and the level shifts encountered in Fig. 15.23a and b are intolerable.

In circuits in which speed is not a problem, the emitter-follower oscillations can be easily eliminated if a large amount of stabilization is applied. However, in high-speed circuits one cannot be so generous if the high-speed capabilities of the circuit are to be retained. It is standard practice to make polar plots similar to Fig. 15.22 under the packaging and load conditions that will be used in the final system and to apply stabilization accordingly. Two other factors have an important bearing on

† This approach was suggested by E. J. Rymaszewski of International Business Machines Corp., Poughkeepsie, N.Y.

the stability of emitter followers. The first is the value of the collector return voltage. In Fig. 15.5, it was shown that the frequency cutoff of a transistor was a function of the collector-to-base voltage and the collector current. In the emitter follower the collector-to-base voltage is a function of the input level, and if the signal swing is large, the transistor can have two significantly different values of cutoff frequency corresponding to the input up-and-down signal levels. It is possible to construct emitter-follower circuits that will oscillate at one input level and not at the other. In general, the signal level that results in the smaller collector-to-base voltage will be the worst case.

The second factor concerns the phase shift of α_{fb}, the collector-current generator. In the analysis presented here it was assumed that at frequency cutoff, the phase was shifted 45° (refer to Fig. 15.21). In the high-frequency drift transistors that are now commercially available, this assumption will be found to be grossly in error. Phase

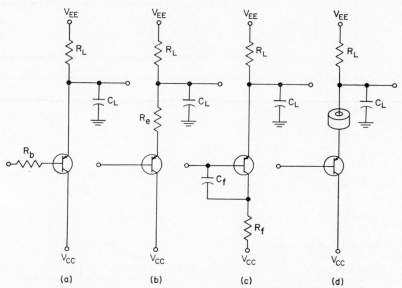

FIG. 15.23. Methods of preventing emitter-follower oscillations.

shifts at frequency cutoff $(0.707\alpha_{fb})$ as large as 90° have been measured. This additional phase shift will cause the input resistance to become negative at a lower value of frequency, and the total impedance curve will not approach the origin at higher frequencies as shown in Fig. 15.21 but curve back into the fourth quadrant. The net result is usually a larger magnitude of negative resistance that extends over a greater frequency range. This will mean that emitter followers using these transistors will require more stabilization. The assumption of a 45° phase shift at frequency cutoff will generally be found to be correct to within 10° where alloy transistors are used.

15.4. Triggers. The trigger or Eccles-Jordan circuit consists of two inverters in cascade with the output of the second inverter tied back to the input of the first. It is well known that such a circuit can be made bistable; i.e., one transistor is conducting while the other is off or one transistor is in a high-current state while the other transistor is in a low-current state and conduction or change of state can be switched from one transistor to the other by appropriate triggering means.

15.4a. Requirements for Saturated-off Operation. The most straightforward trigger circuit is shown in Fig. 15.24. Inspection shows that this circuit is composed of two of the saturating inverters shown in Fig. 15.8.   Stable steady-state operating conditions for this trigger require that the voltage at the base of the "off" transistor be negative with respect to ground by an amount sufficient to cause this transistor to be in saturation.   The steady-state design procedure that was used in Sec. 15.2a for the saturating inverter is directly applicable here.   A saturating inverter that is designed to drive three other inverters can be used as half of a trigger and still be able to drive a load of two inverters.   The third inverter load will be the other half of the trigger.

  15.4b. Resetting the Trigger.   Triggers find frequent use in counters, registers, and other storage applications.   It is generally necessary to add to the basic trigger shown in Fig. 15.24 some means by which the circuit can be set into one or the other of its

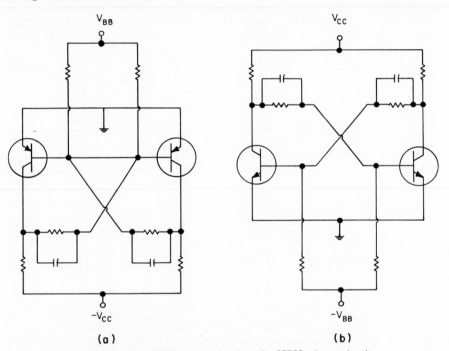

FIG. 15.24. (a) PNP trigger circuit.   (b) NPN trigger circuit.

stable states.   One of the most direct ways to do this is to use the circuit shown in Fig. 15.25a.   Another circuit which is more positive in its action is the collector pullover circuit which utilizes an inverter.   In Fig. 15.25b, the collector of the inverter is connected to the collector of the transistor to be turned on.   A negative pulse applied to the input of the pull-over inverter will initiate the action.   To see how the trigger will turn on under this type of operation, we shall look at the collector input characteristic of a trigger.   This is shown in Fig. 15.26.   This volt-ampere characteristic is obtained by disconnecting one collector load resistor from the trigger and replacing it with a voltage generator.   The current is recorded for various values of collector voltage of the first transistor.   The off section of this curve is the volt-ampere characteristic of the resistor connected between the collector of the first transistor and the base of the second transistor.   The active region is accounted for by the fact that, as the collector voltage is made more positive, the base current of the second transistor decreases, thus allowing it to come out of saturation.   Both transistors are now in their active region.   The current increases because of the positive-feedback action.

When the collector voltage has reached a point where the second transistor is off, there will be no further increase in current. This is represented by the on section of the curve. When the collector voltage is raised to a more positive value, the first transistor enters its saturated region.

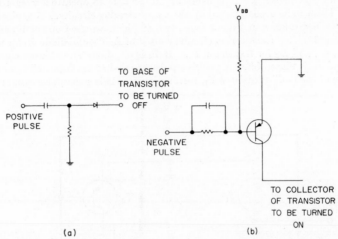

FIG. 15.25. (a) Reset circuit. (b) Inverter pull-over reset circuit.

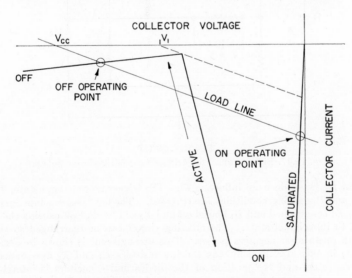

FIG. 15.26. Collector volt-ampere characteristic of trigger.

A load line is superimposed on this volt-ampere characteristic, and the on and off operating points are shown. With a relatively high-impedance drive connected to the trigger, such as the inverter pull-over, the load line is determined by the collector load resistance R_C. To determine how much current the pull-over inverter must supply to turn on the trigger, it is necessary to draw a new load line parallel to itself, as shown dashed. This new load line must be tangent to the volt-ampere characteristic, as shown. It intersects the voltage axis at a voltage V_1. The current the pull-over inverter must supply is therefore $I_C = (V_{CC} - V_1)/R_C$. It is clear this discussion is confined to a trigger without the cross-coupling capacitors or to signals with very long rise times. The problem is quite a bit more complicated when transient conditions are considered.

15.4c. Binary Operation. It is necessary to be able to operate a trigger in binary fashion. This can be accomplished by the use of steering circuits. A typical steering circuit is the resistance-gated diode type, two of which are used on the binary trigger shown in Fig. 15.27. The steering circuits consist of R_1, C_1, and diode D_1 for transistor T_1 and R_2, C_2, and D_2 for transistor T_2. If T_1 is on, diode D_1 is biased close to conduction and D_2 is biased off. A positive pulse applied at the input will be "steered" to the base of the "on" transistor T_1, turning it off. This same pulse cannot override

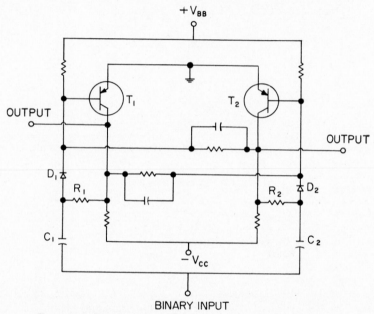

Fig. 15.27. Binary-connected trigger for positive-input pulses.

the bias on D_2, hence does not influence T_2. The trigger now changes state, T_2 is on, T_1 is off, and the gating conditions are reversed. The next positive input pulse will find diode D_2 conditioned and D_1 biased off and T_2 will be shut off causing the trigger to return to its original state. The steering circuit can be rearranged so that the trigger can operate on negative pulses. This arrangement is shown in Fig. 15.28. Note that, in this arrangement, the sensing resistors R_1 and R_2 are connected to opposite collectors and the position of the diodes and capacitors is interchanged. The diodes are also poled to conduct on negative input pulses. If the input potential is at ground and T_2 is on, diode D_1 will be close to conduction but D_2 will have a large reverse bias. When the input moves negative, D_1 will conduct, T_1 will be turned on, and the trigger will change state but the input will not affect T_2 because of the bias on D_2. The next input pulse will find the gating situation reversed, and D_2 will conduct. Whenever the input negative level exceeds the output level in this circuit, trouble will be encountered holding the reversed-biased diode off. This can be overcome by applying sufficient negative bias at points A. Improved operation of the circuits of Figs. 15.27 and 15.28 will generally be realized if diode clamps are placed from the

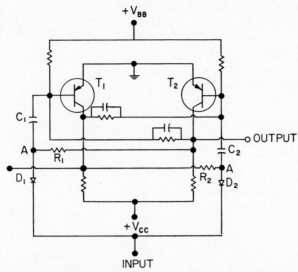

FIG. 15.28. Binary-connected trigger negative-input pulses.

base to ground. This will eliminate large variations in the off base-to-emitter voltage due to variations in I_{CO} from transistor to transistor. Also one should note that where binary operation is not desired, the inputs to the circuits of Figs. 15.27 and 15.28 can be separated into separate set or reset inputs.

A transistor variation of the resistance-gated diode circuit is shown in Fig. 15.29. This circuit depends for its operation on the symmetrical transistor T_3. A good symmetrical transistor is one in which the inverter current gain α_{RB} and the inverted angular frequency cutoff $\omega_{\alpha_{RB}}$ approach the normal values α_{FB} and $\omega_{\alpha_{FB}}$, respectively. In Fig. 15.29, if T_1 is off and T_2 is on, point 1 will be negative and point 2 will be at a potential close to the saturation voltage of T_2, i.e., close to ground potential. A negative input will cause T_3 to conduct, and point 2 will go negative, turning on T_1. Simultaneously, point 1 will go positive, turning off T_2. The trigger has now changed state; T_2 is off, T_1 is on, point 1 is close to ground, and point 2 is negative. Upon application of the next input pulse, point 1 will go positive, point 2 negative,

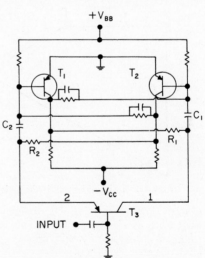

FIG. 15.29. Binary trigger with symmetrical transistor steering circuit.

and the trigger will revert to its original state. In this circuit, input pulses are applied simultaneously at both bases of the trigger and transistor T_3 functions in a normal and then inverted fashion depending on the state of the trigger.

15.4d. Transient Operation. A detailed treatment of the transient operation of a transistor trigger circuit is very difficult and to the author's knowledge has never been attempted. It is interesting, however, to determine in a very informal way the mode of operation that one might expect of a trigger. To do this we shall construct an extremely simple equivalent circuit for the trigger. This is shown in Fig. 15.30. As can be seen, the transistor is idealized and R_c is considered infinite. The equations for this circuit follow:

$$\frac{1}{\omega_{\alpha_{RB}}} \frac{di_{C_1}}{dt} + i_{C_1} = \alpha_{FB} i_{E_2} \tag{15.32}$$

$$\frac{1}{\omega_{\alpha_{FB}}} \frac{di_{C_2}}{dt} + i_{C_2} = \alpha_{FB} i_{E_2} \tag{15.33}$$

$$i_{E_1} = i_{B_1} + i_{C_2} \tag{15.34}$$

$$i_{E_2} = i_{B_2} + i_{C_2} \tag{15.35}$$

$$i_{B_2} = -i_{C_1} \tag{15.36}$$

$$i_{B_1} = -i_{C_2} \tag{15.37}$$

Where these equations are solved for, say $i_{C_1}(t)$, we find that

$$i_{C_1}(t) = \left[\frac{I_{C_1}(0) - I_{C_2}(0)}{2} \right] e^{\omega_{\alpha_{FB}}(2\alpha_{FB}-1)t} + \left[\frac{I_{C_1}(0) + I_{C_2}(0)}{2} \right] e^{\omega_{\alpha_{FB}}t} \tag{15.38}$$

where the $I_{C_1}(0)$ and $I_{C_2}(0)$ are the initial collector currents associated with transistors 1 and 2. The first term on the right of Eq. (15.38) produces a rising exponential mode

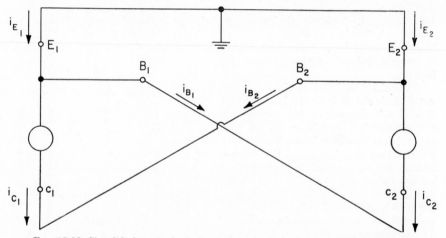

FIG. 15.30. Simplified equivalent circuit for trigger under transient conditions.

of operation. Inspecting the exponent of the first term, it is seen that it reduces to $\omega_{\alpha_{FB}}t$ when α_{FB} is made unity. This is very interesting in view of the fact that the trigger is composed of two inverter stages. We found in Eq. (15.9) that the inverter has a response which contains an exponent of the form $-\omega_{\alpha_{FB}}(1 - \omega_{\alpha_{FB}})t$. The minus sign should cause no trouble because with the positive feedback associated with two inverter stages closed on themselves, one might expect a positive exponential mode of operation. The significant point to be noted is that the speed of operation of the trigger is comparable to a grounded-base stage, not a grounded-emitter stage. This is due to the overdriving action that has been mentioned previously. The cross-coupling capacitors produce a direct connection between collector and opposite base for transients. In this way, almost the full collector current of a transistor is initially available to the base of the other transistor. The speed of a trigger can be improved, therefore, if it is recognized that it is necessary to supply a high current into a rather low impedance. The low impedance is the base impedance of the transistor under transient conditions. If two emitter followers are used for cross coupling in a trigger, the speed of the trigger can be materially increased. This is a technique which has been used in vacuum-tube triggers for some time. Shunt peaking coils or clamp diodes can also be used to advantage in increasing the speed of a trigger.

15.4e. Nonsaturating Triggers. An example of a nonsaturating trigger that employs emitter followers for cross coupling is shown in Fig. 15.31a. In this circuit two of the feedback inverters that were discussed in Sec. 15.2h and shown in Fig. 15.14 are

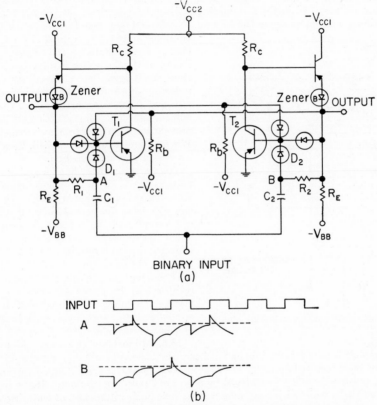

Fig. 15.31. (a) PNP nonsaturating trigger. (b) Timing diagram.

cross-coupled to form the basic trigger. Binary gating is achieved by the resistance-gated diode networks $R_1C_1D_1$ and $R_2C_2D_2$. For moderate loads the upper pulse repetition frequency of the signal that can be applied at the input will generally be limited by the RC time constant of the gating circuits. As shown in the timing diagram of Fig. 15.31b, the recovery of point A and B must occur in one-half the input period. When very high speed operation is desired, the low values of R and C that are necessary for gate recovery make it difficult to couple in enough energy from the driving source to ensure reliable operation. With a 1.0-volt low-impedance, fast-rise-time driving source and R and C values of 200 ohms and 69 pf reliable operation at 30 mc/sec has been achieved. Additional diodes can be added to the base of T_1 and T_2 to provide independent set and reset means.

A faster binary trigger is shown in Fig. 15.32. In this circuit, the basic trigger is formed by cross-coupling two of the inverters of Fig. 15.15.   The emitter diodes of Fig. 15.15 are not necessary in the trigger, since one side or the other is always conducting.   The state of the trigger is sensed by the current switch formed by transistors T_3 and T_4.   If the state of the trigger is such that T_1 is on and T_2 is off, then the base of T_4 will be negative with respect to the base of T_3.   However, the base of the gating transistor T_5 is biased negative so that T_5 conducts and T_3 and T_4 are off. When a positive current pulse is applied at the input, the base of T_5 will go positive and T_5 will shut off and remain off for the time required for the input waveform to propagate down the short-circuited delay line, be inverted and travel back up the line, and be absorbed in the terminating resistor R_0.   With T_5 off, T_4 will turn on, delivering a current pulse to the base of T_1 (through the Zener diode in the cross-coupling network), turning T_1 off, and changing the state of the trigger.   The length of the delay line is such that by the time the trigger has changed state, the reflected pulse from the delay line has returned from the shorted end of the line and turned on T_5, thus shutting off T_4 and preventing the trigger from switching back. When the next input is applied, T_2 will be turned off and T_1 turned on.

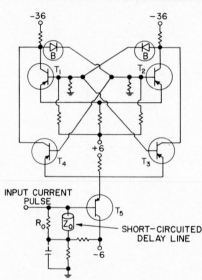

FIG. 15.32. PNP current-switching binary trigger.

The use of the delay line for gating eliminates the recovery problems associated with the resistance-gated diode.   In general, the delay line should have a low value of characteristic impedance in order to avoid termination troubles due to the transient input impedance of T_5.   Drive may be obtained from a suitably biased PNP current switch, or the terminating resistor may be placed in series with the input and a voltage drive used.   With 400- or 500-mc transistors, 75-mc reliable operation has been realized.

15.5. Monostable Circuits.   A monostable circuit is used for obtaining a fixed or variable delay, pulse shaping, etc.   It can be of the blocking-oscillator type or of the cascaded-inverter type.   In the case of the former, positive feedback is achieved by means of a pulse transformer.   In the case of the latter, it is achieved in the same way as it is done in the case of the trigger.

15.5a. Single Shots.   The term single shot is a name generally given to a monostable circuit of the type consisting of two inverters.   The pulse width can be determined by the charging of a capacitor or by a length of short-circuited delay line.   A typical NPN saturating single shot is shown in Fig. 15.33.   In this circuit, a positive input pulse applied to the base of a pull-over transistor causes point C_1 to drop from ground potential to -5.0 volts.   Transistor T_1 is normally off while T_2 is normally on.   The negative-going excursion of point C_1 is coupled to the base of T_2 through C_T, thus cutting off T_2. T_2 going off allows point C_2 to rise until it is caught at ground potential by means of the clamp diode.   Point C_2 going positive is coupled back to the base of T_1 by means of the cross-coupling capacitor and resistor.   This causes T_1 to remain on.   As C_T is charged through R_T, the base of T_2 rises toward $+15$ volts.   When the base of T_2 reaches the potential of the emitter, T_2 turns on, causing T_1 to turn off.   It should be emphasized that the back resistance of the emitter and collector of T_2, in addition to I_{EBO} and I_{CBO}, is important in determining pulse width.   Also the emitter breakdown potential of T_2 should be higher than the signal swing at point C_1. Because the charging of C_T is a function of the I_{CBO} and I_{EBO} of transistor T_2, the pulse width of the circuit of Fig. 15.33 will be a function of temperature. In many applications it is only necessary to obtain a pulse output whose width is greater than some fixed value, and if the temperature effects on I_{CBO} and I_{EBO} are included in the

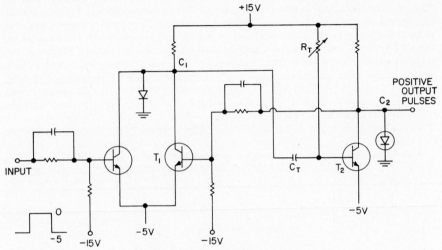

FIG. 15.33. NPN saturating single shot.

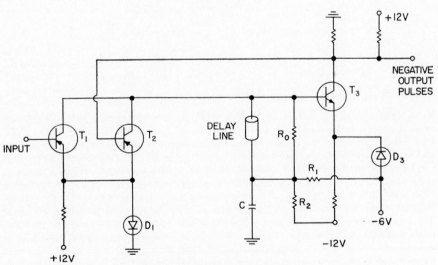

FIG. 15.34. Delay-line single shot.

design, a minimum pulse width can be defined. However, in applications where a fixed pulse width is required over a large temperature range, the delay-line single shot of Fig. 15.34 is more desirable.

This circuit consists of two of the current-switching inverters described in Sec. 15.2i. The input to the NPN current switch consisting of T_3 and D_3 is biased to hold T_3 off by the resistor network R_1, R_2. Since T_3 is off, the output voltage will be above ground, holding T_2 off. T_1 is a pull-over transistor and is assumed to be biased off initially. R_0 serves to terminate the delay line, and C serves to short-circuit the delay line. When a negative input is applied, T_1 conducts and the input to T_3 rises, turning T_3 on; the output voltage goes negative, causing conduction to switch from T_1 to T_2 and, in effect, disconnecting the input. T_3 will remain conducting until the waveform in the delay line travels down line, is inverted, and returns back up the line. At this time, the voltage at the base of T_3 will drop to its initial value and T_3 will turn off, causing the output voltage to rise. This will turn off T_2, but T_1 may start conducting again if the input to T_1 is still negative. At any rate, when current ceases in either T_1 or T_2, a negative wavefront will be propagated down the delay line. However, this negative pulse will not cause T_3 to conduct and hence will not appear in the output. In this circuit, the problem of translating the output of the PNP current switch back to ground level is avoided by the use of the NPN current switch, which has an output around ground but an input around -6.0 volts. More will be said about current-switching circuits of this type in Sec. 15.11.

The output pulse width of the circuit is seen to be twice the electrical length of the delay line.

15.5b. Blocking Oscillator. Another monostable circuit that can be used for obtaining a well-defined pulse output is the blocking oscillator. An example of a

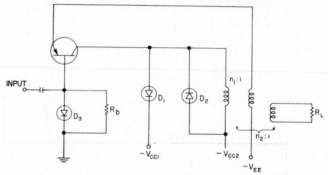

FIG. 15.35. PNP blocking oscillator.

blocking oscillator is shown in Fig. 15.35. The emitter bias supply $-V_{EE}$ is 0.5 volt or so negative with respect to ground in order to bias off the emitter of the PNP transistor. The diode D_3 will present a high resistance to a negative input pulse and at the same time supply a low resistance to the base of the transistor when it is conducting. R_b bypasses the diode D_3 to allow a path for I_{CBO}. When a negative pulse is applied to the input, the transistor conducts and collector current and collector voltage begin to rise. The polarity of the transformer windings is such that the voltage induced in the emitter feedback loop is positive, thus turning the transistor on more. The input pulse can now be removed, and because of the positive feedback, the collector potential will continue to rise until diode D_1 conducts and clamps the collector voltage at $-V_{CC_1}$. Since the induced voltages in the transformer windings are produced by an increase of flux in the core of the transformer, then the magnetizing current which produces this flux is also increasing. Since the collector current is fixed, the increase in magnetizing current must come from the current flowing in the clamp diode D_1. Eventually, the magnetizing current rises to a value equal to the initial current in diode D_1 and the diode is cut off. The magnetizing current now can no longer increase, the induced voltage drops to zero, the emitter becomes reversed-biased, and the transistor is cut off. Since action is terminated because the collector is no longer able to sustain the sum of the reflected load, feedback, and magnetizing currents, the pulse width will be sensitive to loading. If a saturable core is used, then the magnetizing current will increase very rapidly once saturation is reached.

The energy stored in the inductance must now be dissipated in the load R_L. As the magnetizing current decreases, the induced voltage reverses, and if the load impedance is high, the transient voltage will also be high. The transistor collector must withstand the transient voltage plus the collector return supply voltage, or a diode D_2 returned to a safe bias $-V_{CC_1}$ must be employed. Where diodes are used to control the turn-off transient, the recovery time of the circuit will be increased considerably and the pulse repetition frequency will be limited. In the circuit of Fig. 15.35, feedback is from collector to emitter, and in order to have a loop current gain greater than 1, the emitter turns ratio n_1 must be greater than $1/\alpha_{FB}$.

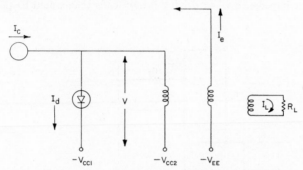

Fig. 15.36. Direction of currents in a PNP blocking oscillator.

The magnetizing inductance L_m that is required for a specific pulse width can be calculated.[5] If we make the reasonable assumption that the magnetizing current is zero when diode D_1 first conducts, then the magnetizing current will increase by an amount equal to the initial value of current in the clamp diode D_1. The initial current directions are shown in Fig. 15.36, and

$$V = L_m \frac{\Delta I}{\Delta T} \tag{15.39}$$

where ΔI is the increase in magnetizing current and ΔT is the pulse width τ,

$$\Delta I = I_D$$

$$I_D = I_C - \frac{I_E}{n_1} - \frac{I_L}{n_2} \tag{15.40}$$

but

$$I_E = \frac{V}{n_1[r_e + r_b(1 - \alpha_{FB})]} \tag{15.41}$$

$$I_C = \frac{\alpha_{FB}V}{n_1[r_e + r_b(1 - \alpha_{FB})]} \tag{15.42}$$

$$I_L = \frac{V}{n_2 R_L} \tag{15.43}$$

Substitutions of Eqs. (15.41) to (15.43) into Eqs. (15.39) and (15.40) yields the following expression for pulse width:

$$\tau = \frac{(\alpha_{FB}n_1 - 1)L_m}{n_1^2[r_e + r_b(1 - \alpha_{FB})]} - \frac{L_m}{n_2^2 R_L} \tag{15.43a}$$

15.6. Power Drivers. The circuits that are described here have the feature of being able to act as buffer amplifiers between low-power circuits and large capacitive or resistance loads. As pointed out in the introduction, most large systems require a building block that has a large pyramiding factor. In addition to the requirement for a circuit with a large pyramiding factor, there is usually a requirement for a circuit capable of charging and discharging large capacitive loads. This is particularly true where fast operation is required.

15.6a. Power Inverters. In the circuit shown in Fig. 15.37, transistor T_2 may be a power transistor capable of supplying a large steady-state load. In this circuit the base current of T_2 is part of the load current of T_1, and in this connection, it can be seen that the total current gain of the circuit approaches the product of the common-emitter current gain of T_1 and T_2. The high current gain permits the circuit to have a higher input impedance when driving heavy loads than would be possible with a

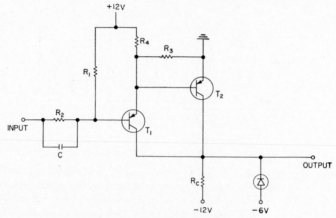

FIG. 15.37. PNP power inverter 1.

single transistor. A second advantage of the circuit is that the grounded-emitter stage which is supplying the bulk of the output current is not driven into saturation. This follows from the method of coupling between T_1 and T_2. Transistor T_2 cannot reach saturation because its base-to-collector voltage can never be less than the emitter-to-collector voltage of transistor T_1 which drives it. Transistor T_1 will saturate, of course, but this transistor is operated at a relatively low current level and is more easily driven out of saturation. The input circuit is designed so that T_1 and T_2 are off for the most negative up level. Transistor T_1 is held off by the voltage divider R_1, R_2, while T_2 is held off by the resistor network R_3, R_4. The turn-off current for T_2 is supplied through resistor R_4, and capacitor C supplies overdrive to T_1. When the input is negative, T_1 and T_2 are on and their collector currents add at the output. The input network is designed so when T_1 is on, it is capable of conducting the base current of T_2 and the current from R_3 and R_4.

This circuit has application where large currents must be delivered to the load with small input loading. The fall time for the circuit is largely determined by the RC time constant of the load. A diode clamp such as shown in Fig. 15.37 can be used to reduce the fall time.

Figure 15.38 shows a power inverter which is very useful for driving capacitive loads. The circuit consists of a saturating inverter (transistor T_1) and a clamping emitter follower (transistor T_2). When the input to the circuit goes negative, transistor T_1 will conduct heavily and charge the load capacitance C_L through diode D_1.

The charging of C_L will continue until transistor T_1 saturates, at which point C_L will be charged to close to ground potential. A positive input to the circuit will cut off transistor T_1, and the collector potential of T_1 will fall toward -12 volts. Transistor T_2 conducts, clamping the collector of T_1 at approximately -6.0 volts. The -6.0- and -12.0-volt power supplies could have the same potential. However, if connected as shown, some improvement in fall time is achieved because of the clamping action of the collector diode of T_2. This circuit has the useful feature of being able to

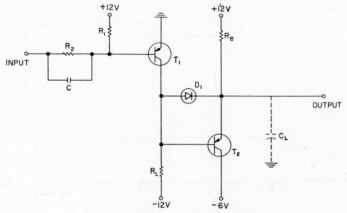

FIG. 15.38. PNP power inverter 2.

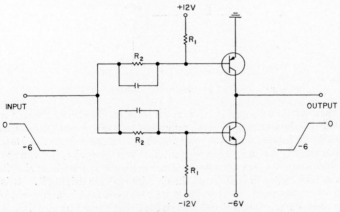

FIG. 15.39. Complemented inverter.

supply a positive drive in both directions. That is, when T_1 turns on, an output current flows through D_1 into the load C_L. When T_1 turns off, current flows out of the capacitor to the emitter follower. Thus the circuit can drive capacitive loads without resorting to small values of R_e and large standby currents in T_2.

15.6b. Complemented Circuits. Another circuit, which has the driving ability of the circuit of Fig. 15.38, is the complemented saturating inverter shown in Fig. 15.39. This circuit consists of a PNP and an NPN saturating inverter. When the input goes negative, the PNP inverter conducts and supplies current to the load. The NPN inverter is off. When the input goes positive, the NPN inverter conducts and draws current from the load. The PNP inverter is off. Note that no collector return resistor is required and therefore all output current is available for driving the load.

The driving ability of the emitter follower can also be improved by the addition of a complementing transistor. In the complemented emitter follower shown in Fig.15.40, the NPN transistor provides drive in the positive direction while the PNP transistor provides drive in the negative direction. Although the addition of the complementing transistor will improve the driving ability of a single emitter follower, it will not alter the stability problem discussed previously.

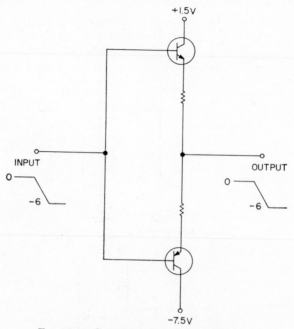

FIG. 15.40. Complemented emitter follower.

15.7. Indicators. In a large system, some form of visual indication is a desirable servicing aid. Indicators are usually connected across the output of critical lines or triggers to give an indication of the state the line or trigger is in. The ideal indicator for transistor circuits would be a low-current–low-voltage device, low voltage to enable it to be driven from the low voltages that are common to transistor circuits and low current to reduce its loading effect on the circuits that are driving it. It is common practice to use either neon bulbs or low-voltage–low-current incandescent bulbs, and usually the situation (signal level and load) is such that a separate amplifier is required. An incandescent-bulb indicating circuit is shown in Fig. 15.41. Here transistor T_1 is operated as a conventional grounded-emitter saturating inverter similar to the circuit discussed in Sec. 15.2a. The overdrive capacitor across R_1 is not necessary where visual indication is required and is omitted in order to reduce the transient load on the driving source. When T_1 is on and in saturation, point 1 is essentially at ground and R_4 and the collector return potential (-12 volts) are such that sufficient current flows and the incandescent bulb lights. When T_1 is off, a resistor R_3 is added in series with the -12-volt supply, current is greatly reduced, and the lamp emits little or no visible light. In Fig. 15.42a, the same saturating inverter is used to control a neon bulb. The volt-ampere characteristic of the neon bulb will rise as the rectified 120-cycle input voltage rises, and the neon will ignite when the rectified input plus the negative collector return exceeds V_1 in Fig. 15.42b. The neon will remain on until the rectified input falls below the conduction threshold V_2.   When T_1 is on, point 1 will be essentially at ground, and even when the rectified input is at full amplitude, the neon will not conduct.   An alternative solution would be simply to return the neon bulb to a positive d-c voltage of, say, +45 volts.   However, when the rectified a-c return

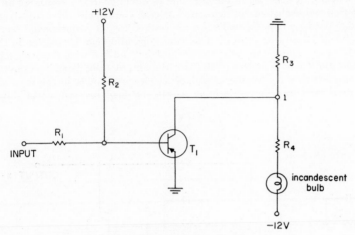

FIG. 15.41. Indicator circuit.

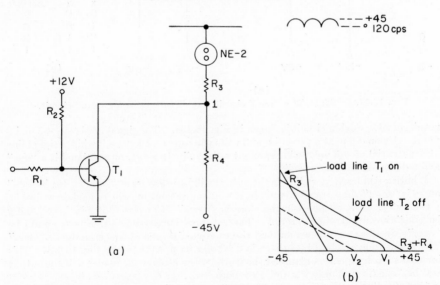

FIG. 15.42. (a) Neon indicator circuit.   (b) Volt-ampere characteristic of neon and load line.

is used, the problem of specifying a turn-off level for the neon (V_2 in Fig. 15.42b) is eliminated.

15.8. Performing Logic.   In previous sections of this chapter we have discussed individual circuits.   In the following sections the circuits already discussed are combined to form different logical building blocks.   If we were to analyze a large computing system and separate the system into functional units, we would find such units as decoders, adders, counters, shifting registers, and in particular a large section which can be called a control unit. The control unit serves to connect and control the various registers, decoders and the adder, etc. If we now investigate each of the functional units, we would find that they are made up of combinations of various logical building blocks. A basic set of building blocks would generally consist of an "and," "or" inverter and exclusive "or" circuit. A basic storage circuit such as one of the triggers discussed previously would also be required for the counters and registers.

15.8a. "And" Operation $(x \cdot y)$. The "and" operation can be written in the symbolic form $x \cdot y$. This means that the x signal is "and"-ed with the y signal, which implies that both inputs must be "one" for the output to be "one." Conversely, it can be regarded as a circuit the output of which corresponds to the most negative input. PNP emitter followers driving a common load resistance will satisfy this

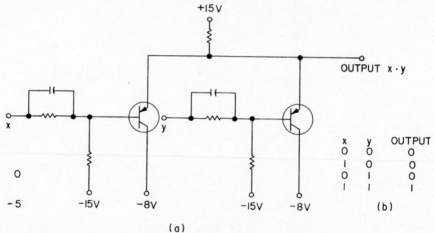

(a)

FIG. 15.43. (*a*) Transistor "and" circuit. (*b*) Truth table for "and" circuit.

requirement. Such a circuit is shown in Fig. 15.43*a*. The signal levels are -5 and 0 volts. A signal line at a potential of 0 volts will represent a "one," while a signal line at a potential of -5 volts will represent a "zero." In short, an up signal is a "one" and a down signal is a "zero."

If both x and y are "zero," then the output will be -5 volts or "zero." If x is "one" and y is "zero," the x transistor will be cut off and the output will be held down by the y transistor. The output will therefore be "zero." Conversely if x is "zero" and y is "one," the output will be "zero." The last condition possible is that both x and y be "one." In this case, the output will rise to ground level and hence produce a "one." This description can best be written in a tabular form, as shown in Fig. 15.43*b*. This is called a truth table. A glance at the truth table will show the reader that the output will be "one" if and only if x and y are both "one."

15.8b. "Or" Operation $(x + y)$. The "or" operation is denoted by the symbol $x + y$. The plus sign denotes logical addition and not algebraic addition. The rules for the "or" operation will become clear when we develop the truth table. The output of an "or" circuit will correspond to the most positive input. NPN emitter followers driving a common-load resistor will satisfy this requirement. This can be seen by referring to Fig. 15.44*a*. If both x and y are "zero," then the output will be "zero." If either x or y is "one," the output will be" one." If both x and y are "one," the output will also be "one." The truth table is shown in Fig. 15.44*b*, and we see that the output will be "one" if either x or y or both are "one."

15.8c. The Operation $(\bar{x} \cdot \bar{y})$. The inverter has been studied previously, but no symbol was used for its logical operation. Remembering how the inverter inverts a signal, we see that if a "one" signal is applied to the input of an inverter, the output will be a "zero." This can be represented symbolically thus: $\bar{x}$. The $\bar{x}$ is called "not

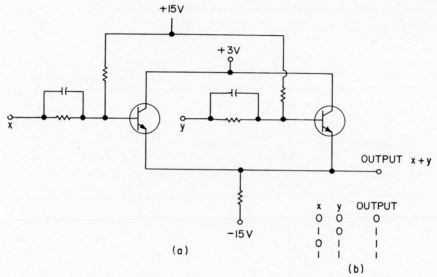

x	y	OUTPUT
0	0	0
1	0	1
0	1	1
1	1	1

(b)

Fig. 15.44. (*a*) Transistor "or" circuit. (*b*) Truth table for "or" circuit.

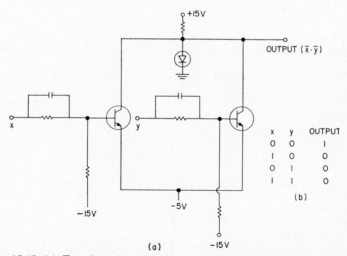

x	y	OUTPUT
0	0	1
1	0	0
0	1	0
1	1	0

(b)

Fig. 15.45. (*a*) Transistor $(\bar{x} \cdot \bar{y})$ circuit. (*b*) Truth table for $(\bar{x} \cdot \bar{y})$ circuit.

x." If a signal x is applied to the input of an inverter, then the output signal will be "not x," or $\bar{x}$. We see that to produce the operation $\bar{x} \cdot \bar{y}$ the outputs of two inverters should be "and"-ed together. A circuit to produce $\bar{x} \cdot \bar{y}$ should have a positive output only if both inputs are negative. A moment's thought will convince the reader that PNP inverters will not work but NPN inverters driving a common load will do the job.   These are shown in Fig. 15.45a.   The truth table shows that the output will be "one" if there is a "zero" at both inputs.

15.8d.   The Operation $(x \cdot \bar{y})$.   This operation can be achieved by combining a PNP emitter follower with an NPN inverter, as shown in Fig. 15.46a.   The truth table shows that the circuit performs the operation $(x \cdot \bar{y})$.   The operation $x \cdot \bar{y}$ can also be performed using one transistor.   This is shown in Fig. 15.47a.

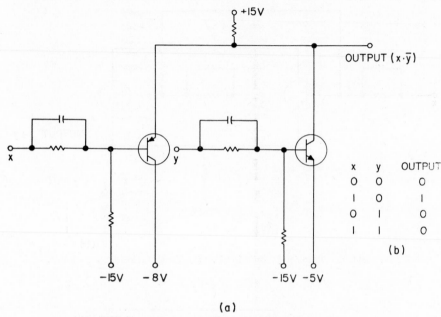

FIG. 15.46.   (*a*) Transistor $x \cdot \bar{y}$ circuit.   (*b*) Truth table for $x \cdot \bar{y}$ circuit.

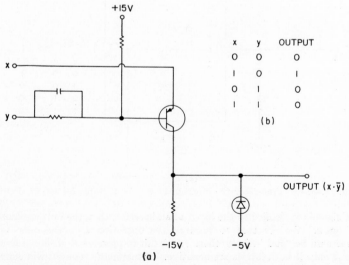

FIG. 15.47.   (*a*) Single transistor $x \cdot \bar{y}$ circuit.   (*b*) Truth table for $x \cdot \bar{y}$ circuit.

15.8e. Exclusive "Or" Circuit ($x \cdot \bar{y} + \bar{x} \cdot y$). If two circuits of the type shown in Fig. 15.47a are coupled to drive a common load and their inputs are cross-connected, we have a very useful circuit called an exclusive "or" circuit. This is shown in Fig. 15.48a. The truth table states that the output will be a "one" if either x or y input is "one" but not both. While this circuit is conservative with respect to the number of transistors used, it requires large driving currents, since the emitter is used as an input terminal.

15.8f. Trigger Functional Units. In order to give the reader a feeling for how triggers are used in more complex assemblies, two simple structures will be described. The first of these is a shifting register.

A shifting register must be capable of storing digital information and shifting it forward or backward in the register upon command. If a register is designed to

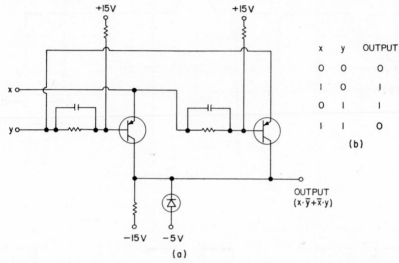

x	y	OUTPUT
0	0	0
I	0	I
0	I	I
I	I	0

(b)

OUTPUT
($x \cdot \bar{y} + \bar{x} \cdot y$)

(a)

FIG. 15.48. (a) Transistor exclusive "or" circuit. (b) Truth table for exclusive "or" circuit.

operate in a number system of radix 2, which is the simplest case, then each stage will contain either a "one" or a "zero." As an example, a number such as 18 in the radix 10, or decimal system, becomes 10010 in the radix 2, or binary system of numbers. A shift register capable of storing, say, seven binary bits of information would have seven stages. If the number 18 were stored in this register, the seven stages would be "ones" and "zeros" in the following pattern: 0010010. If this information were shifted right one stage, the register would contain 0001001. A "zero" would shift out of the end of the register. Another shift to the right would shift a "one" out of the register, and the register would contain 0000100. This process can continue until the register is empty.

With the d-c type of building blocks described here, triggers would be used for each state of the register. The triggers would not need to be provided with binary inputs. They could be of the form shown in Fig. 15.49. A symbol for the trigger is also shown in this figure. The trigger operates on positive pulses and has set and reset inputs at C and D and a binary input E which is not used in a shifting register. A positive pulse applied to terminal C will turn the left transistor off and the right one on. Terminal B will be at ground potential, while A will be at -5 volts. When the trigger is in this state, we shall say it is on and therefore is storing a "one." A positive

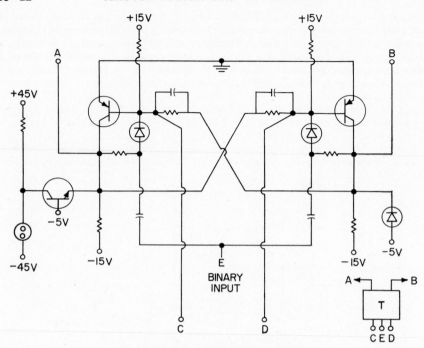

FIG. 15.49. Transistor trigger and symbol.

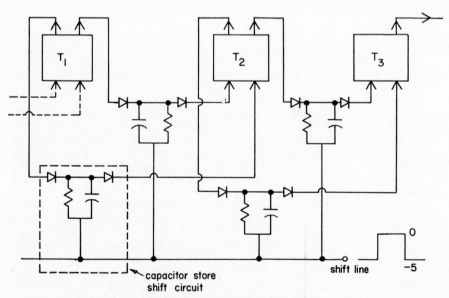

FIG. 15.50. Section of a shifting register.

pulse at D will turn the trigger off and therefore read a "zero" into it. All that needs to be done now is to provide some means of shifting information out of a stage from the left. It is clear that additional memory is needed aside from that available in each stage. Other triggers could be used for temporary memory, but a simpler arrangement is to use a capacitor and isolation diode as shown in Fig. 15.50. The capacitor store shift circuit† is shown in the square drawn with dashed lines.

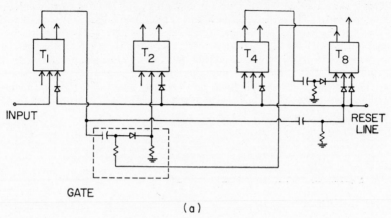

(a)

Decimal number	T_1	T_2	T_4	T_8
0	0	0	0	0
1	1	0	0	0
2	0	1	0	0
3	1	1	0	0
4	0	0	1	0
5	1	0	1	0
6	0	1	1	0
7	1	1	1	0
8	0	0	0	1
9	1	0	0	1

(b)

FIG. 15.51. Binary-coded decimal counter: (*a*) diagram, (*b*) 10 stable states.

The next system to be described is a binary-coded decimal counter. It has been shown previously that a trigger can be connected in binary fashion by the addition of simple gating circuits. A cascaded set of binary triggers will provide a counter that is capable of counting in the binary number system up to $2N$, where N is the number of triggers in cascade. If such a counter has been initially set to zero, then each trigger in the counter contains a zero. If one pulse is applied to the counter, only the first stage will be on. If a total of two pulses is applied, only the second stage will be on. Four pulses will leave only the third stage on, and with eight pulses only the fourth stage will be on. The stages will have a numeric weight of 1, 2, 4, 8, etc. Four stages can count up to 15, and the sixteenth pulse will turn all the stages off. Human beings,

† This circuit was developed independently by D. J. Crawford of International Business Machines and A. W. Holt of the National Bureau of Standards.

probably because they have ten fingers, use the decimal system; therefore, it is desirable to have a counter that has ten stable states. This can be done with four triggers and a gate, as shown in Fig. 15.51a.

The reset line normally is at a potential of -5 volts and is brought up to a potential of $+1$ volt. This will reset all the triggers to zero, and the left-hand output terminal of the triggers will be at ground potential. The first positive input pulse will turn T_1 on. This is shown in Fig. 15.51b by a 1 in column T_1 and the row corresponding to a decimal number 1. The second pulse will turn T_1 off, and T_1 going off passes a positive pulse through the gate to T_2, turning it on. The gate passes this pulse because the left-hand output of T_8 is at ground potential; therefore, the diode in the gate has no bias across it. The positive pulse produced by T_1 going off is also coupled over to the right-hand input of T_8. Since T_8 is off, this causes no change. The third pulse turns T_1 on. This process continues until the eighth pulse. Just before the eighth pulse T_1, T_2, and T_4 are on. Since they have the numerical weight of 1, 2, 4, it is seen that their

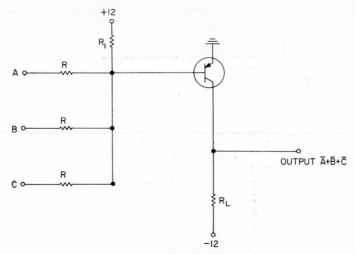

Fig. 15.52. NOR circuit.

being on gives a count of $1 + 2 + 4 = 7$. The eighth pulse turns off T_1, which turns off T_2, which turns off T_4, which turns on T_8. T_8 going on causes the diode gate to be biased in the reverse direction by 5 volts. The ninth pulse turns on T_1, and the tenth pulse turns T_1 off. Since the diode in the gate is biased by 5 volts in the reverse direction, T_2 is not turned off. T_1 going off, however, does turn T_8 off. The tenth pulse therefore turns off T_1, which going off turns off T_8. T_8 going off can transmit a carry signal to the next stage corresponding to a higher decimal digit.

15.9. The NOR Circuit. The circuit of Fig. 15.52 is similar to the inverter of Fig. 15.8a except that a number of additional resistor inputs have been provided and no overdrive capacitors are used. In this circuit, the design is such that a negative signal applied to any of the resistor inputs will cause the transistor to conduct and go into saturation. If ground level is defined as a binary "one" and the down level as a binary "zero," the circuit performs the function $\bar{A} + \bar{B} + \bar{C}$ and is called a NOR circuit.[6] The NOR circuit is logically complete; that is, any logical expression can be achieved by a combination of NOR's. This circuit is found to be quite useful in the control section of a digital computer where chains of logic are often made up of cascaded "and-or" circuits. The fact that the circuit always inverts the signal can often be neglected because in a logical chain of an even number of stages, the inversions will cancel out. Triggers can be constructed by simply cross-coupling two NOR circuits. This circuit has the advantage of permitting inexpensive resistors to be used for logic. The disadvantages of the circuit are that only a small amount of overdrive is available to the transistor and therefore switching is slow. Also the transistor will be

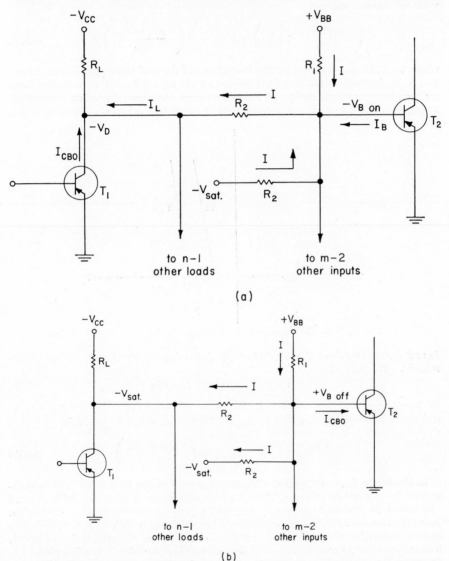

(a)

(b)

Fig. 15.53. (a) On case loading conditions. (b) Off case loading conditions.

driven very deep into saturation when two or more inputs are negative, and therefore, the delay due to minority carrier storage will be long.

In the d-c design of NOR circuits, the required pyramiding factor and speed generally necessitate that resistor values be used that allow significant leakage currents to flow, and these, in turn, effect the pyramiding factor. In Fig. 15.53, a NOR circuit is driving a load of n other NOR circuits each of which have m input resistors. In the on case, that is, when we wish to turn all the loads on, we can have a situation where $m - 1$ inputs to all the n loads can be up. This will significantly increase the load current for which the circuit must be designed. Referring to Fig. 15.53a, we can write for the on case

$$n\left(\frac{E_{BB} + V_{B,\text{on}}}{R_1} + I_B\right) + n(m - 1)\left(\frac{V_{B,\text{on}} - V_{\text{sat}}}{R_2}\right) = I_L \qquad (15.44)$$

where V_B on is the on voltage at the base of any of the load transistors (T_2 et al.) and V_{sat} is the saturation voltage of the driving blocks that drive the $m - 1$ other input resistors in the n loads. Since PNP transistors are used here, V_B on will be approximately -0.4 volt, while V_{sat} would generally be less than -0.1 volt. The load current

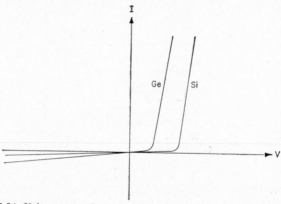

Fig. 15.54. Volt-ampere characteristics of germanium and silicon diodes.

I_L and I_{CBO} of transistor T_1 will add in R_L to determine V_D, the down level input to the n loads. We can write

$$V_D = V_C - (I_L + I_{CBO})R_L \qquad (15.45)$$

In the off case, it is necessary to bias the base of T_2 above ground and the inputs to m resistors will be slightly negative ($-V_{\text{sat}}$). From Fig. 15.53b we can write

$$\frac{V_{BB} - V_{B,\text{off}}}{R_1} = I_{CBO} + m\left(\frac{V_{B,\text{off}} + V_{\text{sat}}}{R_2}\right) \qquad (15.46)$$

15.10. Diode Logical Circuits. Diode switching circuits have been used in computers for a number of years. The diode is still an attractive switching element because of its low cost and small size, which permits relatively dense packaging. Also the recent availability of very fast recovery diodes makes diode switching circuits quite competitive with transistor switching circuits from the standpoint of speed. The volt-ampere characteristics of typical germanium and silicon bonded diodes are shown in Fig. 15.54. In general, the silicon diode will have a larger turn-on voltage than the germanium diode and will have a leakage current that is less than that found in germanium diodes.

Three input diode "and" and "or" circuits are shown in Fig. 15.55. In the "and" circuit, the junction of the diodes is returned to a constant-current source $+V/R$, while in the "or" circuit, the junction of the diodes is returned to a constant-current sink $-V/R$. A little thought will convince the reader that in the case of the "and" circuit, the output potential will be up only when all three inputs are up, while in the case of the "or" circuit, the output will be up if one or more of the inputs are up. In the "and" circuit, the output potential will be determined by the most negative input signal, while in the "or" circuit, the output will be determined by the most positive input signal. In these respects, it is seen that diode logical circuits are much the same

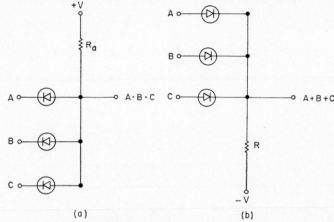

FIG. 15.55. (a) Diode "and" circuit. (b) Diode "or" circuit.

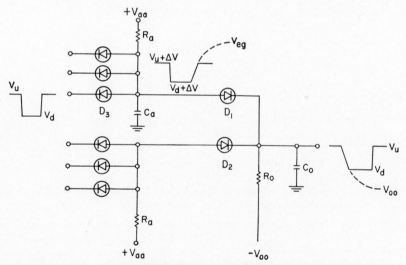

FIG. 15.56. Diode "and-or" chain.

as the emitter-follower logical circuits of Figs. 15.43 and 15.44 and both circuits are characterized by no voltage gain and by a small shift in potential from input to output caused by the drop across the conducting diode.

It is common practice to use diode circuitry to form short chains of logic. The input to the chain might come from a low-impedance driving source such as an emitter follower, while the output of the chain would drive a voltage amplifier which would reestablish the signal level and drive another chain. The simplest chain would be the "and-or" circuit of Fig. 15.56. If the voltage drop across the "and" and "or" diodes is the same, the input-signal levels V_U, V_D will equal the output-signal levels, the positive voltage shift across the "and" diodes being just canceled by the negative voltage shift across the "or" diodes.   If a negative step of voltage is applied at diode D_1, stray capacitance C_a will discharge through D_3, the potential at this node will drop from $V_U + \Delta V$ to $V_D + \Delta V$ (ΔV is the drop across a conducting diode), and diode D_1 will cut off.   The output potential will drop to V_D if the input to diode D_2 is at V_D, and we can say that the fall time at the output will be

$$T_F = R_0 C_0 \ln \left(1 - \frac{V_U - V_D}{V_{00}} \right) \tag{15.47}$$

We have assumed that the back resistance of D_2 is many times R_0.   The rise time at

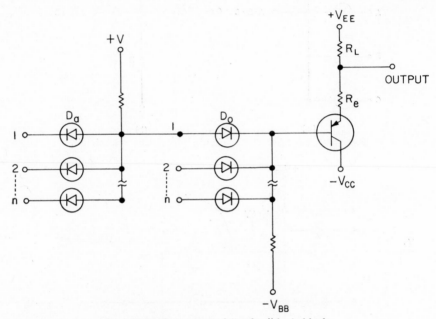

Fig. 15.57. Compensated "and-or" logic block.

the output is controlled by the sum of C_a and C_0 and the parallel combination of R_a and R_0.   We can write for a positive input step of voltage

$$T_R = \frac{R_a R_0}{R_a + R_0} (C_a + C_0) \ln \left(1 - \frac{V_U - V_D}{V_{eq}} \right) \tag{15.48}$$

where V_{eq} is the Thévenin equivalent voltage formed by $+V_{aa}$, $-V_{00}$ and R_a, R_0. These simple calculations hold only where the transients are such that the recovery time of the diodes is insignificant.   In high-speed applications, this is not the case and the fall time of the "and" circuit will generally be determined by the time required to turn off conducting diodes.

Diode chains of logic are reasonably flexible, and if some care is taken to compensate for level shifts, several stages can usually be cascaded before the required input signal swing becomes objectionably large.   An example is shown in Fig. 15.57.   In this circuit, germanium diodes are paralleled to form the "and" circuit while silicon diodes are used to form the "or" circuit.   An emitter follower is used to drive several other "and" inputs.   If the inputs to the "and" diodes are at ground potential, the junction of the "and-or" diodes will be slightly positive.   Because of the larger voltage drop in the silicon diodes, the input to the emitter follower will be slightly negative.   However, the output of the emitter follower will be shifted positive by the drop across the emitter base diode and stabilization resistor R_e.   By the use of alternate silicon and germanium diodes, the level shifts are in the ideal case canceled out and in the practical case where diode voltage drops do differ, the total level shift is minimized.   Good speed can be obtained from the circuit of Fig. 15.57 if the "and" and "or" diodes are mounted close to the input to the emitter follower and the emitter followers are used to drive the lines that must be long.   The inputs to all "and" diodes, then, would come from other emitter followers.

A complemented diode "and-or" block is shown in Fig. 15.58.   This circuit has advantages where large capacitive loads must be driven but requires the use of both

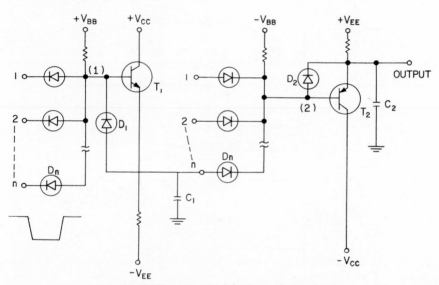

FIG. 15.58. Complemented diode "and-or" circuit.

PNP and NPN transistors.   Circuit operation is as follows: Assume that the "and" circuit diodes are driven from low-impedance sources.   Then a negative input-voltage step will cut off transistor T_1 and load capacitance C_1 will discharge through diode D_1, the "and" circuit diode, and into the driving source.   The "or" circuit diode D_n will cut off, and assuming that all other inputs to "or" diodes are down, point 2 will fall toward $-V_{BB}$.   This will cause transistor T_2 to conduct, and load capacitance C_2 will discharge into T_2.   An input positive step will cut off the "and" circuit diode D_n, and assuming that all other "and" diodes are up, point 1 will rise toward $+V_{BB}$.   This will cause transistor T_1 to conduct, C_1 will be charged up, and current will flow through "or" diode D_n, through D_2, and charge up load capacitance C_2.   By close packaging, load capacitance C_1 can be made very small and the principal load will be C_2.   In this circuit, transistors T_1 and T_2 are combined to form a complemented emitter follower. In a chain of these circuits, an effective complemented drive will be available at all outputs within the chain.

After several stages of diode logic, it will usually be necessary to amplify the signal and restore the d-c level.   All the inverters or triggers previously discussed can be employed for this purpose.

15.11. Current-switching Circuits. The basic current-switching circuit is shown in Fig. 15.59. This circuit is seen to be a differential amplifier in which the signal is applied to one base and the other base is returned to a reference voltage which in this case is ground. When the input potential is at −0.6 volt, transistor T_1 is conducting and 6 ma from the emitter-current source flows into transistor T_1, causing its output potential to rise from −6.6 to −5.4 volts. The input potential of −0.6 volt is sufficient to bias T_2 off, and its output potential falls to 6.6 volts. When the input potential is raised to +0.6 volt, transistor T_1 is shut off and conduction switches to T_2. This circuit illustrates a method by which a well-defined current is switched by a relatively small input signal. The input signal need only be large enough to ensure

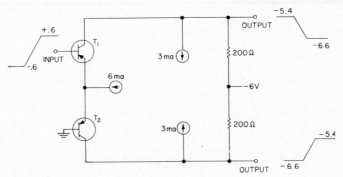

Fig. 15.59. PNP current switch.

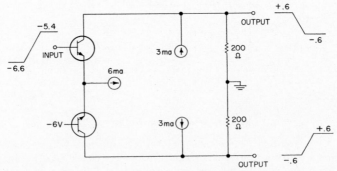

Fig. 15.60. NPN current switch.

that the potential at the emitter node rise sufficiently above or below ground to ensure switching of T_2.

From Fig. 15.59 it is seen that the collector is returned to −6 volts through a small load resistor and a suitable current bias is applied to obtain a signal swing about −6 volts. Because of the 6-volt difference between input and output, a PNP current switch cannot drive another PNP switch. This difficulty can be overcome by constructing the complementary NPN switch shown in Fig. 15.60.

In the NPN circuit of Fig. 15.60, the reference input is returned to −6 volts, so that this circuit can be driven by a PNP circuit. The NPN and PNP switches of Figs. 15.59 and 15.60 are basic to current switching, and one basic rule in their use is that PNP switches always drive NPN switches, which in turn always drive PNP switches.

15.11a. Logical Circuits. When additional transistors are provided, the basic current switches can be extended to perform logic. For this discussion, let us continue to define a binary "one" as the most positive input to a switch regardless of whether the signal in question is referenced to ground or −6 volts. Two logical circuits capable of performing the "and," "or," and inversion connectives are shown in Fig. 15.61. In Fig. 15.61a, the "and" statement is obtained from the bottom transistor, which will conduct only provided inputs A, B, and C are positive. In Fig. 15.61b, the "or" statement is obtained from the bottom transistor, which will be off if one or

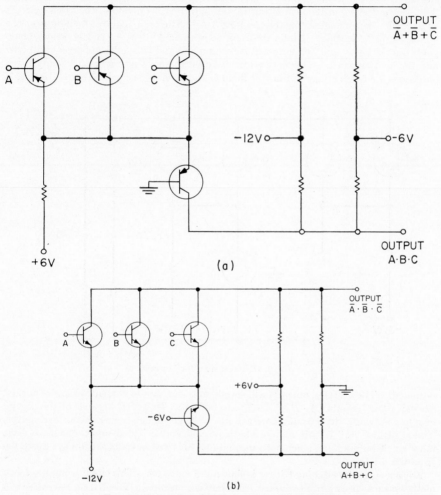

FIG. 15.61. (a) "And" circuit. (b) "Or" circuit.

more inputs to the top transistors are positive. One logical feature of current-switching circuits can immediately be seen from Fig. 15.61. That is, there are two logical outputs and they are complements of each other. As a logical "one" is defined here, the top outputs are inverted and the bottom outputs are normal. The fact that inverted outputs are always available eliminates the need for a separate inverter building block.

When use is made of the normal and inverted outputs and transistors are added, the two logical blocks of Fig. 15.61 can be extended to generate all the necessary logical connections required in a system. However, a separate exclusive "or" building block would be an advantage, since three of the logical blocks of Fig. 15.61 would be required to generate the exclusive "or" statement and also there would be a delay of two logical blocks in the cascade involved. The arrangement of logical blocks shown in Fig. 15.62 will generate an exclusive "or" statement with a delay of only one logical block. This exclusive "or" circuit consists of two parallel "and" circuits which generate $A \cdot \bar{B}$ and $\bar{A} \cdot B$. With the four inputs connected as shown, only one of the "and" circuit (bottom) outputs can be conducting at any one time. Therefore, the "and" circuit outputs can be connected together to form the "or" circuit required to complete the exclusive "or" function. Under the input conditions $\bar{A} \cdot \bar{B}$ or $A \cdot B$, the inverted outputs (top) of both "and" circuits will be conducting and two units of current will flow into the load network. This network is designed to give a normal output only when both sides are conducting, and in this manner the inverted exclusive "or" statement is

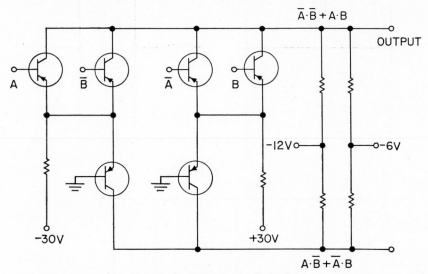

FIG. 15.62. Exclusive "or" circuit.

obtained. The inverted outputs will supply only one unit of current when the normal exclusive "or" inputs $(A \cdot \bar{B} + \bar{A} \cdot B)$ are present. However, because of the special coupling network, the output signal will not be large enough to switch the load stages. The exclusive "or" circuit requires both normal and inverted input signals. This, however, is no problem, since both normal and inverted outputs are always available from the driving source.

A basic current-switching trigger is shown in Fig. 15.63. This circuit consists of two of the basic switches cross-coupled from bottom outputs. The trigger can be set in either position through the pull-over transistors on either side. An "or" function can be built into the trigger by simply adding more transistors in parallel with the pull-over transistor. Operation is in no way different from the logical block circuits of Fig. 15.61. A binary trigger and a single shot have already been discussed, and the reader is referred to Figs. 15.32 and 15.34 for schematics of these circuits.

The basic logical circuits of Fig. 15.61 can be made more useful by the use of an inhibit signal. In Fig. 15.64, if the signal level at the inhibit input I is more negative than the level at inputs A, B, and C, then transistor T_1 will conduct all the current from the emitter-current source and T_2, T_3, T_4, and T_5 will be off. When a clock pulse

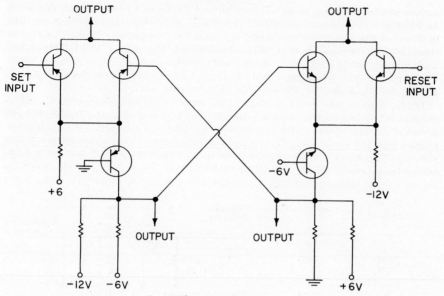

FIG. 15.63. Trigger.

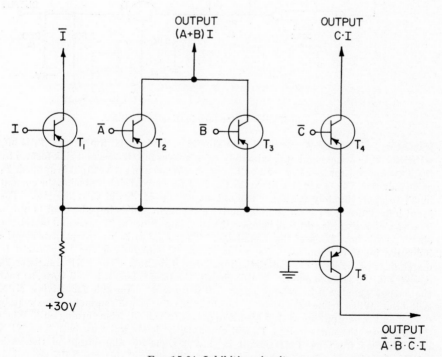

FIG. 15.64. Inhibiting circuit.

arrives at the inhibit input, T_1 will turn off and T_2, T_3, or T_4 will conduct, depending on which of these inputs are negative.   In this circuit, we have assumed that the input to T_4 will not be negative if the inputs to T_2 and T_3 are negative.   Under these conditions, we have the logical output expressions shown in Fig. 15.64.   This inhibit scheme finds frequent use in a computer where it is desired to sample the state of various lines. The outputs can be joined together to form an "or" statement as in the case of T_1 or T_2, or lines can be individually sampled as in the case of T_4.

15.11b. Transmission-line Circuits.   In any high-speed computing system situations are encountered where it is necessary to drive loads located at a considerable distance from the driving source.   This can be done by driving a conventional coaxial transmission line and terminating the coaxial transmission line with either of the circuits shown in Fig. 15.65.   These circuits serve to terminate the coaxial line and provide adequate signals for driving the loads.   Both of the circuits shown in Fig. 15.65 are driven by the basic current switch consisting of transistors T_1 and T_2.   The NPN

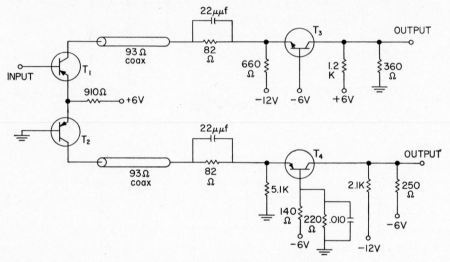

FIG. 15.65. Circuits for terminating coaxial line.

transistor T_3 is a class A grounded-base amplifier.   When the top output T_1 is off, transistor T_3 conducts and approximately 6.5 ma flows into the current sink formed by the 660-ohm resistor and the -12-volt supply.   When a negative input is applied, T_1 will conduct and 6 ma will flow down the line into the current sink, reducing the current in T_3 to approximately 0.5 ma.   The output voltage of T_3 will therefore rise.   The input impedance of T_3 has a small inductive component and an impedance of 11 ohms. The 82-ohm resistor is added to increase the total impedance to 93 ohms and match the characteristic impedance of the coaxial line.   The 22-$\mu\mu$f capacitor compensates for the inductive input component.   The value of the 82-ohm resistor can be changed to match lines of different characteristic impedance if desired.   The PNP transistor T_4 operates in the same manner.   In this circuit, the base is biased to -3 volts, so that the output signal will be referenced to -6 volts and be suitable for driving NPN switches.   When driving transistor T_2 is off, transistor T_4 will conduct approximately 0.5 ma and the output network is biased to prevent the loads from turning on.   When T_2 conducts, the current into T_4 will rise and the loads will turn on.   The NPN circuit differs from the PNP circuit in that it translates the output of the basic PNP switch from -6 volts up to ground level.   Because of this, the NPN grounded-base amplifier can also be used as a coupling means between two PNP logical blocks. In this respect the circuit is similar to the Zener diode translating circuit of Fig. 15.17a.

15.11c. D-C Design Considerations. The d-c design considerations for current-switching blocks are straightforward. In the preceding discussion we have assumed a perfect emitter-current source and equal output currents from the top and bottom transistors. Actually the output current from the top and bottom transistors will differ, since the negative input to the top transistor will act to increase the current from the emitter source and consequently increase the top output current. This difference between top and bottom output currents can be made increasingly small by using small signals and by increasing the emitter-current source supply voltage. This, however, raises the total power dissipated by the circuit, which is undesirable, particularly in view of the fact that satisfactory design can be achieved with far less than a perfect current source. Under these conditions then, the minimum output current will come from the bottom transistor. The maximum value of off current from a current switch will come from the top output and be the sum of the I_{CBO}'s of the individual transistors that make up the top output. We then have the on-off conditions shown in Fig. 15.66, where an NPN current switch consisting of m transistors in the top output is driving a load of n PNP switches. We can write for the minimum output current

$$I_{\min} = \frac{V_{EE} - V_{EB}}{R_e} \alpha_{FB} \tag{15.49}$$

In the on case, that is, transistor T_1 on, the common-emitter node must be at or below ground potential to ensure that T_2 is off, so that

$$I_B = \frac{V_{EE}}{R_e}(1 - \alpha_{FB}) \tag{15.50}$$

and for the on condition for n loads

$$I_{\min} = \frac{V_{BB} + V_{EB}}{R_1} + \frac{V_{EB}}{R_2} + \frac{nV_{EE}}{R_e}(1 - \alpha_{FB}) \tag{15.51}$$

In the off case, the base of T_1 must be equal to or more positive than V_{EB} of T_2. We can write

$$\frac{V_{BB} - V_{EB}}{R_1} = \frac{V_{EB}}{R_2} + (n + m)I_{CBO,\max} \tag{15.52}$$

and since the transistors operate well out of saturation, power dissipation will be large enough to increase I_{CBO} significantly.

It is necessary to know the maximum value of the on signal level in order to arrive at an optimum value of voltage for the emitter constant-current source. We may postulate a situation in which a slightly larger signal from the top output of one block would result in a larger voltage swing at the input of a load block, which would result in a larger output from the load block, and this might continue, the signal growing ever larger as it progresses through top outputs in successive blocks. This cannot happen if the emitter-current-source power supply is greater than a minimum value. This problem can be investigated by considering what happens to a signal in an infinite chain of blocks where the infinite chain is simulated by a trigger in which the top outputs are cross-coupled. Such a circuit is shown in Fig. 15.67a, and a plot of the maximum "on" signal level versus emitter-current supply voltage is shown in Fig. 15.67b. To obtain this curve the emitter current is held constant by increasing the value of the emitter resistor as the power-supply voltage is increased. As one would expect, the curve shows that the signal level will approach a constant minimum value as the power supply is

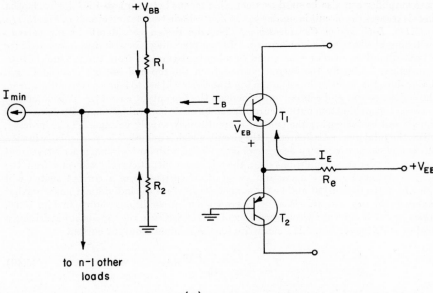

(a)

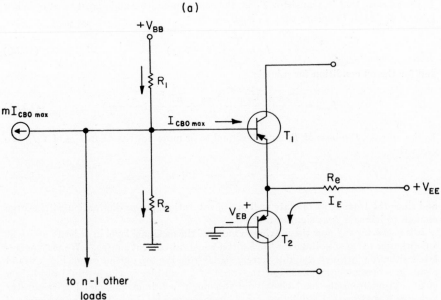

(b)

FIG. 15.66. (a) On case ($T_{1,\ \text{on}}$). (b) Off case ($T_{1,\ \text{off}}$).

increased or as a real constant-current source is approached. At lower values of voltage the signal level is seen to approach fairly large steady-state values, and finally at a very low voltage the curve goes off to infinity. This would mean that the signal can grow large enough at some point in the chain to drive a stage into saturation. The values on the curve will, of course, depend on the tolerance of the components used.

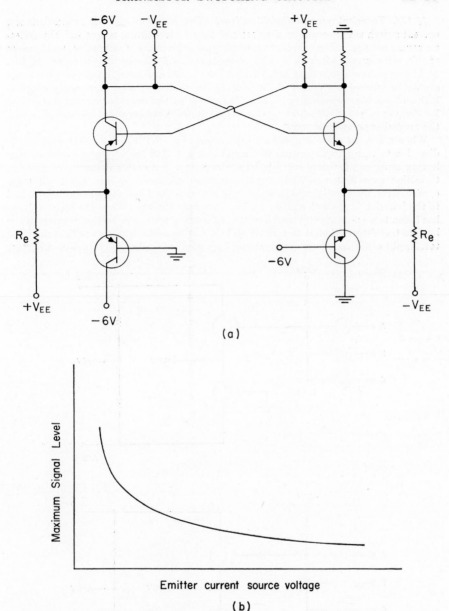

(a)

(b)

FIG. 15.67. (a) Circuit for determining maximum signal level.   (b) Curve of maximum on level versus emitter-current-source voltage.

In one case using 3 per cent resistors and power supplies, the signal to all practical purposes reached its lower limit at 20 volts.   Where really good current control is desired, the bottom output of a current switch should be used.   In the trigger of Fig. 15.63, the bottom outputs were cross-coupled instead of the top outputs in order to gain a better degree of control over the current in the top outputs.

15.11d. Transient-response Considerations. The on and off operating conditions of a current switch are governed by the choice of the emitter-current source and the collector return voltage. The transistors may be operated well out of saturation, and because of this, the current-switching circuits are quite fast. By inspecting the curves of Fig. 15.5, the reader can convince himself that the operating point of a current switch can always be located in a region of the collector characteristic where frequency cutoff is high and collector capacitance is low. The exception to this is the very small region of low-frequency cutoff which occurs at very low collector current and through which the operating point must move.

When a current pulse is applied to the input of a PNP current switch and is in a direction to turn this circuit on, the initial rate of fall of the voltage waveform, neglecting stray capacitance, will be determined by the collector capacitance and the transition capacitance. (These capacitances are discussed in Sec. 4.5e.) Of these capacitances, the transition capacitance will generally predominate, since it is returned to the junction of the two emitters, a low-impedance point. When the input voltage has fallen to a value slightly less than the emitter voltage of the bottom transistor, the bottom transistor will start to turn off and the top transistor will start to turn on. The total input capacitance across the emitter base diode of the bottom transistor will start

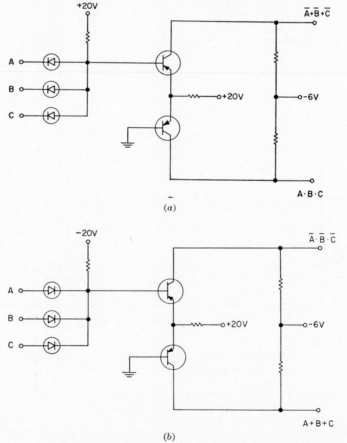

(a)

(b)

Fig. 15.68. (a) PNP diode current switch. (b) PNP diode current to decrease while the capacitance across the emitter base diode of the top transistor will increase owing to the fact that current is starting to flow and because of an increase in the transition capacitance. The emitter base capacitances in the top and bottom transistors are in series, and at some point during the turn-on transient, they will present a maximum series equivalent to the driving source. This will generally cause an inflection in the turn-on transient, or if very low frequency transistors are being used and the input current pulse is small enough, a distinct plateau will be seen. A further decrease in current in the bottom transistor will cause the inflection in the turn-on transient to disappear, the slope of the turn-on transient will return to nearly its original value, and the input voltage will continue to fall toward its final steady-state value. The turn-off transient is similar to the turn-on transient, and a point of inflection will also be seen. The points of inflection are determined by the conduction threshold, which for the turn-on condition (top transistor turning on) is determined by the sum of the emitter base drops of the top and bottom transistors. Likewise the turn-off threshold is also determined by the sum of the emitter base drops in the top and bottom transistors.

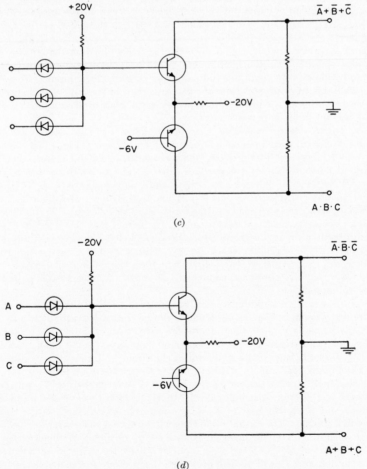

(c)

(d)

switch. (c) NPN diode current switch. (d) NPN diode current switch.

The conduction threshold can significantly affect the turn-on and turn-off delay of a current-switching circuit.   Consider the case where a current switch is driving a load of three other current switches and the bottom transistors in the loads are conducting. Assume that the bottom transistors in loads 1 and 2 have an emitter base voltage drop greater than the emitter base voltage drop in load 3.   Also the emitter base voltage drops in the top transistors of loads 1 and 2 are smaller when conducting than the same voltage drop in load 3.   Under these conditions, during the turn-on transient, loads 1 and 2 will conduct before load 3 and the combined effect of their input capacitance will produce an inflection in the input voltage waveform that can significantly delay the turning on of load 3.   In the turn-off case the situation is reversed.   The load that turns off last would have a smaller emitter base drop in the bottom transistor and a large emitter base drop in the top transistor.   This effect is called "base robbing" and is generally associated with parallel loads of circuits that have no series passive networks to determine their input impedance.   In the saturating circuits that were discussed previously, the effect is negligible because the input impedance to each stage is determined by resistor-capacitor networks that act to assure each stage in the load an equal amount of overdrive.   The base-robbing effect can be limited by specifying the maximum spread in emitter base diode drops.   It can also be made negligible by providing a large amount of drive which swamps out the effect of the input load capacitance.

Because a current switch has an effective capacitive load at the emitter node, it will, under suitable conditions, present a negative input impedance to the driving source and will oscillate if suitable inductance is present at the input.   This stability problem is in no way different from the one described in the emitter-follower section. A practical solution to the problem is to place a small resistor in series with each input to make the net input impedance positive.

15.11e. Diode Current-switching Circuits.   Diodes can be used with current-switching circuits.   Four possible combinations are shown in Fig. 15.68.   The diode inputs would be driven from emitter followers which would be, in turn, driven from the top and bottom outputs of a current switch.   The general rule that is followed is to use PNP emitter followers to drive "and" circuit diodes and NPN emitter followers to drive "or" circuit diodes.   When this is done, the diode circuit load resistor will also serve as the load resistor for the emitter follower.   The diode current-switching circuits have several advantages.   The first is that they tend to reduce the number of transistors used and substitute cheaper diodes.   Second, the use of diodes will eliminate the base-robbing effect, for now when a load of several stages turns off, each stage will receive its own turn-off current from the diode load resistor.   In the turn-on case, the low output impedance of the emitter followers tends to swamp out the base-robbing effect.

Some increased logical flexibility can be achieved with diodes.   However, of the four circuits shown in Fig. 15.68, b and c can be eliminated with little loss.   Some circuits can be made simpler when diodes are used.   An example is the combination exclusive "or" and trigger circuit of Fig. 15.69.   Assume for the moment that transistors T_2, T_4, and Zener diode Z are not in the circuit.   Under these conditions, we have an exclusive "or" circuit.   If both inputs A and B are up or down, the base of T_3 will be negative with respect to the base of T_1 and transistor T_3 will conduct. When there is a difference in input levels, that is, when we have A up and B down or A down and B up, the base of T_1 will be negative with respect to the base of T_3 and T_1 will conduct.   The output of T_1 then will be the normal exclusive "or" output, while the output of T_3 will be inverted exclusive "or" output.   With normal exclusive "or" inputs present and with the clear input at T_2 up, the inverted output will drop, T_4 will conduct, and T_1 will be held on.   The Zener diode serves merely to translate -6-volt collector output of T_2 up to ground level.   At some later time, conduction can be switched back to T_2 by dropping the clear input. This input would have a large enough down level to override inputs A and B and ensure that T_2 is conducting. It is seen that the circuit can serve the function of a trigger and an exclusive "or" circuit.

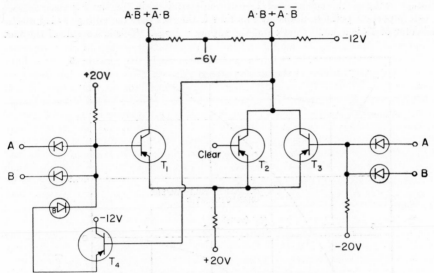

FIG. 15.69. Exclusive "or" trigger combination.

15.12. Direct-current Transistor Logic (DCTL) Circuits. Up to this point, we have confined our attention to the operation of transistors in what might be termed a voltage mode. By using the term voltage mode, we mean to imply that the presence or absence of a signal at a terminal is determined primarily by the voltage of the terminal. We have seen in the previous discussion that a signal representing a "one" is present at a terminal if the potential of the terminal is at ground level. A "zero" is represented by the terminal having a potential of, say, -5 volts. It has been shown that it is just as reasonable to speak of current as the information-carrying element.[7] In this case, the current is switched through a system in order to perform complex logical operations. When transistors are used in this fashion, they are operating in what we shall call a current mode and the circuits in which they are used are called d-c transistor logic circuits (DCTL).

In order to obtain a better understanding of the current mode of operation, let us consider a simple two-stage amplifier as shown in Fig. 15.70.

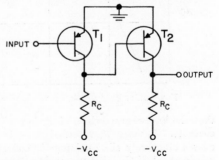

FIG. 15.70. Two-stage amplifier (current mode).

Transistor T_1 has, as its load, the base volt-ampere characteristic of transistor T_2 in parallel with R_c returned to $-V_{CC}$. The base volt-ampere characteristic of T_2 is shown in Fig. 15.71, along with the volt-ampere characteristic of R_c returned to $-V_{CC}$. The composite volt-ampere characteristic of R_c in parallel with the base characteristic of T_2 is shown dashed. The collector volt-ampere characteristic of T_1 is shown in Fig. 15.72 with the composite curve of Fig. 15.71 superimposed as a load "line." The operating point, for a given value of base current or voltage of T_1, is located at the intersection of the given base current or voltage with the composite load line. The base current of T_2 can readily be determined. The voltage swing at the collector of T_2 can be determined in the usual manner.

An important point to notice at this time is the fact that the voltage swing at the collector of T_1 is a small fraction of the supply voltage. This is a result of the fact

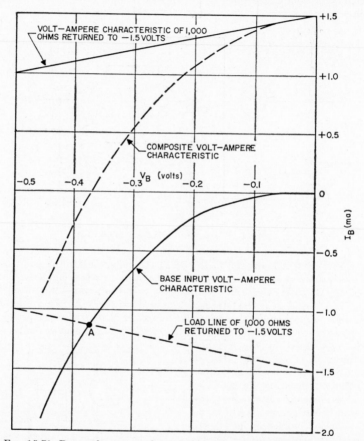

Fig. 15.71. Base volt-ampere characteristics of a surface-barrier transistor.

that the base characteristic of T_2 has a low variational impedance at moderate base currents. Resistor R_c returned to $-V_{CC}$ acts like a constant-current bias. This causes practically all the change in collector current of T_1 to appear as a change in base current of T_2. Let us consider that T_1 is cut off, and for the moment we shall neglect its collector leakage current. The base current of T_2 is found in the usual way by applying the volt-ampere characteristic of R_c returned to $-V_{CC}$ as a load line on the base characteristic of T_2. The resulting operating point is shown in Fig. 15.71 as point A. Typical values for surface-barrier transistors are $R_c = 1,000$ ohms and $V_{CC} = -1.5$ volts. Under these conditions, the base current of T_2 is found to be 1.22 ma. When a current of this magnitude is caused to flow out of the base terminal of a surface-barrier or alloy transistor, the voltage drop from collector to emitter is quite small as seen in Fig. 15.72. It makes very little difference whether the load on the transistor T_2 is a 1,000-ohm resistor returned to -1.5 volts (dashed line) or the parallel combination of this load with the base characteristics of a transistor (composite load line).

It was assumed at the start of this discussion that T_1 was cut off and its collector leakage current could be neglected. From the plot of I_C versus V_B of Fig. 15.73, it can be seen that I_C will be small if V_B has a small negative value. However, this small value of I_C must be considered in the design. First, let us discuss the various DCTL circuits.

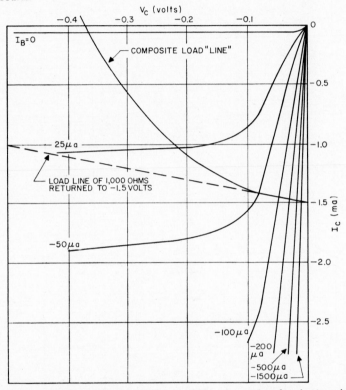

Fig. 15.72. Collector volt-ampere characteristics of a surface-barrier transistor.

15.12a. The NOR Operation. The most basic DCTL circuit is formed by simply paralleling transistors as shown in Fig. 15.74. In this circuit, the output will be a "one" if any of the parallel transistors are "on" or if one or more of the inputs are negative. Under these conditions, the circuit is logically equivalent to an "or" circuit in series with an inverter. This combination is logically equivalent to the NOR circuit which was discussed in Sec. 15.9. This is the most important DCTL circuit, and it is logically complete. That is, all the necessary complex logical statements that might be required in a computer can be achieved by interconnections of NOR circuits.

15.12b. Trigger. A trigger can be constructed by cross-coupling two inverters, as shown in Fig. 15.75. It is seen that the basic current-mode trigger uses only two transistors and two resistors. This represents quite a reduction in the number of components over what is required by a trigger operating in the voltage mode. To

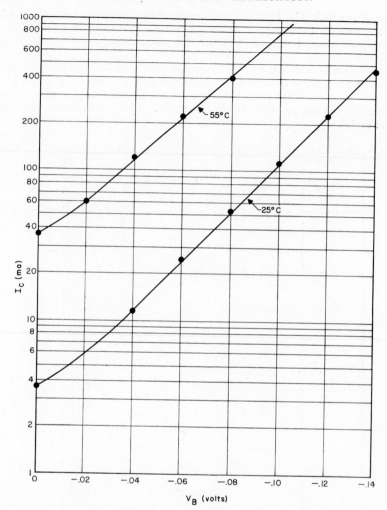

Fig. 15.73. Collector current versus base voltage for a surface-barrier transistor.

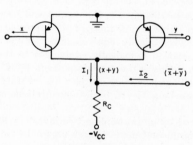

Fig. 15.74. NOR circuit.

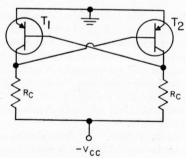

Fig. 15.75. Basic DCTL (current-mode) trigger.

provide set and reset facilities, two more transistors are needed, as shown in Fig. 15.76. In order to describe the operation of this circuit, we shall assume that transistor T_1 is conducting and that T_2, T_3, and T_4 are cut off. Under these conditions, the collector of T_1 is at a potential of about -0.03 volt, and the potential at the collector of T_2 is determined by the base volt-ampere characteristics of T_1. Normally, the potential of the collector of T_2 would be about -0.35 volt. The trigger will remain in this state until it is reset. The trigger can be reset by causing transistor T_4 to turn on momentarily. This causes the potential of the collector of T_2 and, hence, the potential of the base of T_1 to increase about -0.03 volt, thereby turning off T_1, which turns on T_2. Transistor T_4 is turned on momentarily when the potential of its base is caused to drop from -0.03 to -0.35 volt for a short interval of time. Other tran-

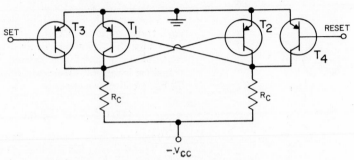

FIG. 15.76. DCTL (current-mode) trigger with set and reset inputs.

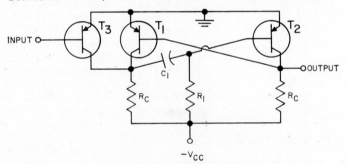

FIG. 15.77. Single shot.

sistors are driven from this trigger when their bases are connected to the collector to T_1 or T_2.

15.12c. Single Shot. A single shot can be constructed in the same fashion as was used for the voltage-mode circuits. Actually, a combination of the voltage mode and current mode is used in constructing a single shot, as seen in Fig. 15.77. Normally, transistor T_2 is conducting until a short negative pulse is applied to the base of T_3. This causes the collectors of T_1 and T_3 to be raised to within 0.03 volt of ground. A positive signal is coupled through capacitor C_1 to the base of transistor T_2, turning it off. Transistor T_1 is therefore turned on. The potential at the base of T_2 decays exponentially toward $-V_{cc}$ with a time constant R_1C_1. When the potential at the base of T_1 becomes slightly negative, regeneration takes place and the circuit returns to its initial state. It is to be noted that transistors T_1 and T_3 are operating in the voltage mode. This is necessary in order to use reasonable values of capacitance C_1 and resistance R_1.

Astable operation can be achieved if R_1 is increased to the point where T_2 is biased lightly out of saturation. Transistor T_1 will be in its active region, and relaxation oscillations will take place.

15.12d. "And" Circuit. The "and" operation can most easily be performed by connecting the transistors in series, as seen in Fig. 15.78. In this case, the current I_{C3} is represented by the logical statement $(\bar{x} \cdot \bar{y} \cdot \bar{z})$. Consideration must be given to the voltage appearing between the collector of T_3 and the emitter of T_1 when all three transistors are conducting. If this voltage is too large, then the transistor that is driven from this stage will not completely turn off. If such a cascade of transistors has as its load resistor the load resistor of a trigger, then the collector of T_3 must reach a potential of about -0.1 volt to ensure the setting of the trigger. With a load resistor $R_c = 1,000$ ohms and a collector supply voltage of -1.5 volts, the collector current of T_3 will be 1.4 ma when the potential of the collector of T_3 is -0.1 volt.

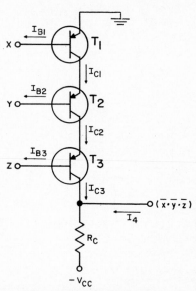

Fig. 15.78. "And" circuit.

Let us assume that the voltage drop across each transistor is 0.033 volt. It can be seen from Fig. 15.72 that the required base current for T_3 is about 200 μa and that the transistor is well into saturation. Transistor T_2 has a collector current of

$$1.4 + 0.2 = 1.6 \text{ ma}$$

and requires a base current in excess of 200 μa. Transistor T_1 has a collector current of $1.4 + 0.2$ ma plus the base current of T_2 and requires a larger base current than T_2. There are problems involved in the use of the series DCTL circuit which will be apparent to the reader after the next section.

15.12e. Design Considerations.[8,9] There are two basic requirements that transistors used in DCTL circuits must provide if good d-c stability is to be realized. First, there must be a voltage margin Δ between the maximum collector-to-emitter saturation voltage of an "on" transistor and the minimum base-to-emitter voltage of an "off" transistor. Δ must be large enough to guarantee definite on and off states in the circuits and must provide adequate protection from cross talk and other sources of noise. In this respect silicon transistors offer an advantage over germanium in that a base-to-emitter voltage of the order of 0.7 volt is required to turn on a silicon transistor and collector-to-emitter voltage drops of the order of 0.3 volt or less are realized from silicon units deep in saturation. Also, silicon units usually exhibit lower values of "off" collector current. The second transistor requirement concerns the allowable spread in the emitter base voltage drop. DCTL circuitry, like the current-switching circuits previously discussed, is subject to the base-robbing effect. Consider a DCTL circuit driving a load of several other parallel DCTL circuits. If one transistor in the load has a small base-to-emitter voltage drop, when on, it will tend to rob most of the current from the current source and the other transistors in the load may not go into saturation or may be only marginally in saturation. To ensure that all the transistors in the load will switch completely, the allowable spread in the emitter base voltage specification must be restricted.

Consider the general DCTL circuit shown in Fig. 15.79. In this figure an m-input logic block consisting of m parallel transistors is shown driving a load of n other blocks.

A current sink I is formed by the resistor R returned to the voltage V. From Fig. 15.79 we can write the following d-c expressions:

$$mI_C + nI_B \leq I \qquad (15.53)$$

$$\alpha_{FE}I_B \geq I \qquad (15.54)$$

$$V_{BE,\,\text{off}} = V_{CE,\,\text{on}} \qquad (15.55)$$

which are sufficient to guarantee d-c stability. To expand the above equations further we must determine how the transistor parameters affect the various terms. To do this we make use of the generalized transistor equations of Ebers and Moll.[4] These equations are reproduced here as Eqs. (15.56) and (15.57). They were derived neglecting the ohmic voltage drops in the transistor.

$$I_E = \frac{I_{EBO}}{1 - \alpha_{FB}\alpha_{RB}}\,(e^{qV_{EB}/kT} - 1) + \frac{\alpha_{RB}I_{CBO}}{1 - \alpha_{FB}\alpha_{RB}}\,(e^{qV_{CB}/kT} - 1) \qquad (15.56)$$

$$I_C = \frac{\alpha_{FB}I_{EBO}}{1 - \alpha_{FB}\alpha_{RB}}\,(e^{qV_{EB}/kT} - 1) - \frac{I_{CBO}}{1 - \alpha_{FB}\alpha_{RB}}\,(e^{qV_{CB}/kT} - 1) \qquad (15.57)$$

where $\alpha_{RB}I_{CBO} = \alpha_{FB}I_{EBO}$. The voltages V_{EB} and V_{CB} are the voltages from emitter to base and collector to base. These voltages are positive if the PN junction across

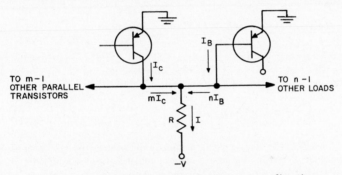

FIG. 15.79. General DCTL circuit showing current directions.

which they are applied is biased in the forward direction. Assuming that the positive sense of the emitter, base, and collector currents is into the respective terminals, we have

$$I_E + I_B + I_C = 0 \qquad (15.58)$$

Solving Eqs. (15.56), (15.57), and (15.58) for operation in the saturated region, we find that

$$I_B = I_{EBO}(e^{qV_{EB}/kT} - 1) - (1 - \alpha_{RB})I_C \qquad (15.59)$$

$$V_{CE} = \pm\,\frac{kT}{q}\ln\left[\frac{\alpha_{RB}(1 - I_C/I_B\alpha_{FE})}{1 + (1 - \alpha_{RB})I_C/I_B}\right] \qquad (15.60)$$

Since the effects of collector and emitter body resistance are not included in Eqs. (15.56) and (15.57), we must add to V_{CE} a voltage V' where R_c and R_e are the ohmic respective body resistances.

$$V' = I_C R_C + (I_C + I_B)R_E \qquad (15.61)$$

Then the total value of V_{CE} is

$$V_{CE} = \frac{kT}{q}\ln\left[\frac{\alpha_{RB}(1 - I_C/I_B\alpha_{FE})}{1 + (1 - \alpha_{RB})I_C/I_B}\right] + V' \qquad (15.62)$$

In Eq. (15.60) the plus sign should be used for PNP transistors and the minus sign for the NPN transistors in order that V_{CE} represent a voltage drop from c to e. The voltage V_{CE} is quite small in saturation ($I_C < |\alpha_{FE}I_B|$). At room temperature

$$\frac{kT}{q} = 0.026 \text{ volt}$$

and the argument of the logarithmic term of Eq. (15.62) ranges from α_{RB} to zero. The voltage V_{CE} ranges from about $-kT/q \ln{(1/\alpha_{RB})}$ to about -0.08 volt for a surface-barrier transistor with reasonable values of I_C/I_B and α_{FB} and α_{RB} as can be seen in Fig. 15.72. It is also seen that the α_{RB} for the particular transistor from which these curves were obtained is close to unity. The slope of the curves in the saturated region shows that the resistance between the collector and emitter is low. From Eq. (15.59) we obtain for V_{BE}

$$V_{BE} = \frac{kT}{q} \ln \left[\frac{I_B + (1 - \alpha_{RB})I_C}{I_{EBO}} \right] \tag{15.63}$$

To the above we must add the contributions of the base spreading resistance[10] and the emitter body resistance. This results in

$$V_{BE} = I_B R_b + (I_C + I_B)R_e + \frac{kT}{q} \ln \left[\frac{I_B + (1 - \alpha_{RB})I_C}{I_{EBO}} \right] \tag{15.64}$$

where R_b represents the base spreading resistance. It is important to know the slope of the V_{BE} curve, since this will enter into determining the maximum allowable spread in V_{BE}. Accordingly, $\partial V_{BE}/\partial I_B$ from Eq. (15.64) is

$$r_i = R_b + R_e + \frac{kT}{qI_C} \ln \left[\frac{1}{I_B/I_C + 1 - \alpha_{RB}} \right] \tag{15.65}$$

For most transistors the slope will be primarily determined by the R_b term.

The resistance between the emitter and collector terminals can be obtained by taking the derivative of Eq. (15.60) with respect to I_C.

$$\frac{dV_{CE}}{dI_C} = \pm \frac{kT}{q} \left[\frac{1}{\alpha_{FB}I_B/(1 - \alpha_{FB}) - I_E} + \frac{1}{I_B/(1 - \alpha_{RB}) + I_C} \right] \tag{15.66}$$

The minus sign applies to PNP transistors, and the plus sign to NPN transistors. It can be seen from Fig. 15.72 that the slope of I_C versus V_C is reasonably constant in the saturated region. The collector-to-emitter resistance can be approximated by the relationship

$$r_{ec} \approx \frac{kT}{qI_B} \left(\frac{1 - \alpha_{FB}}{\alpha_{FB}} + 1 - \alpha_{RB} \right) \tag{15.67}$$

An approximate equivalent circuit for the transistor in the saturation region is shown in Fig. 15.80. Diode D_1 has the characteristic

$$I_{EBO}(e^{qV_{EB}/kT} - 1) \tag{15.68}$$

An experimental verification for the equivalent resistance of the collector-to-emitter circuit is shown in Fig. 15.81. It is seen that r_{ec} is proportional to $1/I_B$. The straight lines do not intersect the origin because of the ohmic resistances of the transistor. For the particular transistor measured, it is seen that the sum of r_e and r_c of the equivalent circuit amounts to 7 ohms. The effect of temperature is clearly seen from Fig.

15.81. In order to determine the effect of temperature changes on current-mode circuits, it is also necessary to consider the transistor in the cutoff region of operation. In order that the transistor be cut off, the potential of the base must be within 20 or 30 mv of the emitter. In a system operating in the current mode, the collector is

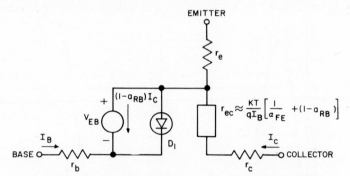

FIG. 15.80. Equivalent circuit for a transistor in saturation.

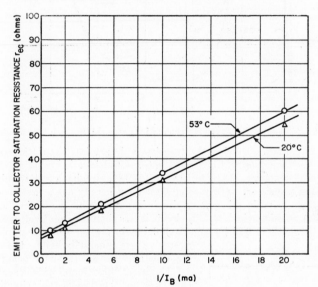

FIG. 15.81. Saturation resistance versus the reciprocal of the base current for a surface-barrier transistor.

reversed-biased about 0.3 volt. Under these conditions, Eqs. (15.56), (15.57), and (15.58) can be solved for I_C and I_B.

$$I_C = \frac{\alpha_{RB} I_{CBO}}{1 - \alpha_{FB}\alpha_{RB}}\, e^{qV_{EB}/kT} + \frac{1 - \alpha_{RB}}{1 - \alpha_{FB}\alpha_{RB}}\, I_{CBO} \qquad (15.69)$$

$$I_B = \frac{(1 - \alpha_{FB})I_{EBO}}{1 - \alpha_{FB}\alpha_{RB}}\,(e^{qV_{EB}/kT} - 1) - \frac{(1 - \alpha_{RB})I_{CBO}}{1 - \alpha_{FB}\alpha_{RB}} \qquad (15.70)$$

It is seen from Eq. (15.69) that a slight increase in base voltage can cause a large increase in collector current. This is particularly true if α_{FB}/α_{RB} is close to unity. Figure 15.73 is an experimental verification of the form of Eq. (15.69).

Where it is desired to use a series DCTL "and" circuit and maintain the same "on" to "off" voltage margin Δ at the output of the series chain, then the sum of the "on" voltages of each transistor in the chain must equal the "on" voltage of a single transistor in the parallel NOR circuit. This requires that each transistor in the series chain be driven deeper into saturation or that transistors with high values of α_{FE}

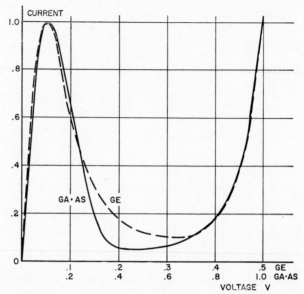

Fig. 15.82. Volt-ampere curves for germanium and gallium arsenide Esaki diodes.

be used in the chain. Driving the transistors deeper into saturation to achieve a smaller "on" voltage drop will increase the turn-off delay.

The transient-response characteristics of DCTL circuits are determined almost entirely by the transistor. Stray capacitance is generally not a first-order problem, since the voltage swing in this type of circuit is quite small. Since the "on" collector voltage of any transistor in a DCTL circuit is less than the "on" voltage at the base of any transistor, there will be some overdrive during the turn-off transient. This overdrive is in general limited by the base spreading resistance of the transistor being turned off. DCTL circuits have found wide acceptance in the computer field because of their simplicity.

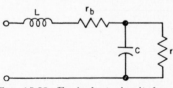

Fig. 15.83. Equivalent circuit for the Esaki diode.

15.13. Esaki Tunnel Diode Circuits. An interesting component which promises to be useful in switching circuits is the Esaki diode, or tunnel diode. A discussion of the physical attributes of the device is contained in Sec. 3. The device has been made in several compounds, but those of principal interest are germanium and gallium arsenide. The volt-ampere characteristic of a germanium and a gallium arsenide Esaki diode is shown in Fig. 15.82. Here the current axis has been normalized because Esaki diodes are made with a wide range of peak currents extending from fractions of a milliampere to hundreds of milliamperes. Note that the valley is broad and the valley voltage is not so well defined as the peak voltage. This will be shown to cause trouble in the circuit applications that follow. An inspection of Fig. 15.82 reveals that the Esaki diode is for all practical purposes a low-impedance device over the entire volt-ampere characteristic, particularly in the third quadrant, where conventional switching diodes exhibit a high impedance. Consequently, the Esaki diode will exhibit none of the unidirectional properties of the transistor or the conventional diode, and special techniques must be employed to use Esaki diodes in switching circuits.

A small-signal equivalent circuit for the Esaki diode is shown in Fig. 15.83. In this figure L represents the lead inductance and r_b the bulk resistivity of the semiconductor. L depends greatly on how the Esaki diode is packaged, while r_b for a typical germanium unit would be of the order of 0.25 ohm. C represents the depletion-layer capacitance of the junction which, since Esaki diodes have relatively abrupt junctions, varies inversely as the junction voltage raised to the half power.

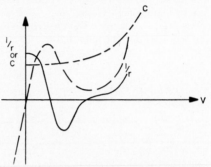

A plot of junction capacitance versus applied voltage is shown in Fig. 15.84. r represents the real-part impedance of the Esaki diode and may be positive or negative. Since the bulk resistivity of Esaki diodes is quite small, r may, to a good approximation, be represented by the reciprocal of the small-signal derivative of the volt-ampere characteristic of Fig. 15.82. A plot of $1/r$ versus voltage for a germanium Esaki diode is also shown in Fig. 15.84. A quick multiplication of r and C at several different voltages in Fig. 15.84 will convince the reader that the Esaki diode has a very small time constant and consequently is capable of very fast switching. Time constants in the negative-resistance region in the range of 10^{-10} to 10^{-11} sec have been realized.

FIG. 15.84. Junction capacitance and the reciprocal of signal resistance versus voltage.

15.13a. Transient Response. To study the transient response of the Esaki diode we make use of the equivalent circuit of Fig. 15.85 consisting of a voltage source V_i and a load resistor R_i. The bulk resistivity of the Esaki diode is considered a part of R_i. When the equation for this circuit is solved for the output voltage $V_o(t)$ with an input step function for V_i, we have in operational form

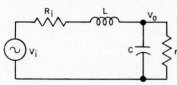

FIG. 15.85. Equivalent circuit for the transient response of the Esaki diode.

$$V_o(s) = \frac{V_i}{LC} \frac{1}{s^2 + s\frac{1}{rC} + \frac{R_i}{L} + \frac{1}{LC} + \frac{R_i}{rLC}}$$

(15.71)

where r may be positive or negative. For positive values of r

$$s = \frac{-\left(\frac{1}{rC} + \frac{R_i}{L}\right) \pm \left[\left(\frac{1}{rC} - \frac{R_i}{L}\right)^2 - \frac{4}{LC}\right]^{1/2}}{2}$$

(15.72)

For a negative r

$$s = \frac{-\left(\frac{1}{rC} + \frac{R_i}{L}\right) \pm \left[\left(\frac{1}{rC} + \frac{R_i}{L}\right)^2 - \frac{4}{LC}\right]^{1/2}}{2}$$

(15.73)

In general, a complete solution of the above equations for a particular circuit is an involved boundary-value problem. This is due to the fact that r and C are nonlinear and in most practical applications the circuit operating point, for a positive step-function input, will move from the low-voltage positive-resistance region of the Esaki diode across the negative-resistance region into the high-voltage positive-resistance region. We can, however, use the above equations to define the necessary conditions for a stable operating point. It is clear from an inspection of Eq. (15.72) that for positive values of r there are three possible regions of operation corresponding to an overdamped case, a critically damped case, and an underdamped case. The case of particular interest is the underdamped case. There are applications where one wishes to interrogate the Esaki diode and sense whether the diode is biased in the low-voltage or high-voltage state, and a damped oscillation in such applications may cause false switching. Damped oscillations can be avoided by satisfying the following condition for the load line R_i:

$$R_i > \frac{L}{rC} - \frac{2L}{\sqrt{LC}} \tag{15.74}$$

Where damped oscillations occur, the solution to Eq. (15.71) will be of the form

$$V_o(t) = \frac{V_i}{LC}\left[\frac{1}{\alpha^2 + \beta^2} - \frac{e^{-\alpha t}}{\beta(\alpha^2 + \beta^2)^{1/2}}\cos\left(\beta t - \frac{\alpha}{\beta}\right)\right] \tag{15.75}$$

where the damping factor is α, the frequency of damped oscillation is β, and the oscillation lags the applied input step by α/β radians. α and β can be written as

$$\alpha = \frac{1}{2}\left(\frac{1}{rC} + \frac{R_i}{L}\right) \tag{15.76}$$

$$\beta = \frac{1}{2}\left[\left(\frac{1}{rC} - \frac{R_i}{L}\right)^2 - \frac{4}{LC}\right]^{1/2} \tag{15.77}$$

Where r is negative, three general conditions of interest arise from Eq. (15.73). These are:

1. A switching condition, where the output voltage will rise exponentially while the operating point is in the negative-resistance region.

2. An oscillatory condition, where the load line and the reactive circuit parameters are such that the circuit oscillates.

3. A stable condition, where small input perturbations result in an output voltage which is a decaying exponential. Under these conditions a stable operating point will be realized in the negative-resistance region. This condition is of interest when one wishes to design a curve tracer to display the volt-ampere characteristic of the Esaki diode.

Two typical switching conditions are shown in Fig. 15.86. Figure 15.86a illustrates the use of a bistable load line with stable operating points at 1 and 2. Figure 15.86b illustrates what is called a continuous-control load line. In this case the operating point is under continuous control of the input signal and there is no bistable situation as in Fig. 15.86a. In the continuous-control case the steady-state operating point will be at 1 or 2 and will depend on the value of the input signal. For the continuous-control case a solution for Eq. (15.71) for the negative-resistance region is

$$V_o(t) = \frac{V_i}{LC}\left[\frac{1}{\alpha^2 - \beta^2} + \frac{e^{(\alpha+\beta)t}}{2(\beta^2 + \alpha\beta)} + \frac{e^{(\alpha-\beta)t}}{2(\beta^2 - \alpha\beta)}\right] \tag{15.78}$$

where

$$\alpha = \frac{1}{2}\left(\frac{1}{rC} - \frac{R_i}{L}\right) \tag{15.79}$$

and

$$\beta = \frac{1}{2}\left[\left(\frac{1}{rC} + \frac{R_i}{L}\right)^2 - \frac{4}{LC}\right]^{1/2} \tag{15.80}$$

To realize the solution of Eq. (15.78) certain conditions must be placed on the value of R_i, the load line. These are

$$R_i < \frac{L}{rC} \tag{15.81}$$

This condition ensures a positive exponential in Eq. (15.78). The reader will note that if $|\beta| > |\alpha|$, one exponential term in Eq. (15.78) will be negative and, although switching will occur, a longer triggering pulse will be required. An example of this case would be the bistable load line of Fig. 15.86a. If the value of the load line is

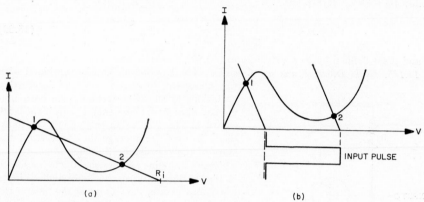

Fig. 15.86. (a) Bistable load line for an Esaki diode. (b) A continuous-control load line for an Esaki diode.

less than the value of negative resistance at all points on the volt-ampere characteristic, then $|\beta| < |\alpha|$. That is,

$$|\beta| < |\alpha| \qquad \text{if } R_i < r$$

A further condition necessary to realize Eq. (15.78) is

$$R_i > \frac{2L}{\sqrt{LC}} - \frac{L}{rC} \tag{15.82}$$

This condition is necessary if oscillations are to be avoided.

For an oscillatory condition the solution to Eq. (15.71) is

$$V_o(t) = \frac{V_i}{LC} \frac{1}{\alpha^2 + \beta^2} - \frac{e^{\alpha t}}{\beta(\alpha^2 + \beta^2)^{1/2}} \cos\left(\beta t - \frac{\alpha}{\beta}\right) \tag{15.83}$$

To guarantee oscillations two conditions are necessary:

$$R_i < \frac{L}{rC} \tag{15.84}$$

$$R_i < \frac{2L}{\sqrt{LC}} - \frac{L}{rC} \tag{15.85}$$

Here, α and β, the frequency of oscillation, are given by Eqs. (15.79) and (15.80), respectively.

If the following parameter conditions are met, a stable operating point can be realized in the negative-resistance region. These conditions,

$$R_i > \frac{L}{rC} \tag{15.86}$$

$$R_i < r \tag{15.87}$$

$$R_1 > \frac{2L}{\sqrt{LC}} - \frac{L}{rC} \tag{15.88}$$

are of interest when one wishes to design a plotter. These conditions result in the following solution to Eq. (15.71):

$$V_o(t) = \frac{V_i}{LC} \left[\frac{1}{\alpha^2 - \beta^2} + \frac{e^{-(\alpha+\beta)t}}{2(\beta^2 + \alpha\beta)} + \frac{e^{-(\alpha-\beta)t}}{2(\beta^2 - \alpha\beta)} \right] \tag{15.89}$$

α and β are defined by Eqs. (15.79) and (15.80), respectively.

15.13b. Esaki Diode, Transistor Circuits. The Esaki diode can be combined with the transistor to create new and interesting variations of the circuits that have been previously discussed. One such circuit is the latch shown in Fig. 15.87. In this circuit the Esaki diode is used for storage and to control the state of the transistor. Resistor R constitutes a bistable load line on the Esaki diode (as shown in Fig. 15.86a). When the Esaki diode is in its low-voltage state, the voltage at the base of the transistor will be too small to turn the transistor on and therefore the collector potential of the transistor will rise to $V_{CC} - I_{c,\text{off}} R_L$. When the Esaki diode is in its high-voltage state, the voltage drop across the Esaki diode will be sufficient to cause the transistor to go into saturation.

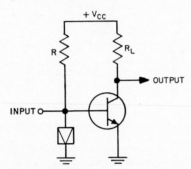

FIG. 15.87. Esaki diode transistor latch.

The d-c operating conditions of the circuit can be determined by drawing on the Esaki diode volt-ampere characteristic the composite load line consisting of the parallel combination of R returned to $+V_{CC}$ and the transistor emitter base diode plot. This construction is shown in Fig. 15.88. Although the value of the transistor collector current is quite small when the Esaki diode is in its low-voltage state, it will be influenced by significant changes in the ambient temperature, and this should be considered in the design.

The circuit can be gated in a number of ways. A typical example of a complete circuit is shown in Fig. 15.89. In this circuit diode D_1 clamps the output level when the transistor is off, thus making the output voltage less sensitive to temperature variations of the "off" collector current. The Esaki diode may be set in its high-voltage state by a positive input applied to the resistance-gated diode circuit consisting of C, R_3, D_3. The circuit is reset by a negative input applied to the pull-over emitter follower T_1 which pulls the collector voltage down through diode D_2 and switches the Esaki diode to its low-voltage state through R_2. Resistor R_1 returned to $+12$ forms a current source for the Esaki diode and transistor. The emitter-follower input is normally biased to ensure that the emitter follower is off except during reset time.

The basic latch circuit of Fig. 15.87 can be modified to construct the nonsaturating inverter circuit of Fig. 15.90. In this circuit the sum of R_L and R_F in parallel with the input resistor R_i constitute the load line of the Esaki diode. If we assume that the input signal is up, that is, at its most positive potential, then the Esaki diode will be in its high-voltage state and the transistor will conduct. When the transistor conducts, the collector voltage will drop and the voltage across the Esaki diode will drop because of feedback through resistor R_F. When the voltage across the Esaki diode decreases, the collector current of the transistor will decrease and the collector

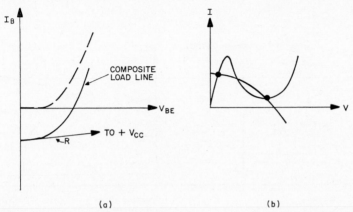

(a) (b)

FIG. 15.88. (a) Construction of composite load line. (b) Composite load line for latch of Fig. 15.87.

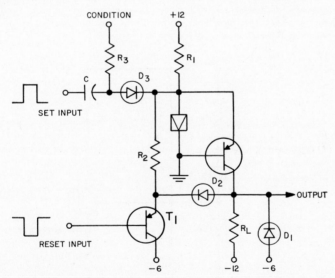

FIG. 15.89. Esaki diode, transistor latch showing input gating circuitry.

voltage will rise, which will increase the drop across the Esaki diode, increase the collector current, and cause the collector voltage to drop. The circuit thus hunts for a stable operating point. A stable "on" operating point can be determined in the following way: The reader will notice that the circuit is composed of two parts: the Esaki diode and its associated load resistors R_F, R_i, and R_L and the transistor and its load resistors R_F and R_L. The voltage across the Esaki diode is also the input voltage to the transistor. If we plot the voltage across the Esaki diode versus the collector or output voltage, and if we plot the output voltage of the transistor versus the input voltage or the voltage across the Esaki diode, we obtain two curves whose intersection defines the stable "on" operating point.   A sample plot is shown in Fig. 15.91.

When the input signal goes negative, the Esaki diode switches to its low-voltage state and the transistor will shut off.   In this respect the circuit is identical with

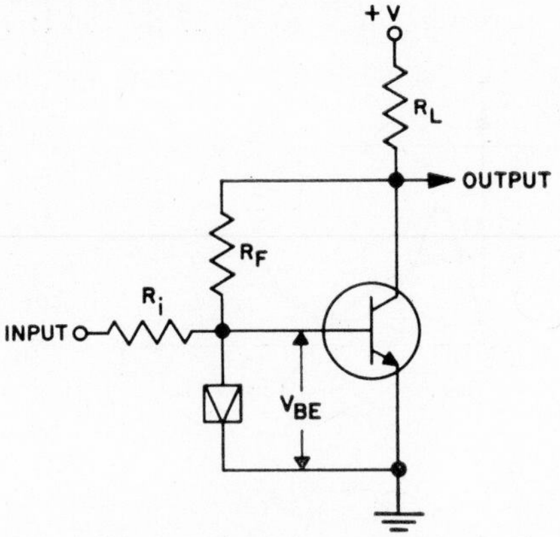

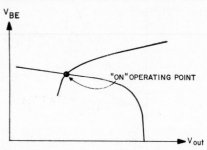

FIG. 15.90. A nonsaturating Esaki diode, transistor inverter.

FIG. 15.91. Curves to determine the on operating point of the nonsaturating Esaki diode inverter.

the latch circuit of Fig. 15.87.   The feedback circuit of Fig. 15.90 has the disadvantage of being susceptible to changes in collector voltage caused by different loads.   These changes directly affect the feedback loop.   They can be minimized by using an emitter follower at the collector to drive the actual load.

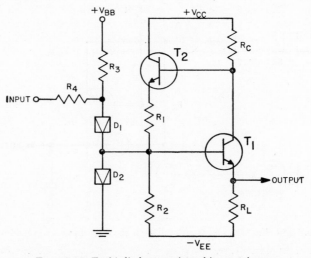

FIG. 15.92. Esaki diode, transistor binary trigger.

An Esaki diode, transistor binary trigger is shown in Fig. 15.92.   The circuit consists of two Esaki diodes in series where the top diode D_1 is returned to a suitable voltage bias V_{BB}.   The junction of the Esaki diodes is coupled to a phase splitter (transistor T_1), and the collector output of the phase splitter is coupled to a feedback network consisting of transistor T_2 and resistors R_1 and R_2.   The operation of the circuit can be understood by referring to Fig. 15.93. In this figure diode D_1 is plotted as a load line on diode D_2. The feedback network acts to shift diode D_1 up or down with respect to D_2 by applying a suitable current bias through the feedback network. Assume that the operating point is at 1. A positive-going input signal will move diode D_1 to the right, as indicated by the dashed characteristics, and the operating point will then transfer to 2. The input voltage to T_1 then drops, and the collector voltage of T_1 will rise. This

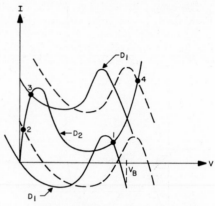

rise in collector voltage is coupled through the feedback loop (T_2, R_1, R_2) and shifts the load line (diode 2) up. The operating point then moves from 2 to 3. The next positive input will shift diode 2 to the right, and the operating point will move from 3 to 4. The input voltage to T_1 has now gone positive, and the collector voltage of T_1 will therefore drop, moving the load line down and moving the operating point from 4 to 1. The reader will note that the circuit behaves as an inverter when the operating point moves from 1 to 3 and as an in-phase amplifier when the operating point moves from 3 to 4. Very little change in output voltage will be seen when the feedback network shifts the operating point from 2 to 3 or from

FIG. 15.93. Composite load line for the Esaki diode, transistor binary trigger.

4 to 1. This is because of the constant-voltage characteristic of the Esaki diode in these regions. The circuit operation requires that there be a suitable delay in the feedback loop. This delay must be longer than the time required for the operating point to shift from 1 to 2 or from 3 to 4. Without this delay operating point 2 or 3 might appear in the negative-resistance region of diode 2 and the circuit would oscillate. Generally the phase splitter will provide the necessary delay.

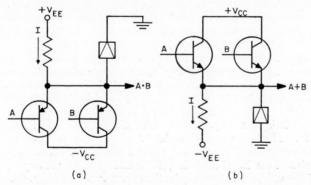

FIG. 15.94. (a) Emitter-follower Esaki diode "and" circuit. (b) Emitter-follower Esaki diode "or" circuit.

This circuit has the advantage that the input signal is not required to move the operating point under the relatively long valley of Esaki diode D_2. Consequently, the circuit will exhibit good voltage gain.

The Esaki diode can be combined with the emitter-follower circuits that were discussed in Sec. 15.8 to obtain circuits that may be of advantage where high speed is required. The two basic circuits are shown in Fig. 15.94. The reader will recall that emitter followers were shown to exhibit good current gain, a low output impedance, and a voltage gain of less than unity. Also, parallel PNP emitter followers were shown to form an "and" circuit while parallel NPN emitter followers were shown to perform the "or" function. In the circuits of Fig. 15.94 logic is performed by the parallel emitter followers while voltage gain is supplied by the Esaki diode. The emitter followers provide good drive for the Esaki diode, and consequently the circuits are fast.

The composite load lines for the circuits are shown in Fig. 15.95. Note that the Esaki diode in the NPN circuit of Fig. 15.95b is reversed so that a negative output swing can be obtained to drive the PNP circuit of Fig. 15.95a. The composite load line for these circuits represents the parallel combination of the emitter base diodes of all the parallel emitter followers. In Fig. 15.94 only two parallel emitter followers

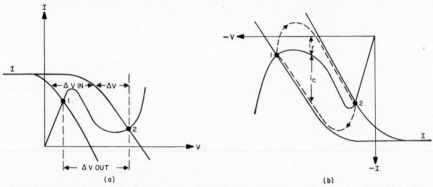

(a)   (b)

FIG. 15.95. (a) Load line for the "and" circuit of Fig. 15.94a. (b) Load line for the "or" circuit of Fig. 15.94b.

are shown. One indication of the speed capabilities of a circuit is the amount of transient driving current that can be supplied to charge capacitances. In Fig. 15.95b, the approximate path of the operating point during switching is shown by the dashed line. Also shown for one particular time during the transient are the two principal components of transient current. These are i_r, the real current required for the Esaki diode, and i_c, the current required to charge the depletion-layer capacitance of the Esaki diode. The reader will note that when the Esaki diode is switched to its low-voltage state, the low output impedance of the emitter follower makes available a good amount of current to charge the Esaki diode capacitance, and when the Esaki diode switches to its high-voltage state, a good drive is supplied by the current sink I. The value of the current sink I can be adjusted to obtain equal turn-off and turn-on times. This, however, cannot be done without first considering the question of voltage gain. Maximum gain is obtained from an Esaki diode amplifier when the load line matches the negative resistance of the Esaki diode. However, the negative-resistance region of the Esaki diode is quite nonlinear while the slope of the emitter base diode of the emitter follower is quite linear and to a good approximation is given by kT/qI_E. From the standpoint of maximum voltage gain the optimum value of a linear load line to use with the Esaki diode is given by

$$R = \frac{V_V - V_P}{I_P - I_V}$$

where the subscripts V and P refer to the peak and valley points, respectively, of the Esaki diode. When a linear load line is used, the nonlinearity of the Esaki diode negative resistance serves only to reduce the voltage gain. Generally in the range of 5.0 ma the slope of the transistor emitter base diode will be of the order of 5 to 10 ohms, while an Esaki diode with a peak current of 5.0 ma would require a load resistor of the order of 40 ohms. The solution is to add a padding resistor in series with the emitter to bring the slope up to the optimum value. The gain situation is further complicated by the fact that the load line will vary according to the number of parallel emitter followers that are used. Specifically, as emitter followers are paralleled, the load line becomes steeper. The best solution to this problem is a compromise. One designs for the number of inputs that are most used and adds the optimum padding resistor to obtain the best match. It is important that the input signal be large enough to ensure that the high-voltage operating point (point 2 in Fig. 15.95a) be out of the negative-resistance region. This is necessary in order to prevent oscillations. The problems of parallel emitter followers can be eased by

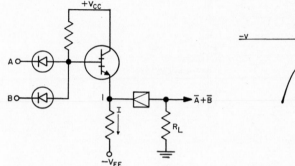

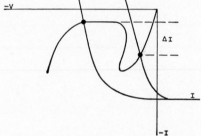

FIG. 15.96. Esaki diode, transistor NOR circuit.

FIG. 15.97. Load-line composite characteristic for the NOR circuit of Fig. 15.96.

using only one emitter follower and using parallel switching diodes to perform logic at the input to the emitter follower. In Fig. 15.95a, the output-voltage change ΔV_o is shown to be the sum of the input-voltage change ΔV_i plus ΔV, the amount of voltage by which the output signal is increased. To guarantee a voltage gain greater than unity, the sum or net effect of all circuit tolerances, i.e., the tolerance on power supplies, transistors, emitter base voltage drops, etc., must be less than ΔV.

An Esaki diode, transistor NOR circuit is shown in Fig. 15.96. In this circuit the "and" function is formed by the two switching diodes at the input to the emitter follower and the inversion is obtained from the combination of the Esaki diode and the series load resistor R_L. A load line and volt-ampere construction for the NOR circuit is shown in Fig. 15.97. In this figure, looking into the circuit at point 1 (refer to Fig. 15.96) one will see that the Esaki diode is in series with the load resistor R_L. The particular composite characteristic shown in Fig. 15.97 is the series combination of a 50-ohm resistor and a 5.0-ma Esaki diode. It is not obvious from Fig. 15.97 why the Esaki diode and load resistor R_L function as an inverter. However, the reader will note that a negative input at the base of the emitter follower will switch the Esaki diode from the low-voltage state to the high-voltage state. In the high-voltage state less current will flow through the Esaki diode and the load resistor and therefore the output voltage must rise. Another viewpoint is to note that a small positive-going signal at point 1 will cause a large increase in the voltage drop across the Esaki diode. Therefore the voltage across the resistor must drop, and consequently the output voltage will rise. From this argument one concludes that the output voltage is the difference between the input-voltage change and the voltage change across the Esaki diode. Or the output-voltage change must equal $\Delta I R_L$, where ΔI, from Fig. 15.97, is the current change that occurs when the Esaki diode is switched. In general, the NOR circuit of Fig. 15.96 will yield less gain than the emitter-follower circuit of Fig. 15.94. This is because the output voltage is the difference between the input voltage change and the total voltage change across the Esaki diode, while in the emitter-follower circuits the output voltage is not a difference but a sum of the input signal and an increment ΔV, where ΔV represents the increase in amplitude of the output signal.

15.13c. Twin Esaki Diode Circuits. The series connection of two Esaki diodes that is shown in Fig. 15.98 is often called a twin-pair amplifier and possesses some

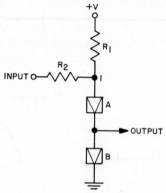

Fig. 15.98. Esaki diode twin-pair amplifier.

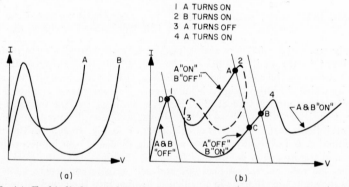

Fig. 15.99. (*a*) Esaki diodes used in the twin-pair amplifier to obtain Fig. 15.99*b*. (*b*) Volt-ampere characteristic and load line for the twin-pair amplifier.

interesting properties. Consider that diodes A and B have the volt-ampere characteristics shown in Fig. 15.99*a*, where diode A is shown to have a lower peak current and a higher valley current than diode B. The total volt-ampere characteristic that one would see looking into point 1 (refer to Fig. 15.98) is shown in Fig. 15.99*b*. For the convenience of the reader in tracing out this characteristic, significant points on the characteristic are tabulated. The regions of primary interest here are the three regions of positive resistance where both diodes are off (low-voltage state) or diode A is on (high-voltage state) and diode B is off or the third region where diode B is on and diode A is off. Also shown in Fig. 15.99*b* is a load line consisting of the parallel combination of R_1 and R_2 returned to a suitable positive bias.

This circuit is capable of operating as an in-phase or as an inverting latch. To obtain an in-phase latch it is necessary that diode B occupy the bottom position in the series chain. With the help of the idealized waveforms shown in Fig. 15.100a one can trace out the path of the operating point for the case of the in-phase latch.

Assume that the operating point is at A (Fig. 15.99b). Under these conditions diode A is on and diode B is off. The positive-set input pulse will move the operating point first to B and then to C when the input pulse falls. Diode B has now been switched to the high-voltage state, and the output voltage will rise. The operating point will remain at C until the negative reset pulse arrives, at which time latch diodes are reset to their low-voltage state, the output voltage falls, and the operating

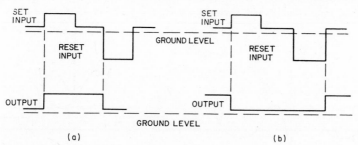

FIG. 15.100. (a) Waveforms for in-phase latch. (b) Waveforms for inverting latch.

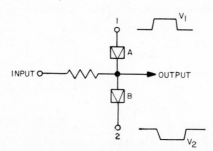

FIG. 15.101. Goto twin-pair amplifier.

point moves from C to D. The operating point will remain at D until the reset pulse rises, at which time the operating point will transfer back to A, turning diode A on again and completing the cycle.

To obtain an inverting latch it is only necessary to interchange diodes A and B. With diode A in the bottom position of the series chain, the circuit will be an inverting latch. The circuit operation will differ from the in-phase version only in the fact that reset takes place on the trailing edge of the reset pulse and not on the leading edge, as is the case for the in-phase latch. Idealized waveforms for the inverting latch are shown in Fig. 15.100b. Both of the latch circuits require careful control of the set input pulse. Too large a positive input will push the operating point into the region where both diodes are on. The circuit also requires a large negative pulse for reset.

An interesting twin-pair circuit has been developed by E. Goto and associates.[11] In the basic circuit shown in Fig. 15.101 clock pulses (V_1 and V_2) of equal amplitude and opposite polarity are applied at points 1 and 2. The Esaki diodes are assumed to be identical. A current input is supplied through a resistor to the junction of the two diodes. The current input serves to apply a positive or negative bias at the junction of the two diodes. The output is also taken from the junction of the two diodes. For an explanation of the circuit operation, the reader is referred to Fig. 15.102. Figure 15.102a illustrates the two diodes before the clock pulses are applied. Points 1 and 2 are at ground level, and the output is at ground level. When the clock pulses are applied, they are of an amplitude such that the negative resistances of both Esaki diodes intersect, as shown in Fig. 15.102b. The circuit then has two stable operating points at X_1 and X_2. Point X_0 will be an unstable operating point. The input signal establishes whether the stable operating point will be at X_1 or X_2. If the input signal is positive, then current will flow into the junction of the two diodes and a positive bias will be applied. This will bias the peak current point of diode A above that of diode B, and the stable operating point will be X_2. If the input signal is negative, then current will flow away from the junction of the two diodes and a

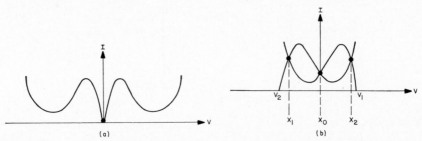

FIG. 15.102. (a) Before clock pulses are applied. (b) Operating points for the twin-pair amplifier.

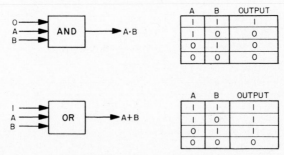

A	B	OUTPUT
I	I	I
I	0	0
0	I	0
0	0	0

A	B	OUTPUT
I	I	I
I	0	I
0	I	I
0	0	0

FIG. 15.103. Majority logic "and" and "or" blocks.

negative bias will be applied. This will bias the peak current point of diode A below that of diode B, and the stable operating point will be at X_1.

Logic is performed by paralleling resistors at the input. The net or total logical signal represents a summation of all the input signals. Logic of this type is called majority logic. The "and" and "or" functions are special cases of majority logic and can be obtained from a majority logic circuit by applying a suitable bias to one of the inputs. As an example, consider the simple two-way "and" and "or" circuits which are shown in Fig. 15.103 along with their respective truth tables. A positive bias (a "one" bias) is required to make an "or" circuit, while a negative bias (a "zero" bias) will make an "and" circuit. Specifically, we can say that in the case of the "and" circuit both inputs must be "one" to overcome the effect of the "zero" bias and make the output "one." In the "or" circuit case the bias supply is "one," so if either A or B or both A and B are "one," the output will be a "one."

In this circuit the input and output are separated only by the coupling resistors, and special steps must be taken to make the circuit unidirectional. This can be done by employing a three-phase clocking system which, by gating groups of circuits at particular times, serves, in effect, to make the circuits unidirectional. In this approach all the circuits in a system are grouped in three different groups. These groups are separately excited by three different periodic clock pulses which are separated from one another in time by one-third of a period. A timing diagram of the clock pulses is shown in Fig. 15.104. In a clock system of this type, amplifiers in the clock phase 1 group drive only amplifiers in the clock phase 2 group, while the amplifiers in the 2 group drive amplifiers in the 3 group, which in turn can drive only amplifiers in the 1 group. The following simple example will describe how the system works: Consider a chain of three amplifiers—a group 1 amplifier driving a group 2 amplifier which in turn drives a group 3 amplifier. At time zero the 2 amplifier is

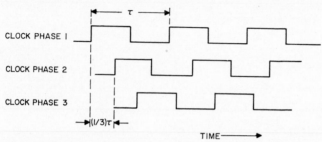

FIG. 15.104. A timing diagram of a three-phase clocking system.

excited by group 2 clock pulses. This amplifier will supply a signal to the group 3 amplifier it is driving, but also a signal must go to the group 1 amplifier because the circuit is bilateral. The group 3 amplifier will turn on when excited by group 3 clock pulses, and it will amplify the signal from the 2 amplifier. The clock pulses of group 2 and group 3 are overlapped by one-third of a clock period to ensure that the signal from the 2 amplifier locks into the 3 amplifier. The backward signal from the 2 amplifier to the 1 amplifier cannot be amplified because all group 1 amplifiers are not excited during this time. This is a unidirectional form of coupling achieved even though bilateral resistors are used as coupling elements.

The majority circuit requires that diodes be closely matched if speed and a high pyramiding factor are to be realized.

15.13d. Conclusion. It is the author's desire that by this time the reader has gained an insight into some of the characteristics of transistors and diodes that make them desirable for switching circuits. Because of the space limitations it is not possible to go into extensive detail, and in general the author has confined himself to the d-c type of logic circuits rather than pulse logic. Space limitations have also prevented a discussion of the use of magnetic cores with transistors, and a discussion of the point-contact transistor is not included, since these transistors are no longer in general use.

REFERENCES

1. Shea, R. F.: "Principles of Transistor Circuits," John Wiley & Sons, Inc., New York, 1953.
2. Kestenbaum, A. L., and N. H. Ditrick: *RCA Rev.*, vol. 18, p. 12, March, 1957.
3. Brooks, N. G., and H. S. Long: A Program for Computing the Transient Response of Transistor Switching Circuits—PE TAP, *IBM Tech. Rept.* TR 00.11000.700.
   Branin, F. H.: D.C. Analysis Portion of PE TAP—A Program for the Analysis of Transistor Switching Circuits, *IBM Tech. Rept.* TR 00.11000.701.
4. Ebers, J. J., and J. L. Moll: Large Signal Behavior of Junction Transistors, *Proc. IRE*, vol. 42, pp. 1761–1772, December, 1954, and J. L. Moll, Large Signal Transient Response of Junction Transistors, *Proc. IRE*, vol. 42, pp. 1773–1784, December, 1954.

5. Linvill, J. G., and R. H. Matson: Junction Transistor Blocking Oscillators, *Proc. IRE*, vol. 43, pp. 826–834, 1955.
6. Rowe, W. D.: Transistor NOR Circuit Design, *Electronic Design*, vol. 6, no. 3, pp. 26–29, Feb. 5, 1958.
7. Bradley, W. E., R. B. Brown, M. Rubinoff, and R. H. Better: Surface Barrier Transistor Computer Circuits, IRE Convention Record, part 4, Computers, Information Theory and Automatic Control, pp. 139–145, 1955.
8. Harris, J. R.: Direct Coupled Transistor Logic Circuitry, *Trans. IRE*, vol. EC-7, pp. 2–6, March, 1958.
9. Easley, J. W.: Transistor Characteristics for Direct-coupled Transistor Logic Circuits, *Trans. IRE*, vol. EC-7, pp. 6–16, March, 1958.
10. Early, J. M.: Design Theory of Junction Transistors, *Bell System Tech. J.*, vol. 32, pp. 1271–1312, November, 1953.
11. Goto, E., K. Murata, K. Nakazawa, K. Nakagawa, T. Moto-oka, Y. Matsuoka, Y. Ishibashi, H. Ishida, T. Soma, and E. Wada: Esaki Diode High Speed Logical Circuits, *Trans. IRE*, vol. EC-9, pp. 25–29, March, 1960.

Section 16

MICROWAVE APPLICATIONS

W. R. Beam

Rensselaer Polytechnic Institute, Troy, N.Y.

16.1. Microwave Mixer and Detector Diodes. *16.1a. Mixer Diode Characteristics and Equivalent Circuits.* Diodes used as mixers in microwave superheterodyne receivers are invariably of the point-contact type and usually employ a silicon wafer. Very early in the development of radio the galena crystal with movable "cat whisker" formed the most essential part of radio receivers. With the advent of vacuum diodes, the crystal diode went out of fashion for broadcast reception but remained the only suitable detector for ultrahigh frequencies. During World War II, research efforts at the MIT Radiation Laboratory, Bell Telephone Laboratories, and elsewhere yielded microwave point-contact diodes of excellent quality, useful to wavelengths of 1 cm or less.[1] Today, despite the availability of microwave tubes capable of mixing, the cheap and simple point-contact diode still holds a unique position as a microwave mixing device.

The voltage-current characteristic of a point-contact silicon diode is exemplified by Fig. 16.1. In the forward direction, a relatively short region of exponential V-I relationship gives way at a few tenths of a volt to a region of essentially constant forward resistance. This resistance is associated with the spreading of current in the crystal and may range from, say, 5 to 50 ohms or more. In the reverse direction, the

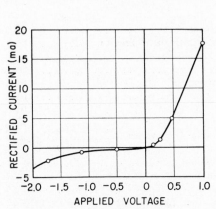

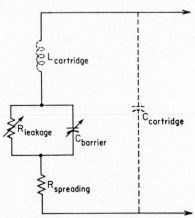

FIG. 16.1. A typical voltage-current characteristic of a silicon mixer diode.

FIG. 16.2. Equivalent circuit of microwave mixer diode.

diode characteristically has leakage current (high by the standards applied to junction devices); above its useful range of operation is a double-valued-current region. Continuous operation in this region leads to irreversible damage to the unit.

In terms of front-to-back ratio, the microwave point-contact diode is far inferior to the usual junction devices used at lower frequencies. The applicability of the device stems mainly from the small size of the contact and the resulting small capacitance which it represents. The usually accepted equivalent circuit for a point-contact microwave diode is shown in Fig. 16.2. The variable shunt resistance represents the injected current, the capacitance represents the barrier layer capacitance, which also varies with the voltage; this variation plays little or no part in the usual operation. The capacitance is typically a few tenths to 1 pf (10^{-12} farad). Parameters vary depending on the frequency band; at higher frequencies, a lower-capacitance diode is desired to match the impedance of the circuits used. As a result, diodes for the highest frequencies, having the smallest contact areas, are the most fragile. Diodes for experimental purposes in the low-millimeter wavelengths are generally laboratory built and adjusted and may frequently be equipped with a new contact point.

A variety of types of crystals are now available; however, certain standard types have been in existence since the war for radar applications. Type 1N21 is the standard diode for S band (10 cm), 1N23 for X band (3 cm), and 1N26 for 1.25 cm. These diodes are generally constructed from boron-doped silicon and have a pressure contact between cat whisker and wafer. During the war a novel diode was made by passage of high current through the contact in the forward direction. This "welded-contact" germanium diode[2] gave interestingly low conversion loss results but yielded poorer noise performance than pressure-contact diodes. The occasionally observed conversion *gain* (rather than loss) and negative-resistance characteristic is thought now to have been due to the "tunnel-diode" phenomenon.[3] Considerable improvements have

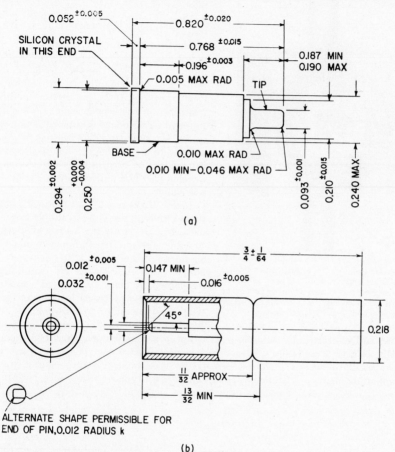

Fig. 16.3. Standard diode dimensions: (*a*) ceramic cartridge, used to 3-cm wavelength, (*b*) coaxial cartridge used at 1.25-cm wavelength.

since been made in the performance of the "standard" diode types (over-all receiver noise figure being the most important characteristic). The 1N23F has significantly lower spreading resistance than early models. The 1N263 diode[4] is an optimized germanium point-contact unit which is reported to deliver, when properly biased, substantially better performance than earlier 1N23-series units. Diodes have been built experimentally using gallium arsenide, which perform comparably to the best germanium and silicon units. Studies[5,6] have shown that considerable improvement can be obtained by further materials investigation and new processing and fabrication techniques.

16.1b. Crystal Cartridges. During World War II, standard crystal cartridges were developed, the external dimensions of which have remained in use. A single size of ceramic-insulated cartridge is used down to 3-cm wavelengths, while for the smaller circuitry at 1 cm, diodes are built into a coaxial cartridge. These two standard cartridges are illustrated in Fig. 16.3.

Figure 16.4 shows a crystal for 70,000 mc which is commercially available.† This is mounted directly into a section of RG-98/U waveguide for good matching at that frequency.

The tungsten whisker, which is bent to provide spring pressure, represents an appreciable inductance. This, together with the capacitance across the ceramic insulator and between electrodes (Fig. 16.2), can produce an internal resonance in the crystal which makes it more frequency-dependent and more lossy. At frequencies where cartridge dimensions are comparable to a wavelength, standard cartridges can seldom be used unless they are made an integral part of a uniform transmission line or waveguide.

16.1c. Microwave Mixer Circuits. The superheterodyne principle is almost universally used in high-sensitivity microwave receivers[7] to achieve selectivity and provide most of the signal amplification at a frequency at which simple and inexpensive i-f amplifiers are available. A block diagram of a microwave superheterodyne receiver is shown in Fig. 16.5. The local oscillator is customarily a reflex klystron, mechanically tunable over a wide band and electronically tunable over a few per cent bandwidth. The mixer generally is a crystal diode. Adjustment is provided to control the strength of the local oscillator drive. Highest sensitivity mixers have signal tuning and coupling adjustments. Untuned mixers, which generally have poorer noise performance, provide a reasonably constant impedance at the signal frequency over a frequency

Fig. 16.4. Diode in mount suitable for 70,000-mc operation. Type 1N2793. Noise figure is reported to be just over 10 db. (*Photograph courtesy of Philco Corporation, Lansdale Division.*)

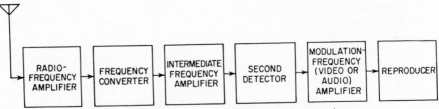

Fig. 16.5. Block diagram of a superheterodyne receiver.

band as great as 1 octave. The intermediate frequency, for typical radar applications, is 30 or 60 mc, and the i-f amplifier may develop up to 100 db gain over a bandwidth of a few megacycles. Most mixers employ a single crystal, although a pair of matched crystals in a *balanced-mixer* arrangement can be used to cancel unwanted sidebands.[8]

† Philco Corporation, Lansdale, Pa. Type 1N2792.

Let us assume that the local oscillator voltage e_0 and the signal voltage e_1 are applied additively to the crystal. The current-voltage characteristic of the diode can be expanded in a series:

$$i = i_0 + a_1 e + a_2 e^2 + a_3 e^3 + \cdots \qquad (16.1)$$

The most important contribution to mixer action comes from the a_2 (quadratic) term, since in general the magnitude of the higher-order a's decreases rapidly. The a_2 term, with $e = e_0 + e_1$ substituted, yields a term $e_0 e_1$ containing upper and lower sideband frequencies $f_0 \pm f_1$. It is usually of little importance at microwave frequencies which sideband is used because of the small frequency difference. The amount of the input signal power converted to intermediate frequency depends strongly on the shape of the diode voltage-current curve, the tuning of the mixer, the amplitude of the local oscillator voltage, and whether the unused sideband frequencies are allowed to develop power. As local oscillator drive level is increased, the conversion loss becomes smaller, as shown in Fig. 16.6. Crystal current is usually monitored as a measure of the local oscillator drive. In a balanced mixer, the r-f currents from the two crystals are arranged so as to subtract and the signal and local oscillator frequency are added in the opposite phase $(e_0 - e_1)$ in the second diode. Fewer current components of significant frequencies are produced, and a lower conversion loss results. The added complexity of balanced mixers and their dependence on well-matched diodes are some handicap to their use.

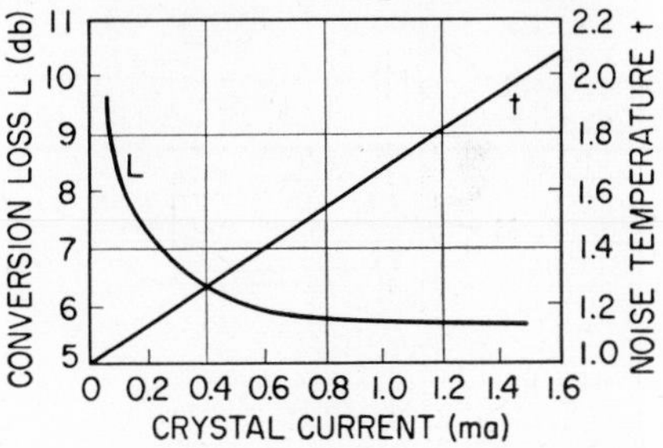

FIG. 16.6. Conversion loss L and noise temperature T_n as a function of rectified current (local oscillator drive) for a typical 1N23B crystal rectifier.

Since crystal mixers operate because of their variable resistance, they must have conversion loss. If the diode were a perfect switch, changing from zero to infinite resistance in going from forward to reverse directions, it would, in principle, be possible to reduce the conversion loss as much as desired, though at great cost in circuit complexity. Measured conversion power of the best microwave crystals under optimized conditions has been almost as much as one-third of the incident power.[6]

Figure 16.7 shows a cross-sectional view of a typical untuned mixer for frequencies around 3,000 mc. It provides separate inputs for signal and local oscillator, a bypassed and shielded i-f output connection, and means for adjusting the local oscillator coupling. Such a mixer can be made to cover a 50 per cent bandwidth, but at a compromise in noise performance.

16.1d. Noise Properties of Microwave Receivers Using Crystal Mixers. The noise properties of microwave and lower-frequency receivers are usually defined by the *noise figure,* as suggested by Friis:[9]

$$NF = \frac{\dfrac{\text{Available noise power output}}{\text{Available noise power input}}}{\dfrac{\text{Available signal power output}}{\text{Available signal power input}}} \qquad (16.2)$$

The lower part of the expression in Eq. (16.2) is merely the power gain. Since the noise power output contains a contribution from noise introduced within the amplifier, the noise figure can never be less than unity.   An alternative expression is

$$NF = 1 + \frac{P_{\text{eff}}}{kT_0 \, \Delta f} \qquad (16.3)$$

where P_{eff} is the effective noise power introduced in the device, referred to the input. $kT_0 \, \Delta f$ is (according to thermodynamic noise theory) the available noise power from an antenna or source impedance.   With the use of amplifiers in radioastronomy, the actual antenna may be matched to a source of very low T_0 (order of 50°K), so that the conventional noise-figure definition,[10] based on $T_0 = 290°$K, may not be a useful measurement of receiver sensitivity.   In this case, the device may better be described

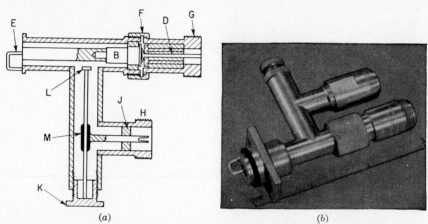

(a)   (b)

FIG. 16.7. (a) Cross section of untuned 3,000-mc crystal mixer: B, mixer diode; E, signal coupling loop; L, local oscillator coupling probe; H, local oscillator input connection; K, local oscillator adjustment; D, r-f bypass capacitance; G, i-f output terminal.   (b) Photograph of 3,000-mc crystal mixer.

in terms of a *noise temperature* T_n, where the actual noise figure and noise temperature are related by

$$NF = 1 + \frac{T_n}{T_0} \qquad (16.4)$$

Noise figures of microwave receivers are usually measured using a gas-discharge-tube noise source, the effective noise temperature of which is about 11,000°K.   If the discharge-tube noise is known, the noise figure of a receiver can be found by comparing the outputs of the amplifier with gas-discharge tube operating and nonoperating.[11] Gas-discharge tubes are available for frequencies from 200 mc up to the 25,000-mc band. They are well suited for noise measurement of crystal-mixer receivers and give accurate measurements from about 2- to over 20-db noise figures (the noise figure in decibels is defined as 10 $\log_{10} NF$).

Crystal mixers always have conversion loss, and consequently the noise performance of the i-f amplifier plays a significant part in the over-all receiver noise figure.   An amplifier containing two cascaded stages which have respective gains G_1 and G_2 and noise figures NF_1 and NF_2 will have an over-all noise figure NF_{12} given by

$$NF_{12} = NF_1 + \frac{NF_2 - 1}{G_1} \qquad (16.5)$$

If G_1 is less than unity, as is the case in the microwave mixer, the noise figure of the i-f amplifier NF_2 is made more significant. This is one reason for using intermediate frequencies of less than 100 mc, for the i-f amplifier tubes which are commonly used have noise figures which increase rapidly in the ultra-high-frequency range; 30-mc i-f amplifiers with 1.5-db noise figures are available. Actual receiver noise figure is a function of matching of mixer and i-f amplifier, so it may be necessary to modify the amplifier or adjust it for use with a particular mixer. Transistor amplifiers, because of their presently poorer noise performance at high frequencies compared with tubes such as the 6AG5, are not yet used in microwave receivers to any extent.

The noise in any device stems from (1) the amount of loss which the signal must pass through before being substantially amplified and (2) the effective temperature of the medium. Thus, conversion loss in the mixer adds directly to the noise figure, and the resistive impedance which the mixer presents to the i-f amplifier represents a source of thermal noise. An inherent characteristic of the rectifying contact is an extraneous noise which can be expressed in terms of the ratio by which the noise power available from the diode (at intermediate frequency) exceeds the $kT\,\Delta f$ value. This ratio, defined as t in early references,[12] is slightly above unity for good diodes; values less than unity which have been reported appear paradoxical from thermodynamical considerations and may be due to particular matching situations. At low intermediate frequencies (a few hundred kilocycles), t becomes very large. It has been observed to have a $1/f$ spectral variation, frequently observed in semiconductor devices.[13] In terms of the conversion loss

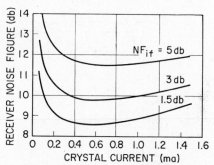

Fig. 16.8. Over-all receiver noise figure using the diode characterized in Fig. 16.6, for several different values of i-f amplifier noise figure.

L (= signal power/i-f output power), the temperature ratio t, and the noise figure of the i-f amplifier NF_{if}, the over-all receiver noise figure is

$$NF_{rec} = L(t + NF_{if} - 1) \tag{16.6}$$

The conversion loss as mentioned earlier is reduced as LO drive increases. The value of t, on the other hand, increases with drive (Fig. 16.6) because the source of the excess noise is a shot-noise process at the contact; therefore the mean-squared shot noise increases with the current drawn through the diode. As a result of the variation of L and t with drive, the over-all noise figure behaves as shown in Fig. 16.8. Most diodes operate successfully near zero bias, but the 1N263 delivers best noise performance with a slight positive bias.

Crystal mixers operating as high as the limit of available local oscillator drive (almost 100 kmc) have been operated. Conversion losses increase with frequency. Noise figures of 4.8 db can be achieved at 3,000 mc with today's crystals. This increases to 6 or 7 db at 10,000 mc and 10 db at 70,000 mc. The results that can be obtained under field conditions may be 2 to 6 db worse. Figure 16.9 shows the relative noise performance, as a function of frequency, of various receiver input devices. *Above* about 40,000 mc, no competitive devices exist at the present. Diode performance at far higher frequencies is so good as to discourage work on more expensive devices such as klystrons and traveling-wave tubes. Parametric amplifiers and masers form the significant competition.[14]

16.1e. Crystal Matching and Mixer Adjustment. The r-f and i-f impedance levels of low-noise microwave mixer crystals are seldom sufficiently uniform to allow replacement of the crystal without adjustment for best noise performance.

Practical mixers designed for optimum noise performance generally have adjustments for local oscillator coupling, signal coupling, and signal tuning. When the mixer is adjusted, the local oscillator coupling is usually set first to the level producing the manufacturer's rated current for lowest noise figure. This is usually in the range of $\frac{1}{10}$ to 1 ma, and currents several times the rated value may irreversibly damage the diode. The next step is tuning of the signal circuit (cavity) to the desired signal frequency. Adjustment is then made for optimum signal coupling, and finally small adjustments are made in all variables for optimization. The process of adjustment is aided materially by use of a noise-figure meter or the presence of a signal not much larger than the noise level.

Generally, no field adjustment is provided for the i-f amplifier input impedance. The input of the amplifier is usually tuned to the i-f band, and a transformer action

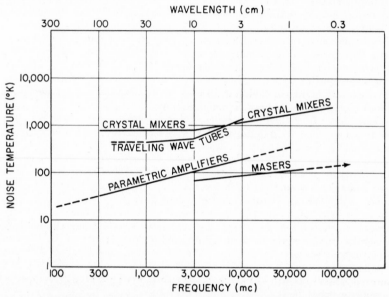

FIG. 16.9. Noise figures of various microwave receive input devices, as a function of frequency. Solid portions indicate "state-of-art" frequency range, dashed portions extrapolated.

provided through a T or pi network prior to the grid of the first tube to transform the high input conductance to a somewhat lower value. Because the tube is a voltage-sensitive device, performance does not suffer if the i-f amplifier input resistance which the diode faces is somewhat higher than the i-f source resistance of the diode. The chief precaution to be observed in connecting a mixer to an i-f amplifier is to minimize the length of the connecting cable; this cable is usually a low-capacitance type which is not matched at either end, but is made short so as to introduce minimum excess capacitance. Excess capacitance at the input of the amplifier will reduce the gain-bandwidth product of the amplifier stage, and higher noise figure will result. In circumstances where the mixer and the i-f amplifier must be remote from one another, a small i-f preamplifier with cathode-follower output is frequently used to raise gain to a safe level and allow the low-frequency i-f signal to be transmitted via cable.

The noise figure of a receiver with an untuned mixer is always higher than that with a tuned mixer, because thermal noise entering the receiver in the image-frequency band contributes to the i-f output. The tuning of the mixer should, therefore, be selective enough to reject any noise input at image frequencies. If the noise figure of a tuned mixer is expressible as $NF_t = 1 + T_n/T_0$, the noise figure of a similar, but untuned mixer admitting image-frequency noise will be $NF_u = 2 + T_n/T_0$. Signal-circuit selectivity of a tuned mixer, therefore, need not be as narrow as the i-f bandwidth, but should effectively eliminate image-frequency noise.

For a comprehensive treatment of matching and impedance transformation of crystal mixers, see reference 1.

16.1f. Crystal Burnout. An important problem in radar systems arises from the high-peak-power r-f pulses which are applied to the antenna during transmission. The crystal mixer forms the first stage of the receiver, operating from the same antenna, and would be destroyed by the first transmitter pulse except for the action of a *duplexer*,[15] which prevents application of more than a small amount of the transmitted energy to the crystal. This duplexer in earlier systems was invariably a gas-filled tube placed across the transmission line before the crystal mixer. The transmitter pulse itself ignites a glow discharge in the duplexer (or TR, for transmit-receive) tube. Because the discharge cannot ignite instantly, a short power pulse (of duration a fraction of a microsecond) does impinge on the crystal. The pulse is generally so short that it is best measured in terms of its total energy. Diodes for military radar systems must pass specification tests which require them to endure short pulses of total energy around 1 erg (10^{-17} watt-sec) without damage.[16] High-burnout types will withstand somewhat higher power, while very high frequency types (because their active parts are smaller and will absorb less energy) have burnout around 0.1 erg. Modern diodes, because of improved materials and processing, may have considerably higher burnout levels.[17]

Although the gas-tube TR switch remains in use, new methods are available which serve to limit the power absorbed by the crystal. Ferrite circulators[18,19] provide an additional 30 db or more of isolation but in high-power systems must be backed up by a TR tube. Some new power tubes[20] produce final transmitter output and at the same time have very low loss in the direction traveled by the received signal. The problem of burnout in single-antenna systems remains a serious one because of the shutdown which results from damage to the crystal; considerable time may be required for replacement and readjustment. Thus while the crystal, a semiconductor device, has potentially longer life than the magnetrons or high-powered klystrons used in radar transmitters, useful life is often much shorter because of pulse burnout or excessive local oscillator drive.

16.1g. Crystal-video Receivers. In applications where utmost simplicity and freedom from tuning adjustments are desired and where ultimate sensitivity is not necessary, a crystal-video receiver can be employed. Such a receiver may have some form of band-limiting tuner ahead of the crystal, but the output of the crystal itself goes directly to an audio or video amplifier. Thus, noise from the entire r-f bandwidth is amplified. A typical application is a radar beacon, where the exact frequency of the source may not be known and where unattended operation is customary. Direct-rectifying crystals can also be used for instrumentation or calibration applications. A minimum sensitivity of about 10^{-8} watt can be obtained with crystal-video receivers.[21] This compares to sensitivities down to almost 10^{-15} watt for superheterodyne receivers of modest bandwidth and good noise figure.

A variable-resistance diode, having a voltage-current curve marked by a constant-resistance region, will operate as a *linear detector* at large voltages. In other words, the rectified current which flows in the diode will be nearly proportional to the applied r-f voltage. Operation at lower applied voltages can be analyzed by expanding the voltage-current characteristic in a power series, as in Eq. (16.1). The d-c component produced by the application of a sine wave will stem from current terms containing an even power of the voltage; the lowest of these is the a_2e^2 term. [If $e = V \sin \omega t$,

$e^2 = V^2/2(\frac{1}{2} - \frac{1}{2}\cos 2\,\omega t).$] Since the coefficient of e^4 is much smaller than that of e^2, the output current will be proportional to the square of the input voltage. Therefore, provided the input match is reasonably good, the diode will serve as a power detector.

A good detector crystal will generate a large current output per unit input. In terms of low-noise performance, the equivalent resistance which the diode presents at the amplifier input is also important. If this is too low, the voltage generated by the diode cannot compete with the induced grid noise of the input tube.[22] The best video detector crystal, therefore, is not the one with the lowest resistance but the one which generates the most square-law current and has the highest effective resistance. A

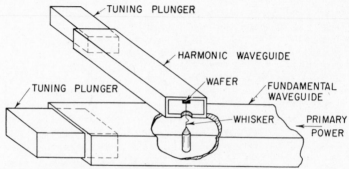

Fig. 16.10. Crossed-guide harmonic generator circuit.

figure of merit for video crystals[23] is

$$M = \frac{\beta R}{\sqrt{R + R_A}} \tag{16.7}$$

where β is the diode sensitivity in amperes per watt, R is the slope of the V-I curve of the crystal at the operating point, and R_A is the effective input noise resistance of the amplifier tube (generally around 1,000 ohms). A typical value for M is 100.

The noise properties of crystal *linear* detectors are of little concern, since these detectors operate with applied voltages considerably above kT/q and therefore signal far exceeds noise.

The ability of a linear detector to indicate true peak r-f voltage is limited by its leakage resistance and the load into which it operates.

16.1h. Variable-resistance Diode Harmonic Generators. A power-series expansion of the diode V-I relation [Eq. (16.1)], with an applied voltage $V \sin \omega t$, will yield currents of all harmonics of the applied frequency. The amplitudes of higher harmonics will be smaller than those of lower harmonics; the sharpness of the bend in the V-I curve will largely determine how effectively harmonics are generated. The losses within the diode, external to the rectifying contact, will also play an important part in determining efficiency. Consequently, diodes for harmonic generation should be chosen to have low spreading resistance. Low capacitance is also to be desired, in the reverse direction, so that a high-frequency voltage can build up rapidly during the reverse half of the voltage cycle. Since the harmonic power output at the nth harmonic varies approximately as (input power)^n, high input powers are required for high efficiency. Other things being equal, a diode for harmonic generation should have the largest possible power-dissipating capacity.

Harmonic generators may operate either tuned or untuned; i.e., in a tuned harmonic generator, power at harmonics other than the one desired may not be allowed to flow from the diode; efficiency is greater than in an untuned generator, which produces output at all frequencies.

The most important region of the spectrum for harmonic generation is in the millimeter wavelengths where no primary power sources are available. While at lower frequencies a harmonic generator can be tuned by means of a resonant cavity, dimensions become too small at millimeter wavelengths. By use of the waveguide arrangement shown in Fig. 16.10, it is possible, if not to tune for maximum efficiency, at least to eliminate all harmonics of lower order than that desired in the output. The primary power is fed in through a large waveguide adequate in size to handle the primary frequency. The crystal diode itself is located partly in this waveguide and partly in a smaller waveguide at right angles to the first. Harmonic power is generated at the diode contact itself, which is located in the smaller waveguide. Therefore, most of the harmonic energy goes into the smaller waveguide at frequencies above its cutoff frequency. Such a harmonic generator can operate with reasonable efficiency over a fair range of frequencies without mechanical tuning. Mechanical adjustment of the pressure of the tungsten whisker should be provided to enable optimization of diode resistance. Figure 16.11 illustrates the performance of such a harmonic generator for several harmonics.

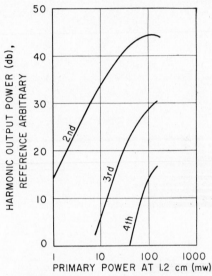

Harmonic output from point-contact diodes has been obtained at wavelengths as low as 0.9 mm[24] using a source around 25,000 mc. Although power obtained in this way is always small, it is sufficient for much physical spectroscopy. At the present time, primary sources above 60,000 mc are unavailable; hence harmonic generation must be relied on above that frequency range.

Fig. 16.11. Performance of variable-resistance diode harmonic generator at millimeter wavelengths. (*After Nethercot, Trans. PGMTT, IRE, pp. 17–20, September, 1954.*)

16.2. Variable-capacitance Diode Applications. *16.2a. Diode Characteristics and Equivalent Circuit.* A PN junction biased in the reverse (low-current) direction establishes a *depletion layer* at the junction, the thickness of which increases with the applied voltage. Shockley[25] has shown that the resulting capacitance of the depletion layer, for planar geometry, is given by

$$C(V) = K(\phi - V)^{-n} \qquad (16.8)$$

where $n = \frac{1}{2}$ for an abrupt junction and $n = \frac{1}{3}$ for a graded junction. This characteristic is shown in Fig. 16.12. V is the actual applied voltage, but the significant voltage is $\phi - V$, which includes the contact potential. The junction carries a conductive current which can be expressed in terms of a conductance G, where

$$G(V) = \frac{qI_0}{kT} e^{qV/kT} \qquad (16.9)$$

G is also plotted in Fig. 16.12. Since variable-reactance circuits operate best with the largest possible change of capacitance, it is desirable to drive the diode as far as possible in the forward direction. Since, however, G produces power loss, the junction should not be operated closer than one-tenth or a few tenths of a volt from the point $V = \phi$.[26] Under these conditions, the shunt conductance G can usually be

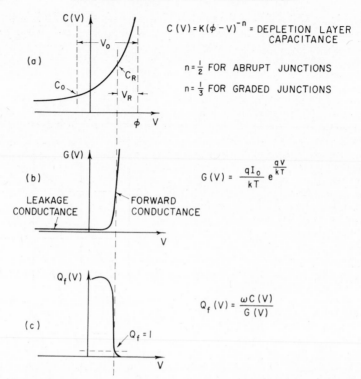

$$C(V) = K(\phi - V)^{-n} = \text{DEPLETION LAYER CAPACITANCE}$$

$$n = \tfrac{1}{2} \text{ FOR ABRUPT JUNCTIONS}$$

$$n = \tfrac{1}{3} \text{ FOR GRADED JUNCTIONS}$$

$$G(V) = \frac{qI_0}{kT} e^{\frac{qv}{kT}}$$

$$Q_f(V) = \frac{\omega C(V)}{G(V)}$$

FIG. 16.12. (*a*) Capacitance, (*b*) conductance, and (*c*) quality factor of a parametric diode as a function of voltage. (*After fig. 2 of RCA Rev., vol. 20, p. 232, June, 1959.*)

neglected. Of greater importance is the series "spreading" resistance which originates in the base of the diode and in the leads. This resistance is approximately constant, except for surface-current ("skin") effects which set in at very high frequencies.[†]

Figure 16.13 shows the equivalent circuit of the diode with encapsulation. It is quite possible that the inductance of the "whisker" and the cartridge capacitance can produce an internal resonance which will be below the desired frequency of operation. This will not prevent higher-frequency operation, but the energy storage in the cart-

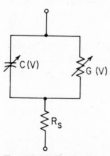

FIG. 16.13. Equivalent circuit of parametric diode, neglecting stray reactance of encapsulation.

ridge may limit the bandwidth of the complete circuit. Losses of the cartridge may also be high. To prevent this problem, manufacturers of variable-reactance diodes for special purposes frequently build special encapsulations which are smaller and fit the circuits more integrally than standard cartridges. Since the "cat-whisker" type of connection is not required for junction units, the standard encapsulation offers little fabrication advantage. A particular type of mount, for example, may solder directly between the copper sheets of a printed circuit.

It has been customary for diode manufacturers to specify, as a figure of merit, a "cutoff frequency" ω_c for these diodes. This is defined as the frequency at which the capacitive react-

† Torrey and Whitmer (reference 1, p. 427) show the effect to be small in mixer diodes. This is probably not so for parametric diodes because of the small spreading resistance.

ance of the junction just equals the series equivalent resistance (the Q becomes unity). ω_c is usually defined at the maximum reverse bias which can be applied without breakdown; this results in an artificially and unusably high frequency. Generally, oscillation or parametric amplification can be obtained from a diode at frequencies little higher than one-tenth the quoted "cutoff frequency,"[27] while harmonic generation or up-conversion applications may apply a signal up to perhaps $0.3\omega_c$.

The best parametric diode description from an applicational viewpoint is (1) the capacitance-versus-voltage curve and (2) the series resistance, corrected for any high-frequency effects. Specification of an operating bias, the possible variation of C, and the series resistance at bias are helpful, but not complete. Typical diodes for microwave applications have maximum capacitance of a few picofarads, minimum capacitance (including capsule) of 1 pf or less, and series resistance around 1 ohm. These diodes can be used as oscillators or amplifiers in the low microwave frequencies or as harmonic generators at output frequencies considerably higher.

At time of writing, several manufacturers advertise and sell variable-reactance diodes suitable for S-band (around 3,000 mc) amplifiers, and some experimental units can be obtained which are useful as amplifiers around 10,000 mc. Generally speaking, the higher-frequency units are not uniform in characteristics and are easy to damage by overcurrent, vibrations, etc. It may eventually be possible to build amplifiers for wavelengths less than 1 cm by refinements of the fabrication processes to yield substantially lower spreading resistance.

16.2b. Manley-Rowe Relations for Nonlinear Reactor Circuits. J. M. Manley and H. E. Rowe[28] have developed formulas applicable to any lossless nonlinear reactance circuit. These formulas show the relation between the power flow at various frequencies to and from the circuit. The formulas do not include the effect of losses in the reactor, and since all practical variable reactances have associated losses, the formulas are not exact. They should, therefore, not be looked upon as design formulas but are capable of demonstrating the *principles* of operation of all known variable-reactance devices.

It is assumed that two incommensurate frequencies f_0 and f_1 are applied to the reactor circuit and that certain of the possible mixing frequencies $mf_0 + nf_1$ are allowed to produce power in loads attached to the variable reactance. If the power flowing from the reactance at frequency $mf_0 + nf_1$ is $W_{m,n}$ (positive sign means power flow into and negative sign power flow out of the reactance), the Manley-Rowe relations are

$$\sum_{m=0}^{+\infty} \sum_{n=-\infty}^{+\infty} \frac{mW_{m,n}}{mf_0 + nf_1} = 0 \qquad \sum_{n=0}^{+\infty} \sum_{m=-\infty}^{+\infty} \frac{nW_{m,n}}{mf_0 + nf_1} = 0 \qquad (16.10)$$

The sums include each frequency of interest only once because of the incommensuracy requirement. The *two* relations, which relate *all* frequencies, tell us that in a device using k frequencies, we can apply only $k - 2$ independent adjustments of the power flow.

The relations in their full generality are not easy to understand. For all amplifiers we shall consider, we need employ only the frequencies $f_0 + f_1 = f_+$ and $f_0 - f_1 = f_-$ as well as f_0 and f_1. The relations then simplify to

$$\frac{W_-}{f_-} + \frac{W_0}{f_0} + \frac{W_+}{f_+} = 0 \qquad -\frac{W_-}{f_-} + \frac{W_1}{f_1} + \frac{W_+}{f_+} = 0 \qquad (16.11)$$

We can now identify the frequencies and the power-flow conditions for several useful parametric devices.

1. THREE-FREQUENCY PARAMETRIC AMPLIFIER. If $W_+ = 0$, the signal frequency is f_1 and the source of motive power in the amplifier, which is termed the "pump" frequency, is f_0. (This terminology is *not* unique.) The third frequency $f_0 - f_1$, which is essential to the operation of the device, is termed the "idle" frequency. (An early investigator enjoyed the analogy between its function and that of an idler gear on a gear train; while it appears at neither input nor output, it is important to the transmission of power in the device.) The relations show that if W_0 is positive, then W_1 and W_-, which must be of the same sign, will be negative; this is the usual parametric amplifier operation. If we provide a strong enough pump drive to ensure that W_0 is positive, then the device will put out power at the other two frequencies in the form of oscillations. If the drive is less strong, any small signals introduced will be regeneratively amplified, whether they be at f_1 or f_-. The amount of power involved at each frequency is proportional to the frequency; this is true for all parametric devices.

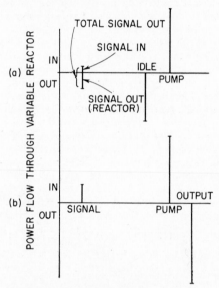

The power flow can be represented by a sort of "energy-level" diagram, as in Fig. 16.14a. This diagram applies exactly only to lossless circuits and shows that the only power wasted is in the idle circuit. This idle power must flow from the reactor; otherwise the device cannot produce signal output.

2. UP-CONVERTER. If W_- is zero, Eqs. (16.10) indicate that if power is put *into* the reactance at f_0 *and at* f_1, the power must come out at f_+. The ratio of the power output at f_+ to the signal input at f_1 is f_+/f_1. This *up-converter* has a conversion gain which is limited by the frequency ratio, but since net power *must* be put *into* the reactor at the signal frequency, the up-converter is inherently stable. Power flow is shown in Fig. 16.14b.

3. DOWN-CONVERTERS. It is possible to down-convert (i.e., apply a high input

FIG. 16.14. Power flow at various frequencies for ideal parametric circuits: (*a*) three-frequency parametric amplifier, (*b*) parametric up-converter.

frequency and obtain a low output frequency). In practice, this is useless, because the Manley-Rowe relations show that the power input at the higher frequency must be considerably larger than the output at low frequency. The variable-resistance converter, which can have relatively low conversion loss, is normally used in conjunction with parametric devices where down-conversion is required to convert frequency to a low value.

4. REGENERATIVE UP-CONVERTER. If power at all four frequencies in Eq. (16.11) is allowed to flow in the circuit, output at f_+ can be enhanced by allowing power to be dissipated at f_-.[29] This, as can be found from the relations (16.10), allows eventual instability. The limitation of up-converter gain by the frequency ratio, however, is removed.

Harmonic and subharmonic generators, both extremely useful applications of parametric principles, involve only two frequencies, the pump frequency and the output frequency. The Manley-Rowe relations do not apply readily to these commensurate frequencies, but in a lossless reactor the output must equal the input. Demonstration of the principle of the subharmonic oscillator is given in Sec. 16.2l.

The Manley-Rowe relations are quite powerful for expressing gain limits and stability of parametric devices. The facts that reactors are in practice lossy and circuits do not uniquely discriminate frequency make it necessary to perform complete detailed analyses of any parametric devices for which gain and noise relations are required.

16.2c. Three-frequency Parametric Amplifiers Using Crystal Diodes. The Manley-Rowe relations tell us that such an amplifier must have signal terminals, pump input terminals, and a termination for the idle-frequency output. The signal circuit of a simple parametric device is very different from that of a conventional transistor amplifier because the parametric device acts like a simple negative resistance at signal frequency. Signal input and output are at the same terminals. At low frequencies, the internal network can best be characterized as a negative resistance; the equivalent circuit of Fig. 16.15a describes the gain process. This circuit is somewhat paradoxical, for although the input signal generator has an available power of $E^2/4R_L$, the power in the generator and internal resistance, separately, appears to be very large. This has no practical implications, because the description of a signal generator by a voltage generator and series impedance does not attach any physical significance to an individual element of the equivalent circuit.

At higher frequencies, a transmission-line viewpoint can be assumed, in which case the termination of the line by a negative resistance, as in Fig. 16.15b, merely produces a larger reflected wave back to the left end of the line. A *ferrite circulator*[18] may be, and often is, used to separate input and output, as shown in the figure.

The gain of a parametric amplifier must obviously be affected seriously by the idle circuit. An excellent analysis of operation of three-frequency amplifiers is that of Heffner and Wade.[30] They begin with the equivalent circuit of Fig. 16.16a. From the circuit equations can be derived the equivalent circuit of Fig. 16.16b. This demonstrates the impedance transformation reflecting a positive idle-circuit resistance as a negative resistance in the signal circuit.

The gain of the amplifier of Fig. 16.16a at center band is

$$\text{Gain} = \frac{4G_g G_l}{(G_{T_1} - G)^2} \tag{16.12}$$

where

G_g = signal source conductance
G_l = load conductance
G_1 = signal-circuit loss conductance
$G_{T_1} = G_1 + G_g + G_l$ = total signal-circuit conductance
$G = \omega_{\text{sig}}\omega_{\text{idle}}C_3^2/4G_{T_2}$ = magnitude of negative conductance appearing at the signal terminals
C_3 = amplitude of varying part of reactor capacitance
G_{T_2} = total idle-circuit conductance

If the Q of the idle circuit is large, the voltage gain-bandwidth product of the amplifier is

$$G_v f = \frac{2}{Q_{\text{idle}}} \frac{\omega_{\text{sig}}}{\omega_{\text{idle}}} \frac{G_g G_l}{G} \tag{16.13}$$

where Q_{idle} is the Q of the idle circuit.

Obviously, the Q of the idle circuit plays a major role in limiting the gain and bandwidth. More complete formulas show that the Q of the signal circuit also limits the gain and bandwidth. For a maximum gain-bandwidth product, Q_{idle} should be very low; the static and stray capacitance of the circuit and reactor set a lower limit to Q_{idle}. (If Q_{idle} is too low, of course, the assumptions of the theory may be violated.)

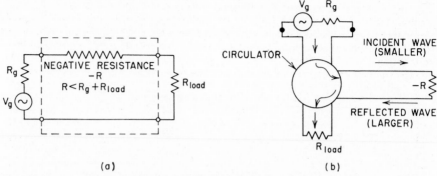

(a)   (b)

FIG. 16.15. (a) Simple equivalent circuit using lumped constants for negative-resistance amplifiers. (b) Distributed-constant equivalent circuit for negative-resistance amplifiers.

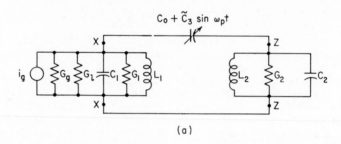

(a)

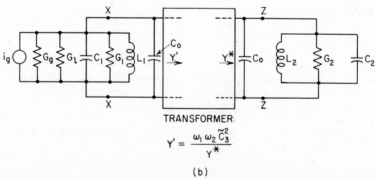

(b)

FIG. 16.16. (a) Equivalent circuit for gain calculation of three-frequency parametric amplifier. (*After Heffner and Wade, J. Appl. Phys., vol. 29, pp. 1321–1331, fig. 2, September, 1958.*) (b) Circuit viewed from signal-frequency tank, demonstrating impedance inversion of variable reactor.

The most important parameter for large gain and bandwidth is G, or (equivalently) C_3.

Actual circuit design is not straightforward, for resonance at ω_{sig} and ω_{idle} must appear at reactor terminals in addition to a large pump voltage. Some typical designs are shown in the following section.

The internal noise in a completely lossless parametric amplifier originates only in the idle-frequency load. A lossless variable reactance, not having internal fluctuations or *resistance*, cannot generate thermal noise (or, in other words, cannot act as a medium for heat transmission from its environment). In this ideal case, the noise figure of the device would have only the contribution from the idle frequency. From the Manley-Rowe theory, a noise power P applied at the idle terminals will produce at the signal terminals a power $(f_1/f_-)P$; the pump power readjusts to allow this. For the simplest parametric amplifier, then, the noise figure will be of the form

$$NF = 1 + \frac{f_1 T_i}{f_- T_0} = 1 + \frac{\omega_{\text{sig}} T_i}{\omega_{\text{idle}} T_0} \tag{16.14}$$

where T_i is the temperature of the idle-current loss and T_0 the reference, usually 290°K. The expression derived by Heffner and Wade[30] for the circuit of Fig. 16.16a is

$$NF = 1 + \frac{G_1}{G_g} + \frac{G f_1}{G_g f_-} + \left(\begin{array}{c}\text{terms due to fluctuations of}\\ \text{capacitance, shot noise, etc.}\end{array}\right) \tag{16.15}$$

The best noise figure accompanies low signal tank loss G_1. The larger the conductance G reflecting idle-circuit loss, the larger the noise figure also. The simple expression

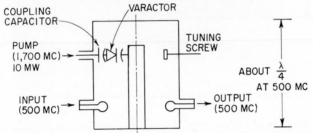

FIG. 16.17. Schematic cross section of simple microwave parametric amplifier using two resonances of a single cavity for signal and idle frequencies. The circuit is not resonant at the pump frequency. (*After "Varactors," published by Microwave Associates, Burlington, Mass., February, 1959.*)

(16.14), however, points out a significant possibility for reduced noise figure, namely, the use of a signal frequency lower than the idle frequency. This is possible only if the pump source frequency can be increased. Another possibility, though inclined to be tedious, is the immersion of the complete amplifier (including idle load and reactor) into a low-temperature bath. This has been demonstrated by Knechtli[31] to reduce substantially the noise figure. Diodes having mechanical stability at low temperatures are required.

16.2d. Performance and Design of Some Typical Parametric Amplifiers. Three general circuit configurations have been used for three-frequency parametric amplifiers using single diodes. The circuit may be basically a waveguide, a coaxial line, or a printed-circuit strip. The differences in these approaches are only in the details of construction. Figure 16.17 illustrates an amplifier using a coaxial cavity, as designed by F. S. Harris.[32] The signal and idle resonances are produced by two resonances (the one-quarter- and three-quarter-wavelength resonances) of the cavity, while the pump frequency is applied through an untuned coupling. The entire cavity can be tuned to a different signal frequency, which requires readjustment of the pump frequency.

Figure 16.18 shows the cavity of Heffner and Kotzebue,[33] which through fortunate circumstances was found to have three independent resonances at signal, pump, and difference frequencies. The separate input and output connections are for convenience only and do not imply electrical separation. This amplifier has the same instability problems as any other similar device.

The input instability problem can be eliminated through the use of two diodes in a circuit resembling a balanced mixer.   If the diodes are perfectly matched and driven by pump voltages of the same amplitude, it is possible in principle to cancel signal power reflected to the input.   It is also possible in principle, using three diodes in a highly symmetrical circuit, to obtain complete separation of signal input, signal output, and idle output.

FIG. 16.18. Parametric amplifier using waveguide cavity simultaneously resonant at signal, idle, and pump frequencies.   (*From Heffner and Kotzebue, Proc. IRE, vol.* 46, *p.* 1301, *June,* 1958.)

The performance of various amplifiers which have been reported in the literature is tabulated in Table 16.1.   Circuit details can be obtained from the references cited.

Work is continuing toward higher frequencies; the availability of suitable diodes is the chief limitation.   At the time of writing, little work has been done on circuit optimization to achieve maximum gain-bandwidth product.   The problem of circuit stability has been more or less neglected, it being assumed that diodes of sufficient uniformity and stability would ultimately become available.   At the present, however, sensitivity of these amplifiers to changes of pump level and to matching is great; applications are ordinarily limited to laboratory-like environments.   The up-converter, because of its inherent stability, is not subject to these limitations and can be operated with fair reliability under conditions where adjustments cannot easily be made.

TABLE 16.1. SINGLE-DIODE PARAMETRIC AMPLIFIERS

Source	Signal band, kmc	Pump freq., kmc	Gain, db	Band-width, %	Noise figure, db	Refer-ence No.
Bell Telephone Laboratories.	6	12	18	0.13	6	34
Stanford..................	1.2	3.5	19	0.08	4.8	33
A.I.L.....................	0.4	8.9	18	0.63	<1†	35
Bell Telephone Laboratories.	6	12	16	0.43	0.3†	36
Hughes..................	3.1	?	?	?	1.3†	31
Bell Telephone Laboratories.	11.5	3	19	0.46	3.2†	37

† Double-sideband operation (*NF* about 3 db higher for single sideband).

16.2e. Traveling-wave Parametric Amplifiers. The operation of a simple parametric amplifier can be described in terms of a negative resistance. A distributed-
constant parametric device, as shown in Fig. 16.19, can produce waves propagating
with negative attenuation; signal and idle waves will build up exponentially as they
propagate along the line. The simplest form of this device, proposed originally by
Tien and Suhl,[38] is a transmission line loaded periodically with variable reactances.
A pump-frequency wave is sent down the line along with the signal wave. Tien shows
that a signal wave and idle wave traveling along the line in the *same* direction as the
pump wave will be amplified but if traveling in the *opposite* direction will *not* be
amplified. This makes possible a considerable increase in stability. This unilateral
property holds only if the spacing between diodes on the line is considerably less than
1 wavelength (signal frequency). If diodes are spaced by integral-wavelength distances, the proper phase relations among certain signal, pump, and idle frequencies
can be set up in either direction.

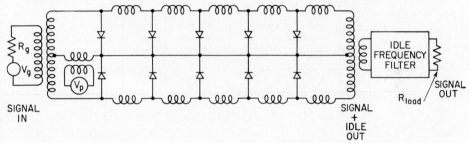

FIG. 16.19. Traveling-wave parametric amplifier using lumped-constant circuits and
balanced to prevent pump voltage appearance in signal circuit.

Placing high-impedance diodes directly across a line of, say, 50-ohm characteristic
impedance may not produce substantial gain per diode (or per unit length, for sensible
diode spacings). The diode impedance should be more nearly matched to that of the
line; this can be done through transformers connecting the diodes to the line. Complicated coupling networks, of course, will make the bandwidth and matching problems
more severe, however.

Good parametric operation can be achieved in such a loaded transmission line only
if frequencies greater than the pump frequency are not allowed to propagate on the
line.[39] A traveling-wave parametric amplifier, therefore, must be a low-pass or
bandpass circuit *rejecting* all sum frequencies which could result from the signal and
pump frequencies employed. The diodes discontinuously load the line, producing
a pass- and stop-band spectrum, characteristic of a filter. With proper diode spacing,
the desired sum-frequency cutoff can be obtained.

In practical traveling-wave devices, the application of pump power at the input end
of the line causes strong pumping of the first few diodes while the ones nearer the
output are more weakly pumped. As a result the waves on the line do not grow
exponentially. A possible but expensive solution to this problem is a separate pump
transmission line of the same phase velocity from which a small power is tapped to
feed each diode. Filtering in one or both lines is necessary to keep respective frequencies to their proper lines. All practical traveling-wave parametric amplifiers
have used a balanced system, with two diodes at each tap on the line; this effectively
prevents cross coupling of pump frequency with the other frequencies.

The gains (per diode) obtainable from traveling-wave parametric amplifiers are
relatively low, but bandwidths are large. Table 16.2 gives a summary of results
obtained from this type of device.

16.2f. Gain and Noise-figure Measurements on Three-frequency Parametric Amplifiers. Because of inherent instability, measurement of an unisolated parametric amplifier is very difficult. Whenever possible, a ferrite circulator should be used to separate input and output terminals. The isolation of the circulator must, of course, exceed the amplifier gain, or oscillation may still be possible. It may also be difficult, particularly with high-gain parametric amplifiers, to keep the gain and noise properties sufficiently constant over a long enough time interval to get a useful measurement.

TABLE 16.2

Source	Signal band, mc	Pump frequency, mc	Gain, db	Band-width, mc	Noise figure, db	Number of diodes	Reference No.
Bell Telephone Laboratories.......	400	890	10	100	1.0	8	40
Bell Telephone Laboratories.......	665	1,330	8–10	200	?	32	40
Airborne Instruments Laboratory........	2.5	5.0	6	3.8	1.5	24	41

For *gain measurements* on high-gain amplifiers, a simple isolator or a large attenuation can be placed in the input and output, as shown in Fig. 16.20. Input level and output level can then be calculated.

Noise figure must usually be measured with minimum attenuation in the circuit but with high-gain amplifiers (15 db or above). The use of an attenuator in the input and output may enable measurement to be made more readily than with the "bare" amplifier. Since the excess noise of a gas-tube noise source is about 15 db, no more than 10 db of input-circuit attenuation should be used. Attenuation which can be

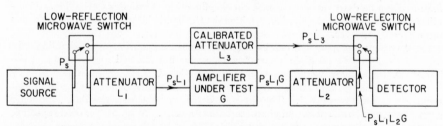

Fig. 16.20. Circuit which can be used to measure gain of high-sensitivity parametric amplifiers. A similar arrangement can be used to measure noise figure if noise source temperature (effective) and amplifier gain are large.

placed in the output circuit is limited by the noise figure of the following stage. The difficulty in noise measurement arises because the change in input or output match (of a negative-resistance amplifier) may change the gain appreciably. A gas-discharge noise source may change its match from perhaps 1.0 to 1.1 voltage-standing-wave ratio as the discharge is switched off and on. A parametric amplifier producing over 20-db gain can easily be forced into oscillation by such a change. When a noise measurement is being made, a change in gain, or oscillation, may be indistinguishable from the effects of an extremely good (or bad!) noise figure. Particular care must be observed when using an automatic indicating noise-figure meter.

In the case of extremely low-noise amplifiers, a noise source of lower effective temperature than the usual gas-discharge tube is permissible. A simple resistive termination which is alternately plunged into a liquid nitrogen bath and operated at room temperature will produce two calculable noise levels. A conventional termination may (depending on materials and construction) exhibit substantial difference in voltage-standing-wave ratio at the two temperatures; such a termination would not be useful for this purpose. This method is desirable if the noise introduced by the amplifier corresponds to an effective temperature of 50° or thereabouts, since even the $kT_0 \, \Delta f$ noise at 290° will be large compared with the internal noise.

By various techniques such as described, values of gain and noise figure can be obtained for an amplifier which is very "touchy"; this amplifier will hardly be practical, however, *unless* it can be operated in an isolated environment.

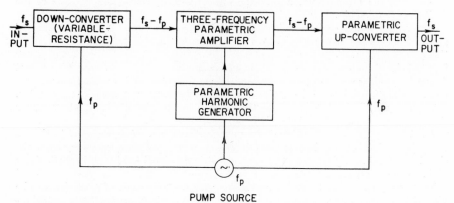

PUMP SOURCE

Fig. 16.21. Composite parametric amplifier having externally stable characteristics and using pump frequency lower than the signal frequency. (*After Chang, Proc. IRE, vol.* 47, *p.* 81, *January,* 1959.)

Some final cautions about parametric amplifier measurements: A circuit using a wideband detector may give incorrect results because of unwanted sidebands in the output. Also, in measurements on a high-gain parametric device, spurious oscillations sometimes occur which may or may not be recorded as output but which reduce gain in the band of interest. A spectrum analyzer is handy for detecting these unwanted frequencies.

16.2g. Parametric Up-converters. The Manley-Rowe relations show that the parametric up-converter is stable and should therefore be a highly useful device. The theoretical power gain, equal to the ratio of output to input frequency, can be approached (from below) only in practice. The noise performance, because there is no idle-circuit source of thermal noise, is excellent, the best of all parametric devices. The system problem of an up-converter is that the output frequency is much higher than the signal frequency. It must be followed by a down-converter, i.e., a conventional crystal mixer. K. K. N. Chang[42] has described a four-diode parametric device, schematically illustrated in Fig. 16.21, which up-converts, amplifies, and down-converts, using only a single pump source of frequency below the signal frequency. The first stage of the device is a parametric up-converter, the second stage a parametric amplifier, and the final stage a variable-resistance down-converter. A harmonic generator raises the effective pump frequency for lower noise figure. The device is said to be inherently stable without the need for isolators; this assumes that it is *internally* stable.

In *regenerative* up-converters, the gain is not limited, but there are the added complications of a fourth frequency and the noise generated by the termination at this frequency. The more the up-conversion gain is increased, the more effect the noise from the idle termination has on the noise figure. There has been little practical application of the regenerative up-converter principle, no doubt owing in part to the added circuit complexity.

Design of normal up-converters is similar to that of conventional crystal mixers, except that resonance should be provided at both input and output frequencies. If separate resonators are not used, care must be taken that feed-through will not disturb other parts of the system.

Up-converters at ultra high frequency (400 mc) have been reported[35] to produce 1.9-db noise figure and a gain only 2 db less than the frequency ratio. Bandwidth was about 7 per cent. The majority of the excess noise in this measurement was due to second-stage noise figure, a common difficulty in up-conversion because of the limited available gain.

16.2h. Modulation and Demodulation Using Parametric Diodes. The process of parametric modulation of a carrier by a low-frequency signal is equivalent to regenerative up-conversion. The Manley-Rowe relations show us that with very small power input at signal frequency f_1, power at the upper and lower sideband frequencies f_+ and f_- can be produced by the pump action. Thus, the parametric modulator can have large modulation gain. If the device is not properly matched, oscillations can occur.

The parametric demodulator, like the down-converter, is not a useful device, for the power output must be substantially less than the input.

16.2i. Low-frequency Pumping of Parametric Amplifiers. A frequent objection to normal parametric amplifiers is that they must be pumped by a frequency *above* the signal frequency. This may not be convenient if the signal frequency is particularly high. Chang and Bloom[43] have shown that parametric amplification can be produced using a pump frequency below the signal frequency. This mode of operation can be viewed in several ways. One can assume that the diode generates the second harmonics of the actual pump frequency and then proceeds to use this just as if it were the actual pump power. The other view is that the diode uses the low pump frequency directly. In any case, the idle frequency is $2f_0 - f_1$. The Manley-Rowe relations [Eqs. (16.10)], allowing only f_0, f_1, and $2f_0 - f_1$, become

$$\frac{W_0}{f_0} + \frac{2W_i}{2f_0 - f_1} = 0 \qquad \frac{W_1}{f_1} - \frac{W_i}{2f_0 - f_1} = 0 \qquad (16.16)$$

These relations show that it is not necessary for power at frequency $2f_0$ to flow *to* or *from* the reactor, for output will still occur at both signal and idle frequencies in the same ratio as in the normal parametric amplifier. To say that frequency $2f_0$ *does not appear* at the diode is incorrect, for the voltage across the diode will contain such a frequency component; the voltage need not produce external power, however.

No matter which way one looks at the low-frequency-pumped parametric amplifier, it is necessary to have reactor nonlinearity of one order higher than required for normal first-order parametric amplification. All diodes have higher-order nonlinearities, but they are not so pronounced as first-order (first order requires only linear variation of capacitance with voltage higher order requires square law or more). Because the nonlinearities are not so large, pump power must be greater for low-frequency pumping, and the losses within the reactor will become more important. In general, therefore, low-frequency pumping should be used only as an expedient to eliminate need for a higher-frequency pump source. The added pump power required may eliminate the advantage gained.

16.2j. Parametric Harmonic Generators. At frequencies where losses are not excessive, parametric diodes are most efficient harmonic generators. Figure 16.22

shows calculated loss versus harmonic for a parametric generator.[44] Loss per harmonic is considerably less than with a resistance diode. While the parametric device should have no loss if the diode and circuit were lossless, in practice the loss is substantial. Parametric diodes should be superior to resistive diodes at all frequencies; however, parametric diodes for millimeter wavelengths are not yet available. At high frequencies where the reactance of the depletion layer becomes considerably less than the spreading resistance, the parametric harmonic generator becomes almost useless, whereas the variable-resistance diode may still operate in this region.

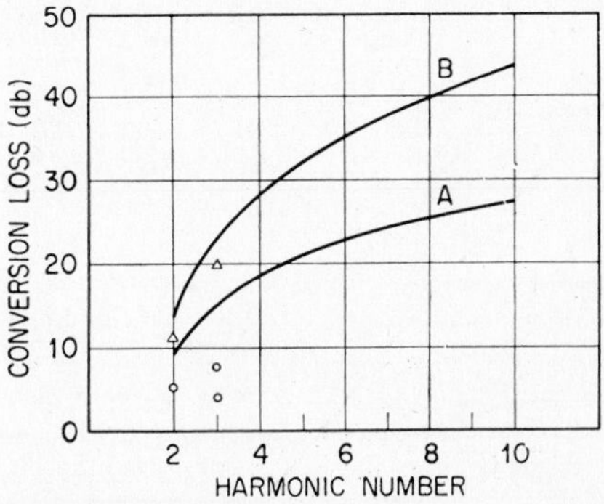

Power-dissipation capability, as for variable-resistance diodes, is the major power limitation, though considerably greater

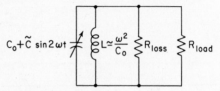

Fig. 16.22. Performance of parametric diode harmonic generator, calculated from actual diode parameters.[44]

Fig. 16.23. Equivalent circuit of a diode subharmonic oscillator.

power can be handled by junction parametric diodes than by point-contact diodes. Power in excess of 1 watt has been pumped into diodes to generate S-band output, while one diode producing useful output at 48 kmc has been stated to be capable of 300-mw dissipation.

Construction of parametric diode harmonic generator circuits is essentially identical with those using resistance diodes. Some form of external bias may be required for optimization of the former, however.

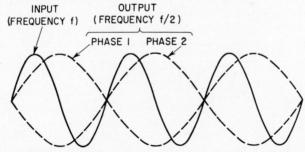

Fig. 16.24. Phase relationships between pump voltage and the two possible output voltages of a subharmonic oscillator.

16.2k. Parametric Subharmonic Generators, Bistable Oscillators. The circuit equation describing the circuit shown in Fig. 16.23 (where the capacitance variation is produced, in practice, by a pump voltage) can be reduced to the Mathieu equation

$$\frac{d^2E}{dt^2} + (a + 2q \cos 2t)E = 0 \tag{16.17}$$

The solutions of this equation grow exponentially with time for $q > 0$ when $a = 1$, 4, 9, . . . , n^2. This implies the growth of oscillations at frequency $nf_0/2$ on such a circuit when pumped at frequency f_0. The $f_0/2$ oscillation is the only one of great importance, because at larger n, extremely large values of q (pump power) are required for oscillation.

When the variation of the reactance is nonsinusoidal, oscillations may be obtained at any subharmonic f_0/m of the pump frequency as well as at other rationally related frequencies. Again, the $f_0/2$ case requires least pump power.

The case of frequency halving can be illustrated by a simple pendulum, using a weight on a piece of string. If the length of the string is altered periodically at twice the average frequency of the pendulum, the natural oscillations will increase with time. While the exponential *growing* oscillation is a mathematical idealism, it can readily be demonstrated that any loss in the circuit demands an incipient growth of oscillations to maintain *constant* oscillation amplitude. Diode losses and pump source impedance limit the amplitude of practical oscillators.

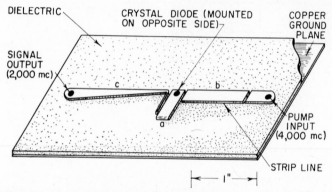

Fig. 16.25. Drawing of printed-circuit parametric oscillator pumped at 4,000 mc. (*From Sterzer, Proc. IRE, vol. 47, pp. 1317–1324, August, 1959.*)

Figure 16.24 illustrates the relations between the pump source and the oscillations. Two stable phases of oscillation are possible (corresponding to the two symmetrical locations of the pendulum at a time when the pump is at a particular point in its cycle). Either of these two oscillations, once started, will continue in the same phase as long as the pump continues and no oscillation-frequency voltage or transient comparable to the amplitude of the sustained oscillations is applied. Because of this bistability, parametric bistable oscillators have been used in binary computers.

Figure 16.25 shows a printed-circuit microwave PLO (phase-locked oscillator) which is pumped at 4,000 mc and oscillates at 2,000 mc.[45] A single output point appears on the circuit, which indicates that it is a two-terminal device.

The most important external characterization of a parametric oscillator, from a dynamic point of view, is how rapidly its oscillations grow to the saturation point once pump voltage is applied and oscillations begin to build up (from noise or an impressed voltage). A useful bistable device must be capable of changing its state rapidly from one oscillation phase to the other; this can be accomplished with a small locking signal of the desired phase. The pump is turned off (or the diode short-circuited) to damp oscillations in the original phase; the injected signal is applied; then normal pumping or diode operation is resumed. If the oscillator can increase its oscillation amplitude rapidly, it can either (1) be locked by a very small locking signal or (2) be completely changed in phase in a very short time. Gain and rise time serve to distinguish this device, analogously to gain and bandwidth in a linear amplifier.

Figure 16.26 shows some rise-time curves taken by Onyshkevych and Kosonocky†

† RCA Laboratories, Princeton, N.J.

from an oscillator operating around 3 mc. The time for the curves to rise by a factor $e = 2.718$ approximated 2 cycles of the oscillation frequency. Analysis by Hilibrand and Beam[26] shows that for ideal junction diodes in circuits with minimum parasitic capacitance, rise time can be almost as small as 1 cycle. The rise time depends almost entirely on the relative variation of diode capacitance which can be achieved. The static, nonvarying capacitance component of the diode sets the lower limit to rise time. Loss in the diode or circuit or extraneous capacitance in the circuit will cause

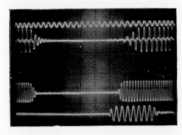

REFERENCE $(f_p/2)$

OSCILLATOR OUTPUT $(f_p/2)$

PUMP BURST

LOCKING SIGNAL

FIG. 16.26. Illustrating rise time of parametric oscillator after application of pump voltage to diode. (*From Onyshkevych, Kosonocky, and Lo, IRE Trans. on Electronic Computers, vol. EC-8 pp. 277, 286, fig. 13, September, 1959.*)

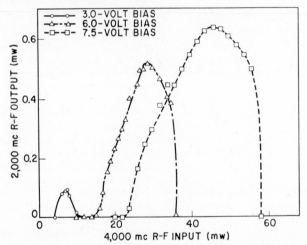

FIG 16.27. Power input-output characteristics of a typical oscillator of the type shown in Fig. 16.25. (*From Sterzer, Proc. IRE, vol. 47, pp. 1317–1324, August, 1959.*)

an increase in the rise time. It can be shown that the rise time of a diode in a parametric oscillator is directly related to the maximum gain-bandwidth product which can be achieved in a parametric amplifier circuit using the diode.

The rise time of the 2,000-mc oscillator of Fig. 16.25 is about 4 cycles of the oscillation frequency. Thus, in 2×10^{-9} sec, the diode can produce a voltage amplified by a factor of 2.7 from the voltage which selected its oscillation phase. This oscillator could presumably be used in binary computer circuitry operating at pulse repetition rates exceeding 100 mc.

The relation between input and output power of the oscillator of Fig. 16.25 is shown in Fig. 16.27 for several bias levels.

16.2l. Computer Applications of Bistable Parametric Oscillators. One of the simplest computer applications is in the shift register shown in Fig. 16.28. This mode of operation was used by the Japanese[46] in the first parametric-oscillator computer; the parametric oscillators in this machine, which are made from ferrite cores and utilize magnetic nonlinearity, are called "parametrons." Diode oscillators can be used in the same way.

In the shift register circuit, three separate pump power bursts are shifted in time and slightly overlapped (Fig. 16.29). The output of the first parametric oscillator is

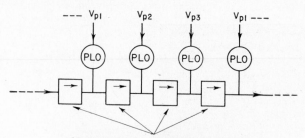

ATTENUATORS OR NONRECIPROCAL
ELEMENTS (IF ISOLATORS USED,
THREE-PHASE PUMP SUPPLY NOT
ESSENTIAL)

FIG. 16.28. Parametric-oscillator shift register using three-phase pump-voltage bursts. (*After Goto, Proc. IRE, vol. 47, pp. 1304–1316, August, 1959.*)

connected to the input of the second, etc. When the first parametric oscillator is operating, it produces a locking signal for the second, and so forth. If the coupling is sufficiently small between units, the problem of feed through may not be serious; at microwave frequencies, ferrite isolators can be used[45] to prevent signal power from progressing in the wrong direction along the shift register.

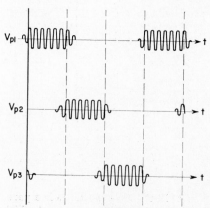

FIG. 16.29. "Three-phase" pump voltages applied to parametric-oscillator logic circuits such as shift register in preceding figure.

Logic elements such as "and" gates[47] can be constructed readily with the use of parametric oscillators. The phase properties of the binary outputs can be used in a novel way to get a logical function which is called a "majority" function. If the outputs from a number of oscillators are added together, the resultant will have the phase of the majority of the inputs; i.e., two signals of opposite phase will completely cancel each other. Output amplitudes from all oscillators must be equal. A two-input "and" gate is shown schematically in Fig. 16.30. In the more complicated circuits such as this one, care must be taken that the outputs (such as the sum output) are of the proper phase regardless of which combination of inputs produces the output.

Storage using parametric oscillators is simple in principle. The oscillator simply oscillates steadily at its desired phase, and to change the phase, the pump is removed from one oscillator without disturbing the other oscillators in the memory. A selection scheme similar to the coincident current method used in ferrite-core memories[48] is possible. If all oscillators are fed from two separate pump sources, either of which will sustain oscillations when applied alone, only that oscillator in the array which has both sources of pump power removed together will drop out of oscillation. "Reading" is more difficult than selection; in principle, the output of the "dying" oscillator can be sensed. To "write," a small locking signal of the desired phase is applied to all oscillators. Only the one not already oscillating is affected; it thus builds up oscillations in the desired phase.

Simple as these schemes may appear, building a complete computer with parametric oscillators is a difficult project. Maintaining and controlling the application of pump power to perhaps 10,000 diodes so as to maintain uniform output are not easy. Particularly where very high speed is desired, the location and interconnection of so large a number of diodes will critically affect the performance of the machine.

A parametric-oscillator computer, if operated at sufficiently large pump frequency, has a potential speed advantage over transistor or vacuum-tube computers at the present stage of device development. At pump frequency of 20,000 mc, pulse repetition rates up to 1,000 mc may be possible; systems techniques to handle these speeds are not presently available. At these pulse speeds, only the tunnel diode offers competition, and because of its greater simplicity, the tunnel diode may prove the victor.

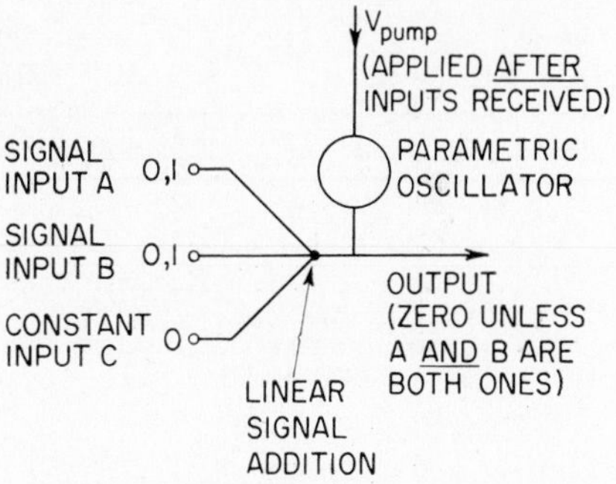

16.2m. Biasing Parametric Diodes. Best parametric operation is obtained when the diode is driven positive by the pump voltage to a point at which its capacitance is a maximum but the shunt loss is still small; on the opposite half cycle, the diode should be driven to some voltage safely short of reverse breakdown.

Bias may be applied by means of an external d-c supply. Fixed-voltage bias, with external voltage adjustment, is the best way to operate when the average capacitance of the diode must be adjusted precisely to match the circuit or to match other diodes. The most common bias method is to leave the diode open-circuited to direct current. It is then self-biased to a level which limits the shunt conductance at peak drive to a reasonable value. This bias gives very strong parametric action and is much less sensitive to pump drive level than fixed bias. A combination of fixed bias with external resistance is probably the best for most purposes, for the external resistor affords some degree of insensitivity to pump level while the bias voltage allows the capacitance value to be adjusted somewhat.

Fig. 16.30. Parametric "and" gate. Two inputs of opposite phase will cancel, hence the presence of a third, constant input of phase corresponding to the digit "zero" will cause the oscillator to synchronize to "zero" phase unless *both* inputs A and B are of "unity" phase.

If the parametric device is to be modulated by the application of time-varying bias voltages (as in some computer logic applications), the total resistance external to the diode must be made low and comparable to the source impedance of the bias modulator or the diode will not respond rapidly to bias changes. Driving the diode in the forward direction is particularly to be avoided in such applications, since the storage of minority carriers will produce long relaxation time.

16.3. Tunnel-diode Applications. *16.3a. Equivalent Circuit and Typical Parameters.* The tunnel diode typically has the voltage-current characteristic shown in Fig. 16.31a. A negative-resistance (negative-slope) region occurs in the range from around 100 to perhaps 350 mv (for good germanium units). The equivalent circuit of Fig. 16.31b applies approximately in the negative-resistance range. The capacitance, as usual, is not constant, but for normal operation the variation is small.

The capacitance of a typical germanium tunnel diode in the negative-resistance region is of the order of 5 μf/cm^2, so that even a junction of dimensions equivalent to those of a high-frequency transistor will have a capacitance in the vicinity of 25 to 100 $\mu\mu$f.[49] A capacitance of 100 $\mu\mu$f is typically accompanied by a negative resistance of about 1 ohm. The spreading resistance itself is small, because the diode material is very heavily doped, but lead resistance may contribute greatly to the total series resistance R_s.

The upper frequency limit is set by the frequency at which the *total* impedance of the diode no longer has a negative resistance component. Assuming the equivalent circuit of Fig. 16.31b, this will be at frequency

$$\omega = \frac{\sqrt{R - R_s}}{\sqrt{R_s}\,RC} \qquad (16.18)$$

where R is the *absolute value* of the negative resistance. This also indicates the obvious point that, to develop negative resistance at all, the diode must have a spreading resistance less than its negative resistance. Welded-contact germanium diodes in World War II sometimes showed negative resistance; more often it was masked by high spreading resistance.

16.3b. Tunnel-diode Circuits, General. Present-day tunnel diodes are limited by manufacturing techniques to junctions a mil or more in diameter, though there is no fundamental reason why smaller junctions could not be made. As a result, the low diode impedances must be matched with equally low circuit impedances. At frequencies in excess of 2,000 mc, the reactance of a 100-$\mu\mu$f capacitor is less than 1 ohm, so that a tunnel diode of that capacitance does not readily match impedance to that of a normal 50-ohm transmission line. Most crystal diodes of the mixer varieties are small perturbations when placed in high-impedance circuits,

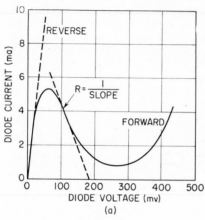

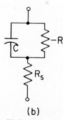

Fig. 16.31. (a) Voltage-current characteristic of typical tunnel diode. (*After Sommers, Proc. IRE, vol. 47, p. 1202, August, 1959.*) (b) Equivalent circuit.

hence are located near points of voltage maximum in a cavity or transmission line. Tunnel diodes, on the other hand, act more like short circuits than open circuits and in high-impedance lines must be located at points where the voltage is nearly zero and the current is large. In attempts to use high-impedance transmission lines with tunnel diodes, problems arise because of the high resistance of the small conductors which adds to the spreading resistance and reduces performance. If printed-circuit transmission lines of very low impedance are employed, the diode can be made a relatively small perturbation across the line. The resistance of the conductors of the line must be small if the maximum capabilities of the diode are to be attained. A special *diode mount* is important, for if the standard type of crystal cartridge were used, the extraneous inductance and lead losses would seriously affect performance. Special diode mounts have been devised which incorporate broad connections to both sides of the junction in order to reduce both inductance and resistance (Fig. 16.32).

The parametric oscillator develops negative resistance only at certain frequencies and is easily restrained from producing serious parasitic oscillations. The tunnel-diode oscillator (or for that matter, any tunnel-diode circuit) has negative resistance down to zero frequency and has serious problems of parasitic oscillation. Referring to the V-I characteristic of Fig. 16.33, if a diode has a d-c supply voltage supplied to it through a very small resistance, as in case I, there is only one possible intercept of the characteristic on the load line and operation is stable; the device is said to be "short-circuit stable." If (as in case II) the resistance of the power supply or any other resistance in the line through which the diode receives power is large, two stable operating points, X and Y, together with an intermediate unstable intercept, are possible. In addition, if the a-c impedance in the supply circuit, at some frequency f, is purely resistive and equivalent to the load line III, oscillations will occur at that frequency. Precautions are required to prevent oscillations at frequencies determined by power-supply connections or some other (presumably inactive) part of the circuit. In the absence of such precautions, it is customary to find several frequencies of oscillation, none of which is the desired value, all of them at frequencies lower than the one of interest.

FIG. 16.32. A tunnel diode mount having very low losses and inductance. (*By permission of Radio Corporation of America and Electronic Industries, vol.* 19, *January,* 1960, *p.* 82, 1960.)

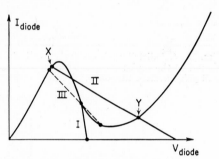

FIG. 16.33. Stable and unstable operating conditions of a tunnel diode.

To eliminate low-frequency oscillations, a shunting resistance smaller in value than the negative-resistance value may be located in the power-supply leads, as near as possible to the diode. Several such resistors may be needed, in certain cases, to prevent all possible spurious modes of oscillation. These damping resistors have an undesirable effect at very low frequencies, since they may absorb more power than that used by the diode itself. Nevertheless, they appear to be the best way of eliminating undesired oscillations. Figure 16.34 shows a simple tunnel-diode oscillator and the desired mode of oscillation. The damping resistance is located very near the diode itself, at a voltage null on the transmission-line resonator. At frequencies of several thousand megacycles, the resistance may be located only a small fraction of an inch from the diode (the distance depending on the frequency range of operation) and must be very small. A power-dissipation problem may arise; however, the broad metal conductors used in these devices can dissipate large amounts of heat. Both the damping resistor and the power-supply connections are located at voltage-zero points of the line. While, in principle, they may be coincident, it is usually easier to locate the power-supply connection at a different null point, farther from the diode.

In circuits employing short-circuit-stable negative resistances such as the tunnel diode, the use of "bypass" capacitors to provide a-c short circuits at certain points may be unsatisfactory because the capacitance used must be many times greater than that of the diode for effective bypassing.   Capacitors of sufficient capacitance generally have high-inductance leads which render them of little value.

16.3c. Tunnel-diode Oscillators.   Several types of tunnel-diode oscillators have been reported in the literature.   At Bell Laboratories, oscillations above 2,000 mc were obtained using the very small cavity illustrated in Fig. 16.35.[50]   This cavity acts

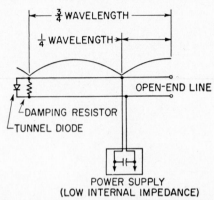

FIG. 16.34. A distributed-constant tunnel-diode oscillator circuit.   The power supply is connected to the tank resonator at a voltage null point.   The diode damping resistor, at the null point nearest the diode, prevents modes of oscillation of longer wavelength.

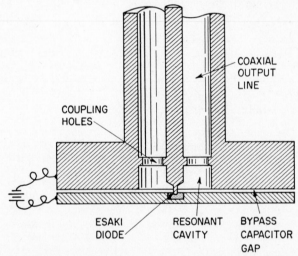

FIG. 16.35. Tunnel-diode oscillator cavity.   The cavity here is much smaller than an unloaded cavity because of the large diode capacitance.   (*M. E. Hines, Bell System Tech. J., vol.* 39, *May,* 1960, *and courtesy of Bell Telephone Laboratories.*)

essentially as a very small one-turn inductance; the capacitance of the diode determines the resonant frequency.   Output is taken from the end connections.   This cavity is much smaller than an unloaded cavity of the same resonant frequency and illustrates one difficulty in going to higher frequencies with high-capacitance diodes.

Output power of tunnel-diode oscillators is sufficient to recommend their application as pump sources for parametric amplifiers or local oscillators for crystal mixers.   Since the voltage range, for negative resistance, of tunnel diodes is a few hundred millivolts, single-diode oscillators must rely on higher current to generate larger power.   As yet, no practical series-connection stacking of diodes has been achieved to increase the voltage. Such stacking would have serious circuit problems; from external measurements, it could not be determined which stable condition each diode of the stack assumed.

16.3d. Tunnel-diode Amplifiers. Since the tunnel diode is a two-terminal negative-resistance device, it is not possible to build unilateral amplifier circuits without the aid of ferrite circulators or isolators. Signal input and output coupling must be similar to that of parametric amplifiers. A simple narrow-band tunnel-diode amplifier can be built from a tunnel-diode oscillator circuit such as shown in Fig. 16.34. External coupling circuits are attached for input and output, and the impedance reflected by a load resistance prevents oscillation. The equivalent circuit of Fig. 16.15a can be used to predict performance.

The traveling-wave tunnel-diode amplifier shows considerably more promise as a practical device. If the diodes are located along a transmission line of such low impedance that they represent small *negative conductances* relative to line impedance level, signal waves sent along the line will grow exponentially. Waves sent in from either end will grow in this fashion; isolators placed along the line will restrict growth to the desired direction. Since building and coupling to a low-impedance line are difficult and ferrite isolators are very difficult to apply to such a line, it is more sensible to couple the diodes to the line by means of impedance transformers. Each diode will then have its associated damping resistance nearby and consequently may not amplify over large bandwidths. Very broadband operation is seldom necessary, however, and involves serious parasitic oscillation problems.

The gain-bandwidth product of a tunnel-diode amplifier depends, as in all R-C networks, on the inverse product $1/RC$, where R is again the magnitude of the negative resistance and C the junction capacitance. A diode having 1-ohm negative resistance and 100-$\mu\mu$f capacitance would have a voltage-gain–bandwidth product around 1,600 mc, which exceeds that of most parametric diodes. Chang[51] has reported an amplifier with a gain of 27 db and a bandwidth of 0.8 mc at a center frequency of 30 mc.

The noise performance of tunnel diodes is somewhat inferior to that of parametric diodes, because the tunnel diode uses a conduction current rather than a variable (lossless) reactance to produce amplification. The sources of noise in a tunnel diode, furthermore, can be described in terms of the "shot current" across the junction. Chang's[51] lowest measured noise figure was 4.5 db, not fantastically low but low enough to make the device of interest. The parametric amplifier can be expected to yield better noise performance at any frequency but the added complexity of the pump and idle circuits is a practical disadvantage.

16.3e. Tunnel-diode Applications in High-speed Computers. Since the gain-bandwidth product of a tunnel diode is over 1,000 mc (at the present state of development), it is promising as a device for high-speed computer logic. The switching speed of the device can be approximated as $T_s = RC$, which gives a theoretical value of about 10^{-10} sec. This is faster than any other known device compatible in size, cost, etc., with computer applications.

In computer applications, the diode will normally come to rest in one of its stable conditions of d-c operation, so that the parasitic-oscillation problem is not quite so severe. It can be readily put to use as a storage element, for the two stable operating points give distinguishable storage states.

Consider the circuit of Fig. 16.36a. The input current-voltage characteristic is as shown in Fig. 16.36b. If no current is applied to selection terminals X and Y (simulating a matrix arrangement), the diode may operate at either V_A or V_B. If at V_A, the introduction of a momentary current which exceeds I' will cause switching to V_B. Similarly, a negative current will cause switching to V_A from V_B. The device operates analogously to a magnetic memory core, except that amplified output power can be obtained from the circuit. This circuit can be read in several ways, none of them apparently so convenient as that used in magnetic core memories. For example, the switching transient contains high-frequency components which can be sensed externally. The same type of circuit can be used as a logic gate or switch, but because tunnel diodes are two-terminal devices, a stability problem arises in computer applications, just as in linear amplifiers. The input terminals cannot be distinguished from the output terminals, and steps must be taken to ensure that the signal information

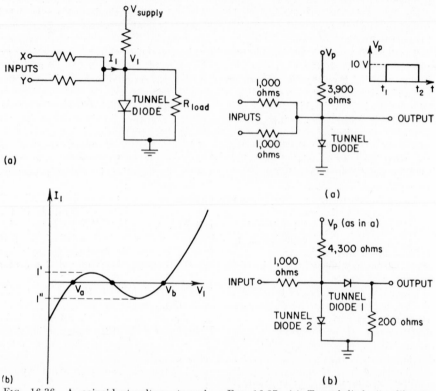

Fig. 16.36. A coincident-voltage tunnel-diode storage element: (a) circuit; (b) characteristics.

Fig. 16.37. (a) Tunnel-diode "and" gate, including typical circuit constants. (b) Tunnel-diode inverter.[52]

moves in the desired direction through the logic system. In computers operating with "baseband" signals, which have spectra down to direct current, it is not possible to use ferrite isolators to enable one-way transmission. On the other hand, since the elements are sensitive to the direction of the voltage or current, rectifying diodes may be employed in certain positions.

Logic elements which have two stable states (a high-voltage state and a low-voltage state) should be switched from the low-voltage to the high-voltage state by a relatively small input signal. By adjustment of circuit parameters, the current required to return the element to the low-voltage state may be increased, so that a circuit cannot be reset by current fed back to an earlier stage. Since the reset to the lower voltage state cannot be done through the signal circuit, an external reset mechanism must be provided. Lewin[52] has proposed a system of logic elements using a three-phase square-wave constant-current power source which operates in much the same way as that used in the Japanese parametron computer.[46] When the power source pulse is removed, all elements are automatically reset. Logic circuits for the "and" and "invert" functions are shown in Fig. 16.37. The "and" gate in Fig. 16.37a has a V-I characteristic similar to that shown in Fig. 16.36b, when the power pulse is applied. The diode, in the absence of current through the input resistors, will assume its low-voltage stable condition. If current totaling I' is injected through input resistors, the diode will switch to V_B and remain there until the power pulse ends or a negative current exceeding I'' is applied. The latter situation is not permitted in the over-all circuit arrangement. The inverter ("not" gate) of Fig. 16.36b must produce a low-voltage output if triggered with positive input current, otherwise (when not pulsed by positive input) the high-voltage output. The diode D_1 is the important part of this circuit, for the diode D_2 always remains in the high-voltage stable region when power is applied. Diode D_1, however, is not sufficiently motivated in the absence of input and has low voltage across it. The result is a large output voltage. The introduction of input current raises the voltage on the D_1–200-ohm resistor combination sufficiently to cause D_1 to switch to its high-voltage condition and remain there, producing a low drop across the output load resistor. Inversion is thus achieved.

Lewin[52] constructed 1-mc pulse-rate logic subsystems which demonstrate performance of these units. Impedance levels used for input and load resistances were somewhat high, which yielded a 50-nsec switching time. Tunnel diodes capable of 1,000-mc gain-bandwidth product should be capable of considerably shorter switching times.

REFERENCES

1. Torrey, H. C., and C. A. Whitmer: "Crystal Rectifier," Radiation Laboratory Series vol. 15, McGraw-Hill Book Company, Inc., New York, 1948. Other volumes in this series deal extensively with microwave receivers.
2. Reference 1, pp. 398–416.
3. Esaki, L.: New Phenomenon in Narrow Ge P-N Junctions, *Phys. Rev.*, vol. 109, p. 603, 1958.
4. Messenger, G. C., and C. T. McCoy: A Low Noise-figure Microwave Crystal Diode, *IRE Conv. Record*, part 8, pp. 68–73, 1955.
5. Jenny, D. A.: A Gallium Arsenide Microwave Diode, *Proc. IRE*, vol. 46, pp. 717–722, April, 1958.
6. McCoy, C. T.: Present and Future Capabilities of Microwave Crystal Receivers, *Proc. IRE*, vol. 46, pp. 61–65, January, 1958.
7. Van Voorhis, S. N.: "Microwave Receivers," Radiation Laboratory Series, vol. 23, McGraw-Hill Book Company, Inc., New York, 1943.
8. Pound, R. V.: "Microwave Mixers," chap. 6, Radiation Laboratory Series, vol. 16, McGraw-Hill Book Company, Inc., New York, 1948.
9. Friis, H. T.: Noise Figures of Radio Receivers, *Proc. IRE*, vol. 32, pp. 419–422, July, 1944.
10. IRE Standards on Receivers, Standard 52IRE 17.51, *Proc. IRE*, vol. 40, p. 1684, December, 1952.
11. Mumford, W. W.: A Broad-band Microwave Noise Source, *Bell System Tech. J.*, vol. 28, p. 608, October, 1949.
12. Reference 1, p. 30.
13. van der Ziel, A.: "Noise," pp. 190ff, Prentice-Hall, Inc., Englewood Cliffs, N.J., 1954.
14. Heffner, H.: Masers and Parametric Amplifiers, *IRE WESCON Conv. Record*, part 3, pp. 3–7, 1958.
15. Smullin, L., and C. G. Montgomery: "Microwave Duplexers," Radiation Laboratory Series, vol. 14, McGraw-Hill Book Company, Inc., New York, 1948.
16. Reference 1, p. 431.
17. Messenger, G. C.: New Concepts in Microwave Mixer Diodes, *Proc. IRE*, vol. 46, pp. 1116–1121, June, 1958.
18. Fox, A. G., S. E. Miller, and M. T. Weiss: Behavior and Application of Ferrites in the Microwave Region, *Bell System Tech. J.*, vol. 34, pp. 5–103, January, 1955.
19. Arams, F. R., and G. Krayer: Low-loss L-band Circulator, *Proc. IRE*, vol. 47, p. 442, March, 1959.

20. Brown, W. C.: Description and Operating Characteristics of the Platinotron—A New Microwave Tube Device, *Proc. IRE*, vol. 46, pp. 1209–1222, September, 1957.
21. Reference 1, p. 333.
22. Reference 13, pp. 139ff.
23. Reference 1, p. 346.
24. Burrus, C. A., and W. Gordy: *Phys. Rev.*, vol. 93, p. 897, 1954.
25. Shockley, W.: The Theory of P-N Junctions in Semiconductors and P-N Junction Transistors, *Bell System Tech. J.*, vol. 28, p. 435, July, 1949.
26. Hilibrand, J., and W. R. Beam: Semiconductor Diodes in Parametric Subharmonic Oscillators, *RCA Rev.*, vol. 20, pp. 229–253, June, 1959.
27. Reference 26, p. 239.
28. Manley, J. M., and H. E. Rowe: Some General Properties of Nonlinear Elements: I. General Energy Relations, *Proc. IRE*, vol. 44, pp. 904–913, July, 1956.
29. Hsu, Hsiung: Multiple Frequency Parametric Devices, in "Digest of Technical Papers," Solid State Circuits Conference, Philadelphia, Pa., 1959.
30. Heffner, H., and G. Wade: Gain, Bandwidth and Noise Characteristics of the Variable-parameter Amplifier, *J. Appl. Phys.*, vol. 29, pp. 1321–1331, September, 1958.
31. Knechtli, R. C., and R. D. Weglein: Low Noise Parametric Amplifier, *Proc. IRE*, vol. 47, p. 584, April, 1959.
32. Uhlir, Jr., A. H.: "Varactors," Microwave Associates, Burlington, Mass., February, 1959.
33. Heffner, H., and K. Kotzebue: Experimental Characteristics of a Microwave Parametric Amplifier Using a Semiconductor Diode, *Proc. IRE*, vol. 46, p. 1301, June, 1958.
34. Herrman, G. F., M. Uenohara, and A. Uhlir, Jr.: Noise Figure Measurements on Two Types of Variable Reactance Amplifiers Using Semiconductor Diodes, *Proc. IRE*, vol. 46, pp. 1301–1303, June, 1958.
35. Lombardo, P. P.: Low Noise 400 Mc Reactance Amplifiers, in "Digest of Papers," Solid State Circuits Conference, Philadelphia, Pa., 1959.
36. Uenohara, M., and W. M. Sharpless: An Extremely Low-noise 6 KMc Parametric Amplifier Using Gallium Arsenide Point-contact Diodes, *Proc. IRE*, vol. 47, pp. 2114–2115, December, 1959.
37. DeLoach, C. B., and W. M. Sharpless: An X-band Parametric Amplifier, *Proc. IRE*, vol. 47, pp. 1664–1665, September, 1959, also p. 2115, December, 1959.
38. Tien, P. K., and H. Suhl: A Traveling-wave Ferromagnetic Amplifier, *Proc. IRE*, vol. 46, pp. 700–706, April, 1958.
39. Roe, G. M., and M. R. Boyd: Parametric Energy Conversion in Distributed Systems, *Proc. IRE*, vol. 47, pp. 1213–1218, July, 1959.
40. Englebrecht, R. S.: Non-linear Reactance (Parametric) Traveling-wave Amplifier for UHF, in "Digest of Papers," Solid State Circuits Conference, Philadelphia, Pa., 1959.
41. Lombardo, P. P., and E. W. Sard: Low-frequency Prototype Traveling-wave Reactance Amplifier, *Proc. IRE*, vol. 47, pp. 995–996, May, 1959.
42. Chang, K. K. N.: Four-terminal Parametric Amplifier, *Proc. IRE*, vol. 47, p. 81, January, 1959.
43. Chang, K. K. N., and S. Bloom: A Parametric Amplifier Using Lower-frequency Pumping, *Proc. IRE*, vol. 46, pp. 1385–1386, July, 1958.
44. Leenov, D., and A. Uhlir, Jr.: Generation of Harmonics and Subharmonics at Microwave Frequencies with P-N Junction Diodes, *Proc. IRE*, vol. 47, pp. 1724–1729, October, 1959.
45. Sterzer, F.: Microwave Parametric Subharmonic Oscillator for Digital Computing, *Proc. IRE*, vol. 47, pp. 1317–1324, August, 1959.
46. Goto, E.: The Parametron, a Digital Computing Element Which Utilizes Parametric Oscillation, *Proc. IRE*, vol. 47, pp. 1304–1316, August, 1959.
47. Phister, Jr., M.: "Logical Design of Digital Computers," pp. 21ff, McGraw-Hill Book Company, Inc., New York, 1959.
48. Reference 47, pp. 195ff.
49. Sommers, Jr., H. S.: Tunnel Diodes as High-frequency Devices, *Proc. IRE*, vol. 47, pp. 1201–1206, July, 1959.
50. Batdorf, R. L.: "An Esaki-type Diode in InSb," reported at Solid State Devices Research Conference, Cornell University, Ithaca, N.Y., June, 1959.
51. Chang, K. K. N.: Low-noise Tunnel-diode Amplifier, *Proc. IRE*, vol. 47, pp. 1268–1269, July, 1959.
52. Lewin, M.: Negative Resistance Elements as Digital Computer Components, *Proc. of the 1959 Eastern Joint Computer Conference* (Boston, Dec. 1–3).

Section 17

POWER SUPPLIES

L. P. HUNTER

IBM Corporation, Poughkeepsie, N.Y.

17.1. Unregulated A-C to D-C Power Supplies. The rectifying properties of a semiconductor junction provide the basis for designing simple low-cost power supplies. Semiconductor power rectifiers must be treated differently from vacuum-tube rectifiers because they are much more easily destroyed by momentary overloads. A semiconductor junction is capable of delivering an indefinitely large amount of surge current, since it is not limited by space-charge or cathode-emission effects. If, then, a sudden surge is drawn from a semiconductor junction, the I^2R heating in the very small volume of the junction region may very well melt the material and destroy the rectifier. This fusing action can be extremely rapid and is difficult to protect against except by proper initial design aimed at limiting surges.

In Fig. 17.1 is shown a log-log plot of the ratio of the surge-current rating to the d-c rating (i_{SR}/I_{DCR}) of some typical silicon power rectifiers as a function of the duration of the surge. It can be seen that for times longer than 1 cycle of 60-cycle current the alloy types show the same slope, indicating a power law dependence ($i_S^n t$ = constant, where $n \sim 5.6$). Most manufacturers plot surge ratings only down to 1 cycle.

For times very much shorter than 1 cycle the power n might be expected to approach 2, since $i_S^2 t$ is proportional to the total energy in the surge. Indeed one manufacturer

† Adapted from the original text of H. C. Hurtig, Sec. 13, 1st ed.

suggests that for surges of duration less than 1 cycle such a law is followed and gives a value for the constant to be used in calculating the surge rating. From Fig. 17.1 it seems unlikely that the power should drop from 5.6 to 2 very suddenly at 1 cycle, and it is probably safer to extrapolate the power law dependence shown if it is desired to estimate allowable surges for times shorter than one cycle.

The real limitation involved in surge rating is the maximum permissible temperature of the semiconductor junction. For very short surges the temperature is determined by the total energy in the surge and the heat capacity of the material in the immediate neighborhood of the junction. The amount of material involved decreases as the

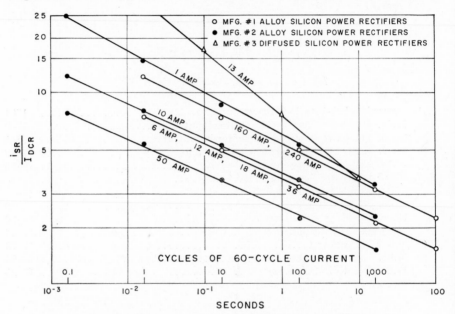

Fig. 17.1. Surge current ratings of silicon power rectifiers.

duration of the surge decreases, since the heat created has a shorter time to diffuse away an appreciable distance. This effect may account for the power n remaining greater than 2 for even very short surges.

All but one of the curves of Fig. 17.1 represent silicon alloy-junction rectifiers. In the case of manufacturer 1, all his units appear to fall on two curves. If a family of rectifiers is designed using identical materials in the alloy junction, the heat-conducting stud, and the solder attaching the semiconductor crystal to the stud, and if the area of the junction together with the cross-sectional area of the connection to the stud is the only variable, it is to be expected that the units would be rated in direct proportion to their areas and should have identical surge curves, since, in effect, the larger units merely represent several smaller units in parallel. On the other hand it is more difficult to get uniform high-quality junctions in large-area alloy junctions, so that it is to be expected that the larger units of a family should be rated somewhat lower than a strict scaling of their areas would imply. Such behavior is shown by the alloy units of manufacturer 2. If different materials are used in alloying to give a higher fusing point of the alloy, or if a higher melting solder is used, it is possible to improve the surge rating even though the d-c rating is relatively unchanged. This follows from the fact that the d-c rating is determined by a junction temperature at which the rectification ratio is still good whereas the surge rating is determined by the temperature at which permanent damage occurs to the unit. The temperature at which the rectification ratio is still good is strictly determined by the type of semi-conductor material and its level of doping (see Fig. 10.6).

The surge curve of the diffused silicon rectifier unit shown in Fig. 17.1 indicates that diffused rectifiers have better surge tolerance than alloy rectifiers. Diffused units have an inherent advantage in that there is no alloy to melt during a surge. On the other hand they do have to have some sort of solder attachment to the stud, and this material must be able to withstand the heat of the surge without fusing.

17.1a. Half-wave Rectifier, Capacitor-input Filter.[1] This circuit is the simplest power-supply circuit which can be used. The circuit arrangement is shown in Fig. 17.2. The circuit for which the power supply is being designed determines the maximum direct current I_{DC} required as well as the full-load d-c voltage (V_{DCL}), the voltage regulation, and the permissible ripple. The voltage regulation will be expressed in terms of a voltage reduction increment V_{red}, defined as the fraction by which the no-load or open-circuit voltage V_{CO} is reduced to give the full-load voltage.

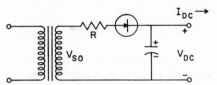

Fig. 17.2. Half-wave rectifier, capacitor-input filter.

$$V_{red} = \frac{V_{CO} - V_{DCL}}{V_{CO}} \tag{17.1}$$

In order to specify the components of this circuit we must calculate:

1. With respect to the transformer:
   The open-circuit secondary voltage V_{so}
   The effective secondary winding resistance r_s
   The rms current in both windings I_s and I_p
2. With respect to the rectifier:
   The peak inverse voltage v_P
   The peak turn-on surge current i_S
   The peak recurring surge current i_{RS}
   The duration of the surges
   The average d-c output voltage and direct current
3. The total surge-limiting resistance of the circuit R
4. With respect to the capacitor:
   The capacitance C
   The rms current in the capacitor I_c

The exact analysis of even this simple circuit is time-consuming because of the non-linearity of the semiconductor rectifier characteristic. However, good results can be obtained from some simple curves and formulas.

Let us first consider qualitatively what to expect in one or two simple cases. If we assume that we have a charging time constant RC which is short compared with one half cycle of the alternating current and a discharging time constant $R_L C$ which is long compared with one half cycle, we can hold our voltage reduction V_{red} constant at a relatively low value. Now for a constant C on each positive half cycle of current the capacitor will receive a fixed charge Q, even though we vary R, as long as RC is short compared with 1 cycle. On the negative half cycle for a constant voltage reduction this fixed Q will be drained away by the load, and the direct current I_{DC} will be constant and independent of RC. The turn-on surge current i_S, however, will vary as

$1/RC$, so that in this case ($RC \ll 1$ cycle) we see that the quantity $(i_S/I_{DC})RC$ is constant.

In the case where RC is comparable to or longer than 1 cycle, the amount of charge supplied to the condenser during each positive half cycle will be proportional to $1/RC$ and so will the direct current I_{DC}, since it can only bleed away the same amount of charge from the capacitor on each negative half cycle (if the voltage reduction is to be held constant). In this case then the ratio i_S/I_{DC} is constant and independent of RC.

We can now deduce that we have the following relation for a constant value of reduced voltage:

$$\frac{i_S}{I_{DC}} = \frac{A}{\omega RC} + B \tag{17.2}$$

For a half-wave rectifier with capacitor-input filter A and B can be represented very closely for V_{red} up to 0.5 by the equations

$$A = \frac{2}{V_{\text{red}}} + 1$$
$$B = \frac{9}{V_{\text{red}}} - 10 \tag{17.3}$$

We can relate the rms ripple voltage V_r to i_S/I_{DC} for the same rectifier case if we express V_r as a fraction of V_{DCL}.

$$\frac{i_S}{I_{DC}} = \frac{1.85 + 1.5(V_r/V_{DCL})}{\omega RC(V_r/V_{DCL})} \tag{17.4}$$

We are now in a position to consider the design of a half-wave rectifier power supply. There are at least three criteria we might use for our choice of components. The most likely of these is the voltage regulation required. This puts a maximum limit on the amount of voltage reduction from no-load to full-load. In combination with this specification we generally want to use a rectifier with as low a current rating as will be reliable and also minimize ripple. Often these last two conditions are mutually exclusive, and a specific choice must be made. To illustrate this let us first calculate the conditions for minimum current rating. From Fig. 17.1 we see that the power law followed by the alloy rectifiers can be expressed as

$$t\left(\frac{i_S}{I_{DC}}\right)^n = D \tag{17.5}$$

where D is a constant depending on the rating of the rectifier and $n = 5.6$ as read from the slope of the curves. In order to find the minimum rating for a given V_{red} we must equate i_S/I_{DC} in Eqs. (17.2) and (17.5) and minimize by setting $dD/dt = 0$. Here $t = RC$, the time constant of the circuit. From this process we obtain the expression

$$\omega RC = (n - 1)\frac{A}{B} = (n - 1)\frac{2 + V_{\text{red}}}{9 - 10V_{\text{red}}} \tag{17.6}$$

Similarly we can calculate the ωRC value for a specified ripple, V_r/V_{DCL}, and V_{red} by solving Eqs. (17.2) and (17.4) simultaneously, giving

$$\omega RC = \frac{1.85V_{\text{red}}}{(9 - 10V_{\text{red}})(V_r/V_{DCL})} = \frac{2 - 0.5V_{\text{red}}}{9 - 10V_{\text{red}}} \tag{17.7}$$

From Eqs. (17.6) and (17.7) it is clear that we cannot simultaneously specify V_{red} and V_r/V_{DCL} and expect to get a minimum solution for rectifier current rating.

Let us assume specific conditions to illustrate the magnitude of the quantities involved.

$$\text{Maximum direct current } I_{DC} = 3 \text{ amp}$$
$$\text{Full-load voltage } V_{DCL} = 100 \text{ volts}$$
$$\text{Fractional full-load voltage reduction } V_{red} = 0.1$$
$$\text{A-c line frequency} = 60 \text{ cycles}$$

First we determine the value of ωRC for minimum rectifier rating from Eq. (17.6) as 1.21. For 60 cycles, $\omega RC = 1.21$ represents a time constant RC of 3.2×10^{-3} sec during which the turn-on surge current i_S will flow. Substituting in Eq. (17.2) we find $i_S/I_{DC} = 97$, and for $I_{DC} = 3$ we have $i_S = 291$ amp. Referring now to Fig. 17.1 we see that the lower curve of manufacturer 1 gives $i_S/I_{DC} = 10$ at 3.2×10^{-3} sec. This means that we must choose the 36-amp rating of this alloy rectifier family to withstand the 291-amp turn-on surge. As an alternative the 13-amp diffused rectifier of manufacturer 3 would also stand the turn-on surge.

The open-circuit d-c voltage will be the loaded d-c voltage plus the voltage reduction. $V_{CO} = V_{DCL}/(1 - V_{red}) = 100/0.9 = 111$ volts. This, after adding the drop in the rectifier, is the peak a-c voltage required of the transformer secondary. A silicon rectifier does not draw appreciable current in the forward direction until about 0.8 volt is applied. (This would be 0.4 volt for germanium.) The rms secondary voltage is then $V_{so} = 0.707(111 + 0.8) = 80$ volts.

The surge-limiting resistance R can now be calculated from i_S and the peak secondary voltage v_{SO}. $R = 112/291 = 0.38$ ohm. This resistance will include the internal rectifier dynamic resistance (see Fig. 17.3), the transformer secondary winding resistance, and the reflected primary resistance.

The filter capacitor can now be calculated from $RC/R = 3.2 \times 10^{-3}/0.38 = 0.0084$ farad. We can now see the price we have paid to minimize the rectifier rating even though the turn-on surge still requires a rectifier current rating of about ten times the value of the average d-c requirement. One might suppose that the value of ωRC could be maintained at 1.21 and C reduced as the R is increased. This is tantamount to changing i_S/I_{DC} while still maintaining ωRC. Equation (17.2) shows that such a procedure will change V_{red}. This is not permissible, since V_{red} is one of our specified conditions.

If, for practical reasons, we wish to hold C to a value of say 2,000 μf, we can calculate the effect on the rectifier by substituting v_{SO}/R for i_S in Eq. (17.2) and solving for R, using $V_{red} = 0.1$, $I_{DC} = 3$, $C = 2 \times 10^{-3}$, and $v_{SO} = 112$. This gives $R = 0.119$ ohm and $\omega RC = 0.09$. i_S/I_{DC} now becomes 314, and the turn-on surge current $i_S = 942$ amp. By extrapolation we find from Fig. 17.1 that the 36-amp unit of manufacturer 1 will no longer handle the turn-on surge current and something like a 50- or 60-amp unit of a similar family would be required. Regardless of the choice of rectifier current rating the rectifier must have a peak inverse voltage rating of $2V_{CO}$ plus a safety factor. In usual practice $3.5V_{CO}$ is used. We can now select a specific rectifier.

If there is a maximum allowable ripple we can calculate from Eq. (17.7) the necessary value of ωRC, or in the present case, since ωRC has been fixed, we can calculate the amount of ripple given by $\omega RC = 0.09$ and $V_{red} = 0.1$. After having chosen the rectifier and the capacitor value, it remains to calculate the ripple current I_C in the capacitor; $I_C = (V_r/V_{DCL})V_{DCL}\omega C$. We can now select a capacitor with the right capacitance, rms current, and voltage ratings.

The remaining design problem is to calculate the rms current I_s in the transformer secondary. This is equal to the rms current in the rectifier. Again this current can

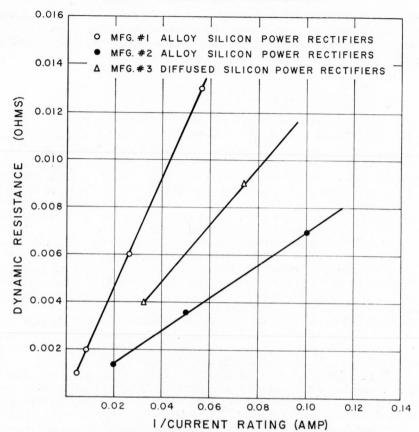

FIG. 17.3. Rectifier internal dynamic resistance.

be calculated from a fairly simple empirical equation:

$$\frac{I_s}{I_{DC}} = \frac{1.6 + E(i_s/I_{DC})\omega RC}{1 + F(i_s/I_{DC})\omega RC} \tag{17.8}$$

and E and F are constants which depend on i_s/I_{DC} and can be represented closely by

$$E = 0.5 + 5\,\frac{I_{DC}}{i_s}$$
$$F = 0.15 + 3\,\frac{I_{DC}}{i_s} \tag{17.9}$$

for values of I_{DC}/i_s greater than 0.01.   For smaller values the curves of Fig. 17.4c should be used.

In Fig. 17.4 are given curves which allow the above-described calculations to be made graphically.   In Fig. 17.4a a set of curves representing Eqs. (17.2) and (17.3) is given.   The representations are given in the form of straight lines for simplicity and ease of reading.   A typical procedure might be to find the curve corresponding to the required voltage regulation V_{red}.   On this curve a point should be chosen to give a reasonably low value of turn-on surge current i_S/I_{DC} without requiring an excessive value of ωRC. The point will then allow the determination of the ripple from Fig. 17.4b and the rectifier (or secondary winding) rms current from Fig. 17.4c. In using Fig. 17.4c one computes the product $(i_S/I_{DC})\omega RC$ and reads the value of the numerator of Eq. (17.8) from the member of the upper set of curves with the proper i_S/I_{DC} value.

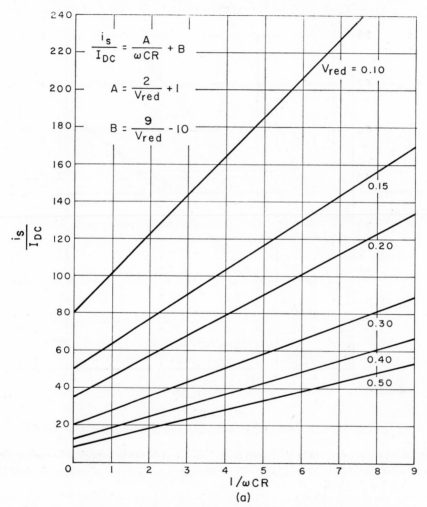

Fig. 17.4a. Half-wave rectifier, capacitor-input filter: normalized surge current.

The denominator is read in a similar manner from the lower set of curves. These two numbers are then divided to give the normalized rms current I_s/I_{DC} in the rectifier and the secondary winding. Two ranges of variables are given in Fig. 17.4c. The calculation of C, R, v_P, v_{SO}, etc., are the same as before.

In some cases it is necessary to examine the recurring peak surge current i_{RS} of the rectifier in order to be sure it will not be used beyond its rating. Usually in a half-wave rectifier circuit the turn-on surge requirement automatically provides enough derating to take care of the recurring peak surge current. A simple rule of thumb which is quite accurate states that the normalized recurring peak surge current i_{RS}/I_{DC} is very nearly equal to the square of the normalized rms rectifier current I_s/I_{DC}. This means that we need merely square the result which we obtain from Eqs. (17.8) and (17.9) to obtain i_{RS}/I_{DC}. This result can be seen to be reasonable if one considers an idealized recurring surge to be a square wave. In this case $I_s = \sqrt{i_{RS}^2(\tau/\tau_0)}$, where τ is the time of the surge and τ_0 is the time of 1 cycle. Since a

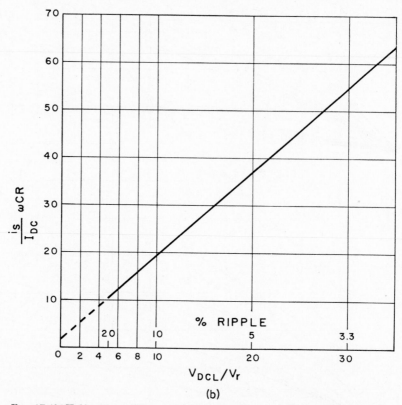

FIG. 17.4b. Half-wave rectifier, capacitor-input filter: normalized ripple voltage.

constant charge Q must be delivered to and removed from the capacitor in each cycle, we know that $i_{RS}\tau = Q = I_{DC}\tau_0$. This gives $I_s = \sqrt{i_{RS}I_{DC}}$, which is equivalent to $(I_s/I_{DC})^2 = i_{RS}/I_{DC}$.

One word of caution concerning switching transients is in order for half-wave rectifier circuits. On either input or output switching, the energy stored in the magnetic field of the transformer may have to be dissipated through the rectifier biased in its reverse direction. Under certain conditions this energy may be sufficient to carry a silicon rectifier, with a low reverse leakage current, beyond its inverse breakdown voltage. Protection can be most simply gained by shunting the transformer secondary with a series R-C network designed to keep the switching transient peak below the breakdown voltage of the rectifier.

17.1b. Full-wave Rectifier, Capacitor-input Filter. There are two common types of full-wave rectifier circuits which are shown in Fig. 17.5. The bridge circuit is somewhat more efficient in that it yields more direct current per unit of rms current in the

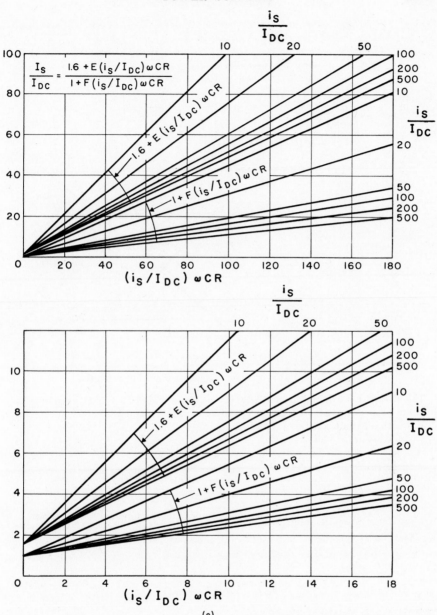

FIG. 17.4c. Half-wave rectifier, capacitor-input filter: factors of the rectifier rms current equation.

secondary winding at a given value of V_{red}. Since there are always two rectifiers in opposite arms of the bridge in the conducting mode when the a-c voltage is at its maximum, it follows that the remaining two rectifiers are never back-biased by more than the peak value of the a-c voltage. This means that the bridge circuit requires only half the voltage rating for its rectifiers that either a half-wave or center-tap full-wave rectifier circuit would require. Both of these latter circuits apply the sum of the peak a-c voltage and the capacitor voltage in the maximum back-bias condition.

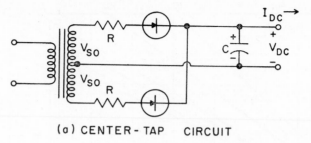

(a) CENTER-TAP   CIRCUIT

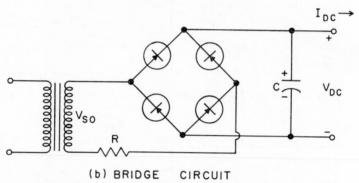

(b) BRIDGE   CIRCUIT

FIG. 17.5. Full-wave rectifier, capacitor-input filter circuits.

The design procedure is essentially the same as before. Again the normalized turn-on surge current i_S/I_{DC} can be approximated by an equation of the form of Eq. (17.2) with different constants α and ℬ.

$$\alpha = \frac{6.7}{\sqrt{V_{red}}} - 11$$

$$\mathcal{B} = \frac{5.5}{V_{red}} - 10$$

$$(17.10)$$

Equations (17.10) are valid for values of V_{red} below 0.3 only. For extended ranges of V_{red} see Fig. 17.6a.

The rms ripple voltage V_r again expressed as a fraction of V_{DCL} is given by

$$\frac{i_S}{I_{DC}} = \frac{0.8}{\omega RC(V_r/V_{DCL})}$$

$$(17.11)$$

This relation is plotted in Fig. 17.6b.

In calculating the rms current in a single rectifier of the bridge or center-tap full-wave rectifier circuit, we can use the curves of Fig. 17.4c, remembering that the effective frequency of a fully rectified wave is double the line frequency, so that $2\omega RC$ must be used in computing the value of the abscissa. In the case of the parameter i_S/I_{DC} we must remember that we have computed this ratio for a single rectifier of the circuit in terms of the total direct current. Since only half of this current flows through a single rectifier, the effective i_S/I_{DC} ratio must be doubled in finding I_s/I_{DC}. This

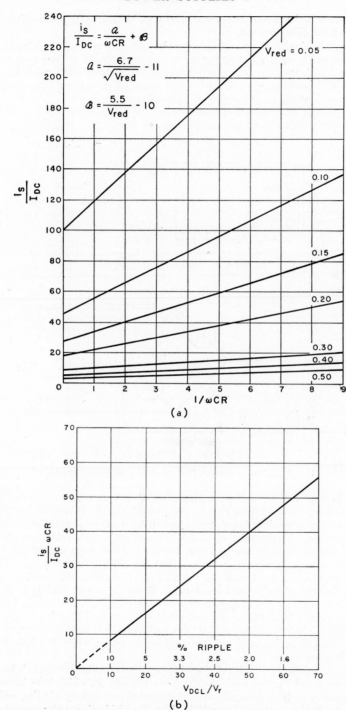

FIG. 17.6. Full-wave rectifier, capacitor-input filter: (a) normalized surge current; (b) normalized ripple voltage.

resulting normalized rms rectifier current must then be divided by 2 before determining I_s from the total direct current.

An advantage of a full-wave rectifier over the half-wave rectifier described before is that it is inherently self-protecting against switching transients. Any need suddenly to dissipate the magnetic energy of the transformer will inevitably bias one rectifier forward as it biases another backward. The magnetic energy can then be stored in the capacitor without significant voltage transients in the circuit.

17.1c. Full-wave Rectifier, Choke-input Filter.[2] It is easier to obtain good voltage regulation with a choke-input filter rectifier circuit than with a capacitor-input filter.

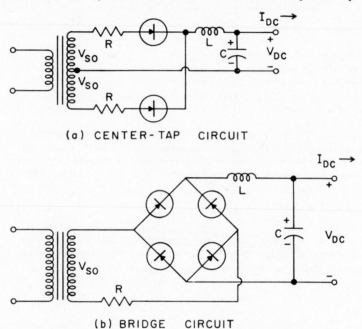

(a) CENTER-TAP CIRCUIT

(b) BRIDGE CIRCUIT

Fig. 17.7. Full-wave rectifier, choke-input filter circuits.

As shown in Fig. 17.7 the full-wave choke-input circuits are the same as the corresponding capacitor-input filter circuits except that a choke is inserted in series with the direct current preceding the storage capacitor. In normal practice the choke is made large enough to maintain current flow through some of the rectifiers at all times. In order to accomplish this, the L/R time constant of the choke and all resistance in series with it must be greater than $1/3\omega$. Here the effective resistance must include the choke resistance, the transformer secondary resistance, the rectifier dynamic resistance, and the effective load resistance. If continuous current is to be drawn under all circumstances including the open-load circuit case, it is necessary to provide a small bleeder resistance across the output in order to avoid having to provide an inordinately high inductance choke. If a swinging choke is used, care must be taken to fulfill the condition[3] $L/R \geq 1/3\omega$ at maximum current where the inductance of the choke is a minimum.

The voltage regulation V_{red} is calculated by determining the difference between the bleeder current and the full-load I_{DC} dropping through R, which here includes the choke resistance, rectifier dynamic resistance, and the secondary winding resistance. The difference in these voltage drops divided by V_{CO} yields V_{red}. For example (using the same numbers as in the case of the half-wave rectifier), letting

$$I_{DC} = 3 \text{ amp}$$
$$\text{Bleeder current} = 100 \text{ ma}$$
$$V_{DCL} = 100 \text{ volts}$$
$$V_{\text{red}} = 0.1$$

we find $V_{CO} = 110$ volts, so that $3R = 10$, giving $R = 3.3$ ohms to be divided among the choke, transformer secondary, and rectifier. The load resistance is

$$\frac{V_{DCL}}{I_{DC}} = 33.3 \text{ ohms}$$

so the inductance of the choke L must be $(33.3 + 3.3)/3\omega = 0.032$ henry at full load. Under open-circuit conditions, with only the bleeder current flowing, the effective series resistance is essentially the bleeder resistance $110/0.1 = 1,100$ ohms. Now an inductance of $L = 1,100/3\omega = 0.98$ henry is required. These values of inductance are quite reasonable for a swinging choke, and so is the total resistance value of 3.3 ohms.

A choke large enough to maintain continuous current also maintains the average value of the rectified alternating current at its output. Since the average value of a fully rectified sine wave is 0.9 of its rms value, we can calculate the necessary open-circuit transformer secondary voltage $V_{so} = (V_{CO} + 0.8)/0.9$. The 0.8 is the effective forward voltage threshold of a silicon rectifier. A rectifier must be chosen which will have a d-c rating of I_{DC} and a peak inverse voltage rating of $3.5v_{so}$, if a center-tap circuit is used, or a rating of $1.8v_{so}$ if a bridge circuit is used.

The turn-on surge situation is not nearly so critical in the case of a choke-input filter as it is for a capacitor-input filter. The surge in this case originates from the shock excitation of the series-resonant circuit comprising the choke and the storage capacitor. The normalized turn-on surge current is given by[4]

$$\frac{i_S}{I_{DC}} = (1 + V_{\text{red}})R_L \sqrt{\frac{C}{L}} \tag{17.12}$$

where R_L is the load resistance. This surge will last only for a time L/R_L (assuming R_L large compared with the other resistances present). The rms ripple voltage V_r can be closely approximated by the relation

$$\frac{V_r}{V_{DCL}} = \frac{0.2}{\omega^2 LC} \tag{17.13}$$

We now have the choice of determining the capacitor from either Eq. (17.13) or (17.12). For example, we may decide to choose C from Eq. (17.12) so that a rectifier of the lower family of manufacturer 1 (Fig. 17.1) with a rating of 3 amp could withstand the turn-on surge. To do this we calculate L/R_L for our example to be $0.032/33.3 = 10^{-3}$ sec. From Fig. 17.1 the rectifier family in question will withstand a normalized surge current of $i_S/I_{DC} \simeq 10$. Equation (17.12) then gives $C = L[(i_S/I_{DC}R_L)(1 + V_{\text{red}})]^2 = 0.032(^{3}\%_0 \times 33.3 \times 1.1)^2 = 2,400$ μf. This capacity will give $V_r/V_{DCL} = 0.2/1.42 \times 10^5 \times 0.032 \times 2.4 \times 10^{-3} = 0.018$, or 1.8 per cent rms ripple, from Eq. (17.13). If we do not need this low a ripple value, and if we wish to lower the capacitance value, we may select a lower value of capacitance with impunity, since from Eq. (17.12) it is clear that this would lower the turn-on surge current. On the other hand if one desires an even lower ripple voltage, one must pay the price of using both a larger capacitor and a larger rectifier.

In the above discussion Eq. (17.12) was normalized by dividing by the total direct current flowing in the load. Actually the direct current flowing in each rectifier of a center-tap full-wave rectifier circuit is only $I_{DC}/2$, and in the bridge circuit it is even less than this. If the designer is having trouble finding a rectifier of the proper rating, he may take cognizance of this fact as long as the turn-on surge current does not require a larger unit.

Graphical representations of the normalized turn-on surge current and the rms ripple voltage are given in Fig. 17.8. To use the set of curves of Fig. 17.8a one must first calculate $(1 + V_{\text{red}})R_L$ and the time constant L/R_L. After referring to Fig. 17.1

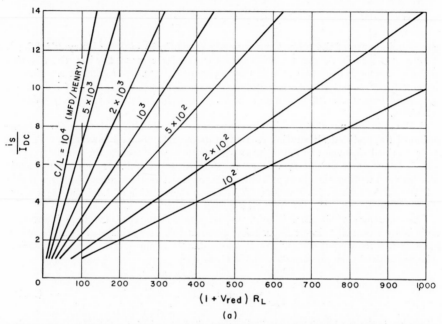

Fig. 17.8a. Full-wave rectifier, choke-input filter: normalized turn-on surge current.

to find the value of i_S/I_{DC} possible for the type of rectifier desired at the surge duration of the calculated time constant, one can determine the C/L parameter value corresponding to the i_S/I_{DC} value of the chosen rectifier and the calculated value of $(1 + V_{\text{red}})R_L$. Multiplying by L will give the necessary capacitance value in microfarads. As indicated above this process will yield a maximum value of capacitance compatible with a rectifier of about twice the minimum possible I_{DC} rating. To minimize the rectifier rating, choose an L/C parameter value corresponding to twice the $(1 + V_{\text{red}})R_L$ value and a rectifier rated at $I_{DC}/2$.

If a choke large enough to maintain a continuous current flow is used, the rectifier rms current is only about 1.5 times the rectifier direct current. This means that the current I_s in each half of the center-tapped transformer secondary winding is about $0.75I_{DC}$. In the bridge circuit there is only one secondary winding and $I_s \simeq I_{DC}$.

It is possible to excite the resonance of the filter circuit by a switching action in the load circuit. In this case the action of the choke in maintaining a constant current will produce a voltage peak across the capacitor and hence the load. This may upset the operation of a voltage regulator if the resonance is inadequately damped by the choke and bleeder resistances.

If for some reason a choke is used which is below the inductance value necessary to maintain continuous current, the turn-on surge current in the rectifiers will have a value somewhere between the values calculated for a choke-input filter and a capacitor-input filter. Analysis is quite difficult for this situation, and it should be avoided when using semiconductor rectifiers.

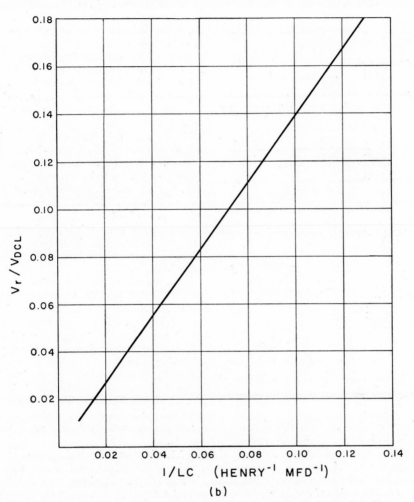

Fig. 17.8b. Full-wave rectifier, choke-input filter: normalized rms ripple voltage.

17.1d. Voltage-multiplying Circuits. It is sometimes desirable to obtain a higher d-c voltage than the peak voltage of the available a-c power. Such a situation arises usually from a desire to save transformer weight or expense. It is possible to charge capacitors in parallel and discharge them in series by suitable arrangements of rectifiers. In Fig. 17.9 are shown several examples of such circuits. In Fig. 17.9a is shown a half-wave voltage-doubler circuit. C_1 is charged through rectifier D_1 on one half cycle and C_2 is charged through C_1 and D_2 on the next half cycle while D_1 is back-biased. On the half cycle in which D_1 is conducting, there is no current being added to C_2, so that the ripple has the same frequency as the a-c line. C_2, D_2, and D_1 must be able to withstand double the a-c peak voltage, while C_1 need be rated only for the peak voltage.

In Fig. 17.9b is shown a full-wave voltage-doubler circuit. Here again C_1 and C_2 are charged on alternate half cycles, but since the capacitors are in series across the load at all times, the ripple will have twice the line frequency. C_1 and C_2 need be rated only for the peak a-c voltage, but D_1 and D_2 must be able to withstand twice the peak voltage.

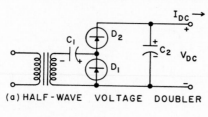

(a) HALF - WAVE   VOLTAGE   DOUBLER

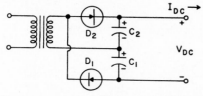

(b) FULL - WAVE   VOLTAGE   DOUBLER

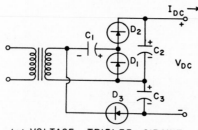

(c) VOLTAGE   TRIPLER   CIRCUIT

FIG. 17.9. Voltage-multiplying rectifier circuits.

In Fig. 17.9c a simple cascade of the first two circuits is shown to give a voltage-tripler circuit. Here the ripple has a component of twice the line frequency, since C_2 and C_3 are charged on alternate half cycles, but unless component values are carefully adjusted, the two charging impulses will not be equal, thus giving a line frequency component to the ripple. C_2 must be rated for twice the peak line voltage, but C_1 and C_3 need withstand only the peak value. The rectifiers must all withstand twice the peak value.

In a similar manner it is possible to cascade the first two circuits to form voltage quadruplers and higher,[5] but it is not worth pursuing here.

17.2. Regulated Power Supplies. Of the two general types of voltage regulators, shunt and series, the most efficient and the most widely used is the series type. The shunt type, in which voltage regulation is achieved by a series dropping resistor and diverting current between the load and a parallel path provided by some device with a constant-voltage characteristic, is inefficient but possesses the significant advantage that it is not destroyed under short-circuit conditions. For this reason such regulators are useful in the laboratory, and a short discussion of the shunt type will be given.

17.2a. Shunt Voltage Regulation. In Fig. 17.10a is shown the arrangement of the simplest type of shunt voltage regulator. The Zener diode[6] used as the voltage clamping device has a characteristic shown in Fig. 17.10b. The important considerations in the design of such a regulator can be understood by reference to the graphical representation of Fig. 17.10c. Here the solid curve labeled $R_L + R_D$ is the characteristic curve of the load resistance and the Zener diode in parallel. The two load lines shown for the series resistance R represent the extreme instantaneous values of the unregulated voltage V_U. The value of R_L used must represent the minimum load resistance required (maximum current rating I_R divided into the regulated voltage V_R). Under conditions of maximum I_R and minimum V_U (point B) the value of R must be chosen to intersect the characteristic below the knee of the curve in order to give good voltage regulation. At point B the power in the load is $V_R I_R$, the power in the diode is $V_R(I_B - I_R)$, and the power in the resistor is $I_B^2 R$. At point A for maximum V_U we must determine the power rating required of the diode. For open-circuited load the entire current I_A must flow through the diode dissipating $V_R I_A$

watts. If a short circuit occurs in the load, all the current flows through the load, and the resistance R must withstand $I_C^2 R$ watts dissipation until some protective device acts. (Note that this condition puts no strain on the diode.)

From the above discussion the inherent inefficiency of this type of regulator should be apparent. If one wishes to reduce the power lost in the series resistor by reducing

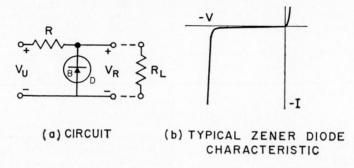

(a) CIRCUIT   **(b) TYPICAL ZENER DIODE CHARACTERISTIC**

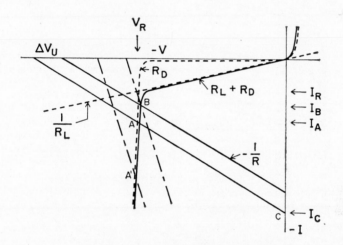

(c) GRAPHICAL REPRESENTATION

FIG. 17.10. Zener diode shunt voltage regulator.

its value (see the two parallel dashed lines in Fig. 17.10c), one is faced with poorer voltage regulation for a given ΔV_U and a much higher diode power dissipation for an open-circuited load $(V_R I_A')$.

The effective internal resistance of such a voltage regulator is the reciprocal of the slope of the composite characteristic curve below B. This ranges from 1 to 100 ohms for typical Zener units. Such diodes are available up to 50 watts dissipation.

If it is necessary to lower the internal resistance of the regulator or to carry more current, a power transistor must be used in conjunction with the Zener diode as shown in Fig. 17.11a. Here the diode will be required to carry only the current diverted from the base of the transistor, which is less than the current diverted from the load by a factor equal to the α_{FE} of the transistor.

To help understand the operation of this circuit again a graphical representation is given. In Fig. 17.11b is shown the output characteristic of the transistor in parallel with the load resistance R_L. This composite characteristic is loaded by R_1. The two load lines shown with slopes of $1/R_1$ are drawn for the minimum I and maximum II values of the unregulated voltage V_U. In Fig. 17.11c is shown the transferred load lines of Fig. 17.11b in the base input characteristic plane. Curves I_O and II_O are

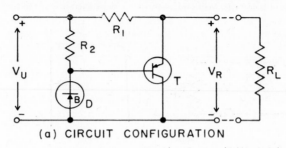

(a) CIRCUIT CONFIGURATION

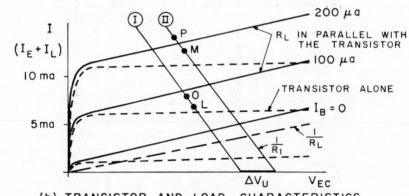

(b) TRANSISTOR AND LOAD CHARACTERISTICS

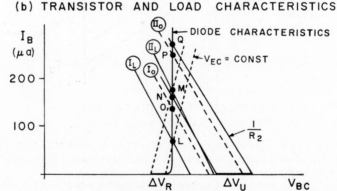

(c) DIODE AND TRANSFERRED LOAD CHARACTERISTICS

Fig. 17.11. Power-transistor shunt voltage regulator.

drawn for the open-circuit load case. (For a discussion of transferred load lines see Sec. 18.) Superimposed upon the transferred load lines is the Zener diode characteristic. The curves I_L and II_L are seen to intersect this characteristic at the points L and M. The dotted curves through these two points are curves of constant V_{EC} and represent the change in V_R when V_U shifts from its minimum to its maximum. The slope of these curves together with the slope of the diode characteristic determines the magnitude of ΔV_R. The internal base resistance of the transistor largely determines the slope of the V_{EC} curves, and a transistor with a low r_b will give better regulation. If a resistance equal to r_b is inserted in series with the regulator diode, the resultant characteristic will lie parallel to the V_{EC} parameter lines and the ΔV_R can be reduced to a very small value, depending on the linearity of the V_{EC} curves.

The open-circuit transferred load lines intersect the diode characteristic at O and P, showing the effect of load on V_R. We are now in a position to choose R_2. The maximum current required by the base of the transistor is given by the I_B value of the point P. This occurs with V_U at its maximum, so we must choose R_2 so that a load line representing it drawn from the maximum V_U value will intersect the diode characteristic above P. Q is this intersection point. Since the difference in current between P and Q is the diode current, care must be taken to be sure that its magnitude is greater than the range of current covering the nonlinear knee of the diode characteristic. Usually when R_2 is chosen in this manner, it will pass enough current when V_U is at the minimum to provide sufficient current for point O.

We shall now return to the choice of R_1. Until now we have assumed a value for R_1 in order to draw the transferred load lines. A little thought will show that the smaller we make R_1, the greater the value of the shunt current and the poorer the regulation. (All points L, M, O, and P will be farther apart.) The larger we make R_1, the better the regulation but the more power is lost in R_1. The minimum value of R_1 is determined by the power rating of the transistor relative to the transferred point P in Fig. 17.11b.

It is worth noting again that a short-circuited load will merely reduce the current and voltage applied to the transistor, so that there is no chance of destroying the regulator circuit as long as R_1 can stand the short until some protective device acts.

17.2b. Series Voltage Regulation. In series voltage regulation the power dissipated in the regulating circuit is substantially less than in the shunt regulating circuits. However, the regulation is still achieved by a controlled dissipation in the series power transistor. In Fig. 17.12 is shown a simple circuit of this type. The input voltage V_U is understood to be substantially larger than the regulated voltage V_R. Control is achieved by fixing the base voltage of the transistor at the desired level of V_R by means of the Zener diode D with breakdown voltage BV_D. When $V_R = BV_D$, the transistor is cut off and the $V_U - V_R$ appears across the

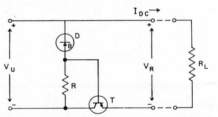

FIG. 17.12. Single-series transistor voltage-regulating circuit.

collector junction. When $V_R < BV_D$, the emitter is positive with respect to the base, base current flows, and the transistor conducts enough to allow the voltage $I_{DC}R_L = V_R$ to rise to the value of BV_D less the voltage threshold of the emitter-base diode of the transistor.

The internal impedance of such a regulator will be the impedance of the emitter-base diode of the transistor plus the impedance of the Zener diode reduced by a factor equal to the current gain of the transistor. The response time of the circuit will be the rise time of the power transistor. If a capacitor of capacitance C is placed across the output, this response time will be limited by the time constant $R_L C$.

The resistance R is chosen to allow the passage of the rated current I_{DC} divided by α_{FE} when driven by $V_U - I_{DC}R_L$ for the minimum instantaneous value of V_U when supplying I_{DC}. R must be reduced slightly below this value in order to avoid the knee of the Zener diode characteristic.

A series regulator circuit has no inherent overload protection, since a short-circuited load will draw massive currents through the power transistor and destroy it in a few microseconds. The only really adequate protection is provided by some electronic means of biasing the power transistor off in a matter of microseconds when an overload occurs.

Two series-regulator constant-voltage supplies are shown in Fig. 17.13a and b. In Fig. 17.13a the series transistor is a PNP and the amplifier is an NPN. In Fig. 17.13b both transistors are PNP's. The supplies differ in the polarity of the unregulated input voltage and the regulated output voltage. The transistors in either supply

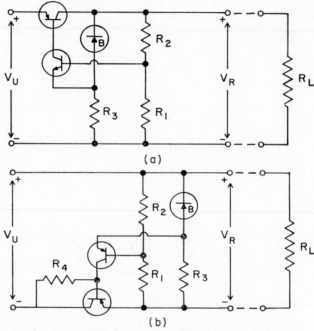

Fig. 17.13. Two-transistor series voltage-regulating circuits.

can be replaced by complementary transistors (and the diodes reversed), with a consequent reversal of the polarity of all voltages. The approximate value of the regulated output voltage V_R is given in terms of the breakdown voltage BV_D of the silicon diodes and the bridge resistor values by the relation $V_R = BV_D(1 + R_1/R_2)$.

The voltage regulators consist of three basic parts: a series power transistor, a nonlinear device used as an error detector, and a d-c amplifier. The voltage drop across the series transistor from the collector to the emitter is a function of the base current and the d-c load across the transistor. The base current of the series transistor is a function of the collector current of the d-c amplifier which is controlled by the base-to-emitter voltage. The two circuits shown differ in the mode of operation of the nonlinear device. In Fig. 17.13a the NPN transistor conducts heavily when the output voltage is less than the nominal regulated value, while the opposite is true for Fig. 17.13b. In Fig. 17.13b the emitter of the amplifier stage is held constant with respect to the positive terminal of the output. An increase in the output voltage causes the base of the amplifier to become more negative, increasing the collector current. The base current of the series transistor is decreased, and this decrease is amplified by the current gain of the series transistor, thereby causing a decrease in the output voltage.

A regulator circuit employing three transistors and two diodes is shown in Fig. 17.14. The nominal regulated voltage of the circuit was 20 volts; the full-load current, 80 ma. The breakdown voltage of the particular silicon diodes D_1 and D_2 was approximately 10 volts. When the output voltage of the supply exceeds the sum of the breakdown voltages of the diodes, the emitter of the first stage T_1 of the d-c amplifier becomes forward-biased. The second stage of the amplifier T_2 employs an NPN transistor in a grounded-collector connection. The use of this combination results in the proper phase shift in the amplifier for negative feedback and permits direct coupling without

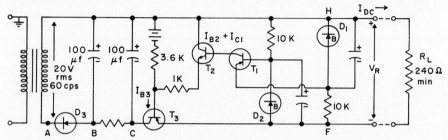

Fig. 17.14. Circuit diagram of a complete regulated voltage supply.

auxiliary interstage bias sources. The emitter of the NPN transistor and the base of the series power transistor T_3 are connected through a high (3,600 ohms) resistance to an external supply. The use of an external supply rather than the unregulated input voltage increases the allowable variation of the rectified input voltage and load resistance for which the output voltage remains regulated. By use of an auxiliary low-current-capacity supply, the battery can be eliminated. Tables 17.1 and 17.2 list the regulation characteristics of the voltage supply.

The output voltage of the supply is a function of temperature. The temperature coefficient of the breakdown voltage is 0.08 per cent/°C. From Fig. 17.14 the expres-

TABLE 17.1. REGULATION CHARACTERISTICS OF THE TRANSISTOR SUPPLY WITH
LOAD VARIATIONS

Load current, ma	Voltage, volts d-c			Ripple, peak-to-peak volts	
	B	C	F	C	F
0	27.5	27.5	19.60	0.11	
40	25.3	24.5	19.58	2.5	0.005
80	23.5	22.3	19.55	3.9	0.014

TABLE 17.2. REGULATION CHARACTERISTICS OF THE TRANSISTOR SUPPLY WITH
INPUT-VOLTAGE VARIATIONS

Input C, volts d-c	No load F, volts d-c	Full load F, volts d-c
22	19.60	19.55
30	19.60	19.58
40	19.62	19.60
50	.....	19.62

sion for the output voltage as a function of the breakdown voltages BV_{D_1} and BV_{D_2} of the diodes and the saturation current of the transistor used in the first stage of the d-c amplifier is

$$V_R \approx \frac{BV_{D_1} + BV_{D_2} - R_1 I_{CO}}{1 + [(1 - \alpha_{FB_3})(1 - \alpha_{FB_2})R_X/\alpha_{FB_1}R_L]} \qquad (17.14)$$

where R_1 is the static value of emitter and base resistances and R_X is the static resistance from point F to H measured through the two diodes. For typical values of transistor parameters, the term $R_1 I_{CO}$ is negligible compared with the variation caused by the temperature change in $BV_{D_1} + BV_{D_2}$. For a temperature change from 0 to 60°C, the output voltage will vary by +4.8 per cent. By use of thermistors or other temperature-sensitive components it is possible to reduce this variation.

17.2c. Switching Regulator. There are two general types of switching regulators. In one the a-c voltage itself is gated synchronously to pass just enough charge to the filter conducer to maintain its voltage at a fixed level and supply the current to the load. In the second type the alternating current is rectified normally and the unregulated direct current is then chopped at a chosen frequency with a pulse width controlled to pass the required amount of charge to the final filter capacitor to maintain its prescribed voltage under load.

Switching regulators have the advantage that they are quite efficient and the disadvantage that they have a slower response than the regulators described before. They are efficient because the only power dissipated is during the transition of the switching transistors. When a transistor is either off or in saturation, it dissipates very little power.

In Fig. 17.15 is shown a schematic circuit of a switching regulator of the chopper type. In normal operation the chopper frequency is kept constant and the duration of the conduction pulse of the transistor is varied to supply the load at the prescribed

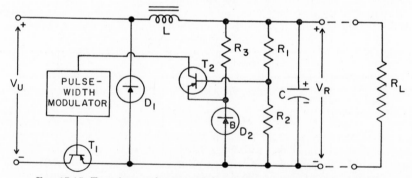

Fig. 17.15. Transistor voltage regulator of the chopper-switching type.

voltage. In this circuit the designer is free to choose the chopper frequency so as to minimize L and C within the reasonable dissipation limits of the transistor. This usually results in L and C values significantly smaller than those needed for the filter of a 60-cycle rectifier.

To outline briefly the operation of the circuit, we see that the pulse-width modulator receives an error signal from the bridge circuit comprised by R_1, R_2, R_3, and D_2 amplified by T_2. The modulator creates a pulse width linearly related to the size of the error signal. This pulse gates the transistor T_1 full on for the duration of the pulse. The current which flows through the transistor divides between the load and the capacitor C and returns through the inductance L. During the on period of the transistor this current tends to increase, since the unregulated input voltage is significantly larger than the regulated output voltage and the excess voltage is balanced by the emf of the current rising in L. During this part of the cycle the diode D_1 is back-biased by the full input voltage less the normally negligible collector saturation drop in T_1 and energy is stored in both the choke and the capacitor.

After T_1 is turned off, its collector must withstand the full value of V_U and diode D_1 will become forward-biased to complete the current path of the choke. The load current will be drawn from the energy stored both in C and in L, and the dropping current in L will produce an emf equal to V_R minus the forward drop of D_1. In all this it has been assumed that V_U is sufficiently filtered that it never drops instantaneously below V_R. If this is not the case, a capacitor must be placed across the input to supply this condition.

V_R can be set at any value significantly below V_U less the saturation drop of T_1, and I_{DC} can be any value significantly less than that current supplied by V_U with T_1 continually conducting. As these limits are approached, the regulation will become progressively worse until at the limit with T_1 continuously conducting there will be no regulation other than the additional filtering supplied by L and C. If the chopping frequency is greater than about five times the ripple frequency of V_U, the circuit will effectively reduce ripple as well as changes in the average value of V_U.

17.2d. Current Regulation. Here we shall be concerned with maintaining a high internal impedance of the regulator. The grounded-base characteristics of a typical junction transistor with constant-current emitter drive give good constant-current output with something like a megohm internal impedance. In Fig. 17.16 is shown a simple current-regulator circuit using this characteristic of a junction transistor.

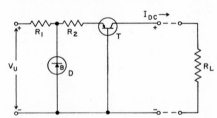

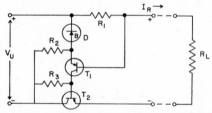

FIG. 17.16. Simple series transistor current-regulator circuit.

FIG. 17.17. Two-transistor current-regulator circuit.

Here the constant-current supply to the emitter consists of a Zener diode constant-voltage source and a large series resistor R_2. Since the emitter input impedance is about 50 ohms, even $R_2 = 5$ kilohms will give about 1 per cent regulation to the emitter current (assuming that R_1, BV_D, and V_U are chosen to give only a 1 per cent variation in the voltage applied to R_2 as V_U ranges over its extreme values).

The voltage-regulator circuit of Fig. 17.13b can be converted to a current-regulator circuit simply by comparing the drop across a series resistance with the standard voltage. The circuit of Fig. 17.17 shows this arrangement. If the variation of V_U is large enough to cause an appreciable variation of BV_D along the breakdown characteristic of the diode, the circuit can be improved by returning R_2 to the negative terminal of a battery.

17.3. Power Converters.[7] It is often necessary to convert d-c to a-c power or to convert d-c power at one level of voltage and current to d-c power at another level of voltage and current as efficiently as possible. For the d-c to a-c case one can take a transistor oscillator to convert the input d-c power to a-c power and use an output transformer to set the desired output level of voltage. To do this efficiently the oscillator must be an overdriver push-pull type so that the transistors spend as little time as possible in their active characteristic region where high-power dissipation occurs but rather spend most of their time either cut off or in saturation where power dissipation is small. In the d-c to d-c case the output transistor is followed by a rectifier and filter to recreate the d-c power at the new voltage level.

17.3a. D-C to A-C Conversion. In Fig. 17.18 is shown a typical basic connection for a d-c to a-c power converter. The bleeder network comprised of resistors R_1 and R_2 serves the purpose of starting oscillations in the circuit. When V_{CC} is applied, its full value instantaneously appears across both transistors and the bleeder network in parallel. The drop in R_1 tends to bias both bases negative with respect to the emitters of the two transistors and tends to turn them on. As the collector currents begin to rise, they will be in opposition in the two halves of the primary winding. This is

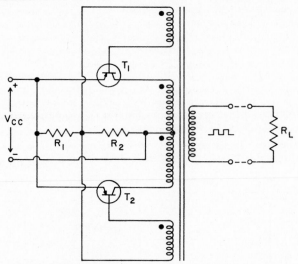

Fig. 17.18. Typical basic d-c to a-c power-converter circuit.

clearly a case of unstable equilibrium. Let us assume that transistor T_1 predominates and that it begins to magnetize the core material in the direction of its collector current. The changing flux through the two base feedback windings will now be of such a direction as to bias T_1 more strongly on and to cut off T_2. As long as the core material is far from saturation, a reasonable current will produce a large enough $d\varphi/dt$ to maintain the full value of V_{CC} across the primary winding in the collector circuit of T_1. This represents a relatively high impedance. When the core material approaches saturation, the $d\varphi/dt$ begins to drop. This simultaneously applies more of V_{CC} to the transistor collector and reduces the base bias. The latter effect starts turning the transistor off, while the former puts a spike on the collector current just before turn off. When T_1 cuts off, the core material relaxes along its saturation characteristic, giving a small $d\varphi/dt$ in the opposite direction which biases the base of transistor T_2 in the direction to turn it on. The whole process is now repeated by transistor T_2 by remagnetizing the transformer core material in the opposite direction.

The period of the oscillation is determined by the time required to reverse the magnetization of the transformer core. This process will depend upon the amount of core material, its saturation magnetization, the saturation current of the transistor at a given V_{CC}, and base feedback bias. All other factors being equal, the frequency of oscillation will tend to increase with V_{CC} and decrease with the size of the transformer core.

For efficient operation the transistors must be turned on and off rapidly. This requires a transformer core material with a "square" hysteresis loop, since the more abruptly the material saturates, the more rapid will be the drop in $d\varphi/dt$ at the end of a magnetizing cycle. Also for a given core material and hence a given hysteresis loop the over-all efficiency will be better at the lower frequency obtained by lower V_{CC}. This follows from the fact that an amount of energy equal to the area of the hysteresis loop is lost during each cycle by heating of the core material.

17.3b. D-C to D-C Conversion. The basic power converter illustrated in Fig. 17.18 can be used for conversion of d-c to d-c power by the addition of a rectifier-filter combination across the output before the load. Here the frequency can be chosen to give the best compromise between efficiency of conversion and minimizing the size of the filter components.

In a power converter regulation is preferably done in the oscillator circuit. One system is to insert a transistor in series with the base bias circuit of the oscillator transistors. This transistor can then act as a variable resistance controlled by a suitably rectified current proportional to the primary voltage to give a constant primary voltage. It is also necessary to protect the circuit against excessive spikes in V_{CE} of the oscillator transistors as they turn off. Since, as explained above, these spikes are due to the dropping $d\varphi/dt$ as the transformer core material approaches saturation, they are easily removed by placing a suitable capacitor across the primary winding to hold the voltage momentarily while the feedback windings have time to switch the transistors and start the remagnetizing cycle.

REFERENCES

1. Schwartz, S.: "Selected Semiconductor Circuits Handbook," p. 8–2, John Wiley & Sons, Inc., New York, 1960.
2. Langford-Smith, F.: "Radiotron Designers Handbook," 4th ed., p. 1182, Wireless Press for Amalgamated Wireless Valve Co. Pty. Ltd., Sydney, Australia. Reproduced and distributed by RCA Victor Division, Radio Corporation of America, Harrison, N.J.
3. Schade, O. H.: Analysis of Rectifier Operation, *Proc. IRE*, vol. 31, p. 356, July, 1943.
4. Reference 2, p. 1185.
5. Reference 2, p. 1188.
6. McAfee, K. B., E. J. Ryder, W. Shockley, and M. Sparks: Observations of Zener Current in Germanium P-N Junctions, *Phys. Rev.*, vol. 83, p. 650, Aug. 1, 1951.
7. Reference 1, part 9.

PART IV

Reference Material

Section 18

METHODS OF CIRCUIT ANALYSIS

H. FLEISHER

IBM Research Center, Yorktown Heights, N.Y.

MATRIX METHODS

Although a matrix is similar in appearance to a determinant in that they both are rectangular arrays of coefficients, fundamentally they are different. A determinant, which always has the same number of rows as columns, is a convenient symbol for a series of mathematical operations which results either in a number or in a polynomial involving symbols. A matrix, on the other hand, is a device for describing a state of affairs, for example, the coefficients of a set of linear equations (or transformations), and is a means of simplifying the work involved in handling such a set of equations.

18.1. Matrix Algebra. Our descriptions of matrix algebra will be based on the set of two linear equations derived from four-terminal-network analysis. We shall indicate those results which we get that are general and those which are specific; a more complete treatment of matrix algebra will be found in the references.

We first consider the set of equations

$$a_{11}x_1 + a_{12}x_2 = y_1$$
$$a_{21}x_1 + a_{22}x_2 = y_2 \tag{18.1}$$

We shall call the array of coefficients

$$[a] = \begin{bmatrix} a_{11} & a_{12} \\ a_{21} & a_{22} \end{bmatrix} \tag{18.2}$$

the matrix [a].

Consider further another set of equations involving a relation among y's and z's:

$$b_{11}y_1 + b_{12}y_2 = z_1$$
$$b_{21}y_1 + b_{22}y_2 = z_2 \tag{18.3}$$

with a matrix of coefficients

$$[b] = \begin{bmatrix} b_{11} & b_{12} \\ b_{21} & b_{22} \end{bmatrix} \tag{18.4}$$

Now, since the x's are linearly related to the y's by (18.1), the y's to the z's by (18.3), it is reasonable to expect linear relations among the x's and z's:

$$c_{11}x_1 + c_{12}x_2 = z_1$$
$$c_{21}x_1 + c_{22}x_2 = z_2 \tag{18.5}$$

with a matrix of coefficients

$$[c] = \begin{bmatrix} c_{11} & c_{12} \\ c_{21} & c_{22} \end{bmatrix} \tag{18.6}$$

Substituting (18.1) into (18.3), we find

$$z_1 = x_1(b_{11}a_{11} + b_{12}a_{21}) + x_2(b_{11}a_{12} + b_{12}a_{22})$$
$$z_2 = x_1(b_{21}a_{11} + b_{22}a_{21}) + x_2(b_{21}a_{12} + b_{22}a_{22}) \tag{18.7}$$

From (18.5), (18.6), and (18.7), we write

$$c = \begin{bmatrix} c_{11} & c_{12} \\ c_{21} & c_{22} \end{bmatrix} = \begin{bmatrix} b_{11}a_{11} + b_{12}a_{21} & b_{11}a_{12} + b_{12}a_{22} \\ b_{21}a_{11} + b_{22}a_{21} & b_{21}a_{12} + b_{22}a_{22} \end{bmatrix} \tag{18.8}$$

If we compare matrices [a] and [b] with the expanded form of [c] in Eq. (18.8), we note that c_{11} is the product of the first row of [b] with the first column of [a], taken term by term. Continuing, c_{12} is the product of the first row of b with the second column of [a], and so on.

We can go further and define matrix multiplication in the sense just described. The symbolism is

$$[c] = [b][a] \qquad c_{ik} = \sum_{j=1}^{n} b_{ij}a_{jk} \tag{18.9}$$

where it is clear that the matrix [a][b] is, in general, different from the matrix [b][a]. Thus, matrix multiplication is not generally commutative. However, it is associative, since [a][[b][c]] = [[a][b]][c]. It is also distributive, since [[a] + [b]][c] = [a][c] + [b][c].

Using this basic definition of multiplication, we can write the set of linear equations, viz., (18.1), in the following symbolic form:

$$[y] = [a][x] \tag{18.10}$$

where [a] is as defined in (18.2) and

$$[x] = \begin{bmatrix} x_1 \\ x_2 \end{bmatrix} \qquad [y] = \begin{bmatrix} y_1 \\ y_2 \end{bmatrix}$$

Note that both $[x]$ and $[y]$ are single-column two-row matrices.

We similarly rewrite (18.3):

$$[z] = [b][y] \tag{18.11}$$

which enables us to write

$$[z] = [b][a][x] \tag{18.12}$$

from which $[c] = [b][a]$, which was our first example of matrix multiplication. Multiplication of a matrix by a constant is obtained by multiplying each term of the matrix with that constant:

$$k[a] = \begin{bmatrix} ka_{11} & ka_{12} \\ ka_{21} & ka_{22} \end{bmatrix} \tag{18.13}$$

Adding or subtracting matrices is possible where the numbers of rows and columns are the same and is done by adding or subtracting the corresponding individual terms:

$$[a] \pm [b] = [c] \qquad \text{when } a_{ij} \pm b_{ij} = c_{ij} \tag{18.14}$$

Expanding the concept of matrix multiplication, we note that we require multiplication of individual terms of a row of the matrix on the left with the corresponding individual terms of a column of the matrix on the right. Therefore, the number of columns in the matrix on the left must be equal to the number of rows in the matrix on the right. Thus, in the matrix product

$$[a][b] = [c]$$

where $[a]$ has m rows and n columns, $[b]$ has n rows and k columns. The product $[c]$ accordingly has m rows and k columns. For example, let

$$[a] = \begin{bmatrix} a_{11} & a_{12} & a_{13} \\ a_{21} & a_{22} & a_{23} \end{bmatrix} \qquad [b] = \begin{bmatrix} b_1 \\ b_2 \\ b_3 \end{bmatrix}$$

Then

$$[c] = \begin{bmatrix} a_{11}b_1 + a_{12}b_2 + a_{13}b_3 \\ a_{21}b_1 + a_{22}b_2 + a_{23}b_3 \end{bmatrix}$$

which is a two-row one-column matrix.

Although division by a matrix is not allowed, multiplication by means of the inverse matrix is equivalent. The inverse matrix can be obtained with reference to Eqs. (18.1) by writing the equations in terms of the y's:

$$\frac{a_{22}}{\Delta} y_1 - \frac{a_{12}}{\Delta} y_2 = x_1$$
$$-\frac{a_{21}}{\Delta} y_1 + \frac{a_{11}}{\Delta} y_2 = x_2 \tag{18.15}$$

where Δ is the determinant of the set of equations

$$\Delta = \begin{vmatrix} a_{11} & a_{12} \\ a_{21} & a_{22} \end{vmatrix} = a_{11}a_{22} - a_{12}a_{21} \tag{18.16}$$

The symbol for the inverse matrix is $[a]^{-1}$, and in this example

$$[a]^{-1} = \frac{1}{\Delta} \begin{bmatrix} a_{22} & -a_{12} \\ -a_{21} & a_{11} \end{bmatrix} \tag{18.17}$$

Consider the product of a matrix and its inverse, in particular, the 2×2 matrix of our example:

$$[a][a]^{-1} = \begin{bmatrix} a_{11} & a_{12} \\ a_{21} & a_{22} \end{bmatrix} \frac{1}{\Delta} \begin{bmatrix} a_{22} & -a_{12} \\ -a_{21} & a_{11} \end{bmatrix} = \begin{bmatrix} 1 & 0 \\ 0 & 1 \end{bmatrix} \tag{18.18}$$

This matrix is called the unit matrix. It is clear that multiplying a matrix with its inverse in the other sense, namely, $[a]^{-1}[a]$, also yields the unit matrix. Similarly, a matrix whether pre- or postmultiplied by the unit matrix yields the original matrix.

18.2. Four-terminal Networks. With this brief introduction to matrix algebra, we proceed to the discussion of four-terminal networks. A network, symbolized

Fig. 18.1. Four-terminal network.

in Fig. 18.1, has four externally measurable quantities which characterize it: two currents and two voltages. Any two may be selected as the independent variables; the choice generally will depend on the use to which the network will be put. There are thus six different functional relations:

I: $V_1 = V_1(I_1, I_2)$ II: $I_1 = I_1(V_1, V_2)$
     $V_2 = V_2(I_1, I_2)$ $I_2 = I_2(V_1, V_2)$
III: $V_1 = V_1(V_2, I_2)$ IV: $V_2 = V_2(V_1, I_1)$
     $I_1 = I_1(V_2, I_2)$ $I_2 = I_2(V_1, I_1)$
V: $I_1 = I_1(V_1, I_2)$ VI: $V_1 = V_1(I_1, V_2)$
     $V_2 = V_2(V_1, I_2)$ $I_2 = I_2(I_1, V_2)$

A linear expansion can be made for a small excursion about a given operating point, and these six functions can be stated as linear equations. The following definitions for the linear coefficients are, in terms of the differentials of the variables,

I: $z_{11} = \dfrac{\partial V_1}{\partial I_1}\Big]_{I_2}$ $z_{12} = \dfrac{\partial V_1}{\partial I_2}\Big]_{I_1}$ $z_{21} = \dfrac{\partial V_2}{\partial I_1}\Big]_{I_2}$ $z_{22} = \dfrac{\partial V_2}{\partial I_2}\Big]_{I_1}$

II: $y_{11} = \dfrac{\partial I_1}{\partial V_1}\Big]_{V_2}$ $y_{12} = \dfrac{\partial I_1}{\partial V_2}\Big]_{V_1}$ $y_{21} = \dfrac{\partial I_2}{\partial V_1}\Big]_{V_2}$ $y_{22} = \dfrac{\partial I_2}{\partial V_2}\Big]_{V_1}$

III: $a_{11} = \dfrac{\partial V_1}{\partial V_2}\Big]_{I_2}$ $a_{12} = \dfrac{\partial V_1}{\partial I_2}\Big]_{V_2}$ $a_{21} = \dfrac{\partial I_1}{\partial V_2}\Big]_{I_2}$ $a_{22} = \dfrac{\partial I_1}{\partial I_2}\Big]_{V_2}$

IV: $b_{11} = \dfrac{\partial V_2}{\partial V_1}\Big]_{I_1}$ $b_{12} = \dfrac{\partial V_2}{\partial I_1}\Big]_{V_1}$ $b_{21} = \dfrac{\partial I_2}{\partial V_1}\Big]_{I_1}$ $b_{22} = \dfrac{\partial I_2}{\partial I_1}\Big]_{V_1}$

V: $m_{11} = \dfrac{\partial I_1}{\partial V_1}\Big]_{I_2}$ $m_{12} = \dfrac{\partial I_1}{\partial I_2}\Big]_{V_1}$ $m_{21} = \dfrac{\partial V_2}{\partial V_1}\Big]_{I_2}$ $m_{22} = \dfrac{\partial V_2}{\partial I_2}\Big]_{V_1}$

VI: $h_{11} = \dfrac{\partial V_1}{\partial I_1}\Big]_{V_2}$ $h_{12} = \dfrac{\partial V_1}{\partial I_2}\Big]_{I_1}$ $h_{21} = \dfrac{\partial I_2}{\partial I_1}\Big]_{V_2}$ $h_{22} = \dfrac{\partial I_2}{\partial V_2}\Big]_{I_1}$

The linear equations can now be written, using lower-case letters for the total derivatives:

I: $v_1 = z_{11}i_1 + z_{12}i_2$ II: $i_1 = y_{11}v_1 + y_{12}v_2$
    $v_2 = z_{21}i_1 + z_{22}i_2$ $i_2 = y_{21}v_1 + y_{22}v_2$
III: $v_1 = a_{11}v_2 + a_{12}i_2$ IV: $v_2 = b_{11}v_1 + b_{12}i_1$
    $i_1 = a_{21}v_2 + a_{22}i_2$ $i_2 = b_{21}v_1 + b_{22}i_1$
V: $i_1 = m_{11}v_1 + m_{12}i_2$ VI: $v_1 = h_{11}i_1 + h_{12}v_2$
    $v_2 = m_{21}v_1 + m_{22}i_2$ $i_2 = h_{21}i_1 + h_{22}v_2$

The matrices of the coefficients of these linear equations are as follows:

I: $\quad [z] = \begin{bmatrix} z_{11} & z_{12} \\ z_{21} & z_{22} \end{bmatrix}$ $\qquad\qquad$ II: $\quad [y] = \begin{bmatrix} y_{11} & y_{12} \\ y_{21} & y_{22} \end{bmatrix}$

III: $\quad [a] = \begin{bmatrix} a_{11} & a_{12} \\ a_{21} & a_{22} \end{bmatrix}$ $\qquad\qquad$ IV: $\quad [b] = \begin{bmatrix} b_{11} & b_{12} \\ b_{21} & b_{22} \end{bmatrix}$

V: $\quad [m] = \begin{bmatrix} m_{11} & m_{12} \\ m_{21} & m_{22} \end{bmatrix}$ $\qquad\qquad$ VI: $\quad [h] = \begin{bmatrix} h_{11} & h_{12} \\ h_{21} & h_{22} \end{bmatrix}$

We note that the following inverse relations hold among these matrices:

$$[y] = [z]^{-1}$$
$$[b] = [a]^{-1}$$
$$[h] = [m]^{-1}$$

Certain relations among the determinants of these matrices are of interest, and we tabulate each determinant in terms of the z coefficients:

$$|z| = \frac{1}{|y|} = z_{11}z_{22} \pm z_{12}z_{21}$$

$$|a| = \frac{1}{|b|} = -\frac{z_{12}}{z_{21}}$$

$$|h| = \frac{1}{|m|} = \frac{z_{11}}{z_{22}}$$

The usefulness of these various ways of representing a network becomes apparent when we consider the handling of the network. The $[z]$ matrix is used for series coupling, and the $[y]$ matrix is the best description of the network for parallel coupling. For cascade coupling, we use the $[a]$ or $[b]$ matrices, depending on whether we look at the network from the left (i.e., input) or the right (i.e., output). The other two general types of coupling are series parallel, for which the $[h]$ matrix is used, and parallel series, for which the $[m]$ matrix is used.

There are, of course, couplings of networks which cannot be handled by matrix methods: those will not be considered here, since an adequate treatment is to be found in the references.

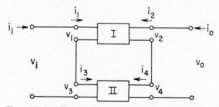 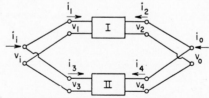

FIG. 18.2a. Two networks in series coupling. $\qquad$ FIG. 18.2b. Two networks in parallel coupling.

In addition, not all the coefficients involved lend themselves readily to direct measurement. However, the relations among the coefficients are such that if one set is determined, or even if a properly selected hybrid set is determined, then all the other coefficients can be calculated.

Figure 18.2a shows two networks in series coupling; Fig. 18.2b shows parallel coupling; Fig. 18.2c shows cascade coupling. Series-parallel coupling is shown in Fig. 18.2d, and parallel-series coupling is shown in Fig. 18.2e.

18.2a. Series Coupling. We shall use a prime to denote the matrix of the II network. Thus, for the series coupling of Fig. 18.2a, network I is described by the $[z]$ matrix, network II by the $[z']$ matrix. For this coupling we have these relations

$$i_i = i_1 = i_3 \qquad v_i = v_1 + v_3$$
$$i_o = i_2 = i_4 \qquad v_o = v_2 + v_4 \tag{18.19}$$

Writing the matrix equations for each network we find that the z matrix allows us to make use of the input and output currents which, respectively, are common to each network:

$$\begin{bmatrix} v_1 \\ v_2 \end{bmatrix} = \begin{bmatrix} z_{11} & z_{12} \\ z_{21} & z_{22} \end{bmatrix} \begin{bmatrix} i_1 \\ i_2 \end{bmatrix}$$

$$\begin{bmatrix} v_3 \\ v_4 \end{bmatrix} = \begin{bmatrix} z'_{11} & z'_{12} \\ z'_{21} & z'_{22} \end{bmatrix} \begin{bmatrix} i_3 \\ i_4 \end{bmatrix}$$

Making use of the relations in (18.19) and the addition rule of matrices, we directly write

$$\begin{bmatrix} v_i \\ v_o \end{bmatrix} = \begin{bmatrix} v_1 + v_3 \\ v_2 + v_4 \end{bmatrix} = \begin{bmatrix} z_{11} + z'_{11} & z_{12} + z'_{12} \\ z_{21} + z'_{21} & z_{22} + z'_{12} \end{bmatrix} \begin{bmatrix} i_i \\ i_o \end{bmatrix} \tag{18.20}$$

18.2b. Parallel Coupling. For the parallel coupling in Fig. 18.2b we have

$$v_i = v_1 = v_3 \qquad i_i = i_1 + i_3$$
$$v_o = v_2 = v_4 \qquad i_o = i_2 + i_4 \tag{18.21}$$

In this case, the common voltages show that the y matrix makes the handling of this coupling easier:

$$\begin{bmatrix} i_1 \\ i_2 \end{bmatrix} = \begin{bmatrix} y_{11} & y_{12} \\ y_{21} & y_{22} \end{bmatrix} \begin{bmatrix} v_1 \\ v_2 \end{bmatrix}$$

$$\begin{bmatrix} i_3 \\ i_4 \end{bmatrix} = \begin{bmatrix} y'_{11} & y'_{12} \\ y'_{21} & y'_{22} \end{bmatrix} \begin{bmatrix} v_3 \\ v_4 \end{bmatrix}$$

The resultant matrix of the parallel coupling of the two networks is obtained by using relations in (18.21) and the matrix addition rule as was done for series coupling:

$$\begin{bmatrix} i_i \\ i_o \end{bmatrix} = \begin{bmatrix} i_1 + i_3 \\ i_2 + i_4 \end{bmatrix} = \begin{bmatrix} y_{11} + y'_{11} & y_{12} + y'_{12} \\ y_{21} + y'_{21} & y_{22} + y'_{22} \end{bmatrix} \begin{bmatrix} v_i \\ v_o \end{bmatrix} \tag{18.22}$$

18.2c. Cascade Coupling. For the cascade coupling of Fig. 18.2c, we have

$$v_2 = v_3 \qquad i_i = i_1 \qquad i_o = i_4$$
$$i_2 = -i_3 \qquad v_i = v_1 \qquad v_o = v_4 \tag{18.23}$$

Looking at this coupling from the left, we make use of network equations III which involve the $[a]$ matrix. For the second network we replace the variables v_3, i_3 by v_2, $-i_2$ from Eqs. (18.23):

$$\begin{bmatrix} v_2 \\ i_2 \end{bmatrix} = \begin{bmatrix} a'_{11} & a'_{12} \\ -a'_{21} & -a'_{22} \end{bmatrix} \begin{bmatrix} v_4 \\ i_4 \end{bmatrix} \tag{18.24}$$

Thus, for the first network

$$\begin{bmatrix} v_1 \\ i_1 \end{bmatrix} = \begin{bmatrix} a_{11} & a_{12} \\ a_{21} & a_{22} \end{bmatrix} \begin{bmatrix} v_2 \\ i_2 \end{bmatrix} \tag{18.25}$$

Insert (18.24), which is the rewritten set of equations for the second network, into Eq. (18.25):

$$\begin{bmatrix} v_i \\ i_i \end{bmatrix} = \begin{bmatrix} v_1 \\ i_1 \end{bmatrix} = \begin{bmatrix} a_{11} & a_{12} \\ a_{21} & a_{22} \end{bmatrix} \begin{bmatrix} a'_{11} & a'_{12} \\ -a'_{21} & -a'_{22} \end{bmatrix} \begin{bmatrix} v_o \\ i_o \end{bmatrix} \tag{18.26}$$

where further substitutions have been made from (18.23). To get the matrix for this coupling we use the rule for matrix multiplication:

$$\begin{bmatrix} v_i \\ i_i \end{bmatrix} = \begin{bmatrix} a_{11}a_{11}' - a_{12}a_{21}' & a_{11}a_{12}' - a_{12}a_{22}' \\ a_{21}a_{11}' - a_{22}a_{21}' & a_{21}a_{12}' - a_{22}a_{22}' \end{bmatrix} \begin{bmatrix} v_o \\ i_o \end{bmatrix} \tag{18.27}$$

Similarly, if we look at this coupling from the right, then we must use the [b] matrix formulation:

$$\begin{bmatrix} v_o \\ i_o \end{bmatrix} = \begin{bmatrix} b_{11}' & b_{12}' \\ b_{21}' & b_{22}' \end{bmatrix} \begin{bmatrix} b_{11} & b_{12} \\ -b_{21} & -b_{22} \end{bmatrix} \begin{bmatrix} v_i \\ i_i \end{bmatrix} \tag{18.28}$$

Multiplying through,

$$\begin{bmatrix} v_o \\ i_o \end{bmatrix} = \begin{bmatrix} b_{11}'b_{11} - b_{12}'b_{21} & b_{11}'b_{12} - b_{12}'b_{22} \\ b_{21}'b_{11} - b_{22}'b_{21} & b_{12}'b_{12} - b_{22}'b_{22} \end{bmatrix} \begin{bmatrix} v_i \\ i_i \end{bmatrix} \tag{18.29}$$

The primes still designate network II; v_o, i_o are the voltage and current on the right; v_i, i_i are still the voltage and current on the left.

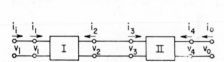

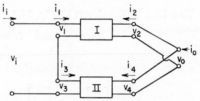

FIG. 18.2c. Two networks in cascade coupling.

FIG. 18.2d. Two networks in series-parallel coupling.

18.2d. Series-Parallel Coupling. For the series-parallel coupling in Fig. 18.2d, the connection is series on the left and parallel on the right. This is clearly a "hybrid" between straightforward series and parallel coupling, and a hybrid formulation of the networks will best describe them. The [h] matrix is used for this coupling because of these relations:

$$i_i = i_1 = i_3 \qquad i_o = i_2 + i_4$$
$$v_i = v_1 + v_3 \qquad v_o = v_2 = v_4 \tag{18.30}$$

Thus

$$\begin{bmatrix} v_1 \\ i_2 \end{bmatrix} = [h] \begin{bmatrix} i_1 \\ v_2 \end{bmatrix}$$
$$\tag{18.31}$$

and

$$\begin{bmatrix} v_3 \\ i_4 \end{bmatrix} = [h'] \begin{bmatrix} i_3 \\ v_4 \end{bmatrix}$$

From Eqs. (18.30),

$$\begin{bmatrix} i_1 \\ v_2 \end{bmatrix} = \begin{bmatrix} i_3 \\ v_4 \end{bmatrix} = \begin{bmatrix} i_i \\ v_o \end{bmatrix}$$

Hence we add Eqs. (18.31):

$$\begin{bmatrix} v_1 + v_3 \\ i_2 + i_4 \end{bmatrix} = [h + h'] \begin{bmatrix} i_i \\ v_o \end{bmatrix} \tag{18.32}$$

Also from (18.30) we write

$$\begin{bmatrix} v_i \\ i_o \end{bmatrix} = \begin{bmatrix} h_{11} + h_{11}' & h_{12} + h_{12}' \\ h_{21} + h_{21}' & h_{22} + h_{22}' \end{bmatrix} \begin{bmatrix} i_i \\ v_o \end{bmatrix} \tag{18.33}$$

In a similar way, we write the matrix formulation for the coupling shown in Fig. 18.2e: parallel input, series output:

$$\begin{bmatrix} i_i \\ v_o \end{bmatrix} = \begin{bmatrix} i_1 + i_3 \\ v_2 + v_4 \end{bmatrix} = \begin{bmatrix} m_{11} + m_{11}' & m_{12} + m_{12}' \\ m_{21} + m_{21}' & m_{22} + m_{22}' \end{bmatrix} \begin{bmatrix} v_i \\ i_o \end{bmatrix} \tag{18.34}$$

18.2e. Network Termination. If a network is terminated, as shown in Fig. 18.3, then the [a] matrix can be used to determine the impedance looking into the ①-① terminals. This impedance, which is the ratio of v_1 to i_1, is the slope of the "transferred" load line, as is discussed in the section on graphical analysis. Similarly, if the ①-① terminals were terminated, then the impedance looking into the ②-② terminals would be the slope of the "transferred" generator if the termination of ①-① were a generator.

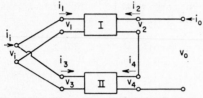

Fig. 18.2e. Two networks in parallel-series coupling.

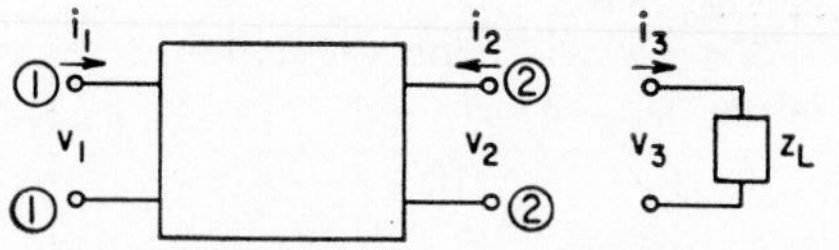

Fig. 18.3. Network termination.

To return to the circuit of Fig. 18.3,

$$v_2 = v_3 \quad \text{and} \quad i_2 = -i_3 \qquad z_L = \frac{v_3}{i_3} = -\frac{v_2}{i_2} \tag{18.35}$$

We rewrite the [a] matrix formulation of the network as follows:

$$\begin{bmatrix} v_1 \\ i_1 \end{bmatrix} = [a] \begin{bmatrix} v_2 \\ i_2 \end{bmatrix} = [a] \begin{bmatrix} -z_L i_2 \\ i_2 \end{bmatrix} = [a] i_2 \begin{bmatrix} -z_L \\ 1 \end{bmatrix} \tag{18.36}$$

Since i_2 is common, it can be factored out, and the [a] matrix can be multiplied into the single-column matrix $\begin{bmatrix} -z_L \\ 1 \end{bmatrix}$:

$$\begin{bmatrix} v_1 \\ i_1 \end{bmatrix} = i_2 \begin{bmatrix} -a_{11}z_L + a_{12} \\ -a_{21}z_L + a_{22} \end{bmatrix} \tag{18.37}$$

The input impedance z_i is the ratio of v_1 to i_1:

$$z_i = \frac{v_1}{i_1} = \frac{a_{12} - a_{11}z_L}{a_{22} - a_{21}z_L} \tag{18.38}$$

To bring this expression (18.38) into a more familiar form, we make use of these relations among the constituents of the [a] and [z] matrices:

$$a_{11} = \frac{z_{11}}{z_{21}} \qquad a_{12} = -\frac{|z|}{z_{21}}$$

$$a_{21} = \frac{1}{z_{21}} \qquad a_{22} = -\frac{z_{22}}{z_{21}} \tag{18.39}$$

where $|z|$ is the determinant of z, $|z| = z_{11}z_{22} - z_{12}z_{21}$. Substituting (18.39) into (18.38),

$$z_i = \frac{z_{11}z_{22} + z_L z_{11} - z_{12}z_{21}}{z_{22} + z_L} = z_{11} - \frac{z_{12}z_{21}}{z_{22} + z_L} \tag{18.40}$$

18.3. Matrix Formulation of the Transistor. As was shown in general terms in the previous section, the general functional relations for a transistor can be expanded into a set of linear equations provided the excursion about a set of operating conditions is such that linearity is kept for the parameters. This is the small-signal representation of the transistor and is written below in matrix form for the grounded base:

$$\begin{bmatrix} V_e \\ V_c \end{bmatrix} = \begin{bmatrix} r_{11} & r_{12} \\ r_{21} & r_{22} \end{bmatrix} \begin{bmatrix} I_e \\ I_c \end{bmatrix} \tag{18.41}$$

where subscripts e, c refer to emitter and collector, respectively. The $[z]$ impedance matrix is replaced by an $[r]$ resistance matrix, since we assume that the network representation of the transistor is resistive at low frequencies. The circuit is shown in Fig. 18.4a.

We can determine the matrix formulations of the transistor by suitably manipulating Eq. (18.41).

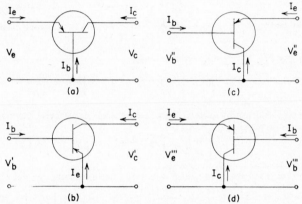

(a) (c)

(b) (d)

FIG. 18.4. (a) Grounded-base emitter input, (b) grounded-emitter base input, (c) grounded-collector base input, (d) grounded-collector emitter input.

In Fig. 18.4b, the emitter is grounded and these relations hold:

$$\begin{aligned} I_e &= -(I_b + I_c) \\ V'_b &= -V_e \\ V'_c &= V_c - V_e \end{aligned} \tag{18.42}$$

The variables are V'_b, V'_c, I_b, I_c, and what is wanted is the matrix equation

$$\begin{bmatrix} V'_b \\ V'_c \end{bmatrix} = \begin{bmatrix} r'_{11} & r'_{12} \\ r'_{21} & r'_{22} \end{bmatrix} \begin{bmatrix} I_b \\ I_c \end{bmatrix} \tag{18.43}$$

where the primed r's are to be expressed in terms of the original r's as stated in Eq. (18.41). The handling of (18.41) is as follows:

$$\begin{bmatrix} V'_b \\ V_c \end{bmatrix} = \begin{bmatrix} -V_e \\ V_c \end{bmatrix} = \begin{bmatrix} -r_{11} & -r_{12} \\ r_{21} & r_{22} \end{bmatrix} \begin{bmatrix} I_e \\ I_c \end{bmatrix}$$

from (18.41) and (18.42) by substitution. Continuing,

$$\begin{bmatrix} V'_b \\ V'_c \end{bmatrix} = \begin{bmatrix} -V_e \\ V_c - V_e \end{bmatrix} = \begin{bmatrix} -r_{11} & -r_{12} \\ r_{21} - r_{11} & r_{22} - r_{12} \end{bmatrix} \begin{bmatrix} I_e \\ I_c \end{bmatrix}$$

by adding the first row to the second row.

From (18.42), $I_e = -(I_b + I_c)$, and multiplying the first column of the $[r]$ matrix by -1, we get

$$\begin{bmatrix} V_b' \\ V_c' \end{bmatrix} = \begin{bmatrix} r_{11} & -r_{12} \\ r_{11} - r_{21} & r_{22} - r_{12} \end{bmatrix} \begin{bmatrix} I_b + I_c \\ I_c \end{bmatrix}$$

By adding the first column to the second column, we eliminate I_c from the first row of the current matrix and obtain the form shown in Eq. (18.43),

$$\begin{bmatrix} V_b' \\ V_c' \end{bmatrix} = \begin{bmatrix} r_{11} & r_{11} - r_{12} \\ r_{11} - r_{21} & r_{11} - r_{12} + r_{22} - r_{21} \end{bmatrix} \begin{bmatrix} I_b \\ I_c \end{bmatrix} \tag{18.44}$$

where
$$\begin{aligned} r_{11}' &= r_{11} & r_{12}' &= r_{11} - r_{12} \\ r_{21}' &= r_{11} - r_{21} & r_{22}' &= r_{22} - r_{21} + r_{11} - r_{12} \end{aligned}$$

For the grounded-collector base-input emitter-output transistor shown in Fig. 18.4c, we have

$$\begin{aligned} V_b'' &= -V_c \\ V_e'' &= V_e - V_c \\ I_c &= -(I_b + I_e) \end{aligned} \tag{18.45}$$

The variables are V_b'', V_e'', I_b, I_e, and we want

$$\begin{bmatrix} V_b'' \\ V_e'' \end{bmatrix} = \begin{bmatrix} r_{11}'' & r_{12}'' \\ r_{21}'' & r_{22}'' \end{bmatrix} \begin{bmatrix} I_b \\ I_e \end{bmatrix} \tag{18.46}$$

We start with the original matrix (18.41) and then change the arrangement of the voltage and current matrices:

$$\begin{bmatrix} V_c \\ V_e \end{bmatrix} = \begin{bmatrix} r_{22} & r_{21} \\ r_{12} & r_{11} \end{bmatrix} \begin{bmatrix} I_c \\ I_e \end{bmatrix} \tag{18.47}$$

Using (18.45) and manipulating the matrix rows and columns, we get the result

$$\begin{bmatrix} V_b'' \\ V_e'' \end{bmatrix} = \begin{bmatrix} r_{22} & r_{22} - r_{21} \\ r_{22} - r_{21} & r_{22} - r_{21} + r_{11} - r_{12} \end{bmatrix} \begin{bmatrix} I_b \\ I_c \end{bmatrix} \tag{18.48}$$

where
$$\begin{aligned} r_{11}'' &= r_{22} & r_{12}'' &= r_{22} - r_{21} \\ r_{21}'' &= r_{22} - r_{12} & r_{22}'' &= r_{22} - r_{21} + r_{11} - r_{12} \end{aligned}$$

For the emitter-input grounded-collector transistor shown in Fig. 18.4d, the variables are the same as for the base-input grounded collector shown in Fig. 18.4c. The matrix description of this case is simply obtained by rearrangement of (18.48):

$$\begin{bmatrix} V_e''' \\ V_b''' \end{bmatrix} = \begin{bmatrix} r_{11} - r_{12} + r_{22} - r_{21} & r_{22} - r_{12} \\ r_{22} - r_{21} & r_{22} \end{bmatrix} \begin{bmatrix} I_e \\ I_b \end{bmatrix} \tag{18.49}$$

where
$$\begin{aligned} r_{11}''' &= r_{11} - r_{12} + r_{22} - r_{21} & r_{12}''' &= r_{22} - r_{12} \\ r_{21}''' &= r_{22} - r_{21} & r_{22}''' &= r_{22} \end{aligned}$$

The rules for such a rearrangement are as follows: (1) interchanging the position of the terms of the dependent variable matrix ($[V]$ matrix) interchanges the rows of the $[r]$ matrix; (2) interchanging the terms of the independent variable matrix ($[I]$ matrix) interchanges the columns of the $[r]$ matrix.

18.3a. Equivalent T Network. If a specific equivalent circuit, such as a T, is desired for the transistor, then the matrix of (18.41) can be written in terms of the components of the T:

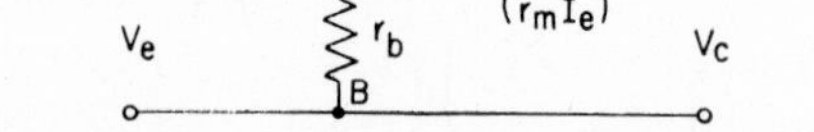

FIG. 18.5. Equivalent T representation of transistor.

$$\begin{bmatrix} r_{11} & r_{12} \\ r_{21} & r_{22} \end{bmatrix} = \begin{bmatrix} r_e + r_b & r_b \\ r_m + r_b & r_c + r_b \end{bmatrix} \tag{18.50}$$

This can be directly deduced from Fig. 18.5.

Equivalent T networks can also be constructed for the other transistor configurations. For example, consider the grounded-emitter base-input collector-output matrix of (18.44)

$$\begin{bmatrix} r_{11} & r_{11} - r_{12} \\ r_{11} - r_{21} & r_{22} - r_{21} + r_{11} - r_{12} \end{bmatrix} = \begin{bmatrix} r_e + r_b & r_b \\ r_e - r_m & r_c + r_e - r_m \end{bmatrix} \qquad (18.51)$$

by term-by-term substitution from Eq. (18.50).

However, the equivalent T would be written as the following matrix:

$$\begin{bmatrix} r'_e + r'_b & r'_b \\ r'_m + r'_b & r'_c + r'_b \end{bmatrix} = \begin{bmatrix} r'_{11} & r'_{12} \\ r'_{21} & r'_{22} \end{bmatrix} \qquad (18.52)$$

From (18.52) and (18.51), by equating terms, we obtain these relations:

$$\begin{matrix} r'_e = r_e & r'_m = r_e - (r_m + r_b) \\ r'_b = r_b & r'_c = r_c + r_e - (r_m + r_b) \end{matrix} \qquad (18.53)$$

In order to discuss the matrix treatment of terminating a transistor, we first write

$$\alpha_{fb} = -\left.\frac{\partial I_c}{\partial I_e}\right]_{V_c} \text{ in terms of the various matrix coefficients:}$$

$$\alpha_{fb} = \frac{z_{21}}{z_{22}} = -\frac{y_{21}}{y_{11}} = -h_{21} = -\frac{1}{a_{22}} \qquad (18.54)$$

This α_{fb} is the current gain for the grounded-base transistor, emitter in, collector out. A similar current gain for this transistor with collector in, emitter out, is defined as

$$\alpha_{rb} = -\left.\frac{\partial I_e}{\partial I_c}\right]_{V_e} \text{ and is also a useful term in characterizing transistor-circuit perform-}$$

ance. These alphas will also be determined for the other configurations; they will be designated by the appropriate primes. In terms of the matrix coefficients we have

$$\alpha_{rb} = \frac{z_{12}}{z_{11}} = -\frac{y_{12}}{y_{22}} = -\frac{1}{b_{22}} = -m_{12} \qquad (18.55)$$

For the grounded-emitter base-input transistor,

$$\alpha_{fe} = \frac{z'_{21}}{z'_{22}} = \frac{r_{11} - r_{21}}{r_{22} - r_{12} + r_{11} - r_{21}} \approx \frac{\alpha_{fb}}{\alpha_{fb} - 1} \qquad (18.56)$$

$$\alpha_{re} = \frac{z'_{12}}{z'_{11}} = \frac{r_{11} - r_{12}}{r_{11}} = 1 - \alpha_{rb}$$

when these inequalities hold,

$$r_{11}, r_{12} \ll r_{22}, r_{21} \qquad (18.57)$$

For the grounded-collector, base-input transistor,

$$\alpha_{fc} = \frac{z''_{21}}{z''_{22}} = \frac{r_{22} - r_{12}}{r_{22} - r_{12} + r_{11} - r_{21}} \approx \frac{1}{1 - \alpha_{fb}} \qquad (18.58)$$

$$\alpha_{rc} = \frac{z''_{12}}{z''_{11}} = \frac{r_{22} - r_{21}}{r_{22}} = 1 - \alpha_{fb}$$

for the same inequalities of (18.57).

The grounded-base transistor, emitter in, has an [a] matrix which can be written in terms of the impedance matrix of the transistor of Eq. (18.41) [see Eqs. (18.39)]:

$$
\begin{bmatrix} a_{11} & a_{12} \\ a_{21} & a_{22} \end{bmatrix} = \begin{bmatrix} \dfrac{r_{11}}{r_{21}} & -\dfrac{r_{11}r_{22} - r_{12}r_{21}}{r_{21}} \\[3mm] \dfrac{1}{r_{21}} & -\dfrac{r_{22}}{r_{21}} \end{bmatrix}
\tag{18.59}
$$

If the collector is shorted to the base, then to apply Eq. (18.38) we set $z_L = 0$, and the result is

$$
z_i = \frac{a_{12}}{a_{22}} = \frac{r_{11}r_{22} - r_{12}r_{21}}{r_{22}}
\tag{18.60}
$$

Making use of Eqs. (18.54) and (18.55), we write

$$
z_i = r_{11}(1 - \alpha_{fb}\alpha_{rb})
\tag{18.61}
$$

We thus state the short-circuit input impedance to the emitter in terms of the collector and emitter current gains. We see from Eq. (18.61) that this input impedance will be negative when the $\alpha_{fb}\alpha_{rb}$ product is greater than 1.

For the grounded-emitter base-input transistor, the [a] matrix is written in terms of the impedance matrix of Eq. (18.43):

$$
\begin{bmatrix} a_{11}' & a_{12}' \\ a_{21}' & a_{22}' \end{bmatrix} = \begin{bmatrix} \dfrac{r_{11}'}{r_{21}'} & -\dfrac{r_{11}'r_{22}' - r_{12}'r_{21}'}{r_{21}'} \\[3mm] \dfrac{1}{r_{21}'} & -\dfrac{r_{22}'}{r_{21}'} \end{bmatrix}
\tag{18.62}
$$

In terms of the grounded-base-transistor parameters,

$$
\begin{bmatrix} a_{11}' & a_{12}' \\ a_{21}' & a_{22}' \end{bmatrix} = \begin{bmatrix} \dfrac{r_{11}}{r_{11} - r_{21}} & -\dfrac{r_{11}(r_{22} - r_{21} + r_{11} - r_{12}) - (r_{11} - r_{12})(r_{11} - r_{21})}{r_{11} - r_{21}} \\[3mm] \dfrac{1}{r_{11} - r_{21}} & -\dfrac{r_{22} - r_{21} + r_{11} - r_{12}}{r_{11} - r_{21}} \end{bmatrix}
\tag{18.63}
$$

Thus, for the shorted collector, the input impedance, looking into the base, is

$$
\begin{aligned}
z_i' &= \frac{a_{12}'}{a_{21}'} = \frac{r_{11}(r_{22} - r_{12} + r_{11} - r_{21}) - (r_{11} - r_{12})(r_{11} - r_{21})}{r_{22} - r_{21} + r_{11} - r_{12}} \\[3mm]
&= \frac{r_{11}r_{22} - r_{12}r_{21}}{r_{22} - r_{12} + r_{11} - r_{21}}
\end{aligned}
\tag{18.64}
$$

In terms of α_{fb} and α_{rb} as defined for the grounded base,

$$
z_i' = \frac{r_{11}(1 - \alpha_{fb}\alpha_{rb})}{(1 - \alpha_{fb}) + \dfrac{r_{11}}{r_{21}}(1 - \alpha_{rb})}
\tag{18.65}
$$

In contrast to the grounded-base transistor, we note that the base input impedance is positive when $\alpha_{fb}\alpha_{rb} > 1$ and $\alpha_{fb} > 1$ but becomes negative for $\alpha_{fb} > 1$ and $\alpha_{fb}\alpha_{rb} < 1$.

For the grounded-collector base-input transistor, the [a] matrix stated in terms of the grounded-base parameters is

$$
\begin{bmatrix} a_{11}'' & a_{12}'' \\ a_{21}'' & a_{22}'' \end{bmatrix} = \begin{bmatrix} \dfrac{r_{22}}{r_{22} - r_{12}} & -\dfrac{r_{22}(r_{11} - r_{12} + r_{22} - r_{21}) - (r_{22} - r_{12})(r_{22} - r_{21})}{r_{22} - r_{12}} \\[2em] \dfrac{1}{r_{22} - r_{12}} & -\dfrac{r_{11} - r_{12} + r_{22} - r_{21}}{r_{22} - r_{12}} \end{bmatrix}
$$

(18.66)

For shorted emitter, the input impedance, looking into the base, is

$$
z_i'' = \frac{a_{12}''}{a_{22}''} = \frac{r_{22}(r_{11} - r_{12} + r_{22} - r_{21}) - (r_{22} - r_{12})(r_{22} - r_{21})}{r_{11} - r_{12} + r_{22} - r_{21}}
$$

$$
= \frac{r_{22}r_{11} - r_{12}r_{21}}{r_{11} - r_{12} + r_{22} - r_{21}}
$$

(18.67)

In terms of α_{fb} and α_{rb} as defined for the grounded-base transistor,

$$
z_i'' = \frac{r_{11}(1 - \alpha_{fb}\alpha_{rb})}{(1 - \alpha_{fb}) + (r_{11}/r_{21})(1 - \alpha_{rb})}
$$

(18.68)

We note that this base-input impedance (18.68) is the same as the base-input impedance (18.65) for the grounded emitter. This obviously must be the case, since both are short-circuit impedances and in both cases the collector is shorted to the emitter. In general, however, for an arbitrary load, these input impedances (no longer short circuit) will be different.

18.4. Note on High-frequency Representation of a Transistor. On a purely formal basis, the matrix representation of a transistor at high frequencies requires that all the resistive parameters be replaced by complex impedances. But two important effects at high frequency are (1) the barrier capacitance and (2) the effect of transit time in decreasing alpha. Because of this, some of the parameters may still be assumed to be resistive, while the remaining must be complex in order to incorporate these two effects.

Thus, if we write the impedance matrix of a grounded-base transistor, as an example, we replace r_{21} with z_{21}, r_{22} with z_{22}, retaining r_{11} and r_{12} as resistive elements:

$$
\begin{bmatrix} r_{11} & r_{12} \\ z_{21} & z_{22} \end{bmatrix}
$$

(18.69)

Certain conclusions can be stated as to the analytic form of z_{21} and z_{22}: (1) The barrier capacitance C_c can be considered as being in parallel with r_{22} (for small r_{12}). Thus

$$
z_{22} = \frac{r_{22}}{1 + j\omega C_c r_{22}}
$$

(18.70)

where $j\omega = j2\pi f$. (2) The $|\alpha_{fb}|$ versus frequency curve approximates that of the amplitude versus frequency curve of a passive R-C network.[5] Thus, we can write

$$
\alpha_{fb} \approx \frac{\alpha_{fb0}}{1 + jf/f_{ab}}
$$

(18.71)

where f_{ab} is the "3-db" frequency for α_{fb}.

From (18.70) and (18.71), we write an approximate expression for z_{21}:

$$
z_{21} \approx \frac{\alpha_{fb0}}{1 + jf/f_{ab}} \cdot \frac{r_{22}}{1 + j\omega C_c r_{22}}
$$

(18.72)

In the other transistor configurations, the corresponding terms will be more complicated, viz., matrices (18.44) and (18.48). For example, the effective α for the grounded-emitter base-input transistor from (18.44) and (18.71) is

$$\alpha_{fe} = \frac{z'_{21}}{z'_{22}} = \frac{\alpha_{f \nvdash 0}}{\alpha_{fb0} - 1} \cdot \frac{1}{1 - \dfrac{jf}{f_{\alpha_b}} \dfrac{1}{\alpha_{fb0} - 1}} \tag{18.73}$$

More recent work has introduced expressions for the frequency dependence of α_{fb} of a junction transistor that are based on refined physical models of the transistor. A recent message[6] to the *Proceedings of the IRE* has summarized some of these considerations and concludes with the following formula:

$$\frac{\alpha_{fb}}{\alpha_{fb0}} = \frac{1 - \tfrac{1}{5}jf/f_{\alpha b}}{1 + jf/f_{\alpha b}} \tag{18.74}$$

where $j\omega$, α_{fb0}, and $f_{\alpha b}$ have the same meaning as for (18.71) above.

It is not difficult to show, however, that, in magnitude, for frequencies at $f_{\alpha b}$ or below, the ratio of (18.74) to (18.70) differs from unity by 2 per cent or less.

Clearly, this justifies the use of (18.70) for most circuit design purposes.

GRAPHICAL METHODS

Two-terminal linear networks are by custom analyzed in terms of algebraic statements which relate the proper currents and voltages. Plotting of current versus voltage has been used in a pictorial sense for these linear networks, with little effort being made to handle these plots in a quantitative way. But when nonlinear devices are brought into the network, then the quantitative plotting of current versus voltage proves itself, since many times we find that an analysis would be very difficult to do in any other way. Rough sketching of the graphical volt-ampere characteristics may also prove useful; enough insight and knowledge of the network may be gained in this way to make more precise graphical work unnecessary.

Similarly, we shall see that four-terminal networks containing nonlinear devices, such as diodes, transistors, and vacuum tubes, can be handled with graphical analysis.

FIG. 18.6. Two-terminal network.

Some advantages which will become apparent in the discussion are (1) the direct viewing of the negative-resistance region(s) of individual devices, if they have them; (2) the types of negative resistance, i.e., whether open-circuit stable or closed-circuit stable; and (3) the way in which other components modify or change these characteristics. As was stated previously with reference to two-terminal networks, a qualitative analysis of the network will frequently yield the desired information, and graphical analysis, in the sense to be discussed here, is admirably suited for that.

The graphical analysis which we shall discuss deals directly with measured currents and voltages, plots the relations as IV plots, and presents such information as input resistance in the form of slopes of the IV plots. We shall develop the method from the point of view of resistive devices and later introduce the graphical method of handling reactive devices in circuits. In this way, we shall be able to introduce such concepts as "switching time" in a direct way.

18.5. Two-terminal Networks. *18.5a. Linear Network.* A two-terminal network, symbolized in Fig. 18.6, can be characterized by the functional relation

$$I = f(V) \tag{18.75}$$

But if the network contains linear components, each of which can be characterized by

$$I = GV \qquad (18.76)$$

where G is a constant, of different value for each component in the network, then Eq. (18.75) can be written as

$$I = KV \qquad (18.77a)$$

where K will also be a constant. Moreover, if the network also contains active elements, i.e., batteries, then Eq. (18.75) would be written as

$$I = KV + I_0 \qquad (18.77b)$$

where I_0 is a constant determined by both the emfs and the (linear) resistances in the network.

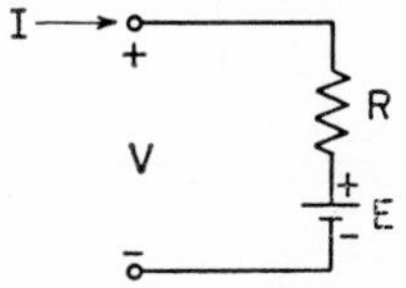

Equations (18.76) and (18.77a), when plotted, yield straight lines passing through the origin, while Eq. (18.77b) also produces a straight line, but with an intercept on the I axis.

FIG. 18.7. Series battery resistance network.

To illustrate the IV plots associated with Eqs. (18.77a) and (18.77b), let the two-terminal network consist of a resistance R in series with a battery E. This is shown in Fig. 18.7. If the battery is shorted, then $I = GV = (1/R)V$, and the plot of this is labeled A in Fig. 18.8. However, with the battery E in the circuit, the IV relation must be of the form of Eq. (18.77b):

$$I = GV - GE = \frac{1}{R}(V - E) \qquad (18.78)$$

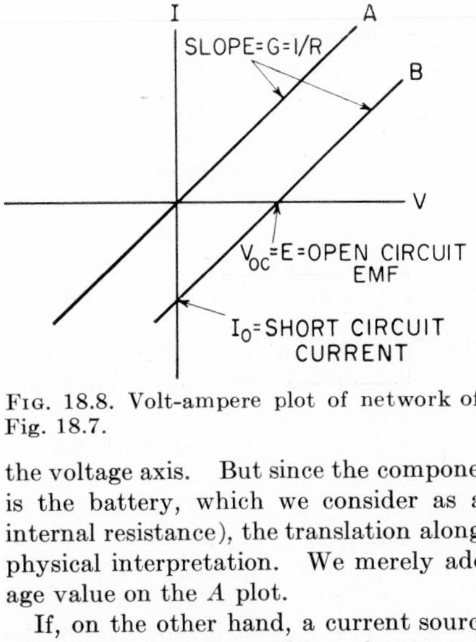

when the battery is of the polarity as shown in Fig. 18.7. The corresponding IV plot is labeled B in Fig. 18.8. We also show the short-circuit current and the open-circuit voltage which are the I-axis intercept and the V-axis intercept, respectively, of the B plot. On comparing B with A, we see that B results from having translated the A plot parallel to itself either along the current axis or along the voltage axis. But since the component which physically produced the translation is the battery, which we consider as a source of constant emf (ideally with zero internal resistance), the translation along the voltage axis is the one with a more direct physical interpretation. We merely add E volts to each voltage value on the A plot.

FIG. 18.8. Volt-ampere plot of network of Fig. 18.7.

If, on the other hand, a current source were introduced into the circuit, then it would have been more direct to add the fixed value of current to the current values of the original plot.

We show a voltage-divider network in Fig. 18.9 and demonstrate by means of the IV plots in Fig. 18.10 the construction of the composite IV plot of the network from the separate graphs of the components. It is clear that the principle of superposition applies, and this is done by adding the appropriate currents or voltages. Thus, for the circuit in Fig. 18.9, we observe that the R_2 branch is in parallel with the R_1, E branch; hence the currents in each branch must be added, at common voltages, to yield the total current entering (and leaving) the network. The graphical construction which does this is shown in Fig. 18.10. We have labeled the open-circuit voltage,

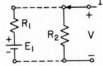

FIG. 18.9. Voltage-divider network.

short-circuit current, and circulating current in the network when no load is applied. Thus, all the pertinent information is available at a glance. For comparison, we have drawn the dot-dash line which has a slope of $-1/R_1$ and, therefore, is the load-line representation of that branch of the network. The intersection of the dot-dash line with the R_2 line also yields the circulating no-load current and the open-circuit voltage.

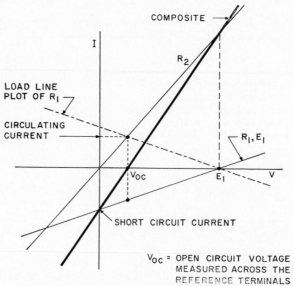

FIG. 18.10. Volt-ampere plots of voltage divider.

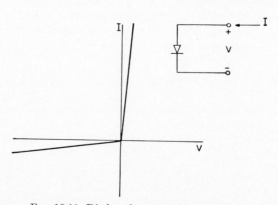

FIG. 18.11. Diode volt-ampere characteristic.

However, not only does the composite plot, the heavy solid line, yield the open-circuit voltage and, with a simple construction, the circulating no-load current, but the slope of the line is the reciprocal of the internal resistance of the entire network. We can, therefore, determine the effect of a load on the network by using the composite IV plot and the load line superposed on it in the conventional way.

    18.5b. Crystal Diode as a Nonlinear Element. The volt-ampere plot of a crystal diode is shown in Fig. 18.11, and a simple network is shown in Fig. 18.12.

    We plot the separate volt-ampere characteristics in Fig. 18.13 and show the composite.   The composite plot is diode-like in appearance but with a "back" resistance nearly equal to R.   The effect on the diode is to maintain a small forward bias across it.   If the battery E were replaced with another of E', then the composite would be B with a new open-circuit voltage V'_{oc}.   Thus, we observe that if the battery were to swing between E and E' the open-circuit emf or the network would swing between V_{oc} and V'_{oc}, a comparatively small excursion.   This type of circuit operation is known as clamping.   Clearly, if a battery were inserted in series with the diode, the diode would then clamp to the emf of the battery; in the circuit shown, the clamping is to ground potential.

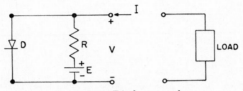

FIG. 18.12. Diode network.

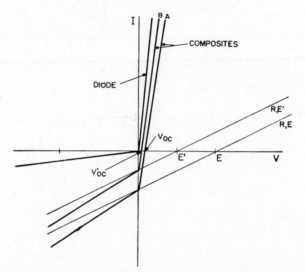

FIG. 18.13. Volt-ampere plots of diode network of Fig. 18.12.

18.5c.   Generation of a Nonlinear Load.   As an example of a nonlinear load we shall discuss a load which approximates a constant power-dissipation line.   This nonlinear load when applied to the appropriate device will tend to keep the device in a state such that, throughout its operating region, its power dissipation is constant.

Consider the constant power line plotted in the third quadrant in Fig. 18.14a.   When reflected in the horizontal voltage axis, this becomes a load line on a device whose characteristics can be plotted in the fourth quadrant, such as the collector IV plot of a PNP transistor.   We shall generate the nonlinear network by means of its IV plots in the third quadrant and then by reflection show that it is the desired constant power load.

A constant power-dissipation curve (a hyperbola) is plotted in Fig. 18.14a, and in the same figure a broken-line approximation is also shown.   It is this broken-line approximation which will be generated.   We note that there are two break points in the broken line which indicate that two diodes are to be used in this network.   The lower break point, labeled A, occurs at 3.4 ma and -26.5 volts, and the upper break point, labeled B, occurs at 7.2 ma and -12 volts. The high-resistance part of the approximation, R_3, will be obtained by keeping the two diodes cut off, i.e., in their back-resistance region, while the middle resistance R_2 will be obtained by keeping one diode cut off and the other diode conducting. The low resistance R_1 will be obtained with

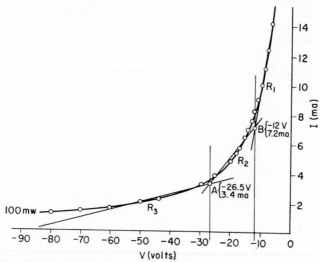

FIG. 18.14a. Constant-power-dissipation curve and approximation.

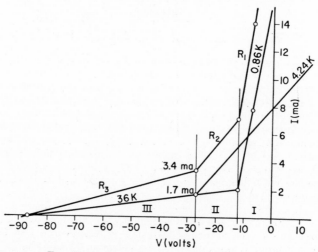

FIG. 18.14b. Reproduction of broken-line plot.

both diodes conducting. Each diode will be in a separate branch of the network, the two branches being placed in parallel to produce the required load.

It is arbitrary whether the synthesis is started from the high-resistance end or the low-resistance end, but a starting point must be specified and so must an initial set of values for the diodes. Thus, we shall choose diodes with nominal forward and reverse resistances of 500 ohms and 500 kilohms, respectively, and we shall start from the high-resistance end.   The broken-line plot is reproduced in Fig. 18.14b.   Light lines are drawn through A and B parallel to the current axis until they intersect the voltage axis.   Three regions are thus marked off: I, low resistance; II, middle resistance; and III, high resistance.

In region III, the choice of resistors is made simple by inserting identical resistors in the two branches of the network.   Graphically, this is done by halving the current for the same drop in voltage.   Thus the straight line labeled 36 kilohms is drawn in region III from the open-circuit emf point of -87 volts (obtained from the intersection of R_3 with the V axis) to 1.7 ma at -26.5 volts and is extended through region II until it intersects the boundary between regions I and II.

The diode which is cut off in region II is represented by the extension of the 36-kilohm line from region III.   The other diode is conducting, and its effective forward characteristic is obtained by subtracting the current passing through the first (cutoff)

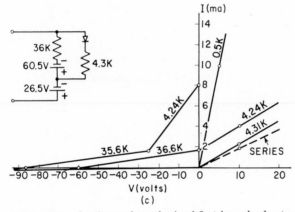

Fig. 18.14c. Reproduction and synthesis of first branch of network.

diode from the total current passing through R_2.   This produces the straight line labeled 4.24 kilohms, which is extended into region I.   Thus, the diode circuitry for one branch of the network has been determined: in region III, the diode is cut off and the branch has an effective resistance of 36 kilohms; in regions II and I, the diode is conducting and the branch has an effective resistance of 4.24 kilohms.

On continuing this analysis into region I, we find that the current for the second diode is determined by subtracting the current passing through the 4.24-kilohm resistor from the current through R_1.   This enables us to draw the line labeled 0.86 kilohm. Thus, the second branch is specified: when its diode is cut off, in regions III and II, the branch resistance is 36 kilohms; when its diode is conducting, in region I, the branch resistance is 0.86 kilohm.

Figure 18.14c reproduces the broken-line characteristic of the first branch of the network (36 and 4.24 kilohms), and its resolution into its component parts is shown in the circuit diagram in the insert.   Thus, the diode is in series with a 4.3-kilohm resistor. This series combination is in parallel with the 36-kilohm 60.5-volt battery series combination.   A 26.5-volt battery in series with the foregoing completes the branch.

Similarly, in Fig. 18.14d, the broken-line characteristic of the second branch of the network (35.6 kilohms and 0.86 kilohm) is reproduced, and it is resolved into its component parts, as shown in the circuit diagram in the insert.   This diode is in series with 0.38 kilohm.   The combination is in parallel with the 36-kilohm 75-volt battery series combination, and a 12-volt battery in series with the foregoing completes this branch.

The two branches are placed in parallel to produce the broken-line characteristic which approximates the given constant-power-dissipation load. In order to obtain a load-line representation, the *IV* plot shown in Fig. 18.14*b* is reflected in the voltage axis. Figure 18.15 shows a diagram of the complete network.

Although the open-circuit emf for each branch of this network is the same, it is not possible to use a single power supply of this emf, with appropriate taps. The reason is that this would force the two 36-kilohm resistors to be in parallel whether or not the diodes were conducting. Thus, the switching action required to achieve the *IV* characteristic of region II would not be obtained.

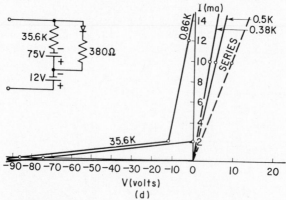

FIG. 18.14*d*. Reproduction and synthesis of second branch of network.

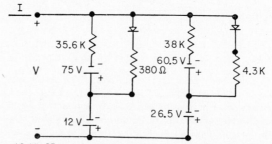

FIG. 18.15. Network for constant-power-load approximation.

18.6. Four-terminal Networks. *Mathematical Introduction.* A four-terminal network consisting of linear components can be characterized by its impedance matrix, which can be obtained from a set of linear equations relating the input and output currents and voltages. However, when nonlinear devices are introduced into the network, the impedance matrix becomes a useful idea only for small excursions about a given operating point. We prefer then to view the network operationally and deal directly with the measured input and output currents and voltages.

A general four-terminal network is shown in Fig. 18.16 with the input and output currents and voltages labeled as to polarity. This convention of polarity will also be used in the discussion of the matrix analysis of circuits.

$$I_1 = I_1(V_1, V_2)$$
$$I_2 = I_2(V_1, V_2) \tag{18.79}$$

Linearity can be brought in provided we restrict the operation of the network to small excursions about a given operating point. Then a first-order Taylor's expansion of Eqs. (18.79) is allowed and in this form expresses the small-signal linearity of the network. As we shall see on a graphical basis, this is the same as determining the appropriate slopes of the IV plots at the given operating point. The first-order Taylor's expansion is shown in Eqs. (18.80) as the expression for the total differential of I_1 and I_2 and in Eqs. (18.81) with lower-case letters substituting for the differentials, both total and partial, as is commonly done.

$$dI_1 = \frac{\partial I_1}{\partial V_1}\bigg)_{V_2} dV_1 + \frac{\partial I_1}{\partial V_2}\bigg)_{V_1} dV_2$$

$$dI_2 = \frac{\partial I_2}{\partial V_1}\bigg)_{V_2} dV_1 + \frac{\partial I_2}{\partial V_2}\bigg)_{V_1} dV_2 \qquad (18.80)$$

$$i_1 = g_{11}v_1 + g_{12}v_2$$
$$i_2 = g_{21}v_1 + g_{22}v_2 \qquad (18.81)$$

The interpretation of the partials as slopes of the appropriate plots is straightforward. Thus, from Eqs. (18.79), we can plot I_1 versus V_1, with V_2 as a parameter.

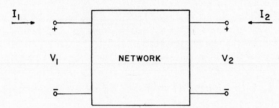

FIG. 18.16. Four-terminal network.

This will yield a family of curves each being labeled with a value of the parameter V_2. Clearly, then, $\frac{\partial I_1}{\partial V_1}\bigg)_{V_2}$ is the slope of the plot of I_1 versus V_1 for the parameter value of V_2 at an arbitrary operating point. Similarly, $\frac{\partial I_2}{\partial V_2}\bigg)_{V_1}$ is the slope of the plot of I_2 versus V_2 with V_1 as the parameter. Transfer plots can also be made: I_1 versus V_2 with V_1 as the parameter and i_2 versus V_1 with V_2 as the parameter. The slopes of these plots are $\frac{\partial I_1}{\partial V_2}\bigg)_{V_1}$ and $\frac{\partial I_2}{\partial V_1}\bigg)_{V_2}$, respectively.

In a similar way, the relations among the four variables can be stated so that the currents are the independent variables:

$$V_1 = V_1(I_1, I_2)$$
$$V_2 = V_2(I_1, I_2) \qquad (18.82)$$

with a corresponding set of equations for the small-signal approximation:

$$dV_1 = \frac{\partial V_1}{\partial I_1}\bigg)_{I_2} dI_1 + \frac{\partial V_1}{\partial I_2}\bigg)_{I_1} dI_2$$

$$dV_2 = \frac{\partial V_2}{\partial I_1}\bigg)_{I_2} dI_1 + \frac{\partial V_2}{\partial I_2}\bigg)_{I_1} dI_2 \qquad (18.83)$$

$$v_1 = r_{11}i_1 + r_{12}i_2$$
$$v_2 = r_{21}i_1 + r_{22}i_2 \qquad (18.84)$$

From Eqs. (18.82) we can plot V_1 versus I_1 with I_2 as the parameter, as well as V_2 versus I_2 with I_1 as the parameter. We note that these are not the same plots as the

V_1 versus I_1 plot and V_2 versus I_2 plot obtained from (18.79), since now the parameters are different. However, simple relations exist among the slopes of the various curves. These will be stated here but were derived in the section on matrices. Thus

$$\left(\frac{\partial I_1}{\partial V_1}\right)_{V_2} = \frac{(\partial V_2/\partial I_2)_{I1}}{\Delta} \qquad \left(\frac{\partial I_2}{\partial V_1}\right)_{V_2} = -\frac{(\partial V_2/\partial I_2)_{I2}}{\Delta}$$

$$\left(\frac{\partial I_1}{\partial V_2}\right)_{V_2} = -\frac{(\partial V_1/\partial I_2)_{I1}}{\Delta} \qquad \left(\frac{\partial I_2}{\partial V_2}\right)_{V_1} = \frac{(\partial V_1/\partial I_1)_{I2}}{\Delta} \tag{18.85}$$

where

$$\Delta = \begin{vmatrix} \left(\dfrac{\partial V_1}{\partial I_1}\right)_{I_2} & \left(\dfrac{\partial V_1}{\partial I_2}\right)_{I_1} \\ \left(\dfrac{\partial V_2}{\partial I_1}\right)_{I_2} & \left(\dfrac{\partial V_2}{\partial I_2}\right)_{I_1} \end{vmatrix}$$

$$= \left(\frac{\partial V_1}{\partial I_1}\right)_{I_2}\left(\frac{\partial V_2}{\partial I_2}\right)_{I_1} - \left(\frac{\partial V_2}{\partial I_1}\right)_{I_2}\left(\frac{\partial V_1}{\partial I_2}\right)_{I_1} \tag{18.86}$$

Δ is known as the determinant of Eqs. (18.83). (There will be no ambiguity in our graphs when we plot I versus V, as though V were the independent parameter but with the other current as the parameter.)

We identify the partials of Eqs. (18.83) with the slopes of the appropriate plots:

$$\frac{\partial V_1}{\partial I_1}\bigg)_{I_2} \text{ is the slope of } I_1 \text{ versus } V_1 \text{ with } I_2 \text{ as the parameter;}$$

$$\frac{\partial V_1}{\partial I_2}\bigg)_{I_1} \text{ is the slope of } I_2 \text{ versus } V_1 \text{ with } I_1 \text{ as the parameter;}$$

$$\frac{\partial V_2}{\partial I_1}\bigg)_{I_2} \text{ is the slope of } I_1 \text{ versus } V_2 \text{ with } I_2 \text{ as the parameter;}$$

$$\frac{\partial V_2}{\partial I_2}\bigg)_{I_1} \text{ is the slope of } I_2 \text{ versus } V_2 \text{ with } I_1 \text{ as the parameter.}$$

18.6a. Volt-Ampere Characteristics of Passive Four-terminal Networks. Equations (18.84) describe a linear passive four-terminal network in general as well as for small-signal use provided we set $r_{21} = r_{12}$. The plotting of a family of input (V_1 versus I_1) curves and output (V_2 versus I_2) curves with the proper parameters for such a network becomes a matter of showing a family of straight-line plots. For the V_1 versus I_1 family, the parameter is represented by the potential drop $I_2 r_{12}$. This potential drop shows itself on the IV plot as the intercept on the voltage axis. Similarly, for the V_2 versus I_2 family, the parameter is the $I_1 r_{12}$ potential drop. If, now, the network is terminated, for example, if the $V_2 I_2$ terminals are closed by a two-terminal device, then the relation between V_2 and I_2 is also determined by this terminating device.

Graphically, this is shown by placing the IV characteristic of the device as a load line on the $V_2 I_2$ family of curves. The intersection of this load line with each member of the family yields, for a given intersection, information about three of the four parameters associated with the four-terminal network. For this example, V_2, I_2, and the I_1 parameter are determined. The remaining unknown is V_1. But in the $V_1 I_1$ family of curves (I_2 being the parameter), I_2 and I_1 are known from the intersections in the $V_2 I_2$ plot. It is a simple matter then to determine that point in the $V_1 I_1$ set of curves which corresponds to a given intersection of the load line with the $I_2 V_2$ set of curves. The set of points in the $I_1 V_1$ plane, formed in this way, becomes the volt-ampere characteristic of the terminated network, looking into the $I_1 V_1$ terminals.

This plot has also been called the "transformed load line," since the four-terminal network which couples the load may be thought of as a transformer.

Figure 18.17a shows a linear T network, which is terminated by a diode. The diode characteristic is drawn in Fig. 18.17c as a load line intersecting the $V_2 I_2$ family. The information is read off this plot and is tabulated in the table inserted in Fig. 18.17b. The corresponding plot in the $V_1 I_1$ plane is then made by using (I_1, I_2) as the

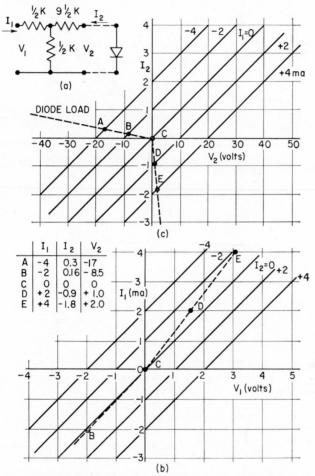

	I_1	I_2	V_2
A	-4	0.3	-17
B	-2	0.16	-8.5
C	0	0	0
D	+2	-0.9	+1.0
E	+4	-1.8	+2.0

FIG. 18.17. Passive linear four-terminal network with diode load.

number pair to locate the points. We see that the result, which is the "transformed load line," is also a diode-like characteristic which has been strongly modified by the network to which the diode has been coupled.

Passive networks containing nonlinear elements such as diodes are analyzed and generated by similar graphical means. A T network involving a single diode as the common element between the two branches is shown in Fig. 18.18a. The input and output open-circuit characteristics are plotted in Fig. 18.18b and 18.18c, respectively. We note that an "open-circuit characteristic" is obtained where current entering (and leaving) the other terminal pair is the parameter. Similarly, a "short-circuit characteristic" is obtained when voltage across the other terminal pair is the parameter.

The characteristics shown in Fig. 18.18b and 18.18c are superficially similar to the plots of a moderately high α junction transistor. More properly, these characteristics

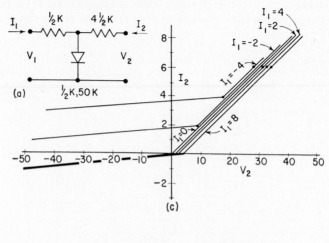

(c)

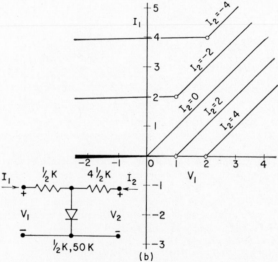

(b)

Fig. 18.18. Passive nonlinear four-terminal network.

look like those of a junction transistor with shorted emitter and collector. The difference, however, between this network and a junction transistor is very real, as can be seen graphically. Figure 18.19 shows the IV plot of the "base input" to the network of Fig. 18.18a: this clearly is a set of displaced diode characteristics with no power gain.

18.6b. The Transistor. The transistor is an active four-terminal device ($r_{12} \neq r_{21}$), and it must be discussed graphically with two sets of volt-ampere plots.[7,8] In the case of high-alpha point-contact transistors, the parameter generally used is current, since this results in a family of single-valued curves. For junction transistors with alpha less than 1, either current or voltage can be used as a parameter.

As was described in the previous section, a set of volt-ampere characteristics, each plot labeled with an appropriate parameter value, uses three of the four variables available to describe a four-terminal network. The termination of the pair of terminals for which this set is drawn is shown graphically by drawing the load line on the set of characteristics. For each intersection, values of each of these three variables are uniquely determined, and the appropriate two variables (of the three) have their values plotted in the volt-ampere plane of the other set of characteristics. This is the "transferred load line," and it describes, graphically, the two-terminal volt-ampere characteristic of the terminated four-terminal device.

The two sets of volt-ampere characteristics, emitter current versus emitter voltage, collector current as parameter, and collector current versus collector voltage, emitter current as parameter, adequately describe the low-frequency-network behavior of the

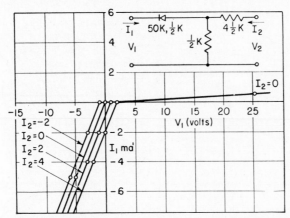

Fig. 18.19. "Base-input" volt-ampere characteristic of network of Fig. 18.18a.

point-contact transistor. From these sets of characteristics, we can determine input plots for different terminations. In this section we shall show how to obtain a base-input plot and also how to modify the emitter-input characteristic of a point-contact transistor.

The transistor symbol is shown in Fig. 18.20a, with currents and voltages labeled as to sign convention. The emitter set is shown in Fig. 18.20b, the collector set is in Fig. 18.20c. Also shown in Fig. 18.20c is the load line for the collector.

The intersections of the load-line characteristic with the set of collector curves determine the values of I_E and I_C, which in turn fix the points in the emitter plane of the transferred collector load. This transferred load line can now be used to determine the base volt-ampere characteristic for the same load on the collector and for a grounded emitter.

The circuit is shown in Fig. 18.21. The third and fourth quadrants of Fig. 18.20b are used to display the base-input characteristic. Note that the $+V_E$ axis is the $-V_B$ axis and that the $-I_E$ axis is the $+I_B$ axis. The reason is clear, since all potentials are measured relative to ground, and to obtain the emitter plot, the base is grounded; to obtain the base plot, the emitter is grounded.

The base current is obtained by adding algebraically the emitter and collector currents for each point of the transferred load line. This current is then plotted against the base voltage (which is the negative of the emitter voltage). This plot can be obtained when the excursion of base (or emitter) voltage is small compared with $|V_{CC}|$. If it is not, then this voltage must be added algebraically to V_{CC} and the load line moved. This produces a shift in the transferred load line, too.

Figure 18.22b shows the equivalent circuit for the emitter-input volt-ampere plot with an external resistance R_B in the base lead; Fig. 18.22a shows the circuit.

This equivalent circuit shows that, in order to present the new characteristic V_E^* versus I_E^*, the voltage drop across R_B must be added to V_E. This drop is determined by $V_B = R_B(I_E + I_B)$, with the condition that $V_B \ll |V_{CC}|$. Graphically, the I_E, I_B sum was obtained for the base-input plot of Fig. 18.20b. If R_B, in series with a battery

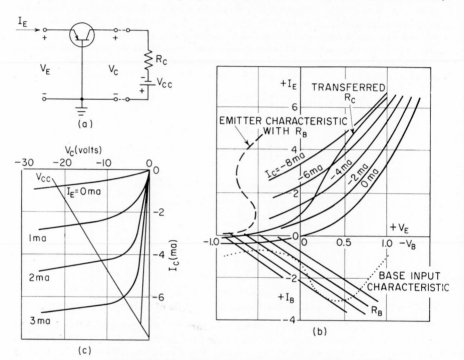

FIG. 18.20. Transistor volt-ampere characteristics.

V_{BB}, is placed as a load across this base-input characteristic as shown in Fig. 18.20b, the points of intersection will determine the emitter current I_E^*; the battery emf V_{BB} will be the new emitter voltage V_E^*. To trace out the characteristic, we vary the battery emf. This translates the R_B line parallel to itself, changing the points of intersection.

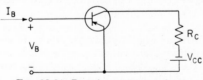

FIG. 18.21. Base input to transistor.

This characteristic is also plotted in Fig. 18.20b as the dashed line.

We can readily see that the base-input characteristic will show a negative-resistance region if, for the given load line, the ratio of an incremental change of collector current to an incremental change of emitter current is greater than unity. Once this is satisfied, an external resistance in the base connection will produce a negative-resistance region in the new emitter characteristic as shown above, provided this resistance is greater than the absolute value of the negative resistance of the base-input characteristic. It can also be demonstrated by this same graphical technique that, if the original emitter characteristic has a negative-resistance region, then the base-input characteristic will have two negative-resistance regions.

18.7. Analysis of Some Transistor Circuits. *18.7a. Negative Resistance.* Negative resistance is related to positive resistance: a positive resistance is a device which dissipates energy in the sense of transferring it from a wanted form into an unwanted form, i.e., from electrical energy to heat. A negative resistance also has the property of transferring energy, but not by dissipation. Instead, it is capable of transferring electrical energy from one form into another, i.e., from direct current to alternating current. It does this in conjunction with associated circuitry, but it itself can be considered as the source of power.

Graphically, the existence of a negative resistance is shown in the volt-ampere characteristic of a device as either an S-shaped plot or an N-shaped plot. For both of

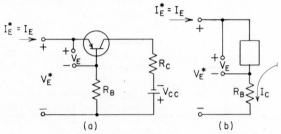

Fig. 18.22. (a) Emitter input to transistor with external R_B and (b) equivalent circuit.

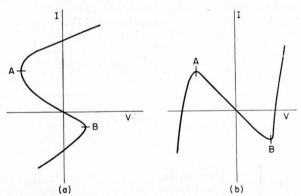

Fig. 18.23. Negative-resistance volt-ampere characteristics: (a) S curve, open circuit stable; (b) N curve, short circuit stable.

these plots, the current is plotted vertically, the voltage is plotted horizontally (see Fig. 18.23a and b).

The negative-resistance region in both plots is between the points marked A and B. The S curve describes a device which is open-circuit stable in that a stable (not self-oscillatory) circuit results if the device is terminated with a load which has a greater impedance than that represented by the slope of the line AB. The N curve describes a device which is short-circuit stable, since stable operation is achieved if the terminating load has an impedance less than that represented by the slope of the line AB in Fig. 18.23b.

As we showed in the previous section, a transistor with a sufficiently high $\alpha_{fb}\alpha_{fe}$ product and with its collector shorted will present an S curve as its emitter characteristic and an N curve as its base characteristic. If the emitter were shorted, its collector characteristic would also be an S curve.

The N-type negative-resistance volt-ampere characteristic obtained above for a properly terminated point-contact transistor has recently been obtained for a two-terminal device known as the Esaki tunnel diode.[10] There are important physical differences, of course, in terms of the obtainable currents, voltages, and speed of switching.

The most important distinction, however, is that the diode is a true two-terminal device displaying this characteristic without attending circuitry. Thus, circuitry based on the Esaki diode may possibly be simpler to design and may result in fewer components to do a given job.

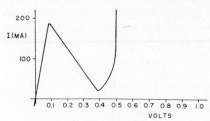

FIG. 18.24. Typical Esaki diode volt-ampere characteristic.

A typical Esaki diode volt-ampere characteristic is shown in Fig. 18.24. Note values of currents and voltages for the negative resistance region and that the characteristic of the device in the fourth quadrant is that of a very low resistance.

A single Esaki diode will oscillate when coupled with circuitry involving inductance. Such circuits have been devised that oscillate in the kilomegacycle region.[11]

However, of more direct interest for use in switching are circuits that involve pairs of these diodes, with the two states of a circuit being determined by which of the two diodes is conducting.

Figure 18.25a shows the circuit consisting of two Esaki diodes, I and II, in series, and Fig. 18.25b shows their individual volt-ampere characteristics, in one quadrant only, and their series-composite volt-ampere characteristic.

Several points can be noted about the series-composite characteristic. Note first that the curve displays two negative-resistance resistances. This is obtained under the assumption the diodes are not exactly identical. The physical operating conditions of these regions are different. In the region on the left, diode I fired but diode

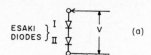

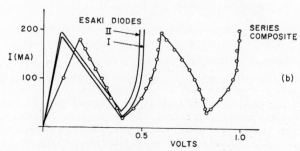

FIG. 18.25. Twin Esaki diode switching circuit.

II did not fire; in the region on the right, diode I is in its normal diode forward-conducting region and diode II has fired.

Hence, there are regions in the composite series characteristic in which each diode can be uniquely identified. We do not have space here to go into circuit details.

18.7b. Modifying the Characteristic. Three examples will be given of modifying a volt-ampere characteristic of a point-contact transistor. These will concern a base-input circuit, an emitter-input circuit, and a collector-input circuit.

A base-input circuit is shown in Fig. 18.26a, and the solid line in Fig. 18.26b represents the volt-ampere characteristic of the base. A dashed line is also drawn in Fig. 18.26b as the load to show operation as a bistable circuit. It is desirable to modify the volt-ampere characteristic of the base for the following reason. The circuit operating as shown dissipates a relatively high collector power when the transistor is in the "off" position. This will produce heating which can change the base characteristic enough so that the circuit will spontaneously turn itself "on."

Adding a diode in the polarity as shown in Fig. 18.26c to the base input will change the input volt-ampere characteristic in the direction of reduced collector-power dissipation, at the same time preserving the bistable nature of the circuit. The resulting volt-ampere plot is the solid line labeled "composite" in Fig. 18.26d. Both the

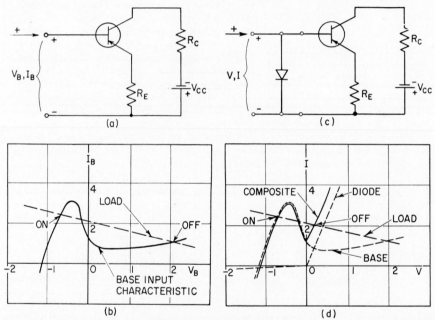

Fig. 18.26. (a) Base-input circuit and (b) volt-ampere plot with load. (c) Circuit modified with diode and (d) construction of composite base-input volt-ampere characteristic.

diode characteristic and the original base characteristic are shown in this figure as dashed lines. The construction of the composite is as follows: Since the diode and the base input are in parallel, we must add the diode current to the base current at common values of voltage. The dashed line, representing the load, is also shown in this figure. We note that there is a small shift in the current-voltage values for the "on" position, but that a considerable change is made in the current-voltage values for the "off" position. This change produces the desired result—reduced power in the collector, while preserving the negative resistance for the bistable circuit.

The circuit shown in Fig. 18.27a is an example of changing the collector volt-ampere characteristic to make the triggering action of a bistable circuit more definite. The dashed line of Fig. 18.27b shows a collector characteristic which has a sharp break from the cutoff region to the negative-resistance region and a smooth transition from the negative-resistance region to the saturation region. The object of the external circuitry is to produce this abrupt change on both sides of the negative-resistance region and, in so doing, improve the triggering action of the circuit.

The creation of the desired composite volt-ampere characteristic is shown in the sequence Figs. 18.27b to 18.27d. In Fig. 18.27b, the dashed line which is the VI plot of R_1 in series with V_{CC_1} is paralleled with the collector characteristic. The result is the solid line labeled "parallel composite." This composite is reproduced in Fig. 18.27c as a short-dashed line, and the diode characteristic as the long-dashed line. These are combined in series, by adding voltages at a common current, and the resultant composite is the solid line of Fig. 18.27c. Note that the diode was put in the circuit in such a way that its back resistance was placed in series with the saturation part of the collector characteristic.

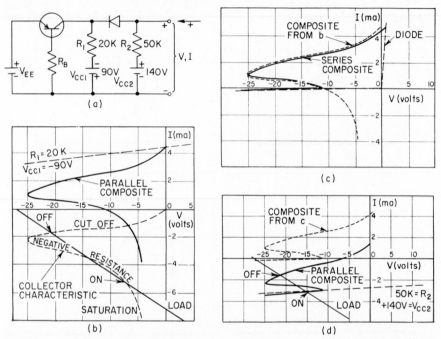

Fig. 18.27. Collector volt-ampere characteristic modification: (a) circuit showing nonlinear collector load, (b) generation of modified characteristic, (c) generation of modified characteristic, (d) generation of modified characteristic.

This composite, in turn, is reproduced in Fig. 18.27d as the short-dashed line, and the series combination of R_2 and V_{CC_2} as the long-dashed line. These are combined in parallel, and the result is the solid line labeled "parallel composite." A load line is drawn so that it intersects the composite characteristic to get bistable operation of the circuit. If we compare the composite characteristic of Fig. 18.27d with the original collector characteristic in Fig. 18.27b, we observe that we have made the sharp transition from the negative-resistance region to the saturation region and have changed only slightly the transition from cutoff to the negative resistance.

Comparing the circuit operation by means of the load-line intersection, we note that the composite network produces intersections which are well away from the transition points and, hence, are more stable.

As the third example, we shall consider the modifying of the emitter characteristic by means of a nonlinear load on the collector. The aim will be to preserve the negative-resistance region, at the same time making more definite the transitions into the region. The circuit is shown in Fig. 18.28a with the nonlinear load on the collector

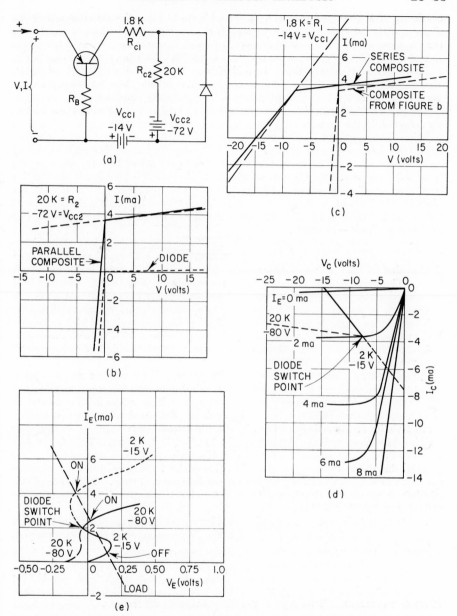

FIG. 18.28. Modification of emitter characteristic: (a) circuit showing nonlinear collector load, (b) construction of desired collector load, (c) construction of desired collector load, (d) collector characteristic with nonlinear load, (e) modified emitter volt-ampere characteristic.

consisting of a diode and several resistors.   Figure 18.28*b* and *c* show the generation of the nonlinear volt-ampere characteristic of the load network.   Thus, in Fig. 18.28*b*, the short-dashed line is the diode characteristic and the long-dashed line is the plot of R_2 and V_{CC_2}.   The solid line is the parallel composite.   This line is reproduced in Fig. 18.28*c* as the short-dashed line.   In this figure, we plot the characteristic of R_1 and V_{CC_1} as the long-dashed line.   As we see from the circuit, these must be placed in series.   The result is the solid line which is labeled "series composite."

This is the desired generator characteristic of the load to be applied to the collector. By reflection in the voltage axis, the generator characteristic becomes a load characteristic.   This is shown in Fig. 18.28*d*.   Because of the compressed scale, this non-linear load line seems to be made of pieces of two straight lines.   These are shown by the dashed-line extensions.   One segment, 2 kilohms at -15 volts, is the effective load when the diode conducts; the other segment, 20 kilohms at -80 volts, is the effective load when the diode is cut off.   However, if the diode were ideal, the load when the diode is cut off would be R_{c_1} plus R_{c_2} (1.8 kilohms) at a voltage of V_{CC_1} plus V_{CC_2} (-86 volts) and the load on the collector when the diode is conducting would be R_{c_1} (1.8 kilohms) at V_{CC_1} (-14 volts).

Figure 18.28*e* shows the transfer of the nonlinear collector load into the emitter-input characteristic.   The solid lines are transferred as solid lines, the dashed load lines as dashed lines in the emitter plane.   The diode switch point is shown in both plots.   The actual emitter characteristic is the solid line in Fig. 18.28*e*.   If we had not introduced a nonlinear collector load and had kept the 2 kilohms at -15-volt collector load, as we see from the load line placed on the emitter characteristic, the switching action is poorly defined.   The addition of the diode switched high-resistance load changes the "on" operating point and makes the transition from the negative-resistance region to the "on" region more abrupt.   This is the desired "sharpening" of the characteristic.

18.8. Graphical Analysis of Transient Response.   The transient response of a network can be analyzed by a graphical means similar to that discussed previously in this section.   The reactive elements in the network are themselves described in terms of volt-ampere characteristics which, in turn, are combined with the volt-ampere characteristics of the resistive elements of the network.   Both linear and nonlinear reactive as well as resistive devices can be handled in this way.   Time becomes a parameter in the volt-ampere representation of reactive devices, in that a set of curves properly describes the operation of the reactive device for a given time interval, each curve of this set being labeled with the appropriate value of time.   By means of this labeling, it becomes a simple matter to determine the appropriate current and/or voltage as a function of time.

To illustrate this method, we shall consider a resistance-capacitance network in which either element or both may be nonlinear.   We shall consider the linear case first.

Thus, for a linear capacitor we write

$$I = C \frac{dV}{dt} \tag{18.87}$$

where C is constant.   If we replace the differentials by differences,

$$I = C \frac{\Delta V}{\Delta t} \tag{18.88}$$

or

$$I = \frac{C}{\Delta t} (V - V_0) \tag{18.89}$$

replacing ΔV by $V - V_0$, where V_0 is the voltage across the capacitor at the beginning of the time interval Δt.   Clearly, for a fixed Δt and C, Eq. (18.89) is linear in (I, V).

We diagram the capacitor with the appropriate sign conventions in Fig. 18.29a and plot Eq. (18.89) in Fig. 18.29b.

Also shown in Fig. 18.29 is R, which is the load across the capacitor. For the first time interval Δt, Eq. (18.89) represents the capacitor undergoing the change from its initial voltage V_0 to a voltage V, the slope of the line being $C/\Delta t$. For the successive time intervals Δt, the V_0 of Eq. (18.89) symbolizes the voltage across the capacitor at the beginning of the time interval.

The analysis of the circuit of Fig. 18.29a for a given time interval Δt can be done by means of Eq. (18.89). Thus, for the capacitor,

$$I = \frac{C}{\Delta t}(V - V_0)$$

and for the resistor,

$$I = -\frac{V}{R}$$

Equating and rewriting,

$$\frac{V - V_0}{V} = \frac{\Delta V}{V} = -\frac{\Delta t}{RC} \quad (18.90)$$

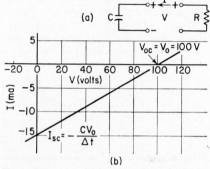

Fig. 18.29. (a) R-C network and (b) capacitor volt-ampere characteristics Δt.

Equation (18.90) states that the fractional change in voltage across the capacitor is constant, since Δt is fixed, and we have previously stated R and C to be constant.

Graphically, we do this analysis in the way shown in Fig. 18.30a and b.

A time interval Δt is chosen. A criterion for this is to make the fraction $\Delta t/RC$ as small as is needed for the precision required of the linear approximation. Thus, for

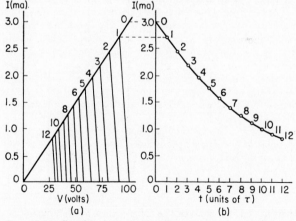

Fig. 18.30. Graphical analysis of linear capacitor discharge.

example, $\Delta t/RC = \frac{1}{10}$ for 1 per cent precision. The slope of Eq. (18.89) is now determined, and this is plotted from the voltage axis intercept V_0. The load line labeled R is also drawn, starting from the origin. The intersection of the capacitor characteristic with the resistor load line is labeled (1), and a line is projected from that intersection parallel to the current axis until that line intersects the voltage axis. This intersection determines the voltage which becomes the V_0 for the next time interval. In the same way, the second capacitor characteristic is drawn (parallel to the first) until it intersects the resistor load.   The V_0 for the third time interval is determined, and the procedure is repeated.   In this way, a succession of voltages and currents, each determined for the proper time interval, is obtained.   Current versus time is plotted in Fig. 18.30b.

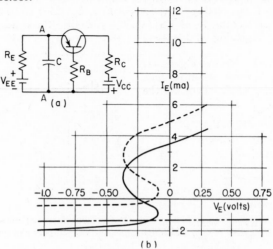

FIG. 18.31. Emitter-input volt-ampere plot.

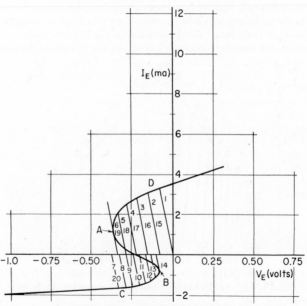

FIG. 18.32. Emitter-input capacitor load.

As a second example, we shall keep the linear capacitor and introduce a nonlinear resistance.   To make the example more specific, the resistance will be that determined by obtaining the volt-ampere characteristic of the emitter of a high-alpha transistor whose collector is effectively shorted.   This results in the characteristic shown in Fig. 18.31b.   The circuit is shown in Fig. 18.31a.   The dashed line in Fig. 18.31b is the characteristic of the R, V_{EE} biasing network for the emitter, and the heavy line is the composite characteristic observed at terminals AA. This represents the resistance which the capacitor "sees," and this characteristic is reproduced in Fig. 18.32. The set of parallel lines represents the capacitor which has been placed across the terminals AA, and from the intersections, labeled 0, 1, 2, . . . , the values of voltage and/or current can be determined with respect to time. These are plotted in Figs. 18.33 and 18.34. Note that the composite characteristic, as shown in Fig. 18.32,

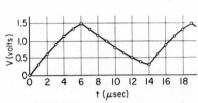

FIG. 18.33. Emitter voltage versus time. 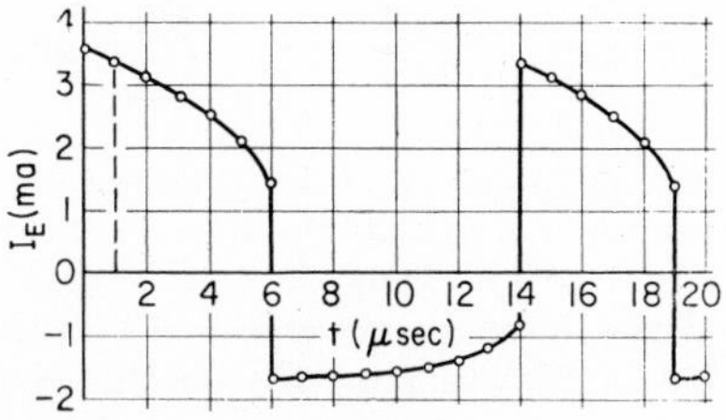   FIG. 18.34. Emitter current versus time.

intersects the voltage axis with its negative-resistance region. This is the part of the characteristic between the points labeled A, B. This is necessary in order to maintain a relaxation oscillation. Thus, the capacitor charges to a negative potential along the path (1) to A; at A, the presence of the negative resistance acts to attempt to "discharge" the capacitor while continuing to force charge into it (i.e., positive current). This seeming contradiction means that the capacitor maintains its potential but "breaks through" and proceeds to discharge along the CB path.

Similarly, at B, the negative resistance attempts to "charge" the capacitor while simultaneously withdrawing charge (i.e., negative current). This also forces the capacitor to "break through," and it charges along the DA path. The result is plotted in Figs. 18.33 and 18.34.

A nonlinear capacitance may have a charge-voltage characteristic such as shown in Fig. 18.35, wherein the dielectric material is assumed to have a narrow hysteresis loop. Then, the functional relation between Q and V can be thought of as single-valued, and the derivative of Q with respect to V will also be single-valued but, nevertheless, a function of V. It is this derivative which defines a differential capacitance for the nonlinear capacitor:

$$C(V) = \frac{dQ(V)}{dV}$$

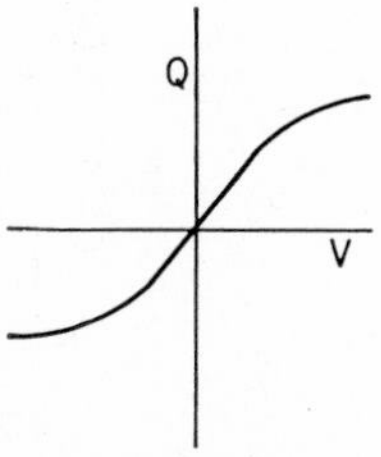

FIG. 18.35. Charge-voltage characteristic for nonlinear capacitance.

On writing the equation for the voltage-current relation for the nonlinear capacitor, we find that the differential capacitance appears and must therefore be used in the following analysis. (For a linear capacitor, the differential capacitance is obviously constant and identical with the linear capacitance.) Thus

$$Q = Q(V)$$

and

$$I = \frac{dQ}{dt} = \frac{dQ(V)}{dV}\frac{dV}{dt}$$

where

$$C(V) = \frac{dQ(V)}{dV}$$

by definition, so that

$$I = C(V) \frac{dV}{dt} \tag{18.91}$$

Equation (18.91) is identical in form with Eq. (18.87), and in a similar way, the differential equation is replaced by a difference equation, yielding a volt-ampere relation for the nonlinear capacitor, for a small time interval Δt,

$$I = \frac{C(V)}{\Delta t} (V - V_0) \tag{18.92}$$

The introduction of the (differential) capacitance as a function of voltage across the capacitor means that the slope of the straight-line plot will be different for each time interval Δt if a change in voltage occurs. The set of parallel lines which characterized the linear capacitor must be replaced with a set of lines each of different slope.

To do this with a specific example, consider a nonlinear capacitor initially charged to

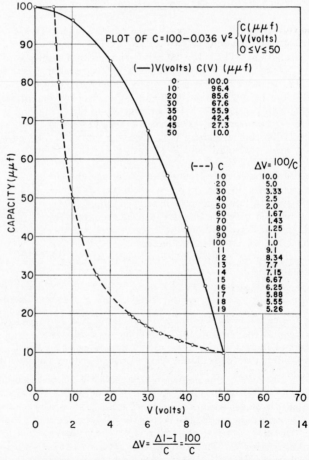

FIG. 18.36. Plot of $C = 100 - 0.036V^2$ and plot of ΔV versus C.

50 volts and required to discharge through a linear 1-megohm resistor.   The capacitance will be assumed to be the following function of voltage:

$$C = 100 - 0.036V^2 \tag{18.93}$$

where V is in volts and C is in micromicrofarads.   This relation is assumed valid over the range of 0 to 50 volts.   A fixed time interval $\Delta t = 2$ μsec is chosen to yield about 5 per cent precision initially, although the precision rapidly increases as the capacitor value increases.

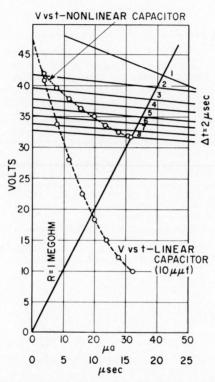

FIG. 18.37. Graphical analysis of R-C network involving a nonlinear capacitor.

Equation (18.93) is plotted as the solid line in Fig. 18.36.   The hyperbolic plot in Fig. 18.36 (dashed line) is a plot of ΔV versus C for a constant transfer of charge (= 50 μa $\times$ 2 μsec) of 100 $\mu\mu$coulombs.   This plot will help to determine the family of lines which will describe the operation of the nonlinear capacitor.   These lines are plotted in Fig. 18.37.

At $t = 0$, the initial value of the capacitor is 10 $\mu\mu$f, and it is charged to 50 volts. In the time interval $\Delta t = 2$ μsec, the capacitor will discharge and will be described by the straight line labeled 1.   The voltage on the capacitor at the end of the first time interval is determined by the intersection of this straight line with the resistor load line.   This value of voltage becomes the new V_0 in Eq. (18.92), and from the solid-line plot in Fig. 18.36 we obtain the value of C at this voltage.   From the dashed-line plot we determine the value of ΔV at this value of C, which then enables us to plot the next straight line labeled 2.   This line, in turn, intersects the resistor load line, and the same procedure is followed.   The result is a set of intersections.   The voltages at each intersection can now be plotted against time, which is obtained by summing the time intervals. This relation is plotted as the dotted line in Fig. 18.37. For comparison there is also a dashed-line plot which is the exponential of a linear 10-$\mu\mu$f capacitor charged initially to 50 volts and discharging through a linear 1-megohm resistor.

This method can be extended, with little difficulty, to the case of a network consisting of a nonlinear capacitance and a nonlinear resistance. We must note that these examples are analyzed by a "closed" method, in that for the two elements involved one acts as the generator, the other as the load.

REFERENCES

1. Guillemin, E. A.: "The Mathematics of Circuit Analysis," chap. 2, John Wiley & Sons, Inc., New York, 1949.
2. Guillemin, E. A.: "Communication Networks," vol. II, John Wiley & Sons, Inc., New York, 1935.
3. LeCorbeiller, P.: "Matrix Analysis of Electrical Networks," Harvard University Press, Cambridge, Mass., 1950.
4. Pipes, L. A.: "Applied Mathematics for Engineers and Physicists," 2d ed., chap. 4, McGraw-Hill Book Company, Inc., New York, 1958.
5. Pritchard, R. L.: Frequency Variations of Current Amplification Factor for Junction Transistors, *Proc. IRE*, vol. 40, pp. 1476–1481, November, 1952.
6. Rollett, J. M.: Another Approximation for the Alpha of a Junction Transistor, *Proc. IRE*, vol. 47, p. 1784, October, 1959.
7. Hunter, L. P., and H. Fleisher: Graphical Analysis of Some Transistor Switching Circuits, *Proc. IRE*, vol. 40, no. 11, pp. 1559–1562, November, 1952.
8. Hunter, L. P.: Graphical Analysis of Transistor Characteristics, *Proc. IRE*, vol. 38, no. 12, pp. 1387–1391, December, 1950.
9. Preisman, A.: "Graphical Constructions for Vacuum Tube Circuits," McGraw-Hill Book Company, Inc., New York, 1943.
10. Esaki, L.: New Phenomenon in Narrow Ge P-N Junctions, *Phys. Rev.*, vol. 109, p. 603, Apr. 1, 1958.
11. Rutz, R. F.: A 3000 mc Lumped-parameter Oscillator Using an Esaki Negative Resistance Diode, *IBM J. Research Develop.*, vol. 3, pp. 372–374, October, 1959.

Section 19

MEASUREMENT OF SEMICONDUCTOR DEVICE PARAMETERS

E. J. RYMASZEWSKI

and

D. F. SINGER

IBM Corporation, Poughkeepsie, N.Y.

The choice of a device suitable for a specific application and/or the choice of operating conditions for the best performance are based on two groups of data. The maximum ratings, such as power dissipation or breakdown voltage, belong to the first group. These ratings are prescribed by the device designer.

The second group of data should characterize the device as a circuit component. For example, the transistor is an active nonlinear device, and a large variety of parameters can be used for its characterization. Four-pole parameters of any kind might seem to be adequate because of the general operation of the transistor with one lead common to the input and output terminals. These parameters either can be used in a pure tabulated (or graphical) form or can be lumped into an equivalent circuit.

There is, however, one transistor model which seems to be the most versatile because of its usefulness to the circuit designer as well as to the device designer. This model reflects the physical phenomena in the transistor by means of equivalent-circuit elements like junction capacitances or bulk resistances. These phenomena are related to the technology of the device, and the equivalent circuit is as useful as an abstract equivalent circuit obtained from any set of four-pole parameters.

Many elements of this model cannot be measured directly, since they cannot be extracted from the physical device. A purpose of this section is to describe how the most important elements can be obtained from a relatively small number of four-pole parameters, directly measurable with the transistor considered as a "black box."

In addition, the d-c characteristics, the maximum rating, and the switching characteristics are included for a more complete characterization.

The selection of the parameters to be specified for the given device type depends on the intended application of the device as well as on the practicality of the techniques needed to determine the value of these parameters. An efficient control of the specified parameter values during the manufacturing process can be established if the relationship between the specified electrical parameters and the technology of the device manufacturing is known.

19.1. D-C Characteristics. The d-c or static characteristics represent the performance of a transistor at zero or low frequency. Of the number of graphs possible, only two are required to (1) construct all others and (2) obtain sufficient data to characterize the transistor completely for low-frequency small or large signals.

Linear equations are generally used in describing the behavior of the transistors at small-signal levels. These, however, are valid only to the extent that the signal is small and that the coefficients are properly defined for the operating point. For a more complete analysis, information regarding the variation of small-signal parameters with the operating point and a description of large-signal nonlinear action are necessary. The characteristic curves are perhaps most useful for the large-signal analysis, since the linear equations cannot easily be applied as their coefficients are functions of the operating point.

For example, in class A power-amplifier design (Sec. 11) not only is a certain power output desired but it is required at a specified maximum degree of distortion. The most fruitful approach, therefore, is a graphical analysis in conjunction with the characteristic curves.

In addition to large signals, the characteristics are also useful in obtaining the approximate small-signal parameters by allowing appropriate increments about the desired operating points. Such a graphical approach is generally made in lieu of the small-signal measurements or linear analysis and, although not so accurate, can be justified when measurements are inconvenient.

Two of the more common static curves are the common-base collector characteristics I_C versus V_{CB} with I_E constant and the common-emitter collector characteristics I_C versus V_{CE} with I_B constant. Because of the general acceptance of these curves to determine transistor performance, they warrant further interpretation and will be considered in some detail.

19.1a. Common-base Collector Characteristics. Figure 19.1 shows the common-base collector characteristics with I_E as the parameter. The cutoff region occurs where the emitter junction is reversed-biased. The transistor is operating in the saturation region when both emitter and collector junctions are forward-biased. For the collector current constrained to zero in the saturation region, the collector-junction voltage is given by[1]†

$$\phi_C = \frac{kT}{q} \ln\left(\frac{\alpha_{FB} I_E + I_{co}}{I_{co}}\right) \quad (19.1a)$$

In addition, the total emitter current must flow through the base bulk resistance R_B. Consequently, the total terminal collector-to-base voltage is given by

$$V_{CBO(S)} = R_B I_E + \frac{kT}{q} \ln\left(\frac{\alpha_{FB} I_E + I_{co}}{I_{co}}\right) \quad (19.1b)$$

The slope in the saturation region is initially R_B with a gradual increase or rounding of the curve near the knee due to the series collector ohmic resistance R_{CC}. At the entry into the active region ϕ_C is zero and the terminal voltage is approximately

$$I_E[R_B(1 - \alpha_{FB}) - R_{CC}\alpha_{FB}] \quad (19.2)$$

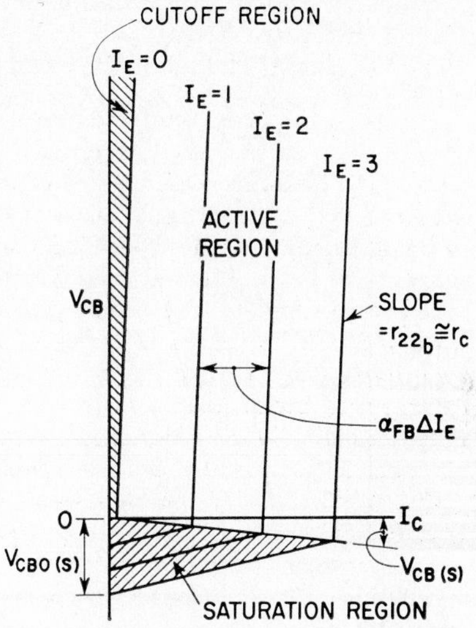

In the active region the collector-current increments are determined by the static short-circuit current-gain factor α_{FB}.‡ The common-base collector characteristics are generally not suited for an accurate measurement of this parameter. This inaccuracy

$$V_{CBO\,(S)} \cong I_E R_B + \frac{kT}{q} \ln\left(\frac{\alpha_{FB} I_E + I_{co}}{I_{co}}\right)$$

$$V_{CB\,(S)} \cong I_E \left[R_B(1 - \alpha_{FB}) - \alpha_{FB} R_{CC}\right]$$

FIG. 19.1. Common-base collector characteristics with I_E constant.

also applies to the output resistance, which is determined from the slope of the constant-emitter-current lines. Since the transistor is not a unilateral device, the output resistance is dependent upon the constant parameter of the emitter. Thus r_{22b} with constant V_{EB} (shorted source) will not be identical with r_{22b} with I_E constant. For the latter condition, r_{22b} consists of r_b, r_{cc}, and the effective collector-junction resistance r_c in series. For all practical cases, r_b and r_{cc} can be considered negligible. The junction resistance r_c can be broken down further into two effectively parallel resistors: a resistance R_{SL} to account for surface leakage and a resistance r_c' which accounts for a change in collector current due to the effect of V_{CB} on α_{FB}. r_c' can be expressed by

$$r_c' = \left.\frac{\Delta V_{CB}}{\Delta I_C}\right|_{I_E} \cong \frac{\Delta V_{CB}}{\Delta \alpha_{FB}} \frac{1}{I_E}$$

The two primary factors contributing to changes in α_{FB} with V_{CB} are:

1. An increase in collector voltage reduces the effective base width with a consequent increase in α_{FB}.

† It is assumed in this chapter that the emitter current varies as exp (qV_{EB}/kT). In practical cases, however, the exponent is generally found to be $(qV_{EB}/\lambda kT)$, where λ is a number between 1 and 2 and is a function of current density.

‡ See reference 33 for standard use of subscripts.

2. The total current gain must include the multiplication occurring at the collector junction (see Sec. 4). This factor causes I_C to increase at larger collector voltages.

Thus, for larger values of emitter current, the slope of the I_E curves in the active region decreases owing to the reduction of r_c'. Consideration must also be given to the effect of I_E on α_{FB}. For larger values of emitter current the injection efficiency is reduced owing to the increased conductivity of the base region. This results in an additional decrease in r_c'. The above effects are hardly noticeable on the common-base collector characteristics but become quite evident when the transistor is operated in common-emitter mode.

The breakdown voltage is the eventual limit of the collector-to-base voltage V_{CB}. This breakdown is not shown in Fig. 19.1, and details are reserved for Sec. 19.2, where voltage limits are considered.

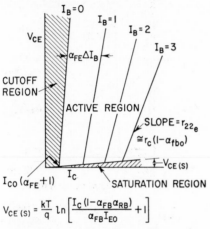

$$V_{CE(S)} = \frac{kT}{q} \ln \left[\frac{I_C(1 - \alpha_{FB}\alpha_{RB})}{\alpha_{FB} I_{EO}} + 1 \right]$$

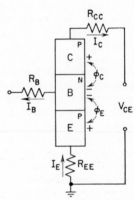

FIG. 19.2. Common-emitter collector characteristics with I_B constant. (Well below breakdown.)

FIG. 19.3. Schematic diagram illustrating transistor voltages.

19.1b. Common-emitter Collector Characteristics. The common-emitter characteristics with I_B as the parameter are shown in Fig. 19.2. The collector junction is neither forward- nor reversed-biased at the boundary between the active and saturation region and can, therefore, be considered the $\phi_C = 0$ locus. If the voltages across R_{EE} and R_{CC} are negligible, the terminal voltage V_{CE} is equal to the emitter junction voltage ϕ_E (see Fig. 19.3), which is then

$$\phi_E = V_{CE(S)} = \frac{kT}{q} \ln \left[\frac{I_C(1 - \alpha_{FB}\alpha_{RB})}{\alpha_{FB} I_{EO}} + 1 \right] \tag{19.3}$$

To analyze more fully this low-voltage region a general expression for I_C is used.†

$$I_C = \frac{\alpha_{FE}(\epsilon^{qV_{CE}/kT} - 1/\alpha_{RB})I_B + I_0(\epsilon^{qV_{CE}/kT} - 1)}{\epsilon^{qV_{CE}/kT} + \alpha_{FE}/\alpha_{RE}} \tag{19.4}$$

where $$I_0 = I_{CO} \frac{1 - \alpha_{FB}\alpha_{RB}}{1 - \alpha_{FB}}$$

This equation is plotted in Fig. 19.4 for different values of I_B. The alphas were assumed constant, although in practical cases some variation can be expected. It is

† Private communication with W. P. Dumke, IBM, Poughkeepsie, N.Y.

noted that the constant I_B curves converge and cross at a value of V_{CE} greater than zero. This convergence occurs at

$$I_C = I_{CO}(1 - \alpha_{RB})$$

$$V_{CE} = \frac{kT}{q} \ln \frac{1}{\alpha_{RB}}$$

The slope of the I_B curves between the active and saturation regions is relatively constant over a narrow range of values of V_{CE}. This slope is approximately

$$\frac{\Delta I_C}{\Delta V_{CE}} = \frac{\alpha_{FE} I_B}{4} \frac{q}{kT}$$

Since only two characteristic curves are to be considered in detail, the analysis of the common-emitter output characteristics with I_B constant will be presented as they pertain in comparison with the common-base characteristic of Fig. 19.1.

The collector-current increments between the constant-base-current curves are $\alpha_{FE} \Delta I_B$. Since $\alpha_{FE} = \alpha_{FB}/(1 - \alpha_{FB})$, small variations in α_{FB} produce large changes in α_{FE}. Thus, the calculated value of α_{FB} from these characteristics is more accurate.

The slope of the constant I_B curves determines the output resistance r_{22e} for the base current of consideration. This resistance can be expressed as

$$r_{22e} \cong r_c(1 - \alpha_{FB})$$

With careful measurement of α_{FE} and r_{22e}, r_c can also be computed far more accurately.

The transition from the active to the cutoff region occurs when the base cur-

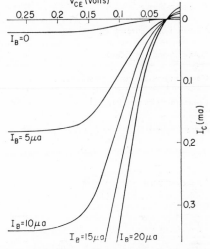

Fig. 19.4. Low-voltage low-current common-emitter collector characteristics.

rent is zero. Since the total base current consists of recombination current $I_E(1 - \alpha_{FB})$ and I_{CO} in opposition, the condition that $I_B = 0$ is met when $I_{CO} = I_E(1 - \alpha_{FB})$. The resulting collector current is then $I_{CO}(\alpha_{FE} + 1)$. Thus, the common-emitter "standby" condition results in a much larger collector current. For values of I_C less than this (operation in the cutoff region) the net base current must be negative or I_{CO} must be larger than $I_E(1 - \alpha_{FB})$.

The effects of the emitter current, collector multiplication, and the decrease in α_{FB} at higher emitter currents are quite evident in the common-emitter characteristics. For larger values of I_B the slope (or r_c) is reduced.

In the region of low voltage and high collector current a decrease in α_{FE} is observed. This effect, referred to as "alpha crowding," is the result of the decrease in α_{FB} for larger values of I_E (see Sec. 10). The distortion caused by operation in this region must be considered when designing large-signal linear amplifiers.

Table 19.1 lists some of the more useful common-base and common-emitter static-characteristic curves and the significance of the constant-parameter slope. Since the slope is determined by the choice of the ordinate and abscissa, the variable parameters are listed under the X and Y ordinates necessary to produce the slope indicated.

TABLE 19.1. SMALL-SIGNAL PARAMETERS OBTAINED FROM THE
STATIC-CHARACTERISTIC SLOPES

Static-characteristic family	Parameters			Slope of constant parameters
	Variable X　Y		Constant	
Common-base collector..............	I_C vs V_C		I_E	$\left.\dfrac{\partial V_C}{\partial I_C}\right\vert_{I_E} = r_{22b} \cong r_c$
Common-base input................	I_E vs V_E		V_C	$\left.\dfrac{\partial V_E}{\partial I_E}\right\vert_{V_C} = h_{11b} \cong r_e + r_b(1 - \alpha_{fb0})$
Common-base transconductance......	V_E vs I_C		V_C	$\left.\dfrac{\partial I_C}{\partial V_E}\right\vert_{V_C} = y_{21b}$
Common-base collector..............	V_C vs I_C		V_E	$\left.\dfrac{\partial I_C}{\partial V_C}\right\vert_{V_E} = y_{22b}$
Common-base current transfer........	I_E vs I_C		V_C	$\left.\dfrac{\partial I_C}{\partial I_E}\right\vert_{V_C} = h_{21b} = h_{fb0} = -\alpha_{fb0}$
Common-emitter collector...........	I_C vs V_C		I_B	$\left.\dfrac{\partial V_C}{\partial I_C}\right\vert_{I_B} = r_{22e} \cong r_c(1 - \alpha_{fb0})$
Common-emitter current transfer.....	I_B vs I_C		V_C	$\left.\dfrac{\partial I_C}{\partial I_B}\right\vert_{V_C} = h_{21e} = h_{fe0} = \alpha_{fe0}$
Common-emitter collector..........	V_C vs I_C		V_B	$\left.\dfrac{\partial I_C}{\partial V_C}\right\vert_{V_B} = y_{22e}$
Common-emitter input..............	I_B vs V_B		V_C	$\left.\dfrac{\partial V_B}{\partial I_B}\right\vert_{V_C} = h_{11e} = \dfrac{r_e}{1 - \alpha_{fb0}} + r_b$

19.1c. Point-by-point Method.　The point-by-point method of obtaining the characteristics requires appropriate d-c power supplies and a means of monitoring the voltages and currents.[2]　A curve can be drawn by plotting recorded values of voltage current, while another voltage current is changed stepwise.　For example,

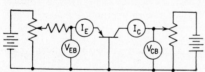

FIG. 19.5. Circuit arrangement for determining d-c common-base characteristics for a PNP transistor.

$$h_{11b} = \left.\frac{\Delta V_{EB}}{\Delta I_E}\right\vert_{V_{CB}}$$

can be obtained by recording values of I_E at different settings of V_{EB} while V_{CB} is kept constant at the desired collector voltage.　Since transistors are inherently temperature-sensitive, care must be taken, particularly at larger values of bias, to account for the temperature.　In addition, in order to prevent possible damage to the transistor, values of voltage or current should not exceed the safe collector-dissipation limit.　Figure 19.5 shows a circuit arrangement for determining the common-base characteristics of a PNP transistor.

19.1d. Visual Display.　The visual display is particularly useful for a rapid observation of the transistor parameters.　Thus, it is an important testing procedure for fabricators, preliminary design, final test, etc.　Although the parameters obtained by this method are generally not so accurate as by a point-by-point method, it does allow quick evaluation of such important parameters as leakage current, breakdown voltages, and common-emitter gain.　In addition, small irregularities which might not show up in the point-by-point procedure can be observed.　Because of the number of commercial plotters available, a detailed description of a display circuit will not be given.　Figure 19.6, however, illustrates the basic principles involved.　The characteristics to be obtained are the common-emitter collector characteristics with I_B constant.   For a PNP transistor a negative increasing voltage between collector and emitter is required.   This voltage is obtained from the induced 60-cycle source which is rectified by the diode.   The negative portion of the signal appears across the transistor, while the positive portion is across the diode.   This provides the negative increasing collector voltage necessary for display purposes.   To obtain a family of constant I_B curves, the base current must increase in stepwise fashion during the successive voltage sweeps.   This is shown in Fig. 19.6 as a stepwise current generator.

PRECAUTIONS.   Some devices may appear unstable and oscillate owing to an effective negative resistance presented to the curve plotter.   This is particularly true for point-contact transistors and for Esaki tunnel diodes.   It has also been observed on some very high frequency transistors with low base resistance.[3]   If instability is

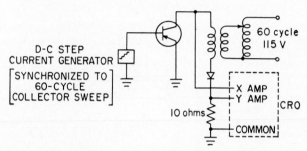

FIG. 19.6. Circuit for visual display of common-emitter characteristics for a PNP transistor.

present, long leads and parasitic capacitances will affect the resulting trace.   A series resistance is sometimes necessary to prevent instability.

Under continuous sweep for the display, an average temperature rise of the junction is anticipated owing to the average power dissipated.   If the dissipated power exceeds the dissipation limit, the accumulative heating effect is evidenced by a gradual shift in the observed characteristics.   Under such conditions, the voltages should be removed before permanent damage results.   Heating can also produce a hysteresis loop (a loop caused by outgoing and return traces not coinciding), particularly when the curves are extended out onto the high-power regions.   This effect can also be noted when moisture is trapped in the transistor can and settles on the semiconductor surfaces.

19.1e. Pulse Method.   For the case where characteristics are desired beyond the thermal limit set by the point-by-point procedure, the pulse method is applicable. The voltage is then applied repeatedly but for short periods of time.   Since the average power dissipated can be made very small, the danger of thermal runaway is all but eliminated.   Accumulated heating will occur, however, for large pulse width and high recurrence frequency.   The pulse width should be sufficiently large to ensure negligible distortion due to capacitance and hole storage effects.[4]   A simple circuit illustrating the principle of the pulse method is shown in Fig. 19.7.   Either oscilloscope display or meters can be used to determine the characteristics.   If moving-coil d-c meters are used, average values will be indicated.   Thus for a 2-msec pulse duration and a repetition rate of 60 cps, the meters will indicate 12 per cent of the pulse amplitudes.   The ratio of the dissipated power to the peak power will also be 12 per cent.   By proper choice of pulse width and repetition rate any convenient power ratio can be obtained.   It should be obvious, however, that for larger values of power ratio, the effects of heating must be considered.

19.2. Maximum Ratings.   Semiconductor devices have inherently a long operating lifetime.   However, the degree to which this long life is utilized is determined largely by the operation of the device. Since the maximum ratings determine the limits of device measurement as well as circuit application, a brief description of these limits is given. Particular emphasis is placed on the visual display of the voltage breakdowns. In some cases the maximum current must be specified. This is particularly true for devices having large bulk resistances.

Since a semiconductor device incorporates at least one junction, the voltage breakdown of this junction must be considered as a limiting condition. For transistors at least two junctions are involved, and consequently more voltages are necessary to specify the limits of operation. For a typical transistor the maximum junction voltages are commonly referred to as

$$\text{Collector-to-base breakdown } V_{CB,\text{max}} = BV_{CBO}$$
$$\text{Emitter-to-base breakdown } V_{EB,\text{max}} = BV_{EBO}$$
$$\text{Collector-to-emitter breakdown } V_{CE,\text{max}}$$

Since the maximum voltages are here considered as the breakdown voltages, it should be obvious that the maximum ratings specified by a manufacturer would necessarily be

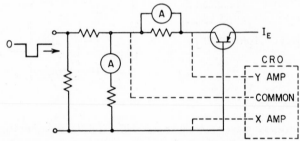

Fɪɢ. 19.7. Circuit for determining the common-base collector characteristics for a PNP transistor by the pulse method.

lower to avoid operation in this region. Both $V_{CB,\text{max}}$ and $V_{EB,\text{max}}$ are limits set by their respective junctions and, therefore, can be considered equal to BV_{CBO} and BV_{EBO}, respectively. $V_{CE,\text{max}}$, however, is dependent upon the transistor action and consequently is a function of the circuit operation.

None of the breakdowns are by themselves damaging. The heat developed from the large power dissipated during the breakdown, however, can result in permanent fracture or degradation of the transistor.

19.2a. Avalanche Breakdown. Avalanche breakdown is due to an effect similar to the breakdown of a gas tube (Townsend breakdown). Carriers crossing the junction arrive at the other side with energies dependent upon the junction voltage. If sufficient energy is acquired in transit, an electron may be ionized when the carrier collides with a germanium atom. This allows another carrier to traverse the junction, and an accumulated current increase results. The rate of extra carrier generation is given by the symbol m and is called the carrier multiplication factor. As the reverse junction voltage is increased, m goes from 1 to infinity with a sharp rise near the avalanche-breakdown voltage BV_A. Both the collector and emitter junctions are usually limited by this breakdown phenomenon. For materials with high impurity concentrations the Zener effect or "tunnel current" may cause breakdown. Here the additional carriers are produced by a high field "stripping" the valence electrons. This breakdown occurs most often at the emitter junction. Generally if the breakdown is larger than 2 volts, it is considered avalanche. For lower values it is considered Zener breakdown or a combination of Zener and avalanche. The Zener effect does not involve the multiplication process.

Figure 19.8 shows typical common-base characteristics with the collector breakdown due to the avalanche effect. The voltage BV_{CBO} is usually obtained from a visual display of these characteristics. Note that for a specific collector voltage the multiplication (or m) is constant. Thus, if it is assumed that α_{FB} and emitter-current increments are constant, the distance between the emitter-current curves will be the same for any specific voltage. They will increase, however, as the voltage is increased owing to the multiplication factor.

The destruction of the transistor due to avalanche breakdown generally results in an open between collector and base.

19.2b. Alpha Multiplication. Alpha multiplication is closely related to the avalanche effect (see Sec. 4.1d), since it depends upon the collector multiplication factor m.

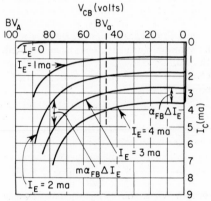

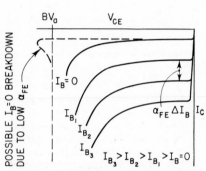

FIG. 19.8. Collector characteristic families showing avalanche-breakdown voltage BV_A and $\alpha = 1$ breakdown BV_a.

FIG. 19.9. Typical common-emitter collector characteristics with I_B constant. Breakdown due to alpha multiplication.

It differs, however, in that the transistor is operated in common-emitter mode. For this condition the collector current is given by

$$I_C = \frac{m}{1 - \alpha_{FB}m}(\alpha_{FB}I_B + I_{CO}) \tag{19.5}$$

It is evident that I_C is infinite when $\alpha_{FB}m = 1$. Since the requirement of this breakdown is that the total current gain be unity, this breakdown is sometimes referred to as the alpha-equal-one breakdown. The voltage necessary to produce this m is much lower than the avalanche-breakdown voltage BV_A and must be considered a limiting voltage that may be applied between collector and emitter.

Alpha-multiplication breakdown is usually observed on a visual display of the common-emitter collector characteristics. It differs from punch through in that the breakdown appears to be dependent upon the base current. That is, as I_B is increased, the knee of the breakdown occurs at lower values of collector voltage. This is shown in Fig. 19.9.

In some cases, the curve for $I_B = 0$ will extend beyond the apparent breakdown BV_a. This is because α_{FB} is generally lower at very low values of I_E and the required m or voltage necessary for breakdown is increased.

19.2c. Maximum Collector-to-emitter Voltage. Voltages larger than the alpha-multiplication breakdown can be applied between collector and emitter, depending on the circuit configuration. For the common-emitter collector characteristics, as normally observed on a visual display, the base current I_B is increased in steps from zero to larger positive values. (Positive here is taken as the direction of base recombination current or coming out of the base lead for PNP transistors.) Thus, for these curves the emitter is forward-biased and contributes current to the multiplication process. For this condition, the breakdown occurs at BV_a. On the other hand, when the emitter current is constrained to zero, I_{CO} only is involved and the breakdown is that of the collector junction BV_A.

These two breakdowns can be considered as limits of $V_{CE,\max}$ with possible values

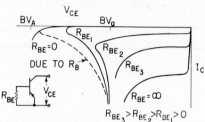

FIG. 19.10. Typical collector characteristics as a function of base-to-emitter resistance R_{BE}.

occurring between them, depending on the source impedance or circuit configuration.

Figure 19.10 shows a common-emitter collector characteristic as a function of base-to-emitter external resistance. Note that once breakdown occurs, V_{CE} drops to BV_a unless I_C is limited by an external resistance. Voltage surges must be avoided, since once $V_{CE,\max}$ is exceeded, the transistor may stay in the breakdown condition even after the voltage surge is removed.

Curves similar to Fig. 19.10 can also be drawn for constant values of reverse base current I_B or reverse-biasing voltage V_{BE}.

The general requirement for values of $V_{CE,\max}$ larger than BV_a is to prevent the emitter junction from conducting. Once the threshold voltage of the emitter is reached, additional current is contributed to the multiplication process, with $\alpha_{FB}m >$ 1. This results in a negative over-all α_{FE}, and the collector current increases until limited by an external resistance.

19.2d. Punch Through. Punch through occurs when the collector space-charge region extends to the emitter, causing an effective emitter-to-collector short. As the collector voltage is increased, the space-charge layer widens, penetrating further into the base region. At a sufficiently high voltage, the effective base width is reduced to zero while the space-charge region touches the emitter.

Punch through can be observed by noting the breakdown of the common-emitter collector characteristics on a visual display. If the collector resistance is low, the breakdown voltage can be considered independent of the base or collector current. Figure 19.11 shows a typical common-emitter collector characteristic with the breakdown due to punch through. Generally this breakdown is not destructive, and normal operation is restored when the voltage is removed.

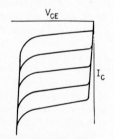

FIG. 19.11. Common-emitter collector characteristics illustrating punch-through breakdown.

19.2e. Thermal Runaway. This condition is discussed under power limitations. As mentioned, thermal runaway is a function of the ambient temperature, thermal resistance, collector dissipation, and collector voltage. For a given circuit, the limit can be expressed as a maximum allowable applied voltage.

19.2f. Power Limits. A limiting factor of the power capabilities of a semiconductor device is the maximum temperature which the material or junction can tolerate. This temperature limit can be set by any one, or a combination, of the following effects:

1. A deterioration of the junction which is accelerated at elevated temperatures, believed to be due to increased surface contamination as a result of outgassing

2. A temperature where transistor action is modified, owing to increased density of thermally generated carriers

3. Thermal runaway

The last condition occurs because of the positive temperature coefficient of I_{CO}.   As the junction temperature increases, I_{CO} increases with a resulting further increase in dissipation.   If the total dissipation causes the junction temperature to increase at a rate greater than that at which the heat is carried away, thermal runaway results, with probable destruction of the junction.   For a specific transistor circuit, thermal runaway is usually considered as a collector-voltage limit, since it is dependent upon the circuit stability factor as well as ambient temperature, dissipation resistance, and power dissipation.

For germanium transistors, the maximum temperature ranges from 85 to 100°C with lower values for some high-frequency units.   For silicon transistors, the junction can be operated as high as 150 or 200°C.   Under operating conditions, the locus of maximum safe operation is that for which the internal temperature rise plus the ambient temperature T_A equals the maximum allowed junction temperature $T_{j,\max}$.

This relationship can be expressed as

$$P_{\max} K + T_A = T_{j,\max} \qquad (19.6)$$

where $P_{\max}$ is the maximum safe transistor power dissipation which is usually attributed entirely to the collector junction.   Then $P_{\max} = P_{C,\max} = (V_{CB}I_C)_{\max}$. K is the thermal resistance, which can be defined as the effective temperature rise per unit power dissipation of the junction above the temperature of an external reference point under steady-state conditions.   Thus, it is an indication of the ability to carry heat away from the junction.   Since the geometry, metallurgy, package, and socket all contribute to the removal of the heat generated at the junction, all must be included in determining the total thermal resistance.

19.3. Small-signal Parameters.   As the name implies, the small-signal or incremental parameters give the incremental current-voltage, current-current, or voltage-voltage dependence measured on the same lead or on pairs of device leads.   The magnitudes of the increments are assumed to be sufficiently small so as not to affect the value of the parameters.   The parameters are usually functions of the d-c operating point as well as functions of the frequency and temperature.

If the device has only two leads, then it has only one small-signal parameter—the impedance (or its inverse—the admittance).   If the device has more than two leads, then several different sets of parameters may be defined to represent different dependencies.   The sets, however, are mutually interrelated.[6-8]

The definition of the parameters usually relates only two variables, and it simultaneously requires zero increment in the value of some other current or voltage.   The zero requirement cannot always be satisfied in the actual measurement without violating the small-signal condition.†

This restriction and the difficulty of combining a broadband a-c open circuit of sufficiently high impedance with a low-resistance d-c path are the main reasons for measuring the short-circuit parameters on the device input.   If, however, an extremely low-impedance a-c short is required, the open-circuit parameters may be favored.   As a result, the h (hybrid) parameters and the y (admittance) parameters are most widely used for device analysis, for the equivalent-network representation of a device, and for circuit design.   The parameter definitions are listed in Tables 19.2 and 19.3.‡

Since the operating frequencies of a semiconductor device may embrace a wide range from direct current to many hundreds or thousands of megacycles, radically different types of measuring equipment may be needed to measure the same parame-

---

† Example: to measure $z_{11} = v_1/i_1$, $i_2 = 0$ (the open-circuit input impedance) the output must be open-circuited at the measuring frequency.   If a transistor is operated in such a circuit, a large a-c collector voltage results and the small-signal condition is violated.

‡ For more details see reference 33.

ter of the same device. Equipment suitable for correct measurement of the small-signal parameters should comply with the following requirements:

1. The a-c voltages and alternating currents in the sample device should be sufficiently small with respect to the corresponding d-c voltages and direct currents in order to ensure quasi-linear (tangential) measurements.

2. It should contain means to establish any desired d-c operating point.

3. It should provide for either an a-c short circuit or an a-c open circuit between certain device leads according to the definition of the particular small-signal parameter.

TABLE 19.2. THE h AND y PARAMETERS OF A TWO-PORT NETWORK

$$V_1 = h_{11}I_1 + h_{12}V_2 \qquad I_1 = y_{11}V_1 + y_{12}V_2$$
$$I_2 = h_{21}I_1 + h_{22}V_2 \qquad I_2 = y_{21}V_1 + y_{22}V_2$$

$h_{11} = \dfrac{V_1}{I_1} = \dfrac{1}{y_{11}}$ $V_2 = 0$ Short-circuit input impedance

$h_{12} = \dfrac{V_1}{V_2}$ $I_1 = 0$ Open-circuit reverse-voltage transfer ratio

$h_{21} = \dfrac{I_2}{I_1} = \dfrac{y_{21}}{y_{11}}$ $V_2 = 0$ Short-circuit forward-current transfer ratio

$h_{22} = \dfrac{I_2}{V_2} = \dfrac{1}{z_{22}}$ $I_1 = 0$ Open-circuit output admittance

$y_{11} = \dfrac{I_1}{V_1} = \dfrac{1}{h_{11}}$ $V_2 = 0$ (Short-circuit) input admittance

$y_{12} = \dfrac{I_1}{V_2}$ $V_1 = 0$ (Short-circuit) reverse transadmittance

$y_{21} = \dfrac{I_2}{V_1} = \dfrac{h_{21}}{h_{11}}$ $V_2 = 0$ (Short-circuit) forward transadmittance

$y_{22} = \dfrac{I_2}{V_2}$ $V_1 = 0$ (Short-circuit) output admittance

4. Facilities to maintain a particular value of the device (junction) temperature may be desirable in some cases.[9]

Unless the equipment has been specifically designed for this kind of measurement,† it would hardly satisfy the requirements 2 and 3. In addition, the device leads are most likely to be unsuitable for a satisfactory direct connection to the equipment terminals. The usual solution is then to design an adapter (jig, fixture, etc.) whose complexity depends upon the required performance features.

Though it may seem simple, one of the most difficult things to do is to design an adapter which in no way distorts the value of the desired parameter. A more sophisticated adapter may either transform the parameter value or convert the parameter type to suit the performance capabilities of the available equipment. All these adapter types are described in the following subsections.

† Such as General Radio Type 1607-A Transfer Function and Immittance Bridge. See reference 10.

Due attention must be paid to the region between the equipment terminals and the actual device. This region consists of the combination of the adapter structure and the device leads and package. At direct current and at low-frequency alternating current this region can often be neglected. With increasing frequency, however, the significance of this region increases,[3] and, if ignored, it may lead to serious errors in measured results.

An equivalent electrical representation of the region is a network whose configuration and elements reflect the electric and magnetic fields as well as resistances possibly

TABLE 19.3. NOTATIONS USED FOR THE h AND y PARAMETERS OF TRANSISTORS†

Small-signal four-pole parameter	Mode of operation		
	Common-base	Common-emitter	Common-collector
$h_{11} = \dfrac{1}{y_{11}}$	h_{11b} h_{ib}	$h_{11e} = h_{11c}$ h_{ie}	$h_{11c} = h_{11c}$ h_{ic}
h_{12}	h_{12b} h_{rb}	h_{12e} h_{re}	h_{12c} h_{rc}
$h_{21} = \dfrac{y_{21}}{y_{11}}$	$h_{21b}(\alpha)$ $h_{fb} = -\alpha_{fb}$	$h_{21e}(\beta)$ $h_{fe} = \alpha_{fe}$	h_{21c} h_{fc}
$h_{22} = \dfrac{1}{z_{22}}$	h_{22b} h_{ob}	$h_{22e} = h_{22c}$ h_{oe}	$h_{22c} = h_{22e}$ h_{oc}
$y_{11} = \dfrac{1}{h_{11}}$	$y_{11b} = y_{22c}$ y_{ib}	$y_{11e} = y_{11c}$ y_{ie}	$y_{11c} = y_{11e}$ y_{ic}
y_{12}	y_{12b} y_{rb}	y_{12e} y_{re}	y_{12c} y_{rc}
$y_{21} = \dfrac{h_{21}}{h_{11}}$	y_{21b} y_{fb}	y_{21e} y_{fe}	y_{21c} y_{fc}
y_{22}	$y_{22b} = y_{22e}$ y_{ob}	$y_{22e} = y_{22b}$ y_{oe}	$y_{22c} = y_{11b}$ y_{oc}

† Subscript zero can be added after the shown subscripts to indicate a d-c (or very low frequency a-c) value of the parameter.

present in the region. The network connects the sample device to the terminals of the measuring equipment. Since the field configuration and, hence, at least the values of the equivalent-network elements depend on the geometry of the region, either it should remain constant throughout the measurements or any changes should be known in order to obtain consistent results.

In the very high frequency range from 30 to 300 mc, the suitable measurement techniques change from the lumped-parameter circuits to the distributed-parameter circuits based on transmission-line phenomena.[11] With further increasing frequency the common concepts of the device terminals[12,13] and of the definition of the impedance (or admittance) disappear, and their definition becomes more restricted and even somewhat arbitrary.[14]

Adapters to the lumped-parameter equipment, such as admittance bridges, can be designed to have an equivalent network whose effect is nearly eliminated during the initial zero balancing, preceding the actual measurements. The device-terminal plane is placed at the boundary plane of the adapter. The device leads are, as a rule, lumped either into an equivalent inductance or into an equivalent capacitance, depending upon the value of the respective parameter.

The same design philosophy regarding the device-terminal plane can be applied to adapters designed using transmission-line technique up to about 1,000 mc. The inhomogeneous fields in the boundary plane and in its vicinity may require introduction of correcting terms, still in the form of lumped equivalent inductances and/or capacitances.[15]

At frequencies higher than about 1,000 mc the dimensions of the device package and the length of the adapter line containing the distorted field region gradually become comparable to the wavelength of the signal. An equivalent-circuit representation of the region is then no longer frequency-independent, although it may require fewer elements.[16] The possibility of determining such an equivalent representation is discussed at the end of the following subsection.

19.3a. One-port (Driving Point) Admittances. Measurement of these parameters is frequently equivalent to the measurement of the physical parameters described in Sec. 19.4.

The selection of the measuring equipment depends upon the intended evaluation. If the equivalent-circuit representation calls for a series connection of the resistance and reactance, then an impedance meter will yield the desired values directly. An admittance meter will measure the equivalent parallel-connection values. In the latter case, a conversion of the measured values into their series equivalent is required. If a great variety of parameters must be measured, then an admittance bridge, especially one which is also capable of measuring the transadmittances, may be the most useful instrument, since it can be made to measure virtually all values of admittances and transadmittances.

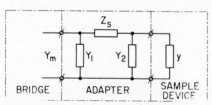

FIG. 19.12. Equivalent adapter network.

An adapter for such a bridge usually has to facilitate the establishment of the desired d-c operating point. If the sample device has more than two leads, then the adapter also has to provide a-c short circuits between the specified leads. The measuring equipment may or may not have a d-c conducting path between its terminals, and the permissible value of the current through this conducting path may be below the desired values. The value of the external d-c voltage across these terminals may be limited as well. These facts may determine the details of the adapter design, but basically the adapters will be similar.

An equivalent adapter network for a two-lead device is shown in Fig. 19.12. The admittance Y_1 represents the stray electric fields of the adapter body directly attached to the equipment terminals. The admittance Y_2 is given by the socket which accommodates the device leads and, if present, by the a-c admittance of the d-c conducting path. The series connection of the d-c blocking capacitor and its lead inductance determines the impedance Z_S. The admittance Y_0 is determined by the adapter itself.

$$Y_0 = Y_1 + \frac{Y_2}{1 + Z_S Y_2} \tag{19.7}$$

This admittance is usually tuned out during the initial zero balancing of the bridge.

If the range of the balancing means is not sufficient, then Y_0 should be measured and its value deducted from the measured device admittance.

The actual device admittance y is transformed by the adapter network into an admittance Y_T which appears across the bridge terminals.

$$Y_T = Y_1 + \frac{y + Y_2}{1 + Z_S(y + Y_2)} \tag{19.8}$$

Y_T contains Y_0, which is already balanced out. Hence, the measured admittance Y_m will be

$$Y_m = Y_T - Y_0 = \frac{y}{(1 + Z_S Y_2)[1 + Z_S(y + Y_2)]} \tag{19.9}$$

The rationalized measurement error δ is then

$$\delta = \frac{Y_m - y}{y} = \frac{Z_S[Y_2 + (y + Y_2)(1 + Z_S Y_2)]}{(1 + Z_S Y_2)[1 + Z_S(y + Y_2)]} \tag{19.10}$$

δ vanishes for $Z_S = 0$; this also can be seen by inspection of Fig. 19.12.

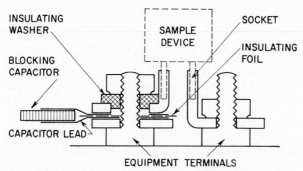

FIG. 19.13. Adapter with a negligible series impedance Z_S.

In a well-designed adapter, Z_S must be kept small. Then $\delta \leq Z_S(y + 2Y_2)$. The error δ has its greatest value δ_{max} for the highest measurable value of the sample admittance $y = y_{max}$. In this case $2Y_2$ can usually be neglected. If the value of δ_{max} is specified, then the adapter series impedance Z_S should be

$$Z_S \leq \frac{\delta_{max}}{y_{max}} \tag{19.11}$$

A sufficient reduction of Z_S may keep the error δ small enough to permit its inclusion into the accuracy figure of the measuring equipment as a correcting term.

The value of Z_S at the lower end of the frequency range of interest is determined by the reactance of the blocking capacitor, whose proper selection is hardly a problem. At the upper end the inductances of the capacitor leads and of any other connections determine the value of Z_S. These inductances can be made extremely small by using very closely spaced wide copper ribbons for the capacitor leads and by placing the sample socket very close to the equipment terminals, as shown in Fig. 19.13. Similar techniques are well suited to provide for a-c short circuits between selected leads of devices having more than two leads.

If a coaxial slotted line is used for the measurements on a two-lead device, the d-c bias can be supplied to the device through the line by means of commercially available components† according to the circuit shown in Fig. 19.14. Note the arrangement of the signal source and the signal detector permitting operation at very low signal levels across the sample device.

In such a case the sole function of the adapter is to mate the device package to the sample connector of the slotted line. The device-terminal plane is determined by short-circuiting the adapter in this plane and then using one of the corresponding voltage minima on the slotted line as the reference plane.

Figure 19.15 shows a photograph and a schematic drawing of the device end of an adapter constructed with the microstrip-line technique.[17] The cross-sectional geometry of the microstrip line permits a great reduction of the undefined region consisting of the device leads and the section of the adapter line containing distorted fields. The

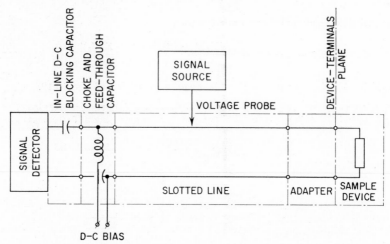

Fig. 19.14. D-c biasing of a two-pole device through the coaxial slotted line.

a-c short circuit for a third device lead is provided by a capacitor whose leads are similar to those shown in Fig. 19.13.

To fabricate an adapter of this kind, first, a microstrip line is made which is slightly longer than twice the final adapter length. Connectors matching the measuring equipment are attached to both ends of the line. The sample-lead clamp and, if required, the d-c blocking capacitor‡ and the d-c conducting choke (or a set of insertable chokes, usually in form of quarter-wavelength helical transmission lines) are installed. All distortions of the characteristic impedance of the line which may eventually occur can be conveniently detected and compensated for during this state of fabrication. As the next step, the line is cut into two unequal halves. The adapter half of the line should be shorter. The other half is gradually made shorter and shorter to match the electrical length of the adapter. The second line is then permanently short-circuited at its end. The purpose of this line is to establish the reference plane of the device terminals quickly.

As already mentioned in this section, the equivalent adapter network may be frequency-dependent when operating in the kilomegacycle range. However, only a small

† Such as described in reference 30.
‡ A further advantage of the microstrip techniques is due to the field concentration in the insulator between the strip and the ground plane. If a component, such as the blocking capacitor, is placed above the strip, then the resulting distortion of the characteristic impedance is fairly small. It can be easily compensated for by narrowing the strip in the vicinity of the capacitor.

number of frequency-dependent elements is required to describe completely the adapter and the device package. In particular, if no appreciable losses (resistances and/or conductances) are present, then the network reduces to an ideal transformer with a single reactance either in series or in parallel. This network may also include a tuner used to transform the device immittance into a more suitable range. In certain cases, such as measuring the series resistance of a parametric-amplifier diode, there is an evaluation technique which permits the determination of the coefficient

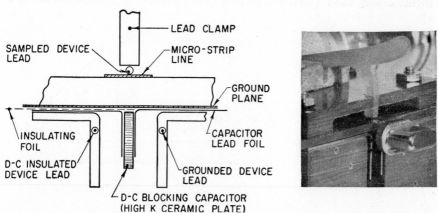

FIG. 19.15. Front view of the microstrip-line adapter for measurement of one-port admittance. (*Courtesy of International Business Machines Corporation.*)

of transformation of the ideal transformer and eliminates the necessity for knowing the value of the reactance.[18]

The inherent diode equivalent circuit is assumed to be frequency-independent and consists of the junction capacitance C_j in series with the bulk resistance R_S. The inductances and capacitances of the diode package are considered to be a part of the adapter network, as shown in Fig. 19.16. The input impedance of the diode is measured at the desired microwave frequency ω with variable d-c bias voltage. The results are then plotted on a Smith chart. The curve A in Fig. 19.17 is an idealized curve of this kind. A concentric rotation of this curve in the chart means changing the position of the (arbitrary) reference plane along the line. This is a permissible operation. The angle of rotation ϕ has been chosen to bring the measured curve A into the new position B which is located on a circle of constant real part. The constant real part complies with the assumption of the constant series resistance R_S in the diode equivalent circuit.

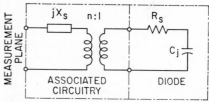

FIG. 19.16. An equivalent-circuit representation of the parametric-amplifier diode and its associated circuitry (package, adapter, and a possible tuner).

The true value of the resistance can be easily computed if the winding ratio n of the ideal transformer is known.

To obtain the value of n, the true increments in the diode reactance ΔX are computed from the capacitance increments ΔC_j measured at a low frequency and then related to the actually measured reactance increments ΔX_m.

$$ n^2 = \frac{\Delta X_m}{\Delta X} = \frac{\Delta X_m}{\omega \, \Delta C_j} \qquad (19.12) $$

The true series resistance R_S is then obtained from the measured value R_m.

$$R_S = \frac{1}{n^2} R_m = \frac{\omega \, \Delta C_j}{\Delta X_m} R_m \tag{19.13}$$

19.3b. Transadmittances. These parameters are defined as the complex ratio of the current in a shorted pair of terminals to the voltage across the other pair, considering currents flowing into the device as positive (Table 19.2). The transadmittances are

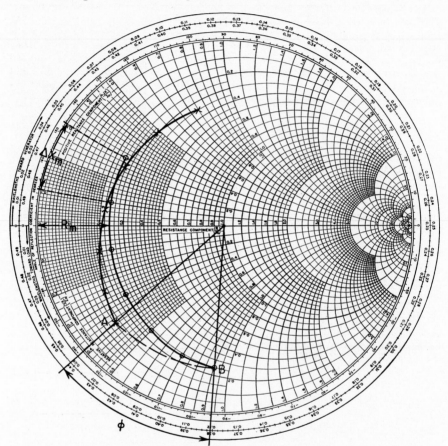

FIG. 19.17. Evaluation of the measured impedance of a parametric-amplifier diode.

most frequently used in amplifier design[19] and in some equivalent device representations. The forward transadmittance y_{21} can also be used along with the input admittance y_{11} for determining the short-circuit current transfer ratio $h_{21} = y_{21}/y_{11}$.

When a transadmittance is measured, its sign is determined by comparing the actual direction of the a-c flow with the definition. For example, in a common-base transistor the actual collector current flows out of the device when the emitter current is flowing in. Hence, $-y_{21b}$ is measured.

Beginning at fairly low frequencies up to very high frequencies the transadmittances can be measured by using three-terminal bridges, such as the Wayne Kerr B-601 (15 kc to 5 mc) and B-801 (1 to 100 mc).[8,20] Using the General Radio Type 1607-A

Transfer Function and Immittance Bridge[10] will extend the frequency range beyond the 1,000-mc mark. If the Rohde and Schwarz Diagraph[15] is used to measure the driving-point admittance y_{22} and the insertion voltage gain V_o/V_i,† then the forward transadmittance y_{21} can be computed from these measured parameters[21] as follows:

$$-y_{21} = \frac{V_o}{V_i}\left(y_{22} + \frac{1}{Z_0}\right) \qquad (19.14)$$

Adapters for the transadmittance-measuring equipment can be designed in a manner similar to those described in Sec. 19.3a. If the available equipment measures only the transadmittances whose actual conductance is positive but the device conductance is negative (such as y_{feo}), then two solutions exist: (1) Other admittances can be measured and used to compute the device admittance.[8,9] (2) The adapter can be equipped with an additional admittance shunting that of the device. This makes the total conductance a positive value. The same technique can also be used to expand the range of measurable susceptances.

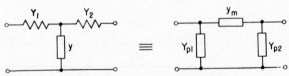

FIG. 19.18. Equivalent π and T networks.

A further application of a three-terminal admittance bridge is the measurement of very high values of a one-port admittance. The bridge can measure the transadmittance y_m of the π network in Fig. 19.18, discarding the other two admittances Y_{p1} and Y_{p2}. If the adapter is designed in the equivalent-T-network configuration, then the measured transadmittance y_m is a function of the fixed admittances Y_1 and Y_2 as well as a function of the device admittance y.

$$y_m = \frac{Y_1 Y_2}{Y_1 + Y_2 + y} \qquad (19.15a)$$

Making $Y_1 = Y_2 = Y$ simplifies Eq. (19.15a) to

$$y_m = \frac{Y^2}{2Y + y} \qquad (19.15b)$$

The transadmittance y_m has its greatest value for $y = 0$ and decreases with an increasing y. This can be used to determine the value of Y from the maximum measurable y_m. The sample admittance y is found from y_m and Y as follows:

$$\frac{y}{Y} = \frac{Y}{y_m} - 2 \qquad (19.16)$$

19.3c. Short-circuit Current Transfer Ratio (Current Gain). Two of the most important parameters used to describe a transistor are the common-base short-circuit current gain h_{fb} and the common-emitter short-circuit current gain h_{fe}. They are defined as the complex ratio of the collector alternating current to the emitter (for h_{fb}) or to the base (for h_{fe}) current, with the collector-to-base or collector-to-emitter a-c voltage equal to zero. Aside from the device geometry and type of doping used, these four-pole parameters are dependent upon d-c operating point, frequency, and temperature.

† This is the voltage transfer ratio with the load impedance Z_0.

At very low frequencies, the values of the parameters are real. They can be determined either by differentiating the proper d-c characteristics (Table 19.1) or by using various known techniques to measure small alternating currents or the ratio of the two currents. There is a large number of designs of measuring equipment commercially available. In selection of the equipment, suitable ranges of d-c voltages and direct currents should be checked. In addition, the peak-to-peak values of the alternating currents must be sufficiently smaller than the corresponding direct operating-point currents at which the measurements are to be performed.

The dependency of the current gain on frequency and on d-c operating point is a very important factor in device characterization as well as in circuit design. Therefore, the initial or low-frequency (sometimes also called "d-c") values of these parameters are often specified along with either the common-base cutoff (3 db down) frequency f_{ab} or the common-emitter unity-gain frequency f_T.

At higher frequencies the current gain becomes a complex number. Its value can be found from the measured y parameters, since $h_{21} = y_{21}/y_{11}$. However, this method

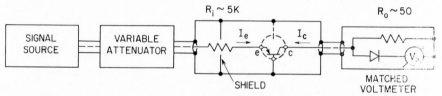

Fig. 19.19. The a-c part of a circuit for measuring the magnitude of h_{fb}.

is time-consuming and laborious, and hence, it is hardly suitable for plotting such representations as the common-base cutoff frequency contours (see Sec. 15.1). Neither is it practical for measurements on a large number of devices. However, it can be used to check the accuracy of other methods.

Figure 19.19 shows the a-c part of a rather simple circuit to measure the current-gain magnitude. R_i is a large resistance placed in the input lead to approximate a constant-current source. R_o is a small resistance in the output lead for use in conjunction with voltmeter V_o as a current-indicating device. The finite voltage V_o violates the requirement of the zero output voltage in the definition of a short-circuit current gain. The error (usually on the pessimistic side) can be kept small by using a sensitive voltmeter and keeping R_o as small as practicable (50 ohms or less).

At the beginning of measurement, a short circuit is placed between the terminals e and c. The value of the voltage V_o which indicates the input current is noted. Then the short circuit is removed, and the device is inserted. Now the voltage V_o indicates the output current. The same value of V_o would, for instance, indicate unity current gain. Either a calibrated voltmeter or a variable attenuator can be used to measure current-gain magnitudes different from unity. A fixed attenuation of about 10 to 28 db may be needed to isolate the source in order to ensure accurate operation of the attenuator. If proper precautions are met in the realization of this circuit, it can operate with reasonable accuracy up to several hundred megacycles. The limitations of this circuit are:

1. The input impedance of the transistor can be high enough to violate the assumption of a constant value of I_e.†

2. High source voltage is needed owing to the high value of R_i.

3. A calibration with the short circuit is usually needed at every frequency, especially when operating at frequencies higher than about 10 mc.

The above limitations are eliminated in the circuit whose a-c part is shown in Fig.

† Especially in common-emitter configuration and/or at low direct emitter currents.

19.20. This circuit is capable of performing fast and fairly accurate measurements, especially if used with a sweep-frequency generator.

The prime virtue of this circuit is the direct measurement of the device input current by converting it into a voltage across an unbalanced (one end grounded) resistance. The conversion is performed by means of a circuit known as a *balun*. The balun consists of an unbalanced transmission line (a coaxial line in Fig. 19.20) whose outer conductor is isolated from ground.†

In this circuit, the isolation is accomplished by means of a conducting sleeve whose upper edge is connected to the ground. The transmission line is placed inside the sleeve with its outer conductor connected to the bottom of the sleeve. The imped-ance between the upper end of the outer conductor and the ground is that of a short-circuited transmission line formed by the sleeve and by the outer conductor of the

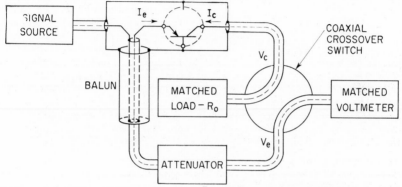

FIG. 19.20. Coaxial-line circuit to measure magnitude of the input and output alternating currents.

original line. This impedance is different from zero as long as the sleeve length differs from one-half wavelength or an integral multiple thereof; it is always different from zero if the sleeve is filled with a lossy material. Therefore, a voltage can be established between the upper end of the outer conductor and the ground plane. If the trans-mission line is terminated at the lower end with its characteristic impedance, then this impedance appears to connect the outer to the center conductor at the upper end, independent of the frequency. The signal source drives a current I_e through this impedance into the device input lead connected to the center conductor.

To terminate the lines correctly, the characteristic impedance of the attenuator, the voltmeter input impedance, and the load resistance should match the characteristic impedance of the line R_o.

The coaxial crossover switch also has the same characteristic impedance. It is used to measure the voltages V_e and V_c with the same voltmeter in order to eliminate dif-ferences in the nonlinear rectifier characteristics. This switch allows the use of the same cathode-ray tube to display both voltages as a function of the frequency when a sweep-frequency generator provides the signal.

The value of the voltage V_e depends, of course, on the attenuator setting, while the value of the voltage V_c is equal to the product of the output current I_c and the resist-ance R_o. Hence, for $|V_c| = |V_e|$ the attenuator setting corresponds to the magnitude of the current gain. For magnitudes of gain greater than unity the attenuator should be placed in the output line.

The frequency and/or the d-c operating point can be varied to achieve $|V_e| = |V_c|$

† The original application of the BALUN was to mate the BALanced to the UNbalanced transmission lines or other circuit components; see also reference 22.

for the given attenuator setting.   These measurements can yield either the frequency of unity current gain f_T or the cutoff frequency $f_{\alpha b}$ at a given d-c operating point or contours of the constant cutoff frequency (see Sec. 15.1).   In the past case, it should be considered that the dynamic (fast switching) contour is somewhat different from the static one measured with thermal equilibrium reached at every given d-c operating point.

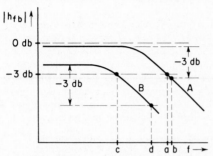

FIG. 19.21. Plot of magnitude of h_{fb} versus frequency.

PRECAUTIONS.   When the attenuator is preset, the initial (low-frequency) current gain should be known in order to prevent erroneous measurements.   For example, curve A in Fig. 19.21 is the response of a typical junction transistor under normal operating conditions.   If the 3-db value is set on the attenuator to find the cutoff frequency, then point a is the measured cutoff frequency (3 db down from unity).   Point b is the actual cutoff frequency (3 db down from h_{fb0}).   On the other hand, curve B represents the response of a transistor operated under conditions such that h_{fb0} is not close to unity (0 db).   Point c is the measured cutoff frequency, and point d is the actual cutoff frequency.   Under the latter conditions, the initial attenuation must be taken into account by correspondingly increasing the value set on the attenuator.   This precaution applies to all similar measurements.

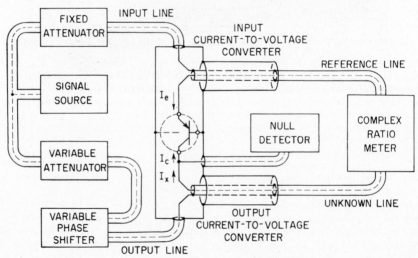

FIG. 19.22. Circuit for measuring the complex value of the short-circuit current transfer ratio.

The phase angle of h_{fb} at higher frequencies is important for device analysis (see Sec. 19.4b) as well as for circuit design.   Since not all devices behave like minimum phase-shift networks, the phase angle cannot always be obtained from the amplitude response and the phase-angle measurements may have to be made to complement the amplitude measurements.

Figure 19.22 shows a circuit for accurately measuring the complex output-to-input current ratio with the output voltage equal to zero.   The signal is fed to the input current-to-voltage converter through a fixed attenuator. The output converter obtains its signal through a variable attenuator and a variable phase shifter to facilitate the adjustment of the magnitude and phase angle of the current I_x flowing out of the output converter. If the current I_x equals the device output current I_c, then no current branches into the finite impedance of the null detector. Thus, the device output voltage is zero.

Two electrically identical transmission lines connect the input and output converters to the terminals of a complex ratio meter. The measured complex voltage ratio is then the desired complex ratio of the device output current I_c to the input current I_e with the output voltage being equal to zero.

A realization of the above circuit using the microstrip technique is shown in Fig. 19.23. To make the connecting lines, two adjacent strips were cut from the row sheet material in order to achieve equal electrical properties. The complex ratio meter is the Rohde and Schwarz Diagraph,[15] which yields the measured results directly on a

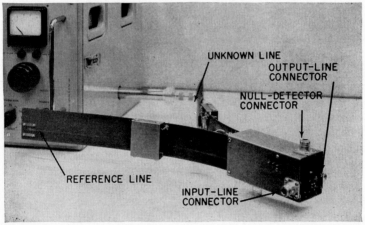

FIG. 19.23. Adapter of Fig. 19.22 devised in the microstrip technique. (*Courtesy of International Business Machines Corporation.*)

polar coordinate chart. The charts are available with either a linear or a logarithmic (decibel) magnitude scale.

An alternative technique for the point-by-point measurement of the real and imaginary parts of various transfer parameters in a wide frequency range has been developed by W. R. Thurston and R. A. Soderman of General Radio.[10]

19.3d. Maximum Frequency of Oscillation. The definition of this parameter may be different for different devices. For devices with an inherent negative resistance, it may be the highest achievable frequency of oscillation given either by the nature of the negative resistance or by the possibility of constructing the necessary tuning circuitry.[29] Since the magnitude of the oscillation is limited by nonlinearities in the device characteristics, this parameter does not strictly comply with the definition of the small-signal parameters. If the device can operate in a two-port circuit, then the maximum frequency of oscillation signifies the frequency at which the falling power gain approaches unity. In this case, the small-signal assumptions and measurement techniques can be applied, at least to make the initial adjustments.

Figure 19.24 shows a circuit to measure the power gain. The required reflectionless transmission of the power is achieved by matching all input and output impedances to the characteristic impedance of the transmission line used for the interconnections. The signal source and the power meter may be available with matching impedances.

However, the device will generally need tuners at its input and output terminals. The following tuning procedure is recommended:

1. Terminate the input tuner with the characteristic impedance of the line.   Observe the voltage-standing-wave ratio at the terminals of the output tuner and operate it to achieve minimum voltage-standing-wave ratio.

2. Terminate the output tuner and repeat 1 for the input tuner.

3. Continue repeating 1 and 2 until both of the voltage-standing-wave ratios equal unity.   The power meter can be used for the termination, while a slotted line or a directional coupler can serve as the voltage-standing-wave-ratio indicator.

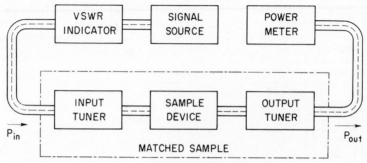

FIG. 19.24. Measurement of power gain.

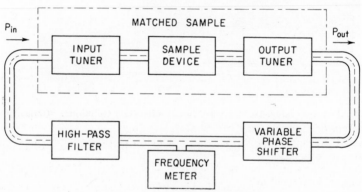

FIG. 19.25. Oscillator circuit.

The device input power delivered by the signal source is measured and then compared with the device output power.   As long as the output power is greater than the input power, an oscillator circuit can be devised by feeding the output power back into the input terminals.   The feedback path should satisfy the classical conditions for the signal magnitude and phase angle.   The magnitude condition is already satisfied, since the power gain is still greater than unity.   The phase condition can be easily satisfied by using a line stretcher as a variable phase shifter in the feedback loop.   The complete block diagram is presented in Fig. 19.25.   In addition to the components mentioned, a matched high-pass filter is included in the feedback loop in order to prevent unintended oscillations at lower frequencies.[30]   A frequency meter is loosely coupled to the system to detect the oscillation and indicate its frequency.

19.4. Physical Parameters.   To design any circuit about a device, a knowledge of that device is necessary.   For simple devices, a theoretical analysis is often sufficient for characterization.   Generally, however, devices are too complex and information is better obtained by measurement.   It is possible in circuit design to treat the device as a black box and characterize it by input and output measurements.   This method, though valid, is not generally accepted by design engineers unless the measurements are reduced to an equivalent electrical circuit.   The equivalent circuit, particularly the T, is also more meaningful to device fabricators, since specific parameters can be related to the device without analysis of a particular black-box measurement.   Since all small-signal measurements on a device can ultimately be considered as black-box measurements, this particular section will deal primarily with the analysis of these measurements in relation to obtaining specific equivalent-circuit parameters.   In addition, background material of the particular parameter is given to aid the reader not yet familiar with them.

Since a transistor consists basically of two semiconductor diodes, the discussion of the equivalent-circuit parameters will be confined to the transistor with the understanding that similar procedures can be used on other devices.   Also, transistors differ

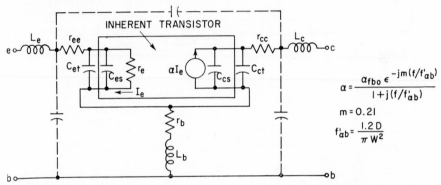

$$\alpha = \frac{\alpha_{fbo}\,\epsilon^{-jm(f/f'_{ab})}}{1+j(f/f'_{ab})}$$

$$m = 0.21$$

$$f'_{ab} = \frac{1.2\,D}{\pi\,W^2}$$

FIG. 19.26. High-frequency equivalent circuit for an alloy transistor illustrating extrinsic and inherent parameters.

in regard to types, fabrication, structure differences, etc., which means that the interpretation of measurements may not be the same.   A complete description of measurement analysis is beyond the scope of this section; rather the basic principles in regard to conventional alloy and graded-base transistors will be presented, leaving further modifications to the reader.   However, to illustrate the different measurement interpretations sometimes necessary, a transistor with a distributed collector capacitance is discussed in some detail.

A transistor or another device can be considered in terms of "inherent" and "extrinsic" parameters.   The inherent are those parameters which account for the basic action of the device.   The extrinsic can be considered as those parameters which are due primarily to the physical structure and consequently do not contribute to the basic device action.   For an alloy transistor the diffusion mechanism of carrier transport across the base and its associated effects are considered the primary part of the inherent structure.   The complete transistor, however, must include the bulk resistances of the base, collector, and emitter; the stray and junction transition capacitances; and at very high frequencies the inductance of the device leads.   These, then, are considered extrinsic parameters.   Figure 19.26 shows an equivalent circuit illustrating the inherent and extrinsic portions of a transistor.   The complete transistor action is determined by the combined parameters, with the extrinsic being particularly important at high frequencies where they can reduce the over-all gain.

To determine these circuit parameters, some form of black-box measurement is usually made. Then by proper choice of the variable, such as frequency or bias current, a specific parameter can be deduced.

The capacitances of primary importance in transistors are the storage or diffusion capacitance and the depletion or transition capacitance. Both types appear across the emitter and collector junctions. Stray capacitances are also present but will be considered when specific measurements are interpreted. For alloy transistors the emitter storage capacitance C_{es} is much larger than the emitter transition capacitance C_{et}, and the latter, therefore, is often neglected. The reverse is true for the collector junction, where the collector transition capacitance C_{ct} predominates. Because of the importance of the storage capacitance at the emitter junction, the brief introduction of this pseudocapacitance will be considered as it applies to this junction.

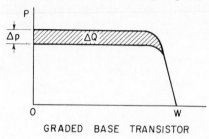

GRADED BASE TRANSISTOR

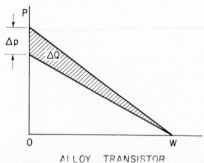

ALLOY TRANSISTOR

Fig. 19.27. Variation of the hole distribution due to the emitter voltage of a PNP transistor.

19.4a. Storage Capacitance. The storage capacitance is a direct result of the diffusion mechanism of charge transfer. Since a charge gradient is necessary to establish a diffusion current, a change in junction voltage results in a change in gradient and consequently a change in charge. Figure 19.27 shows the distribution of injected holes in the base region of PNP alloy and graded-base transistors with the resulting ΔQ as the emitter junction voltage changes.

This change in charge with voltage can be represented by a storage capacitance C_{es}. Since this pseudocapacitance is an integral part of the diffusion mechanism, it has a direct relationship to the response of the transistor and is considered a parameter of the inherent equivalent circuit. First-order approximations use the time constant of the forward resistance of the emitter junction r_e and C_{es} to account for the transistor phase shift and loss of gain at high frequencies. This approximation results in an error of 20 per cent at the half-power point for alloy transistors and is in greater error for drift transistors. It will be shown in Sec. 19.4h that more correctly $r_e C_{es}$ determines the frequency at which the magnitudes of the inherent base and collector currents are equal.

For alloy transistors C_{es} is given by

$$C_{es} = I_E \frac{q}{kT} \frac{W^2}{2D} \tag{19.17}$$

For graded-base transistors,

$$C_{es} = I_E \frac{q}{kT} \frac{W^2}{D} \frac{1}{r}\left(1 - \frac{1}{r}\right) \tag{19.18}$$

where

$$r = \frac{\Delta V}{V_T} \qquad V_T = \frac{kT}{q}$$

and ΔV is the "built-in" drift potential across the base. It is seen that C_{es} is directly dependent upon the direct bias current I_E. Measurements made on the transistor give a total emitter capacitance consisting of C_{et} and C_{es} in parallel. The fact that C_{es} is a function of I_E will allow separation of these capacitances.

19.4b. Transition Capacitance. The transition capacitance (or depletion-layer capacitance) occurs at the junction of two regions of opposite impurity as a result of the contact or "built-in" potential plus any externally applied voltage. In the interior of an impurity semiconductor, the density of mobile majority carriers is approximately equal to the concentration of fixed ions in the crystal lattice. At a PN junction, the density of mobile charge carriers is reduced virtually to zero when a reverse voltage is applied. As the voltage increases, the region of zero carrier density (depletion region) becomes wider. The effect is somewhat analogous to a parallel-plate capacitor. As the distance between the plates is increased (by increasing reverse voltage), the capacitance is decreased. The capacitance of a reverse-biased junction as a function

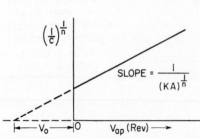

FIG. 19.28. Plot of $(1/c)^{1/n}$ versus applied voltage.

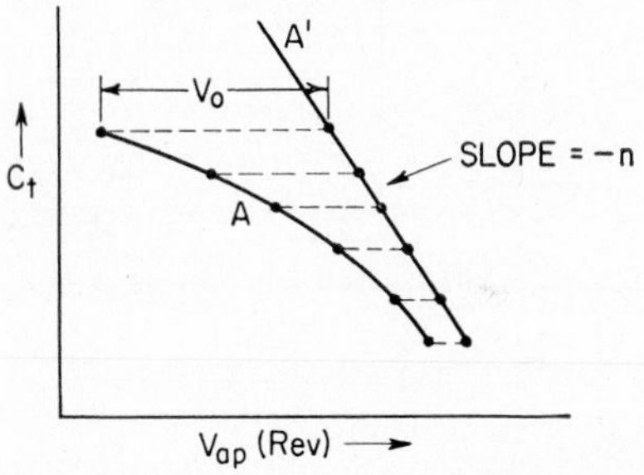

FIG. 19.29. Transition capacitance versus external voltage using log-log scale.

of voltage can be derived from Poisson's equation. A general expression for the capacitance per unit area of a reverse-biased semiconductor junction is given by

$$\frac{C_t}{A} = \frac{K}{(V_{ap} + V_0)^n} \tag{19.19a}$$

where K = constant dependent upon type of material and charge-density distribution
n = exponent dependent upon charge-density distribution
C_t = transition capacitance
V_0 = magnitude of contact potential
V_{ap} = magnitude of the externally applied reverse voltage

If n is known, V_0 can be determined graphically by plotting $(1/C_t)^{1/n}$ versus V_{ap} (see Fig. 19.28). The plot will result in a straight line, since from Eq. (19.19a)

$$\left(\frac{1}{C_t}\right)^{1/n} = (\text{constant})(V_{ap} + V_0) \tag{19.19b}$$

The intercept of the straight line with the voltage axis will give the magnitude of the contact potential V_0. If n is not known, both n and V_0 can be determined graphically using the following procedure: Several measurements of capacitance at different values of applied reverse voltage must be made. Plot C_t versus V_{ap} using log-log scales. The resulting curve should not be a straight line for values of V_{ap} which are comparable to V_0 [see Eq. (19.19b)] but will resemble curve A in Fig. 19.29.

The contact potential at a given PN junction is constant. In a reverse-biased semiconductor junction, the contact potential and the externally applied voltage are additive. If a constant value of voltage is found such that, when it is added to each experimentally measured point, all resulting points lie on a straight line, then that value is equal to the contact potential at the junction. Hence, the voltage coordinate has been changed so that the straight line satisfies Eq. (19.19c). The slope of the straight line is equal to $-n$.

$$\log C_t = -n \log (V_{ap} + V_0) + \text{constant} \tag{19.19c}$$

The transition capacitance is present across both collector and emitter junctions. Since it does not contribute to the basic transistor action, it is considered a parameter of the extrinsic equivalent circuit. Generally, the collector storage capacitance C_{cs} is considered negligible or included in C_{ct}. If separation is desired, measurements of the collector capacitance can be made in the usual manner (Sec. 19.4d) but at different emitter currents. C_{cs} is then proportional to the current (see Sec. 19.4c).

19.4c. Emitter Capacitance Measurement, y_{11e} Method. The total emitter capacitance can be obtained from the y_{11e} measurements. As previously indicated, the capacitance of the forward-biased emitter junction C_e consists of the emitter transition

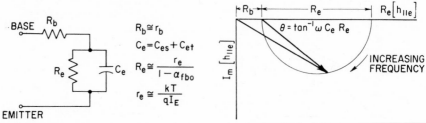

FIG. 19.30. Equivalent circuit for y_{11e} and h_{11e} measurements.

FIG. 19.31. Complex plot of h_{11e} as a function of frequency.

capacitance C_{et} and the emitter storage capacitance C_{es}. Stray capacitances are also present. However, they are normally negligible compared with C_e. Since the y_{11e} measurement has the collector at a-c ground potential, the collector junction appears in parallel with the emitter junction. Thus, if sufficiently large, the collector capacitance C_c must be considered a part of the total measured capacitance. To simplify the analysis, C_c will be neglected. It should be clear, however, that since C_c is an additional parallel capacitance, it can easily be accounted for once it has been obtained by an independent measurement (see Sec. 19.4d).

The approximate transistor equivalent circuit for the y_{11e} (or h_{11e}, since $h_{11e} = 1/y_{11e}$) measurement is shown in Fig. 19.30.

If the ohmic emitter resistance r_{ee} is neglected,

$$R_b = r_b \qquad R_e = \frac{r_e}{1 - \alpha_{fb0}}$$

Then for conditions such that $r_e/(1 - \alpha_{fb0}) \gg r_b$ and $\omega C_e r_b \ll 1$, the susceptance and conductance are given by

$$b_{11e} = \omega C_e$$
$$g_{11e} = \frac{1}{R_e} \tag{19.20}$$

and the total emitter capacitance can be obtained directly.

A more general method, which does not require any of the above restrictions, involves a plot of h_{11e} as a function of frequency. Analysis of the equivalent circuit (Fig. 19.30) shows that the impedance subscribes a semicircle as the frequency is increased. Thus, when a semicircle is completed through the points of measurement (h_{11e} at different frequencies), the value of C_e can be calculated. This is shown in Fig. 19.31. An added advantage of this method is that the high-frequency intercept gives the ohmic base resistance R_b. Generally three measurements at different frequencies, keeping emitter current and collector voltage constant, are sufficient to draw the semicircle. The emitter capacitance C_e can then be calculated from $\tan \theta = \omega C_e r_e$. If the ohmic emitter resistance is not negligible, the following corrections must be made:[23]

$$R_e = \frac{r_e + \alpha_{fb0} r_{ee}}{1 - \alpha_{fb0}} \qquad (19.21)$$

$$R_b = r_b + r_{ee} \qquad (19.22)$$

Since this method gives the total emitter capacitance, the transition capacitance C_{et} (also possibly stray and collector capacitances) must be subtracted to obtain the storage capacitance. C_{et} can be measured independently using a technique similar to that described for the collector transition capacitance in Sec. 19.4d. Because of

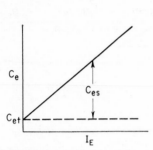

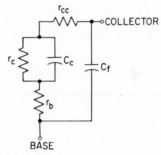

FIG. 19.32. Plot of emitter capacitance C_e as a function of I_E.

FIG. 19.33. Equivalent circuit for h_{22b} measurements.

the difference in bias voltage, however, a slight error will result unless the extrapolated value of C_{et} is used.

A better method of separating the emitter transition and storage capacitance is to determine C_e at different emitter currents I_E while keeping V_C constant. C_{et} is independent of I_E, while C_{es} is directly proportional to it. Thus, a plot of C_e versus I_E will produce a line with a slope corresponding to C_{es} and an intercept at C_{et} (see Fig. 19.32). This method requires more measurements; however, it is generally more accurate and involves only h_{11e} measurements.

For transistors that differ from the conventional alloy, the interpretation of the h_{11e} measurement must be modified to satisfy the particular device. An example of the departure of the semicircle and its significance in regard to r_b is given in Sec. 19.4f. For this case, the transistor has a graded base and a distributed collector capacitance. Owing to the higher resistivity of the base material at the collector junction, the collector is isolated at lower frequencies. Consequently, even though C_{et} is not negligible with respect to C_{es}, it does not affect the h_{11e} measurements until higher frequencies are reached. The measurements, therefore, are confined to the low frequencies where the interpretation can be carried out as previously indicated.

PRECAUTIONS. Since C_{es} is a function of emitter current, it is important that the peak-to-peak value of the input signal current I_b be kept small to minimize error.

19.4d. Collector Capacitance. The most common method of obtaining the collector capacitance is from the open-circuit output admittance h_{22b}. The equivalent circuit for this condition is shown in Fig. 19.33. Neglecting the bulk collector resistance r_{cc}, which is normally small compared with r_b, the output capacitance $C_{22b} = C_c + C_f$ providing $(\omega r_b C_c)^2 \ll 1$; $r_c \gg r_b$. C_f is the stray collector-to-base capacitance, consisting primarily of interlead and lead-to-case capacitances. Generally C_f is negligible.

However, where precise measurements are required or on high-frequency transistors where C_c is low, this capacitance should be accounted for.

The collector capacitance C_c is composed of the collector transition capacitance and the collector storage capacitance. Since the storage capacitance is proportional to emitter current, separation of the two can be accomplished by repeated measurements at different values of emitter current, with a constant collector voltage. For many transistors sufficient accuracy is obtained by treating the collector-base junction as a diode, thus allowing the emitter to float. The collector capacitance measured in this manner is approximately C_{ct}. Any good-quality bridge can be used to measure the output capacity providing it complies with the requirements given in Sec. 19.3.

A number of commercial capacitance meters particularly suitable for quick measurement of the collector capacitance are available. The principle of operation of most of these is the resonance method, whereby resonance is obtained with and without the device. The change in the value of capacitance necessary to produce resonance is the value of the capacitor under test. The primary requirement of this method is a relatively high Q. For most transistors, the reverse-biased conductance is sufficiently low to present little problem. Figure 19.34 shows a circuit used for measuring the

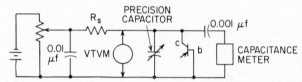

Fig. 19.34. Circuit for quick measurement of collector capacitance.

collector capacitance. No connection is made to the emitter, although it can be easily included. The circuit may include a precision capacitor for additional accuracy. Since the capacitor measured is the output capacitance C_{22b}, the header capacitance must be subtracted to obtain the collector capacitance. This is accomplished by producing resonance with a dummy header inserted in place of the transistor.

19.4e. Base-resistance–Collector-capacitance Product. At high frequencies (see Sec. 12.5) or in pulse applications the product of the base resistance r_b and the collector capacitance C_c is necessary to characterize the performance of a transistor. A method of obtaining this product by measuring the grounded-base open-circuit reverse voltage ratio h_{12b} was given by R. L. Pritchard.[24] With a voltage applied to the collector, the voltage at the emitter consists of the voltage across r_b plus μ_{ec}. This is shown in Fig. 19.35. Assuming $r_c \gg r_b \gg r_{cc}$ and $(\omega C_c r_b)^2 \ll 1$, then $h_{12b} = h_{12bo} + j\omega C_c r_b$, where h_{12bo} is the low-frequency value of h_{12b} and includes the Early feedback ratio as well as the base-to-collector inherent conductance. The capacitance in this case is the collector capacitance and does not include stray or header base-to-collector capacitance. The frequency of measurement is dependent upon the $r_b C_c$ time constant and h_{12bo}. In particular, it is convenient to choose a frequency such that $\omega r_b C_c \gg h_{12bo}$, for which case the product can be obtained by one measurement. Values of $\omega r_b C_c$ of 10^{-3} are generally sufficient. For questionable units, it is best to plot $|h_{12b}|$ as a function of frequency and obtain the product from the slope. The idealized case is shown in Fig. 19.36. A circuit set up for a PNP transistor is shown in Fig. 19.37. R_E must be sufficiently high to approach open-circuit condition. Since R_E appears in parallel with r_b, a general condition is that $R_E > 10r_b$. The only requirement of R_C is that sufficient voltage be developed between collector and base to obtain measurable voltages at the emitter. The generator voltage should be constant; this can be achieved by monitoring the collector voltage with a vacuum-tube voltmeter. The emitter voltmeter must be capable of measuring millivolts, and its input capacity should be very low to prevent erroneous readings due to its shunting action.

PRECAUTIONS. This method is particularly useful for alloy transistors with larger values of $r_b C_c$. Low values of this time constant require higher frequencies where stray capacitances can give erroneous results. In general, for alloy transistors, the base resistance as seen from the collector side is approximately the same as that seen

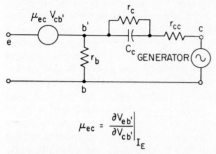

$$\mu_{ec} = \left. \frac{\partial V_{eb'}}{\partial V_{cb'}} \right|_{I_E}$$

FIG. 19.35. Equivalent circuit for h_{12b} measurement.

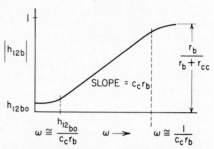

FIG. 19.36. Ideal plot of $|h_{12b}|$ as a function of ω.

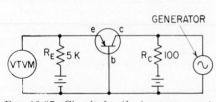

FIG. 19.37. Circuit for $|h_{12b}|$ measurement of PNP transistor.

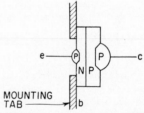

FIG. 19.38. Cross section of a PNP transistor with distributed collector capacitance.

from the emitter side. This is not true for all transistors. For example, the transistor of Fig. 19.38 has a much lower effective base resistance as measured from the collector than that measured from the emitter (using the technique of Sec. 19.4f). It is the former, however, which is primarily responsible for the loss of gain at high frequencies.

19.4f. Base-resistance Measurement, h_{11e} Method. As shown in Sec. 19.4c the semicircle resulting from a complex plot of h_{11e} gives r_b at the high-frequency intercept.

This method is particularly useful when the base resistance can be considered "lumped," as is generally the case for alloy transistors. Structures not fitting this category can result in errors. One such unit having a distributed collector capacity is shown in Fig. 19.38.

The base is graded by diffusing N-type impurities into original P-type germanium. The collector junction is the natural intrinsic region resulting from this process. At low frequencies the base resistance appears in lumped form. At higher fre-

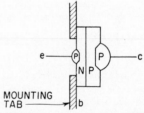

$$R_e = \frac{r_e}{1 - \alpha_{fbo}}$$

$$C_e = C_{es} + C_{et}$$

FIG. 19.39. h_{11e} high-frequency equivalent circuit considering effects of distributed C_c for transistor of Fig. 19.38.

quencies, the distributed collector capacitance creates a shunt which effectively reduces r_b. An approximate equivalent circuit for this condition is shown in Fig. 19.39. This distributed collector capacitance results in a departure of the complex impedance plot from the semicircle at higher frequencies. Generally, however, a sufficient number of measurements can be made at low frequencies (where the effect of C_c is negligible) to complete the semicircle and determine r_b.†

The base resistance can also be obtained by plotting the real part of h_{11e} as a function of frequency.

As the frequency is increased, the contribution from the parallel combination of $R_e C_e$ diminishes until only r_b remains. If C_c is distributed, a decrease occurs at higher frequencies owing to its shunting effect (see Fig. 19.40).

PRECAUTIONS. The type of transistor determines the frequency of measurement. Alloy units with their large emitter capacity can level off at r_b for frequencies as low as 1 mc. Drift units require a higher frequency, in some cases as high as 200 mc. If the collector has a distributed capacitance, the flat portion of the curve decreases

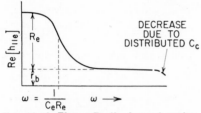

FIG. 19.40. Plot of Re $[h_{11e}]$ as a function of ω.

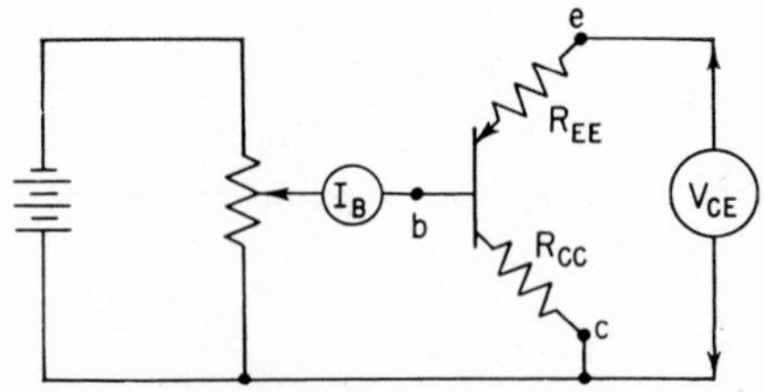

FIG. 19.41. Circuit to measure series resistances R_{EE} and R_{CC}.

as C_c/C_e increases, until only a narrow range of frequencies produces r_b. In the extreme case, the curve levels off at a value of

$$R \cong \frac{r_b}{(1 + C_c/C_e)^2} \tag{19.23}$$

The measured r_b includes the emitter bulk resistance r_{ee}. For most practical cases, this contribution is negligible.

19.4g. Measurement of Series Emitter and Collector Resistance. The measurement of R_{EE} and R_{CC} can be obtained by a method suggested by B. Kulke and S. L. Miller.[25] The general requirement of this measurement is to monitor the collector-to-emitter voltage as the base current is changed. The current of the uncommon lead (emitter or collector) is constrained to zero by allowing it to float. Figure 19.41 shows the circuit for measuring R_{CC} of a PNP transistor. The collector is common. The voltage from emitter to collector is measured as function of base current. No connection other than the vacuum-tube voltmeter is made to the emitter, and its current, therefore, is zero.

For these conditions, the voltage V_{CE} is given by

$$V_{CE} = \frac{kT}{q} \ln \alpha_{FB} + I_B R_{CC} \tag{19.24}$$

Thus, a plot of V_{CE} as a function of I_B gives a straight line, the slope of which is R_{CC}, with the intercept occurring at $(kT/q) \ln \alpha_{FB}$.

To determine the emitter resistance R_{EE}, the transistor is inverted so that the emitter lead is grounded while the collector current is zero.

---

† An evaluation of h_{11e} measurements which includes possible sources of error was developed by Dr. P. A. Ligomenides, IBM, San Jose. By use of a computer, the equivalent-circuit parameters can be obtained with two low-frequency measurements.

The equation for V_{CE} is then

$$V_{CE} = \frac{kT}{q} \ln \alpha_{RB} + I_B R_{EE} \qquad (19.25)$$

Figure 19.42 shows the results of the measurements performed on an experimental PNP germanium transistor.

PRECAUTIONS.   The straight-line relationship is dependent upon a constant α_{FB} and α_{RB}.   For operations such that these are not constant, as at very high or very low current densities, there may be considerable departure from the straight line.   In case of a very narrow base layer and high base resistance, it is possible that these measurements include a contribution from the lateral base resistance.†   This is related to the discussion in Sec. 4.3, where this lateral base resistance results in an additional voltage drop across the transistor.

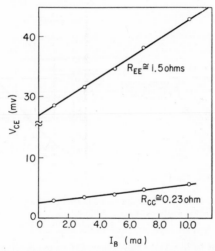

FIG. 19.42. Plot of V_{CE} as a function of I_B to determine R_{CC} and R_{EE}.

19.4h. Frequencies $f'_{\alpha b}$ and f'_T.   The cutoff frequency $f_{\alpha b}$ is the frequency at which the common-base short-circuit current gain α_{fb} is 0.707 of its low-frequency value α_{fb0}.   The inherent cutoff frequency $f'_{\alpha b}$ appears in equations for gain, pulse response, and maximum frequency of oscillation and is therefore of interest to designers.   Unfortunately, as the state of transistor art progresses, this term becomes increasingly more obscure owing to the high-frequency dependence on the extrinsic parameters.[3]   Consequently, the measured cutoff frequency may give no indication of the inherent cutoff point.   Another important consideration is the phase shift associated with $f'_{\alpha b}$.   For the conventional alloy transistor $\phi'_{\alpha b}$ is 57°, while the graded-base transistor can theoretically have values from 57 to approximately 138°.

A reference which restricts the phase variation to a relatively narrow range and yet gives a good indication of its high-frequency capabilities is the frequency at which the real part of the inherent alpha is one-half its low-frequency value.[26]   With normally negligible error, α_{fb0} can be assumed equal to 1.   Then f'_T can be defined as the frequency at which $R_e(\alpha'_{fb}/\alpha_{fb0}) = \frac{1}{2}$ or $R_e(\alpha'_{fb}) = \frac{1}{2}$.   If α'_{fb} is represented by

$$\alpha'_{fb} = a - jb$$

then

$$\alpha'_{fe} = \frac{\alpha'_{fb}}{1 - \alpha'_{fb}} = \frac{a - jb}{(1 - a) + jb} \qquad (19.26)$$

† Personal discussion with S. L. Miller.

When $R_e(\alpha'_{f_o}) = \frac{1}{2}$,

$$\alpha'_{f_e} = \frac{\frac{1}{2} - jb}{(1 - \frac{1}{2}) + jb} = \frac{\frac{1}{2} - jb}{\frac{1}{2} + jb} \qquad \text{or} \qquad |\alpha'_{f_e}| = 1$$

Thus, the frequency f'_T at which the real part of the inherent common-base current gain is $\frac{1}{2}$ is identical with the frequency at which the inherent common-emitter current gain is unity. It should be noted that no restrictions are placed on the form of the functions representing the behavior of a and b with frequency, and therefore the conditions hold for graded-base transistors as well as for the conventional alloy transistor.

Figure 19.43 shows the variation of α'_{fb} as a function of frequency for an alloy and a graded-base transistor. Note that the locus of f'_T occurs at $R_e(\alpha'_{fb}) = \frac{1}{2}$ and that the difference in phase angle between the two transistors is small along this line. The

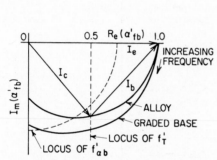

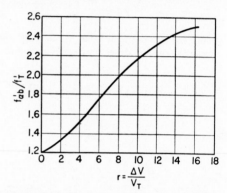

FIG. 19.43. Complex plot of inherent alpha for an alloy and a graded-base transistor.

FIG. 19.44. The ratio of inherent cutoff frequency $f_{\alpha b}'$ to the unity frequency f_T' as a function of "built-in" drift potential.

locus of $f'_{\alpha b}$ is also given to illustrate the larger difference in phase angle occurring at these frequencies.

For the alloy transistor $f'_{\alpha b}/f'_T = 1.21$. For the graded-base transistor, however, no simple relationship exists, since the ratio is a function of the built-in field.[27] This is shown in Fig. 19.44.

A decided advantage of using the frequency f_T as a high-frequency parameter is its general simplicity of measurement (see Sec. 19.3c). The basic requirement is to obtain the frequency at which the common-emitter short-circuit current gain is unity. When the common-emitter equivalent circuit is analyzed, α_{fe} can be approximated by

$$\alpha_{fe} = \frac{\alpha_{fe0}}{1 + [j\omega r_e/(1 - \alpha_{fb0})](C_e + C_c)} \tag{19.27}$$

The restrictions on this equation are that the emitter resistance r_{ec} is negligible and $(\alpha_{fb0})^2 \gg (\omega C_e r_e)^2$. This equation shows that $|\alpha_{fe}|$ will fall off at a rate of 6 db/octave. This is true for the graded-base as well as the alloy transistors. For frequencies up to f'_T, the primary difference between these two types can be explained in terms of their respective storage capacitances C_{es} [see Eqs. (19.17) and (19.18)].

Figure 19.45 illustrates the theoretical frequency response of $|\alpha_{fe}|$. It is evident that measurements can be made at lower frequencies and f_T determined by extrapolation. For questionable units, however, more points should be taken.

Because of the extrinsic parameters C_{et} and C_{ct} (assuming that C_{cs} is negligible) the measured frequency f_T will differ from the inherent f_T'.   From Eq. (19.27)

$$\omega_T = \frac{1}{r_e(C_{es} + C_{et} + C_{ct})} \qquad (19.28)$$

The inherent unity frequency, however, is dependent only upon parameters r_e and C_{es}.   Thus

$$\omega_T' = \frac{1}{r_e C_{es}} \qquad (19.29a)$$

where $r_e = kT/qI_E$ and

$$\omega_T' = \frac{W^2}{2D} \qquad \text{for alloy transistors} \qquad (19.29b)$$

$$\omega_T' = \frac{W^2}{Dr}\left(1 - \frac{1}{r}\right) \qquad \text{for graded-base transistors} \qquad (19.29c)$$

Since ω_T' is independent of I_E, it is possible to separate the inherent and extrinsic capacitances by determining f_T at different emitter currents. C_{ct} will be assumed

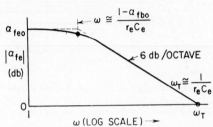

Fig. 19.45. Plot of $|\alpha_{fe}|$ as a function of ω (log scale).

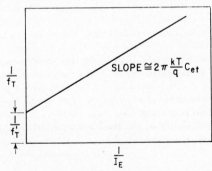

Fig. 19.46. Plot of $1/f_T$ as a function of $1/I_E$.

negligible, since it can easily be accounted for and places no restrictions on the analysis.   Equation (19.28) can then be rewritten as

$$\frac{1}{f_T} = \frac{1}{f_T'} + \frac{kT}{qI_E} 2\pi C_{et} \qquad (19.29d)$$

Thus a plot of $1/f_T$ as a function of $1/I_E$ gives $1/f_T'$ at the intercept and a slope equal to $(kT/q)2\pi C_{et}$.[28]   This is shown in Fig. 19.46.

19.5. Switching Characteristics.   The switching characteristics of a device describe its transient operation from one steady state to another.   The boundary d-c values for any given circuit can be found from the appropriate d-c characteristics of the device and the associated circuit components. The transient behavior of a switching circuit is usually a rather complicated function of many parameters.[31] A nonlinear multiple integral must be solved for each particular case. Three methods are known which provide more or less accurate solutions:

1. Compute the integral by piecewise linearization, using the data obtained from the small-signal equivalent circuit.

2. Compute the redistribution of charges within the device required to change one steady state into another.

3. Use the device as its own analogue computer by performing the actual switching under the specified conditions.

The transient computation may involve a very elaborate device characterization and computer programming effort, but it gives the complete freedom to select any desired values of the device and circuit parameters.[32] This freedom may be used to predict and even to optimize the reliability of the circuit performance.[36] However, this method is often limited by the size of the computer memory and by the difficulties in accurate representation of the device by its equivalent circuit in a wide range of operating conditions.

The second method takes advantage of dealing with the charges which are integrals of the current vs. time.[37] This method is also directly related to the physics of the device, e.g., impurity concentration and distribution, actual dimensions, etc. The measurement of these parameters may be somewhat circuit-dependent; and some parameters needed in this method may be defined rather arbitrarily—as a mean value obtained under certain conditions.[38]

Every bench experiment with the device in a circuit uses essentially the third method, which is, of course, restricted to the values of parameters and their combinations available in the actual devices. The time required to conduct any such experiment may impose additional restriction on the number of the experiments which may be desired to gather statistical data.

The third method is also known as the performance test used for selection and/or acceptance of the devices for a specific application, such as computer switching circuits.

The problem of a sufficient correlation between the test results may arise if one or several of the numerous factors contributing to the result were not adequately reproduced. Some of these factors are:

1. Tolerances in the externally applied d-c voltages and/or currents
2. Variation of temperature
3. Tolerances in the driving function
4. Accuracy and repeatability of the read-out equipment
5. Accuracy of the circuit components
6. Accurate control of the stray fields: capacitive and inductive
7. Parasitic oscillations

Oscilloscopes, including traveling-wave[39] and sampling types for faster devices, are commonly used as the read-out equipment. They provide detailed information about the shape of transients. In the production-type testing, however, nonoscilloscope read-out equipment is preferred, either with analogue or with digitized or with go–no-go output.

REFERENCES

1. Carlson, A. W.: Static Characteristics of Transistors, *Semiconductor Prods.*, vol. 2, no. 6, pp. 31–35, June, 1959.
2. IRE Standards on Methods of Testing Transistors, *Proc. IRE*, vol. 44, no. 11, pp. 1542–1561, November, 1956.

3. Rutz, R. F., and D. F. Singer: Some Properties of Experimental 1000-Mc Transistors, *IBM J.*, vol. 3, no. 3, pp. 230–236, July, 1959.
4. Cooper, B. J.: The Measurement of Transistor Voltage Current Characteristics Using Pulse Techniques, *Electronic Eng.*, vol. 30, no. 365, pp. 440–441, July, 1958.
5. Gates, R. F., and R. A. Johnson: The Measurement of Thermal Resistance, *Semiconductor Prods.*, vol. 2, no. 7, pp. 21–26, July, 1959.
6. Giacoletto, L. J.: Terminology and Equations for Linear Active Four-terminal Networks Including Transistors, *RCA Rev.*, vol. 14, no. 1, pp. 28–46, March, 1953.
7. Follingstad, H. G.: Complete Linear Characterization of Transistors from Low through Very High Frequencies, *Trans. IRE, PGI*, vol. 6, no. 1, pp. 49–63, March, 1957.
8. Paddock, J. P.: Transistor Measurements Using Indefinite Admittance Matrix, *Stanford Engineering Laboratory Tech. Rept.* 20, Stanford, Calif., August, 1957.
9. Credle, A. B.: Effects of Low Temperatures on Transistor Characteristics, *IBM J.*, January, 1958.
10. Thurston, W. R., and R. A. Soderman: Type 1607-A Transfer Function and Immittance Bridge, *Gen. Radio Experimenter*, vol. 33, no. 5, May, 1959.
11. Ginzton, Edward L.: "Microwave Measurements," chap. 5, McGraw-Hill Book Company, Inc., New York, 1957.
12. Meinke, Hans H.: "Theorie der Hochfrequenzschaltungen," sec. 35, R. Oldenbourg-Verlag, Munich, 1951.
13. Meinke-Gundlach: "Taschenbuch der Hochfrequenztechnik," sec. E. 1, Springer-Verlag, Berlin, 1956.
14. Reference 11, chap. 4.
15. Abraham, R. B., and R. J. Kirkpatrick: Transistor Characterization at VHF, *Semiconductor Prods.*, part 1, vol. 2, no. 1, pp. 15–22, January, 1959; part II, vol. 2, no. 2, pp. 25–29, February, 1959.
16. Reference 11, chap. 6.
17. *Trans. IRE, PGMTT*, vol. 3, no. 2, March, 1955.
18. Houlding, Norman: Measurement of Varactor Quality, *Microwave J.*, vol. 3, no. 1, pp. 40–45, January, 1960.
19. Reddi, V. G. K.: Applying Transistor "y" Parameters, *Electronic Ind.*, January, 1960.
20. Scarlett, R. M.: Measuring Transistor Parameters with Wayne Kerr RF Bridges, *Electronic Design*, July 22, 1959.
21. Rymaszewski, E. J.: Extension of Frequency Range of Measurement of Small Signal Four-pole Parameters up to the VHF Region: Final Report under Contract No. AF 19(604)-1906 for Design and Analysis of Circuits Suitable for High Speed Computer Application, sec. XVI, sponsored by the Air Force Cambridge Research Center, Air Research and Development Command, July, 1957.
22. Jordan, Edward C.: Electromagnetic Waves and Radiating Systems, 5th printing, sec. 14.04, Prentice-Hall, Inc., Englewood Cliffs, N.J., November, 1958.
23. Abraham, R. P.: A Wide Band Transistor Feedback Amplifier, *IRE Wescon Conv. Record*, part 2, pp. 10–19, 1957.
24. Pritchard, R. L.: Transistor Tests Predict High Frequency Performance, *Electronic Ind.*, vol. 16, no. 3, p. 62, March, 1957.
25. Kulke, B., and S. L. Miller: Accurate Measurement of Emitter and Collector Resistances in Transistors, *Proc. IRE*, vol. 45, no. 1, p. 90, January, 1957.
26. Sparkes, J. J.: Measurement of Junction Transistor Equivalent Circuit Parameters, *ATE J.*, vol. 14, no. 3, pp. 176–187, July, 1958.
27. Swanson, J. A., and K. Y. Sih: Diffusion Attenuation, Part II, *IBM J.*, vol. 3, no. 1, pp. 18–24, January, 1959.
28. Cripps, L. G.: Transistor High Frequency Parameter f_1, *Electronic Radio Eng.*, vol. 36, no. 9, pp. 341–346, September, 1959.
29. Rutz, R. F.: A 3000-Mc Lumped-parameter Oscillator Using an Esaki Negative-resistance Diode, *IBM J.*, vol. 3, no. 4, October, 1959.
30. Transistor Testing with Type 874 Coaxial Elements, *Gen. Radio Experimenter*, vol. 32, no. 5, October, 1957.
31. Le Can, C.: Transient Behavior and Fundamental Transistor Parameters, *Electronic Applications*, vol. 20, no. 2, pp. 56–83, 1959–1960.
32. Domenico, R. J.: Simulation of Transistor Switching Circuits on the IBM 704, *Trans. IRE, PGEC*, vol. EC-6, December, 1957.
   A later and more detailed description of this work was published by N. G. Brooks and H. S. Long: A Program for Computing the Transient Response of Transistor Switching Circuits—PE TAP, *IBM Tech. Rept.* TR 00.11000.700, December, 1959.
33. IRE Standards on Semiconductor Symbols, *Proc. IRE*, vol. 44, no. 7, pp. 934–937, July, 1956.

34. IRE Standards on Solid State Devices: Methods of Testing Point-contact Transistors for Large-signal Applications, 1958, *Proc. IRE*, vol. 46, no. 5, pp. 878–888, May, 1958.
35. Johnston, R. C., and R. L. Burke: Measurement of Switching Transistor Parameters, *Semiconductor Prods.*, vol. 3, no. 2, pp. 43–46, February, 1960.
36. Hellerman, L., and M. P. Racite: Reliability Techniques for Electronic Circuit Design, *Trans. IRE*, *PGRQC*, vol. 14, September, 1958.
37. DeWitt, D., and A. L. Rossoff: "Transistor Electronics," chap. 2, McGraw-Hill Book Company, Inc., New York, 1957.
38. Ekiss, J. A., and C. D. Simmons: Junction Transistor Transient Response Characterization, *Solid State Abstr. J.*, vol. 2, no. 1, pp. 17–24; no. 2, pp. 24–29, 1961.
39. Edgerton, Germeshausen, and Grier, Inc.: *Engineering Note*, Jan. 26, 1959; Dual Position Operation of the Sub-millimicrosecond Oscilloscope in Diode Recovery Time Measurement, in *Application Note*, Feb. 6, 1959; Measurement of Diode Recovery Time with the Milli-mike System, in *Application Note*, Feb. 17, 1959; Boston, Mass.

Section 20

MEASUREMENTS OF SEMICONDUCTOR PARAMETERS

J. F. WOODS

IBM Research Center, Yorktown Heights, N.Y.

The following measurements are discussed in this section:

1. Resistivity
2. Hall effect, carrier density, conductivity type, carrier mobility
3. Drift mobility
4. Lifetime, diffusion length

They are those most explicitly related to device properties. They depend on the impurities in the crystal and, therefore, vary from crystal to crystal. The intrinsic properties are assumed to be known, so that the use of measurements for the study of intrinsic crystal properties will not be discussed explicitly.

Since the measurements are discussed principally in connection with extrinsic properties, particular emphasis is placed on techniques which are suitable for use on an appreciable volume of samples.   The discussion of theory and analysis of measurements is aimed primarily at the evaluation of device material.   Reference will be made to more detailed treatments of the particular measurements.   The discussion here is intended to provide a guide to the significance of the various measurements and the methods and techniques appropriate to them and a source of references for further study of particular phenomena.   The references are principally to long articles and to books which have comprehensive treatments of the subjects.

MEASUREMENTS AT ROOM TEMPERATURE

The measurements will be discussed first as primarily room-temperature measurements, and then the discussion will be extended to the variation of properties with temperature.

20.1. Resistivity and Conductivity.   Resistivity is a specific property of a material. In the units normally used (ohm-centimeters) resistivity ρ is equal to the resistance R of a cube 1 cm on a side.   For a rectangular prism the resistance is equal to the resistivity multiplied by the ratio of its length to its cross-sectional area $(R = \rho l/A)$ provided the material of the prism is uniform.   The resistivity is a macroscopic property which depends on the density of electrons and holes (Sec. 2.4) and their mobilities (page 2–11).   These more fundamental properties will be considered in some detail separately.

Ohm's law relates resistance R, current I, and voltage V; $V = IR$.   The same law relates resistivity ρ, current density J, and electric field E; $E = \rho J$.   In uniform material $V = El$ and $I = JA$, where l and A are the length and cross-sectional area of a rectangular prism.   In a nonuniform material ρ, E, and J may all vary from point to point within the prism.

Several common types of nonuniformity are (1) polycrystalline material, (2) PN junctions, and (3) resistivity gradients.   In polycrystalline materials there are generally high-resistance layers or potential barriers between the crystallites.   In such a case the apparent resistivity is a function of these barriers.   In single-crystal materials containing junctions, it is generally possible to measure ρ in the interjunction regions once they have been located.   If the junctions are very close together, however, this may not be possible.

In single-crystal material the resistivity may vary smoothly from point to point. In fact, this is generally the case.   The principal question is the amount of this variation rather than any question of its presence.   Often, however, it is conventionally stated that ρ is constant to within some percentage variation, and when the variation does, in fact, fall within this tolerance, it is ignored and the crystal is considered to be of uniform resistivity.

20.1a. Methods of Measuring Resistivity.   The simplest method of measuring the resistivity of a bar is to make contact to the two ends and measure the current and voltage drop across the sample.   This arrangement is illustrated schematically in Fig. 20.1a.   Then $V/I = R = \rho l/A$, as we have discussed above.   The two principal drawbacks to this simple measurement are: (1) the resistance measured includes the resistance of the contacts and (2) there is no indication of sample uniformity.

1. High resistance or rectification appears fairly often in electrical contacts to semiconductors.   Often one will observe that if the current is reversed, its value changes.   This clearly indicates a rectifying contact (see Sec. 3.3).   However, the mere absence of rectification tested in this way is not sufficient evidence of low contact resistance.   High-resistance contacts can be detected by measuring current and voltage for a range of values, since they are generally nonohmic.

2. Unless there are reasons from other observations for being confident that the material is reasonably uniform, it is not clear what the significance may be of resistivity measured in this way.

Error due to contact resistance is avoided by the use of extra contacts (probes), between the current contacts, for measuring the voltage.   The first advantage of probe measurements is that the contact resistances may all be high compared with the sample resistance, provided that the probe contact resistance and the sample resistance are small compared with the effective resistance of the measuring device (voltmeter, potentiometer, or electrometer), without influencing the measured value. In this case, the principal drawback of poor contacts is the fact that they are noisy.

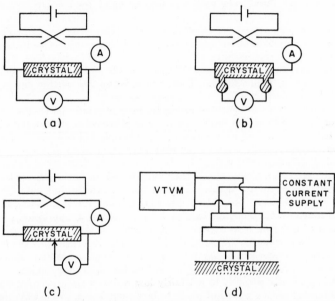

Fig. 20.1. Resistivity measurements: (*a*) arrangement for resistance measurement, (*b*) resistivity measurement with two self-probes, (*c*) single-probe arrangement for location of junctions, and (*d*) resistivity measurement with four-point probes.

This may in some cases limit the accuracy of the measurement.   Current contacts and voltage probes may be soldered, plated, or pressure contacts.   The last are especially useful for sampling different parts of the crystal.

Soldered probe contacts should be kept small in order to avoid disturbing the current flow (shorting out part of the sample) and to avoid ambiguity in the measurement of the probe spacing.   Soldering directly to the body of the sample can affect the sample properties by heating effects and by contamination unless care is taken.

If the sample is cut so that arms of the sample material extend out from its body, the soldering or plating can be done on the arms and the contact size need not be small. The arrangement illustrated in Fig. 20.1*b* has several advantages.   The body of the sample need not be heated, contact noise due to sample current through the probe contacts is avoided, and since the cutting can be done with a die in an ultrasonic cutter, the probe spacings will be constant from sample to sample.

The current I through the sample and the voltage drop V between the probes are measured, and $\rho = VA/IX$, where X is the probe spacing and A is the cross-sectional area of the sample.   There may be three or more voltage probes.   The voltage drop between each pair can then be used to compare the resistivity along the sample in two or more sections. If the current and voltage drop are measured with a potentiometer, the accuracy of ρ will be limited mainly by the measurement of X and A.

The current through the sample should not be large enough to cause heating. A further precaution is necessary to prevent injection effects from affecting the measured value of ρ. Even good contacts, to germanium for example, may inject (see Secs. 3.3 to 3.5). This is minimized by keeping the voltage drop at the contact low. If the surface near the current contacts is rough (lapped surface) and the electric field in the crystal is low, these injected carriers will recombine (see page 3–6, also Sec. 20.4) before reaching the measuring probes.

Since ρ is independent of current, it is possible to determine whether or not any of these effects are interfering with the measurement by measuring ρ at several values of I. *It should be kept in mind that these points of experimental technique affect essentially all the measurements to be described and not the resistivity measurements only.*

A very useful variation of the probe type of resistivity measurement is the use of movable probes. These are generally point pressure contacts. The advantage of these is that the crystal can be "searched" by the probes and the variation of resistivity over the crystal can be measured. There are three variations: the one-probe, two-probe, and four-probe methods.

The one-probe method, illustrated in Fig. 20.1c, is primarily useful for locating PN junctions or potential barriers in a sample. The potential along the crystal is measured with respect to one end (or a ground point) and plotted as a function of distance X along the crystal. The slope of the plot V/X is equal to $\rho I/A$, where I is the current and A the cross-sectional area. Deviations from linearity indicate variation in ρ along the sample. Both current directions should be observed in order to locate rectifying junctions and to distinguish these from nonrectifying potential barriers such as grain boundaries. Unless the cross section is uniform in area and the measuring current constant, the slope of the plot V/X will not be proportional to ρ.

In crystals of uniform cross section the two-probe method can be used to obtain a plot of ρ versus X directly. This method is virtually identical with the fixed-probe method described above except for the movable pressure contacts. The nature of the contact will put a more severe requirement on the measuring device. With fixed contacts it is generally possible to get fairly low resistance contacts by soldering or plating. Pressure contacts are not likely to be so consistent, so a really high impedance voltmeter or electrometer will be more often needed. This type of measurement is easily automated. The sample can be moved past the probes by a screw coupled with a Helipot. The position can then be displayed on one axis of an X-Y recorder, and the resistivity voltage on the other. The probes should be lifted while the sample is moving.

The four-probe method[1] (four-point probe), illustrated in Fig. 20.1d, is still more generally useful. In its usual form the four probes are colinear. The outside probes are the current contacts, and the inside pair the potential probes. When the probes are equally spaced and all edges of the sample are far from the probes (at least $3d$ where d is the probe spacing), $\rho = 2\pi d V/I$. Thus this measurement is independent of the sample shape, and a complete resistivity profile can be obtained over a broad area of a crystal slab. If the sample thickness is less than $5d$, a correction factor is necessary. Figure 20.2 gives the ratio ρ (material)/ρ (measured) as a function of the ratio of thickness to probe spacing when the surface is nonconducting. Figure 20.3 gives the relation between the same two ratios for the case in which the lower surface is a perfect conductor.

With closely spaced probes and point current contacts the precautions given above against heating and injection are even more critical. It is generally necessary to make four-point-probe measurements on a lapped surface in order to have a high recombination rate and a level surface for even probe contact. The measurement can be made with either alternating or direct current. The four-point-probe method can be automated in the same way as the two-point probe. One additional precaution is that the current supply be a constant-current supply (high-impedance source), since the current contact resistances will not generally be constant.

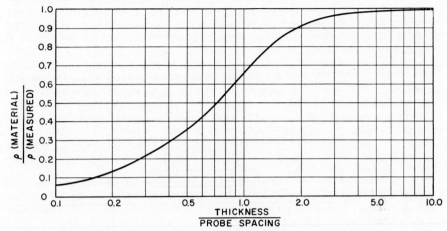

FIG. 20.2. Correction factor for slices with nonconducting surfaces.

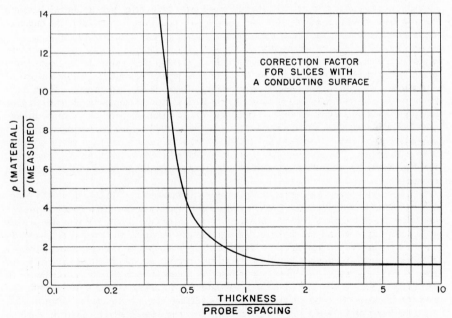

FIG. 20.3. Correction factor for slices with conducting surfaces.

It can be seen from Figs. 20.2 and 20.3 that the material more than $3d$ beneath the surface cannot affect the measurement appreciably, so with closely spaced probes only a thin layer of material is actually measured. For this reason high resolution can be obtained only on thin layers.

The selection of a method of measurement will, therefore, depend on the sample geometry. Both the single probe and two-point probes measure the integrated resistivity over the total depth of the sample but are sensitive to resistivity variations only along the current direction, which is fixed by the sample geometry and the current contacts. In addition, any variation of cross-sectional area complicates the analysis considerably.

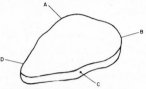

FIG. 20.4. Contacts to disk of arbitrary outline.

There is another method of making resistivity measurements that is very useful for small or odd-shaped samples.[2] Four contacts are made on the periphery of the sample as shown in Fig. 20.4.

With current flowing in A-B the voltage C-D is measured, and then with current in A-D the voltage B-C is measured. If the sample is uniform in resistivity and of uniform thickness, the resistivity is given by

$$\rho = \frac{\pi d}{2 \ln 2} \left(\frac{V_{DC}}{I_{AB}} + \frac{V_{BC}}{I_{AD}} \right) f \tag{20.1}$$

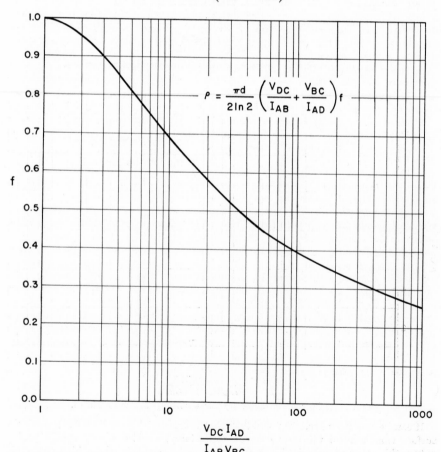

$$\rho = \frac{\pi d}{2 \ln 2} \left(\frac{V_{DC}}{I_{AB}} + \frac{V_{BC}}{I_{AD}} \right) f$$

$$\frac{V_{DC} I_{AD}}{I_{AB} V_{BC}}$$

FIG. 20.5. Function f of Eq. (20.1). (*Adapted from Philips Research Reports.*[2])

where d is the sample thickness, V_{DC} and V_{BC} the measured voltages, I_{AB} and I_{AD} the corresponding currents, and f is a function of $V_{DC}I_{AD}/I_{AB}V_{BC}$. This function is plotted in Fig. 20.5.

There is another technique which sometimes has advantages over the resistivity measurement for examination of crystal uniformity. This is the detection of gradients by means of the "bulk photovoltaic effect."[3] Ohmic contacts are made at two ends of a bar, and a transverse line of light is focused on the bar. When the light falls on a gradient of resistivity, a voltage appears at the contacts. If the line of light is traversed along the bar, the curve of photovoltage versus position can be recorded as in the two-point-probe resistivity measurement. The peaks of the curve will then identify the sections of maximum gradient in the crystal. These data are not directly quantitative but are nevertheless useful.

An alternative method is to measure the photoconductive change by passing a current through the bar while traversing the line of light. If large enough current is used, the photoconductive signal will be very much larger than the photovoltage. The signal will be roughly proportional to $\rho\tau$, where τ is the lifetime (Sec. 20.5).

In both of these experiments, the results are quite sensitive to accidental variations in reflection at the crystal surface and (especially for the photoconductivity) to variations in crystal cross section. Generally, however, these can be kept small without much trouble. The major features of the curves are independent of variations in surface treatment. Figure 20.6 is an example of the two kinds of traces on a germanium zone-leveled crystal.

All the methods described in this section are suitable for use over a limited temperature range. Soldered contacts will soften above ~250°C, and point pressure contacts usually become useless at low temperature. This varies from crystal to crystal. However, we shall consider measurements as a function of temperature in Sec. 20.6.

20.1b. Analysis of Resistivity Measurements. Electronic conduction in solids is discussed in Sec. 2, but we repeat parts of that discussion here in more detail.

Conductivity σ is expressed by the relation

$$\sigma = q(n_1\mu_1 + n_2\mu_2 + n_3\mu_3 + \cdots) \tag{20.2}$$

where q is the electric charge of the current carriers; n_1, n_2, etc., are the densities (per cubic centimeter) of charge carriers in the several energy bands; and μ_1, μ_2, etc., are the mobilities of the carriers in each band. Usually only two bands are considered, the conduction band and the valence band, and n_1 and n_2 are then the densities of electrons and holes, respectively. However, it is known that two-hole bands (heavy holes and light holes)[4] are important in germanium and perhaps three-hole bands in silicon. Nevertheless, for many purposes it is sufficient to consider only electrons and holes without distinguishing the varieties of them. This procedure will generally be followed here, and the discussion will be extended to more than two bands when necessary.

Carrier density is a function of the temperature, band structure, and impurities present in a crystalline solid. In the interior of a conducting material the principle of local charge neutrality holds. Since conduction electrons are negative charges, holes are positive charges, ionized donor impurities are positive charges, and ionized acceptor impurities are negative charges (see Sec. 2.4), we write[5]

$$n + N_A^- = p + N_D^+ \tag{20.3}$$

where N_A^- and N_D^+ are the densities of ionized acceptor and donor impurities, respectively. The fraction of acceptors ionized is given by a Fermi function†

$$f_A = \left(1 + \frac{1}{g_A}\exp\frac{\epsilon_A - \epsilon_0}{kT}\right)^{-1} \tag{20.4}$$

† See Sec. 2.5 and reference 5.

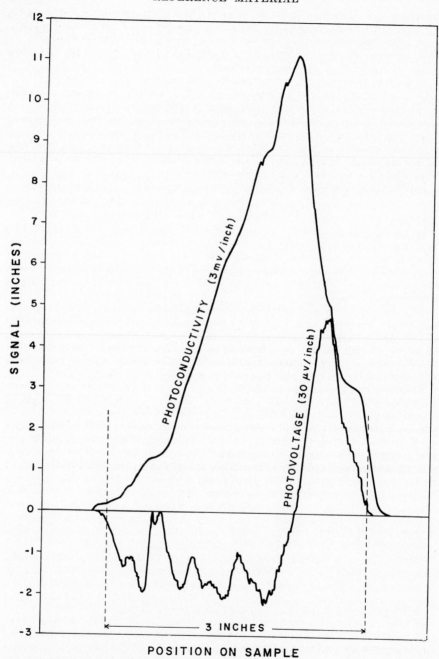

FIG. 20.6. Trace of photoconductivity and photovoltage versus distance along a germanium zone-leveled crystal at −50°C.

where g_A is the degeneracy factor of the energy level of the acceptor, ϵ_A the energy of the level, ϵ_0 the Fermi energy, k the Boltzmann constant, and T the absolute temperature. The Fermi function for a localized energy level gives the probability that it be occupied by an electron. Thus $f_A N_A = N_A^-$ but $f_D N_D = N_D - N_D^+$, since the ionized donors are those which have lost an electron.

In general, there may be many different kinds of donor and acceptor impurities present in a crystal, each with its appropriate Fermi function and density. Furthermore, some of the impurities may accept (or donate) more than one electron, in which case the probability of being singly ionized, doubly ionized, etc., will not be simply Fermi functions but more complex expressions.[6] The charge neutrality equation may then become very complex. However, in Ge and Si, at least, one or two types of impurity usually dominate, so that any others which may be present can be ignored. This problem is discussed further in Sec. 20.6c.

For the case of one kind of donor and one kind of acceptor Eq. (20.3) becomes

$$n + f_A N_A = p + N_D - f_D N_D \tag{20.5}$$

In nondegenerate materials n and p are given by Eqs. (2.3) and (2.4) reproduced here with a simplified symbolism.

$$n = N_c \exp \frac{\epsilon_0 - \epsilon_c}{kT}$$
$$p = N_v \exp \frac{\epsilon_v - \epsilon_0}{kT} \tag{20.6}$$

This system of three equations gives n, p, and ϵ_0 as functions of N_A, N_D, ϵ_A, ϵ_D, g_A, g_D, $\epsilon_c - \epsilon_v$, N_c, N_v, and T. The energy gap $\epsilon_c - \epsilon_v$ is known for many materials, and N_c and N_v are known at least approximately. The energy levels ϵ_A, ϵ_D for many impurities are known in Ge and Si, as are g_A and g_D for some cases.[7,8]

The usual impurities in Ge and Si (B, Al, Ga, In, P, As, Sb, Bi) have energy levels such that either $(\epsilon_c - \epsilon_D) \ll (\epsilon_c - \epsilon_v)$ or $(\epsilon_a - \epsilon_v) \ll (\epsilon_c - \epsilon_v)$, and this leads to certain simplifications of Eq. (20.5) in some temperature ranges.

1. At high temperature both n and p become much larger than the absolute value of $N_D - N_A$. This is the intrinsic region. Equation (20.5) becomes essentially $n = p$, and n and p are given by Eq. (20.6).

2. In the intrinsic region and for some range of temperature below it $f_A \doteq 1$ and $f_D \doteq 0$. In this range Eq. (20.5) is equivalent to

$$n + N_A = p + N_D \tag{20.7}$$

This is the near-intrinsic region.

3. At somewhat lower temperatures either $p \ll n$ or $n \ll p$ and Eq. (20.7) is equivalent to

$$\begin{aligned} n &= N_D - N_A & &n \text{ type} \\ \text{or} \qquad p &= N_A - N_D & &p \text{ type} \end{aligned} \tag{20.8}$$

This is the exhaustion region. It is in this range of temperature that transistors are used. For transistor material, therefore, room temperature falls in this range. For high-resistivity material room temperature is above the exhaustion region (e.g., 40-ohm-cm Ge at room temperature is near-intrinsic).

4. At still lower temperatures either $f_A < 1$ (p type) or $f_D > 0$ (n type) and Eq. (20.5) is equivalent to either

$$\begin{aligned} n &= N_D - N_A - f_D N_D \\ \text{or} \qquad p &= f_A N_A - N_D \end{aligned} \tag{20.9}$$

The behavior of n as a function of T is shown in Figs. 20.20 and 20.21 for several values of N_D and N_A. We shall return to this dependence on temperature again in Sec. 20.6. For now it will be assumed that the measurements are made in the exhaustion region.

From Eqs. (20.2) and (20.8) it is apparent that in this region either

$$\frac{1}{\rho} = \sigma = ne\mu_n$$

or

$$\sigma = pe\mu_p$$

So if it is known whether the material is n- or p-type, and if the mobilities are known, then the carrier concentration can be determined directly from the measured resistivity. In device material usually the doping agent and, therefore, the carrier type are known (see Sec. 6). Methods of determining carrier type are discussed in Sec. 20.2.

Mobility is a function of the band structure, temperature, and impurities present in a crystal. The carrier mobility characteristic of the crystal is due to thermal vibration of the lattice[9] (see Sec. 2.2).† This "lattice-scattering mobility" has been shown empirically to follow a law of the form $\mu(T) = \mu_0 T^{-x}$ for many materials. The values of μ_0 and x for germanium and silicon are given in Table 20.1. This law is followed for a finite range of temperatures, which include those given in the table. The extent to which these values can be extrapolated beyond the listed temperature ranges has not been established. For normal single-crystal material which is not very highly compensated,‡ the mobilities will have their lattice-scattering values above room temperature for 10^{15} material and above 100°K for 10^{14} material. It is probable, in Ge, that below about 80°K lattice-scattering mobility varies as $T^{-\frac{3}{2}}$ for both holes and electrons.

TABLE 20.1. LATTICE-SCATTERING MOBILITY AS A FUNCTION OF TEMPERATURE FOR GE AND SI

	Germanium†	Silicon‡
Electrons.........	$4.9 \times 10^7 T^{-1.66}$ (100–300°K)	$2.1 \times 10^9 T^{-2.5}$ (160 − 400°K)
Holes.............	$1.05 \times 10^9 T^{-2.33}$ (100–300°K)	$2.3 \times 10^9 T^{-2.7}$ (150 − 400°K)

† Morin, *Phys. Rev.*, vol. 93, p. 62, 1954.
‡ Ludwig and Watters, *Phys. Rev.*, vol. 101, p. 1699, 1956.

The carrier mobility characteristic of the impurities in the crystal is due to the interaction between the charge carriers and irregularities in the lattice fields caused by the impurities. There are two laws of behavior characterizing "ionized impurity scattering" and "neutral impurity scattering," neither of which is so accurately established quantitatively as the "lattice-scattering mobility" because of the uncertainty in comparing theory with the experimental results. This is mainly due to difficulties in determining the densities of ionized and neutral impurities, accurate evaluation of mobilities of majority carriers, and calculation of mobility when two or more scattering mechanisms are simultaneously effective.[10] However, the general behavior seems well established in principle with only increased accuracy and detail required. The uncertainties are, however, sufficiently large to restrict the usefulness

† See also reference 5, sec. 8.5, and reference 8, chap. 5.
‡ See Sec. 7.2.

of mobility measurements as a materials-evaluation tool. This subject will be discussed further in connection with mobility measurements.

Enough data are available that an empirical relation between resistivity and carrier density at 300°K can be constructed (Fig. 20.7). This curve is limited to the case in which ionized impurity density is approximately equal to the carrier density. This is probably the most common case in good materials in the exhaustion region.

20.2. Conductivity Type. The intrinsic region was defined above as the region in which $n = p$. However, the word intrinsic per se implies more than merely carrier density. Intrinsic resistivity is the resistivity of a perfectly pure crystal, and resistivity depends on both carrier density and mobility. It is possible if $(N_D - N_A)/N_D \ll 1$ for impurity scattering to be effective while the carrier densities are intrinsic.

The product of the hole and electron densities np is given by

$$np = \left(\frac{2\pi k T}{h^2}\right)^3 (m_n m_p)^{3/2} \exp\left(-\frac{\Delta \epsilon}{kT}\right) \tag{20.10}$$

in which equation there appear only intrinsic properties of the material. Therefore, this product is independent of impurity concentration.† It is common practice to write

$$np = n_i^2 \tag{20.11}$$

since when $p = n$, both n and p have the intrinsic value. When the total carrier density is greater than the intrinsic value, the gain is in either holes or electrons, but not both. Since $np = n_i^2$ in all cases, p must decrease as n increases and vice versa. Then one type of carrier becomes dominant very rapidly when the carrier concentrations become greater than intrinsic. The dominant carrier determines the conductivity type of the sample. Conductivity type has meaning and is observable only in the extrinsic range.

The most generally useful methods of determining conductivity type are the polarity of the thermoelectric[11] voltage, direction of rectification, and the Hall effect. Thermoelectric power and rectification are discussed here briefly and only in this connection. The Hall effect is treated in more detail.

20.2a. Thermoelectric Effect. If two contacts are made to a sample and the contacts are kept at different temperatures (either by cooling one or heating the other), a potential will appear between them. The polarity of the cool probe is positive for p-type and negative for n-type material. It is convenient to use a small soldering iron as the hot probe and a zero center galvanometer as the detector. The required sensitivity of the detector is determined by the thermoelectric power, temperature difference, resistivity, and probe spacing. For extrinsic germanium a microammeter or millivoltmeter is most convenient. A schematic diagram of this experimental arrangement is shown in Fig. 20.8.

A p-type surface layer on n-type material can produce a p-type indication on this test. In this case a higher probe temperature and contact pressure can produce the proper reading. However, on high-resistance p-type material (near intrinsic) a high temperature on the probe can produce n-type readings.

This is brought about by the hot material immediately beneath the probe being driven into the intrinsic conductivity range by the heat from the probe. Since the electrons are more mobile than holes, intrinsic material will appear n-type in this test. If the material is cooled until extrinsic, this difficulty is avoided.

20.2b. Rectification. If an ohmic contact is made to a semiconductor by soldering, plating, or making a pressure contact on a lapped surface and the circuit is completed

---

† This is true for nondegenerate material. At room temperature this is effectively material having less than 10^{18} impurities. For further discussion see reference 5, sec. 10.3, and reference 8, chap. 4.

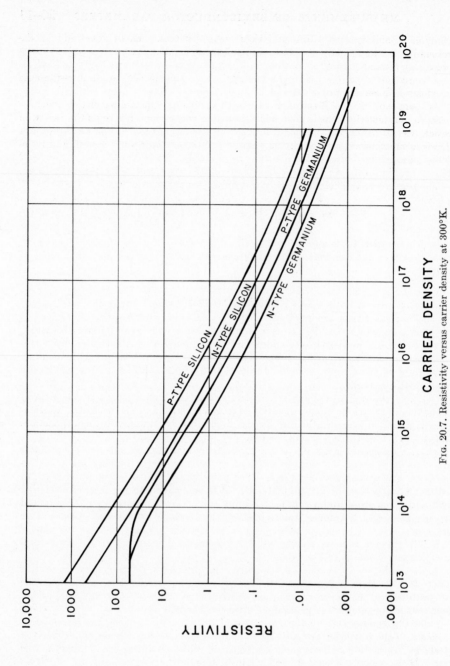

FIG. 20.7. Resistivity versus carrier density at 300°K.

through a point applied to an etched surface, rectification can be observed. If the resistance is highest with the point contact positive, the material is p type and vice versa (see Sec. 3.3).

A convenient arrangement by which the characteristic can be displayed on an oscilloscope is shown in Fig. 20.9.

An extension of this method is to alloy† a material containing either donor or acceptor elements into the sample and to observe whether or not a rectifying junction results between the alloyed material and the semiconductor. For example, if a donor element produces a rectifying junction and an acceptor element does not, the material must be p type.

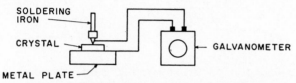

FIG. 20.8. Hot probe for carrier-type indication.

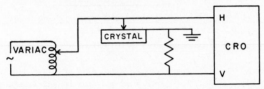

FIG. 20.9. Circuit for observation of carrier type by rectification.

20.3. The Hall Effect. When a conductor carrying a current is placed in a magnetic field and oriented so that the current is in the x direction and the magnetic field in the z direction of a right-handed coordinate system, a field is produced in the conductor in the direction y. This is the direction opposite to that of the force on the conductor due to the current and magnetic field. The field produced is related to the current density and magnetic field strength by the expression

$$\vec{E}_H = -R(\vec{J} \times \vec{H}) \tag{20.12}$$

If the conductor is a uniform prism of dimensions l, w, t as shown in Fig. 20.10 and the magnetic field is uniform, the proportionality constant R (the Hall coefficient) is given by

$$R = \frac{V_H t \times 10^8}{IH} \tag{20.13}$$

where R is the Hall coefficient, V_H is the Hall voltage $= wE_H$, t the sample thickness (in centimeters) in the direction of H, I the current in amperes $= jwt$, and H the magnetic field in gauss. The factor 10^8 adjusts for the mixed units. R is then given in cubic centimeters per coulomb, the normal units.

20.3a. Measurement of the Hall Effect. The measurement usually requires four readings. The voltage appearing between the Hall probes is not, in general, the Hall voltage alone. There are other galvanomagnetic and thermomagnetic effects (Nernst effect, Rhighi-Leduc effect, and Ettingshausen effect[12]) which can produce voltages between the Hall probes. In addition, the IR drop due to probe misalignment and the thermoelectric voltage due to a transverse thermal gradient may be present. All of these except the Ettingshausen effect are eliminated by the method of

† See Sec. 7.6 for a description of the alloy process.

averaging four readings. The Ettingshausen effect is negligible in materials in which a high thermal conductivity is primarily due to lattice conductivity or in which the thermoelectric power is small.

When the voltage between the Hall probes is measured for both directions of current, only the Hall voltage, IR drop, and the voltage due to the Ettingshausen temperature difference reverse. Therefore, the average of these two readings elimi-

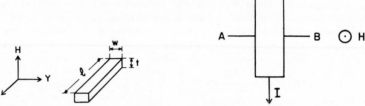

FIG. 20.10. Arrangement in Hall-effect measurement.

FIG. 20.11. Schematic of Hall voltage polarity.

nates the influence of the other effects. When the Hall probe voltage is measured for both directions of the magnetic field, the IR drop does not reverse and is therefore eliminated. Referring to Fig. 20.11 we may define:

V_1 is the voltage $A \to B$ with current downward and H out of the page (as in the figure).

V_2 is the voltage $A \to B$ with current upward and H out of the page.

V_3 is the voltage $A \to B$ with current upward and H into the page.

V_4 is the voltage $A \to B$ with current downward and H into the page.

$$V_H = \frac{V_1 + V_3 - V_2 - V_4}{4} \tag{20.14}$$

The addition is algebraic. When A is positive with respect to B, V is positive. When B is positive, the voltage V is negative. The sign of V_H is the sign of the Hall coefficient, which is the sign of the principal current-carrying particle.

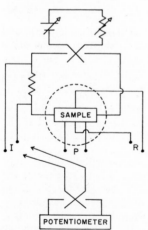

FIG. 20.12. Circuit for Hall-effect and resistivity measurements.

The direction of H is conventionally from a north-seeking pole to a south-seeking pole. The easiest test for the direction of H in strong fields is to observe the direction of motion of a wire carrying a current in the magnetic field. If the conventional current ($+ \to -$) is downward and the wire is forced toward the observer, then the magnetic field direction is left to right. Figure 20.12 shows schematically a d-c method of making a Hall coefficient measurement.

If for a new material it has not been established that the Ettingshausen effect is negligible, the Hall voltage should be measured with alternating current. The Ettingshausen effect involves a thermal gradient and does not establish itself quickly. It requires a time of the order of seconds. Therefore, an alternating current eliminates the effect, since it cannot follow the rapid current reversals. Agreement between the d-c and a-c Hall effects is assurance of the negligibility of the Ettingshausen effect. The average of the a-c Hall effect for both magnetic field directions will eliminate the other effects as in the d-c case.

In cases where the Ettingshausen effect may be important or where space-charge effects prevent d-c measurement, an a-c measurement will have advantages.   Several methods have been described in the literature.[13]   Also there is a chopper square-wave method[14] which has some of the advantages of both a-c and d-c methods.   The d-c method is quite straightforward.   The simple circuit of Fig. 20.12 is sufficient for a wide range of materials.   The usual precautions in semiconductor measurements apply to the Hall effect.   If too large a current is used, joule heating and carrier injection may cause erroneous results.   Usually, no more than a few volts per centimeter should be put across the sample.   In new materials especially, it is necessary to make Hall measurements as a function of current in order to verify the linear relationship at the particular value of current to be used.

The surface at the probe contacts is important.   If pressure contacts are used, the surface should be lapped in order that the surface recombination velocity† may be high.   With ohmic solder contacts this requirement is automatically met.   A rectifying contact will measure the nonequilibrium density of minority carriers beneath it.   A spurious floating potential will be present with rectifying contacts if there is any injection of excess carriers by electrical, optical, or thermal means.[15]

20.3b. Analysis of the Hall Effect.   The Hall voltage is not linear in the magnetic field (in general, R is a function of H), and therefore only for the limiting cases of very small and very large magnetic fields is R independent of H.   The form of the variation of R with H for different impurity densities and crystal orientations is quite complicated and not suitable for detailed discussion here.[16]‡   However, some discussion is required for an appreciation of the advantages and limitations of the phenomenon as an evaluation tool.

In what follows, the value of R (when not otherwise specified) is the "zero field value," i.e., the limiting value which R approaches as H becomes very small.

In metals and degenerate semiconductors R is not a function of H and the interpretation of the Hall effect is most straightforward.

$$R = \frac{1}{nq} \tag{20.15}$$

where n is the carrier density and q the charge of an electron.   Since $\sigma = nq\mu$ the product

$$R\sigma = \mu \tag{20.16}$$

gives the carrier mobility directly and $1/Rq$ gives the carrier density.

In nondegenerate semiconductors the situation is more complex.   (1) In nondegenerate semiconductors the thermal energy of the current carriers has a distribution which produces an additional factor in the expression.   (2) The energy bands in semiconductors do not, in general, have spherical symmetry, and this introduces an additional orientation-dependent factor.   (3) There may be two or more bands effective in conduction.

The mobilities are defined in Sec. 2 as the ratio v/E, where v is the average acquired velocity of the charge carriers and E is the field producing the velocity.   In the absence of the field, the carriers are in random motion owing to their thermal energy and are in thermal equilibrium with the crystal lattice.   This means that the carriers in colliding with the atoms of the lattice neither lose nor gain energy on the average.   The average kinetic energy of the electrons is $\frac{3}{2}kT$, and most carriers have energies near this value, but there are appreciable numbers of carriers having kinetic energies over the whole range from zero to several times kT.

The frequency of collisions and the amount of scattering per collision are functions

---

† See Sec. 8.3a.
‡ See also reference 8, chap. 5.

of the energy of the carrier. When an electric field is applied, the acceleration due to the field adds a component of velocity to the thermal velocity of the carrier. Because of the energy dependence of the scattering, the added velocity component is different for carriers in different energy ranges. Therefore, the current produced by the field is the result of an average of the different velocities of the carriers.

In the presence of a magnetic field, the force on the carriers, as well as the scattering, is a function of their velocities. Therefore, the Hall field is a function of an average over the velocities of the carriers, and this average is not, in general, the same as that for the current. In the degenerate case the carriers effective in conduction are restricted essentially to a narrow range of energy, so that virtually all the carriers have the same velocity and any type of average is essentially equal to any other type.†

Because of the distribution of velocity of the carriers

$$R = \frac{r}{nq} \quad \text{and} \quad R\sigma = r\mu \tag{20.17}$$

We can define a Hall mobility μ_H by the product $R\sigma$, and then $r = \mu_H/\mu$. Since we now have two kinds of mobilities for the same carriers, we shall write the conductivity mobility as μ_σ in order to avoid ambiguity. The factor r is a function of H, the scattering mechanisms effective in the sample, and the shape of the energy surfaces. For spherical energy surfaces and H small ($H \to 0$), r has the value $3\pi/8$ and $315\pi/512$ for lattice and ionized impurity scattering, respectively, with a minimum value of about unity for some particular mixture of impurity and lattice scattering. As H is increased, the value of r decreases and approaches unity at high fields.

For nonspherical symmetry the values of r are reduced. For materials such as germanium and silicon, having ellipsoidal energy surfaces and cubic symmetry, the anisotropy factor is

$$\frac{3K(K + 2)}{(2K + 1)^2} \tag{20.18}$$

where K is the anisotropy ratio of the individual ellipsoidal energy surfaces. $K = 20$ in n-type germanium, which gives 0.785 for the value of the anisotropy factor [Eq. (20.18)]. Combined with the value $3\pi/8$ for lattice scattering this leads to $R = 0.93/nq$ for germanium. This value is in good agreement with experimental results.[16,17]

As H is increased, the anisotropy factor also approaches unity. This effect at very high fields is a general result.[18]

When two kinds of carriers are effective simultaneously, the expression for the Hall coefficient becomes

$$R = \frac{p_1\mu_{\sigma1}\mu_{H1} + p_2\mu_{\sigma2}\mu_{H2} - n_3\mu_{\sigma3}\mu_{H3} - \cdots}{q(p_1\mu_{\sigma1} + p_2\mu_{\sigma2} + n_3\mu_{\sigma3} + \cdots)^2} \tag{20.19}$$

where the equation is written for two kinds of holes of density p_1 and p_2 and one kind of electrons of density n_3 and the dots indicate that as many terms of the same type can be added as there are kinds of carriers in significant quantity. For two bands, (one kind each of electrons and holes) the expression is

$$R = \frac{p\mu_{\sigma p}\mu_{Hp} - n\mu_{\sigma n}\mu_{Hn}}{q(p\mu_{\sigma p} + n\mu_{\sigma n})^2} \tag{20.20}$$

† This material is well covered in reference 5, especially chaps. 8 and 11.

When $r = 1$ for both electrons and holes, this becomes

$$R = \frac{p - b^2 n}{q(p + bn)^2} \tag{20.21}$$

where the mobility ratio $b = \mu_{\sigma n}/\mu_{\sigma p}$.

In Ge and Si there are at least two types of holes with different mobilities. Assuming $r = 1$ for both kinds of holes (high magnetic fields) the Hall mobility for p-type material is

$$R\sigma = \mu_H = \frac{p_1 \mu_1^2 + p_2 \mu_2^2}{p_1 \mu_1 + p_2 \mu_2} \tag{20.22}$$

This is a sort of average mobility, but not an obviously useful one. The effective conductivity mobility is

$$\mu_\sigma = \frac{\sigma}{q(p_1 + p_2)} = \frac{p_1 \mu_1 + p_2 \mu_2}{p_1 + p_2} \tag{20.23}$$

To sum up, interpretation of Hall-effect measurements is not simple or straightforward except in metals or degenerate materials. In all nondegenerate materials (except at very large magnetic fields, which are not always attainable) the factor r, or the possibility of two or more energy bands, introduces an uncertainty in the interpretation. The most serious, of course, is the case of multiple bands, in which case the Hall coefficient is meaningless without additional information. In the case of single bands r ranges only from about 0.90 to about 1.8 in cases observed so far. Thus, carrier densities and mobilities can be ascertained at least to within these uncertainties.

20.4. Drift Mobility. Measurement of Hall effect and resistivity can, within the limitations described, give both carrier concentration and carrier mobility of a sample. In effect, the Hall coefficient is the reciprocal of a charge concentration (density of carriers times charge per carrier) and the resistivity is equal to the Hall coefficient divided by the carrier mobility. We measure then the product $n\mu$ and the density n from which we calculate μ. It is possible, however, to measure μ directly and by means of measurements of ρ and μ calculate n. In the Hall measurement, the principal source of uncertainty is the ratio $r = \mu_H/\mu_\sigma$. The Hall mobility μ_H and conductivity mobility μ_σ are not equal in general. The mobility which may be measured directly is the "drift mobility" μ_D. The conductivity mobility is the majority-carrier mobility, while the drift mobility as measured is that of the minority carriers. For this reason μ_σ and μ_D can never be measured for the same sample. None of these mobilities is necessarily equal to the "microscopic mobility" μ[†] in a particular sample, since "trapping" (Sec. 20.5b) may occur in some samples.

The "microscopic" mobility is defined in terms of the acceleration of the charge carriers in an electric field and their mean free path or mean free time between scattering collisions. It is a theoretical concept.

The conductivity mobility given by Eq. (20.23) is defined as the average conductivity per charge carrier. In general, $\mu_\sigma = \mu$.

Drift mobility is defined operationally by measuring the rate of drift in an electric field of minority carriers in extrinsic material. When the scattering is due to lattice vibrations (lattice scattering), the drift mobility of electrons should be independent of the crystal; i.e., it should be the same in p-type or in n-type material. The same is true for holes. If no trapping occurs, the drift mobility in this case is equal to the microscopic mobility. Drift mobility measured when impurity scattering is important is harder to interpret. A majority carrier "sees" an array of attractive centers

† See reference 5, p. 209.

(ionized impurities) screened by a cloud of repulsive particles (the majority carriers). A minority carrier "sees" a repulsive center screened by attractive particles. It is not clear that $\mu_D = \mu_\sigma$ in this case. The experimental observations of impurity-scattering drift mobility are in agreement with theory within their uncertainties, but these are still fairly large.

When both impurity and lattice scattering are effective, the uncertainty is greater. It is quite uncertain just how, quantitatively, the drift mobility of a sample of 0.1-ohm-cm p-type Ge with 4×10^{16} acceptors is related to the conductivity mobility of a sample of n-type 0.05-ohm-cm Ge with 4×10^{16} donors.

Drift-mobility measurements in the lattice-scattering region in Ge and Si have been invaluable in determining the actual values of μ and of μ_H/μ_σ.

The schematic diagram of a circuit suitable for making such a measurement with an error of only a few per cent is shown in Fig. 20.13.[19] The operation of this circuit is as

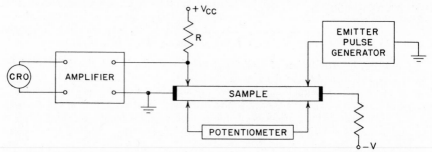

Fɪɢ. 20.13. Schematic diagram of a circuit for measuring carrier-drift mobility.

follows: The batteries produce an electric field inside the rod of single-crystal semi-conducting material, which results in a steady flow of current. When minority carriers are injected into the rod by a short pulse from the emitter pulse generator, they drift toward the collector because of the presence of the field. When they arrive at the collector, they produce a voltage pulse across the resistor R, so it is possible to determine the velocity of these injected carriers by measuring on the cathode-ray oscilloscope the time between the center of the emitter injection pulse and the maximum of the pulse at the collector. Since the mobility of carriers in an electric field is, by definition, the ratio of their average velocity to the strength of the field and since the electric field inside the filament is approximately equal to the ratio of the voltage between the emitter and the collector (which can be measured by the potentiometer) to the distance between them, the mobility of the minority carriers can be computed from the formula

$$\mu_D = \frac{L/t}{V/L} = \frac{L^2}{Vt}$$

The mobility measured in this way is found to be a function of the amplitude of the emitter current pulse because the injected carriers modulate the conductivity of the bar. This effect can be eliminated by measuring the mobility with several values of pulse amplitude and extrapolating to the zero-amplitude value.

Errors may be introduced because of the nonuniformity of the electric field near the emitter and collector electrodes, but these errors become negligible if the electrodes are sufficiently far apart.†

Inhomogeneity in the crystal (which causes the field to vary) can also introduce error. If the resistivity along the sample is known, the field may be corrected. If

† A separation of 1 cm was found to be adequate for measurements on germanium (see reference 20).

trapping occurs, the apparent mobility will be low. Serious trapping can be detected by the shape of the voltage pulse. When trapping is present, the trailing edge of the pulse will fall much more slowly than the leading edge, so the pulse will be skewed.

Since the mobility is a function of the temperature, it is essential to specify the temperature at which the measurements are made. For this reason it is desirable to limit the flow of current through the sample. On the other hand, it is desirable to have strong fields to minimize the spreading of the injected pulse through diffusion and to reduce the loss of injected carriers due to recombination. One solution is to pulse both the sweeping field and the injected carriers, the sweeping-field pulse starting before the injection pulse and finishing after the collection pulse. In this way, the heating effect of the sweeping current can be greatly reduced even when strong fields are present during the operating part of the cycle.[20]

An alternative solution is to pulse the sweeping field but to use a steady, though small, emitter current.[21] In this case a distribution of minority carriers builds up in the neighborhood of the emitter between pulses of the sweeping field, this distribution falling off exponentially with distance from the emitter because of the finite lifetime of the injected carriers. When the sweeping field is applied, this distribution moves down the filament to the collector. The time between the application of the sweeping pulse and the arrival of the peak of the minority-carrier distribution at the collector is taken as the transit time of the carriers.

20.5. Lifetime. The concentration of carriers satisfying the charge neutrality condition and the appropriate statistics (Sec. 20.1b) is the equilibrium concentration determined by the impurity densities and the temperature. The operation of semiconductor devices is, however, usually effected by means of nonequilibrium concentrations, e.g., injected minority carriers in a transistor or excess densities of carriers generated by light in a photodevice. At all times electrons and holes are being generated by thermal processes within the crystal, and simultaneously electrons from the conduction band are recombining with holes, thus removing both from the conduction process. At equilibrium the rates of generation and recombination are equal, so the density of carriers is constant.

The rate of change of a carrier density is given by

$$\frac{dn}{dt} = G - U \tag{20.24}$$

where G is the rate of generation (per unit volume per second) and U is the rate of recombination. In equilibrium $G = U$ and $dn/dt = 0$. It is assumed that G is a function of temperature, but not of n. U is a function of n. The various recombination processes and trapping are studied by means of their effect on U.

When n is disturbed by an influence g, we write

$$\frac{d(n_0 + \Delta n)}{dt} = G + g - U - u \tag{20.25}$$

where n_0 is the equilibrium value of n. Since $dn_0/dt = G - U = 0$, the equation need be written only for the disturbance.

$$\frac{d(\Delta n)}{dt} = g - u \tag{20.26}$$

understanding that Δn, g, and u are all zero at equilibrium. When u in Eq. (20.26) is proportional to Δn (this is approximately the case in some experimental measurements), we write

$$\frac{d \Delta n}{dt} = g - \frac{\Delta n}{\tau} \tag{20.27}$$

If g is a constant $\neq 0$, the solution of (20.27) is

$$\Delta n = g\tau(1 - e^{-t/\tau}) \tag{20.28}$$

If, after some time t, g is removed ($g = 0$), we have

$$\Delta n = \Delta n_0 e^{-t/\tau} \tag{20.29}$$

where Δn_0 is the value of Δn at the time g is removed and τ is seen to be the average length of time that the excess carriers exist. From this there are, in principal, three ways of determining the lifetime τ:

1. As $t \to \infty$ from Eq. (20.28)

$$\tau = \frac{\Delta n}{g} \tag{20.30}$$

This is a "steady-state" equation $d\,\Delta n/dt = 0$.

2. When t is finite from Eq. (20.28)

$$\tau = \frac{\Delta t}{\ln\left(\dfrac{\Delta n_1 - \Delta n_2}{\Delta n_2 - \Delta n_3}\right)} \tag{20.31}$$

where Δn_1, Δn_2, and Δn_3 are measured at times t_1, t_2, and t_3 and $\Delta t = t_2 - t_1 = t_3 - t_2$. This is a "build-up" equation ($d\,\Delta n/dt = ge^{-t/\tau}$).

3. From Eq. (20.29)

$$\tau = \frac{\Delta t}{\ln(\Delta n_1/\Delta n_2)} \tag{20.32}$$

This is a "decay" equation ($d\,\Delta n/dt = -(\Delta n_0/\tau)e^{-t/\tau}$).

In the simplest case $\Delta n = \Delta p$, so the above equations pertain equally to electrons, holes, and electron-hole pairs.

It is not generally true that u is simply proportional to Δn, and therefore, τ (defined by $\tau = \Delta n/u$) is not independent of Δn. The simple exponential behavior described above is observed only in special experimental situations.

A general discussion of recombination of electrons and holes is given in Sec. 5. There are two types considered, radiative recombination[22] across the energy gap and recombinations taking place through the action of "recombination centers."[23]

The radiative recombination rate can be given as $u = P(n_0 + \Delta n)(p_0 + \Delta p)$, where P is the recombination probability and $(n_0 + \Delta n)$ and $(p_0 + \Delta p)$ are the electron and hole concentrations. Thus for radiative recombination, since $\Delta n = \Delta p$, we have, for small signals, $\Delta n = \Delta p \ll n_0 + p_0$ and the lifetime τ is given by

$$\tau = \frac{\Delta n}{u} = \frac{1}{P(n_0 + p_0)} \tag{20.33}$$

The τ for this process is large, since P is small. The small value of P results from the necessity of conserving momentum in the radiative recombination process with the aid of either a three-particle collision (the so-called phonon-assisted process) or else an exact momentum match between the hole and electron involved. τ will be independent of Δn if $\Delta n \ll (n_0 + p_0)$ and Eqs. (20.27) to (20.32) apply.

If the semiconductor material has a significant density of impurity atoms or lattice defects which act as "recombination centers," a different situation exists. An electron captured by such a center is localized; i.e., it is bound to the lattice. This has the consequence that the electron can exchange energy and momentum with the lattice. Now the electron can make a transition to the valence band (recombine with a hole) with greater freedom than in the radiative case, since lattice vibrations (phonons) can assist more efficiently in securing conservation of momentum in the process. This has the effect of increasing the transition probabilities. This is normally the dominant recombination process.

Recombination through localized states is the process described by the "Shockley-Read" theory. It is a more complicated process statistically than radiative recombination, since there are four processes which must be considered (transitions to the centers from the conduction band and from the valence band and transitions from the centers to the conduction band and to the valence band). Since the rate of loss of electrons from the conduction band is the rate of transition of electrons to the centers minus their rate of reexcitation to the conduction band and the rate of loss of holes is also their net rate of capture by the centers, it is not necessary that $d \, \Delta n/dt = d \, \Delta p/dt$. Obviously, then, Δn need not equal Δp.

In Sec. 5.1b the action of recombination centers is described. In Eq. (5.2) the values of Δn and Δp in the steady state are given as

$$\Delta n = \frac{g}{v_n s_n N_p} \quad \text{and} \quad \Delta p = \frac{g}{v_p s_p N_n} \qquad (20.34)$$

where v_n and v_p are the velocities of the electrons and holes, s_n and s_p are the capture cross sections for the electron and hole centers, N_p is the density of centers occupied by holes, and N_n is the density of centers occupied by electrons. The respective lifetimes are

$$\tau_n = \frac{1}{v_n s_n N_p} \quad \text{and} \quad \tau_p = \frac{1}{v_p s_p N_n} \qquad (20.35)$$

and are in general not equal.[24]

There is also a difference between "steady-state" lifetime and "transient" lifetimes. Phenomena such as d-c photoconductivity or diffusion-length measurements in which a steady state has been established are characterized by the condition $d \, \Delta n/dt = d \, \Delta p/dt$. In other phenomena such as photoconductive decay or diode recovery this condition is not generally satisfied. When the density of recombination centers is small compared with the carrier density and the signal (Δp and Δn) is small, the lifetimes reduce to the simplest case $\tau_n = \tau_p$ and τ (steady state) $= \tau$ (transient). When these conditions are satisfied,

$$\tau = \frac{1}{v_n s_n N_p} \frac{n_0 + n_1}{n_0 + p_0} + \frac{1}{v_p s_p N_n} \frac{p_0 + p_1}{n_0 + p_0} \qquad (20.36)$$

where n_1 and p_1 are properties of the centers defined by the equations

$$n_1 = N_c \exp \frac{\epsilon_t - \epsilon_c}{kT}$$
$$\qquad (20.37)$$
$$p_1 = N_v \exp \frac{\epsilon_v - \epsilon_t}{kT}$$

in which N_c and N_v are related to the densities of states in the conduction and valence bands, ϵ_c and ϵ_v are the energies of the bottom of the conduction band and the top of the valence band, and ϵ_t is the energy of a captured electron. From Eqs. (20.36) and (20.37) it can be seen that the lifetime is quite temperature-dependent.

The lifetime discussed in this section is called the "bulk" lifetime. The effective lifetime observed in various measurements is not necessarily equal to the bulk lifetime, but under proper conditions of experiment the bulk lifetime can be determined.

The expression "bulk" lifetime explicitly distinguishes it from surface-recombination lifetime.   Surface recombination is not a property of the material, since it is subject to change by surface treatment or even by change of the ambient atmosphere.   It is not a parameter of interest in evaluating material, although it is a phenomenon of interest in the study of crystal surfaces and devices.

20.5a. Surface Recombination.   When the surface recombination is high, the excess carriers near the surface recombine much more quickly than those deep in the bulk. As a result, the density of excess carriers is lowered near the surface, causing a density gradient.   Carriers diffuse† toward the surface, thus extending the effect of the surface recombination into the crystal bulk.   The numbers of carriers per unit area diffusing to the surface and recombining there constitute a current density of charge carriers which is expressed in terms of the excess carrier density Δn near the surface and an average velocity s, which is called the surface recombination velocity.

In a fairly thick sample (in which s does not completely dominate the bulk recombination) the surface recombination has two effects.   Consider for simplicity a case

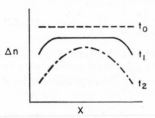

Δn

FIG. 20.14. Schematic view of variation of excess carriers with distance from surface at several times.

in which Δn is uniform throughout the sample at the time when the generating source is removed.   In the center, the concentration Δn will decrease at the rate $\Delta n/\tau_b$ as in Eq. (20.27) with $g = 0$.   Near the surface, however, the rate will be $\Delta n/\tau_b + K$, where K is the number of carriers lost per unit time by recombination at the surface, and a density gradient is established near the surface.   Now Δn is no longer uniform, so we write $\Delta n(x)$, where x is the distance into the crystal. In every volume element, the rate of decrease $d(\Delta n)/dt$ is composed of a sum $(\Delta n(x)/\tau_b) + D_n[\partial^2 \Delta n(x)/\partial x^2]$, where D_n is the diffusion constant and $d^2 \Delta n/dx^2$ is the spatial rate of change of the gradient; i.e., $D(d^2 \Delta n/dx^2)$ gives the variation of the diffusion current with distance from the surface.

In Fig. 20.14 the dashed line represents an initially uniform distribution.   The solid line represents the distribution after a short time in which the decrease in the center is about equal to $\Delta n/\tau_b$, while that at the ends is $\Delta n/\tau_b + K$.   Sometime later the distribution would come to resemble the dot-dash line.   At this time $\Delta n/\tau_b$ near the surface is much smaller than $\Delta n/\tau_b$ near the middle, but $D_n(d^2 \Delta n/dx^2)$ is much larger at the edges than in the center.   As the ratio $(\Delta n \text{ surface}/\Delta n \text{ center})$ becomes smaller and as $D_n(\partial^2 \Delta n/\partial x^2)$ becomes appreciable in the interior, the rates of loss in the two regions become more nearly equal.   Shockley‡ has shown that $\Delta n(x)$ approaches the form $A \cos b(B - x)$, where b is a function of the recombination velocity and the sample dimensions and $2B$ is the sample thickness.   At this point $\partial^2 \Delta n/\partial x^2$ becomes $-b^2 \Delta n$, so

$$\frac{d \Delta n(x)}{dt} = - \frac{\Delta n(x)}{\tau_b} - D_n b^2 \Delta n(x) = - \Delta n(x) \left(\frac{1}{\tau_b} + D_n b^2 \right) = \frac{\Delta n(x)}{\tau_m} \quad (20.38)$$

where b is defined by the equation $b \tan bB = s/D_n$. b is not a function of x. Therefore,

$$\left(\frac{d \Delta n}{dt} \right)_{\text{total}} = \frac{d}{dt} \int_{-B}^{B} \Delta n(x)\, dx = - \left(\frac{\Delta n}{\tau_m} \right)_{\text{total}} \quad (20.39)$$

and the total density of excess carriers along our dimension x is decaying with the effective decay rate $1/\tau_m = (1/\tau_b) + D_n b^2$.   While the distribution was changing,

† See Sec. 3, p. 3–7.
‡ Reference 5, sec. 12.6.

this was not true and the decay was not exponential. For this reason the initial decay cannot be used for lifetime measurement; so the first effect of s is the non-exponential initial decay and the second is the term $D_n b^2$ in the effective time constant.

Shockley has discussed this problem for a rectangular sample for the case both of uniform generation along the sample and of generation at one point. His more general expressions are

$$\frac{1}{\tau_b} + D_n(b^2 + c^2) = \frac{1}{\tau_m} \tag{20.40}$$

where c is defined by $c \tan cC = s/D_n$ and $2C$ is the sample width. For the case $s \to \infty$

$$\frac{1}{\tau_b} + \frac{\pi^2 D_n}{4}\left(\frac{1}{B^2} + \frac{1}{C^2}\right) = \frac{1}{\tau_m} \tag{20.41}$$

and for $s \to 0$

$$\frac{1}{\tau_b} + s\left(\frac{1}{B} + \frac{1}{C}\right) = \frac{1}{\tau_m} \tag{20.42}$$

This simplification, in decay, occurs for any initial distribution of Δn. For build-up and steady state, no such simplification is possible. The distribution $\cos bx$ is but one term of a Fourier expansion of the actual distribution. Each term of the expansion has its own recombination constant. For this reason, build-up and steady-state lifetime measurements require that surface recombination be negligible. It is necessary to note that in this respect drift-length or diffusion-length measurements[†] are decay rather than steady-state measurements.

20.5b. Trapping. The problem of trapping is extremely complicated, and we shall attempt only a qualitative description of its general effects. Trapping is a property of the material, and its presence or absence may be decisive in selecting materials for device use.

The term "trapping" is used somewhat ambiguously in the literature. Consider a set of centers N. The capture cross sections of these centers for electrons and holes were defined alternately. That is, s_n is defined for a center which is empty of electrons and s_p is defined for a center which is occupied by an electron. Thus, only two states of the center are considered.[25] The statistics of these states involves (as mentioned previously) a balance of four processes (the capture of electrons and their reexcitation and the capture of holes and their reexcitation). A recombination consists in the capture of an electron and then a hole (in p-type material). A hole capture in this case completes a recombination. We shall assume, for simplicity, that reexcitation of electrons and holes is small. This is certainly the case for recombination states near the center of the forbidden energy gap at low temperatures.

Now if the capture cross sections for holes and electrons are comparable, electrons will spend little time on the centers. In p-type material Δn may be $0.01 p_0$ (small-signal conditions). A center which has captured an electron will capture a hole very quickly. If $s_p = 0.1 s_n$, then on the average a captured electron will wait ten times longer to recombine. For any finite ratio of capture cross sections there will be some density of centers for which the density of electrons in the centers waiting for hole captures will be comparable to the density of electrons in the conduction band. In this case $\Delta n < \Delta p$. This is one sense in which the term "trapping" has been used. This case has a definite effect on lifetime measurement. When the density of excess carriers is changing, $d\,\Delta n/dt \neq d\,\Delta p/dt$, and when the densities are steady, $\Delta n \neq \Delta p$ because some of the electrons are lost to the trap while the holes are lost only by recombination.

† See Sec. 20.5c.

If the cross section for holes becomes much less than that for the electrons, it may happen that the rate of reexcitation of electrons from the centers may become comparable to the rate of hole capture. If the electrons are captured and reexcited several times before recombining, it is the length of time they spend in the conduction band that determines their lifetime and not the total time between generation and recombination.

This case is almost indistinguishable from the case in which one set of centers traps electrons while another set serves as recombination centers. If a set of trapping centers were more dense or had a higher capture cross section for electrons than a set of recombination centers, then the electrons would, on the average, be trapped several times before recombining.

In either of the latter two cases, the drift mobility of the electrons will be reduced, since they will spend some fraction of their transit time in traps. This is another sense in which the word trapping has been used. These two phenomena should be distinguished. It is necessary to be a little cautious in reading the literature, since many unqualified statements about trapping assume the reexcitation and recapture case and, therefore, do not necessarily refer to the weaker case of $\Delta n \neq \Delta p$.

If the density of traps (of either kind) is not very large, the trapped electrons begin to fill the traps, so that each successive increment of Δn is less strongly trapped. In such a case it is possible to create enough excess carriers to saturate the traps, and then any excess carrier density beyond this point is not affected by trapping. The interpretation of lifetime measurements made in this way s, however, not obvious.

20.5c. Lifetime Measurement. The various methods of measuring lifetime vary in the method and manner of generating Δn, the parameter used to observe Δn, and the technique by which its time dependence is determined. These choices are controlled essentially by the material properties, sample shapes, and range of lifetimes to be measured and practically by the available equipment. Some of the possible variety of choices are enumerated in the following paragraph.

The source of Δn may be incident light (or X rays, electrons, protons, etc.) injection (or exclusion) at contacts (or PN junctions) or impact ionization within the bulk at low temperatures. In the case of incident radiation the type of source used depends on the wavelength (or energy) and the flux required. The radiation may be applied in step functions, square waves, square pulses, sinusoidal modulation, etc.

The parameter observed may be conductance, photoelectromagnetic current or voltage, a point collector current or potential, free carrier absorption, or the current in a reverse-biased junction.

Time dependence may be observed directly on an oscilloscope, by means of frequency response or phase change, by spatial distribution of free carriers due to diffusion or drift in an electric field.

The variety of possible lifetime measurements is large, and in fact, a large number of the possible combinations have actually been used and results reported in the literature. A comprehensive survey of methods, however, will not be attempted here.† The methods described in this section are fairly typical of the variety and are widely used.

PHOTOCONDUCTIVE DECAY. This is the most direct method of measuring lifetimes. It is suitable for values of τ ranging from about 1 μsec to about 1 msec. The arrangement is shown in Fig. 20.15.

A constant current is provided in the sample by a high-impedance source, and the voltage drop across the sample is applied to the vertical input of an oscilloscope through a wideband preamplifier. The resistance of the sample is reduced by absorbed light, and the return to dark value after the light has been removed is observed on the oscilloscope.

† See reference 12, sec. 7.4.

The light (from a tungsten filament, Nernst glower, spark, etc.) is chopped at a convenient frequency either mechanically by a rotating mirror or slotted wheel or electrically by a capacitor discharge in a spark gap. The frequency is governed by the requirements that:

1. The light must be on the sample long enough to get a measurable signal. This depends on the intensity of the source.

2. The light must be off the sample long enough to permit the excess conductivity to decay away. This requires several times the effective lifetime and, therefore, depends on the sample.

3. The light must be extinguished in much less than a lifetime. The lens system is used to focus the light in the plane of the chopping wheel in order to minimize the cutoff time. It is helpful to use a second light source and photocell chopped by the same light chopper to trigger the scope. This permits greater control of triggering.

The electrical circuit must, of course, be shielded. The precautions given previously in connection with resistivity measurements concerning contacts and fields should be

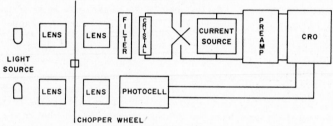

FIG. 20.15. Arrangement for photoconductive decay measurement.

observed. The contacts and adjacent area of the sample should be masked in order to avoid carrier sweep-out and photovoltaic effects at the contacts.

The samples should be fairly large in all dimensions (e.g., 0.5 by 0.5 by 2.5 cm). In thin samples the decay may be completely dominated by surface recombination. Since it is not generally possible to know or to control the surface recombination velocity accurately, it is recommended that ground or sandblasted surfaces be used. In this case one can be sure at least that s is large, and the expression for $s \to \infty$ [Eq. (20.41)] is used to calculate the bulk lifetime.

Unless the decay is exponential, there is no obviously meaningful lifetime. In order to ascertain that the observed decay is exponential it is convenient to prepare an exponential face mask for the cathode-ray oscilloscope and to match the decay curve to it by adjusting gain and sweep. In general, the first part of the decay will be nonexponential owing to surface recombination, and if trapping is present, there may be a slow decay (long tail) at the end.

The lifetime is most easily calculated by observing the time (using a calibrated sweep) in which the signal falls from any value (in an exponential region) to half that value. The observed lifetime is then $\tau = \Delta t/\ln 2 = 1.44 \Delta t$.

DRIFT LENGTH, DIFFUSION LENGTH. This method uses the techniques of the drift-mobility measurement already described. In the drift-mobility measurement only the time of arrival of the pulse is used. However, the pulse of excess carriers decays as it drifts, and this decay can be measured to determine lifetime.

The drift-mobility measurement is essentially a one-dimensional case. When carriers are injected steadily at x_0 and swept down the bar, the concentration is given as a function of x by

$$\Delta n = \Delta n_0 \exp \alpha(x - x_0)\dagger \qquad (20.43)$$

† Reference 5, sec. 12.6.

in which

$$\alpha = \frac{-\mu E \tau + [(\mu E \tau)^2 + 4D\tau]^{1/2}}{2D\tau} \qquad (20.44)$$

and μ and D are the free carrier ambipolar mobility and diffusion constant, respectively.

$$\mu = \frac{p - n}{(n/\mu_p) + (p/\mu_n)}$$

$$D = \frac{p + n}{(n/D_p) + (p/D_n)} \qquad (20.45)$$

By the Einstein relation

$$D_n = \frac{\mu_n k T}{q}$$

$$D_p = \frac{\mu_p k T}{q} \qquad (20.46)$$

In addition to the experimental precautions noted in the drift-mobility experiment, it is necessary to maintain injection and collector response constant as either E or x is varied in order that Δn be a function of α and x only and that collector current be proportional to Δn.

There are two limiting cases for α:

1. When $(\mu E \tau)^2 \gg 4D\tau$ or $E^2 \gg (4kT/q)/\mu\tau$ (in practical units $k/q = 8.617 \times 10^{-5}$ volt/deg),

$$\alpha \to (\mu E \tau)^{-1} \qquad (20.47)$$

2. When $E = 0$,

$$\alpha = (D\tau)^{-1/2} = \frac{1}{L_D} \qquad (20.48)$$

The first case is a drift-length measurement, while the second is a diffusion-length measurement. L_D is called the diffusion length. In either case the first part of the decay ($x - x_0$ small) is not exponential and it is necessary to verify the exponential behavior just as in photoconductive decay.

The decay as a function of x is independent of trapping. Any trapping of the carriers decreases the effective mobility in the same proportion that it increases the effective τ, so that $\mu\tau$ and $D\tau$ are independent of trapping.

In large samples the one-dimensional analysis is not adequate. The Morton-Haynes method[26] is adapted to this case. This method permits the observation of lifetime locally (within several diffusion lengths). A narrow rectangle of chopped light is used to inject carriers. The collector signal is observed as a function of distance as the rectangle of light is moved. A comparison of a curve of collector current versus distance with the solution of the diffusion equation for the appropriate boundary conditions permits an evaluation of the diffusion length L_D from which the lifetime can be computed.

The function $n(r)/n_0$ is plotted in Fig. 20.16 with diffusion length as parameter. $n(r)/n_0$ represents the relative excess carrier density as a function of the distance r from the line of light. The experimental data are plotted on semilog paper (log of collector current versus separation), and the diffusion length L_D is determined by a comparison of slope with the curves of Fig. 20.16. τ can then be calculated from Eqs. (20.46) and (20.48).

For accurate measurements, the width of the illuminated area must be less than one-fifth the minimum value of r, the length of the illuminated area must be at least four times the maximum value of r, and the illuminated region must be at a distance at least 1.5 times the minority-carrier diffusion length from the sides of the crystal. Also, the electric field introduced by the collector must be sufficiently small so that it does not affect the flow of the injected carriers.

The solutions given in Fig. 20.16 neglect the effect of surface recombination velocity. Careful etching[27] and cleaning can produce surfaces with $s < 200$. Lifetimes in the range 2 to 500 μsec can be measured with this technique.

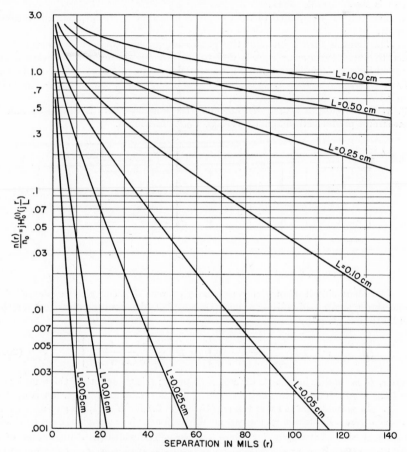

Fig. 20.16. Minority-carrier diffusion length.

The analysis has been extended[28] to include the effect of surface recombination and to other geometrical arrangements.

PHOTOELECTROMAGNETIC EFFECT. The photoelectromagnetic effect[29] measures τ indirectly as the Hall effect measures mobility indirectly. Its interpretation therefore depends strongly on an adequate theory, which exists for the effect only in fairly ideal form. For this reason application of the technique to new materials, the technology of which may not be under control, must be done with caution.

The effect is produced by illuminating one face of a crystal with strongly absorbed radiation. A magnetic field parallel to the illuminated crystal face causes the electrons and holes diffusing into the crystal to be deflected in opposite directions. If connection is made between the faces of the crystal toward which the carriers are deflected, a current will flow in the external connection (the short-circuit current), or if a voltmeter is connected across them, an open-circuit voltage will be measured. The interpretive difficulties lie in the quantitative correlation of the measurable effect with the mobilities, lifetimes, etc., of the current carriers.

As with any other measurement there are a number of modifications of the basic measurement. The one we describe is apparently the simplest. The electrical circuit is shown in Fig. 20.17.

1. The voltage V_0 applied to the sample is measured with light and the magnetic field off.

2. The light is turned on, and the photoconductive signal ΔV is measured. In order to avoid extraneous signals due to heating by the light (bolometer effect), chopped light should be used and ΔV measured on a-c equipment. For small signals $\Delta V/V_0 = -\Delta g/g$, and the error is about equal to the signal; i.e., if $\Delta g/g = 5$ per cent, then $\Delta V/V_0 = -0.95\Delta g/g$.

3. With the current source disconnected, the magnetic field is turned on and the open-circuit photoelectromagnetic voltage V_{OC} is measured.

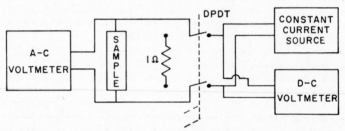

Fig. 20.17. Circuit for photoelectromagnetic effect measurement.

4. The short-circuit photoelectromagnetic current I_{SC} can also be measured by connecting a small load resistor across the sample and measuring the drop across it. The lifetime is given by

$$\tau = D\left[\frac{L\Delta g}{I_{SC}}\frac{\theta}{(\mu_n + \mu_p)}\right]^2 = D\left[\frac{L\Delta g}{gV_{OC}}\frac{\theta}{(\mu_n + \mu_p)}\right]^2 \tag{20.49}$$

where τ, D, μ_n, and μ_p have been defined previously; L is the length of the sample; and $\theta = (\mu_{nH} + \mu_{pH})H \times 10^{-8}$. This relation for τ is valid only for fields such that $\theta^2 \ll 1$. In germanium at room temperature $\theta \approx 0.1$ for $H = 1,300$ gauss.

There is also a limitation on the sample dimensions. The sample should be thicker (in the direction of the light flux) than $3\sqrt{D\tau}$. The width (in the direction of H) should be greater than $15\sqrt{D\tau}$ in order to minimize the effect of surface recombination. In order to avoid superfluous fields at the end contacts they should be shielded from the light and the sample in this direction should be about three times the width.

On the samples thinner than $\sqrt{D\tau}$ the surface recombination at the back surface (opposite the illuminated surface) becomes dominant. For a thickness less than $\sqrt{D\tau}/10$ we have

$$\frac{\Delta g}{I_{SC}} = \frac{\Delta V}{V_0 V_{OC}} = \frac{\mu_n + \mu_p}{LD\theta}\frac{D + st}{s + t/\tau} \tag{20.50}$$

where t is half the thickness and s the surface recombination velocity on the back surface. This condition has been used for the study of the effect of surface treatments on surface recombination velocity.[30]

Some additional precautions are:

1. With light on and no current flowing, observe the photovoltage if present. Subtract from the photoconductive signal.

2. If photovoltage is observed, V_{OC} should be measured with both directions of the magnetic field.

3. Contacts must be low-resistance ohmic contacts.

4. Observations should be made as a function of chopping frequency, light intensity, and magnetic field strength. The simple expression for τ is valid only in the range where it is independent of all three.

MEASUREMENTS AT LOW TEMPERATURE

At sufficiently high temperature all single crystals of a given semiconductor (with the possible exception of heavily doped degenerate material) become intrinsic. No electrical measurements would be able to distinguish one sample from another. As the temperature is lowered, the intrinsic (radiative recombination) lifetime becomes long, so that the extrinsic (recombination center) lifetime is the limiting one. At lower temperatures the intrinsic carrier concentration becomes smaller than the net impurity concentration, so the carrier density also becomes extrinsic, and the intrinsic relaxation time (lattice scattering) becomes long, so that the extrinsic (impurity scattering) relaxation time becomes effective in limiting mobility.

As these successive degrees of change from intrinsic to extrinsic behavior are passed, individual crystals become more and more distinguishable. As the temperature is lowered, also, the impurity levels in the upper half of the energy gap (lower half in p-type) change from empty to full as the Fermi level moves from the center of the gap toward the band edge. As this takes place, more varieties of behavior of different samples are distinguishable. Crystals which are virtually identical at one temperature may exhibit markedly different behavior at a lower temperature. For this reason, measurements at reduced temperatures are most useful in determining extrinsic properties of materials. All the measurements discussed in the first half of this section can be made at low temperature as well as at high temperature, although the experimental problems become more severe. These problems are least complicated in the case of resistivity and Hall effect measurements, especially the former, and we shall concentrate our attention on these in the remainder of the chapter.

20.6. Variation of Resistivity with Temperature. The variation of carrier concentration and mobility with temperature was discussed in Sec. 20.1b. We continue the discussion here with the aid of several figures in order to emphasize the characteristics which may be used for comparison of material samples.

Figure 20.18 illustrates the variation of resistivity with temperature for n-type Ge with group V impurity (or p-type with group III). From top to bottom the curves are:

1. Intrinsic (at room temp) $N_D - N_A = 5 \times 10^{12}$
2. Extrinsic $N_D - N_A = 6 \times 10^{14}$
3. Low resistance $N_D - N_A = 3 \times 10^{15}$
4. Nearly degenerate $N_D - N_A = 2 \times 10^{18}$
5. Degenerate (at room temp) $N_D - N_A = 2.7 \times 10^{19}$

In curves 1 to 3 the decrease in resistance with increasing temperature at both low temperature (depletion region) and high temperature (intrinsic range) is due to increasing carrier concentration. The increase in the temperature range in which the resistance increases with temperature (in all five samples) is due to decreasing mobility with carrier concentration constant (exhaustion region).

In curve 4 there is a shallow maximum at about 80°K. This is apparently due to impurity band conduction.[31] At about 4×10^{18} this feature no longer appears, and the curves for crystals of larger carrier concentrations all resemble curve 5. For lower carrier concentrations, down to about 2×10^{17}, this maximum becomes more pronounced and moves to lower temperatures. For concentrations below 2×10^{17} there is no longer a maximum, but only a change in slope. This is apparently the threshold at which an impurity band is formed. The abrupt change in slope is observed in

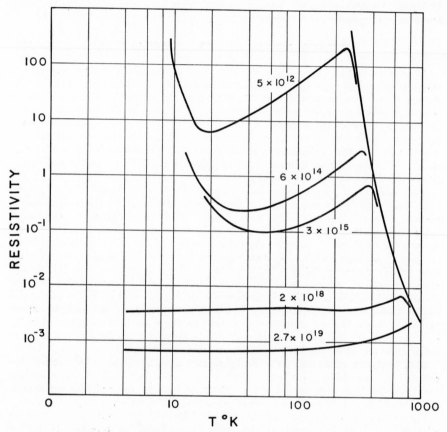

Fig. 20.18. Various resistivity-versus-temperature behaviors.

crystals with impurity densities between 2×10^{17} and 5×10^{15} and occurs at lower temperatures for lower concentrations.

These phenomena occur also in other semiconductors, but at different doping values. We shall not discuss impurity conduction further in this book but point it out as a feature which provides a natural lower temperature limit to the discussion that follows, since that discussion is concerned with electrons and holes in the conduction band and valence band. The actual temperature at which impurity conduction or impurity band conduction appears depends on carrier concentration, compensation, and activation energy of the majority impurity. Figure 20.18 shows the "normal" variation of resistivity with temperature in the various impurity ranges. Figure 20.19 illustrates the principal large deviation from "normal" behavior in homogeneous single crystals. These are calculated curves for the case of an impurity level at 0.26 electron volt below the conduction band in Ge, having a degeneracy factor 0.125.   The curves are calculated for a net impurity density of shallow levels ($N_D - N_A$) equal to 5×10^{14}. The densities of deep-level impurity are:

Curve 1	7×10^{14}
Curve 2	3×10^{14}
Curve 3	1×10^{14}
Curve 4	5×10^{13}
Curve 5	0

(Note: This is the computed effect of a -0.26-electron-volt level.   It does not represent quantitatively the effect of copper impurity, since the two lower levels of copper

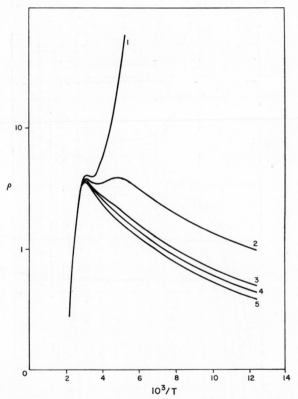

Fig. 20.19. The effect of deep-level impurities on the resistivity-versus-temperature measurement.

are not included in this calculation, nor is the effect of the ionized copper impurities on the mobility.   It illustrates the general appearance of a resistivity curve when a deep-level impurity is present.)

In crystals of different doping levels, a deep level in concentration approximately equal to 60 per cent of the net shallow-level density would have the same general appearance as curve 2 but shifted to higher or lower temperatures according to whether the impurity density was greater or less.   Also, a level nearer the center of the gap would tend to merge the two maxima which are clearly separated in curve 2, while one closer to the band edge would allow a greater temperature difference between the two maxima.

For deep-level concentrations greater than 60 per cent the second maximum increases until at 100 per cent and greater the resistivity increases indefinitely as in curve 1. When the deep level is close to the center of the gap, these second maxima

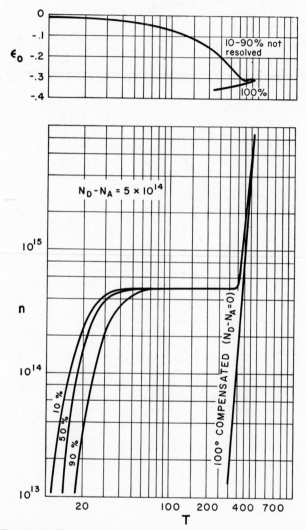

FIG. 20.20. The effect of compensation on carrier concentration.

may be much more prominent than the "normal" maxima, and there have been cases in which this phenomenon has been mistaken for intrinsic behavior. This error can be avoided either by close scrutiny of a resistivity versus temperature curve or by a plot such as Fig. 20.23 in which the value of a "normal" resistivity maximum is graphed as a function of the temperature at which it occurs. A secondary maximum will have a lower value than a "normal" maximum would have at the same temperature.

The effects of the difference in donor and acceptor concentration (net donor concentration) and of the ratio of donors and acceptors (compensation) on carrier concentration and Fermi level are shown in Figs. 20.20 and 20.21. It is seen that carrier concentration is a function of net impurity concentration in the exhaustion range and

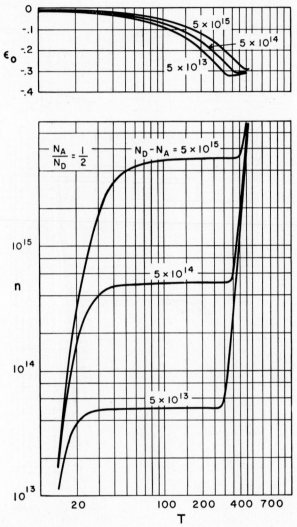

FIG. 20.21. Carrier concentration and Fermi level as a function of temperature for different impurity densities but equal compensation.

of compensation in the depletion range. The curves in Fig. 20.21 all merge at low temperature.

Figure 20.22 illustrates the variation of n and ϵ_0 for the deep-level cases shown in Fig. 20.19. It can be seen that when the density of the deep level is greater than the net donor density the Fermi level does not rise much above the deep impurity level, so the shallow donor impurities remain ionized at all temperatures.

These sets of curves have been calculated using values of parameters appropriate to Ge. If the numerical values of T, $N_D - N_A$, and ρ are ignored, however, the shapes of the curves may be considered as general types. Thus the features of semiconductor behavior illustrated in the figures can be used to compare samples of any semiconductor.

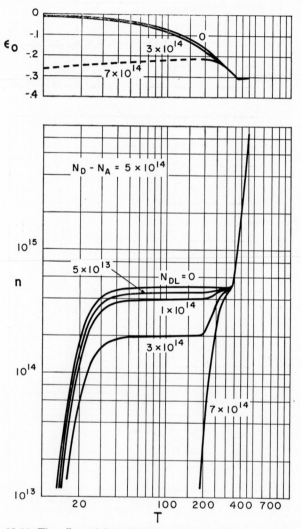

FIG. 20.22. The effect of deep-level impurity on carrier concentration.

Various features of the ρ versus temperature curves can be used as comparison criteria for the evaluation of crystals even without detailed analysis of the data.

The temperature of the resistivity maximum, the value of the maximum resistivity, and the shape of the curve around the maximum are often useful, especially when small, irregularly shaped samples are to be checked. It is difficult to inspect such samples for homogeneity, and also the dimensions are uncertain if they are irregular.

Appreciable inhomogeneity will tend to broaden the resistivity maximum, as will impurity centers near the center of the forbidden energy gap. If the sample is otherwise normal, the values at the resistivity maximum will permit evaluation of the effective dimensional factor.

In Fig. 20.23 is plotted the value of the resistivity maximum as a function of the temperature at which it occurs. It is calculated for shallow (0.01 electron volt) levels

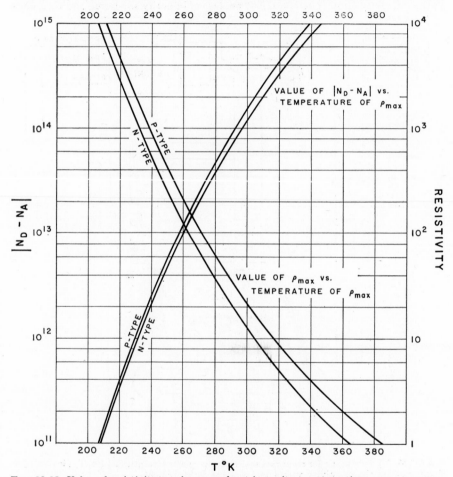

FIG. 20.23. Value of resistivity maximum and net impurity concentration versus temperature at which resistivity maximum occurs (theoretical) for germanium.

and lattice scattering mobility in Ge. In the same figure is a graph of net carrier density as a function of the temperature at which the resistivity maximum occurs.

At temperatures below that of the resistivity maximum, since carrier concentration is constant, the variation in ρ will be due to mobility change only (barring a deep-level impurity). This will be true until carrier depletion begins. To give an idea of the range of temperatures involved, consider 8 ohm-cm p-type Ge ($N_A - N_D = 4 \times 10^{14}$). The resistivity maximum will be 9.4 ohm-cm at 320°K. Between 300 and 200°K its resistivity will vary as $T^{2.33}$.† At some temperature below 200°, depending

† μ_p (lattice) $= 1.05 \times 10^7 \, T^{-2.33}$ (cm/sec)/(volt/cm) between 100 and 300°K.

on total impurity density, impurity scattering will cause the resistivity to vary less strongly than $T^{2.33}$. At some temperature in the vicinity of 100°K (depending on compensation) the carrier density will begin to decrease, and the resistivity will go through a minimum in the neighborhood of 50°K. Both impurity scattering and carrier depletion become apparent at higher temperatures for higher impurity densities.

As temperature is decreased, the resistivity of less pure samples will increase relative to the resistivity of purer samples, first because of impurity scattering and then more

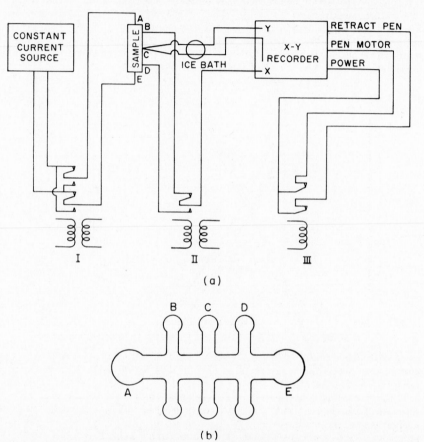

FIG. 20.24. (a) Schematic for recording resistivity versus temperature. (b) Typical sample shape used for the resistivity versus temperature measurement.

strongly because of carrier depletion. As the temperature is further lowered, this trend will be reversed for materials with impurity concentrations greater than about $5 \times 10^{15}/cm^3$. This is due to the impurity conduction which was discussed in relation to Fig. 20.18.

20.6a. Measurement of Resistivity versus Temperature. From the previous discussion, it can be seen that a measurement of resistivity versus temperature provides a number of points of comparison by which crystal samples can be rated empirically. By making use of automatic recording, it becomes quite practical to use measurements of resistivity versus temperature for routine testing. If a thermocouple is soldered to the crystal and the results recorded on an X-Y or other type of recorder, warm-up rates may be used such that a liquid nitrogen to above room temperature run can be completed in ½ to ¾ hr or less, depending on sample size and cryostat design.

It is not really necessary to strive too much for speed in warm-up. It may be more advantageous to measure several samples per run. Although many curves on a single chart could lead to difficulty in reading the information, by the use either of several pen recorders or of digital recording, the data on numbers of samples can be kept unmixed. If the measurement results are to be used quantitatively, digital recording is a considerable advantage, especially if combined with automatic calculation.

A simple, useful system for the automatic recording of resistivity data is shown in Fig. 20.24a. In this system, the sample is of a standard size, cut with an ultrasonic cutter, in the shape shown in Fig. 20.24b. The form shown has more arms than required for the particular use to be described, but it provides also for Hall effect measurements on three sections of the crystal if this should prove desirable. Current

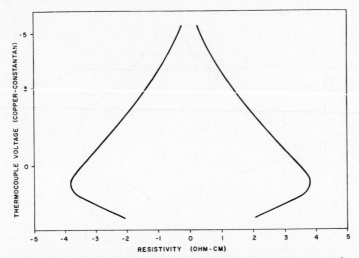

Fɪɢ. 20.25. Temperature variation of resistance for a uniform crystal.

leads are soldered to A and E, probe leads to B and D, and a thermocouple to C. One lead of the thermocouple serves as a common lead for both the thermocouple and resistivity measurements.

With this technique two sections of the crystal are measured in order to give a rough estimate of sample uniformity. (It sometimes happens that nonuniformity is grossly evident at low temperatures and not at room temperature.) The relay I in Fig. 20.24a reverses the current at twice the rate at which relay II switches between the two halves of the crystal. Relay III causes the recorder pen to print a dot for each combination. The resultant plot on the X-Y recorder is of the form of Fig. 20.25 if the crystal is uniform and of Fig. 20.26 if the crystal is not. The resistivity voltage is recorded on the X axis with zero in the center, and the thermocouple voltage is recorded on the Y axis with the zero placed conveniently for the particular temperature range to be recorded.

It is easy to make this record direct-reading in resistivity. Since the pen deflection is equal to GV_ρ where G is the calibration in inches per volt,

$$\rho = \frac{V_\rho wt}{IL} = \frac{Dwt}{GIL}$$

where w, t, and L are, respectively, the width, thickness, and length of the measured portion of the sample; V_ρ and I are, respectively, the measured voltage and applied current; and D is the pen deflection in inches. It is only necessary to choose G and I so that $wt = GIL$ in order to have $\rho = D$. By varying G or I by factors of 10 it is then possible to have $\rho = 10D$, etc., in order to handle a wide range of resistivity values.

In Fig. 20.26 at the lower part of the graph (where there are only two curves) the crystal is intrinsic. As the temperature is lowered, the resistivity passes through a maximum (the extreme left and right portions of the curves) and the crystals become extrinsic. In the extrinsic region the curves marked A and D give the resistivity voltage of one part of the crystal (A for positive current, D for reversed current) and curves B and C give the resistivity of the other half of the crystal (C for positive current and B for reversed current).

If there are no extraneous voltages (thermal gradients, rectifying contact, etc.) curves A and B will be symmetrical with D and C, respectively. When there are

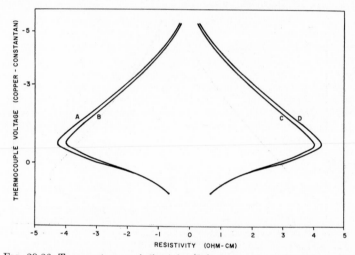

FIG. 20.26. Temperature variation of resistance for a nonuniform crystal.

extraneous voltages present, the distance between A and D will be equal to twice the resistivity, since stray emfs will not reverse with the current.

This system is very convenient for the examination of ρ versus temperature down to about liquid nitrogen temperature using a copper-constantan thermocouple. Below that temperature it is necessary to introduce some additional complication to compensate for the decreased sensitivity of the thermocouple. If Au (2.1 atomic per cent Co) versus copper thermocouples are used, sensitivity will be sufficient down to about 30°K.

If care is taken to avoid stressing the thermocouple, the temperature-versus-chart position can be kept reproducible from run to run. When this is done, the behavior of crystals under test can be compared directly with an empirical or theoretical standard curve without the necessity for taking numerical data from the recorder chart.

20.6b. Magnetoresistance at Low Temperatures. Comparison of crystal purity can be made at a single temperature, e.g., liquid-nitrogen temperature, by means of a mobility measurement or by measurement of some function of mobility if the impurity density is great enough to produce appreciable impurity scattering at that temperature. This is true at nitrogen temperature for Ge and Si containing approximately 10^{14} impurities or more.

Magnetoresistance, the change in resistance due to the application of a magnetic field, is to the first approximation proportional to the square of the mobility and is therefore quite sensitive to impurity scattering. Since the change in resistance is measured, precision and sensitivity of the electrical measurement and the reproducibility of the magnetic field strength are the sole controlling factors in the measurement. Sample dimensions and probe spacings are not involved, nor is the carrier concentration.

This measurement can be "calibrated" in terms of magnetoresistance change, $[\rho(H) - \rho_0]/\rho_0 H^2$ versus $(N_D + N_A)$ for any particular majority impurity in any particular host crystal. The total impurity concentrations for a group of crystals can be determined by the method discussed in Sec. 20.7 and the value of magnetoresistance measured for these crystals. These data can be used to provide a "calibration" curve from which $N_D + N_A$ may be determined from measurements of $\Delta\rho/\rho H^2$. Such a curve has been published for boron-doped silicon.[35] This paper (reference 35) has a detailed discussion of the analysis involved.

20.6c. Current/Voltage Breakdown. At liquid helium temperature the resistivities of pure samples are very high at low electric fields. As the applied field is increased, the few free carriers present acquire sufficient energy to ionize neutral donors (n-type) by impact. This means that at some threshold value of electric field the sample will "break down" reversibly and the current will increase by orders of magnitude for a very small increase in applied voltage.[32]

When the breakdown occurs, the resistance of the sample is much reduced, so the breakdown voltage can be measured at an effective sample resistivity of perhaps 10^5, although the low field resistivity may be very much larger. The breakdown voltage is a function of the compensation of the crystal.

In the absence of an electric field the carrier density at liquid helium temperature is given by†

$$n = \frac{N_D - N_A}{N_A} F(T) \qquad (20.51)$$

$F(T)$ represents the ratio of the probability for thermal excitation of carriers from neutral donors to their recapture probability. When an electric field is applied, we have approximately[33]

$$n = \frac{(N_D - N_A)A_T}{N_A B_T - A_I(N_D - N_A)} \qquad (20.52)$$

where $A_T/B_T = F(T)$ in Eq. (20.51) and A_I is the probability of excitation of carriers by impact ionization. A_I is a function of applied field. At some value of the applied field $A_I = (N_A/N_D - N_A)B_T$ and the denominator of Eq. (20.52) approaches zero. This field is called the "breakdown" field. From the expression it is seen that more compensated samples will require higher fields.

This measurement can also be "calibrated" for particular impurities by determining $N_D - N_A$ and $N_D + N_A$ on a number of samples and by measuring breakdown voltage on the same samples. A curve of $(N_D - N_A)/N_A$ versus E_{BD} can then be prepared which, in conjunction with the determination of $N_D - N_A$ in the exhaustion region, can be used to determine total impurity on other samples.

20.7. Determination of Impurity Activation Energy and Impurity Density. For many purposes a requirement on basic properties such as impurity density can be translated either empirically or theoretically into a requirement in terms of resistivity or a ratio of resistivities at two different temperatures or some other easily measured parameter. Since resistivity is the most easily measured property of semiconductors, we have considered in some detail in Sec. 20.6 the direct comparison of crystals by means of resistivity measurements.

† See Sec. 20.7.

This is not always sufficient, however. It is sometimes necessary to determine impurity densities directly, as, for example, in the "calibration" of the magneto-resistance measurement (Sec. 20.6b). Such a determination depends on Hall effect measurements interpreted by means of Eqs. (20.4), (20.6), and (20.9). Combining these equations we get, for n-type material,

$$n = (N_D - N_A) - \frac{nN_D}{n + (Nc/g_D) \exp (\epsilon_D/kT)} \tag{20.53}$$

in which energy is measured from the edge of the conduction band so $\epsilon_c = 0$ and $\epsilon_D < 0$ (i.e., energies in the forbidden gap are negative). For p-type material the equation is exactly symmetrical:

$$p = (N_A - N_D) - \frac{pN_A}{p + (Nv/g_A) \exp (\epsilon_A/kT)} \tag{20.54}$$

in which energy is measured from the valence band edge so $\epsilon_v = 0$. Energies in the forbidden gap are negative in this equation also.

These equations are to be fitted[34] to Hall effect measurements in the depletion region. At low temperature the mobilities of holes and electrons are large in most semiconductors, so the product $\mu H \times 10^{-8}$ approaches and exceeds unity (μ in practical units, H in gauss) for practical values of magnetic field. $\mu H \gg 1$ is the condition for large field approximations, so that the factor $r = \mu_H/\mu_\sigma$ (Sec. 20.3) approaches unity. Equations (20.19) and (20.22) for two or more types of carriers are valid only for small field conditions $\mu H \ll 1$. In the high field approximation the Hall coefficient in p-type Ge and Si approaches

$$R = \frac{1}{ep}$$

in which p is the sum of light and heavy holes.

We can, therefore, when the condition

$$\mu_H H \times 10^{-8} \gg 1 \qquad (cm^2\text{-gauss/volt-sec})$$

is satisfied, compute n or p simply from $(Re)^{-1}$, where R is measured in practical units [Eq. (20.13)] and $e = 1.601 \times 10^{-19}$ coulomb.

Fitting the data to Eq. (20.53) is done most conveniently in several steps:

1. In the exhaustion region $n = N_D - N_A$, which determines one term of the equation.

2. At low T, $n \ll N_D - N_A$, which reduces the equation to

$$n = \frac{N_D - N_A}{N_A} \frac{N_c}{g_D} \exp \frac{\epsilon_D}{kT} \tag{20.55}$$

N_c is equal to a constant multiplied by $T^{3/2}$. Therefore a plot of $nT^{-3/2}$ should produce a straight-line graph on semilog paper when plotted against $1/T$. From the slope of this graph ϵ_D can be found.

Values of the density of states are known fairly accurately for Ge and Si.[8]

$$N_c = 2 \times 10^{15}T^{3/2} \qquad \text{for Ge}$$
$$N_v = 1.17 \times 10^{15}T^{3/2} \qquad \text{for Ge}$$
$$N_c = 5.4 \times 10^{15}T^{3/2} \qquad \text{for Si}$$
$$N_v = 1.95 \times 10^{15}T^{3/2} \qquad \text{for Si}$$

Also, for group V impurities in Ge and Si, $g_D = 2$, and for group III, $g_A = 4$. Thus there are sufficient data to determine N_A from Eq. (20.55) and therefore N_D.

3. Using the determined values of N_D, N_A, ϵ_D, g_D, and N_c compute n as a function of T from Eq. (20.53) to compare with the measured curve.

This procedure depends on the applicability of Eq. (20.53) to the sample under study. If there is more than one impurity present, the levels of which are either above the Fermi level or within 3 or $4kT$ below it, in the temperature range in which the curve fitting is carried out, the equation does not apply. The comparison in step 3 above provides a fair test for the applicability of the equation but is not sufficient. For example, a sample contains N_1 donors with energy ϵ_1, N_2 donors with energy ϵ_2, and N_3 acceptors. $N_1 + N_2 > N_3$ and $\epsilon_1 > \epsilon_2$ (ϵ_1 closer to the band edge). The equation at low temperatures is

$$ n = N_1 + N_2 - N_3 - \frac{nN_1}{n + A_1} - \frac{nN_2}{n + A_2} $$

in which $A_1 = (N_c/g_1) \exp (\epsilon_1/kT)$ and $A_2 = (N_c/g_2) \exp (\epsilon_2/kT)$. If it happened that $N_3 > N_1$ and $\epsilon_1 - \epsilon_2 > 3kT$ at temperatures below the exhaustion range, then we would have

$$ n = N_1 + N_2 - N_3 - \frac{nN_2}{n + A_2} $$

since donor N_1 would remain ionized at all temperatures. If we now applied Eq. (20.53), we would get, in step 1, $N_D - N_A = N_1 + N_2 - N_3$. In step 2 we would calculate $N_A = N_3 - N_1$, which would give $N_D = N_2$. Now in step 3 we would get a good fit, but when we calculate $N_D + N_A$, we would get $N_2 + N_3 - N_1$ instead of $N_1 + N_2 + N_3$. This would be an error of $2N_1$, which could be appreciable. Silicon containing both boron and indium is a case in which a significant boron impurity could be masked.

In view of the possibility of "masking" of one level by another, it is well to resort to an additional supporting experiment to check for consistency. The magnetoresistance measurement (Sec. 20.6b) in the exhaustion region would provide such a check, provided a number of samples were examined covering some range of $N_D + N_A$ values.

Another case in which Eq. (20.53) does not apply is that of multilevel impurities, i.e., impurities which can accept or give up more than one electron per impurity atom, such as copper or selenium in germanium.

In the case of Cu the first electron accepted is very strongly bound, lying only 0.04 electron volt above the valence band. The next electron accepted makes the Cu doubly ionized, the coulomb repulsion between the electrons decreases the binding strength, and they now lie 0.33 electron volt above the valence band (nearly at the center of the gap). The third electron (making a triply negative center) raises the energy to 0.26 electron volt below the conduction band. These energy levels are obviously not independent, and this gives rise to a complication in the statistics of multilevel centers.

If there are three distinct types of impurity (one having an energy level 0.04 electron volt from the valence band, the second a level 0.33 from the valence band, and the third a level 0.26 from the conduction band) then each would contribute a term fN in Eq. (20.56), where the sum over i includes all donor levels and the sum over j includes both donors and acceptors,

$$ n = p + \sum_i N_i - \sum_j f_j N_j \qquad (20.56) $$

Since these levels in Cu are all on one center and the occupation of each level is influenced by the occupation of the other levels, the density of electrons localized on the copper centers is given[6] (neglecting possible excited states) by

$$n' = \frac{G_1\lambda + 2G_1G_2\lambda^2 + 3G_1G_2G_3\lambda^3}{1 + G_1\lambda + G_1G_2\lambda^2 + G_1G_2G_3\lambda^3} N \tag{20.57}$$

in which n' = density of electrons localized

$\quad\quad N$ = density of copper atoms

$\quad\quad G_i = g_i \exp\left(-\epsilon_i/kT\right)$

$\quad\quad \lambda = \exp\left(\epsilon_0/kT\right)$

$\quad\quad \epsilon_i$ = energy of ith level

$\quad\quad g_i$ = degeneracy factor of ith level

If $\epsilon_3 - \epsilon_2$ and $\epsilon_2 - \epsilon_1$ are greater than $5kT$ (as in the case for copper at not too high temperatures) the expression is essentially equal to

$$n' = (f_1 + f_2 + f_3)N \tag{20.58}$$

just as if there were three independent centers. However, in some cases (e.g., Zn in Ge, in which $\epsilon_2 - \epsilon_1 = 0.06$ electron volt) Eq. (20.58) may not be a sufficient approximation.

When deep-level or multilevel impurities are present in significant quantity, considerable care must be taken in choosing the proper method of analysis. In particular, the choice of terms to be ignored in an equation such as (20.56) and the validity of approximating (20.57) by a sum of Fermi functions must be justified. There are, however, many cases in which considerable simplification can be achieved, and Eq. (20.53) is very often correct.

FIG. 20.27. Apparatus for automatic digital recording of Hall effect and resistivity.

With presently available amplifiers and digital voltmeters measurements can be made to four significant figures with a sensitivity of ± 1 or 2 mv. A digital voltmeter can operate equipment which will print the voltage on tape or punch it on tape or cards. By means of suitable control circuits, the various parameters—thermocouple voltage, current, resistivity voltage, Hall voltage, etc.—can be presented successively to the voltmeter for recording. The same circuits can switch current and magnetic fields. By these means measurements can be made more quickly than it is possible to do by manual methods. Figure 20.27 is a photograph of such an automatic apparatus used for recording Hall voltage and resistivity over a wide temperature range.

Use of punched cards or tape and a programmed computer will also save the labor of calculation, since the data can be fed into the computer. This can lend itself to quite sophisticated treatment of data, since programs can be written to calculate any function of the data for which a relation can be written.

REFERENCES

1. MacDonald, A. L., J. Soled, and C. A. Stearns: Four-probe Instrument for Resistivity Measurements of Germanium and Silicon, *Rev. Sci. Instr.*, vol. 24, p. 884, 1953; L. B. Valdes: Resistivity Measurements on Germanium for Transistors, *Proc. IRE*, vol. 42, p. 420, 1954; and F. M. Smits: Measurement of Sheet Resistivities with the Four-point Probe, *Bell System Tech. J.*, vol. 37, p. 711, 1958.
2. van der Pauw, L. J.: A Method of Measuring Specific Resistivity and Hall Effect of Discs of Arbitrary Shape, *Philips Research Repts.*, vol. 13, p. 1, 1958; and J. Hornstra and L. J. van der Pauw: Measurement of the Resistivity Constants of Anisotropic Conductors by Means of Plane-parallel Discs of Arbitrary Shape, *J. Electronics and Control*, vol. 7, p. 169, 1959.
3. Tauc, J.: Generation of an EMF in Semiconductors with Nonequilibrium Current Carrier Concentrations, *Rev. Mod. Phys.*, vol. 29, p. 308, 1957; and J. Oroshnik and A. Many: Evaluation of the Homogeneity of Germanium Single Crystals by Photovoltaic Scanning, *J. Electrochem. Soc.*, vol. 106, p. 360, 1959.
4. Willardson, R. K., T. C. Harman, and A. C. Beer: Transverse Hall and Magnetoresistance Effects in *p*-type Germanium, *Phys. Rev.*, vol. 96, p. 1512, 1954; and E. M. Conwell: Properties of Silicon and Germanium: II, *Proc. IRE*, vol. 46, p. 1281, 1958.
5. Shockley, W.: "Electrons and Holes in Semiconductors," chap. 10, D. Van Nostrand Company, Inc., Princeton, N.J., 1950.
6. Landsberg, P. T.: Some Statistical Problems in Semiconductors, in "Semiconductors and Phosphors, Proceedings of the International Colloquium 1956 at Garmisch-Partenkirchen," p. 46, Interscience Publishers, Inc., New York, 1958.
7. Burstein, E., and P. H. Egli: The Physics of Semiconductor Materials, in "Advances in Electronics and Electron Physics," vol. 7, Academic Press, Inc., New York, 1955.
8. Smith, R. A.: "Semiconductors," chaps. 10 and 11, Cambridge University Press, New York, 1959.
9. Blatt, F. S.: Theory of Mobility of Electrons in Solids, in "Solid State Physics," vol. 4, p. 199, Academic Press, Inc., New York, 1957.
10. Conwell, E. M.: Properties of Silicon and Germanium: II, *Proc. IRE*, vol. 46, p. 1281, 1958.
11. Johnson, V. A.: Theory of the Seebeck Effect in Semiconductors, in "Progress in Semiconductors," vol. 1, p. 65, John Wiley & Sons, Inc., New York, 1956.
12. Scanlan, W. W.: Other Transverse Galvanomagnetic and Thermomagnetic Effects, in "Methods of Experimental Physics," vol. 6B, sec. 8.3, Academic Press, Inc., New York, 1959.
13. Russell, B. R., and C. Wahlig: A New Method for the Measurement of Hall Coefficients, *Rev. Sci. Instr.*, vol. 21, p. 1028, 1950; J. J. Donoghue and W. P. Eatherly: A New Method for Precision Measurement of the Hall and Magneto-resistive Coefficients, *Rev. Sci. Instr.*, vol. 22, p. 513, 1951; E. M. Pell and R. L. Sproull: Sensitive Recording Alternating-current Hall Effect Apparatus, *Rev. Sci. Instr.*, vol. 23, p. 548, 1952; and J. R. MacDonald and J. E. Robinson: AC Hall and Magnetostrictive Effects in Photoconducting Alkali Halides, *Phys. Rev.*, vol. 95, p. 44, 1954.
14. Dauphinee, T. M., and E. Mooser: Apparatus for Measuring Resistivity and Hall Coefficient of Semiconductors, *Rev. Sci. Instr.*, vol. 26, p. 660, 1955.

15. Bardeen, J.: Theory of Relation between Hole Concentration and Characteristics of Germanium Point Contacts, *Bell System Tech. J.*, vol. 29, p. 469, 1950; R. Landauer and J. Swanson: Diffusion Currents in the Semiconductor Hall Effect, *Phys. Rev.*, vol. 91, p. 555, 1953; and L. P. Hunter, E. J. Huibregtse, and R. L. Anderson: Current Carrier Lifetimes Deduced from Hall Coefficient and Resistivity Measurements, *Phys. Rev.*, vol. 91, p. 1315, 1953.

16. Pearson, G. L., and J. Bardeen: Electrical Properties of Pure Silicon and Silicon Alloys Containing Boron and Phosphors, *Phys. Rev.*, vol. 75, p. 865, 1949; and W. M. Bullis and W. E. Krag: Hall Effect in Oriented Single Crystals of n-type Germanium, *Phys. Rev.*, vol. 101, p. 580, 1956.

17. Abeles, B., and S. Meiboom: Theory of the Galvanomagnetic Effects in Germanium, *Phys. Rev.*, vol. 95, p. 31, 1954; M. Shibuya: Magnetoresistance Effect in Cubic Semiconductors with Spheroidal Energy Surfaces, *Phys. Rev.*, vol. 95, p. 1385, 1954; L. Gold and L. M. Roth: Galvanomagnetic Theory for n-type Germanium and Silicon: Hall Theory and General Behavior of Magnetoresistance, *Phys. Rev.*, vol. 107, p. 358, 1957; and C. Herring and E. Vogt: Transport and Deformation-potential Theory for Many-valley Semiconductors with Anisotropic Scattering, *Phys. Rev.*, vol. 101, p. 944, 1956.

18. Swanson, J. A.: Saturation Hall Constants of Semiconductors, *Phys. Rev.*, vol. 99, p. 1799, 1955.

19. Haynes, J. R., and W. C. Westphal: The Drift Mobility of Electrons in Silicon, *Phys. Rev.*, vol. 85, p. 680, 1952.

20. Haynes, J. R., and W. Shockley: The Mobility and Lifetime of Injected Holes and Electrons in Germanium, *Phys. Rev.*, vol. 81, p. 835, 1951.

21. Lawrance, R., and A. F. Gibson: The Measurement of Drift Mobility in Semiconductors, *Proc. Phys. Soc.*, ser. B, vol. 65, p. 994, 1952.

22. van Roosbroeck, W., and W. Shockley: Photon-radiative Recombination of Electrons and Holes in Germanium, *Phys. Rev.*, vol. 94, p. 1558, 1954.

23. Shockley, W., and W. T. Read, Jr.: Statistics of the Recombinations of Holes and Electrons, *Phys. Rev.*, vol. 87, p. 835, 1952.

24. Bemski, G.: Recombination in Semiconductors, *Proc. IRE*, vol. 46, p. 990, 1958.

25. Shockley, W.: Electrons, Holes, and Traps, *Proc. IRE*, vol. 46, p. 973, 1958.

26. Valdes, L. B.: Measurement of Minority Carrier Lifetimes in Germanium, *Proc. IRE*, vol. 40, p. 1420, 1952.

27. Ellis, S. G.: Surface Studies on Single-crystal Germanium, *J. Appl. Phys.*, vol. 28, p. 1262, 1957.

28. van Roosbroeck, W.: Injected Current Carrier Transport in a Semi-infinite Semiconductor and the Determination of Lifetimes and Surface Recombination Velocities, *J. Appl. Phys.*, vol. 26, p. 380, 1955.

29. Garreta, O., and J. Grosvalet: Photo-magneto-electric Effect in Semiconductors, in "Progress in Semiconductors," vol. 1, p. 167, John Wiley & Sons, Inc., New York, 1956.

30. Buck, T. M., and F. S. McKim: Experiments on the Photomagnetoelectric Effect in Germanium, *Phys. Rev.*, vol. 106, p. 904, 1957.

31. Hung, C. S., and J. R. Gliessman: Resistivity and Hall Effect of Germanium at Low Temperatures, *Phys. Rev.*, vol. 96, p. 1226, 1954; and H. Fritzche: Electrical Properties of Germanium at Low Temperatures, *Phys. Rev.*, vol. 99, p. 406, 1955; Resistivity and Hall Coefficient of Antimony-doped Germanium at Low Temperatures, *J. Phys. Chem. Solids*, vol. 6, p. 69, 1958.

32. Sclar, N., E. Burstein, W. J. Turner, and J. W. Davisson: Low Temperature "Breakdown" Effect in Germanium, *Phys. Rev.*, vol. 91, p. 215, 1953.

33. Koenig, S. H.: Rate Processes and Low-temperature Electrical Conduction in n-type Germanium, *Phys. Rev.*, vol. 110, p. 986, 1958.

34. Geballe, T. H., and F. J. Morin: Ionization Energies of Groups III and V Elements in Germanium, *Phys. Rev.*, vol. 95, p. 1085, 1954; and P. P. Debye and E. M. Conwell: Electrical Properties of n-type Germanium, *Phys. Rev.*, vol. 93, p. 693, 1954.

35. Long, D., C. D. Motchenbacker, and J. Myers: Impurity Compensation and Magnetoresistance in p-type Silicon, *J. Appl. Phys.*, vol. 30, p. 353, 1959.

BIBLIOGRAPHY ON TRANSISTORS, SEMICONDUCTORS, AND RECTIFIERS

Compiled by

WAYNE A. KALENICH

IBM Corporation, New York, N.Y.

and

LLOYD P. HUNTER

IBM Corporation, Poughkeepsie, N.Y.

This bibliography on semiconductors, transistors, rectifiers, and related materials was compiled by using such indexes and abstracts as Science Abstracts, Engineering Index, Industrial Arts Index, etc. No attempt was made to cover the patent literature or the material which is covered by the U.S. Government Research Reports, formerly called Bibliography of Technical Reports.

For the most part, only the literature from 1940 onward was considered; however, some references of earlier periods are given because it was felt that they should be included.

1936

Mott, N. F., and H. Jones: "The Theory of the Properties of Metals and Alloys," Oxford University Press, New York, 1936.

Wilson, A. H.: "Theory of Metals," Cambridge University Press, New York, 1936.

1937

Seitz, F., and R. P. Johnson: Modern Theory of Solids, *J. Appl. Phys.*, vol. 8, pp. 84–97, 186–199, 246–260, 1937.

1939

Wilson, A. H.: "Semiconductors and Metals," Cambridge University Press, New York, 1939.

1940

Bauer, K.: Electrical and Optical Behavior of Semiconductors. XV. Electrical Measurements on Lead Selenide, *Ann. Physik*, vol. 38, pp. 84–98, 1940.

Becker, J. A.: Varistors—Their Characteristics and Uses, *Bell Labs. Record*, vol. 18, pp. 322–327, 1940.

Davydov, B., and I. Shmushkevich: Electrical Conductivity of Semiconductors with an Ionic Lattice in Strong Fields, *J. Phys. (U.S.S.R.)*, vol. 3, no. 4–5, pp. 359–377, 1940.

Hollman, H. E.: Semiconductive Colloidal Suspensions with Non Linear Properties, *J. Appl. Phys.*, vol. 21, pp. 402–413, 1940.

Joffe, A. V., and A. F. Joffe: Semiconductors in Strong Electric Fields, *J. Phys. (U.S.S.R.)*, vol. 2, no. 4, pp. 283–304, 1940.

Mott, N. F., and R. W. Gurney: "Electronic Processes in Ionic Crystals," Oxford University Press, New York, 1940.

1

Scharawskij, P. W.: The Temperature Dependence of the Resistance of Selenium Rectifiers, *J. Phys. (U.S.S.R.)*, vol. 3, no. 4–5, pp. 379–384, 1940.

Schottky, W.: Deviations from Ohm's Law in Semiconductors, *Z. tech. Phys.*, vol. 21, pp.
322–325, 1940; *Physik. Z.*, vol. 41, pp. 570–573, 1940.

Seitz, F.: "The Modern Theory of Solids," McGraw-Hill Book Company, Inc., New York,
1940.

Sisenmann, L.: Electrical and Optical Behavior of Semiconductors. XVI. Electrical
Measurements on Lead Sulphide, *Ann. Physik*, vol. 38, pp. 121–138, 1940.

1941

Aschermann, G., E. Friedrich, E. Justi, and J. Kramer: Supraconducting Compounds with
Extremely High Discontinuity Temperatures, *Physik. Z.*, vol. 42, pp. 349–360, 1941.

Behrens, D. J.: A New Formula for the Reduction of Lammer-plate Fringes, *J. Sci. Instr.*,
vol. 18, pp. 238–239, 1941.

Davydov, B.: Transitional Resistance of Semiconductors, *J. Phys. (U.S.S.R.)*, vol. 4,
pp. 335–339, 1941.

Eckert, F., and A. Kittel: On Measurements of the Hall Effect in Selenium, *Naturwissenschaften*, vol. 29, p. 371, June 13, 1941.

Frenkel, J.: On the Electrification of Dielectrics by Frictions, *J. Phys. (U.S.S.R.)*, vol. 5,
pp. 25–29, 1941.

Kadyschewitsch, A. E.: Theory of Secondary Electron Emission from Dielectrics and
Semiconductors, *J. Phys. (U.S.S.R.)*, vol. 4, pp. 341–381, 1941.

Komar, A., and S. Sidorov: The Arrangement of Atoms in the Alloy $AlCu_3$ and the Hall
Coefficient, *J. Phys. (U.S.S.R.)*, vol. 4, pp. 552–554, 1941.

Lappe, R. F.: Photo-electric Conductivity of ZnSCu Phosphors under the Influence of
X-rays, *Ann. Physik*, vol. 39, pp. 604–618, 1941.

Miller, P. H., Jr.: The Electrical Conductivity of Zinc Oxide, *Phys. Rev.*, vol. 60, pp. 890–
895, 1941.

Richards, E. A.: The Characteristics and Applications of the Selenium Rectifier, *J. Inst.
Elec. Engrs. (London)*, part II, vol. 88, pp. 423–438, 1941; discussion pp. 438–442; *J.
Inst. Elec. Engrs. (London)*, part III, vol. 88, pp. 238–253, 1941; discussion pp. 253–257;
abridgement in *J. Inst. Elec. Engrs. (London)*, part I, vol. 88, pp. 384–387, 1941.

Williams, A. L., and L. E. Thompson: Metal Rectifiers, *J. Inst. Elec. Engrs. (London)*,
part I, vol. 88, pp. 353–371, 1941; discussion pp. 371–383.

1942

Angello, S. J.: Hall Effect and Conductivity of Cuprous Oxide, *Phys. Rev.*, vol. 62, pp.
371–377, 1942.

Croatto, U.: Ionic Electric Conductivity of Fluorite Lattices at a High Degree of Disorder,
Ricerca sci., vol. 13, pp. 830–831, 1942.

Davydov, B. I.: Voltage Fluctuations in Electronic Semiconductors, *J. Phys. (U.S.S.R.)*,
vol. 6, p. 230, 1942.

Earle, M. D.: The Electrical Conductivity of Titanium Dioxide, *Phys. Rev.*, vol. 61, pp.
56–62, 1942.

Fan, H. Y.: Contacts between Metals and between a Metal and a Semiconductor, *Phys.
Rev.*, vol. 62, pp. 388–394, 1942.

Hintenberger, H.: On the Electrical Properties of Lead Sulphide, *Z. Physik*, vol. 119, pp.
1–21, 1942.

Hirone, L., and S. Miyahara: Ferromagnetism of Semiconductors, *Proc. Phys.-Math. Soc.
Japan*, vol. 24, pp. 560–568, 1942.

Schottky, W.: Simplified and Extended Theory of Boundary Layer Rectifiers, *Z. Physik*,
vol. 118, pp. 539–592, 1942.

Seitz, F, and S. Pasternack: Principles of Crystal Rectifiers, NDRC 14–102, University of
Pennsylvania, June, 1942.   (PB 108184.)

Yarmack, J. E.: Selenium Rectifiers and Their Design, *Elec. Eng.*, vol. 61, pp. 488–495, 1942;
Elec. Commun., vol. 20, pp. 275–286, 1942.

1943

Anderson, S.: Luminescence of Valve Metals during Electrolytic Oxidation, *J. Appl.
Phys.*, vol. 14, pp. 601–609, 1943.

Davydov, B. I., and B. Gurevich: Voltage Fluctuations in Semiconductors, *J. Phys.
(U.S.S.R.)*, vol. 7, pp. 138–140, 1943.

Feldman, W.: The Electrical Conductivity and Isothermal Effect in Cuprous Oxide, *Phys. Rev.*, vol. 64, pp. 113–118, 1943.

Goldman, J. E., and A. Lawson: The Photoconductivity of Lead Chromate, *Phys. Rev.*, vol. 64, pp. 11–18, 1943.

Potter, E. V., and R. W. Huber: Use of Manganese Alloys for Electrical Condenser Plates, *U.S. Bur. Mines, Rep. Invest.* 3, February, 1943.

Powell, H., and E. J. Evans: The Hall Effect and Some Other Physical Constants of Alloys. VII. The Aluminium-Silver Series of Alloys, *Phil. Mag.*, vol. 34, pp. 145–161, 1943.

Seitz, F.: "The Physics of Metals," McGraw-Hill Book Company, Inc., New York, 1943.

1944

Benzer, S.: The High Voltage Germanium Rectifier, NDRC 14-342, Purdue University, Nov. 1, 1944.

Cohan, L. H., and M. Steinberg: Conductivity of Tread Stocks, *Ind. Eng. Chem.*, vol. 36, pp. 7–15, 1944.

Kendall, J. T.: The Rectifying Property of Carborundum, *Proc. Phys. Soc. (London)*, vol. 56, pp. 123–129, 1944.

Mullaney, J. F.: Optical Properties and Electronic Structure of Solid Silicon, *Phys. Rev.*, vol. 66, pp. 326–339, 1944.

Shifrin, K.: On the Theory of Electronic Properties of Good Conducting Semiconductors, *J. Phys. (U.S.S.R.)*, vol. 8, pp. 242–252, 1944.

Sillars, R. W.: Metrosil, *Metropolitan Vickers Gaz.*, vol. 20, pp. 304–312, 1944.

1945

Anderson, J. S., and M. C. Morton: Semi-conducting Properties of Stannous Sulphide, *Nature*, vol. 155, p. 112, 1945.

Benzer, S.: Photoelectric Effects in Germanium, NDRC 14-580, Purdue University, Oct. 31, 1945.

Braun, A., and G. Busch: Electrical Conductivity of Silicon Carbide, *Helv. Phys. Acta*, vol. 18, pp. 251–252, 1945.

Joffe, J.: Schottky's Theories of Dry Solid Rectifiers, *Elec. Commun.*, vol. 22, pp. 217–225, 1945.

Kendall, J. T.: The Rectifying Property of Carborundum, *Metropolitan Vickers Gaz.*, vol. 21, pp. 17–20, 1945.

Lark-Horovitz, K.: Preparation of Semiconductor and Development of Crystal Rectifiers, NDRC Final Report 14-585, 1945.

Lewis, M. N., J. H. Taylor, R. J. Gibson, Jr., and W. E. Stephens: High Back Voltage Silicon, NDRC 14-453, University of Pennsylvania, June 28, 1945.

Maurer, R. J.: Deviations from Stoichiometric Proportions in Cuprous Oxide, *J. Chem. Phys.*, vol. 13, pp. 321–326, 1945.

Maurer, R. J.: The Electrical Properties of Semiconductors, *J. Appl. Phys.*, vol. 16, pp. 563–570, 1945.

Pruzhinina-Granovskaya, V.: Non Linear Resistance Material "Vilite" for Arrestors, *Elektrichestvo*, No. 7, pp. 32–35, July, 1945.

Scaff, J. H., and H. C. Theuerer: Preparation of High Back Voltage Germanium Rectifiers, NDRC 14-555, Oct. 24, 1945.

Seitz, F.: The Basic Principles of Semiconductors, *J. Appl. Phys.*, vol. 16, pp. 553–563, 1945.

Snyder, C. L., and T. M. Adaremos: Semiconducting Dielectric Materials, FIAT Evaluation Report 235, August, 1945.

Temperature Dependence of High Voltage Germanium Rectifier D-C Characteristics, NDRC 14-579, Purdue University, Oct. 31, 1945.

The Thermistor, *J. Franklin Inst.*, vol 239, pp. 158–159, 1945.

1946

Ashworth, F., W. Needham, and R. W. Sillars: Silicon Carbide Non-ohmic Resistors, *J. Inst. Elec. Engrs. (London)*, part I, vol. 93, pp. 385–405, 1946.

Becker, J. A., C. B. Green, and G. L. Pearson: Properties and Uses of Thermistors, Thermally Sensitive Resistors, *Trans. AIEE*, vol. 65, pp. 711–725, 1945.

Benzer, S.: The Photo-diode and Photo-peak Characteristics in Germanium, *Phys. Rev.*, vol. 70, p. 105, 1946.

Bleaney, B., J. W. Ryder, and T. H. Kinman: Crystal Valves, *J. Inst. Elec. Engrs. (London)*, part IIIA, vol. 93, pp. 847–854, 1946.

Brattain, W. H.: Rectification Series, *Phys. Rev.*, vol. 69, p. 682, 1946.

Brazier, L. G.: Semi-conducting Porcelain Glazes, *Elec. Industry*, vol. 46, pp. 370–374, October, 1946.

Busch, G.: Electric Conductivity of Silicon Carbide, *Helv. Phys. Acta*, vol. 19, pp. 167–188, 1946.

Busch, G., and H. Labhart: On the Mechanism of the Electrical Conductivity in Silicon Carbide, *Helv. Phys. Acta*, vol. 19, pp. 463–492, 1946.

Busch, G.: Relation between the Constant A and the Activation Energy e in the Conductivity Law of Semiconductors, *Helv. Phys. Acta*, vol. 19, pp. 189–198, 1946.

Conwell, E., and V. F. Weisskopf: Theory of Impurity Scattering in Semiconductors, *Phys. Rev.*, vol. 69, p. 258, 1946.

Cornelius, E. C.: Germanium Crystal Diodes, *Electronics*, vol. 19, pp. 252, 254, January, 1946; pp. 118–123, February, 1946.

Crater, C. W., Jr., A. C. Dickinson, and D. Mitchell: Application of Compandors to Telephone Circuits, *Trans. AIEE*, vol. 65, pp. 1079–1086, 1946.

Gudden, B., and K. Lehovec: Observation on the Diffusion of Thallium in Crystalline Hexagonal Selenium, *Z. Naturforsch.*, vol. 1, pp. 508–512, 1946.

Joffe, A. F.: Electrical Resistance of the Contact between a Semiconductor and a Metal, *J. Phys. (U.S.S.R.)*, vol. 10, pp. 49–60, 1946.

Joffe, A. F.: Semiconductors and Their Application, *Bull. acad. sci. U.R.S.S.*, sér. phys., vol. 10, pp. 3–14, 1946.

Johnson, V. A., and K. Lark-Horovitz: The Theory of Thermoelectric Power in Germanium, *Phys. Rev.*, vol. 69, p. 259, 1946.

Jones, R. C.: Steady-state Load Curves for Semiconductor Bolometers, *J. Opt. Soc. Amer.*, vol. 36, pp. 448–454, 1946.

Kalabuchov, N.: The Nature of the Conductivity of KI Crystals Saturated with Iodine, *J. Phys. (U.S.S.R.)*, vol. 10, pp. 61–63, 1946.

Kikoin, I. K., and D. L. Simonenko: The Influence of a Magnetic Field on the Photoconductivity of Semiconductors, *J. Tech. Phys. (U.S.S.R.)*, vol. 16, pp. 155–158, 1946.

Lark-Horovitz, K., A. E. Middleton, E. P. Miller, and I. Walerstein: Electrical Properties of Germanium Alloys. I. Electrical Conductivity and Hall Effect, *Phys. Rev.*, vol. 69, p. 258, 1946.

Lark-Horovitz, K., A. E. Middleton, E. P. Miller, W. W. Scanlon, and I. Walerstein: Electrical Properties of Germanium Alloys. II. Thermoelectric Power, *Phys. Rev.*, vol. 69, p. 259, 1946.

Lark-Horovitz, K., and V. A. Johnson: Theory of Resistivity in Germanium Alloys, *Phys. Rev.*, vol. 69, p. 258, 1946.

Lehovec, K.: Theory of the Barrier-layer Photo-electric Effect, *Z. Naturforsch.*, vol. 1, pp. 258–263, 1946.

Nelson, J. B., and J. H. McKee: Cerium Tungstate as a Semi-conductor, *Nature*, vol. 158, pp. 753–754, 1946.

Sachs, R. G.: Multicontact Theory of Rectification, *Phys. Rev.*, vol. 69, p. 682, 1946.

Serin, B.: The Energy of Impurity Levels in Semi-conductors, *Phys. Rev.*, vol. 70, p. 104, 1946.

Serin, B.: Heat Treatment of Semiconductors and Contact Rectification, *Phys. Rev.*, vol. 69, pp. 357–362, 1946.

Smyth, C. N.: Total Emission Damping with Space-charge Limited Cathodes, *Nature*, vol. 157, p. 841, 1946.

Starkiewicz, J., L. Sosnowski, and O. Simpson: Photovoltaic Effects Exhibited in High-resistance Semi-conducting Films, *Nature*, vol. 158, p. 28, 1946.

Stephens, W. E., B. Serin, and W. E. Meyerhoff: A Method for Measuring Effective Contact E. M. F. between a Metal and a Semiconductor, *Phys. Rev.*, vol. 69, p. 42, 1946.

Teal, G. I., J. R. Fisher, and A. W. Treptow: A New Bridge Photo-cell Employing a Photo-conductive Effect in Silicon. Some Properties of High Purity Silicon, *J. Appl. Phys.*, vol. 17, pp. 879–885, 1946.

German Research on Rectifiers and Semi-conductors, *BIOS Report* 725, 1946.

1947

Anderson, S. J., and M. C. Morton: Semiconducting Properties of Stannous Sulphide. Thermoelectric Effect, *Trans. Faraday Soc.*, vol. 43, pp. 185–194, 1947.

Baker, G. T.: The Use of Non-linear Resistors for Voltage Correction, *Strowger J.*, vol. 6, pp. 73–78, 1947.

Bardeen, J.: Surface States and Rectification at a Metal-to-Semiconductor Contact, *Phys. Rev.*, vol. 71, pp. 717–727, 1947.

Becker, J. A., C. B. Green, and G. L. Pearson: Properties and Uses of Thermistors—Thermally Sensitive Resistors, *Bell System Tech. J.*, vol. 26, pp. 170–212, 1947.

Benzer, S.: Excess-defect Germanium Contacts, *Phys. Rev.*, vol. 72, pp. 1267–1268, 1947.

Benzer, S.: Ge-Ge Contacts, *Phys. Rev.*, vol. 71, p. 141, 1947.

Benzer, S.: Spontaneous Electrical Oscillations in Germanium Crystals, *Phys. Rev.*, vol. 72, p. 531, 1947.

Brattain, W. H., and W. Shockley: Density of Surface States on Silicon Deduced from Contact Potential Measurements, *Phys. Rev.*, vol. 72, p. 345, 1947.

Brattain, W. H.: Evidence for Surface States on Semi-conductors from Change in Contact Potential on Illumination, *Phys. Rev.*, vol. 72, p. 345, 1947.

Bray, R., and K. Lark-Horovitz: Photo- and Thermo-effects in P-type Germanium Rectifiers, *Phys. Rev.*, vol. 71, pp. 141–142, 1947.

Clark, F. M.: The Dielectric Properties of Cellulose Insulation Impregnated with Semiconducting Liquids, *Trans. AIEE*, vol. 66, pp. 55–63, 1947.

Clark, F. M.: Effect of Semiconducting Liquids on the Dielectric Properties of Cellulose Insulation, *Gen. Elec. Rev.*, vol. 50, pp. 9–17, February, 1947.

Cooper, W. H. B.: Temperature-dependent Resistors, *Wireless Engr.*, vol. 24, pp 298–306, 1947.

Davydov, B. I.: Soviet Investigations on Electronic Semiconductors, *Uspekhi Fiz. Nauk*, vol. 33, pp. 157–164, 1947.

Dunaev, J. A.: Resistance of PbS Close to Absolute Zero, *Compt. rend. acad. sci. U.R.S.S.*, vol. 55, no. 1, pp. 21–24, 1947.

Eck, J. L.: Discontinuities of Potential between a Metal and a Liquid Semiconductor, *Compt. rend.*, vol. 225, pp. 1294–1296, 1947.

Falls, W. H.: Rectifiers—Selenium and Copper Oxide, *Gen. Elec. Rev.*, vol. 50, pp. 34–38, 1947.

Forrest, J. S.: The Electrical Properties of Semiconducting Ceramic Glazes, *J. Sci. Instr.*, vol. 24, pp. 211–217, 1947.

Gillam, G. H.: Stabilized Insulators. An Account of the Properties and Applications of Semi-conducting Ceramic Glazes, *Elec. Times*, vol. 112, pp. 289–293, Sept. 11, 1947.

Gisolf, J. H.: The Temperature Dependence of the Resistivity of Semiconductors, *Ann. Physik*, vol. 1, pp. 3–26, 1947.

Goodman, B., A. W. Lawson, and L. T. Schiff: Thermal Ionization of Impurity Levels in Semi-conductors, *Phys. Rev.*, vol. 71, pp. 191–194, 1947.

Guminski, H.: The Formation of Barrier Anodes of Aluminum at Different Concentrations of Oxalic Acid Solutions, *Bull. intern. acad. polon. sci.*, sér. *A*, 7–10, pp. 133–141, July-December, 1947.

Hepner, W. A.: Response of Photoconductive Lead Sulphide Cells, *Nature*, vol. 159, p. 96, 1947.

Hirahara, E.: Experimental Studies on the Electric Conduction and Heat Capacity of Cuprous Sulphide Semiconductors, *J. Phys. Soc. Japan*, vol. 2, pp. 211–213, 1947.

Hume-Rothery, W.: "Atomic Theory for Students of Metallurgy," Institute of Metals, London, 1947

Johnson, V. A., and K. Lark-Horovitz: Transition from Classical to Quantum Statistics in Germanium Semiconductors at Low Temperatures, *Phys. Rev.*, vol. 71, pp. 374–375, 909, 1947.

Kobayashi, A.: The Relaxation Effect of the Cuprous Oxide Rectifier after the Application of Strong Field, *J. Phys. Soc. Japan*, vol. 2, p. 92, 1947.

Kolomiets, B. T.: The Positive Rectifying Photo-electric Effect in Selenium, *Compt. rend. acad. sci. U.R.S.S.*, vol. 55, pp. 207–208, 1947.

Kolomiets, B. T., and I. T. Sheftel: Temperature Measurement by Semiconductor Resistance Thermometers, *J. Tech. Phys. (U.S.S.R.)*, vol. 17, pp. 1105–1110, 1947.

Leblanc, M.: Application of the Theory of Conduction in Semi-conductors to Crystal Detectors, *Bull. soc. franç. elect.*, vol. 7, pp. 445–452, 1947.

Lehovec, K. Z.: Theory of Barrier-layer Photo-electric Effects, II. *Z. Naturforsch.*, vol. 2a, pp. 398–403, 1947.

Lynshonko, V. T., and A. M. Pavlenko: Enrichment in Current Carriers of a Semiconductor under the Influence of the Contact Field, *J. Tech. Phys. (U.S.S.R.)*, vol. 17, pp. 1097–1104, 1947.

Macfarlane, G. G.: A Theory of Flicker Noise in Valves and Impurity Semiconductors, *Proc. Phys. Soc. (London)*, vol. 59, pp. 366–375, 1947.

Massey, H. S. W.: Semi-conductors, *J. Sci. Instr.*, vol. 24, pp. 220–224, 1947.

Meyer, H., and Neldel: On the Activation Energy of Semiconductors, *Physik. Z.*, vol. 38, p. 1014, 1947.

Meyerhoff, W. E.: Contact Potential Difference in Silicon Rectifiers, *Phys. Rev.*, vol. 71, pp. 727–735, 1947.

Morton, M. C.: Semiconducting Properties of Lead Sulphide, *Trans. Faraday Soc.*, vol. 43, pp. 194–201, 1947.

Muto, T., and J. Yamashita: Theory of the External Photoelectric Effect in Semiconductors. I. BaO, SrO, and Cu₂O Semiconductors. Behaviours of the Photo Sensitivity near Threshold, *J. Phys. Soc. Japan*, vol. 2, pp. 187–190, 1947.

Muto, T.: Theory of the External Photoelectric Effect in Semiconductors. I. BaO, SrO, and Cu₂O Semiconductors. II. Total Photo Sensitivity, *J. Phys. Soc. Japan*, vol. 2, pp. 190–192, 1941.

Muto, T.: Theory of the External Photoelectric Effect in Semiconductors. Colored Alkali Halides, *J. Phys. Soc. Japan*, vol. 2, pp. 193–195, 1947.

Pearson, G. L., and W. Shockley: Measurements of Hall Effect and Resistivity of Germanium and Silicon from 10° to 600°K, *Phys. Rev.*, vol. 71, p. 142, 1947.

Pearson, G. L.: The Physics of Electronic Semiconductors, *Trans. AIEE*, vol. 66, pp. 209–214, 1947; *Elec. Eng.*, vol. 66, pp. 638–642, 1947.

Rose, F., and H. Schmidt: An Interpretation of Forming Phenomena in Selenium Barrier-layer Rectifiers, *Z. Naturforsch.*, vol. 2a, pp. 226–233, 1947.

Scaff, J. H., and R. S. Ohl: Development of Silicon Crystal Rectifiers for Microwave Radar Receivers, *Bell System Tech. J.*, vol. 26, pp. 1–30, 1947.

Selenyi, P.: Effect of Bending on Selenium Rectifier Disks, *Nature*, vol. 160, pp. 197, 326, 1947.

Simpson, O.: Conductivity of Evaporated Films of Lead Selenide, *Nature*, vol. 160, pp. 791–792, 1947.

Sosnowski, L.: Excess-defect Semiconductor Contacts, *Phys. Rev.*, vol. 72, pp. 641–642, 1947.

Sosnowski, L., B. W. Soole, and J. Starkiewicz: Occurrence of Random Photovoltaic Barriers in Photo-conductive Layers, *Nature*, vol. 160, pp. 471–472, 1947.

van der Ziel, A., and A. Versnel: Total Emission Noise in Diodes, *Nature*, vol. 159, pp. 640–641, 1947.

Verwey, E. J. W., P. W. Haayman, and F. C. Romeyn: Semiconductors with Large Negative Temperature Coefficient of Resistance, *Philips Tech. Rev.*, vol. 9, pp. 239–248, 1947.

Yamamoto, T., and S. Takagi: Remarks on the Ferromagnetism of the Semiconductors, *Progr. Theoret. Phys. (Japan)*, vol. 2, pp. 160–161, 1947.

German Developments in Semi-conducting Materials, *JIOA Report* 54, 1947.

Selenium Rectifier Development in Germany, Supplement to *JIOA Report* 56, *FIAT Report* 890, 1947.

Semi-conducting Ceramic Materials, *J. Am. Ceram. Soc.*, vol. 30, pp. 290–296, 1947.

1948

Adam, M.: Une découverte électronique capitale: transistor, *La Nature*, no. 3164, pp. 377–379, December, 1948.

Apker, L., E. Taft, and J. Dickey: Energy Distribution of Photoelectrons from Polycrystalline Tungsten, *Phys. Rev.*, vol. 73, pp. 46–50, 1948.

Apker, L., E. Taft, and J. Dickey: Photoelectric Emission and Contact Potentials of Semiconductors, *Phys. Rev.*, vol. 74, pp. 1462–1474, 1948.

Arnaud, J. P.: Transistor: The Crystal Amplifier and Oscillator, *Rev. Telegr. (Buenos Aires)*, vol. 37, pp. 715–720, October, 1948.

Atkins, C. E.: Crystal That Amplifies, *Radio and Television News*, vol. 40, pp. 181–184, October, 1948.

Bardeen, J., and W. H. Brattain: The Transistor, a Semi-conducting Triode, *Phys. Rev.*, vol. 74, pp. 230–231, 1948.

Becker, J. A.: Recent Developments in Semi-conductors and the Transistor, *Elec. Eng.*, vol. 67, p. 1201, 1948.

Begovich, N. A.: High Frequency Loading, *Phys. Rev.*, vol. 74, p. 1563, 1948.

Belevitch, V.: Linear Theory of Bridge and Ring Modulators Circuits, *Elec. Commun.*, vol. 25, pp. 62–73, 1948.

Benzer, S.: Photoelectric Effects and Their Relation to Rectification at Metal-semiconductor Contacts, *Phys. Rev.*, vol. 73, p. 1256, 1948.

Billig, E.: German Research on Semiconductors, Metal Rectifiers, Detectors and Photocells, *BIOS Report* 1751, 1948.

Blackburn, W. E.: Temperature Coefficient of Electrical Resistivity for Crystalline Selenium Containing Various Percentages of Bromine, *J. Appl. Phys.*, vol. 19, pp. 51–54, 1948.

Boltaks, B. I., and V. P. Zhuse: Physical Properties of Intermetallic Compounds of Constant Composition. (On the Mechanism of Conductivity of Mg_3Sb_2), *J. Tech. Phys. (U.S.S.R.)*, vol. 18, pp. 1459–1477, 1948.

Brattain, W. H., and J. Bardeen: Nature of the Forward Current in Germanium Point Contacts, *Phys. Rev.*, vol. 74, pp. 231–232, 1948.

Brown, F. C.: Temperature-Pressure-Conductivity Relations in Semiconductors, *Phys. Rev.*, vol. 73, p. 1257, 1948.

Chasmar, R. P.: High Frequency Characteristics of Lead Sulphide and Lead Selenide Layers, *Nature*, vol. 161, pp. 281–282, 1948.

Chretien, L.: The Transistor, or the Return of the Crystal, *T.S.F. pour Tous*, vol. 24, pp. 260–262, October, 1948.

Davis, R. E., et al.: Neutron-bombarded Germanium Semiconductors, *Phys. Rev.*, vol. 74, p. 1255, 1948.

Dikman, I. M.: Theory of the Photon and Secondary Electron Emission of Effective Semiconducting Emitters, *J. Tech. Phys. (U.S.S.R.)*, vol. 18, pp. 1426–1442, 1948.

Dilworth, C. C.: The Influence of Surface Films on the Electrical Behavior of Contacts, *Proc. Phys. Soc. (London)*, vol. 60, pp. 315–325, 1948.

Dunlap, W. C., Jr., and E. F. Hennelly: Non-rectifying Germanium, *Phys. Rev.*, vol. 74, p. 976, 1948.

Eley, D. D.: Phthalocyanines as Semiconductors, *Nature*, vol. 162, p. 819, 1948.

Fakidov, I. G., and N. P. Grazhdankina: The Electrical Conductivity of Chromium Sulphide, *Doklady Akad. Nauk S.S.S.R.*, vol. 63, no. 1, pp. 27–28, 1948.

Fan, H. Y.: Theory of Rectification of an Insulating Layer, *Phys. Rev.*, vol. 74, pp. 1505–1513, 1948.

Fassbender, J., F. Moglich, and R. Rompe: The Band Model and the Inertia of Photoelectric Conductivity in Insulators and Semiconductors, *Ann. Physik*, vol. 3, pp. 327–332, 1948.

Frerichs, R., and A. J. F. Siegert: Note on the Photoconductivity of Cadmium-sulphide Crystals, *Phys. Rev.*, vol. 74, p. 1875, 1948.

Gray, T. J.: Application of Measurements of Semi-conductivity to Heterogeneous Reactions, *Nature*, vol. 162, pp. 260–261, 1948.

Grondahl, L. O.: Twenty-five Years of Copper Oxide Rectifiers, *Trans. AIEE*, vol. 67, pp. 403–410, 1948.

Hausner, H. H.: Semi-conducting Ceramic Materials, *J. Am. Ceram. Soc.*, vol. 30, p. 290, 1948.

Haynes, J. R., and W. Shockley: The Trapping of Electrons in Silver Chloride, in Report of Conference on Strength of Solids, pp. 151–157, Physical Society, London, 1948.

Henisch, H. K.: Thermo-electric and Conductive Properties of Blue Titanium Dioxide, *Elec. Commun.*, vol. 25, pp. 163–177, 1948.

Hewitt, W. H.: Microwave Resonance Absorption in Ferromagnetic Semiconductors, *Phys. Rev.*, vol. 73, pp. 1118–1119, 1948.

Hogarth, C. A.: Variation of Thermo-electric Power of Electronic Semiconductors with Vapour Pressure, *Nature*, vol. 161, pp. 60–61, 1948.

Hogarth, C. A.: The Variation with Vapour Pressure of the Properties of Certain Electronic Semi-conductors, *Phil. Mag.*, vol. 39, pp. 260–267, 1948.

Hume-Rothery, W.: "Electrons, Atoms, Metals and Alloys," Iliffe, London, 1948.

Isenberg, I., B. R. Russel, and R. F. Greene: Improved Method for Measuring Hall Coefficients, *Rev. Sci. Instr.*, vol. 19, pp. 685–688, 1948.

Jacottet, P.: Determination of the Electromagnetic Constants of Semiconductors in the Ultra Short Wave Range, *Helv. Phys. Acta*, vol. 21, pp. 251–260, 1948

Jaffray, J., and M. F. Beaufort: The Electrical Conductivity of Chromium Sesquioxide at Moderately High Temperatures, *Compt. rend.*, vol. 227, pp. 1345–1347, 1948.

Joffe, A. V.: Rectification on the Boundary of Two Semiconductors, *J. Tech. Phys. (U.S.S.R.)*, vol. 18, pp. 1498–1510, 1948.

Johnson, V. A., and K. Lark-Horovitz: Semiconductor Research. Final Report, January, 1946–December, 1948, Contract W-36-039 sc-32020, Department of Physics, Purdue University.

Johnson, V. A., and K. Lark-Horovitz: Theory of the Nernst and Ettinghausen Effects in Semiconductors at High Temperatures, *Phys. Rev.*, vol. 73, p. 1257, 1948.

Kobayashi, A.: On Crystal Rectifiers. I., *J. Phys. Soc. Japan*, vol. 3, pp. 41–47, 1948.

Kubo, R.: Interaction between Electrons and Ions in Semiconductors, I., *J. Phys. Soc. Japan*, vol. 3, pp. 254–259, 1948.

Lark-Horovitz, K., et al.: Deuteron-bombarded Semiconductors, *Phys. Rev.*, vol. 73, p. 1256, 1948.

Lashkarev, V. E., and K. M. Kosonogorov: Photo E.M.F. in Copper Oxide, *J. Exptl. Theoret. Phys. (U.S.S.R.)*, vol. 18, pp. 927–936, 1948

Lashkarev, V. E.: The Production of Photo E.M.F. in Semiconductors, *J. Exptl. Theoret. Phys.* (*U.S.S.R.*), vol. 18, pp. 917–926, 1948.

Lashkarev, V. E.: Properties of Badly Conducting Layers between Metal and Semiconductor, *J. Tech. Phys.* (*U.S.S.R.*), vol. 18, pp. 1347–1355, 1948.

Lehovec, K.: The Electrical Conductivity of Micro-crystalline Hexagonal Selenium with Thallium Content, *Z. Physik*, vol. 124, p. 278, 1948.

Lehovec, K.: The Photo-voltaic Effect, *Phys. Rev.*, vol. 74, pp. 463–471, 1948.

McKay, K. G.: Electron Bombardment Conductivity in Diamond, *Phys. Rev.*, vol. 74, pp. 1606–1621, 1948.

Margulis, N. D.: The Problem of the Ionization of Atoms and Neutralization of the Ions on the Surface of a Semiconducting Cathode, *J. Tech. Phys.* (*U.S.S.R.*), vol. 18, pp. 567–572, 1948.

Meixner, J.: Electrical Properties of Solids. VII. Galvanomagnetic, Thermomagnetic and Thermoelectric Effects, *FIAT Rev. Ger. Sci.*, 1939–1946, Physics of Solids II, pp. 131–142, 1948.

Miller, P. H., and J. J. Markham: Work Function and Semiconductors at High Temperatures, *Phys. Rev.*, vol. 74, p. 1218, 1948.

Mochan, I. V.: Electroconductivity of the System Zinc-Antimony, *J. Tech. Phys.* (*U.S.S.R.*), vol. 18, pp. 1485–1493, 1948.

Mott, N. F., and R. W. Gurney: "Electronic Processes in Ionic Crystals," 2nd ed. Oxford University Press, New York, 1948.

Müller, R. H.: Development of the Transistor, *Anal. Chem.*, vol. 20, pp. 25A–26A, September, 1948.

Peterson, L. C.: Equivalent Circuits of Linear Active Four-terminal Networks, *Bell System Tech. J.*, vol. 27, pp. 593–622, 1948.

Pirie, J. H.: The Application of Semi-conducting Glaze to Porcelain Insulators, *CIGRE Report* 202, 1948.

Putseko, E.: Use of the Capacitor Method in Studying the Internal Photo Effect of Sensitizers, *Doklady Akad. Nauk S.S.S.R.*, vol. 59, pp. 471–474, 1948.

Ringer, W., and H. Z. Welker: Conductivity and Hall Effect in Germanium, *Z. Naturforsch.*, vol. 3a, pp. 20–29, 1948.

Rittner, E. S.: Use of Photo-conductive Semi-conductors as Amplifiers, *Phys. Rev.*, vol. 73, pp. 1212–1213, 1948.

Robertson, W. D., and H. H. Uhlig: Electrical Properties of the Intermetallic Compounds Mg_2Sn and Mg_2Pb, *AIMME Tech. Pub.* 2468, 1948.

Rocket, F. H.: Transistor, *Sci. American*, vol. 179, pp. 52–55, September, 1948.

Shmushkevich, I. M.: Dependence of the Contact Resistance of a Semiconductor on the Frequency of the Field, *J. Exptl. Theoret. Phys.* (*U.S.S.R.*), vol. 18, pp. 462–474, 1948.

Shockley, W., J. Bardeen, and W. H. Brattain: Electronic Theory of the Transistor, *Science*, vol. 108, pp. 678–679, 1948.

Shockley, W., and G. L. Pearson: Modulation of Conductance of Thin Films of Semiconductors by Surface Charges, *Phys. Rev.*, vol. 74, pp. 232–233, 1948.

Smith, I. R.: The Copper Oxide Rectifier, *Elec. Eng.*, vol. 67, pp. 1051–1058, 1948.

Sotskov, B. S.: The Application of Thermistors, *Automat. Telemekh.* (*U.S.S.R.*), vol. 9, pp. 39–58, January, 1948.

Tellegen, B. D. H.: The Gyrator, a New Electric Network Circuit, *Philips Research Repts.*, vol. 3, pp. 81–101, 1948.

Tetzner, H.: Investigations of Luminescence Phenomena on Manufactured Silicon Carbide, *Z. angew. Physik.*, vol. 1, pp. 153–161, 1948.

Torrey, H. C., and C. A. Whitmer: "Crystal Rectifiers," McGraw-Hill Book Company, Inc., 1948.

van der Ziel, A., and A. Versnel: Induced Grid Noise and Total Emission Noise, *Philips Research Repts.*, vol. 3, pp. 13–23, 1948.

von Meyeren, W. A.: Electrical Properties of Solids. V. Semiconductors, Rectifiers and Photo-cells, *FIAT Rev. Ger. Sci.*, 1939–1946, Physics of Solids II, pp. 101–122, 1948.

von Meyeren, W. A., and W. A. Frat: Electrical Properties of Solids. III. Conduction of Electricity in Insulators; Photoconductivity, *FIAT Rev. Ger. Sci.*, 1939–1946, Physics of Solids, pp. 63–76, 1948.

Verster, J. L.: The Electrical and Thermal Behavior of Steady State Loaded Thermistors, *Ingenieur*, vol. 60, pp. 62–67, June 11, 1948.

Walker, R. C.: "Photoelectric Cells in Industry," Sir Isaac Pitman & Sons, Ltd., London, 1948.

Wells, W., and S. Y. White: Experimental Germanium Crystal Amplifier (The Transistor), *Audio Engineering*, vol. 32, pp. 6, 8, July, 1948; pp. 28–29, 39, August, 1948.

West, C. F., and J. E. DeTurk: A Digital Computer for Scientific Applications, *Proc. IRE*, vol. 36, pp. 1452–1460, 1948.

White, S. Y.: Clarification of Germanium Trio de Characteristics, *Audio Eng.*, vol. 32, pp. 19–21, 44, December, 1948.

White, S. Y.: Design of Amplifying Crystal Units, *Audio Eng.*, vol. 32, pp. 26–27, 43–45, September, 1948; pp. 32–33, 51–52, October, 1948; pp. 18–19, November, 1948; pp. 40–44, December, 1948.

Amplifying Crystal (The Transistor: A 3-electrode Germanium Contact Device), *Wireless World*, vol. 54, pp. 358–359, 1948.

Bell Laboratories Introduce a Revolutionary Component, *Radio Television News*, vol. 40, p. 84, September, 1948.

Eclipse of the Radio Tube, *Radio-Electronics*, vol. 19, p. 24, September, 1948.

Electronic Applications of Germanium, *Nature*, vol. 162, pp. 982–983, 1948.

Germanium Rectifiers, *Electronic Eng.*, vol. 20, p. 232, 1948.

Germanium Varistors, *Bell Labs. Record*, vol. 26, pp. 485–486, 1948.

Semi-conductor Replaces Vacuum Tubes, *Instruments*, vol. 21, pp. 636–638, July, 1948.

Semi-conductor Replaces Vacuum Tubes, *Product Eng.*, vol. 19, pp. 158–159, September, 1948.

Semi-conductor Triodes May Replace Vacuum Tubes, *Elec. Mfg.*, vol. 42, pp. 126, 128, 188, August, 1948.

The Silicon Crystal Detector, *Bell Labs. Record*, vol. 26, pp. 152–155, 1948.

The Transistor, *Bell Labs. Record*, vol. 26, pp. 321–324, August, 1948.

Transistor: *Sci. American*, September, 1948; *Telephone and Telegraph Age*, vol. 26, pp. 7, 30, August, 1948; *Mech. Eng.*, vol. 70, p. 766, 1948. *Rev. Sci. Instr.*, vol. 19, pp. 724–725, 1948.

The Transistor—A Crystal Triode, *Electronics*, vol. 21, pp. 68–71, September, 1948.

The Transistor—A Crystal Triode, *Power Generator*, vol. 52, pp. 83–85, October, 1948.

Transistor—A New Amplifier, *Elec. Eng.*, vol. 67, p. 740, 1948.

Transistor Amplifier, *Engineering*, vol. 166, pp. 630–631, December, 1948.

Transistors May Replace Vacuum Tubes, *Tele-Tech*, vol. 7, pp. 18–20, August, 1948.

1949

Aberdam, H.: Transistor et transistron, *Ingen. et tech.* (*Paris*), vol. 12, pp. 213–218, 1949.

Aisberg, E.: Transistron-transistor +? *Toute la radio*, vol. 16, pp. 218–220, 1949.

Andrews, J. P.: Semiconductors, *Science Progr.*, vol. 37, pp. 435–449, 1949.

Angello, S. J.: Semi-conductor Rectifiers, *Elec. Eng.*, vol. 68, pp. 865–872, 1949.

Arsenev-Geil, A. N.: Influence of the Temperature on the External Photo-effect for Semiconductors, *Doklady Akad. Nauk S.S.S.R.*, vol. 68, pp. 245–247, 1949.

Auerbach, R.: Die elektrische Leitfaehigkeit fester dispersoide, *Kolloid-Z.*, vol. 112, pp. 60–66, 1949.

Bardeen, J., and W. H. Brattain: Coaxial Transistor, *Electronics*, vol. 22, p. 128, March, 1949; *Electronic Eng.*, vol. 21, p. 394, 1949.

Bardeen, J.: On the Theory of the A-C Impedance of a Contact Rectifier, *Bell System Tech. J.*, vol. 28, pp. 428–434, 1949.

Bardeen, J., and W. H. Brattain: Physical Principles Involved in Transistor Action, *Phys. Rev.*, vol. 79, pp. 1208–1225, 1949; *Bell System Tech. J.*, vol. 28, pp. 239–277, 1949.

Becker, J. A.: Photo Effects in Semi-conductors, *Elec. Eng.*, vol. 68, pp. 937–942, 1949.

Becker, J. A., and J. N. Shive: The Transistor—A New Semi-conductor Amplifier, *Elec. Eng.*, vol. 68, pp. 215–221, 1949.

Becker, M., and H. Y. Fan: Optical Properties of Semiconductors, II. Infra-red Transmission of Germanium, *Phys. Rev.*, vol. 76, pp. 1530–1531, 1949.

Becker, M., and H. Y. Fan: Optical Properties of Semiconductors. III. Infra-red Transmission of Silicon, *Phys. Rev.*, vol. 76, pp. 1531–1532, 1949.

Becker, M., and H. Y. Fan: Photovoltaic Effects of P-N Barriers Produced in Germanium by Alpha and Deuteron Bombardment, *Phys. Rev.*, vol. 75, p. 1631, 1949.

Begovich, N. A.: High Frequency Total Emission Loading in Diodes, *J. Appl. Phys.*, vol. 20, pp. 457–461, 1949.

Benzer, S.: Hall Effect in Metal-semiconductor Point Contacts, *Phys. Rev.*, vol. 76, pp. 150–151, 1949.

Benzer, S.: High Inverse Voltage Germanium Rectifiers, *J. Appl. Phys.*, vol. 20, pp. 804–815, 1949.

Bray, R.: The Barrier Layer in P-type Germanium, *Phys. Rev.*, vol. 76, p. 458, 1949.

Bray, R.: Dependence of Resistivity of Germanium on Electric Field, *Phys. Rev.*, vol. 76, pp. 152–153, 1949.

Broser, I., H. Kallmann, and R. Warminsky: On the Theory of the Conductive Mechanism in Cadmium Sulphide Crystals, *Z. Naturforsch.*, vol. 4a, pp. 631–637, 1949.

Brown, C. B.: Magnetically Biased Transistors, *Phys. Rev.*, vol. 76, pp. 1736–1737, 1949.

Cauville, R.: Electrical Properties of Products of the System Titanium Oxide–Aluminum Oxide Reduced by Hydrogen, *Compt. rend.*, vol. 229, pp. 1228–1230, 1949.

Croatto, V.: Thermal Conductivity and Lattice Disorder in Semi-conductors, *Ricerca sci.*, vol. 19, pp. 696–699, 1949.

Croatto, V.: Thermoelectric Power and Lattice Disorder in Semi-conductors, *Ricerca sci.*, vol. 19, pp. 1324–1326, 1949.

Dudnik, R. L., and V. I. Pruzhinina-Granovskaya: Time Effects in Black Silicon Carbide, *J. Tech. Phys. (U.S.S.R.)*, vol. 19, pp. 1434–1441, 1949.

Dunlap, W. C., Jr.: Germanium, Important New Semi-conductor, *Gen. Elec. Rev.*, vol. 52, pp. 9–17, 1949.

Eberhard, E., R. O. Andres, and R. P. Moore: Counter Circuits Using Transistors, *RCA Rev.*, vol. 10, pp. 459–476, 1949.

Eck, J. L.: Contribution to the Study of Liquid Semiconductors, *Ann. Phys.*, vol. 4, pp. 12–61, 1949.

Eisenstein, A.: Some Properties of the Ba_2SiO_4 Oxide Cathode Interface, *J. Appl. Phys.*, vol. 20, pp. 776–790, 1949.

Estermann, A.: Resistivity of Germanium Samples at Liquid-helium Temperatures, *Phys. Rev.*, vol. 75, pp. 1631–1632, 1949.

Fan, H. Y., and R. Bray: The Barrier Layer on P-type Germanium, *Phys. Rev.*, vol. 76, p. 458, 1949.

Fan, H. Y.: Theory of Photovoltaic Effect of P-N Barrier in a Semiconductor, *Phys. Rev.*, vol. 74, p. 1631, 1949.

Fink, D. G., and F. H. Rockett: The Transistor, a Crystal Triode, *Electronics*, vol. 21, pp. 68–71, September, 1949.

Forrest, J. S.: The Use of Semi-conducting Ceramic Glaze for the Measurement of Temperature, *J. Sci. Instr.*, vol. 26, pp. 254–255, 1949.

Frank, K., and K. Raithel: A Method for the Production of Photoelectric Layers of Very High Resistance with PbS As an Infra-red Sensitive Semiconductor, *Z. Physik*, vol. 126, pp. 377–382, 1949.

Freeman, J. J.: Noise Spectrum of a Diode with a Retarding Field, *J. Research, NBS*, vol. 42, pp. 75–88, 1949.

Frerichs, R.: On the Conductivity Produced by Cadmium Sulphide Crystals by Irradiation with Gamma-rays, *Phys. Rev.*, vol. 76, pp. 1869–1875, 1949.

Fukuroi, T., S. Tanuma, and S. Tobisawa: Electric Resistance, Hall Effect, Magneto-resistance and Seebeck Effect in a Pure Tellurium Film, *Sci. Repts. Research Insts. Tôhoku Univ.*, ser. A, vol. 1, pp. 365–373, 1949.

Fukuroi, T., S. Tanuma, and S. Tobisawa: On the Electro-magnetic Properties of Single Crystals of Tellurium. I. Electric Resistance, Hall Effect, Magnetic Resistance and Thermo Electric Power, *Sci. Repts. Research Insts. Tôhoku Univ.*, ser. A, vol. 1, pp. 373–386, 1949.

Geyer: Oscillographic Presentation of Transistor Characteristics, Master of Science Thesis at MIT, Electrical Engineering Department, 1949.

Gisolf, J. H.: On the Spontaneous Current Fluctuations in Semiconductors, *Physica*, vol. 15, pp. 825–832, 1949.

Gray, T. J.: The Application of Semi-conductivity Measurements in the Study of Catalysis on Copper Oxide, *Proc. Roy. Soc.*, vol. 197A, pp. 314–420, 1949.

Greenwood, N. N., and J. S. Anderson: Conductivity and Thermo-electric Effect in Cuprous Oxide, *Nature*, vol. 164, pp. 346–347, 1949.

Gyulai, Z.: Deviations from Ohm's Law in Additively Coloured Alkali Halide Crystals, *Z. Physik*, vol. 125, pp. 505–516, 1949.

Haegele, R. W.: Crystal Tetrode Mixer, *Electronics*, vol. 22, pp. 80–81, October, 1949; *Sylvania Technologist*, vol. 2, pp. 2–4, July, 1949.

Hannay, N. B., D. MacNair, and A. H. White: Semi-conducting Properties in Oxide Cathodes, *J. Appl. Phys.*, vol. 20, pp. 669–681, 1949.

Haynes, J. R., and W. Shockley: Investigations of Hole Injection in Transistor Action, *Phys. Rev.*, vol. 75, p. 691, 1949.

Henisch, H. K.: "Metal Rectifiers," Oxford University Press, New York, 1949.

Henkels, H. W.: Properties of Single Crystal Selenium Prepared from a Melt, *Phys. Rev.*, vol. 76, pp. 1737–1738, 1949.

Herring, C.: Theory of Transient Phenomena in the Transport of Holes in an Excess Semiconductor, *Bell System Tech. J.*, vol. 28, pp. 401–427, 1949.

Heywang, W.: On the Influence of Isolated Lattice Perturbations on the Electrical Resistance of Electronic Semi-conductors and Its Temperature Dependence, *Z. Naturforsch.*, vol. 4a, pp. 654–664, 1949.

Horton, W. P., and R. M. Kalb: A Preliminary Investigation of Transistors for Complete Circuits, Engineering Research Associates, Inc., St. Paul, Minn., Oct. 7, 1949.

Hungermann, E. H.: Kristallgleichrichter, *Elektron Wiss. u. Tech.*, vol. 3, p. 381, 1949.

Hutcheson, J. A.: Possible Significance of Transistors in the Power Field, *Elec. Eng.*, vol. 68, p. 689, 1949.

James, H. M.: Electronic States in Perturbed Periodic Systems, *Phys. Rev.*, vol. 76, pp. 1611–1624, 1949.

Johnson, V. A.: Theory of Resistivity and Hall Effect in Semiconducting Anisotropic Crystals, *Phys. Rev.*, vol. 75, p. 1631, 1949.

Johnson, W. E., and K. Lark-Horovitz: Neutron Irradiated Semiconductors, *Phys. Rev.*, vol. 76, pp. 442–443, 1949.

Jones, T. K., R. A. Scott, and R. W. Sillars: The Structure and Electrical Properties of Surfaces of Some Semiconductors. I. Silicon Carbide, *Proc. Phys. Soc. (London)*, vol. 62A, pp. 333–343, 1949.

Kobayashi, A., and K. Arita: The Patch Effect of Crystal Rectifiers, *J. Phys. Soc. Japan*, vol. 4, pp. 96–99, 1949.

Kock, W. E., and R. L. Wallace, Jr.: The Coaxial Transistor, *Elec. Eng.*, vol. 68, pp. 222–223, 1949.

Koczynski, G. C.: Elementary Principles of Solid State Physics. I. Metals, *Sylvania Technologist*, vol. 2, pp. 6–9, July, 1949.

Kubo, R.: Interaction between Electrons and Ions in Semiconductors. II-III, *J. Phys. Soc. Japan*, vol. 4, pp. 322–325, 326–329, 1949.

Kushida, T.: On the Anomalous Electrical Properties of Beta Cu_2S. I, *J. Sci., Hiroshima Univ.*, vol. 14, pp. 48–49, 1949.

Landsberg, P. T.: Image Force in Rectifiers, *Nature*, vol. 164, pp. 967–968, 1949.

Lapostolle, P.: Étude theoretique et experimentale de la detection par les cristaux au silicium, *Onde élect.*, no. 273, December, 1949.

Lark-Horovitz, K.: Conductivity in Semiconductors, *Elec. Eng.*, vol. 68, pp. 1047–1056, 1949.

Lark-Horovitz, K., and K. W. Meissner: Optical Properties of Semiconductors. I. The Reflectivity of Germanium Semiconductors, *Phys. Rev.*, vol. 76, p. 1530, 1949.

Lashkarev, V. E.: Kinetics of the Photo-conductivity of Semiconductors, *J. Exptl. Theoret. Phys. (U.S.S.R.)*, vol. 19, pp. 876–886, 1949.

Lehan, F. W.: A Transistor Oscillator for Telemetering. (Memo 4-48, California Institute of Technology, February, 1949), *Electronics*, vol. 22, pp. 90–91, August, 1949.

Lehovec, K.: The Influences of Traces of Thallium on the Selenium Rectifier, *Z. Physik*, vol. 125, pp. 451–454, 1949.

Lehovec, K.: On Hole Current in the Germanium Transistor, *Phys. Rev.*, vol. 75, pp. 1100–1101, 1949.

Lehovec, K.: Testing Transistors, *Electronics*, vol. 22, pp. 88–89, June, 1949.

Little, J. B.: New Structure for Transistors, IRE-Princeton Symposium on Semiconductor Devices, July 21, 1949.

Loosjes, R., and H. J. Vink: The Conduction Mechanism of Oxide-coated Cathodes, *Philips Research Repts.*, vol. 4, pp. 449–475, 1949.

McKay, K. G.: A Germanium Counter, *Phys. Rev.*, vol. 76, p. 1537, 1949.

Mansfield, R.: The Electrical Properties of Bismuth Oxide, *Proc. Phys. Soc. (London)*, vol. 62B, pp. 476–483, 1949.

Markham, J. J., and R. H. Miller, Jr.: The Effect of Surface States on the Temperature Variation of the Work Function of Semiconductors, *Phys. Rev.*, vol. 75, pp. 959–967, 1949.

Markus, J.: Characteristics of Three Transistor Circuits, *Electronics*, vol. 22, pp. 120–121, August, 1949.

Martin, P. S.: Patents on Solid-state Amplifying Devices, *Sylvania Technologist*, vol. 2, pp. 4–6, July, 1949.

Matare, H. F.: Background Noise in Semiconductors I, *J. phys. radium*, vol. 10, pp. 364–372, 1949.

Mitchell, E. W. J., and R. W. Sillars: Observations of the Electrical Behaviour of Silicon Carbide Contacts, *Proc. Phys. Soc. (London)*, vol. 62B, pp. 509–522, 1949.

Mooers, H. T.: Low Frequency Noise in Transistors, *Proc. Natl. Electronics Conf.*, vol. 5, pp. 17–22, 1949.

Mott, N. F.: Notes on the Transistor and Surface States in Semiconductors, *Rept. Brit. Elect. Research Assoc.*, Ref. L/T216, 1949.

Mott, N. F.: Semi-conductors and Rectifiers, *Proc. IRE.*, part I, vol. 96, pp. 253–260, 1949; *Engineering*, vol. 167, pp. 510–511, 1949.

Nekrashevich, I. G., and T. Z. Fisher: Dependence on Frequency of the Uni-polar Conductivity of Contacts, *J. Tech. Phys. (U.S.S.R.)*, vol. 19, pp. 1312–1320, 1949.

Netushil, A. V., and I. V. Korzun: Measurement of Characteristics of Semiconductors by the Substitution Method, *Elektrichestvo*, no. 2, pp. 69–71, February, 1949.

Newton, R. R.: Space Charge Effects in Bombardment Conductivity through Diamond, *Phys. Rev.*, vol. 75, pp. 233–246, 1949.

Pearson, G. L.: Electrical Properties of Crystal Grain Boundaries in Germanium, *Phys. Rev.*, vol. 76, p. 459, 1949.

Pearson, G. L., and J. Bardeen: Electrical Properties of Pure Silicon and Silicon Alloys Containing Boron and Phosphorus, *Phys. Rev.*, vol. 75, pp. 865–883, 1949.

Pekar, S. I.: Theory of Polarons, *J. Exptl. Theoret. Phys. (U.S.S.R.)*, vol. 19, pp. 796–806, 1949.

Pfann, W. G., and J. H. Scaff: The P-germanium Transistor, *Phys. Rev.*, vol. 76, p. 459, 1949; *Proc. IRE*, vol. 38, pp. 1151–1154, 1949.

Pfotzer, G.: Conductivity Profile of the Barrier Layer of the Copper Oxide Rectifier from H. F. Measurements and Its Division in the Space Charge Regions, *Z. Naturforsch.*, vol. 4a, pp. 691–706, 1949.

Pohl, R. W., and F. Stochmann: Enhancing of Electron Current in Irradiated Crystal, *Ann. Physik*, vol. 6, pp. 89–92, 1949.

Posthumus, H. G.: The Transistor, *Elec. Eng.*, vol. 68, p. 643, 1949.

Putley, E. H.: The Electrical Conductivity of Germanium, *Proc. Phys. Soc. (London)*, vol. 62A, pp. 284–292, 1949.

Reich, H. J., and R. L. Ungvary: A Transistor Trigger Circuit, *Rev. Sci. Instr.*, vol. 20, pp. 586–588, 1949.

Renne, V. T.: On the Question of Using Semiconducting Liquids for Impregnating Paper Condensers, *J. Tech. Phys. (U.S.S.R.)*, vol. 19, pp. 218–224, 1949.

Rice, F. O., and E. Teller: "Structure of Matter," John Wiley & Sons, Inc., New York, 1949.

Rothlein, B. J., and P. H. Miller: Measurements of Variation of Work Function of Silicon with Temperature, *Phys. Rev.*, vol. 76, p. 1882, 1949.

Ryder, E. J., and W. Shockley: Interpretation of Dependence of Resistivity of Germanium on Electric Field, *Phys. Rev.*, vol. 75, p. 310, 1949.

Ryder, R. M., and R. J. Kircher: Some Aspects of the Transistor, *Bell System Tech. J.*, vol. 28, pp. 367–401, 1949.

Ryder, R. M.: The Type-A Transistor, *Bell Labs. Record*, vol. 27, pp. 89–93, 1949.

Sato, T., and H. Kaneko: Studies on Selenium and Its Alloys (Report 1), Physical Properties of Selenium, *Tech. Rept. Tôhoku Univ.*, vol. 14, no. 2, pp. 45–54, 1949.

Scaff, J. H., H. C. Theuerer, and E. E. Schumacher: P-type and N-type Silicon and the Formation of the Photovoltaic Barrier in Silicon Ingots, *J. Metals*, vol. 185, pp. 383–388, June, 1949.

Schwarz, E.: Theory of Photoconductivity of Layers of Semiconducting Substances, *Proc. Phys. Soc. (London)*, vol. 62A, pp. 530–532, 1949.

Shive, J. N.: Double-surface Transistors, *Phys. Rev.*, vol. 75, pp. 689–690, 1949.

Shive, J. N.: New Germanium Photo-resistance Cell, *Phys. Rev.*, vol. 76, p. 575, 1949.

Shockley, W., G. L. Pearson, and J. R. Haynes: Hole Injection in Germanium—Quantitative Studies and Filamentary Transistors, *Bell System Tech. J.*, vol. 28, pp. 344–366, 1949.

Shockley, W., M. Sparks, and G. K. Teal: The PN Junction Transistor, *Phys. Rev.*, vol. 76, p. 459, 1949.

Shockley, W.: The Theory of P-N Junctions in Semi-conductors and P-N Junction Transistors, *Bell System Tech. J.*, vol. 28, pp. 435–489, 1949.

Shockley, W., and J. A. Becker: Transistor Characteristics, *Electronics*, vol. 22, pp. 132, 164–165, January, 1949.

Simpson, J. H.: Charge Distribution and Energy Levels of Trapped Electrons in Ionic Solids, *Proc. Roy. Soc. (London)*, vol. 197A, pp. 269–281, 1949.

Simpson, J. H.: Status of Transistor and Crystal Rectifier Theory and Development, National Research Council, Canada, October, 1949.

Slater, J. C.: Electrons in Perturbed Periodic Lattices, *Phys. Rev.*, vol. 76, pp. 1592–1601, 1949.

Smith: Characteristics and Applications of Transistors, Master of Science Thesis, MIT, Electrical Engineering Department, 1949.

Smith, A. H.: Temperature Dependence of the Work Function of Semiconductors, *Phys. Rev.*, vol. 75, pp. 953–958, 1949.

Sosnowski, L.: Investigations of Photo-Effects in Semiconductors, *Compt. rend. soc. sci. et Lettres Varsovie*, Cl III, *Sci. Math. Phys.*, 1949.

Spenke, E.: Non-homogeneous Distributions of Impurity Centers in Dry Rectifiers, *Z. Naturforsch.*, vol. 4a, pp. 37–51, 1949.

Spenke, E.: On the Barrier Layer Theory of Dry Rectifiers, *Z. Physik*, vol. 126, pp. 67–83, 1949.

Straubel, H.: New Applications of Semiconductor Resistors, *Z. angew. Physik*, vol. 1, pp. 506–509, 1949.

Stuetzer, O. M.: Experiments for Controlling the Current Flow through a Metal-semi-conductor Contact, IRE-Princeton Symposium on Electron Devices, June, 1949.

Sueur, S.: Les detecteurs a germanium, *Inform. technique*, January–February, 1949.

Sueur, S.: The Transistor Triode Type PTT 601, *Onde élect.*, vol. 29, pp. 389–397, 1949.

Suhl, H., and W. Shockley: Concentrating Holes and Electrons by Magnetic Fields, *Phys. Rev.*, vol. 75, pp. 1617–1618, 1949.

Taft, E., and L. Apker: Photoelectric Determination of Fermi level at Amorphous Arsenic Surfaces, *Phys. Rev.*, vol. 76, pp. 1181–1182, 1949.

Teszner, S.: Theory of Electronic Semiconductors and of Derived Complexes, *Bull. soc. franç. élect.*, vol. 9, pp. 401–432, 1949.

Tolpigo, K. B.: Thermionic Emission from Thin Semiconducting Films, *J. Tech. Phys. (U.S.S.R.)*, vol. 19, p. 1301, 1949.

Tucker, D. G.: Rectifier Modulators with Frequency Selective Terminations, *J. Inst. Elec. Engrs. (London)*, part III, vol. 96, pp. 422–428, 1949.

Turner, R. P.: Build a Transistor, *Radio-Electronics*, vol. 20, pp. 38–39, May, 1949.

Turner, R. P.: Tubeless Oscillator Uses a IN34 Crystal, *Radio-Electronics*, vol. 20, October, 1949.

van Itterbeck, A.: Measurements on the Electrical Resistivity of Thin Metallic Films, *Physica*, vol. 15, pp. 80–82, 1949.

Webster, W. M., E. Eberhard, and L. E. Barton: Some Novel Circuits for the Three Terminal Semiconductor Amplifier, *RCA Rev.*, vol. 10, pp. 5-16, 1949.

Wright, R. W., and J. P. Andrews: Temperature Variation of the Electrical Properties of Nickel Oxide, *Proc. Phys. Soc. (London)*, vol. 62A, pp. 446–455, 1949.

Yamashita, J.: The Theory of Thermoelectromotive Force in Semiconductors, *J. Phys. Soc. Japan*, vol. 4, pp. 310–315, 1949.

Zworykin, V. K., and E. G. Ramberg: "Photoelectricity and Its Applications," John Wiley & Sons, Inc., New York, 1949.

Characteristics of Three Transistor Circuits, *Electronics*, vol. 22, pp. 120, 122, August, 1949.

The Coaxial Transistor, *Bell Labs. Record*, vol. 27, p. 129, 1949.

Crystal Valves: Their Construction Simply Explained, *Elec. Rev.*, vol. 144, pp. 507–508, March, 1949.

Der dreielektroden-kristall (Transistor), *Elektron Wiss. u. Tech.*, vol. 3, pp. 255–261, July, 1949.

Electrostatic Field Controlled Semiconductors, MCR EE 49-9, Wright-Patterson Air Force Base, Feb. 21, 1949.

Experimental Crystal Amplifier, *Electronic Eng.*, vol. 21, pp. 448–449, 1949.

Modern Materials, *Electrician*, vol. 143, pp. 893–894, 1949.

Photo-effects in Semiconductors, *Elec. Eng.*, vol. 68, pp. 937–942, 1949.

Semiconductor Rectifiers, *Elec. Eng.*, vol. 68, pp. 865–872, 1949.

Semiconductors, *Bell System Tech. J.*, vol. 28, pp. 335–489, 1949.

Transistor, *Elect. News and Eng.*, vol. 58, no. 18, pp. 89, 92, 94, 1949.

Transistor, *Railway Sig. and Commun.*, vol. 42, pp. 507–508, August, 1949.

Transistor—An Amplifying Crystal, *Aerovox Research Worker*, vol. 19, pp. 1–3, February, 1949.

Transistor as a Beat-frequency Oscillator and Amplifier, *Electronics*, vol. 22, pp. 120–121, November, 1949.

Transistor Audiences, *Bell Labs. Record*, vol. 17, pp. 22–23, 1949.

Transistor Characteristics (review of papers presented at a conference), *Electronics*, vol. 22, pp. 132, 164–165, January, 1949.

Le transistor: crystal semiconducteur amplificateur et oscillateur, *Tech. moderne*, vol. 41, pp. 99–101, 1949.

A Transistor Curve Tracer, RCA License Laboratory Bulletin LB882, 1949.

Transistors and the Serviceman, *Radio Service Dealer*, vol. 10, pp. 25–26, May, 1949.

1950

Adam, M.: Transistor et transistron, *Tech. moderne*, vol. 42, pp. 220–224, 1950.

Aigrain, P.: Back Current of Germanium Diodes at High Voltages, *Compt. rend.*, vol. 231, pp. 1047–1048, 1950.

Aigrain, P., and C. Dugas: Characteristics of Transistors, *Compt. rend.*, vol. 230, pp. 377–378, 1950.

Aigrain, P.: On the Surface Conductance of Germanium, *Compt. rend.*, vol. 230, pp. 732–733, 1950.

Aigrain, P.: Reverse Current and Capacitance of Germanium Diodes, *Compt. rend.*, vol. 230, pp. 194–196, 1950.

Aigrain, P.: Reverse Current in Germanium Diodes, *Compt. rend.*, vol. 230, pp. 62–63, 1950.

Albanese, L.: Il transistor: triodo a cristallo semiconduttore, *Poste e telecomun.*, vol. 3, pp. 145–156, May, 1950.

Balakrishnan, C.: Johnson-Rahbeck Effect with Electronic Semi-conductor, *Brit. J. Appl. Phys.*, vol. 1, pp. 211–213, 1950.

Banbury, P. C., C. A. Hogarth, and H. A. Gebbie: Crystal Diode and Triode Action in Lead Sulphide, *Proc. Phys. Soc. (London)*, vol. 63B, p. 371, 1950.

Banbury, P. C., and H. K. Henisch: Frequency Response of Lead Sulphide Transistors, *Proc. Phys. Soc. (London)*, vol. 63B, pp. 540–541, 1950.

Bardeen, J., and W. Shockley: Deformation Potentials and Mobilities in Non-polar Crystals, *Phys. Rev.*, vol. 80, pp. 72–80, 1950.

Bardeen, J., and W. G. Pfann: Effects of Electrical Forming on the Rectifying Barriers on N- and P-germanium Transistors, *Phys. Rev.*, vol. 77, pp. 401–402, 1950.

Bardeen, J.: Theory of Relation between Hole Concentration and Characteristics of Germanium Point Contacts, *Bell System Tech. J.*, vol. 29, pp. 469–495, 1950.

Bardeen, J.: Zero-point Vibrations and Superconductivity, *Phys. Rev.*, vol. 79, pp. 167–168, 1950.

Becker, G., and W. Hubner: Static and Dynamic Characteristics of Indirectly Heated Thermistors, *Elektrotechnik*, vol. 4, pp. 151–156, 1950.

Becker, J. A.: Transistors: Summary of Symposium on Semiconductors and the Transistor, *Elec. Eng.*, vol. 69, pp. 58–64, 1950.

Becker, M., and H. Y. Fan: Photovoltaic Effects of P-N Junctions in Germanium, *Phys. Rev.*, vol. 78, pp. 301–302, 1950.

Bevan, D. J. M., and J. S. Anderson: Electronic Conductivity and Surface Equilibria of Zinc Oxide, *Discussions Faraday Soc.*, no. 8, pp. 238–246, 1950.

Billig, E., and P. T. Landsberg: Characteristics of Compound Barrier Layer Rectifiers, *Proc. Phys. Soc. (London)*, vol. 63A, pp. 101–111, 1950.

Blanc-Lapierre, A., and M. Perrot: On Certain Detector Properties Shown by Thin Silver Film, *Compt. rend.*, vol. 230, pp. 1749–1751, 1950.

Blum, A. I., and N. A. Goryunova: Electrical Properties of Grey Tin, *Doklady Akad. Nauk S.S.S.R.*, vol. 75, pp. 367–370, 1950.

Bode, H. W.: "Network Analysis and Feedback Amplifier Design," D. Van Nostrand Company, Inc., New York, 1950.

Boltaks, B. I.: Dependence of the Coefficient of the Thermo E.M.F. in Semiconductors on the Temperature Difference of the Junctions, *J. Tech. Phys. (U.S.S.R.)*, vol. 20, pp. 1039–1048, 1950.

Borchardt, G.: Transistor-fortschritte: les perfectionnements des montages a transistors, *Fortschr. Radiotech.*, vol. 12, pp. 253–260, 1950/1951.

Brattain, W. H., and G. L. Pearson: Changes in Conductivity in Germanium Induced by Alpha Particle Bombardment, *Phys. Rev.*, vol. 80, pp. 846–850, 1950.

Bray, R., and H. J. Yearian: Dependence of the Germanium High Back Voltage Rectifier Resistance on Frequency, *Phys. Rev.*, vol. 77, p. 760, 1950.

Breckenridge, R. G.: Solid State Electronics, *Electronic Eng.*, vol. 22, pp. 106–109, 1950.

Briggs, H. B.: Infra-red Absorption in Silicon, *Phys. Rev.*, vol. 77, pp. 727–728, 1950.

Briggs, H. B.: Optical Effects in Bulk Silicon and Germanium, *Phys. Rev.*, vol. 77, p. 287, 1950.

Broser, I., and R. Warminsky: Electrical Properties of Cadmium Sulphide Crystals Which Depend on the Electrode Arrangement, *Z. Naturforsch.*, vol. 5a, pp. 62–63, 1950.

Brown, C. B.: High-frequency Operation of Transistors, *Electronics*, vol. 23, pp. 81–83, July, 1950.

Busch, G.: Electron Conduction in Non-metals, *Z. angew. Math. Physik*, vol. 1, pp. 3–31, 81–110, 1950.

Busch, G., J. Wieland, and H. Zoller: Experiments on the Measurement of the Electrical Conductivity of Grey Tin, *Helv. Phys. Acta*, vol. 23, pp. 528–529, 1950.

Chang Chen, Tung: Diode Coincidence and Mixing Circuits in Digital Computation, *Proc. IRE*, vol. 38, pp. 511–514, 1950.

Claussnitzer, W., and H. Heumann: Mapping Electric Fields with the Help of Semiconducting Sheets, *Z. angew. Physik*, vol. 2, pp. 443–446, 1950.

Cleland, J. W., K. Lark-Horovitz, and J. C. Pigg: Transmutation-produced Germanium Semiconductors, *Phys. Rev.*, vol. 78, pp. 814–815, 1950.

Conwell, E. M., and V. F. Weisskopf: Theory of Impurity Scattering in Semiconductors, *Phys. Rev.*, vol. 77, pp. 388–390, 1950.

Crawford, J. H., Jr., and K. Lark-Horovitz: Fast Neutron Bombardment Effects in Germanium, *Phys. Rev.*, vol. 78, pp. 815–816, 1950.

Crawford, J. H., Jr., and K. Lark-Horovitz: Thermal Equilibrium in Neutron-irradiated Semiconductors, *Phys. Rev.*, vol. 79, pp. 889–890, 1950.

Douglas, R. W.: Semiconductors and Their Applications, *Gen. Elec. Co. J.*, vol. 17, pp. 107–124, 1950.

Dunlap, W. C.: Some Properties of High-resistivity P-type Germanium, *Phys. Rev.*, vol. 79, pp. 286–292, 1950.

DuPre, F. K.: Non Linear I-V Characteristics of Germanium at Very Low Temperatures, *Phys. Rev.*, vol. 77, p. 152, 1950.

DuPre, F. K., R. A. Hutner, and E. S. Rittner: On the Interpretation of Conduction and Thermionic Emission of (Ba-Sr)O Cathodes, *Phys. Rev.*, vol. 78, pp. 567–571, 1950.

Ehrenberg, W.: The Electric Conductivity of Simple Semiconductors, *Proc. Phys. Soc. (London)*, vol. 63A, pp. 75–76, 1950.

Ellis, W. C.: Twin Relationships in Ingots of Germanium, *J. Metals*, vol. 188, p. 886, June, 1950.

Engel, A., H. Welker, and H. F. Matare: Crystal Detectors and Their Use at U. H. F. I. General Features of the Problem, *Bull. soc. franç. elect.*, vol. 10, pp. 379–380, 1950.

Erginsoy, C.: Neutral Impurity Scattering in Semiconductors, *Phys. Rev.*, vol. 79, pp. 1013–1014, 1950.

Erginsoy, C.: On the Mechanism of Impurity Band Conduction in Semiconductors, *Phys. Rev.*, vol. 80, pp. 1104–1105, 1950.

Estermann, I., and A. Foner: Magneto-resistance of Germanium Samples between 20° and 300°K, *Phys. Rev.*, vol. 79, pp. 365–372, 1950.

Fan, H. Y.: Temperature Dependence of Energy Gap in Monoatomic Semiconductors, *Phys. Rev.*, vol. 78, pp. 808–809, 1950.

Fan, H. Y., and M. Becker: Temperature Dependence of Photovoltaic Effects on P-N Barriers in Germanium, *Phys. Rev.*, vol. 78, p. 335, 1950.

Fricke, H.: Halbleiter-trioden und -tetroden als verstaerker und mischstufen, *Elektrotech. Z.*, vol. 71, pp. 133–137, 1950.

Frohlich, H.: Conduction Electrons in Non-metallic Solids, *Research*, vol. 3, pp. 202–207, 1950.

Frohlich, H., and J. O'Dwyer: Time Dependence of Electronic Processes in Dielectrics, *Proc. Phys. Soc. (London)*, vol. 63A, pp. 81–85, 1950.

Fukuroi, T., S. Tanuma, and S. Tobisawa: On the Electromagnetic Properties of Single Crystals of Tellurium. II. Ettingshausen-Nernst Effect, *Sci. Repts. Research Insts. Tôhoku Univ.*, ser. A, vol. 2, pp. 233–238, 1950.

Fukuroi, T., S. Tanuma, and S. Tobisawa: On the Electromagnetic Properties of Single Crystals of Tellurium. III. Adiabatic and Isothermal Hall Effect and Ettingshausen Effect, *Sci. Repts. Research Insts. Tôhoku Univ.*, ser. A, vol. 2, pp. 238–248, 1950.

Garner, W. E., T. J. Gray, and F. S. Stone: Reactions on the Surface of Copper Oxide. *Discussions Faraday Soc.*, no. 8, pp. 246–250, 1950.

Gaule, G.: The Transistor—Bibliographical Survey (40 Summaries), *Fernmeldtech. Z.*, vol. 3, pp. 390–400, 1950.

Gebbie, H. A., P. C. Banbury, and C. A. Hogarth: Crystal Diode and Triode Action in Lead Sulphide, *Proc. Phys. Soc. (London)*, vol. 63B, p. 371, 1950.

Gisolf, J. H., On the Back Current in Backing Layer Rectifiers, *Phil. Mag.*, vol. 41, pp. 754–769, 1950.

Goucher, F. S.: The Photon Yield of Electron-hole Pairs in Germanium, *Phys. Rev.*, vol. 78, p. 816, 1950.

Goucher, F. S.: The Quantum Yield of Electron-hole Pairs in Germanium, *Phys. Rev.*, vol. 78, p. 646, 1950.

Gray, T. J.: Semi-conductivity and Catalysis, *Discussions Faraday Soc.*, no. 8, pp. 331–337, 1950.

Guentherschulze, A.: Der heutige Stand der Sperrschichtgleichrichter, *Elektrotech. Z.*, vol. 71, pp. 414–419, 1950.

Gurevich, D. B., N. A. Tolstoi, and P. P. Feofilov: Relaxation of the Photoconductivity of Semiconductors, *J. Exptl. Theoret. Phys. (U.S.S.R.)*, vol. 20, pp. 769–782, 1950.

Haegele, R. W.: The Crystal Tetrode; Its Use as Frequency Converter, *Onde élect.*, vol. 30, pp. 239–241, 1950.

Hall, R. N., and W. C. Dunlap: P-N Junctions Prepared by Impurity Diffusion, *Phys. Rev.*, vol. 80, pp. 467–468, 1950.

Harris, E. J.: Semi-conductors, *Electronic Eng.*, vol. 22, pp. 106–109, 1950.

Hauffe, K., and A. L. Vierk: Electrical Conductivity of Zinc Oxide with Added Foreign Oxides, *Z. physik. Chem.*, vol. 196, pp. 160–180, 1950.

Hauffe, K.: Lattice Defect Phenomena and Diffusion Processes in Semi Conducting Mixed Phases, *Ann. Physik*, vol. 8, pp. 201–210, 1950.

Heins, H.: Germanium Crystal Triodes, *Sylvania Technologist*, vol. 3, pp. 13–18, January, 1950.

Henisch, H. K., and J. Ewels: A Study of Electrical Forming Phenomena at Selenium Contacts, *Proc. Phys. Soc. (London)*, vol. 63B, pp. 861–876, 1950.

Henkel, H. W.: Conductivity of Liquid Selenium—200–500°C, *J. Appl. Phys.*, vol. 21, pp. 725–731, 1950.

Henkel, H. W.: Thermoelectric Power, and Mobility of Carriers in Selenium, *Phys. Rev.*, vol. 77, pp. 734–736, 1950.

Hibi, T.: Electric Conductivity of Semi-conductors, *Science Repts. Research Insts. Tôhoku Univ.*, ser. A, vol. 2, pp. 150–155, 1950.

Hibi, T.: Thermionic Emission of Semi-conductors, *Science Repts. Research Insts. Tôhoku Univ.*, ser. A, vol. 2, pp. 157–166, 1950.

Hoffmann, A.: An Oscillograph Method for the Investigation of Barrier Layer Properties of Metal Rectifiers, *Z. angew. Physik*, vol. 2, pp. 253–259, 1950.

Hofstradter, R., S. H. Liebson, and J. O. Elliot: Terphenyl and Dibenzyl Scintillation Counters, *Phys. Rev.*, vol. 78, p. 81, 1950.

Hollmann, H. E.: Semiconductive Colloidal Suspensions with Non-linear Properties, *J. Appl. Phys.*, vol. 21, pp. 402–413, 1950.

Hung, C. S., and J. R. Gliessman: The Resistivity and Hall Effect of Germanium at Low Temperature, *Phys. Rev.*, vol. 79, pp. 726–727, 1950.

Hung, C. S., and V. A. Johnson: Resistivity of Semiconductors Containing Both Acceptors and Donors, *Phys. Rev.*, vol. 79, pp. 535–536, 1950.

Hung, C. S.: Theory of Resistivity and Hall Effect at Very Low Temperature, *Phys. Rev.*, vol. 79, pp. 727–728, 1950.

Hungermann, E. H.: The Physics and Technic of Transistors, *Elektron Wiss. u. Tech.*, vol. 4, pp. 357–367, 1950.

Hunter, L. P.: Graphical Analysis of Transistor Characteristics, *Proc. IRE*, vol. 38, pp. 1387–1391, 1950.

Hunter, L. P.: Physical Interpretation of Type-A Transistor Characteristics, *Phys. Rev.*, vol. 77, pp. 558–559, 1950.

Hunter, L. P., and R. E. Brown: Production Tester for Transistors, *Electronics*, vol. 23, pp. 96–99, October, 1950.

Hutner, R. A., E. S. Rittner, and F. K. DuPre: Fermi Levels in Semiconductors, *Philips Research Reports*, vol. 5, pp. 188–204, 1950.

Jaffray, J.: The Behaviour of the Electric Conductivity of Some Semiconductors at the Time of Passing through a State of Transformation or Transition, *Compt. rend.*, vol. 230, pp. 525–527, 1950.

Jarret, J. A., and J. E. Jarret: Modulation of Electric Current by Semiconductors of a Rubber Nature, *Rev. gén. caoutchouc*, vol. 27, pp. 341–343, 1950.

Johnson, V. A., R. N. Smith, and H. J. Yearian: D. C. Characteristics of Silicon and Germanium Point Contact Crystal Rectifiers. II. The Multicontact Theory, *J. Appl. Phys.*, vol. 21, pp. 283–289, 1950.

Johnson, V. A., and K. Lark-Horovitz: Electron Mobility in Germanium, *Phys. Rev.*, vol. 79, pp. 409–410, 1950.

Johnson, V. A., and H. Y. Fan: Temperature Dependence of the Energy Gap in Germanium from Conductivity and Hall Data, *Phys. Rev.*, vol. 79, p. 899, 1950.

Johnson, V. A., and K. Lark-Horovitz: Theoretical Hall Coefficient Expressions for Impurity Semiconductors, *Phys. Rev.*, vol. 79, pp. 176–177, 1950.

Kalabukhov, N. P., and N. G. Politov: Secondary Current in Coloured KCI Crystals, *Doklady Akad. Nauk S.S.S.R.*, vol. 70, pp. 805–808, 1950.

Kendall, J. T.: Electrical Conductivity of Gray Tin, *Proc. Phys. Soc. (London)*, vol. 63B, pp. 821–822, 1950.

Konstantinova, V. P., and T. Kh. Chormonov: The Effect of Purification on the Ferroelectric Properties of Crystals of Rochelle Salt, *Doklady Akad. Nauk S.S.S.R.*, vol. 75, pp. 11–14, 1950.

Kuehn, R.: Crystal Diodes in TV Studio Equipment, *Electronics*, vol. 23, pp. 114–116, December, 1950.

Kushida, T.: On the Anomalous Electrical Properties of Beta Cu_2S, *J. Sci., Hiroshima Univ.*, ser. A, vol. 14, pp. 147–150, 1950.

Lashkarev, V. E.: Diffusion of Carriers of Current in Semiconductors with Compound Conductivity, *Doklady Akad. Nauk S.S.S.R.*, vol. 73, pp. 929–932, 1950.

Lashkarev, V. E.: Influence of Electric Field on Photo-E. M. F. in Insulated Semiconductors, *Doklady Akad. Nauk S.S.S.R.*, vol. 70, pp. 813–816, 1950.

Lashkarev, V. E.: Investigation of the Kinetics of Photoconductivity of Semiconductors by a Compensation Method, *Izvest. Akad. Nauk S.S.S.R.*, ser. Fiz., vol. 14, pp. 199–211, 1950.

Levy, I. E.: The Measurement of Contact Difference in Potential on Certain Oxide-coated Cathode Diodes, *Proc. IRE*, vol. 38, pp. 774–776, 1950.

Loosjes, R., and H. J. Vink: Conduction Processes in the Oxide-coated Cathode, *Philips Tech. Rev.*, vol. 11, pp. 271–278, 1950.

Macfarlane, G. G.: Theory of Contact Noise in Semiconductors, *Proc. Phys. Soc. (London)*, vol. 63B, pp. 807–814, 1950.

McKay, K. G.: Electron Bombardment Conductivity in Diamond, *Phys. Rev.*, vol. 77, pp. 816–825, 1950.

Matare, H. F.: Background Noise in Semiconductors II, *J. phys. radium*, vol. 11, pp. 130–140, 1950.

Matare, H. F.: Notes on the Amplification Observed on Semiconductors (The Transistor Phenomenon), *Onde élect.*, vol. 30, pp. 469–475, 1950.

Matare, H. F.: Transistor Measurement Techniques, *Elektron Wiss. u. Tech.*, vol. 4, pp. 368–379, 1950.

Matare, H. F.: Von der Vakuumdiode zum Kristalldetektor, *Elektron Wiss. u. Tech.*, vol. 4, pp. 229–236, 1950.

Meacham, L. A., and S. E. Michaels: Observations of the Rapid Withdrawal of Stored Holes from Germanium Transistors and Varistors, *Phys. Rev.*, vol. 78, pp. 175–176, 1950.

Montgomery, H. C.: Background Noise in Transistors, *Bell Labs. Record*, vol. 28, pp. 400–403, 1950.

Montgomery, H. C., and W. Shockley: Noise in Germanium Related to Fluctuations in Hole Concentrations, *Phys. Rev.*, vol. 78, p. 646, 1950.

Moses, R. C.: Germanium Diode Impulse Noise Limiters, *Sylvania Technologist*, vol. 3, pp. 1–5, October, 1950.

Moss, T. S.: Photoconductivity in Magnesium Antimonide, *Proc. Phys. Soc. (London)*, vol. 63B, pp. 982–989, 1950.

Mott, N. F., and R. W. Gurney: "Electronic Processes in Ionic Crystals," Oxford University Press, New York, 1950.

Muser, H.: The Fermi Level in Electronic Semiconductors, *Z. Naturforsch.*, vol. 5a, pp. 18–25, 1950.

N'Guyen, T. C., and J. Suchet: Semi-conductors with Large Negative Temperature Coefficients: Thermistors, *Ann. Radioelec.*, vol 5, pp. 155–167, 1950.

Okamura, T., Y. Torizuka, and Y. Kojima: Microwave Resonance Absorption of $NiOFe_2O_3$, *Phys. Rev.*, vol. 80, pp. 910–911, 1950.

Okamura, T., Y. Torizuka, and Y. Kojima: Microwave Resonance Absorption in Ferromagnetic Semi-conductor, I. Nickel Ferrite, *Sci. Repts. Research Insts. Tôhoku Univ.*, ser. A, vol. 2, pp. 663–672, 1950.

Okamura, T., and Y. Torizuka: Microwave Resonance Absorption in Semi-conductor. II. Magnetite Single Crystal, *Sci. Repts. Research Insts. Tôhoku Univ.*, ser. A, vol. 2, pp. 822–827, 1950.

Okamura, T., and J. Simoizaka: On the Reaction Kinetics of Spinel-type Ferrite. I. Nickel Ferrite, *Sci. Repts. Research Insts. Tôhoku Univ.*, ser. A, vol. 2, pp. 673–894, 1950.

Okamura, T., and Y. Torizuka: Research on the Specific Heat and the Hall Effect of Magnetite, *Sci. Repts. Research Insts. Tôhoku Univ.*, ser. A, vol. 2, pp. 352–360, 1950.

O'Neill, C. D.: Germanium Photocells, *Proc. Natl. Electronics Conf.*, vol. 6, pp. 266–275, 1950.

Orman, C., H. Y. Fan, G. J. Goldsmith, and K. Lark-Horovitz: Germanium P-N Barriers As Counters, *Phys. Rev.*, vol. 78, p. 646, 1950.

Ortueta, R. L., and E. Y. Garrido: Semiconductors, *Rev. Telecommun. (Madrid)*, vol. 6, pp. 12–22, December, 1950.

Osbahr, B. F.: Characteristics of Germanium Diodes, *Tele-Tech*, vol. 9, pp. 33–34, December, 1950.

Pantchechnikoff, J. I.: On the Nature of a Soldered Contact on a Semiconductor, *Phys. Rev.*, vol. 79, pp. 1027–1028, 1950.

Parker, P.: Semiconductors, *Electronics*, vol. 23, 1950.

Pearson, G. L., J. R. Haynes, and W. Shockley: Comment on Mobility Anomalies in Germanium, *Phys. Rev.*, vol. 78, pp. 295–296, 1950.

Pearson, G. L., and J. D. Struthers: Correlation of Geiger Counter and Hall Effect Measurement in Alloys Containing Germanium and Radioactive Antimony 124, *Phys. Rev.*, vol. 77, pp. 809–813, 1950.

Pearson, G. L., and J. Bardeen: Erratum to Electrical Properties of Pure Silicon and Silicon Alloys, *Phys. Rev.*, vol. 77, p. 303, 1950.

Pekar, S. I., and Yu. E. Perlin: Recombination of Conductivity Electrons of the Colour Centres in Crystals, *J. Exptl. Theoret. Phys. (U.S.S.R.)*, vol. 20, pp. 271–273, 1950.

Pekar, S. I.: Theory of the Recombination of Electrons in Semiconductors, *J. Exptl. Theoret. Phys. (U.S.S.R.)*, vol. 20, pp. 267–270, 1950.

Perlin, Yu. E.: Polarizability of the Colour Center, *J. Exptl. Theoret. Phys. (U.S.S.R.)*, vol. 20, pp. 274–278, 1950.

Petritz, R. L., and A. J. F. Siegert: On the Theory of Noise in Semiconductors, *Phys. Rev.*, vol. 79, pp. 215–216, 1950.

Pfann, W. G., and J. H. Scaff: The P-Germanium Transistor, *Proc. IRE*, vol. 38, pp. 1151–1154, 1950.

Pfann, W. G.: The Transistor As a Reversible Amplifier, *Proc. IRE*, vol. 38, p. 1222, 1950.
Pietenpol, W. J., and R. S. Ohl: Characteristics of Silicon Transistors, paper given at Conference on Electron Devices, University of Michigan, June 22, 1950.
Putseiko, E. K., and A. N. Terenin: Accumulation of Electrons of a Semiconductor at the Organic Dyes Absorbed on It, *Doklady Akad. Nauk S.S.S.R.*, vol. 70, pp. 401–404, 1950.
Read, W. T., and W. Shockley: Dislocation Models of Crystal Grain Boundaries, *Phys. Rev.*, vol. 78, pp. 275–289, 1950.
Richardson, J. M.: The Linear Theory of Fluctuations Arising from Diffusional Mechanisms —An Attempt at a Theory of Contact Noise, *Bell System Tech. J.*, vol. 29, pp.117–141, 1950.
Ronge, G., and C. Wagner: Transference Numbers of Solid Potassium Chloride with Strontium Chloride, Potassium Oxide, and Sodium Sulfide as Additives, *J. Chem. Phys.*, vol. 18, pp. 74–76, 1950.
Rothlein, B. J., and F. A. Stahl: Photo-electric Effect in Germanium, *Sylvania Technologist*, vol. 3, pp. 8–12, April, 1950.
Ryvkin, S. M.: Fundamental Investigation of Photoconductivity. I. Definition of the Problem and the Method of Research, *J. Exptl. Theoret. Phys. (U.S.S.R.)*, vol. 20, pp. 139–151, 1950.
Salow, H.: Secondary Emission from Alloys, *Ann. Physik*, vol. 5, pp. 417–428, 1950.
Schaetti, N., and W. Baumgartner: The Photo-effect of Alkali-germanium Compounds, *Helv. Phys. Acta*, vol. 23, pp. 524–528, 1950.
Scott, T. R.: Crystal Triodes, *Inst. Elec. Engrs. Paper* 990, 1950.
Shive, J. N.: The Phototransistor, *Bell Labs. Record*, vol. 28, p. 289, 1950.
Shockley, W.: "Electrons and Holes in Semiconductors, with Applications to Transistor Electronics," D. Van Nostrand Company, Inc., New York, 1950.
Shockley, W.: Energy Band Structures in Semiconductors, *Phys. Rev.*, vol. 78, pp. 173–174, 1950.
Shockley, W., and J. Bardeen: Energy Bands and Mobilities in Monoatomic Semiconductors, *Phys. Rev.*, vol. 77, pp. 407–408, 1950.
Shockley, W.: Holes and Electrons, *Phys. Today*, vol. 3, pp. 16–24, October, 1950.
Shockley, W.: Hot Electrons in Germanium and Ohm's Law, *Bell System Tech. J.*, vol. 30, pp. 990–1034, 1950.
Shockley, W.: Theories of High Values of Alpha for Collector Contacts on Germanium, *Phys. Rev.*, vol. 78, pp. 294–295, 1950.
Skaupy, F.: The Historical Development of the Semiconductor Problem and of Semiconductor Resistors, *Z. Elektrochem.*, vol. 54, pp. 159–160, 1950.
Slade, B. N.: High-performance Transistor with Wide Spacing between Contacts, *RCA Rev.*, vol. 11, pp. 517–526, 1950.
Sliskovic, J.: Neue Erkenntnisse ueber Transistoren, *Elektrotech. u. Maschinenbau, suppl. Radiotechnik*, vol. 26, pp. 105–109, March, 1950.
Stahelin, P., and G. Busch: Electrical Conductivity of Molybdenum Trioxide, *Helv. Phys. Acta*, vol. 23, pp. 530–531, 1950.
Stockmann, F.: Electric Conduction in Semiconductors, *Naturwissenschaften*, vol. 37, pp. 85–89, 105–111, 1950.
Stuetzer, O. M.: A Crystal Amplifier with High Input Impedance, *Proc. IRE*, vol. 38, pp. 868–871, 1950.
Stuetzer, O. M.: Microspacer Electrode Technique, *Proc. IRE*, vol. 38, pp. 871–876, 1950.
Stuetzer, O. M.: Transistor and Fieldistor, *Electronics*, vol. 23, pp. 167–171, July, 1950.
Sweeney, J. H.: Application of Germanium Diodes in Very High and Ultrahigh TV Sets, *Television Eng.*, vol. 1, pp. 10–11, 36, February, 1950.
Sweeney, J. H.: Use of Germanium Diodes at High Frequency, *Elec. Eng.*, vol. 69, pp. 217–220, 1950.
Taylor, H. S.: Catalysis: Retrospect and Prospect, *Discussions Faraday Soc.*, no. 8, pp. 9–18, 1950.
Taylor, J. H.: Pressure Dependence of Resistance of Germanium, *Phys. Rev.*, vol. 80, pp. 919–920, 1950.
Taylor, W. E., and H. Y. Fan: D-C Characteristics of High Resistance Barriers at Crystal Boundaries in Germanium, *Phys. Rev.*, vol. 78, p. 335A, 1950.
Teal, G. K., and J. B. Little: Growth of Germanium Single Crystals, *Phys. Rev.*, vol. 78, p. 647, 1950.
Teszner, S.: Semiconducteurs electroniques et complexes derives-theories-applications, Gauthier-Villars & Cie, Paris, 1950.
Tillman, J. R.: A Note on the Decay of Current in Germanium Diodes, *Phil. Mag.*, vol. 41, pp. 1281–1283, 1950.
Tonnesen, T. H.: Noen trekk fra utviklingen av transistorkonstruksjoner, *Ingenioren*, vol. 59, pp. 933–937, 1950.

Toth, D. H.: The Potentialities of Transistors in Digital Computing Circuits, Engineering Research Associates, Inc., St. Paul, Minn., July 12, 1950.

Trey, F.: Unipolarity and Applied Voltage, *Z. angew. Physik.*, vol. 2, no. 9, pp. 367–369, 1950.

Turner, R. P.: Crystal Receiver with Transistor Amplifier, *Radio Television News*, vol. 43, pp. 38–39, January, 1950.

Turner, R. P.: Experimental Circuits for Crystal Triodes, *Radio-Electronics*, vol. 21, pp. 66, 68–70, June, 1950.

Turner, R. P.: New Applications for Crystal Diodes, *Radio Television News*, vol. 43, pp. 64–65, 150–151, June, 1950.

Untermann, G.: Measurement of the Electrical and Magnetic Constants of Semiconductors at U. H. F. by the Concentric Line Method, *Z. angew. Physik*, vol. 2, pp. 233–241, 1950.

van der Ziel, A.: Note on the Total Emission Damping and Total Emission Noise, *Proc. IRE*, vol. 38, p. 562, 1950.

van der Ziel, A.: On the Noise Spectra of Semiconductor Noise and of Flicker Effect, *Physica*, vol. 16, pp. 359–372, 1950.

van Itterbeck, A., L. De Greve, and R. Lambeir: Measurements on the Electrical Resistivity of Iron Films at Low Temperatures, *Meded. Koninkl. Vlaam. Acad. Wetenschap.*, vol. 12, 1950.

van Roosbroeck, W.: Theory of the Flow of Electrons and Holes in Germanium and Other Semiconductors, *Bell System Tech. J.*, vol. 29, pp. 560–607, 1950.

van Santen, J. H., and G. H. Jonker: Electrical Conductivity of Ferromagnetic Compounds of Manganese of Perovskite Structure, *Physica*, vol. 16, pp. 599–600, 1950.

Vavilov, V. S.: H.F. Current Amplification with Germanium Crystal Triodes, *Uspekhi Fiz. Nauk, vol. 40, pp. 120–141, January, 1950.*

Veith, W.: The Properties and Mechanism of the Photoelectric Emission of Cs-Sb Layers, *J. phys. et radium*, vol. 11, pp. 507–513, 1950.

Verwey, E. J. W., P. W. Haaijman, F. C. Romeijn, and G. W. van Oosterhout: Controlled Valency Semiconductors, *Philips Research Repts.*, vol. 5, pp. 173–187, 1950.

Vidal, P.: The Semiconducting Properties of a Natural Calcium Carbonate, *Ann. Physik*, vol. 5, pp. 257–309, 1950.

Wagner, C., and P. Hantelmann: Determination of the Concentrations of Cation and Anion Vacancies in Solid Potassium Chloride, *J. Chem. Phys.*, vol. 18, pp. 72–74, 1950.

Wright, D. A.: "Semi-conductors," John Wiley & Sons, Inc., New York, 1950.

Yamaguchi, J., and S. Katayama: On Cadmium Selenide of Selenium Rectifiers, *J. Phys. Soc. Japan*, vol. 5, pp. 386–387, 1950.

Yearian, H. J.: D.C. Characteristics of Silicon and Germanium Point Contact Crystal Rectifiers, *J. Appl. Phys.*, vol. 21, pp. 214–221, 1950.

Germanium Crystal Rectifiers, *Engineer*, vol. 189, pp. 329–330, Mar. 17, 1950.

A New Type of Electric Eye Developed by Bell Labs. *Elec. Eng.*, vol. 69, pp. 476–477, 1950.

The Phototransistor, *Western Union Tech. Rev.*, vol. 4, p. 102, 1950.

Transistor Circuits, *Cornell-Dubilier Capacitor*, vol. 15, pp. 3–7, February, 1950.

Transistor et transistron, *Tech. mod.*, vol. 42, pp. 220–223, July, 1950.

1951

Adam, M. Electronic Rubber, *Nature (Paris)*, no. 3199, pp. 330–332, 1951; *Rev. gen. caoutchouc*, vol. 29, p. 302, 1951.

Adler, R. B.: A Large Signal Equivalent Circuit for Transistor Static Characteristics, MIT, October, 1951.

Aigrain, P., C. Dugas, and J. Germain: Adsorption on Semiconductors, *Compt. rend.*, vol. 232, pp. 1100–1101, 1951.

American Society for Testing Materials: "Quality Control of Materials," ASTM Manual, part III, pp. 55–114, January, 1951.

Anderson, A. E.: Some Switching Characteristics of Transistors, in Bell Telephone Labs., Inc., "The Transistor . . . ," pp. 283–333, New York, 1951.

Anderson, A. E.: A Stabilized Transistor Delay and Switching Circuit, in Bell Telephone Labs, Inc., "The Transistor . . . ," pp. 429–435, 1951.

Anselm, A. I.: Some Problems of Electron Theory of Crystals, *J. Tech. Phys. (U.S.S.R.)*, vol. 21, pp. 489–503, 1951.

Armstrong, L. D.: Crystal Diodes in Modern Electronics, *Radio Television News*, vol. 46, pp. 47–50, 162–166, April, 1951; pp. 66–68, May, 1951; pp. 60–62, 108, June, 1951.

Baltensperger, W.: Contribution to the Theory of Impurity Centers in Silicon, *Phys. Rev.*, vol. 83, pp. 1055–1056, 1951.

Banbury, P. C., H. A. Gebbie, and C. A. Hogarth: Crystal Triode Action in Lead Sulphide, in "Conference on Semi-conducting Materials, Proceedings . . . ," pp. 78–86, New York, Academic Press, 1951.

Bell Telephone Laboratories, Inc.: The Transistor; Selected Reference Material on Characteristics and Applications, Office of Technical Services PB 11054, New York, 1951.

Benda, H.: Measurements of the Electrical Conductivity of Cadmium Sulphide Crystals Due to Bombardment with Electrons of Medium Energy, *Ann. Physik*, vol. 9, pp. 413–422, 1951.

Bennett, A. I., and L. P. Hunter: Pulse Measurement of the Inverse Voltage Characteristic of Germanium Point Contacts, *Phys. Rev.*, vol. 81, p. 152, 1951.

Bettridge, B. R. A.: Germanium Crystal Valves: an Assessment of Characteristics and Applications, *Electronic Eng.*, vol. 23, pp. 414–417, 1951.

Billig, E.: Effect of Temperature on the Height of Potential Barriers and on the Breakdown Voltage of Contact Rectifier, *Proc. Phys. Soc. (London)*, vol. 64A, pp. 752–753, 1951.

Billig, E.: Effect of the Change in Lattice Parameter on the Width of the Forbidden Energy Zone According to Kronig and Penney's One-dimensional Lattice Model, *Proc. Phys. Soc. (London)*, vol. 64A, pp. 878–880, 1951.

Blodgett, K. B.: Surface Conductivity of Lead Silicate Glass after Hydrogen Treatment, *J. Am. Ceram. Soc.*, vol. 34, pp. 14–27, 1951.

Blum, A. I., and A. R. Regel: Electric Properties of Solid Solutions of Mercury-selenide and Selenium, *J. Tech. Phys. (U.S.S.R.)*, vol. 21, pp. 316–327, 1951.

Bogoroditski, N. P., and I. D. Fridberg: Electrical Ceramics and Characteristics of Ionic Crystals, *Elektrichestvo*, no. 5, pp. 52–56, May, 1951.

Bohr, E., and H. French: Tubeless Oscillator Covers Audio to 2 Mc, *Radio-Electronics*, vol. 22, p. 43, June, 1951.

Boltaks, B. I., F. I. Vasenin, and A. E. Salumina: Electric and Thermoelectric Properties of Partially Reduced (Blue) Titanium Dioxide, *Zhur. Tekh. Fiz.*, vol. 21, pp. 537–546, 1951.

Bonch-Bruevich, V. L., and S. V. Tyablikov: On the Theory of Elementary Excitations in a Weak Non-ideal Electron-gas in Crystals, *Doklady Akad. Nauk S.S.S.R.*, vol. 76, pp. 817–819, 1951.

Bowers, W. B.: Transistor Frequency-multiplying Circuit, *Electronics*, vol. 24, pp. 140–141, March, 1951.

Brattain, W. H.: Semi-conductor Surface Phenomena, in "Conference on Semi-conducting Materials, Proceedings . . . ," pp. 37–46, Academic Press, Inc., New York, 1951.

Breckenridge, R.: Solid State Electronics, *Physics Today*, vol. 4, pp. 6–11, September, 1951.

Bridgman, P. W.: Effect of Pressure on Electrical Resistance of Certain Semiconductors, *Proc. Am. Acad. Arts Sci.*, vol. 79, pp. 125–148, 1951.

Buckley, H. E.: "Crystal Growth," John Wiley & Sons, Inc., New York, 1951.

Busch, G., J. Wieland, and H. Zoller: Electrical Properties of Grey Tin, *Helv. Phys. Acta*, vol. 24, pp. 49–62, 1951.

Busch, G., J. Wieland, and H. Zoller: Electronic Properties of Grey Tin, in "Conference on Semi-conducting Materials, Proceedings . . . ," pp. 188–197, Academic Press, Inc., New York, 1951.

Busch, G., and E. Moser: Magnetic Susceptibility of Grey Tin, *Z. physik. Chem.*, vol. 198, pp. 23–29, 1951.

Busch, G., and E. Moser: Magnetism of Free Charge Bearers in Semiconductors, *Helv. Phys. Acta*, vol. 24, pp. 324–331, 1951.

Caruthers, R. S.: Modulators in Carrier Telephone Systems, in Bell Telephone Labs., Inc., "The Transistor . . . ," pp. 415–427, New York, 1951.

Caruthers, R. S.: Some Experimental and Practical Applications of Transistor Oscillators, in Bell Telephone Labs., Inc., "The Transistor . . . ," pp. 397–413, New York, 1951.

Caruthers, R. S.: Some System Applications of Transistor Amplifiers, in Bell Telephone Labs., Inc., "The Transistor . . . ," pp. 335–376, New York, 1951.

Castellan, G. W., and F. Seitz: On the Energy States of Impurities in Silicon, in "Conference on Semi-conducting Materials, Proceedings . . . ," pp. 8–25, Academic Press, New York, 1951.

Chasmar, R. P., and A. F. Gibson: Characteristics of Long Period Photoeffects in Lead Sulphide, *Proc. Phys. Soc. (London)*, vol. 64B, pp. 595–602, 1951.

Chasmar, R. P., and E. H. Putley: Measurement of the Temperature Dependence of Conductivity and Hall Coefficient in Lead Sulphide and Lead Telluride, in "Conference on Semi-conducting Materials, Proceedings . . . ," pp. 208–217, Academic Press, New York, 1951.

Cleland, J. W., J. H. Crawford, Jr., K. Lark-Horovitz, J. C. Pigg, and F. W. Young, Jr.: The Effect of Fast Neutron Bombardment on the Electrical Properties of Germanium, *Phys. Rev.*, vol. 83, pp. 312–319, 1951.

Cleland, J. W., J. H. Crawford, Jr., K. Lark-Horovitz, J. C. Pigg, and F. W. Young, Jr.: Evidence for Production of Hole Traps in Germanium by Fast Neutron Bombardment, *Phys. Rev.*, vol. 84, pp. 861–862, 1951.

"Conference on Semi-conducting Materials, Semi-conducting Materials, Proceedings of a Conference Held at the University of Reading," H. K. Henisch, ed., Academic Press, New York, 1951.

Danko, S. F., and S. J. Lanzalotti: Auto-sembly of Miniature Military Equipment, *Electronics*, vol. 24, pp. 94–98, July, 1951.

Douglas, R. W., and E. G. James: Crystal Diodes, *Proc. Inst. Elec. Engrs. (London)*, part III, vol. 98, pp. 157–168, 177–183, 1951.

Dunoyer, J. M.: Electrical Properties of Thin Layers of Germanium, *J. phys. radium*, vol. 12, pp. 602–606, 1951.

Ehrenberg, W., and J. Hirsch: Conductivity-temperature Characteristics of Lead Sulphides: Influence of Oxygen and of Rate of Heating, *Proc. Phys. Soc. (London)*, vol. 64B, pp. 700–706, 1951.

Fan, H. Y., and M. Becker: Infra-red Optical Properties of Silicon and Germanium, in "Conference on Semi-conducting Materials, Proceedings . . . ," pp. 132–147, Academic Press, New York, 1951.

Fan, H. Y.: Temperature Dependence of the Energy Gap in Semiconductors, *Phys. Rev.*, vol. 82, pp. 900–905, 1951.

Fark, H.: Physical Explanation of Triode Crystals and Their Modern Applications, *Elektrotech. Z.*, vol. 72, p. 690, 1951.

Farley, B. G.: General Considerations Concerning Non-linear Circuits and Negative Resistance, in Bell Telephone Labs., Inc., "The Transistor . . . ," pp. 237–248, New York, 1951.

Felker, J. H.: Notes on the Design of High Speed Digital Computers Using Transistors, in Bell Telephone Labs., Inc., "The Transistor . . . ," pp. 627–751, New York, 1951.

Felker, J. H.: The Transistor As a Computer Component, Bell Laboratories Paper (Association for Computing Machinery), December, 1951.

Fink, D. F., and R. K. Jurgen: The Junction Transistor, *Electronics*, vol. 24, pp. 82–85, November, 1951.

Follingstad, H. G.: A Packaged Angular Position Encoder, in Bell Telephone Labs., Inc., "The Transistor . . . ," pp. 583–609, New York, 1951.

Frerichs, R., and J. E. Jacobs: An Economical Industrial X-ray Detector, *Gen. Elec. Rev.*, vol. 54, pp. 42–45, August, 1951.

Fricke, H.: Amplifiers Using Transistors. I. Mode of Operation and Characteristics, *Arch. tech. Messen*, no. 186, July, 1951.

Fricke, H.: Amplifiers Using Transistors. II. Circuits and Types of Construction, *Arch. tech. Messen*, no. 186, July, 1951.

Fukuroi, T.: On the Width of Forbidden Energy Zone of Tellurium, *Sci. Repts. Research Insts. Tôhoku Univ.*, ser. A, vol. 3, pp. 175–181, 1951.

Geist, D.: The Diode Rectifier, *Z. angew. Physik*, vol. 3, pp. 32–35, 1951.

Genta, V.: Electrical Conductivity and Lattice Disorder of Lead Sulphide, *Ricerca Sci.*, vol. 21, pp. 788–789, 1951.

Gibson, A. F.: The Sensitivity and Response Time of Lead Sulphide Photoconductive Cells, *Proc. Phys. Soc. (London)*, vol. 64B, pp. 603–615, 1951.

Gorelik, S. I.: Electron Conductivity in Polycrystalline Sintered Tellurium Dioxide, *Zhur. Eksptl. i. Teort. Fiz.*, vol. 21, pp. 826–832, 1951.

Gorlich, P.: On the Question of Noise in Light-sensitive Semiconductors, *Optik*, vol. 8, pp. 512–516, 1951.

Goucher, F. S.: Measurement of Hole Diffusion in N-type Germanium, *Phys. Rev.*, vol. 81, p. 475, 1951.

Goucher, F. S., G. L. Pearson, M. Sparks, G. K. Teal, and W. Shockley: Theory and Experiment for a Germanium P-N Junction, *Phys. Rev.*, vol. 81, pp. 637–638, 1951.

Granville, J. W., and C. A. Hogarth: A Study of Thermo-electric Effects at the Surfaces of Transistor Materials, *Proc. Phys. Soc. (London)*, vol. 64B, pp. 488–494, 1951.

Gray, T. J.: The Properties of Semi-conducting Oxides, in "Conference on Semi-conducting Materials, Proceedings . . . ," pp. 180–187, Academic Press, Inc., New York, 1951.

Gubanov, A. I.: On the Theory of Semiconductors with Mixed Conductivity, *J. Exptl. Theoret. Phys. (U.S.S.R.)*, vol. 21, pp. 79–87, 1951.

Gubanov, A. I.: The Theory of Contact of Two Semiconductors of Mixed Conductivity, *J. Exptl. Theoret. Phys. (U.S.S.R.)*, vol. 21, pp. 721–730, 1951.

Gubanov, A. I.: Theory of the Contact of Two Semiconductors of the Same Type of Conductivity, *J. Tech. Phys. (U.S.S.R.)*, vol. 21, pp. 304–315, 1951.

Haegele, R. W.: A Visual Transistor Test Method and Its Application to Collector Forming, *Sylvania Technologist*, vol. 4, pp. 61–63, July, 1951.

Hahn, E. E.: Some Electrical Properties of Zinc Oxide Semiconductors, *J. Appl. Phys.*, vol. 22, pp. 855–863, 1951.

Hall, H. H., J. Bardeen, and G. L. Pearson: The Effects of Pressure and Temperature on the Resistance of P-N Junctions in Germanium, *Phys. Rev.*, vol. 84, pp. 129–132, 1951.

Hall, R. N.: Germanium Rectifier Characteristics, *Phys. Rev.*, vol. 83, p. 228, 1951.

Harris, J. R.: Storage and Addition of Binary Numbers, in Bell Telephone Labs., Inc., "The Transistor . . . ," pp. 523–581, New York, 1951.

Hauffe, K., and J. Block: Disorder Model for a Semiconductor with Characteristic Defect Centers, Taking Chromium Sesquioxide As an Example, *Z. physik. Chem.*, vol. 198, pp. 232–247, 1951.

Hauffe, K., and J. Block: On the Dependence of the Electrical Conductivity of Some Mixed Oxides on Oxygen Pressure, *Z. physik. Chem.*, vol. 196, pp. 438–446, 1951.

Hauffe, K., and H. Grunewald: On Disorder Phenomena and Conduction Processes in Characteristic Semiconductors, *Z. physik. Chem.*, vol. 198, pp. 248–257, 1951.

Haynes, J. R., and W. Shockley: The Mobility and Life of Injected Holes and Electrons in Germanium, *Phys. Rev.*, vol. 81, pp. 835–843, 1951.

Heller, Z. H., and D. J. Tendam: The Stopping Power of Metal and Semiconductors, *Phys. Rev.*, vol. 84, pp. 905–909, 1951.

Henisch, H. K.: The Activation Energy of Disordered Semiconductors, *Z. physik. Chem.*, vol. 198, pp. 41–51, 1951.

Henisch, H. K.: Internal Barriers in Semi-conductors, *Phil. Mag.*, vol. 42, pp. 734–738, 1951.

Henisch, H. K.: On the Activation Energy of Impurity Semiconductors, *Z. physik. Chem.*, vol. 198, pp. 41–51, 1951.

Henisch, H. K., and M. Francois: On the Thermoelectric Properties of Selenium, in "Conference on Semi-conducting Materials, Proceedings . . . ," pp. 234–245, Academic Press, Inc., New York, 1951.

Henisch, H. K., and J. W. Granville: Recent Experiments on Lead Sulphide Contacts, in "Conference on Semi-conducting Materials, Proceedings . . . ," pp. 87–94, Academic Press, Inc., New York, 1951.

Henisch, H. K.: Thermo-electric Measurements on Semiconductors, *Proc. Phys. Soc. (London)*, vol. 64B, p. 1014, 1951.

Henkels, H. W.: Electrical Properties of Selenium.   I. Single Crystals, *J. Appl. Phys.*, vol. 22, pp. 916–925, 1951.

Henkels, H. W.: Electrical Properties of Selenium.   II. Microcrystalline Selenium, *J. Appl. Phys.*, vol. 22, pp. 1265–1278, 1951.

Hensley, E. B.: A Study of the Electrical Properties of Porous Semiconductors, University Microfilms Pub. 2883, 1951.

Herzog, G. B., and A. van der Ziel: Shot Noise in Germanium Single Crystals, *Phys. Rev.*, vol. 84, pp. 1249–1250, 1951.

Hibi, T., and T. Matsumura: On the Aggregation of Trapping Centers in Semiconductors or Insulators, *Phys. Rev.*, vol. 81, pp. 884–885, 1951.

Hirahara, E.: The Electrical Conductivity and Isothermal Hall Effect in Cuprous Sulphide Semiconductors, *J. Phys. Soc. Japan*, vol. 6, pp. 428–437, 1951.

Hirahara, E.: The Physical Properties of Cuprous Sulfide Semiconductors, *J. Phys. Soc. Japan*, vol. 6, pp. 422–427, 1951.

Hogarth, C. A.: Crystal Diode and Triode Action in Lead Selenide, *Proc. Phys. Soc. (London)*, vol. 64B, pp. 822–823, 1951.

Hogarth, C. A.: The Electrical Conductivity of Liquid Germanium, *Phys. Rev.*, vol. 84, pp. 367–368, 1951

Hogarth, C. A.: A Note on the Partial Differential Equations Describing Steady Current Flow in Intrinsic Semiconductors, *J. Appl. Phys.*, vol. 22, pp. 1388–1389, 1951.

Hogarth, C. A.: Some Conduction Properties of Oxides of Cadmium and Nickel, *Proc. Phys. Soc. (London)*, vol. 64B, pp. 691–700, 1951.

Hogarth, C. A.: Some Conduction Properties of the Oxides of Zinc and Copper, *Z. physik. Chem.*, vol. 198, pp. 30–40, 1951.

Horton, C. W.: On the Semiconductor Bornite, *J. Appl. Phys.*, vol. 22, p. 364, 1951.

Hungermann, E. H.: Progress in Transistor Technique, *Elektron Wiss. u. Tech.*, vol. 5, pp. 429–439, 1951/1952.

Hunter, L. P.: The Inverse Voltage Characteristic of a Point Contact on N-type Germanium, *Phys. Rev.*, vol. 81, pp. 151–152, 1951.

Hussey, L. W.: Anti-coincidence or "Not And" Gate, in Bell Telephone Labs., Inc., "The Transistor . . . ," pp. 517–522, New York, 1951.

Hussey, L. W.: Diode Gate, in Bell Telephone Labs., Inc., "The Transistor . . . ," pp. 507–515, New York, 1951.

Ichimura, H.: Statistical Thermodynamics of the Super Conducting State, *Phys. Rev.*, vol. 84, pp. 375–376, 1951.

Ishikawa, Y., T. Sato, K. Okumura, and T. Sasaki: P-N Transition of an Oxide Coated Cathode, *Phys. Rev.*, vol. 84, pp. 371–372, 1951.

Ishuguru, M., and T. Mori: On the Temperature Effect of Crystal Rectifiers and the Negative Resistance, *Mem. Inst. Sci. and Ind. Research, Osaka Univ.*, vol. 8, pp. 74–77, 1951.

Ivanov, L. I., V. I. Pruzhinina, and I. V. Chernina: Some Electrical Properties of Silicon Carbide, *Zhur. Tekh. Fiz.*, vol. 21, pp. 1050–1060, 1951.

Jacobs, J. E.: Electrical Conductivity of Cadmium Sulphide Exposed to Pulsating X Radiation, *Elec. Eng.*, vol. 70, pp. 667–671, 1951.

James, H. M., and K. Lark-Horovitz: Localized Electronic States in Bombarded Semiconductors, *Z. physik. Chem.*, vol. 198, pp. 107–126, 1951.

Johnson, V. A., and K. Lark-Horovitz: The Combination of Resistivities in Semiconductors, *Phys. Rev.*, vol. 82, pp. 977–978, 1951.

Johnson, V. A., and K. Lark-Horovitz: Conversion of a Classical Semiconductor in Thermal Equilibrium from N- to P-type, *Phys. Rev.*, vol. 82, p. 763, 1951.

Johnson, V. A., and M. Hansen: Research on the Element Silicon and Silicon Alloys, Armour Research Foundation, AF TR 6383, June, 1951.

Jones, H.: The Hall Coefficient of Semiconductors, *Phys. Rev.*, vol. 81, p. 149, 1951.

Kalashnikov, S. G., and L. N. Erastov: Formation of Barrier Layers in Alloys by Means of Chemical Compounds, *J. Tech. Physics (U.S.S.R.)*, vol. 21, pp. 129–134, 1951.

Keyes, R. W.: The Electrical Conductivity of Liquid Germanium, *Phys. Rev.*, vol. 84, pp. 367–368, 1951.

Klahr, C. N., and L. P. Hunter: Measurement of Semiconductor Impurity Content, *Phys. Rev.*, vol. 81, pp. 1059–1060, 1951.

Klahr, C. N.: Resistivity and Hall Constant of Semiconductors, *Phys. Rev.*, vol. 82, pp. 109–110, 1951.

Klahr, C. N.: Erratum to Resistivity and Hall Constant of Semiconductors, *Phys. Rev.*, vol. 83, p. 460, 1951.

Kleimack, J. J., R. M. Ryder, R. J. Kircher, and J. N. Shive: Data on Experimental Transistors, in Bell Telephone Labs., Inc., "The Transistor . . . ," pp. 753–792, New York, 1951.

Kmetko, E. A.: Infra Red Absorption and Intrinsic Semiconductivity of Condensed Aromatic Systems, *Phys. Rev.*, vol. 82, p. 456, 1951.

Kock, W. E., and R. L. Wallace, Jr.: The Coaxial Transistor, in Bell Telephone Labs., Inc., "The Transistor . . . ," pp. 111–113, New York, 1951.

Komagata, S., M. Hatoyama, M. Shibuya, W. Sasaki, T. Yamamoto, and M. Kikuchi: A.C. Characteristics of Silicon P-N Junctions, *J. Appl. Phys.*, vol. 22, p. 1290, 1951.

Koops, C. G.: On the Dispersion of Resistivity and Dielectric Constant of Some Semiconductors at Audio Frequencies, *Phys. Rev.*, vol. 83, pp. 121–124, 1951.

Kornilov, I. I.: On the Solid Solutions of Metallic Compounds, *Doklady Akad. Nauk S.S.S.R.*, vol. 81, pp. 597–600, 1951.

Koros, L. L., and R. F. Schwartz: Transistor Frequency Modulator Circuit, *Electronics*, vol. 24, pp. 130–132, 134, July, 1951.

Krantz, E.: Report on the Semiconductor Conference of July 10–15, 1950, *Z. angew. Physik*, vol. 3, pp. 35–38, 1951.

Krebs, H.: On the Crystallization of Semi-metals and the Formation of Lattice Defects, in "Conference on Semi-conducting Materials, Proceedings . . . ," pp. 246–253, Academic Press, Inc., New York, 1951.

Krivoglaz, M. A., and K. B. Tolpygo: The Problem of the Relation between Contact Resistance and Contact P. D., *J. Tech. Phys. (U.S.S.R.)*, vol. 21, pp. 417–426, 1951.

Landsberg, P. T., R. W. Mackay, and A. D. McDonald: Parameters of Simple Excess Semiconductors, *Proc. Phys. Soc. (London)*, vol. 64A, pp. 476–480, 1951.

Lark-Horovitz, K.: Nucleon-bombarded Semiconductors, in "Conference on Semi-conducting Materials, Proceedings . . . ," pp. 47–69, Academic Press, Inc., New York, 1951.

Lawson, W. D.: A Method of Growing Single Crystals of Lead Telluride and Lead Selenide, *J. Appl. Phys.*, vol. 22, pp. 1444–1447, 1951.

Lehovec, K., and H. Kedesdy: Graphical Determination of the Fermi Level in a Simple Impurity Semiconductor, *J. Appl. Phys.*, vol. 22, pp. 65–67, 1951.

Lehovec, K., C. A. Accardo, and E. Jamgochian: Injected Light Emission of Silicon Carbide Crystals, *Phys. Rev.*, vol. 83, pp. 603–607, 1951.

Lempicki, A.: Electrical Conductivity of Simple P-type Semiconductors, *Proc. Phys. Soc. (London)*, vol. 64A, pp. 589–590, 1951.

Lessing, L. P.: The Electronics Era, *Fortune*, vol. 44, pp. 79–83, 1951.

Longini, R. L.: Electrical Forming of N-germanium Transistors Using Donor-alloy contacts, *Phys. Rev.*, vol. 84, p. 1254, 1951.

McAfee, K. B., E. J. Ryder, W. Shockley, and M. Sparks: Observation of Zener Current in Germanium P-N Junctions, *Phys. Rev.*, vol. 83, pp. 650–651, 1951.

McKay, K. G.: Electron-hole Production in Germanium by Alpha Particles, *Phys. Rev.*, vol. 84, pp. 829–832, 1951.

McKay, K. G.: The N-P-N Junction as a Model for Secondary Photoconductivity, *Phys. Rev.*, vol. 84, pp. 833–835, 1951.

Malsch, J.: Physics and Construction of Transistors, *Arch. Elekt. Ubertrag.*, vol. 5, pp. 139–148, 425–433, 467–473, 1951.

Marin, G.: Semiconductors, *L'Electricien (Paris)*, vol. 79, pp. 14–16, January, 1951.

Matare, H. F.: Barrier Layer Changes and Statistical Fluctuations in the Three-electrode Crystal (Transistor), *Z. Physik*, vol. 131, pp. 82–97, 1951.

Mesnard, G., and R. Uzan: On the Conductivity and Some Other Electrical Properties of Thoria under Vacuum, *Vide*, vol. 6, pp. 1052–1062, 1091–1097, 1951.

Mesnard, G.: Semiconducting Properties of Thoria in Vacuo, *Compt. rend.*, vol. 232, pp. 1744–1746, 1951.

Michelssen, F.: Notes on the Development and Application of Infra-red-sensitive Galena, Pbs, PbSe and PbTe Photocells, *Optik*, vol. 8, pp. 75–76, 1951.

Miller, P. H., Jr.: Electrical and Optical Properties of Zinc Oxide, in "Conference on Semiconducting Materials, Proceedings . . . ," pp. 172–179, Academic Press, Inc., New York, 1951.

Mitchell, E. W. J., and J. W. Mitchell: The Work Function of Germanium, in "Conference on Semi-conducting Materials, Proceedings . . . ," pp. 148–150, Academic Press, Inc., New York, 1951.

Mizushima, S., and J. Okada: Notes on the Electrical and Thermal Conductivities of Graphite and Amorphous Carbon, *Phys. Rev.*, vol. 82, pp. 94–95, 1951.

Morin, F. J.: Electrical Properties of Alpha Fe_2O_3 and Alpha Fe_2O_3 Containing Titanium, *Phys. Rev.*, vol. 83, pp. 1005–1010, 1951.

Mostovetch, N., and B. Vodar: Electrical Conductivity of Very Thin Metallic Films Evaporated in High Vacuum, in "Conference on Semi-conducting Materials, Proceedings . . . ," pp. 260–281, Academic Press, Inc., New York, 1951.

Mostovetch, N., and T. Duhautois: Variations As Functions of Temperature and Applied Potential of the Electrical Resistance of Very Thin Metallic Films Deposited on Diamond, Amber and Plexiglass, *Compt. rend.*, vol. 233, pp. 1265–1267, 1951.

Mott, N. F.: Semi-conductors, in "Conference on Semi-conducting Materials, Proceedings . . . ," pp. 1–7, Academic Press, Inc., New York, 1951.

Muller, R. H.: Junction Transistor, *Anal. Chem.*, vol. 23, p. 19A, December, 1951.

Muser, H.: Limits of Performance of Photoresistors (Photoconductors), *Z. Physik*, vol. 129, pp. 504–516, 1951.

Muser, H.: On Localized Decreases of Resistance in Photoconductive Layers, *Z. physik. Chem.*, vol. 198, pp. 52–60, 1951.

Muto, T., and S. Oyama: Theory of the Temperature Effect of Energy Bands in Crystals, *Progr. Theoret. Phys.*, vol. 6, pp. 61–64, 1951.

Netushil, A. V.: Conditions of the Co-existence of Steady Thermal and Electric Fields in the Electric Heating of Concrete, *J. Tech. Phys. (U.S.S.R.)*, vol. 21, pp. 405–409, 1951.

N'Guyen, T. C., and J. Suchet: Conductivity of Electronic Semi-conductors and Thermistors, *Onde élect.*, vol. 31, pp. 473–489, 1951.

N'Guyen, T. C., and J. Suchet: A Study of Semi-conductors at High Temperatures, Refractory Thermistors, *Ann. Radioélec.*, vol. 6, pp. 99–105, 1951.

Pearson, G. L., and H. Suhl: Magnetoresistance Effect in Oriented Single Crystals of Germanium, *Phys. Rev.*, vol. 83, pp. 768–776, 1951.

Pearson, G. L.: The Physics of Electronic Semi-conductors, in Bell Telephone Labs., Inc., "The Transistor . . . ," pp. 17–24, New York, 1951.

Pfann, W. G., and J. H. Scaff: The P-germanium Transistor, in Bell Telephone Labs., Inc., "The Transistor . . . ," p. 97, New York, 1951.

Pfann, W. G.: Significance of Composition of Contact Point in Rectifying Junctions on Germanium, *Phys. Rev.*, vol. 81, p. 882, 1951.

Pietenpol, W. J.: P-N Junction Rectifier and Photocell, *Phys. Rev.*, vol. 82, pp. 120–121, 1951.

Pikus, A. E.: Influence of the Surface Levels on the Chemical Potential and the Work Function of a Semiconductor, *Zhur. Eksptl. i. Teort. Fiz.*, vol. 21, pp. 1127–1138, 1951.

Pikus, A. E.: On the Thermoelectric Properties of Semiconductors, *Zhur. Eksptl. i. Teort. Fiz.*, vol. 21, pp. 852–853, 1951.

Pincherle, L.: Change of Activation Energy with Impurity Concentration in Semi-conductors, *Proc. Phys. Soc. (London)*, vol. 64A, pp. 663–664, 1951.

Plessner, K. W.: Conductivity and Hall Effect of Micro-crystalline Selenium Iodine Impurities, *Proc. Phys. Soc. (London)*, vol. 64B, pp. 681–690, 1951.

Plessner, K. W.: Conductivity, Hall Effect and Thermo-electric Power of Selenium Single Crystals, *Proc. Phys. Soc. (London)*, vol. 64B, pp. 671–681, 1951.

Pohl, R. W.: Electron Trap and Electron Conduction in Irradiated Alkali Halide Crystals, in "Conference on Semi-conducting Materials, Proceedings . . . ," pp. 106–113, Academic Press, Inc., New York, 1951.

Prim, R. C.: A Note on the Partial Differential Equations Describing Steady Current Flow in Intrinsic Semiconductors, *J. Appl. Phys.*, vol. 22, pp. 1388–1389, 1951.

Prim, R. C.: Some Results Concerning the Partial Differential Equations Describing the Flow Holes and Electrons in Semiconductors, *Bell System Tech. J.*, vol. 30, pp. 1174–1213, 1951.

Purdue University, Department of Physics: Semiconductor Research, Final Report PRF-489, September, 1948–Nov. 30, 1951, Contract W-36-039 sc-38151.

Putley, E. H., and J. B. Arthur: Lead Sulphide—An Intrinsic Semi-conductor, *Proc. Phys. Soc. (London)*, vol. 64B, pp. 616–618, 1951.

Queen, I.: New Transistor Circuit Design Method, *Radio-Electronics*, vol. 23, pp. 64, 68, January, 1951.

Queen, I.: Transistor Amplifying Circuits, *Radio-Electronics*, vol. 23, pp. 56, 58, December, 1951.

Queen, I.: Transistors as Multivibrators, *Radio-Electronics*, vol. 23, pp. 92, 94, September, 1951.

Raisbeck, G.: A High-efficiency Untuned Amplifier in Bell Telephone Labs., Inc., "The Transistor . . . ," pp. 389–396, New York, 1951.

Raisbeck, G.: A New High-efficiency Linear Amplifier Using a Transistor and a Vacuum Tube, in Bell Telephone Labs., Inc., "The Transistor . . . ," pp. 377–387, New York, 1951.

Raisbeck, G.: Transistor Circuit Design, *Electronics*, vol. 24, pp. 128–132, December, 1951.

Reich, H. J., P. M. Schultheiss, J. G. Skalnick, T. Flynn, and J. E. Gibson: Effect of Auxiliary Current on Transistor Operation, *J. Appl. Phys.*, vol. 22, pp. 682–683, 1951.

Ridenour, L. N.: Revolution in Electronics, *Sci. American*, vol. 185, pp. 13–17, August, 1951.

Rose, A.: An Outline of Some Photoconductive Processes, *RCA Rev.*, vol. 12, pp. 362–414, 1951.

Rosenberg, W., and E. Fues: The Barrier Layer of a Germanium Rectifier in the Current Region. *Z. Naturforsch.*, vol. 6a, pp. 741–744, 1951.

Rost, R.: Kristalloden, *Radio Mentor*, vol. 14, pp. 190–192, April, 1951.

Rothlein, B. J.: A New High Conductance Crystal Diode, *Sylvania Technologist*, vol. 4, p. 44, May, 1951.

Rothlein, B. J.: A Photovoltaic Germanium Cell, *Sylvania Technologist*, vol. 4, p. 86, August, 1951.

Ryder, E. J., and W. Shockley: Mobilities of Electrons in High Electric Fields, *Phys. Rev.*, vol. 81, pp. 139–140, 1951.

Ryder, R. M.: Aging and Temperature Response of Point-contact Transistors, in Bell Telephone Labs., Inc., "The Transistor . . . ," pp. 123–126, New York, 1951.

Saby, J. S.: Recent Developments in Transistors and Related Devices, *Tele-Tech*, vol. 10, pp. 32–34, 58, December, 1951.

Salow, H.: The Germanium Triode, *Z. angew. Physik*, vol. 3, pp. 231–239, 1951.

Sandstrom, A. E.: Some Experimental Studies of Resistance and Electro-motive Force of Selenium Blocking-layer Cells, in "Conference on Semi-conducting Materials, Proceedings . . . ," pp. 218–233, Academic Press, Inc., New York, 1951.

Scaff, J. H., and H. C. Theuerer: Effect of Heat Treatment on the Electrical Properties of Germanium, *J. Metals*, vol. 191, pp. 59–63, 1951.

Schultheiss, P. M., and H. J. Reich: Some Transistor Trigger Circuits, *Proc. IRE*, vol. 39, pp. 627–632, 1951.

Schulz, O.: The Transistor in Industry, *Funktech.*, vol. 6, pp. 254–259, June, 1951.

Scott, T. R.: Crystal Triodes, *Proc. Inst. Elec. Engrs. (London)*, part III, vol. 98, pp. 169–177, 1951; discussion pp. 177–183; *Elec. Commun.*, vol. 28, pp. 195–208, 1951.

Scott, T. R., and S. E. Mayer: Engineering and Chemical Aspects of Semi-conductors, in "Conference on Semi-conducting Materials, Proceedings . . . ," pp. 254–259, Academic Press, Inc., New York, 1951.

Selis, G. H.: The Measurement of the Electrical Resistance of Semi-conducting Flooring, *Elektrotechnik*, vol. 29, pp. 415–419, 1951.

Shive, J. N.: The Phototransistor, in Bell Telephone Labs., Inc., "The Transistor . . . ," p. 115, New York, 1951.

Shockley, W.: Holes and Electrons, in Bell Telephone Labs., Inc., "The Transistor . . . ," pp. 8–16, New York, 1951.

Shockley, W.: Hot Electrons in Germanium and Ohm's Law, *Bell System Tech. J.*, vol. 30, pp. 990–1034, 1951.

Shockley, W.: New Phenomena of Electronic Conduction in Semi-conductors, in "Conference on Semi-conducting Materials, Proceedings . . . ," pp. 26–36, Academic Press, Inc., New York, 1951.

Shockley, W., M. Sparks, and G. K. Teal: P-N Junction Transistors, *Phys. Rev.*, vol. 83, pp. 151–162, 1951.

Shockley, W.: Transistor Electronics, *Science*, vol. 114, p. 487, 1951.

Simon, I.: Optical Constants of Germanium, Silicon, and Pyrite in the Infra-red, *J. Opt. Soc. Amer.*, vol. 41, p. 730, 1951.

Simpson, O., and G. B. B. M. Sutherland: Photoconductivity in the Infra-red Region of the Spectrum. I. The Preparation and Properties of Photoconductive Film of Lead Telluride. II. The Mechanism of Photoconductivity in Lead Telluride, *Phil. Trans.*, vol. 243A, pp. 547–584, 1951.

Skalnick, J. G., H. J. Reich, J. E. Gibson, and T. Flynn: Auxiliary Current Alters Transistor Characteristics, *Electronics*, vol. 24, pp. 142, 228, 232, 236, September, 1951.

Skaupy, F.: The Physics and Application of Electrical Semiconductors, *Ver. deut. Ing. Z.*, vol. 93, pp. 899–903, 1951.

Slade, B. N.: A Method of Improving the Electrical and Mechanical Stability of Point-contact Transistors, *RCA Rev.*, vol. 12, pp. 651–659, 1951.

Slater, J. C.: Electron Theory of Solids, *Am. J. Phys.*, vol. 19, pp. 368–374, 1951.

Smith, L. P.: The Motion of Electrons and Holes in Silver Chloride, in "Conference on Semi-conducting Materials, Proceedings . . . ," pp. 114–121, Academic Press, Inc., New York, 1951.

Smith, R. A.: The Electrical and Optical Properties of Certain Sulphides, Selenides and Tellurides in "Conference on Semi-conducting Materials, Proceedings . . . ," pp. 108–207, Academic Press, Inc., New York, 1951.

Sommer, A.: "Photoelectric Tubes," 2d edition, Methuen & Co., Ltd., London, 1951.

Sproull, R. L., and W. W. Tyler: Semi-conduction and Photo-conduction in Barium Oxide Crystals, in "Conference on Semi-conducting Materials, Proceedings . . . ," pp. 122–131, Academic Press, Inc., New York, 1951.

Stahl, F. A.: Effect of Probe Metal in Locating a P-N Barrier in Germanium, *Sylvania Technologist*, vol. 4, p. 61, July, 1951.

Stahl, F. A.: Germanium Trigger Photocells, *Elec. Eng.*, vol. 70, pp. 518–520, 1951.

Stansel, F. R.: The Characteristics and Some Applications of Varistors, *Proc. IRE*, vol. 39, pp. 342–358, 1951.

Stelmak, J. P.: Electrical Forming in N-germanium Transistors Using Phosphorus Alloy Contacts, *Phys. Rev.*, vol. 83, p. 165, 1951.

Strutt, M. J. O.: "Verstaerker und Empfaenger," 2d edition, esp. p. 422, Springer-Verlag OHG, Berlin, 1951.

Surdin, M.: A Theory of Electrical Fluctuations in Semiconductors, *J. phys. radium*, vol. 12, pp. 777–783, 1951.

Teal, G. K., M. Sparks, and E. Buehler: Growth of Germanium Single Crystals Containing P-N Junctions, *Phys. Rev.*, vol. 81, p. 637, 1951.

Theuerer, H. C., and J. H. Scaff: Effect of Heat Treatment on the Electrical Properties of Germanium, *J. Metals*, vol. 191, pp. 59–63, 1951.

Trent, R. L.: A Four-stage Binary Counter, in Bell Telephone Labs., Inc., "The Transistor . . . ," pp. 501–505, New York, 1951.

Trent, R. L.: Idealized Negative Resistance Characteristics of the Transistors, in Bell Telephone Labs., Inc., "The Transistor . . . ," pp. 249–281, New York, 1951.

Trent, R. L.: A Stabilized General Purpose Two-transistor Binary Counter, in Bell Telephone Labs., Inc., "The Transistor . . . ," pp. 469–482, New York, 1951.

Trent, R. L.: Stabilized Single Transistor Binary Counter, in Bell Telephone Labs., Inc., "The Transistor . . . ," pp. 463–468, New York, 1951.

Trent, R. L.: A Transistor Packaged Circuit for Multi-functional Switching Applications, in Bell Telephone Labs., Inc., "The Transistor . . . ," pp. 437–461, New York, 1951.

Trent, R. L.: A Transistor Reversible Binary Counter, in Bell Telephone Labs., Inc., "The Transistor . . . ," pp. 483–500, New York, 1951.

Veith, W., and C. Wlerick: An Effect of Light on Semiconductors: A Variation in the Contact Potential Difference, *Compt. rend.*, vol. 233, pp. 1097–1099, 1951.

Verwey, E. J. W., and F. A. Kroger: New Views on Oxidic Semi-conductors and Zinc-sulphide Phosphors, *Philips Tech. Rev.*, vol. 13, pp. 90–95, 1951.

Verwey, E. J. W.: Oxidic Semi-conductors, in "Conference on Semi-conducting Materials. Proceedings . . . ," pp. 151–161, Academic Press, Inc., New York, 1951.

Vine, B. H., and R. J. Maurer: The Electrical Properties of Cuprous Oxide, *Z. physik. Chem.*, vol. 198, pp. 147–156, 1951.

Volger, J.: Some Properties of (La, Sr)MnO₃, in "Conference on Semi-conducting Materials, Proceedings . . . ," pp. 162–171, Academic Press, Inc., New York, 1951.

Wallace, R. L., Jr.: Duality, A New Approach to Transistor Circuit Design, *Proc. IRE*, vol. 39, pp. 702–703, 1951.

Wallace, R. L., Jr., and G. Raisbeck: Duality as a Guide in Transistor Circuit Design, *Bell System Tech. J.*, vol. 30, pp. 381–417, 1951; also in Bell Telephone Labs., Inc., "The Transistor . . . ," pp. 127–164, New York, 1951.

Wallace, R. L., Jr., and W. J. Pietenpol: The Germanium Triode, *Electronic Eng.*, vol. 23, p. 393, 1951.

Wallace, R. L., Jr., and W. J. Pietenpol: The Junction Transistor, *Electronics*, vol. 24, pp. 82–85, November, 1951.

Wallace, R. L., Jr., and W. J. Pietenpol: Some Circuit Properties and Applications of N-P-N Transistors, *Bell System Tech. J.*, vol. 30, pp. 530–563, 1951; *Proc. IRE*, vol. 39, pp. 753–767, 1951.

Watanabe, Y., and N. Honda: Theory of Noise in the Transistor, *Science Repts. Research Insts. Tôhoku Univ.*, ser. B, vol. 1–2, pp. 313–325, 1951.

Welker, H.: On the Theory of Galvanomagnetic Effects for Mixed Conduction, *Z. Naturforsch.*, vol. 6a, pp. 184–191, 1951.

Whalley, W. B., C. Masucci, and N. P. Salz: An Analysis of Germanium Diode as a Video Detector, *Sylvania Technologist*, vol. 4, pp. 25–34, April, 1951.

Wright, R. W.: The Effect of the Mean Free Path of Electrons on the Electrical Properties of Non Metals, *Proc. Phys. Soc. (London)*, vol. 64A, pp. 984–999, 1951.

Wright, R. W.: Residual Resistance in an Extremely Impure Semiconductor, *Proc. Phys. Soc. (London)*, vol. 64A, pp. 949–950, 1951.

Wright, R. W.: The Variation with Temperature of the Electrical Properties of a Degenerate Electronic Semiconductor as Exemplified by Cadmium Oxide, *Proc. Phys. Soc. (London)*, vol. 64A, pp. 350–362, 1951.

Yaeger, R. E.: A Gray to Binary Translator and Shift Register, in Bell Telephone Labs., Inc., "The Transistor . . . ," pp. 611–626, New York, 1951.

Auxiliary Current Alters Transistor Characteristics, *Electronics*, vol. 24, p. 192, September, 1951.

Developments in Germanium Triodes, *Engineering*, vol. 172, p. 329, 1951.

Experimental Germanium Triode R. F. Receiver, *Engineering*, vol. 172, p. 329, 1951.

Germanium Triode, *Electronic Eng.*, vol. 23, p. 393, 1951.

The Junction Transistor, *Bell Labs. Record*, vol. 29, pp. 379–381, 1951.

Junction Transistor, *Electronics*, vol. 24, pp. 82–85, November, 1951.

Junction Transistors Developed by Bell Laboratories, *Tele-Tech*, vol. 10, p. 66, August, 1951; *Radio Television News*, vol. 46, p. 143, September, 1951.

New Type Transistor, *Rev. Sci. Instr.*, vol. 22, pp. 710–711, 1951.

Precision Transistor Oscillator, *Tele-Tech*, vol. 12, pp. 93, 145, March, 1951.

Revolution in the Making; Junction Transistor, *Tech. Rev.*, vol. 54, p. 16, November, 1951.

Semiconductor Diodes, *Electronics*, vol. 24, pp. 112–113, March, 1951.

Semiconductors Will Become a Major Field of Electrical Engineering; Vacuum Tubes to Transistors? *Product Eng.*, vol. 22, pp. 132–134, May, 1951.

Tiny Transistor Invented at the Bell Telephone Laboratories, *Aviation Week*, vol. 55, p. 26, July, 1951.

The Transistor, *Sci. American*, vol. 85, August, 1951.

Transistor Microphone, *Elektron Wiss. u. Tech.*, vol. 4, pp. 359–361, 1951.

1952

Abeles, F.: Determination of the Optical Constants of Solids by Photometric Measurements, *Rev. opt.*, vol. 31, pp. 127–130, 1952.

Adler, R. B.: A Large Signal Equivalent Circuit for Transistor Static Characteristics, MIT Research Laboratory of Electronics, Transistor Group Report T-8, Nov. 12, 1952.

Aigrain, P., J. Lagrenaudie, and G. Liandrat: Modulation of the Conductance of a Semiconductor by an Electric Field, *J. phys. radium*, vol. 13, pp. 587–588, 1952.

Aigrain, P.: Rectification Phenomena and Transistor Action in Germanium, *Ann. phys.*, vol. 7, pp. 140–184, 1952.

Aigrain, P., C. Dugas, J. Legrand des Cloiseaux, and B. Jancovici: Semiconducting Properties of Tellurium, *Compt. rend.*, vol. 235, pp. 145–146, 1952.

Akamatu, H., and H. Inokuchi: Photoconductivity of Violanthrone, *J. Chem. Phys.*, vol. 20, pp. 1481–1483, 1952.

Alexanderson, E. F. W.: Control Applications of the Transistor, *Proc. IRE*, vol. 40, pp. 1508–1511, 1952.

Anderson, A. E.: Transistors in Switching Circuits, *Bell System Tech. J.*, vol. 31, pp. 1207–1249, 1952; *Proc. IRE*, vol. 40, pp. 1541–1558, 1732, 1952.

Anderson, J. S., and N. N. Greenwood: The Semi-conducting Properties of Cuprous Oxide, *Proc. Roy. Soc. (London)*, vol. 215A, pp. 353–370, 1952.

Anderson, R. L., and A. van der Ziel: On the Shot Effect on P-N Junctions, *Trans. IRE*, vol. PGED-1, pp. 20-24, November, 1952.

Anselm, A. I.: The Distribution of the Concentration of the Current Carriers in the Hall Effect in a Semiconductor, *Zhur. Tekh. Fiz.*, vol. 22, pp. 1146–1153, 1952.

Anselm, A. I., and V. I. Klyachkin: Kinetic Processes in Atomic Semiconductors Taking into Account Scattering of Electrons by Ions, *Zhur. Eksptl. i. Teort. Fiz.*, vol. 22, pp. 297–302, 1952.

Armstrong, L. D.: Crystal Diodes in Modern Electronics, *Radio Television News*, vol. 47, pp. 63–65, 127–133, January, 1952; pp. 62–64, 120–123, February, 1952; pp. 56–57, 127–128, March, 1952.

Armstrong, L. D.: P-N Junctions by Impurity Introduction through an Intermediate Metal Layer, *Proc. IRE*, vol. 40, pp. 1341–1342, 1952.

Armstrong, L. D., J. I. Pantchechnikoff, C. W. Mueller, and R. R. Law: Germanium P-N-P Junction Transistors, RCA Industrial Service Laboratory, Bulletin LB-868, June, 1952.

Aronson, M. H.: Instrument Electronics: Solid State Amplifiers, *Instruments*, vol. 25, pp. 608–609, 1952.

Baker, R. H., I. L. Lebow, and R. H. Rediker: A Transistor Switching Circuit with Stabilized Valley Point, MIT Lincoln Laboratory Memo, July 22, 1952.

Banbury, P. C.: Double-surface Lead Sulphide Transistor, *Proc. Phys. Soc. (London)*, vol. 65B, p. 236, 1952.

Baum, R. M., and C. S. Hung: Activation Energy of Heat Treatment Introduced Lattice Defects in Germanium, *Phys. Rev.*, vol. 88, p. 134, 1952.

Becker, W. M., and K. Lark-Horovitz: Semiconductive Films, *Proc. Nat. Electronics Conf.*, vol. 8, pp. 506–509, 1952.

Bell, D. A.: Current Noise in Semi-conductors: A Reexamination of Bernamont's Data, *Phil. Mag.*, vol. 43, pp. 1107–1111, 1952.

Billig, E.: Effect of Minority Carriers on the Breakdown of Point-contact Rectifiers, *Phys. Rev.*, vol. 87, pp. 1060–1061, 1952.

Billig, E.: The Physics of Transistors, *Brit. J. Appl. Phys.*, vol. 3, pp. 241–248, 1952.

Blakemore, J. S.: Carrier Concentrations and Fermi Levels in Semi-conductors, *Elec. Commun.*, vol. 29, pp. 131–154, 1952.

Blakemore, J. S.: The Parameters of Partially Degenerate Semiconductors, *Proc. Phys. Soc. (London)*, vol. 65A, pp. 460–461, 1952.

Blankenburg, G., and K. Kassel: The Semiconducting Properties of Cuprous Oxide. I. Procedure for Preparation Allowing for Conditions of Stability, *Ann. Physik*, vol. 10, pp. 201–210, 1952.

Blankenburg, G., C. Fritzsche, and G. Schubart: The Semiconducting Properties of Cuprous Oxide. III. The Dependence of Electrical Conductivity at Low Temperatures on the Oxygen Pressure during the Preliminary Heat Treatment, *Ann. Physik*, vol. 10, pp. 217–231, 1952.

Blankenburg, G., and O. Bottger: The Semiconducting Properties of Cuprous Oxide. V. The Interpretation of the Dependence of the Electrical Conductivity at Low Temperatures on the Pressure of Oxygen during the Preparation, *Ann. Physik*, vol. 10, pp. 241–252, 1952.

Boer, K. W.: The Influence of Temperature-dependent Fermi Levels on the Conductivity of Semiconductors, *Ann. Physik*, vol. 10, pp. 32–47, 1952.

Boer, K. W.: The Temperature-dependence of the Dark Conductivity of Cadmium Sulphide, *Ann. Physik*, vol. 10, pp. 20–31, 1952.

Boltaks, B.: The Problem of Measuring the Thermo-E. M. F. of Semi-conductors, *Zhur. Tekh. Fiz.*, vol. 22, pp. 892–893, 1952.

Bottger, O.: The Semiconducting Properties of Cuprous Oxide. IV. Conductivity Measurements at High Temperatures, *Ann. Physik*, vol. 10, pp. 232–240, 1952.

Bottom, V. E.: The Hall Effect and Electrical Resistivity of Tellurium, *Science*, vol. 115, pp. 570–571, 1952.

Bridgman, P. W.: The Electrical Resistance of 72 Elements, Alloys and Compounds to 100,000 Kg/Sq. Cm., *Proc. Am. Acad. Arts Sci.*, vol. 81, pp. 169–251, 1952.

Briggs, H. W., and R. C. Fletcher: New Infrared Absorption Bands in P-Type Germanium, *Phys. Rev.*, vol. 87, p. 1130, 1952.

Brown, D. E., and W. C. Dunlap, Jr.: Comparison of P-N Junctions and Radioactive Traces for Measurement of Diffusion, *Phys. Rev.*, vol. 86, p. 616, 1952.

Brownlee, L. D., and E. W. J. Mitchell: On the Variations of Lattice Parameters of Some Semiconducting Oxides, *Proc. Phys. Soc. (London)*, vol. 65B, pp. 710–716, 1952.

Bryan, G. W., Jr.: Application of Transistors to High-voltage Low-current Supplies, *Proc. IRE*, vol. 40, pp. 1521–1523, 1952.

Burgess, R. E.: The Dispersion of Permittivity and Conductivity of Semiconductors, *Phys. Rev.*, vol. 86, pp. 113–122, 1952.

Butler, J. A. V.: "Electrical Phenomena at Interface," Methuen & Co., Ltd., London, 1951.

Carlson, A. W.: A Transistor Flip-flop with Two Stable Non-saturated States, Air Force Cambridge Research Center Report, December, 1952.

Chaplin, G. B. B.: Display of Transistor Characteristics on the Cathode-ray Oscillograph, *J. Sci. Instr.*, vol. 29, pp. 142–145, 1952.

Chirnside, R. C., and H. J. Cluley: Germanium from Coal, *Gen. Elec. J.*, vol. 19, pp. 94–100, 1952.

Coblenz, A., and H. L. Owens: Variation of Transistor Parameters with Temperature, *Proc. IRE*, vol. 40, pp. 1472–1476, 1952.

Conwell, E. M.: Properties of Silicon and Germanium, *Proc. IRE*, vol. 40, pp. 1327–1337, 1952.

Crawford, D. J., and H. F. Heath: Germanium Diode Testing Program, *Proc. IRE*, vol. 40, p. 232, 1952.

Cronemeyer, D. C.: Electrical and Optical Properties of Rutile Single Crystals, *Phys. Rev.*, vol. 87, pp. 876–886, 1952.

Dacker, L., and W. J. Wray: Germanium Photodevice Reads Computer Tapes, *Electronics*, vol. 25, pp. 150–151, 1952.

Danko, S. F., and R. A. Gerhold: Printed Circuitry for Transistors, *Proc. IRE*, vol. 40, pp. 1524–1528, 1952.

Darnell, P. S.: Miniaturized Component Design (Electronic Components for Transistor Circuitry), *Radio Television News*, vol. 48, pp. 10–11, 30, 1952.

Darnell, P. S.: Miniaturized Components for Transistor Action, in Proceedings of Progress in Quality Electronics Components, pp. 51–57, May, 1952.

Debye, P. P., and E. M. Conwell: Mobility of Electrons in Germanium, *Phys. Rev.*, vol. 87, p. 1131, 1952.

Dewold, N., and N. E. Schick: Tester for Germanium Diodes, *Electronics*, vol. 25, pp. 150, 152, 156, 160, December, 1952.

Dexter, D. L., and F. Seitz: Effects of Dislocations of Mobilities in Semiconductors, *Phys. Rev.*, vol. 86, pp. 964–965, 1952.

Doremus, J. A.: Point Contact and Junction Transistors, *Radio-Electronics*, vol. 47, pp. 14–16, 18, 20, April, 1952.

Dunlap, W. C., Jr.: Germanium Photocells, *Gen. Elec. Rev.*, vol. 55, pp. 26–31, March, 1952.

Dunlap, W. C., Jr., and D. E. Brown: P-N Junction Method for Measuring Diffusion in Germanium, *Phys. Rev.*, vol. 86, pp. 417–418, 1952.

Dunlap, W. C., Jr.: Zinc As an Acceptor in Germanium, *Phys. Rev.*, vol. 85, p. 945, 1952.

Early, J. M.: Effects of Space-charge Layer Widening in Junction Transistors, *Proc. IRE*, vol. 40, pp. 1401–1406, 1952.

Ebers, J. J.: Four-terminal P-N-P-N Transistors, *Proc. IRE*, vol. 40, pp. 1361–1364, 1952.

Eckart, F.: Noise Measurements on Thin Lead Sulphide Photolayers, *Ann. Physik*, vol. 11, pp. 166–168, 1952.

Einsele, T.: On the Inertia of Forward Conductivity of Germanium Diodes, *Z. angew. Physik*, vol. 4, pp. 183–185, 1952.

Eisenmann, L.: Electrical and Optical Properties of the Selenides of Copper, *Ann. Physik*, vol. 10, pp. 129–152, 1952.

Engel, L.: Little Gadget with a Large Future, *Harper's Mag.*, vol. 204, pp. 54–60, March, 1952.

Engle, J. F.: A Water Rheostat Using Untreated Water, *Trans. AIEE*, vol. 71, pp. 18–21, 1952.

Engstrom, E. W.: Transistors in Wide Range of Experimental Applications, *J. Franklin Inst.*, vol. 254, pp. 560–561, 1952.

Epstein, G. S., J. A. Bush, and B. Shellhorn: Transistorizing Communication Equipment, *Electronics*, vol. 25, pp. 98–102, May, 1952.

Erginsoy, C.: Energy States of Overlapping Impurity Carriers in Semiconductors, *Phys. Rev.*, vol. 88, pp. 893–894, 1952.

Farley, B. G.: Dynamics of Transistor Negative-resistance Circuits, *Proc. IRE*, vol. 40, pp. 1497–1508, 1952.

Feldman, C., and B. Vodar: The Electrical Conductivity of Thin Films of Platinum Covered with an Evaporated Dielectric Layer, *Compt. rend.*, vol. 235, pp. 414–417, 1952.

Felker, J. H.: Regenerative Amplifier for Digital Computer Applications, *Proc. IRE*, vol. 40, pp. 1584–1596, 1952.

Felker, J. H.: The Transistor as a Digital Computer Component, in AIEE Review of Electronic Digital Computers, pp. 105–109, 1951.

Felker, J. H.: Typical Block Diagrams for a Transistor Digital Computer, *Elec. Eng.*, vol. 71, pp. 1103–1108, 1952; *Commun. and Electronics*, no. 1, pp. 175–183, July, 1952.

Ferguson, T. J.: The G-10 Germanium Rectifier, *Gen. Elec. Rev.*, vol. 55, pp. 29–31, July, 1952.

Finlayson, D. M., V. A. Johnson, and F. M. Shipley: Interpretation of the Low Temperature Hall Curve of a Degenerate Germanium Sample, *Phys. Rev.*, vol. 87, p. 1141, 1952.

Follingstad, H. G., J. N. Shive, and R. E. Yaeger: An Optical Position Encoder and Digit Register, *Proc. IRE*, vol. 40, pp. 1573–1583, 1952.

Freymann, M., and R. Freymann: New Method for the Study by High Frequency Spectroscopy of Defects in the Structure of Semiconductors (ZnO), *J. phys. radium*, vol. 13, pp. 589–590, 1952.

Freymann, M., and R. Freymann: On the Existence of Debye Absorption in Hertzian Spectra: Application to Semiconductors, *Compt. rend.*, vol. 235, pp. 1125–1127, 1952.

Freymann, R., and M. Freymann: The New Method of Studying Lattice Defects in Solids by Debye Absorption: Case of Semiconductors, *J. Chem. Phys.*, vol. 20, pp. 1970–1971, 1952.

Fritsche, H.: Interpretation of the Double Reversal of the Hall Effect in Tellurium, *Science*, vol. 115, pp. 571–572, 1952.

Fuller, C. S., and J. D. Struthers: Copper As an Acceptor Element in Germanium, *Phys. Rev.*, vol. 87, pp. 526–527, 1952.

Fuller, C. S.: Diffusion of Donor and Acceptor Elements into Germanium, *Phys. Rev.*, vol. 86, pp. 136–137, 1952.

Fuller, C. S., H. C. Theuerer, and W. van Roosbroeck: Properties of Thermally Produced Acceptors in Germanium, *Phys. Rev.*, vol. 85, pp. 678–679, 1952.

Gallagher, C. J.: Plastic Deformation of Germanium and Silicon, *Phys. Rev.*, vol. 88, pp. 721–722, 1952.

Geist, D., and K. Seiler: Temperature Dependence of the Backward Current on P-N Junction in Germanium, *Naturwissenschaften*, vol. 39, p. 401, 1952.

Gerecke, E.: Systematic Classification of Electric Valve Apparatus, *Bull. schweiz. elektrotech. Ver.*, vol. 43, pp. 127–130, 1952.

Giacoletto, L. J.: Junction Transistor Characteristics at Low and Medium Frequencies, *Proc. Natl. Electronics Conf.*, vol. 8, pp. 321–329, 1952.

Giacoletto, L. J.: Junction Transistor Equivalent Circuits and Vacuum-tube Analogy, *Proc. IRE*, vol. 40, pp. 1490–1493, 1952.

Gibson, A. F.: Single Contact Lead Telluride Photocells, *Proc. Phys. Soc. (London)*, vol. 65B, pp. 196–214, 1952.

Glaser, H., and A. J. F. Siegert: Electron Distribution in Irradiated N-type Semiconductors, *Phys. Rev.*, vol. 87, p. 191, 1952.

Golay, M. J. E.: The Equivalent Circuit of the Transistor, *Proc. IRE*, vol. 40, p. 360, 1952.

Goldberg, G.: Acceptors Produced in Germanium by Quenching from High Temperatures, *Phys. Rev.*, vol. 88, pp. 920–924, 1952.

Golden, N., and R. Nielsen: Oscilloscopic Display of Transistor Static Electrical Characteristics, *Proc. IRE*, vol. 40, pp. 1437–1439, 1952.

Goldsmith, A. N.: Transistor Lineage, *Proc. IRE*, vol. 40, p. 1284, 1952.

Granville, J. W., and H. K. Henisch: Area Contacts on Germanium, *Proc. Phys. Soc. (London)*, vol. 65B, pp. 650–651, 1952.

Granville, J. W., H. K. Henisch, and P. M. Tipple: Contact Properties of P-type Germanium, *Proc. Phys. Soc. (London)*, vol. 65B, pp. 908–909, 1952.

Groll, H.: Load Measurements by Means of Thermistors at High Frequency, *Fern-meldetech. Z.*, vol. 5, pp. 522–527, 1952.

Gubanov, A. I.: Dynamical Theory of Dry Rectifiers. I. Limits of Application of the Static Theory, *Zhur. Tekh. Fiz.*, vol. 22, pp. 1803–1813, 1952.

Gubanov, A. I.: Dynamical Theory of Dry Rectifiers. II. Frequency Characteristics, *Zhur. Tekh. Fiz.:* vol. 22, pp. 1814-1826, 1952.

Gubanov, A. I.: Theory of Contact between a Semiconductor and Metal (Large Potential Difference), *Zhur. Eksptl. i. Teort. Fiz.*, vol. 22, pp. 204–213, 1952.

Gubanov, A. I.: Theory of Contact Phenomena in Semiconductors, *Zhur. Tekh. Fiz.*, vol. 22, pp. 729–735, 1952.

Guggenheim, E. A.: Electron Spin in Semiconductors, *Proc. Phys. Soc. (London)*, vol. 66A, pp. 121–122, 1952.

Guillaud, C., and R. Bertrand: Study of Conductivity of Semiconductors and Applications to Systems of Mixed Oxides, *J. recherches centre nat. recherches sci., Labs. Bellevue (Paris)*, vol. 4, pp. 118–130, 1952.

Gunn, J. B.: Resistance of Germanium Contacts, *Proc. Phys. Soc. (London)*, vol. 65B, pp. 908–909, 1952.

Hall, R. N.: Electron-hole Recombination in Germanium, *Phys. Rev.*, vol. 87, p. 387, 1952.

Hall, R. N.: P-N Junctions Produced by Rate Growth Variation, *Phys. Rev.*, vol. 88, p. 139, 1952.

Hall, R. N.: Power Rectifiers and Transistors, *Proc. IRE*, vol. 40, pp. 1512–1518, 1952.

Hannahs, W. H., and J. W. Eng: Production Control of Printed Resistors, *Electronics*, vol. 25, pp. 106–109, October, 1952.

Harris, J. R.: A Transistor Shift Register and Serial Adder, *Proc. IRE*, vol. 40, pp. 1597–1602, 1952.

Hatoyama, M., M. Shibuya, and H. Matsumoto: Characteristics of the Low-impurity Density N-type Germanium, Electrochemical Laboratory, Tokyo, Doc. A. G. 100, Comm. VII, 1952.

Hauffe, K., and H. G. Findt: On the Electrical Conductivity and Thermo-electric Power of Nickel Sulphide, *Z. physik. Chem.*, vol. 200, pp. 199–209, 1952.

Haynes, J. R., and H. B. Briggs: Radiation Produced in Germanium and Silicon by Electron-hole Recombinations, *Bull. Am. Phys. Soc.*, vol. 27, p. 14, 1952.

Haynes, J. R., and W. C. Westphal: The Drift Mobility of Electrons in Silicon, *Phys. Rev.*, vol. 85, p. 680, 1952.

Helwig, G.: Electrical Conductivity and Structure of Sputtered Cadmium Oxide Layers, *Z. Physik*, vol. 132, pp. 621–642, 1952.

Henisch, H. K., and J. Ewels: Apparatus for Electrical Measurements on Semiconductors, *F & G Rundschau*, no. 34, pp. 33–38, April, 1952.

Henisch, H. K., and E. W. Saker: The Effect of Mercury on Selenium, *Proc. Phys. Soc. (London)*, vol. 65B, pp. 149–152, 1952.

Henisch, H. K.: Semiconductors, *Research*, vol. 5, pp. 101–107, 1952.

Hensley, E. B.: On the Electrical Properties of Porous Semiconductors, *J. Appl. Phys.*, vol. 23, pp. 1122–1129, 1952.

Herzog, W.: Oscillators with Transistors, *Arch. Elekt. Ubertrag.*, vol. 6, pp. 398–400, 1952.

Herzog, W.: On Transistor Circuits, *Arch. Elekt. Ubertrag.*, vol. 6, pp. 499–501, 1952.

Hogarth, C. A.: Transistor Action in Lead Telluride, *Proc. Phys. Soc. (London)*, vol. 65B, pp. 958–963, 1952.

Hollmann, H. E.: Dielectric and Semiconductive Suspensions, *Tele-Tech*, vol. 11, pp. 56–59, September, 1952.

Hollmann, H. E.: The Electrical Characteristics of Colloidal Solutions and Mixtures and Their Application to the Development of Non-linear Resistances, *Arch. Elekt. Ubertrag.*, vol. 6, pp. 178–186, 1952.

Hollmann, H. E.: Transistor Analysis in Terms of Vacuum Tubes, Memo 77, OSR 32, U.S. NAMTC, Point Mugu, Calif., December, 1952.

Hollmann, H. E.: Vacuum Tube Analogy of Transistors, *Electronics*, vol. 25, pp. 156, 158, 162, 164, 169, July, 1952.

Holm, E.: Contribution to the Theory of the Silicon Carbide Contact, *J. Appl. Phys.*, vol. 23, pp. 509–517, 1952.

Hopkins, E. G.: Self-heating Thermionic Vacuum Tubes, *J. Appl. Phys.*, vol. 23, pp. 1055, 1952.

Howe, G. W.: Duality between Triode and Transistor, *Wireless Engr.*, vol. 29, pp. 57–58, 1952.

Hungermann, E. H.: Advances in Transistor Technique, *Elektron Wiss. u. Tech.*, vol. 5, pp. 429–439, 1952.

Hunter, L. P., and H. Fleisher: Graphical Analysis of Some Transistor Switching Circuits, *Proc. IRE*, vol. 40, pp. 1559–1562, 1952.

Hunter, L. P., H. Fleisher, and C. G. Irish: Some Remarks on the Temperature Dependence of Alpha in Point-contact Transistors, *Trans. IRE*, vol. PGED-1, pp. 25–30, November, 1952.

Iglitsyn, M. I.: On the Electric Properties of Polycrystalline Selenium, *Zhur. Tekh. Fiz.*, vol. 22, pp. 885–887, 1952.

Ingalls, C. E.: Introduction to transistor Theory, Cornell University, School of Electrical Engineering, August, 1952. (Office of Technical Services PB 112631.)

Ioffe, A. V., and A. F. Ioffe: A Simple Method of Measuring Thermal Conductivity, *Zhur. Tekh. Fiz.*, vol. 22, pp. 2005–2013, 1952.

Ishiguro, M., T. Okuno, and A. Ueda: On the Electrical Properties of Silicon Containing Aluminum, *Mem. Inst. Sci. and Ind. Research, Osaka Univ.*, vol. 9, pp. 1–3, 1952.

Jaffe, G.: Theory of Conductivity of Semiconductors, *Phys. Rev.*, vol. 85, pp. 354–363, 1952.

James, E. G., and G. M. Wells: Crystal Triodes, *J. Brit. Inst. Radio Engrs.*, vol. 12, pp. 285–294, 1952.

Job, B., and J. M. Moulon: Transistrons, *J. Telecommun.*, vol. 19, pp. 444–460, 1952.

Jochems, P. J. W., and F. H. Stieltjes: Apparatus for Testing Transistors, *Philips Tech. Rev.*, vol. 13, pp. 254–265, 1952.

Jones, W. R.: Transistor Circuit Reliability, Cornell University, School of Electrical Engineering, August, 1952. (Office of Technical Services, PB 112633.)

Jordan, J. P.: The ABC's of Germanium, *Elec. Eng.*, vol. 71, pp. 619–625, 1952.

Justi, E., and G. Lautz: On Impurity and Intrinsic Semiconductors of Intermetallic Compounds, *Z. Naturforsch.*, vol. 7a, pp. 191–200, 602–613, 1952.

Justi, E., and G. Lautz: On the Semiconducting Properties of Intermetallic Compounds, (CdSb), *Abhandl. braunschweig. wiss. Ges.*, vol. 4, pp. 107–116, 1952.

Kalashnikov, S. G., and Ya. E. Pokrovski: The Influence of the Surface on the Type of Electrical Conduction of a Semiconductor, *Zhur. Tekh. Fiz.*, vol. 22 pp. 883–884, 1952.

Kalbskopf, W.: Phase-controlled Rectifiers, *VDE-Fachber.*, vol. 16, no. 4, pp. 8–10, 1952.

Kanai, Y.: On the P-N Junction of Silicon, Electrical Communication Laboratory, Ministry of Telecommunications, Tokyo, Doc. A. G. 98, Comm. VII, 1952.

Kanai, Y.: On the Transistor Action of Silicon Crystals, *J. Phys. Soc. Japan*, vol. 7, pp. 435–436, 1952.

Kassel, K.: The Semiconducting Properties of Cuprous Oxide. II. The Influence of Defects on the Optical Absorption, *Ann. Physik*, vol. 10, pp. 211–216, 1952.

Katz, E.: Splitting of Bands in Solids, *Phys. Rev.*, vol. 85, pp. 495–496, 1952.

Kaufman, A. B.: Germanium Phenomenon, *Radio-Electronic Eng.*, vol. 48, no. 1, pp. 10, 29, 1952.

Kaufman, A. B.: Potentiometer Leading Errors, *Radio-Electronic Eng.*, pp. 12–13, 26, September, 1952.

Keck, P. H.: Photoconductivity in Vacuum Coated Selenium Films, *J. Opt. Soc. Amer.*, vol. 42, pp. 221–225, 1952.

Keonjian, E., and J. S. Schaffner: An Experimental Investigation of Transistor Noise, *Proc. IRE*, vol. 40, pp. 1456–1460, 1952.

Keonjian, E., and J. S. Schaffner: Noise in Transistor Amplifiers, *Proc. Natl. Electronics Conf.*, vol. 8, pp. 343–345, 1952; *Electronics*, vol. 26, pp. 104–107, February, 1952.

Kikuchi, M.: Effect of the Electrical Field on Crystal Rectifiers, Electrochemical Laboratory, Tokyo, Doc. A. G. 101, Comm. VII, 1952.

Kingsbury, E. F., and R. S. Ohl: Photoelectric Properties of Ionically Bombarded Silicon, *Bell System Tech. J.*, vol. 31, pp. 802–815, 1952.

Kinman, T. H.: Germanium, *Wireless World*, vol. 58, pp. 29–30, 1952.

Klein Knecht, H.: Silicon Single-crystal Rods, *Naturwissenschaften*, vol. 39, pp. 400–401, 1952.

Kohler, M., and G. Zielasek: Der zeitliche Temperaturverlauf in elektrischen Kontakten, *Abhandl. braunschweig. wiss. Ges.*, vol. 4, pp. 116–126, 1952.

Kotterman, C. A.: Production Testing of Selenium Cells, *Electronics*, vol. 25, pp. 272–284, March, 1952.

Koyama, T.: Controlling Initial Current of Electrical Machinery and Apparatus by Semiconductor, *J. Inst. Elec. Engrs. Japan*, vol. 72, no. 759, 1952.

Koyama, T.: Design of Automatic Starter by Semiconductor, *J. Inst. Elec. Engrs. Japan*, vol. 72, pp. 423–427, 1952.

Koyama, T.: An Experimental Interpretation of the Theory of Selenium Rectification by P-N Junction Mechanism, *J. Inst. Elec. Engrs. Japan*, vol. 72, no. 761, 1952.

Krumbiegel, J.: Photoelectric Measurements in ZnS Single Crystals, *Naturwissenschaften*, vol. 39, p. 447, 1952.

Lagrenaudie, J.: Electrical and Optical Properties of Boron, *J. phys. radium*, vol. 13, pp. 554–557, 1952.

Landsberg, P. T.: Further Results in the General Theory of Barrier Layer Rectifiers, *Proc. Phys. Soc. (London)*, vol. 65B, pp. 397–409, 1952.

Landsberg, P. T.: A Note on the Theory of Semiconductors, *Proc. Phys. Soc. (London)*, vol. 65A, pp. 604–608, 1952.

Law, R. R., C. W. Mueller, J. I. Pankove (Pantchechnikoff), and L. D. Armstrong: A Developmental Germanium P-N-P Junction Transistor, *Proc. IRE*, vol. 40, pp. 1352–1357, 1952.

Lawrance, R., and A. F. Gibson: The Measurement of Drift Mobility in Semi-conductors, *Proc. Phys. Soc. (London)*, vol. 65B, pp. 994–995, 1952.

Lehovec, K.: New Photoelectric Devices Utilizing Carrier Injection, *Proc. IRE*, vol. 40, pp. 1407–1409, 1952.

Lindell, A., and G. M. Wells: Industrial Applications of Semiconductors. V, *Research*, vol. 5, pp. 317–323, 1952.

Lingel, F. J.: Germanium Diodes for Indicating Instruments and Relays, *Tele-Tech*, vol. 11, pp. 42–43, 100, 102, 104, April, 1952.

Lingel, F. J.: Germanium Power Rectifier Construction, *Electronics*, vol. 25, pp. 210, 212, June, 1952.

Lo, A. W.: Transistor Trigger Circuits, *Proc. IRE*, vol. 40, pp. 1531–1541, 1952.

Loeb, J.: Transistors in Non-linear Servomechanism (Filters), *Ann. Telecommun.*, vol. 7, pp. 408–410, 1952.

Lindberg, O.: Hall Effect, *Proc. IRE*, vol. 40, pp. 1414–1419, 1952.

Longini, R. L.: Electric Forming on N-germanium Transistors Using Donor-alloy Contacts, *Phys. Rev.*, vol. 84, p. 1254, 1952.

Lovelock, R. T.: The Use of the Germanium Rectifier in Television Receivers, *Proc. Inst. Elec. Engrs. (London)*, part III, vol. 99, pp. 551–559, 1952.

Lucas, O. H.: The Properties of Semi-conducting Ceramic Glaze, *Brit. J. Appl. Phys.*, vol. 3, pp. 293–296, 1952.

MacDonald, D. K. C., and K. Sarginson: Galvanomagnetic Effects in Conductors, *Repts. Progr. Phys.*, vol. 15, pp. 249–274, 1952.

McAfee, K. B., and G. L. Pearson: The Electrical Properties of Silicon P-N Junctions Grown from the Melt, *Phys. Rev.*, vol. 87, p. 190, 1952.

McAfee, K. B., W. Shockley, and M. Sparks: Measurements of Diffusion in Semiconductors by a Capacitance Method, *Phys. Rev.*, vol. 86, pp. 137–138, 1952.

McDuffie, G. E., Jr.: Pulse Duration and Repetition Rate of a Transistor Multivibrator, *Proc. IRE*, vol. 40, pp. 1487–1489, 1952.

McRae, J. W.: Transistors in Our Civilian Economy, *Proc. IRE*, vol. 40, pp. 1285–1286, 1952.

Madelung, O., and H. Welker: On the Theory of Mixed Semiconductors, *Z. angew. Physik*, vol. 5, pp. 12–14, 1952.

Malsch, J: Physics and Construction of the Transistor, *Arch. Elekt. Ubertrag.*, vol. 6, pp. 73–79, 1952.

Margna, C.: Eine Messanlase fuer Transistoren, *Bull. schweiz. elektrotech. Ver.*, vol. 43, pp. 1047–1049, 1952.

Martinet, J.: Physical Processes in Semiconducting Complexes, *Compt. rend.*, vol. 235, pp. 874–876, 1952.

Martinet, J.: Semiconducting Properties of the Oxides of Iron, *Compt. rend.*, vol. 234, pp. 2167–2169, 1952.

Marton, J. A.: New Transistors Give Improved Performance, *Electronics*, vol. 25, pp. 100–103, August, 1952.

Maslakovets, Yu. P., L. S. Stillbans, and T. S. Slavitskaya: On the Temperature Dependence of the Mobility of Charge Carriers in Semiconductors, *Doklady Akad. Nauk S.S.S.R.*, vol. 84, pp. 681–682, 1952.

Matare, H. F.: Interaction of Barrier Layers and Statistical Fluctuations in the Three-electrode Crystal (Transistor), *J. phys. radium*, vol. 13, pp. 112A–127A, 1952.

Matare, H. F.: Progress in the Field of Transistor Technology, *Elektron Wiss. u. Tech.*, vol. 5, pp. 411–420, 1952.

Milner, C. J., and B. N. Watts: Lead Sulphide Photo-cells, *Research*, vol. 5, pp. 267–273, 1952.

Minor, W. H.: The Transistor in Simple Circuits, *Radio-Electronic Eng.*, vol. 48, pp. 14–16, 25, December, 1952.

Mitchell, E. W. J.: Impurity Scattering in Oxide Semiconductors, *Proc. Phys. Soc. (London)*, vol. 65B, pp. 154–161, 1952.

Montgomery, H. C.: Electrical Noise in Semiconductors, *Bell System Tech. J.*, vol. 31, pp. 950–976, 1952.

Montgomery, H. C.: Transistor Noise in Circuit Applications, *Proc. IRE*, vol. 40, pp. 1461–1471, 1952.

Moore, A. R.: The Preparation of Single and Multiple P-N Junctions in Single Crystals of Germanium, RCA Laboratory LB-860, Apr. 25, 1952.

Morton, J. A.: New Transistor Gives Improved Performance, *Electronics*, vol. 25, pp. 100–103, August, 1952.

Morton, J. A.: Present Status of Transistor Development, *Bell System Tech. J.*, vol. 31, pp. 411–442, 1952; *Proc. IRE*, vol. 40, pp. 1314–1326, 1952; *Aero. Eng. Rev.*, vol. 11, pp. 34–45, 87, May, 1952.

Moss, T. S.: Optical Properties of Tellurium in the Infrared, *Proc. Phys. Soc. (London)*, vol. 65B, pp. 62–66, 1952.

Moss, T. S.: "Photoconductivity in the Elements," Butterworth & Co. (Publishers) Ltd., London, 1952.

Moss, T. S.: Properties of Films of Non-metallic Antimony, *Proc. Phys. Soc. (London)*, vol. 65A, pp. 147–148, 1952.

Moulon, J. M.: Semiconductors and Their Applications, *Ann. Telecommun.*, vol. 7, pp. 364–374, 1952.

Mrozowski, S.: Semiconductivity and Diamagnetism of Polycrystalline Graphite and Condensed Ring Systems, *Phys. Rev.*, vol. 85, pp. 609–620, 1952.

Munesue, S., and T. Sakurai: Resistivity of Evaporated Tellurium Films, *Phys. Rev.*, vol. 85, p. 921, 1952.

Muto, T., and S. Oyama: Theory of the Temperature Effect of Electronic Energy Bands in Crystals, Institute of Science and Technology, Tokyo University, Doc. A.G. 93, Comm. VII, 1952.

National Research Council, Committee on Solids: Imperfections in Nearly Perfect Crystals, Symposium held at Pocono Manor, Pa., Oct. 12–14, 1950, editorial committee, W. Shockley, chairman (and others), John Wiley & Sons, Inc., New York, 1952.

Navon, D., R. Bray, and H. Y. Fan: Lifetime of Injected Carriers in Germanium, *Proc. IRE*, vol. 40, pp. 1342–1347, 1952.

N'Guyen, T. C., and J. Suchet: Voltage Regulators with Non-linear Circuit Elements, *Ann. radioelec.*, vol. 7, pp. 189–198, 1952.

Nifontoff, N.: Conductivity and Fluctuation Effect in Very Thin Films of Carbon, *Compt. rend.*, vol. 234, pp. 1755–1757, 1952.

Nifontoff, N.: On the Effect of Fluctuations of Crystal Detectors, *Compt. rend.*, vol. 235, pp. 1117–1118, 1952.

Obenchain, I. R., and W. J. Galloway: Transistors and the Military, *Proc. IRE*, vol. 40, pp. 1287–1288, 1952.

O'Connor, J. A.: What Can Transistors Do? *Chem. Eng.*, vol. 59, pp. 154–156, 370, 372–374, 376, 378, May, 1952.

Ohl, R. S.: Properties of Ionically Bombarded Silicon, *Bell System Tech. J.*, vol. 31, pp. 104–122, 1952.

Ono, K., and Y. Kanai: Studies on Silicon Detector Surface by the Electron Diffraction Method, Electrical Communication Laboratory, Ministry of Telecommunication, Tokyo, Doc. A. G. 95, Comm. VII, 1952.

Oser, E. A., R. O. Endres, and R. P. Moore: Transistor Oscillators, *RCA Rev.*, vol. 13, pp. 369–385, 1952; *Bull. schweiz. elektrotech. Ver.*, vol. 44, pp. 420–422, 1953.

Packer, L., and W. J. Wray, Jr.: Germanium Photodiodes Read Computer Tapes, *Electronics*, vol. 25, pp. 150–151, November, 1952.

Pantchechnikoff, J. I., S. Lasof, J. Kurshan, and A. R. Moore: Use of the Flying Spot Scanner to Study Photosensitive Surfaces, *Rev. Sci. Instr.*, vol. 23, pp. 465–467, 1952.

Pearson, G. L., W. T. Read, and W. Shockley: Probing the Space Charge Layer in P-N Junctions, *Phys. Rev.*, vol. 85, pp. 1055–1057, 1952; vol. 86, p. 467, 1952.

Pearson, G. L., and B. Sawyer: Silicon P-N Junction Alloy Diodes, *Proc. IRE*, vol. 40, pp. 1348–1351, 1952.

Pearson, G. L., and P. W. Foy: Silicon P-N Junction Diodes Prepared by the Alloying Process, *Phys. Rev.*, vol. 87, p. 190, 1952.

Petritz, R. L.: On the Diffusion Theory of Noise in Rectifiers and Transistors, *Phys. Rev.*, vol. 87, p. 189, 1952.

Petritz, R. L.: On the Theory of Noise in P-N Junctions and Related Devices, *Proc. IRE*, vol. 40, pp. 1440–1456, 1952.

Petritz, R. L.: A Theory of Contact Noise, *Phys. Rev.*, vol. 87, pp. 535–536, 1952.

Pfann, W. G.: Improved Transistor, *Radio-Electronics*, vol. 23, p. 110, March, 1952.

Pfann, W. G.: Principles of Zone Melting, *J. Metals*, vol. 4, pp. 747–754, July, 1952.

Pfann, W. G.: Segregation of Two Solutes with Particular Reference to Semiconductors, *J. Metals*, vol. 4, pp. 861–866, 1952.

Pikus, G. E.: Influence of the Surface Levels on the Optical Properties of a Semi-conductor or of a Dielectric, *Zhur. Eksptl. i. Teort. Fiz.*, vol. 22, pp. 231–238, 1952.

Ploke, M.: Alternating Light Amplification with Photo Resistances, *Funk u. Ton*, vol. 6, pp. 305–310, 1952.

Pohl, R. W.: The Significance of Imperfections in Crystal Structure for the Physics of Solids, *Naturwissenschaften*, vol. 39, pp. 9–13, 1952.

Prache, P. M., and H. Billottet: Magnetodynamics of Semiconductors (Application to Ferrites), *Cables et transm.*, vol. 6, pp. 317–332, 1952.

Prince, M. B., and F. S. Goucher: Test of Transistor Equations, *Phys. Rev.*, vol. 86, p. 647, 1952.

Pritchard, R. L.: Frequency Variations of Current-amplification Factor for Junction Transistors, *Proc. IRE*, vol. 40, pp. 1476–1481, 1952.

Putley, E. H.: The Conductivity and Hall Coefficient of Sintered Lead Sulphide, *Proc. Phys. Soc. (London)*, vol. 65B, pp. 736–737, 1952.

Putley, E. H.: Intrinsic Conduction in PbS, PbSe, PbTe, *Proc. Phys. Soc. (London)*, vol. 65B, p. 993, 1952.

Putley, E. H.: Thermo and Galvano-magnetic Coefficients for Semiconductors, *Proc. Phys. Soc. (London)*, vol. 65B, pp. 991–993, 1952.

Raisbeck, G.: Transistor Circuit Design, *Electronics*, vol. 24, pp. 128–134, December, 1952.

Regnault, F., P. Aigrain, C. Dugas, and B. Sancovici: On the Semiconducting Properties of Molybdenite, *Compt. rend.*, vol. 235, pp. 31–32, 1952.

Reich, H. J.: Transistor and Transistor Circuits, *Elec. Mfg.*, vol. 50, pp. 106–112, 324, 326, 328, November, 1952; p. 102, December, 1952.

Renne, H. M.: The Junction Transistor, *Radio Television News*, vol. 47, pp. 38–39, 166, April, 1952.

Rhita, N.: Transistor Oscillators with Crystal Control, *Radio-Electronics*, vol. 23, p. 56, April, 1952.

Rittner, E. S., and F. Frace: Impedance Measurements on PbS Photoconductive Cells, *Phys. Rev.*, vol. 86, pp. 955–958, 1952.

Roessler, E.: Transistor Fundamentals, *Elektrotech. Z.*, vol. 73, pp. 338–339, May, 1952.

Rose, G. M., and B. N. Slade: Transistors Operate at 300 mc/s, *Electronics*, vol. 25, pp. 116–118, November, 1952.

Rosenthal, J. E., and A. Bramley: Mechanism of Conductivity in Semiconducting Phosphors, *J. Chem. Phys.*, vol. 20, p. 1496, 1952.

Rost, R.: Temperature Stable Crystal Diodes, *Fernmeldetech. Z.*, vol. 5, pp. 177–178, 1952.

Roth, I., and W. E. Taylor: Preparation of Germanium Single Crystals, *Proc. IRE*, vol. 40, pp. 1338–1341, 1952.

Rothlein, B. J.: A Photovoltaic Germanium Cell, *Sylvania Technologist*, pp. 86–88, October, 1952.

Roualt, C. L., and G. N. Hall: A High-voltage, Medium-power Rectifier, *Proc. IRE*, vol. 40, pp. 1519–1521, 1952.

Roy-Pochon, C.: The Germanium Photodiode, *Electricité*, vol. 36, p. 131, June, 1952.

Roy-Pochon, C.: Germanium Triodes, *Electricité*, vol. 36, p. 242, December, 1952.

Rudenberg, H. G.: Transistor Sawtooth Oscillator, *Radio-Electronics*, vol. 24, pp. 50–51, November, 1952.

Rugare, A. S.: The Metal Germanium and Its Use in the Electronics Industry, *Metal Progr.*, vol. 62, pp. 97–103, August, 1952.

Saby, J. S.: Fused Impurity P-N-P Junction Transistors, *Proc. IRE*, vol. 40, pp. 1358–1360, 1952.

Saby, J. S.: Germanium Transistors, *Gen. Elec. Rev.*, vol. 55, pp. 21–24, September, 1952; *Product Eng.*, vol. 23, p. 270, December, 1952.

Salow, H.: Progress in Transistor Technique, *Elektron Wiss. u. Tech.*, vol. 5, pp. 421–428, 1952.

Sasaki, W.: Electrical Resistivity of Silicon Carbide, *J. Phys. Soc. Japan*, vol. 7, p. 107, 1952.

Satomuras, S., and M. Ishiguro: Frequency Characteristics of the Negative Resistance of the Germanium Rectifier, *Mem. Inst. Sci. and Ind. Research, Osaka Univ.*, vol. 9, pp. 4–5, 1952.

Savornin, J., and F. Savornin: Thermoelectric Measurements on P-type Silicon, *Compt. rend.*, vol. 235, pp. 465–467, 1952.

Schottky, W.: Zum Hochfrequenzverhalten der Randschichtgleichrichter, *Z. Physik*, vol. 132, pp. 261–285, 1952.

Schulze, A.: Gold-chromium Standard Resistances, *Arch. Tech. Messen*, no. 203, pp. 283–284, 1952.

Schulze, A., and H. Eicke: Metal-film Resistors, *Deut. Elektrotech.*, vol. 6, pp. 616–619, 1952.

Schulze, A., and H. Eicke: On Gold-chromium Resistance Standards, *Z. angew. Physik*, vol. 4, pp. 321–324, 1952.

Schwarz, E.: Industrial Applications of Semi-conductors. 6. Semi-conductor Thermopiles, *Research*, vol. 5, pp. 407–411, 1952.

Science Museum: Bibliography of Semiconductors, 1946—September, 1952, Bibliographical series 711, Science Museum, London, 1952.

Selenyi, P.: The Influence of Mercury Vapour on Selenium Rectifiers and Selenium Photo-elements, *Proc. Phys. Soc. (London)*, vol. 65B, p. 552, 1952.

Shea, R. F.: Transistor Operation: Stabilization of Operating Points, *Proc. IRE*, vol. 40, pp. 1435–1437, 1952.

Shea, R. F.: Transistor Power Amplifiers, *Electronics*, vol. 25, pp. 106–108, 1952.

Shekel, J.: Matrix Representation of Transistor Circuits, *Proc. IRE*, vol. 40, pp. 1493–1497, 1952.

Shive, J. N.: Properties of Germanium Phototransistors, *J. Opt. Soc. Amer.*, vol. 42, p. 869, 1952.

Shive, J. N.: Properties of M-1740 P-N Junction Photocell, *Proc. IRE*, vol. 40, pp. 1410–1413, 1952.

Shockley, W., and W. T. Read, Jr.: Statistics of the Recombinations of Holes and Electrons, *Phys. Rev.*, vol. 87, pp. 835–842, 1952.

Shockley, W.: Transistor Electronics: Imperfections, Unipolar and Analog Transistors, *Proc. IRE*, vol. 40, pp. 1289–1313, 1952.

Shockley, W.: A Unipolar "Field Effect" Transistor, *Proc. IRE*, vol. 40, pp. 1365–1376, 1952.

Sillars, R. W.: Light Emission from Silicon Carbide, *Phys. Rev.*, vol. 85, p. 136, 1952.

Sittner, W. R.: Current Multiplication in the Type-A Transistor, *Proc. IRE*, vol. 40, pp. 448–454, 1952.

Sittner, W. R.: The Transistors Development Status at Bell Telephone Labs., in Proceedings of Progress in Quality Electronic Components, pp. 138–142. May, 1952.

Skalicky, M.: Maximum Power in Load Resistances, *Elektrotech. u. Maschinenbau*, vol. 69, pp. 479–480, 1952.

Slade, B. N.: The Control of Frequency Response and Stability of Point-contact Transistors, *Proc. IRE*, vol. 40, pp. 1382–1384, 1952.

Slade, B. N.: A Method of Improving the Electrical and Mechanical Stability of Point-contact Transistors, *RCA Rev.*, vol. 12, pp. 651–659, 1952.

Slade, B. N.: Survey of Transistor Development, *Radio Television News*, vol. 48, pp. 43–45, 170–171, September, 1952; pp. 64–65, 112, 114–116, October, 1952; pp. 68–69, November, 1952.

Slater, J. C.: The Solid State, *Physics Today*, vol. 5, pp. 10–15, January, 1952.

Slichter, W. P., and E. D. Kolb: Impurity Effects in the Thermal Conversion of Germanium, *Phys. Rev.*, vol. 87, pp. 527–528, 1952.

Smith, D. H.: Automatic Regulation of Metallic Rectifiers by Magnetic Control, *Trans. AIEE*, vol. 71, part I, pp. 111–114, 1952.

Smith, K. D.: Properties of Junction Transistors, *Proc. Natl. Electronics Conf.*, vol. 8, pp. 330–342, 1952.

Soldi, M.: Application of Thermistors to a Bridge for Measuring Low Admittances at Radio Frequency, *Alta frequenza*, vol. 21, pp. 243–259, December, 1952.

Sommer, J.: A New Non-linear Resistance (Lamp), *Funk u. Ton*, vol. 6, pp. 520–526, 1952.

Sparks, M.: The Junction Transistor, *Sci. American*, vol. 187, pp. 28–32, July, 1952.

Steele, E. L.: Theory of Alpha for P-N-P Diffused Junction Transistors, *Proc. IRE*, vol. 40, pp. 1424–1428, 1952.

Stilbans, L. S.: On the Adiabatic and Isothermal Hall Effects in Semiconductors, *Zhur. Tekh. Fiz.*, vol. 22, pp. 77–79, 1952.

Strull, G.: Cadmium Sulphide As a Crystal Rectifier, *Proc. Natl. Electronics Conf.*, vol. 8, pp. 510–521, 1952.

Stuetzer, O. M.: Junction Fieldistors, *Proc. IRE*, vol. 40, pp. 1377–1381, 1952.

Stuetzer, O. M.: Transistors in Airborne Equipment, *Proc. IRE*, vol. 40, pp. 1529–1530, 1952.

Sturzinger, O.: Zusammenstellung der wichtigsten erhaltlichen Kristallrichtleiter, *Funk u. Ton*, vol. 8, pp. 427–439, 1952.

Taft, E. A., and M. H. Hebb: Note on Quenching of Photoconductivity in Cadmium Sulfide, *J. Opt. Soc. Amer.*, vol. 42, pp. 249–251, 1952.

Tauc, J.: Transistor As a New Element for High Frequency Circuits, *Slaboproudy Obzor*, vol. 13, pp. 30–38, February, 1952.

Taylor, W. E., N. H. Odell, and H. Y. Fan: Grain Boundary Barriers in Germanium, *Phys. Rev.*, vol. 88, pp. 867–875, 1952.

Teal, G. K., and E. Buehler: Growth of Silicon Single Crystals and of Single Crystal Silicon P-N Junctions, *Phys. Rev.*, vol. 87, p. 190, 1952.

Teal, G. K., M. Sparks, and E. Buehler: Single-crystal Germanium, *Proc. IRE*, vol. 40, pp. 906–909, 1952.

Thedieck, R.: Mechanism of Point-contact Transistors, *Z. angew. Physik*, vol. 5, pp. 165–166, 1952.

Thomas, D. E.: Low-drain Transistor Audio Oscillator, *Proc. IRE*, vol. 40, pp. 1385–1395, 1952.

Thomas, D. E.: Transistor Amplifier-cutoff Frequency, *Proc. IRE*, vol. 40, pp. 1481–1483, 1952.

Tolpygo, K. B.: On the Determination of the Effective Mass of the Current Carriers in Semiconductors from Their Infrared Absorption, *Zhur. Eksptl. i. Teort. Fiz.*, vol. 22, pp. 378–380, 1952.

Tomlinson, J. W., and H. Inouye: The Electric Conductance of Liquid Iron Oxide, *J. Chem. Phys.*, vol. 20, p. 193, 1952.

Tomura, M., and Y. Abiko: The Magneto-effect in Germanium Point Contacts, *J. Phys. Soc. Japan*, vol. 7, pp. 115–117, 1952.

Tonnesen, T. H.: On the Distribution of Transistor Action, *Proc. Phys. Soc. (London)*, vol. 65B, pp. 737–739, 1952.

Trent, R. L.: Binary Counter Uses Two Transistors, *Electronics*, vol. 25, pp. 100–101, July, 1952.

Trent, R. L.: A Transistor Reversible Binary Counter, *Proc. Natl. Electronics Conf.*, vol. 8, pp. 346–357, 1952; *Proc. IRE*, vol. 40, pp. 1562–1572, 1952.

Valdes, L. B.: Effect of Electrode Spacing on the Equivalent Base Resistance of Point-contact Transistors, *Proc. IRE*, vol. 40, pp. 1429–1434, 1952.

Valdes, L. B.: Measurement of Minority Carrier Lifetime in Germanium, *Proc. IRE*, vol. 40, pp. 1420–1423, 1952.

Valdes, L. B.: Transistor Forming Effects in N-type Germanium, *Proc. IRE*, vol. 40, pp. 445–448, 1952.

van der Ziel, A.: Fluctuation Phenomena, *Advances in Electronics*, vol. 4, pp. 109–155, 1952.

van der Ziel, A.: Shot Noise in Semiconductors, *Bull. Am. Phys. Soc.*, vol. 27, p. 15, May, 1952.

van Roosbroeck, W.: Large Current Amplification in Filamentary Transistors, *J. Appl. Phys.*, vol. 23, pp. 1411–1412, 1952.

Wagener, S.: Industrial Applications of Semi-conductors. 6. Oxide Cathodes, *Research*, vol. 5, pp. 355–362, 1952.

Walker, A. H. B.: The Transbooster, *Electronic Eng.*, vol. 24, pp. 546–550, 1952.

Wallace, R. L., Jr., L. G. Schimpf, and E. Dickten: A Junction Transistor Tetrode for High-frequency Use, *Proc. IRE*, vol. 40, pp. 1395–1400, 1952.

Wallis, J. H.: First Application of Transistors in Railroad Communications, *Railway Sig.*, vol. 45, pp. 774–775, 1952.

Waltz, M. C.: On Some Transients in the Pulse Response of Point-contact Germanium Diodes, *Proc. IRE*, vol. 40, pp. 1483–1487, 1952.

Warfield, G.: "Physics of Transistors," Princeton University, Princeton, N.J., August, 1952. (Office of Technical Services PB 112635.)

Watanabe, Y.: Noise Figures of Transistor Circuits, *Repts. Research Elect. Commun.*, *Tôhoku Univ.*, vol. 3, pp. 151–187, 1952; also Doc. A. G. 97, Comm. VII, 1952.

Watanabe, Y., et al.: On the Crystal Rectifier, *Electrotechnical Papers (Tokyo)*, vol. 4, pp. 100–104, April, 1952.

Watanabe, Y., and J. Nishizawa: On the Rectification Mechanism of Semiconductors, Department of Electrical Engineering, Tôhoku University, Doc. A. G. 94, Comm. VII, 1952.

Watanabe, Y.: Some Circuit Considerations of the Transistor, *Sci. Repts. Tôhoku Univ.*, *ser. B*, vol. 4, no. 2; also Doc. A.G. 96, Comm. VII, 1952.

Watson, D. J.: Transistors, *Eng. J. Canada*, vol. 35, pp. 722–728, 733, 1952.

Weill, M. C.: Applications of Germanium in Telecommunications, *Revue Gen. Elec.*, vol. 61, pp. 154–155, April, 1952.

Welker, H.: On New Semiconducting Compounds, *Z. Naturforsch.*, vol. 7a, pp. 744–749, 1952.

Went, J. J., and E. W. Gorter: The Magnetic and Electrical Properties of Ferroxcube Materials, *Philips Tech. Rev.*, vol. 13, pp. 181–193, 1952.

Whalley, W. B., and C. Masucci: An Analysis of Crystal Diodes in the Millivolt Region, *Tele-Tech*, vol. 11, pp. 40–42, 130, May, 1952.

Whalley, W. B., N. P. Salz, and C. Masucci: An Analysis of Crystal Diodes in the Millivolt Region, *Proc. IRE*, vol. 40, pp. 232–233, 1952.

Wijn, H. P. J.: A New Method of Melting Ferromagnetic Semiconductors BaFe$_{18}$O$_{27}$, a New Kind of Ferromagnetic Crystal with High Crystal Anisotropy, *Nature*, vol. 170, pp. 707–708, 1952.

Witthandt, R.: Simplified Calculation of Logarithmically Divided Stage Potentiometers, *Funk u. Ton*, vol. 6, pp. 378–380, 1952.

Wood, M. L.: Transistor Characteristic Curve Plotter, IBM Engineering Laboratory, Poughkeepsie, N.Y., 1952.

Young, J. R.: Electrical Conductivity and Thermoelectric Power of (BaSr)O and BaO, *J. Appl. Phys.*, vol. 23, pp. 1129–1138, 1952.

Yurkov, V. A.: Change in the Electric Conduction of Sb$_2$S$_3$ and V$_2$O$_5$ on Melting, *Zhur. Eksptl. i. Teort. Fiz.*, vol. 22, pp. 223–229, 1952.

Zeider, H. M.: Transistor Characteristics, *Trans. IRE*, vol. PGED-1, pp. 2–10, November, 1952.

Aging Troubles Transistor Producers, *Aviation Week*, vol. 57, no. 17, pp. 18–19, November, 1952.

Colloquium on Transistors in Theory and Practice, U.S. Naval Research Laboratory, Washington, D.C., May, 1952.

Dick Tracy's Radio Comes to Life, *Radio Television News*, vol. 48, p. 108, September, 1952.

Duality between Triodes and Transistors, *Wireless Engr.*, vol. 29, pp. 57–58, 1952.

Experimental Verification of the Relationship between Diffusion Constant and Mobility of Electrons, *Phys. Rev.*, vol. 88, pp. 1368–1369, 1952.

GE Predicts Germanium Will Miniaturize Electronic Components, *Product Eng.*, vol. 23, p. 179, March, 1952.

Germanium Diode Experience, *Radio-Electronic Eng.*, vol. 47, pp. 20–21, January, 1952.

Germanium Diode Tester, *Instruments*, vol. 25, p. 1230, 1952.

The Junction Transistor, *Electronics*, vol. 24, pp. 82–85, November, 1952.

Latest Transistor Units, *Tele-Tech*, vol. 11, p. 39, May, 1952.

New Tetrode Junction Transistor, *Tele-Tech*, vol. 11, p. 38, November, 1952.

On the Distribution of Transistor Action, *Proc. Phys. Soc. (London)*, vol. 65B, pp. 737–739, 1952.

Transistors, *Radio-Electronics Eng.*, vol. 48, p. 36, August, 1952.

Transistors: A Summary of Progress in Performance, *Tele-Tech*, vol. 11, pp. 36–38, 102–106, July, 1952.

Transistors Enter Telephone Service, *Bell Labs. Record*, vol. 30, p. 439, November, 1952.

1953

Accardo, C. A., and E. Jamgochian: Light Emission Produced by Current Injected into a Green Silicon Carbide Crystal, *Phys. Rev.*, vol. 89, pp. 20–25, 1953.

Aigrain, P., and C. Dugas: Physical Properties of Semiconductors and Applications in Radioelectricity, *Onde élect.*, vol. 33, pp. 5–14, 1953.

Alsberg, D. A.: Transistor Metrology, *IRE Convention Record*, part 9, pp. 39–44, 1953.

Anderson, V. C., and P. Rudnick: A Thermistor Bridge Correlator, *Rev. Sci. Instr.*, vol. 24, pp. 360–361, 1953.

Angell, J. B., and F. P. Keiper, Jr.: The Surface-barrier Transistor. Part III. Circuit Applications of Surface-barrier Transistors, *Proc. IRE*, vol. 41, pp. 1709–1712, 1953.

An'selm, A. I.: Effect of the Resonance Scattering of Current Carriers in the Impurity Centers on Electrical Properties of Atomic Semiconductors, *Zhur. Eksptl. i. Teort. Fiz.*, vol. 24, pp. 83–89, 1953.

Armstrong, H. L.: Thermal Effects in Point Contact Rectifiers, *J. Appl. Phys.*, vol. 24, pp. 1332–1333, 1953.

Armstrong, L. D., and D. A. Jenny: Behavior of Germanium Junction Transistors at Elevated Temperature and Power Transistor Design, *IRE Convention Record*, part 6, pp. 22–26, 1953.

Arnold, A. H. M.: Alternating-current Resistance Standards, *Proc. Inst. Elec. Engrs.*, *(London)*, vol. 100, part II, pp. 319–327, 1953.

Aronson, M. H.: Instrument Electronics; Transistors, *Instruments*, vol. 26, pp. 252–253, 1953.

Avery, D. G.: The Optical Constants of Lead Sulphide, Lead Selenide and Lead Telluride in the 0.5–3μ Region of the Spectrum, *Proc. Phys. Soc. (London)*, vol. 66B, pp. 134–140, 1953.

Baker, G. S., L. M. Slifkin, and J. W. Marx: Germanium under Ultrasonic Stress. I: Anelastic Effects, *J. Appl. Phys.*, vol. 24, p. 1331, 1953.

Baker, G. S., L. M. Slifkin, and J. W. Marx: Germanium under Ultrasonic Stress. II: Dynamic Yield Point, *J. Appl. Phys.*, vol. 24, pp. 1331–1332, 1953.

Baker, R. H., I. L. Lebow, R. H. Rediker, and I. S. Reed: The Phase-bistable Transistor Circuit, *Proc. IRE*, vol. 41, pp. 1119–1124, 1760, 1953.

Ballard, R. C.: Portable Transistor FM Receiver, *Tele-Tech*, vol. 12, pp. 79, 206–207, August, 1953.

Baltensperger, W.: On Conduction in Impurity Bands, *Phil. Mag.*, vol. 44, pp. 1355–1363, 1953.

Banbury, P. C.: Carrier Injection and Extraction in Lead Sulfide, *Proc. Phys. Soc. (London)*, vol. 66B, pp. 50–53, 1953.

Banbury, P. C., H. K. Henisch, and A. Many: On the Theory of Isothermal Hall Effect in Semiconductors, *Proc. Phys. Soc. (London)*, vol. 66A, pp. 753–758, 1953.

Banbury, P. C.: Theory of the Forward Characteristic of Injecting Point Contacts, *Proc. Phys. Soc. (London)*, vol. 66B, pp. 833–840, 1953.

Bassett, H. G., and J. R. Tillman: Some Transient Properties of Transistors, *Brit. J. Appl. Phys.*, vol. 4, pp. 116–117, 1953.

Bauer, B. B.: Miniature Microphone for Transistorized Amplifiers, *J. Acoust. Soc. Am.*, vol. 25, pp. 867–869, 1953.

Bauer, B. B.: A Miniature Microphone for Transistorized Amplifiers, *Trans. IRE*, vol. AU-1, pp. 5–7, November, 1953.

Bello, F.: The Year of the Transistor, *Fortune*, vol. 47, pp. 128–133, March, 1953.

Benedict, T. S., and W. Shockley: Microwave Observation of the Collision Frequency of Electrons in *Germanium, Phys. Rev.*, vol. 89, pp. 1152–1153, 1953.

Benedict, T. S.: Microwave Observation of the Collision Frequency of Holes in Germanium, *Phys. Rev.*, vol. 91, p. 1565, 1953.

Bess, L.: A Possible Mechanism for 1/f Noise Generation in Semiconductor Filaments, *Phys. Rev.*, vol. 91, p. 1569, 1953.

Billig, E., and J. J. Dowd: P-N Junction Revealed by Electrolytic Etching, *Nature*, vol. 172, p. 115, 1953.

Blakemore, J. S., A. E. DeBarr, and J. B. Gunn: Semiconductors Circuit Elements, *Repts. Progr. Phys.*, vol. 16, pp. 160–215, 1953.

Blankenburg, G.: The Semiconducting Properties of Cuprous Oxide. VI: The Temperature Dependence of Electrical Conductivity at Temperatures between 20° and −190°C., *Ann. Physik*, vol. 12, pp. 281–296, 1953.

Blount, F. E.: Transistor Oscillator for Use in Multifrequency Pulsing Current Supply, *Bell System Tech. J.*, vol. 32, pp. 1313–1331, 1953.

Boer, K. W., and K. Junge: On the Frequency Dependence of Semiconductor Noise, *Z. Naturforsch.*, vol. 8a, pp. 753–755, 1953.

Bohr, E.: Transistor Control Relay, *Radio-Electronics*, vol. 24, pp. 53–54, July, 1953.

Bradley, W. E.: The Surface-barrier Transistor. Part I: Principles of the Surface-barrier Transistor, *Proc. IRE*, vol. 41, pp. 1702–1706, 1953.

Brattain, W. H., and J. Bardeen: Surface Properties of Germanium, *Bell System Tech. J.*, vol. 32, pp. 1–41, 1953.

Breckenridge, R. G., and W. R. Hosler: Electrical Properties of Titanium Dioxide Semiconductors, *Phys. Rev.*, vol. 91, pp. 793–802, 1953.

Breckenridge, R. G.: Semiconducting Intermetallic Compounds, *Phys. Rev.*, vol. 90, pp. 488–489, 1953.

Breckenridge, R. G.: Semiconducting Intermetallic Compounds, *Tele-Tech*, vol. 12, pp. 86, 147, November, 1953.

Bridgman, P. W.: Further Measurements of the Effect of Pressure on the Electrical Resistance of Germanium, *Proc. Am. Acad. Arts Sci.*, vol. 82, pp. 71–82, April, 1953.

Briggs, H. B., and R. C. Fletcher: Absorption of Infrared Light by Free Carriers in Germanium, *Phys. Rev.*, vol. 91, pp. 1342–1346, 1953.

Brown, A. H., R. P. Chasmar, and P. B. Fellgett: The Construction of Radiation Thermocouples Using Semi-conducting Thermoelectric Materials, *J. Sci. Instr.*, vol. 30, pp. 195–199, 1953.

Brown, H. V.: Transistor M. C. W. Adaptor, *QST*, vol. 37, p. 51, September, 1953.

Brown, W. L.: N-type Surface Conductivity on P-type Germanium, *Phys. Rev.*, vol. 91, pp. 518–527, 1953.

Burgess, R. E.: Contact Noise in Semiconductors, *Proc. Phys. Soc. (London)*, vol. 66B, pp. 334–335, 1953.

Burgess, R. E.: The Influence of Mobility Variation in High Fields on the Diffusion Theory of Rectifier Barriers, *Proc. Phys. Soc. (London)*, vol. 66B, pp. 430–431, 1953.

Burns, L.: Electroluminescence of Insulated Particles, *J. Electrochem. Soc.*, vol. 100, pp. 572–579, 1953.

Burton, J. A.: Effect of Nickel and Copper Impurities on the Recombination of Holes and Electrons in Germanium, *J. Phys. Chem.*, vol. 57, pp. 853–859, 1953.

Busch, G., and E. Mooser: The Magnetic Properties of Semiconductors with Special Consideration of Grey Tin. I–II, *Helv. Phys. Acta*, vol. 26, pp. 611–656, 1953.

Busch, G., and J. Wieland: Researches on the Mechanism of the Electrical Conductivity of Grey Tin, *Helv. Phys. Acta*, vol. 26, pp. 697–730, 1953.

Butler, W. M.: On the Surface Layer Noise in CdS Single Crystals, *Ann. Physik*, vol. 11, pp. 368–376, 1953.

Butler, W. M.: On the Surface Layer Noise in Semiconductors, *Ann. Physik*, vol. 11, pp. 362–367, 1953.

Carcano, L. D.: Transistor Bridge Null Detector, *Radio Television News*, vol. 50, p. 132, October, 1953.

Carcano, L. D.: Transistor Power Supply, *Radio Television News*, vol. 50, p. 88, October, 1953.

Chaplin, R., P. R. Chapman, and R. H. Griffith: Electrical Properties of Chromium Oxide Alumina Catalyst, *Nature*, vol. 172, p. 78, 1953.

Checinska, H.: Photoconductive and Photovoltaic Lead Selenide, *Acta Phys. Polonica*, vol. 12, pp. 194–224, 1953.

Chow, W. F., and J. J. Suran: Transient Analysis of Junction Transistor Amplifiers. *Proc. IRE*, vol. 41, pp. 1125–1129, 1953; *Electronics*, vol. 26, pp. 189–191, November, 1953; *IRE Convention Record*, part 5, p. 102, 1953.

Clark, E. N., and R. L. Hopkins: Electrical Conductivity of Mechanically Disturbed Germanium Surfaces, *Phys. Rev.*, vol. 91, p. 1566, 1953.

Clark, E. N.: Oxygen-induced Surface Conductivity on Germanium, *Phys. Rev.*, vol. 91, pp. 756–757, 1953.

Clay, R.: Transistor Circuitry, *QST*, vol. 37, pp. 35–38, December, 1953.

Coblenz, A., and H. L. Owens: Transistors: Theory and Application, part I, *Electronics*, vol. 26, pp. 98–102, March, 1953.

Coblenz, A., and H. L. Owens: Transistors: Theory and Application, part II: Energy Levels in Transistor Electronics, *Electronics*, vol. 26, pp. 138–141, April, 1953.

Coblenz, A., and H. L. Owens: Transistors: Theory and Application, part III: Physical Properties of Electrons in Solids, *Electronics*, vol. 26, pp. 162–165, May, 1953.

Coblenz, A., and H. L. Owens: Transistors: Theory and Application, part IV: Transistor Action in Germanium and Silicon, *Electronics*, vol. 26, pp. 166–171, June, 1953.

Coblenz, A., and H. L. Owens: Transistors: Theory and Application, part V: Point-contact Transistor Operation, *Electronics*, vol. 26, pp. 158–163, July, 1953.

Coblenz, A., and H. L. Owens: Transistors: Theory and Application, part VI: Operation of Junction Transistors, *Electronics*, vol. 26, pp. 156–161, August, 1953.

Coblenz, A., and H. L. Owens: Transistors: Theory and Application, part VII: Equivalent Transistor Circuits and Equations, *Electronics*, vol. 26, pp. 156–161, September, 1953.

Coblenz, A., and H. L. Owens: Transistors: Theory and Application, part VIII: Small-signal Transistor Operation, *Electronics*, vol. 26, pp. 158–163, October, 1953.

Coblenz, A., and H. L. Owens: Transistors: Theory and Application, part IX: Grounded Emitter and Collector Circuits, *Electronics*, vol. 26, pp. 166–172, November, 1953.

Coblenz, A., and H. L. Owens: Transistors: Theory and Application, part X: Switching Circuits Using Transistors, *Electronics*, vol. 26, pp. 186–191, December, 1953.

Conwell, E. M.: High Field Mobility in Germanium with Impurity Scattering Dominant, *Phys. Rev.*, vol. 90, pp. 769–772, 1953.

Cunnell, F. A., E. W. Saker, and J. T. Edmond: A Note on the Semiconducting Compound InSb, *Proc. Phys. Soc. (London)*, vol. 66B, pp. 1115–1116, 1953.

Cutteridge, O. P. D.: Four-terminal Networks (Fundamental Theory), *Wireless Engr.*, vol. 30, pp. 61–69, 1953.

Dacey, G. C.: Space Charge Limited Hole Current in Germanium, *Phys. Rev.*, vol. 90, pp. 759–763, 1953.

Dacey, G. C., and I. M. Ross: Unipolar "Field-effect" Transistor, *Proc. IRE*, vol. 41, pp. 970–979, 1953.

Dalfonso, J.: Power Requirements for Transistor Circuits, *Electronics*, vol. 26, pp. 204, 206, 208, 210, 212, 214, June, 1953.

Debye, P. P.: Hall Effect and Conductivity of Ge Containing As or Ga as Impurities, *Phys. Rev.*, vol. 91, p. 208, 1953.

Diestel, R.: Experimental and Theoretical Investigations of Isothermal and Adiabatic Hall Effects in Selenium, *Z. Naturforsch.*, vol. 8a, pp. 453–457, 1953.

Dietrich, K.: Design Principles of Regulating-resistances, *Elektrotech. u. Maschinenbau*, vol. 70, pp. 189–197, 1953.

Dixon, R. K.: Build This Transistor Receiver, *Radio Television News*, vol. 49, pp. 35–37, February, 1953.

Dresselhaus, G., A. F. Kip, and C. Kittel: Observation of Cyclotron Resonance in Germanium Crystals, *Phys. Rev.*, vol. 92, p. 827, 1953.

Dukat, F. M.: Transistor Characteristics, *Radio-Electronic Eng.*, pp. 7–9, 24–25, September, 1953.

Dummer, G. W. A.: Components for Transistors, *Wireless World*, vol. 59, pp. 196–199, 1953.

Dunlap, W. C., Jr.: Electrical Properties of Gold-germanium Alloys, *Phys. Rev.*, vol. 91, p. 1282, 1953.

Early, J. M.: Design Theory of Junction Transistors, *Bell System Tech. J.*, vol. 32, pp. 1271–1312, 1953.

Einsele, T.: A Double-pulse Equipment for Measuring Inertia-phenomena in Crystal Diodes and Transistors, *Funk u. Ton*, vol. 7, pp. 557–569, 1953.

Ellis, R. C., Jr., and S. P. Wolsky: New Etches for Germanium, *J. Appl. Phys.*, vol. 24, pp. 1411–1412, 1953.

Ellis, W. C., and E. S. Greiner: Production of Acceptor Centers in Germanium and Silicon by Plastic Deformation, *Phys. Rev.*, vol. 92, p. 1061, 1953.

Elmer, T. H.: Silicon Carbide Heating Elements—Development, Uses, Chemical and Physical Investigations, *Bull. Am. Ceram. Soc.*, vol. 32, pp. 23–27, 1953.

Enenstein, N. H., and M. E. McMahon: Pulse Response of Junction Transistors, *Trans. IRE*, vol. PGED-3, pp. 5–8, June, 1953.

Enenstein, N. H.: A Transient Equivalent Circuit for Junction Transistors, *Trans. IRE*, vol. PGED-4, pp. 37–54, December, 1953.

Esaki, L.: Properties of Thermally Treated Germanium, *Phys. Rev.*, vol. 89, pp. 1026–1034, 1953.

Fahnestock, J. D.: Experiments Illustrate Transistor Applications, *Electronics*, vol. 26, pp. 112–113, March, 1953; discussion p. 426, April, 1953.

Fahnestock, J. D.: Production Techniques in Transistor Manufacture, *Electronics*, vol. 26, pp. 130–134, October, 1953.

Fahnestock, J. D.: Transistor Organs, *Electronics*, vol. 26, pp. 156, 158, February, 1953.

Fahnestock, J. D.: Transistorized Hearing Aids, *Electronics*, vol. 26, pp. 154–155, April, 1953.

Fahnestock, J. D.: Twenty-five Cent Oscillator, *Electronics*, vol. 26, pp. 194, 198, March, 1953.

Fairweather, A., and E. J. Frost: Dielectric Behavior of Granular Semiconducting Aggregates with Special Reference to Some Magnesium Ferrites, *Proc. Inst. Elec. Engrs. (London)*, part II A, vol. 100, pp. 15–22, 1953; discussion pp 54–60.

Fan, H. Y.: Effect of Traps on Carrier Injection in Semiconductors, *Phys. Rev.*, vol. 92, pp. 1424–1428, 1953.

Fewer, D. R.: Transistor Characteristics Obtained by Pulse Techniques, *IRE Convention Record*, part 9, pp. 53–57, 1953.

Fine, M. E.: Elasticity and Thermal Expansion of Germanium between −195° and 275°C., *J. Appl. Phys.*, vol. 24, pp 338–340, 1953.

Fink, D. G.: Are Better Transistors at Hand? *Aviation Week*, vol. 59, p. 76, Sept. 14, 1953; *Product Eng.*, vol. 24, pp. 278–279, November, 1953.

Finn, G.: Evaporation of Copper from Germanium, *Phys. Rev.*, vol. 91, p. 754, 1953.

Fischer, A.: The Electroluminescence of Semiconducting Phosphors, *Z. Naturforsch.*, vol. 8a, pp. 756–757, 1953.

Fleming, L.: Transistor Oscillator Circuit, *Electronics*, vol. 26, pp. 196, 198, June, 1953.

Folberth, O. G., R. Grimm, and H. Weiss: On the Electrical Properties of InAs, *Z. Naturforsch.*, vol. 8a, p. 826, 1953.

Folberth, O. G., and O. Madelung: The Significance of Conductivity Measurements on Indium Antimonide, *Z. Naturforsch.*, vol. 8a, pp. 673–675, 1953.

Follingstad, H. G.: A Transistor Alpha Sweeper, *IRE Convention Record*, part 9, pp. 64–71, 1953.

Forbes, A. H., and R. L. Riddle: Transistor-controlled Garage Door, *Electronics*, vol. 26, pp. 222, 224, 226, 228, June, 1953.

Frank, H.: Photoelectric Conductivity of Lead Sulphide, *Slaboproudy Obzor*, vol. 14, no. 6, pp. 243–257, 1953.

Frank, V.: On the Geometrical Arrangement in Hall Effect Measurements, *Appl. Sci. Research*, vol. 3B, pp. 129–140, 1953.

Frederikse, H. P. R.: Thermoelectric Power of Germanium below Room Temperature, *Phys. Rev.*, vol. 92, pp. 248–252, 1953.

Frohnmeyer, G., R. Glocker, and D. Messner: On the Wavelength Dependence of the Conductivity Produced in CdS Crystals by x- and γ-Irradiation, *Naturwissenschaften*, vol. 40, p. 338, 1953.

Fuller, C. S., and J. A. Ditzenberger: Diffusion of Lithium into Germanium and Silicon, *Phys. Rev.*, vol. 91, p. 193, 1953.

Gans, F.: Cadmium Sulphide Cells, *Bull. Sci. Assoc. Ingen. Montefiore*, vol. 66, pp. 897–911, 1953.

Gans, F., J. Lagrenaudie, and P. Seguin: The Preparation and Properties of Semiconducting Arsenides, *Compt. rend.*, vol. 237, pp. 310–313, 1953.

Garcia de Gudal, A.: Modulation with Semiconductors, *Rev. cien. Apl. (Madrid)*, vol. 7, pp. 481–492, 1953.

Garner, L. E.: Transistor Code Practice Oscillator, *Radio Television News*, vol. 49, pp. 40–41, 99, April, 1953.

Garner, L. E.: Transistor Electric Organ, *Radio Television News*, vol. 50, pp. 64–65, July, 1953.

Garner, L. E.: Transistor Guitar Amplifier, *Radio Television News*, vol. 50, pp. 74–75, 192–193, November, 1953.

Garner, L. E.: Transistor Operated Photocell Relay, *Radio Television News*, vol. 49, pp. 64–65, 165, May, 1953.

Garner, L. E.: Transistor Timer, *Radio Television News*, vol. 50, pp. 68–69, October, 1953.

Garner, L. E.: Transistorized Audio Oscillator, *Radio Television News*, vol. 50, pp. 68–69, September, 1953.

Garner, L. E.: "Transistors and Their Applications in Television, Radio, Electronics," Coyne Electrical School, Chicago, 1953.

Garner, L. E.: Using a Transistor to Increase Relay Sensitivity, *Radio Television News*, vol. 49, pp. 39, 140–142, June, 1953.

Gaynor, E., and H. J. Tate: Four-quadrant Calibrator, *Electronics*, vol. 26, pp. 236, 238, 240, September, 1953.

Ghandhi, S. K.: Transistor Feedback Amplifiers, *Proc. Natl. Electronics Conf.*, vol. 9, pp. 738–747, 1953.

Giacoletto, L. J.: Bridges Measure Transistor Parameters, *Electronics*, vol. 26, pp. 144–147, November, 1953.

Giacoletto, L. J.: Equipments for Measuring Junction Transistor Admittance Parameter for a Wide Range of Frequencies, *RCA Rev.*, vol. 14, pp. 269–296, 1953.

Giacoletto, L. J.: Special Bridge Equipment for Measuring Junction Transistor Admittance Parameters, *IRE Convention Record*, part 9, pp. 58–63, 1953.

Giacoletto, L. J.: Terminology and Equations for Linear Active Four-terminal Networks including Transistors, *RCA Rev.*, vol. 14, pp. 28–46, 1953.

Giacoletto, L. J.: Transistor Characteristics at Low and Medium Frequency, *Tele-Tech*, vol. 12, pp. 97–99, March, 1953.

Gibson, A. F.: Injected Absorption in Germanium, *Proc. Phys. Soc. (London)*, vol. 66B, pp. 588–596, 1953.

Gobrecht, H., and H. Hamisch: Frequency Dependence of the Electrical Conductivity of Polycrystalline Selenium, *Z. Physik*, vol. 136, pp. 234–247, 1953.

Gobrecht, H., and F. Speer: A Study of the Secondary Electron Emission from Impurity Semiconductors, *Z. Physik*, vol. 135, pp. 602–614, 1953.

Goucher, F. S., and M. B. Prince: Alpha Values in P-N Junction Transistors, *Phys. Rev.*, vol. 89, pp. 651–653, 1953.

Grace, W. H., Jr.: Transistor Receiver Operates Loudspeaker, *Radio-Electronics*, vol. 24, pp. 99–100, March, 1953.

Graf, L., H. R. Lacour, and K. Seiler: Plastic Deformation of Germanium at Elevated Temperatures, *Z. Metallkunde*, vol. 44, pp. 113–114, 1953.

Granville, J. W., and A. F. Gibson: The Reduction of Rectifier Noise by Illumination, *Proc. Phys. Soc. (London)*, vol. 66B, pp. 1118–1119, 1953.

Granville, J. W., and W. Bardsley: Some Properties of Silicon Point-contact Transistors, *Proc. Phys. Soc. (London)*, vol. 66B, p. 429, 1953.

Gremmelmaier, R., and O. Madelung: Preparation of Single Crystals of Semiconducting Compounds of the Type $A^{III}B^{V}$, *Z. Naturforsch.*, vol. 8a, p. 333, 1953.

Gunn, J. B.: Radiative Transitions in Germanium, *Proc. Phys. Soc. (London)*, vol. 66B, pp. 330–331, 1953.

Hauffe, K., and G. Tranckler: Calcium Oxide, an Amphoteric Semiconductor, *Z. Physik*, vol. 136, pp. 166–178, 1953.

Haynes, J. R., and J. A. Hornbeck: Temporary Traps in Silicon and Germanium, *Phys. Rev.*, vol. 90, p. 152, 1953.

Hellmers, A. H.: Transistor Cathode Follower, *Radio Television News*, vol. 50, p. 169, October, 1953.

Hellmers, A. H.: Transistor Wireless Mike, *Radio Television News*, vol. 50, p. 196, October, 1953.

Henisch, H. K., and F. D. Morten: Forward Characteristic of Injecting Area Contacts on Germanium, *Proc. Phys. Soc. (London)*, vol. 66B, pp. 841–844, 1953.

Henkels, H. W., and J. Maczuk: Anisotropic Resistivities of Selenium Crystals at High Frequencies, *Phys. Rev.*, vol. 91, p. 1562, 1953.

Henkels, H. W., and J. Maczuk: Electrical Properties of Liquid Selenium, *J. Appl. Phys.*, vol. 24, pp. 1056–1060, 1953.

Herkart, P. G., and J. Kurshan: Theoretical Resistivity and Hall Coefficient of Impure Germanium near Room Temperature, *RCA Rev.*, vol. 14, pp. 427–440, 1953.

Herman, F., and J. Callaway: Electronic Structure of the Germanium Crystal, *Phys. Rev.*, vol. 89, pp. 518–519, 1953.

Heywang, W.: A Simple Demonstration Model of a P-N Junction, *Naturwissenschaften*, vol. 40, pp. 527–528, 1953.

Hiller, J. E., and H. G. Smolczyk: Spektralanalytische Untersuchungen am Bleiglanz unter Berucksichtigung des photoelektrischen Sowie des Thermo- und Gleichrichtereffektes, *Z. Elektrochemie*, vol. 57, pp. 50–58, 1953.

Hoffman, A., and F. Rose: The Mode of Action of the CdSe Intermediate Layers in Selenium Rectifiers, *Z. Physik*, vol. 136, pp. 152–165, 1953.

Hogarth, C. A.: A Study of Carrier Injecting Properties of Emitter Contacts and Light Spots at Normal and Moderately Elevated Temperatures, *Proc. Phys. Soc. (London)*, vol. 66B, pp. 845–858, 1953.

Hogarth, C. A.: Transistor Action and Related Phenomena in Lead Sulphide Specimens from Various Sources, *Proc. Phys. Soc. (London)*, vol. 66B, pp. 216–220, 1953.

Hollmann, H. E.: Transistor Oscillators, *Arch. Elekt. Ubertragung*, vol. 7, pp. 585–591, 1953.

Hollmann, H. E.: Transistor Oscillators, *Tele-Tech*, vol. 12, pp. 82–83, October, 1953.

Hollmann, H. E.: Transistors in Terms of Vacuum Tubes, *Tele-Tech*, vol. 12, pp. 74–76, 124–126, May, 1953.

Hollmann, H. E.: Transistor Theory and Transistor Circuits, *Arch. Elekt. Ubertragung*, vol. 7, pp. 315–327, 1953.

Howarth, D. J., and E. H. Sondheimer: The Theory of Electronic Conduction in Polar Semiconductors, *Proc. Roy. Soc. (London)*, vol. 219A, pp. 53–76, 1953.

Hoyaux, M.: Theory of Ionized Media with Distant Walls, *Rev. gén. élect.*, vol. 62, pp. 421–438, 1953.

Hughes, J., and H. Strong: The Manufacturing and Testing of Transistor G. E. C. type GET. 1, *G. E. C. Telecommun.*, no. 18, pp. 16–21, 1953.

Humphrey, J. N., F. L. Lummis, and W. W. Scanlon: Capacitance Effects in Thin Conductive Films, *Phys. Rev.*, vol. 90, pp. 111–115, 1953.

Hunter, L. P., E. J. Huibregtse, and R. L. Anderson: Current Carrier Lifetimes Deduced from Hall Coefficient and Resistivity Measurements, *Phys. Rev.*, vol. 91, pp. 1315–1320, 1953.

Hunter, L. P.: Current Carrier Mobility Ratio in Semiconductors, *Phys. Rev.*, vol. 91, pp. 579–581, 1953.

Huntington, H. B.: Extension of Makinson's Theory of Photoelectric Emission to a Periodic Potential, *Phys. Rev.*, vol. 89, pp. 357–358, 1953.

Huntington, H. B., and L. Apker: Transition Probability for Photoelectric Emission from Semi-conductors, *Phys. Rev.*, vol. 89, pp. 352–356, 1953.

Hussy, L. W.: Semiconductor Diode Gates, *Bell System Tech. J.*, vol. 32, pp. 1137–1154, 1953.

Hyde, F. J.: Measurement of Noise Spectra of a Point Contact Germanium Rectifier, *Proc. Phys. Soc. (London)*, vol. 66B, pp. 1017–1024, 1953.

Ichiyo, B.: On the New Method of Measuring Dielectric Constant and Loss Angles of Semiconductors, *J. Appl. Phys.*, vol. 24, pp. 307–311, 1953.

Inuishi, Y., and T. C. Yang: The Influence of Impurity Atoms on Flicker Noise, *J. Phys. Soc. Japan*, vol. 8, pp. 565–567, 1953.

Isay, W. H.: Contribution to the Theory of Conduction in Semiconductors, *Ann. Physik*, vol. 13, pp. 327–348, 1953.

Ishiguro, K.: The Change of the Refractive Index of Semiconducting Film Irradiated by Intense Light, *J. Phys. Soc. Japan*, vol. 8, pp. 269–270, 1953.

Jacobs, H.: Enhanced Alpha in Formed Silicon Point Contact Transistors, *J. Appl. Phys.*, vol. 24, pp. 1410–1411, 1953.

Jacobs, H., F. A. Brand, and W. Matthei: Forming Silicon Point Contact Transistors, *J. Appl. Phys.*, vol. 24, p. 1340, 1953.

James, H. M., and A. S. Ginzberg: Band Structure in Disordered Alloys and Impurity Semiconductors, *J. Phys. Chem.*, vol. 57, pp. 840–848, 1953.

Jenny, D. A.: A Germanium N-P-N Alloy Junction Transistor, *Proc. IRE*, vol. 41, pp. 1728–1734, 1953.

Johnson, V. A., and F. M. Shipley: The Adiabatic Hall Effect in Semi-conductors, *Phys. Rev.*, vol. 90, pp. 523–529, 1953.

Johnson, V. A., and K. Lark-Horovitz: Theory of Thermoelectric Power in Semiconductors with Applications to Germanium, *Phys. Rev.*, vol. 92, pp. 226–232, 1953.

Justi, E., and G. Lautz: The Electrical Behavior of AlSb, *Abhand. braunschweig. Wiss. Gesell.*, vol. 5, pp. 36–47, 1953.

Justi, E., and H. Schultz: On the Formation of Super Conductivity of Disturbance Centre Semi-conductors, *Z. Naturforsch.*, vol. 8a, pp. 149–155, 1953.

Kaden, R. Yu.: The Instability of the Electrical Conductivity of Selenium, *Zhur. Eksptl. i. Teort. Fiz.*, vol. 24, pp. 714–720, 1953.

Kaiser, W., R. J. Collins, and H. Y. Fan: Infrared Absorption in P-type Germanium, *Naturwissenschaften*, vol. 40, pp. 479, 1953.

Kaiser, W., R. J. Collins, and H. Y. Fan: Infrared Absorption in P-type Germanium, *Phys. Rev.*, vol. 91, pp. 1380–1381, 1953.

Kansas, R.: The Surface-barrier Transistor. Part IV: On the High-frequency Performance of Transistors, *Proc. IRE*, vol. 41, pp. 1712–1714, 1953.

Keck, P. H., and M. J. E. Golay: Crystallization of Silicon from a Floating Liquid Zone, *Phys. Rev.*, vol. 89, p. 1297, 1953.

Keesom, P. H., and N. Pearlman: The Atomic Heat of Germanium below 4°K., *Phys. Rev.*, vol. 91, pp. 1347–1353, 1953.

Keilson, J.: More Exact Treatment of the Equations Describing Dielectric Relaxation and Carrier Motion in Semiconductors, *J. Appl. Phys.*, vol. 24, pp. 1198–1200, 1953.

Keilson, J.: On the Diffusion of Decaying Particles of a Radial Electric Field, *J. Appl. Phys.*, vol. 24, pp. 1397–1400, 1953.

Kelen, A.: A Micromanipulator for Electrical Investigations of Semi-conducting Materials, *Appl. Sci. Research*, vol. 3B, pp. 125–128, 1953.

Kendall, J. F.: Electronic Conduction in Silicon Carbide, *J. Chem. Phys.*, vol. 21, pp. 821–827, 1953.

Keonjian, E.: D. C. Amplifiers Employing Junction Type Transistors, *Elec. Eng.*, vol. 72, pp. 961–964, 1953.

Keonjian, E., and J. S. Schaffner: Noise in Transistor Amplifiers, *Electronics*, vol. 26, pp. 104–107, February, 1953.

Kerfoot, B. P.: Vest Pocket Transistor Alpha Meter, *Electronics*, vol. 26, pp. 216–224, December, 1953.

Keyes, R. W.: The Electrical Properties of Black Phosphorus, *Phys. Rev.*, vol. 92, pp. 580–584, 1953.

Kikuchi, M., and T. Onishi: A Thermoelectric Study of the Electrical Forming of Germanium Rectifiers, *J. Appl. Phys.*, vol. 24, pp. 162–166, 1953.

44 REFERENCE MATERIAL

Kittel, C.: "Introduction to Solid State Physics," John Wiley & Sons, Inc., New York, 1953.

Klein, W.: Equivalent Circuits for Transistors, *Frequenz*, vol. 7, pp. 59–60, 1953.

Kluge, W., and S. Weber: Pulse Irradiation of Differently Arranged Photocathodes with Semiconducting Intermediate Layers, *Naturwissenschaften*, vol. 40, p. 315, 1953.

Knight, G., Jr., R. A. Johnson, and R. B. Holt: Measurement of the Small Signal Parameters of Transistors, *Proc. IRE*, vol. 41, pp. 983–989, 1953.

Koerner, L. F.: Oven Control with Thermistors, *Bell Labs. Record*, vol. 31, pp. 115–118, 1953.

Koga, S.: Experimental Study of Surface potential Analysis. II: Metals and Semi-conductors, *J. Sci., Research Inst. Tokyo*, vol. 47, pp. 181–188, 1953.

Kretzmer, E. R.: Amplitude Stabilized Transistor Oscillator, *Electronics*, vol. 26, p. 208, December, 1953.

Krim, N. B.: Transistor Enters Commercial Field, *Product Eng.*, vol. 24, p. 197, March, 1953.

Kromer, H.: The Drift Transistor, *Naturwissenschaften*, vol. 40, pp. 578–579, 1953.

Kromer, H.: Theory of the Germanium Rectifier and the Transistor, *Z. Physik*, vol. 134, pp. 435–450, 1953.

Krull, A. R., ed.: Transistors and Their Applications: A Bibliography, 1948–1953, *Trans. IRE*, vol. ED-1, pp. 40–77, August, 1953.

Kurshan, J., R. D. Lohman, and G. B. Herzog: Cathode Ray Tube Plots Transistor Curves, *Electronics*, vol. 26, pp. 122–127, February, 1953.

Lagrenaudie, J.: Semiconducting Compounds of Boron with Carbon and Aluminum, *J. chim. phys.*, vol. 50, pp. 352–355, 1953.

Lagrenaudie, J.: Semiconducting Properties of Boron, *J. chim. phys.*, vol. 50, pp. 629–633, 1953.

Lagrenaudie, J.: Semiconducting Properties of Zinc Phosphite (Zn_3P_2), *J. chim. phys.*, vol. 50, pp. 545–547, 1953.

Lagrenaudie, J.: A Study of the Properties of Boron, *J. phys. radium*, vol. 14, pp. 14–18, 1953.

Landauer, R., and J. Swanson: Diffusion Currents in the Semiconductor Hall Effect, *Phys. Rev.*, vol. 91, pp. 555–561, 1953.

Landsberg, P. T.: Semiconductor Statistics, *Proc. Phys. Soc. (London)*, vol. 66A, pp. 662–663, 1953.

Laplume, J.: Germanium Rectifiers, *Bull. soc. franç. électr.*, vol. 3, pp. 125–136, 1953; *Rev. gén. élect.*, vol. 62, pp. 1–2, 1953.

Lauckner, H.: Contribution to the Knowledge of Dynamic Characteristics of Selenium Rectifiers, *Z. angew. Physik*, vol. 5, pp. 341–349, 1953.

Lautz, G.: On the Theory of Differential Thermo-power of Semiconductors, *Z. Naturforsch.*, vol. 8a, pp. 361–371, 1953.

Lawrance, R.: The Temperature Dependence of Drift Mobility in Germanium, *Phys. Rev.*, vol. 89, p. 1295, 1953.

Lees, J.: Cuprous Oxide Rectifier Characteristics, *Proc. Phys. Soc. (London)*, vol. 66B, pp. 622–632, 1953.

Lefever, R. A.: Summary of Semiconductor and Transistor Theory, *J. Chem. Educ.*, vol. 30, pp. 554–556, 1953.

Lehovec, K., A. MacDonald, J. Rosen, and J. Broder: Evaporation of Germanium Films from a Carbon Crucible, *J. Appl. Phys.*, vol. 24, pp. 513–514, 1953.

Lehovec, K., C. A. Accardo, and E. Jamgochian: Light Emission Produced by Current Injected into a Green Silicon Carbide Crystal, *Phys. Rev.*, vol. 89, pp. 20–25, 1953.

Lehovec, K., and E. Belmont: Preparation of P-N Junctions by Surface Melting, *J. Appl. Phys.*, vol. 24, pp. 1482–1484, 1953.

Lesk, I. A., and V. P. Mathis: The Double Base Diode, *IRE Convention Record*, part 6, pp. 2–8, 1953.

Lewis, E. L.: Aluminum-Antimony Alloy Has Wide Applications in Electronics, *Light Metal Age*, vol. 11, p. 11, August, 1953.

Linvill, J. G.: Transistor Negative-impedance Converters, *Proc. IRE*, vol. 41, pp. 725–729, 1953.

Logan, R. A.: Thermally Induced Acceptors in Single Crystal Germanium, *Phys. Rev.*, vol. 91, pp. 757–758, 1953.

Lohman, R. D.: Complementary Symmetry Transistor Circuits, *Electronics*, vol. 26, pp. 140–143, September, 1953.

Lukens, L. A.: New Electronics Age Developing and Efforts of Leading Companies, *Mag. Wall Street*, vol. 93, pp. 14–15, Oct. 3, 1953.

MacDonald, A. L., J. Soled, and C. A. Stearns: Four-probe Instrument for Resistivity Measurements of Germanium and Silicon, *Rev. Sci. Instr.*, vol. 24, pp. 884–885, 1953.

MacDonald, J. R.: Theory of A-C Space Charge Polarization Effects in Photoconductors, Semiconductors, and Electrolytes, *Phys. Rev.*, vol. 92, pp. 4–17, 1953.

McKay, K. G., and K. B. McAfee: Electron Multiplication in Silicon and Germanium, *Phys. Rev.*, vol. 91, pp. 1079–1084, 1953.

McQuister, R. B.: Determining Properties of Bulk Semiconductors, *Electronics*, vol. 26, pp. 150–155, June, 1953.

Madelung, O.: The Conductivity Mechanism of Homo-polar Semiconductors, *Ergeb. exakt. Naturw.*, vol. 27, pp. 56–124, 1953.

Madelung, O.: The Theory of Magnetic Effects in Isotropic Semiconductors Having High Mobility, *Z. Naturforsch.*, vol. 8a, pp. 791–795, 1953.

Mallery, P.: Transistors and Their Circuits in the 4A Toll Crossbar Switching System, *Commun. and Electronics*, no. 8, pp. 388–392, 1953.

Mansfield, R.: The Electrical Conductivity and Thermoelectric Power of Magnesium Oxide, *Proc. Phys. Soc. (London)*, vol. 66B, pp. 612–614, 1953.

Mansfield, R., and S. A. Salam: Electrical Properties of Molybdenite, *Proc. Phys. Soc. (London)*, vol. 66B, pp. 377–385, 1953.

Markowitz, R. S.: Transistorized Radar Scope Display Unit, *Electronics*, vol. 26, pp. 182–183, October, 1953.

Martel, C. W.: Transistorize Your Audio Amplifiers, *Radio Television News*, vol. 49, pp. 40–41, March, 1953.

Mason, W. P., W. H. Hewitt, and R. F. Wick: Hall Effect Modulators and "Gyrators" Employing Magnetic Field Independent Orientations in Germanium, *J. Appl. Phys.*, vol. 24, pp. 166–175, 1953.

Mathis, V. P., and J. S. Schaffner: Quick Evaluation of Junction Transistor Characteristics by Oscilloscopic Display, *IRE Convention Record*, part 9, pp. 72–74, 1953.

Matukura, Y., and A. Okazaki: The Photo-voltaic Effect of Selenium Photocells, *Mem. Fac. Sci. Kyūsyū Univ.*, vol. 1B, pp. 89–93, 1953.

Matukura, Y., T. Yamamoto, and A. Okazaki: A Preliminary Study on the Electrical Properties of SnSe Single Crystals, *Mem. Fac. Sci. Kyūsyū Univ.*, vol. 1B, pp. 98–101, 1953.

Mayer, D: Note on the Johnsen-Rahbeck Effect, *Elektrotech. Obzor*, vol. 42, pp. 257–262, 1953.

Maynard, J. E., and R. L. Brock: Kerosene Cooled Transistors, *Electronics*, vol. 26, pp. 202, 204, 206, October, 1953.

Merrithew, R. F.: Noise Analyzer for Transistor Production, *Electronics*, vol. 26, pp. 136–137, May, 1953.

Middleton, A. E., and W. W. Scanlon: Measurement of the Thermoelectric Power of Germanium at Temperatures above 78°K., *Phys. Rev.*, vol. 92, pp. 219–226, 1953.

Mirlin, D. N., and I. L. Sokol'skaya: The Dependence of Capacitance and Rectification of Frequency of a Point Contact Metal-semiconductor (Lead Sulphide), *Zhur. Tekh. Fiz.*, vol. 23, pp. 1582–1590, 1953.

Missen, J. I.: A Crystal Triode Push-pull Amplifier. *Gen. Elec. Co. J.*, vol. 20, pp. 144–150, 1953.

Missen, J. I.: Push-pull Transistor Amplifier, *Wireless World*, vol. 59, pp. 467–470, 1953.

Miyatani, S. Y., and Y. Suzuki: On the Electric Conductivity of Cuprous Sulfide; Experiment, *J. Phys. Soc. Japan*, vol. 8, pp. 680–681, 1953.

Moll, J. L., and J. J. Ebers: Theory of Junction Transistors for Switching, presented at IRE-AIEE Transistor Research Conference, Penn State College, 1953.

Montgomery, H. C., and M. A. Clark: Shot Noise in Junction Transistors, *J. Appl. Phys.*, vol. 24, pp. 1337–1338, 1953.

Montroll, E. J., ed.: Topics in the Theory of the Solid State, University of Maryland, Institute for Fluid Dynamics and Applied Mathematics, Lecture series no. 27, 1953.

Mooser, E.: A Device for the Graphical Determination of the Fermi-energy in Semiconductors, *Z. angew. Math. Phys.*, vol. 4, pp. 433–449, 1953.

Morrison, S. R.: Changes of Surface Conductivity of Germanium with Ambient, *J. Phys. Chem.*, vol. 57, pp. 860–863, 1953.

Morrow, W. E., Jr.: Measurement of Transistor Parameters by C. R. O. and Other Means, *IRE Convention Record*, part 9, pp. 45–52, 1953.

Morton, J. B.: Present Status of Transistor Development, *Bell System Tech. J.*, vol. 31, pp. 411–442, 1953.

Moss, T. S.: Inter-relation between Optical Constants for Lead Telluride and Silicon, *Proc. Phys. Soc. (London)*, vol. 66B, pp. 141–144, 1953.

Moss, T. S.: Photoelectromagnetic and Photoconductive Effects in Lead Sulfide Single Crystals, *Proc. Phys. Soc. (London)*, vol. 66B, pp. 993–1002, 1953.

Moss, T. S., L. Pincherle, and A. M. Woodward: Photoelectromagnetic and Photodiffusion Effect in Germanium, *Proc. Phys. Soc. (London)*, vol. 66B, pp. 743–752, 1953.

Mostovetch, N.: An Experimental Study of the Electrical Conductivity of Very Thin Metallic Deposits Obtained by Thermal Evaporation, *Ann. phys.*, vol. 8, pp. 61–125, 1953.

Moulon, J. M.: Properties and Applications of Transistors, *Onde élect.*, vol. 33, pp. 27–35, 1953.

Mrozowski, S.: Electric Resistivity of Interstitial Compounds of Graphite, *J. Chem. Phys.*, vol. 21, pp. 492–495, 1953.

Mueller, C. W., and J. J. Pankove: P-N-P Triode Alloy Junction Transistor for Radio Frequency Amplification, *RCA Rev.*, vol. 14, pp. 586–598, 1953.

Nelson, B. E.: High Power U. H. F. Wafer Load, *Tele-Tech*, vol. 12, pp. 72–73, 104, August, 1953.

Nelson, S. R.: Transistor I. F. Amplifiers, *Tele-Tech*, vol. 12, pp. 68–69, December, 1953.

Netushvil, A. V., and A. A. Lisenkov: Measurement of the Temperature of Dielectrics and Semiconductors in High Frequency Fields, *Elektrichestvo*, no. 2, pp. 42–44, 1953.

Newman, R.: Optical Studies of Injected Carriers. I. Infra-red Absorption in Germanium, *Phys. Rev.*, vol. 91, pp. 1311–1312, 1953.

Newman, R.: Optical Studies of Injected Carriers. II. Recombination Radiation in Germanium, *Phys. Rev.*, vol. 91, pp. 1313–1314, 1953.

Nifontoff, N.: A Simultaneous Study of the Conductivity and Flicker Effect in Thin Films and in Crystal Detectors, *J. Phys. radium*, vol. 14, pp. 42–44s, 1953.

Niimi, T.: On the Changes in Contact Potential Difference of a Germanium Rectifier during the Electrical Forming, *J. phys. Soc. Japan*, vol. 8, pp. 324–330, 1953.

Okazaki, A., H. Tubota, and H. Suzuki: The Temperature Dependence of the Zero Bias Resistance of Cuprous Oxide Rectifiers, *J. Phys. Soc. Japan*, vol. 8, pp. 431–432, 1953.

O'Neill, B. J., and A. Gutterman: Methods and Equipment for Transistor Testing, *Electronics*, vol. 26, pp. 172–175, July, 1953.

Oser, E. A., R. O. Endres, and R. P. Moore: Transistor Oscillators, *Bull. schweiz. elektrotech. Ver.*, vol. 44, pp. 420–422, 1953.

Pearson, G. L.: A High Impedance Field-effect Silicon Transistor, *Phys. Rev.*, vol. 90, p. 336, 1953.

Pearson, G. L., and M. Tanenbaum: The Magnetoresistance Effect in InSb, *Phys. Rev.*, vol. 90, p. 153, 1953.

Pearson, H. A.: Sonotone 1010 Transistorized Hearing Aid, *Audio Eng.*, vol. 37, pp. 19–21, 49–50, August, 1953.

Pearson, R. M., and F. A. Benson: Direct-reading Thermistor Bridge, *Electronic Eng.*, vol. 25, pp. 51–57, 1953.

Pell, E. M.: Recombination Rate in Germanium by Observation of Pulsed Reverse Characteristics, *Phys. Rev.*, vol. 90, pp. 278–279, 1953.

Pennsylvania State College: Transistor Short Course, Proceedings, June 8–9, 1953, conducted by the Department of Electrical Engineering and General Extension Services of Pennsylvania State College, in cooperation with Bell Telephone Laboratories and others, 1953.

Philbrook, W.: Obtaining Transistor Characteristic Curves, *Radio Television News*, vol. 50, pp. 66–67, September, 1953.

Philco Research Division, Technical Staff: The Surface Barrier Transistor, *Proc. IRE*, vol. 41, pp. 1702–1720, 1953.

Pierce, J. R.: Transistors, *Radio-Electronics*, vol. 24, pp. 42–44, June, 1953.

Prim, R. C.: D. C. Field Distribution in a "Swept Intrinsic" Semiconductor Configuration, *Bell System Tech. J.*, vol. 32, pp. 665–694, 1953.

Prim, R. C., and W. Shockley: Joining Solutions at the Pinch-off Point in Field-effect Transistor, *Trans. IRE*, no. PGED-4, pp. 1–14, December, 1953.

Prince, M. B.: Drift Mobilities in Semiconductors. I. Germanium, *Phys. Rev.*, vol. 92, pp. 681–687, 1953.

Prince, M. B.: Experimental Confirmation of Relation between Pulse Drift Mobility and Charge Carrier Drift Mobility in Germanium, *Phys. Rev.*, vol. 91, pp. 271–272, 1953.

Putseiko, E. K.: Influence of the Adsorption of Gases and Vapors on the Characteristic Photoelectric Effect of ZnO and on the Photoelectric Effect of ZnO Sensitized by Chlorophyll and Similar Pigments, *Doklady Akad. Nauk S.S.S.R.*, vol. 91, pp. 1071–1074, 1953. (English translation: U.S. National Science Foundation NSF-tr-149.)

Putseiko, E. K., and A. N. Terenin: Sensitization of the Internal Photoeffect of Semiconductors by Chlorophyll and Allied Pigments, *Doklady Akad. Nauk S.S.S.R.*, vol. 90, pp. 1005–1008, 1953. (English translation: U.S. National Science Foundation NSF-tr-147.)

Rachel, H.: Dimensioning of Inductive Shunts for Field Weakening of Railway D. C. Series Motors, *Deut. Elektrotech.*, vol. 7, pp. 169–175, 1953.

Reiss, H.: Chemical Effects due to the Ionization of Impurities in Semiconductors, *J. Chem. Phys.*, vol. 21, pp. 1209–1217, 1953.

Reynolds, W. N.: Surface Recombination in Germanium, *Proc. Phys. Soc. (London)*, vol. 66B, pp. 899–901, 1953.

Rhita, N.: Transistor Microammeter, *Radio-Electronics*, vol. 24, p. 49, June, 1953.

Riddle, R. L.: Transistor Test Board Speeds Circuit Choice, *Electronics*, vol. 26, p. 198, October, 1953.

Roddam, T.: Analogue "Field-effect" and Tetrode Transistors. Junction Photocells, *Wireless World*, vol. 59, pp. 543–547, November, 1953.

Roddam, T.: Earthed-emitter and Earthed-collector Circuits as Amplifiers and Oscillators, *Wireless World*, vol. 59, pp. 175–178, 1953.

Roddam, T.: Stabilizing the Working Point, *Wireless World*, vol. 59, pp. 311–313, 1953.

Roddam, T.: Transistors. Introduction to Junction Transistors, *Wireless World*, vol. 59, pp. 205–210, 1953.

Rollin, B. V., and I. M. Templeton: Noise in Semi-conductors at Very Low Frequencies, *Proc. Phys. Soc. (London)*, vol. 66B, pp. 259–261, 1953.

Rose, F. W. G., and E. W. Timmins: A Method of Estimating Impurity Concentrations in Germanium, *Proc. Phys. Soc. (London)*, vol. 66B, pp. 984–986, 1953.

Rose, G. M.: Transistor, or 25 Miles on a Hunk of Germanium, *QST*, vol. 37, pp. 13–15, March, 1953, also RCA Pub. ST-712.

Roth, L., and W. E. Taylor: Preparation of Germanium Crystals, *Proc. IRE*, vol. 41, p. 218, 1953.

Ryder, E. J.: Mobility of Holes and Electrons in High Electric Fields, *Phys. Rev.*, vol. 90, pp. 766–769, 1953.

Sakata, T.: Some Experimental Studies of the Conductivity and Thermo-electromotive Force of Cs_3Sb Photocathodes, *J. Phys. Soc. Japan*, vol. 8, pp. 125–126, 272–273, 1953.

Sakata, T.: Studies on the Cs_3Sb Photocathode, *J. Phys. Soc. Japan*, vol. 8, pp. 723–730, 1953.

Salz, N. P.: Some General Considerations in Semiconductor Power-rectifier Design, *Sylvania Technologist*, vol. 6, pp. 73–75, 1953.

Sarduto, A.: The Faraday Effect in Conductors and Semi-conductors, *Compt. rend.*, vol. 236, pp. 1005–1007, 1953.

Sasaki, W., and M. Kuno: On the Effective Mass of the Conduction Electron in Germanium, *J. Phys. Soc. Japan*, vol. 8, pp. 791–792, 1953.

Sassa, N., and M. Nakamura: On the PbS Photoconductive Cell, *Science of Light (Japan)*, vol. 2, no. 2, pp. 104–115, March, 1953.

Scanlon, W. W.: Interpretation of Hall Effect and Resistivity Data in PbS and Similar Binary Compound Semiconductors, *Phys. Rev.*, vol. 92, pp. 1573–1575, 1953.

Schaffner, J. S.: Junction Transistor Applications, *Advances in Electronics*, vol. 5, pp. 367–398, 1953.

Schaffner, J. S., and J. J. Suran: Transient Response of the Grounded-base transistor Amplifier with Small-load Impedance, *J. Appl. Phys.*, vol. 24, pp. 1355–1357, 1953.

Schon, M.: On the Light Emission of Carborundum Crystals due to Passage of Current, *Z. Naturforsch.*, vol. 8a, pp. 442–446, 1953.

Schottky, W.: On the Problem of Defect Semiconduction in Crystalline Selenium, *Z. Naturforsch.*, vol. 8a, pp. 457–459, 1953.

Schulman, R. G., and D. M. Van Winkle: Pressure-welded P-N Junctions in Germanium, *J. Appl. Phys.*, vol. 24, p. 224, 1953.

Schwarz, R. F., and J. F. Walsh: The Surface-barrier Transistor. Part V: The Properties of Metal to Semiconductor Contacts, *Proc. IRE*, vol. 41, pp. 1715–1720, 1953.

Schwertz, F. A., and J. J. Mazenko: Nonlinear Semiconductor Resistors, *J. Appl. Phys.*, vol. 24, pp. 1015–1024, 1953.

Seiler, K., J. Geist, and K. Keller: Is There a Thermal Disordering Process with Germanium? *Naturwissenschaften*, vol. 40, pp. 56–57, 1953.

Seitz, F.: Survey of Imperfections in Nearly Perfect Crystals, *J. Phys. Chem.*, vol. 57, pp. 737–738, 1953.

Selenya, P.: Sensitization of Se Photoelements to the Infrared by Mercury Vapor, *Acta Phys. Hungary*, vol. 3, no. 2, pp. 65–73, 1953.

Severiens, J. C., and C. S. Fuller: Mobility of Impurity Ions in Germanium and Silicon, *Phys. Rev.*, vol. 92, pp. 1322–1323, 1953.

Shea, R. F., ed.: "Principles of Transistor Circuits," John Wiley & Sons, Inc., New York, 1953.

Shea, R. F.: Correction to Article "Transistor Operation: Stabilization of Operating Points," *Proc. IRE*, vol. 41, p. 992, 1953.

Shive, J. N.: The Properties of Germanium Phototransistors, *J. Opt. Soc. Amer.*, vol. 43, pp. 239–244, 1953.

Shockley, W.: Cyclotron Resonances, Magnetoresistance and Brillouin Zones in Semi-conductors, *Phys. Rev.*, vol. 90, p. 491, 1953.

Shockley, W.: Recent Developments in Transistor Electronics, *Proc. Inst. Elec. Engrs.* (*London*), vol. 100, part 3, pp. 36–38, 1953.

Shockley, W., and R. C. Prim: Space Charge Limited Emission in Semi-conductors, *Phys. Rev.*, vol. 90, pp. 753–758, 1953.

Shockley, W.: Transistor Electronics: Imperfect Ions, Unipolar and Analog Transistors, in Penn State College Transistor Short Course Process, 1953.

Shulman, G. C., and D. M. Van Winkle: Pressure Welded P-N Junctions in Germanium, *J. Appl. Phys.*, vol. 24, p. 224, 1953.

Shulman, R. G., and M. E. McMahon: Recovery Currents in Germanium P-N Junction Diodes, *J. Appl. Phys.*, vol. 24, pp. 1267–1272, 1953.

Simpson, J. H., and H. L. Armstrong: Reverse Characteristics of High Inverse Voltage Point Contact Germanium Rectifiers, *J. Appl. Phys.*, vol. 24, pp. 25–34, 1953.

Slade, B. N., Factors in the Design of Point-contact Transistors, *RCA Rev.*, vol. 14, pp. 17–27, 1953; also RCA Pub. ST-761.

Slichter, W. P., and E. D. Kolb: Solute Distribution in Germanium Crystals, *Phys. Rev.*, vol. 90, pp. 987–988, 1953.

Smith, K. D.: Properties of Junction Transistors, *Tele-Tech*, vol. 12, pp. 76–78, 122–129, 135, January, 1953.

Smith, R. A.: Infra Red Photoconductors, *Advances in Physics*, vol. 2, pp. 321–369, 1953.

Spencer, R. H.: Transistor-controlled Magnetic Amplifier, *Electronics*, vol. 26, pp. 136–140, August, 1953.

Spenke, E.: The Physical Mode of Action of Rectifiers and Transistors, *Z. angew. Physik*, vol. 5, pp. 472–480, 1953.

Stansel, F. R.: The Common-collector Transistor Amplifier at Carrier Frequencies, *Proc. IRE*, vol 41, pp. 1096–1102, 1953.

Stansel, F. R.: Transistor Equations (Reference Sheet), *Electronics*, vol. 26, pp. 156, 158, March, 1953.

Start, H. F.: Transistor D. C. Amplifier, *Radio Television News*, vol. 50, pp. 82–83, December, 1953.

Stevens, D. K., and J. H. Crawford: The Magnetic Susceptibility of Germanium, *Phys. Rev.*, vol. 92, p. 1065, 1953.

Strull, G.: Production of a P-type CdS Rectifier by High Local Heating of N-type Crystals, *J. Appl. Phys.*, vol. 24, p. 1411, 1953.

Strutt, M. J. O.: Transistors in Amplifier Output Stages, *Scientia Electrica*, vol. 1, pp. 2–17, 1953.

Stuckes, A. D.: Electro-thermal Behavior of Point Contacts to Semiconductors, *Proc. Phys. Soc.* (*London*), vol. 66B, pp. 570–587, 1953.

Suhl, H.: Theory of Magnetic Effects on the Noise in a Germanium Filament, *Bell System Tech. J.*, vol. 32, pp. 647–664, 1953.

Suhrmann, R., and C. Kangro: On the Semiconducting Properties of the Systems Potassium-Antimony, Cesium-Antimony, Potassium-Indium, Cesium-Indium, *Naturwissenschaften*, vol. 40, pp. 137–138, 1953.

Sulzer, P. G.: Junction Transistor Circuit Applications, *Electronics*, vol. 26, pp. 170–173, August, 1953.

Sulzer, P. G.: Low-distortion Transistor Audio Oscillator, *Electronics*, vol. 26, pp. 171–173, September, 1953.

Sulzer, P. G.: Precision Transistor Oscillator, *Radio-Electronic Eng.*, pp. 18, 29, May, 1953.

Sulzer, P. G.: Transistor Band Spotter, *Radio Television News*, vol. 49, pp. 52–53, June, 1953.

Sulzer, P. G.: Transistor Broadcast Regenerator, *Electronics*, vol. 26, p. 200, June, 1953.

Sulzer, P. G.: Transistor Frequency Standard, *Electronics*, vol. 26, pp. 206, 208, 210, 212, 214, May, 1953.

Suran, J. J., and W. F. Chow: Transistor Transient Response, *Tele-Tech*, vol. 12, pp. 67–69, November, 1953.

Sziklai, G. C., R. D. Lohman, and G. B. Herzog: A Study of Transistor Circuits for Television, *Proc. IRE*, vol. 41, pp. 708–717, 1953.

Sziklai, G. C.: Symmetrical Properties of Transistors and Their Applications, *Proc. IRE*, vol. 41, pp. 717–724, 1953.

Sziklai, G. C.: Transistor Circuits and Applications, *Electronic Eng.*, vol. 25, pp. 358–364, 1953.

Taft, E., and L. Apker: Photoemission from Caesium and Urbidium Tellurides, *J. Opt. Soc. Amer.*, vol. 43, pp. 81–83, 1953.

Tanenbaum, M., and J. P. Maita: Hall Effect and Conductivity of InSb Single Crystals, *Phys. Rev.*, vol. 91, pp. 1009–1010, 1953.

Tanenbaum, M., and H. B. Briggs: Optical Properties of Indium Antimonide, *Phys. Rev.*, vol. 91, p. 1561, 1953.

Tauc, J., and Z. Trousil: The Effect of Thermal Emission of Holes on the Thermal E. M. F. of N-type Semiconductors, *Czech J. Phys.*, vol. 3, no. 2, pp. 120–125, 1953.

Tauc, J.: An Explanation of Some Anomalous Thermoelectric Phenomena on the Surface of Transistor Materials, *Czech J. Phys.*, vol. 3, p. 259, 1953.

Tauc, J.: Germanium Rectifiers of the P-N Type, *Elektrotech. Obzor*, vol. 42, pp. 495–498, 1953.

Tauc, J.: The Theory of the Thermal E. M. F. of Semiconductors, *Czech J. Phys.*, vol. 3, pp. 282–303, 1953.

Templeton, I. M., and D. K. C. MacDonald: The Electrical Conductivity and Current Noise of Carbon Resistors, *Proc. Phys. Soc. (London)*, vol. 66B, pp. 680–687, 1953.

Teszner, S., P. Seguin, and J. Millet: Aggregates of Some Semiconductors Showing Non-linear Resistance, *Ann. Telecommun.*, vol. 8, pp. 271–298, 1953.

Thedieck, R.: On the Forming of Germanium Surfaces, *Z. angew. Physik*, vol. 5, pp. 163–165, 1953.

Tiley, J. W., and R. A. Williams: The Surface-barrier Transistor. Part II: Electrochemical Techniques for Fabrication of Surface-barrier Transistors, *Proc. IRE*, vol. 41, pp. 1706–1708, 1953.

Tipple, P. M., and H. K. Henisch: Thermal Effects at Point Contact Diodes, *Proc. Phys. Soc. (London)*, vol. 66B, pp. 826–832, 1953.

Tomlinson, L. E.: Transistors: Key to Electronic Simplicity, *Aero Digest*, vol. 66, pp. 22–27, April, 1953.

Tomlinson, T. B., and W. L. Price: Theory of the Flicker Effect, *J. Appl. Phys.*, vol. 24, pp. 1063–1065, 1953.

Toth, E.: Transistorized Superhet Receiver, *Electronics*, vol. 26, pp. 202, 204–205, August, 1953.

Turner, R. P.: Build Transistor Hearing Aid, *Radio-Electronics*, vol. 24, pp. 38–39, September, 1953.

Turner, R. P.: Care of Transistors, *Radio Television News*, vol. 49, pp. 40–41, February, 1953.

Turner, R. P.: Heterodyne Frequency Uses Pair of Transistors, *Radio-Electronics*, vol. 24, pp. 88–90, 94, October, 1953.

Turner, R. P.: Transistor Oscillator Is Powered by Light, *Radio-Electronics*, vol. 24, p. 66, August, 1953.

Turner, R. P.: A Transistor Pre-amp, *Radio-Electronics*, vol. 24, p. 54, February, 1953.

Valder, F. L.: Encapsulated Reference Resistors, *Electronic Eng.*, vol. 25, pp. 332–333, 1953.

van Arkel, A. E., E. A. Flood, and N. F. H. Bright: The Electrical Conductivity of Molten Oxides, *Canadian J. Chem.*, vol. 31, pp. 1009–1019, 1953.

van der Maesen, F., P. Penning, and A. van Wieringen: On the Thermal Conversion of Germanium, *Philips Research Repts.*, vol. 8, pp. 241–244, 1953.

van der Ziel, A.: Note on Shot Effect in Semiconductors and Flicker Effect in Cathodes, *Physica*, vol. 19, pp. 742–744, 1953.

van der Ziel, A.: Shot Noise in Semiconductors, *J. Appl. Phys.*, vol. 24, pp. 222–223, 1953.

van der Ziel, A.: A Simpler Explanation for the Observed Shot Effect in Germanium Filaments, *J. Appl. Phys.*, vol. 24, p. 1063, 1953.

van Roosbroeck, W.: The Transport of Added Current Carriers in a Homogeneous Semiconductor, *Phys. Rev.*, vol. 91, pp. 282–289, 1953.

Vogelsong, J. H.: A Transistor Pulse Amplifier Using External Regeneration, *Proc. IRE*, vol. 41, pp. 1444–1450, 1953.

Wallace, R. L., Jr., L. G. Schimpf and E. Dickten: High Frequency Transistor Tetrode, *Electronics*, vol. 26, pp. 112–113, January, 1953.

Walter, S.: A Transistor in Trigger Circuits, *Proc. IRE*, vol. 41, p. 1190, 1953.

Weill, M. C.: Germanium in Telecommunications Technique, *Onde élect.*, vol. 33, pp. 15–26, 1953.

Weiss, H.: On the Electrical Properties of InSb, *Z. Naturforsch.*, vol. 8a, pp. 463–469, 1953.

Weisshaar, E., and H. Welker: Magnetic Barrier Layers in Germanium, *Z. Naturforsch.*, vol. 8a, pp. 681–686, 1953.

Weisz, P. B., C. D. Prater, and K. D. Rittenhouse: Electrical Conductivity of Chromia-Alumina Dehydrogenation Catalyst, *J. Chem. Phys.*, vol. 21, p. 2236, 1953.

Weisz, P. B., C. D. Prater, and K. D. Rittenhouse: Electrical Conductivity of Hydrocarbon Cracking Catalyst, *J. Chem. Phys.*, vol. 21, pp. 2236–2237, 1953.

Weisz, P. B.: Effects of Electronic Charge Transfer between Adsorbate and Solid on Chemisorption and Catalysis, *J. Chem. Phys.*, vol. 21, pp. 1531–1538, 1953.

Welker, H.: On New Semiconducting Compounds. II, *Z. Naturforsch.*, vol. 8a, pp. 248–251, 1953.

West, C. A.: Transdipper, *Radio Television News*, vol. 50, pp. 60–62, October, 1953.

Whalley, W. B., C. Masucci, and N. P. Salz: The Germanium Diode as Video Detector, *Proc. IRE*, vol. 41, pp. 638–644, 1953.

Wieder, H. H., and N. Cass: FM Transistor Oscillator, *Electronics*, vol. 26, pp. 198, 202, July, 1953.

Willenbrock, F. K., and N. Bloembergen: Paramagnetic Resonance in N- and P-type Silicon, *Phys. Rev.*, vol. 91, p. 1281, 1953.

Williams, F. C., and G. B. B. Chaplin: A Method of Designing Transistor Trigger Circuits, *Proc. Inst. Elec. Engrs. (London)*, vol. 100, part 3, pp. 228–247, 1953.

Williams, F. C., and G. B. B. Chaplin: Transistor Trigger Circuits, *Elec. Rev. (London)*, pp. 152, 379, 1953.

Wilson, A. H.: "The Theory of Metals," 2d ed., Cambridge University Press, New York, 1953.

Wolf, H. C.: "Lattice-source" Interference of Hard X-ray Bremsstrahlung, *Ann. Physik*, vol. 13, pp. 381–403, 1953.

Wright, D. A.: A Survey of Present Knowledge of Thermionic Emitters, *Proc. Inst. Elec. Engrs. (London)*, vol. 99, part 3, pp. 125–139, 1953; discussion pp. 140–142.

Wright, R. W.: Low Temperature Conduction in Extremely Degenerate Semi-conductors, *Proc. Phys. Soc. (London)*, vol. 66B, pp. 273–277, 1953.

Yokota, I.: On the Electrical Conductivity of Cuprous Sulfide: A Diffusion Theory, *J. Phys. Soc. Japan*, vol. 8, pp. 595–602, 1953.

Zadeh, L. A.: A Note on the Analysis of Vacuum Tube and Transistor Circuits, *Proc. IRE*, vol. 41, pp. 989–992, 1953.

Zeidler, H. M.: Transistor Characteristics, *Trans. IRE*, vol. PGED-2, pp. 2–10, January, 1953.

Zhuse, V. P., and S. N. Nikolaev: A Method of Measuring the Hall Effect in Semiconductors, *Zhur. Tekh. Fiz.*, vol. 23, pp. 913–923, 1953.

Zuckler, K.: Influence of Capacitatively Applied Fields on the Conductivity of Thin Semiconductor Layers, *Z. Physik*, vol. 136, pp. 40–51, 1953.

Zworykin, V. K.: Electronic Control for Automatic Driving, *J. Franklin Inst.*, vol. 256, pp. 393–394, 1953.

Bets Remain High, *Steel*, vol. 133, p. 43, Nov. 2, 1953.

How a Transistor Is Born, *Aviation Week*, vol. 59, p. 74, Oct. 26, 1953.

Impurities Create an Industry, *Technology Rev.*, vol. 55, pp. 143–145, January, 1953.

More Transistor Power, *Business Week*, p. 56, Sept. 12, 1953.

New Antimony Type Transistor Hoped for by NBS Research, *Chem. Eng. News*, vol. 31, p. 3892, Sept. 21, 1953.

Overrated? Transistor Hearing Aids, *Business World*, p. 106, Apr. 25, 1953.

Precision Transistor Oscillator, *Tech. News Bull.*, *NBS*, vol. 37, pp. 17–19, February, 1953; *Tele-Tech*, vol. 12, pp. 93, 145, March, 1953.

Slice-away Battery Assemblies Designed for Transistor Use, *Elec. Eng.*, vol. 72, pp. 1044–1045, 1953.

Transistor and Crystal Diode Specification MIL-T-12679A (Sig C), Sept. 23, 1953.

Transistor Miniaturized Hearing Aid, *Elec. Mfg.*, vol. 51, p. 144, March, 1953.

Transistor Research Aid, *Steel*, vol. 132, p. 83, Feb. 16, 1953.

Transistor Research Bulletin, vol. 1, nos. 1-6, December, 1953–December, 1954.

Transistor Standards, *Business World*, p. 48, May 9, 1953.

Transistors; High Hopes vs. Hard Facts, *Business Week*, p. 110, Oct. 3, 1953.

Transistors Multiply, *Business Week*, p. 50, Aug. 1, 1953.

Transistors, a New Use for Antimony, *Eng. Mining J.*, vol. 154, p. 99, June, 1953.

1954

Aarons, M. W., M. Pobereskin, J. E. Gates, and E. B. Dale: Distribution of the Mass Transported from a Collector into a Germanium Crystal by the Forming Process, *Phys. Rev.*, vol. 95, p. 1345, 1954.

Abeles, B., and S. Meiboom: Theory of the Galvanomagnetic Effects in Germanium, *Phys. Rev.*, vol. 95, pp. 31–37, 1954.

Adcock, W. A., M. E. Jones, J. W. Thornhill, and E. D. Jackson: Silicon Transistor, *Proc. IRE*, vol. 42, p. 1192, 1954.

Adirovich, E. I., and V. G. Kolotilova: Towards the Kinetic Formation and Relaxation of Non-equilibrium Current Carriers during the Illumination of a Semiconductor, *Zhur. Eksper. Teort. Fiz.*, vol. 26, pp. 281–292, 1954.

Aigrain, P., and O. Garreta: On the Theory of the Photo-magneto-mechanical Effect, *Compt. rend.*, vol. 238, pp. 1573–1575, 1954.

Aitchison, R. E.: Transparent Semiconducting Oxide Films, *Australian J. Appl. Sci.*, vol. 5, pp. 10–17, 1954.

Aldrich, R. W., and I. A. Lesk: The Double-base Diode: A Semiconductor thyratron Analog, *Trans. IRE*, vol. ED-1, pp. 24–27, February, 1954.

Alexander, F. C., Jr.: Self-keyed Transistor Oscillator, *Electronics*, vol. 27, pp. 214, 216, July, 1954.

Angell, J. B.: Applications of the Surface-barrier Transistor, in Penn State University, Transistor Short Course Proceedings, 1954.

Angell, J. B.: Junction Transistor Amplifiers for Low Level Signals, in Penn State University, Transistor Short Course Proceedings, 1954.

Appel, J.: Experimental Verification of the Semiconducting Characteristics of the Compounds CdTe and In₂Te₃. *Z. Naturforsch.*, vol. 9a, pp. 265–267, 1954.

Appel, J.: The Transverse Galvanomagnetic Effects in Semiconductors, *Z. Naturforsch.*, vol. 9a, pp. 167–174, 1954.

Armstrong, H. L.: Transistor Tester, *Radio Television News*, vol. 51, p. 39, May, 1954.

Armstrong, L. D., and D. A. Jenny: Behavior of Germanium Junction Transistors at Elevated Temperatures and Power Transistor Design, *Proc. IRE*, vol. 42, pp. 527–530, 1954.

Avery, D. G.: Further Measurements on the Optical Properties of Lead Sulphide Selenide and Telluride, *Proc. Phys. Soc. (London)*, vol. 67B, pp. 2–8, 1954.

Backovsky, J., M. Malkovska, and J. Tauc: Photo-voltaic Effect Caused by X-rays at P-N Junctions in Germanium, *Cas. Pest. Fys.*, vol. 4, p. 98, February, 1954.

Baker, D. K.: Flicker Noise in Germanium Rectifiers at Very Low- and Audio-frequencies, *J. Appl. Phys.*, vol. 25, pp. 922–924, 1954.

Baker, R. H., I. L. Lebow, and R. E. McMahon: Transistor Shift Registers, *Proc. IRE*, vol. 42, pp. 1152–1159, 1954.

Baldus, H.: On the Influence of Cathode Sputtering in High Vacuum on the Rectifier Action of Germanium, *Z. angew. Physik*, vol. 6, pp. 241–246, 1954.

Bangert, J. F.: Transistor As a Network Element, *Bell System Tech. J.*, vol. 33, pp. 329–352, 1954.

Barlow, H. M.: Application of the Hall Effect in a Semiconductor to the Measurement of Power in an Electromagnetic Field, *Nature*, vol. 173, pp. 41–42, 1954.

Barton, L. E.: Experimental Transistor Personal Broadcast Receiver, *Trans. IRE*, vol. PGBTR-5, pp. 6-13, January, 1954; *Proc. IRE*, vol. 42, pp. 1062–1066, 1954.

Barut, A. O.: The Mechanism of Secondary Electron Emission, *Phys. Rev.*, vol. 93, pp. 981–984, 1954.

Battey, J. F., and R. M. Baum: Energy of the High-lying Acceptor Level in Copper-doped Germanium, *Phys. Rev.*, vol. 94, p. 1393, 1954.

Beneking, H.: Characteristic Data of Transistors, *Arch. Elekt. Ubertragung*, vol. 8, pp. 69–74, 1954.

Billig, E., and M. S. Ridout: Transmission of Electrons and Holes across a Twin Boundary in Germanium, *Nature*, vol. 173, pp. 496–497, 1954.

Blank, K., D. Geist, and K. Seiler: On the Influence of Special Lattice Defects on the Electrical Properties of Germanium, *Z. Naturforsch.*, vol. 9a, pp. 515–520, 1954.

Blankenburg, G.: On the Semiconducting Properties of Cuprous Oxide. X: Observations of the Electrical Conductivity on Disturbing the Thermodynamic Equilibrium between 600°C and 1000°C within and beyond the Stability Region of Cu₂O, *Ann. Physik*, vol. 14, pp. 290–307, 1954.

Blankenburg, G.: On the Semiconducting Properties of Cuprous Oxide. XI: The Behavior of Cuprous Oxide in the Stability Range of Cupric Oxide, *Ann. Physik*, vol. 14, pp. 308–318, 1954.

Blatter, H : The Reliability and Economic Advantages of the Contact Converter, *Brown Boveri Rev.*, vol. 40, pp. 243–246, 1954.

Blecher, F. H.: Automatic Gain Control of Junction Transistor Amplifiers, *Electronics*, vol. 27, p. 224, January, 1954.

Boer, K. W., E. Borchardt, and W. Borchardt: On Slow Changes of Conductivity with Time for CdS Single Crystals at High Temperatures and under Additional Optical Irradiation. A Contribution to the Clarification of the Conduction-mechanism, *Z. Phys. Chem.*, vol. 203, pp. 145–162, 1954.

Boer, K. W., and U. Kummel: Pure Electrical Excitation of Glow Curves, *Z. Naturforsch.*, vol. 9a, pp. 177–178, 1954.

Boer, K. W.: Some Remarks on Gisolf's Theory of the Electron Fluctuations of Semiconductors, *Ann. Physik*, vol. 14, pp. 87–96, 1954.

Boothroyd, A. R., and J. Almond: A Bridge for Measuring the A. C. Parameters of Junction Transistors, *Proc. Inst. Elec. Engrs. (London)*, vol. 101, part III, pp. 314–316, 1954.

Boothroyd, A. R., and S. K. Datta: A Bridge for Measuring the A. C. Parameters of Point-contact Transistors, *Proc. Inst. Elec. Engrs. (London)*, vol. 101, part III, pp. 294–297, 1954.

Bradley, W. E.: Electroplated Transistors Announced, *Electronics*, vol. 27, p. 10, January, 1954; discussion pp. 420–421, May, 1954.

Brentano, J. C. M., and C. Goldberg: The Electrical Conductance of Pressed Powders, in Particular of Zinc Oxide, *Phys. Rev.*, vol. 94, pp. 56–60, 1954.

Brentano, J. C. M., and J. D. Richard: Evaporated Multiple Layers with Semiconductor Properties, *Phys. Rev.*, vol. 95, pp. 841–842, 1954.

Bright, R. L.: Future Transistor Applications in Machine Tool Control, *Instruments and Automation*, vol. 27, pp. 1296–1298, 1954; *Machine Design*, vol. 26, pp. 282–285, October, 1954; *Tele-Tech*, vol. 13, p. 103, June, 1954.

Brock, R. L.: Transistor Flip-flop Uses Two Frequencies, *Electronics*, vol. 27, pp. 175–177, June, 1954.

Bulliard, H.: Contribution to the Study of the Photo-magneto-electric Effect on Germanium, *Ann. phys.*, vol. 9, pp. 52–83, 1954.

Burstein, E., J. W. Davisson, E. E. Bell, W. J. Turner, and H. G. Lipson: Infrared Photoconductivity due to Neutral Impurities in Germanium, *Phys. Rev.*, vol. 93, pp. 65–68, 1954.

Busch, G., F. Hulliger, and U. Winkler: The Electrical Properties of the Intermetallic Compound Mg_3Sb_2, *Helv. Phys. Acta*, vol. 27, pp. 249–258, 1954.

Busch, G., and O. Vogt: Variation of the Electrical and Magnetic Properties of Sb and InSb at the Melting Point, *Helv. Phys. Acta*, vol. 27, pp. 241–249, 1954.

Buttler, W. M., and W. Muscheid: The Nature of the Electrical Contact by studies on Single Crystals of Cadmium Sulphide I, *Ann. Physik*, vol. 14, pp. 215–219, 1954.

Caldwell, W. H.: Transistor Phase Inverter, *Radio Television News*, vol. 52, p. 71, September, 1954.

Camp, P. R.: Resistivity Striations in Germanium Crystals, *J. Appl. Physics*, vol. 25, pp. 459–463, 1954.

Carlisle, R. W., H. A. Pearson, and W. H. Greenbaum: A Simple Transistor Noise Test Set, *IRE Convention Record*, part 10, pp. 88–91, 1954.

Carswell, D. J., J. Ferguson, and L. E. Lyons: Photo- and Semi-conductance in Molecular Single Crystals, *Nature*, vol. 173, p. 736, 1954.

Chapin, D. M., C. S. Fuller, and G. L. Pearson: A New Silicon P-N Junction Photocell for Converting Solar Radiation into Electrical Power, *J. Appl. Phys.*, vol. 25, pp. 676–677, 1954.

Chaplin, G. B. B.: The Transistor Regenerative Amplifier as a Computer Element, *Proc. Inst. Elec. Engrs. (London)*, vol. 101, part III, pp. 298–307, 1954.

Chase, F. H., B. H. Hamilton, and D. H. Smith: Transistors and Junction Diodes in Telephone Power Plants, *Bell System Tech. J.*, vol. 33, pp. 827–858, 1954.

Cheng, C. C.: Transistor Equations Using H-parameters (Reference Sheet), *Electronics*, vol. 27, pp. 191–192, 194, April, 1954.

Chow, W. F.: High Frequency Transistor Amplifiers, *Electronics*, vol. 27, pp. 142–145, April, 1954; discussion p. 346, July, 1954.

Christensen, H.: Surface Conduction Channel Phenomena in Germanium, *Proc. IRE*, vol. 42, pp. 1371–1376, 1954.

Clarke, E. N.: Hall and Suhl Effects, in Penn State University, Transistor Short Course Proceedings, 1954.

Clarke, E. N.: Oxygen and the Surface Energy-level Structure on Germanium, *Phys. Rev.*, vol. 95, pp. 284–285, 1954.

Cleland, J. W., and J. H. Crawford, Jr.: Radiation Effects in Indium Antimonide, *Phys. Rev.*, vol. 93, p. 894, 1954.

Coblenz, A., and H. L. Owens: Transistors: Theory and Application, part XI: Cascading Transistor Amplifier Stages, *Electronics*, vol. 27, pp. 158–161, January, 1954.

Cochran, K. E.: Semiconductors and Their Applications, *Battelle Tech. Rev.*, vol. 3, pp. 71–74, 1954.

Cohen, J.: Semiconducting Films of Antimony, *J. Appl. Phys.*, vol. 25, pp. 798–801, 1954.

Cohen, R. M.: Application Considerations for RCA Commercial Transistors, *Trans. IRE*, vol. ED-1, pp. 32–46, February, 1954.

Conwell, E. M.: Experimental Evidence concerning Degeneracy in Germanium, *Phys. Rev.*, vol. 93, p. 1118, 1954.

Conwell, E. M.: High Field Effects in Germanium, *Phys. Rev.*, vol. 94, p. 1068, 1954.

Cooke-Yarborough, E. H., C. D. Florida, and J. H. Stephen: The Measurement of the Small-signal Characteristics of Transistors, *Proc. Inst. Elec. Engrs. (London)*, vol. 101, part III, pp. 288–293, 1954.

Cooke-Yarborough, E. H.: A Versatile Transistor Circuit, *Proc. Inst. Elec. Engrs. (London)*, vol. 101, part III, pp. 281–287, 1954.

Crawford, J. H., Jr., and D. K. Holmes: A Chemical Approach to the Treatment of Electronic Spin in Semiconductors, *Proc. Phys. Soc. (London)*, vol. 67A, pp. 294–295, 1954.

Cummerow, R. L.: Photovoltaic Effect in P-N Junctions, *Phys. Rev.*, vol. 95, pp. 16–21, 1954.

Cummerow, R. L.: Use of Silicon P-N Junctions for Converting Solar Energy to Electrical Energy, *Phys. Rev.*, vol. 95, pp. 561–562, 1954.

Curie, G., and D. Curie: Brightness Waves in Electroluminescence and Luminous "Surface" Effects, *J. phys. radium*, vol. 15, pp. 61–62, 1954.

Das, J. N., and V. G. Bhide: Influence of Mechanical Pressure on Barrier Height in Galena Rectifiers, *Current Science*, vol. 23, pp. 185–186, 1954.

Davis, P. D.: Germanium Diode Push Pull Voltmeter, *Electronics*, vol. 27, p. 212, February, 1954.

Dawson, M.: The Problem of Transistor Action, in Penn State University, Transistor Short Course Proceedings, 1954.

Debye, P. P., and E. M. Conwell: Electrical Properties on N-type Germanium, *Phys. Rev.*, vol. 93, pp. 693–706, 1954.

Debye, P. P., and T. Kohane: Hall Mobility of Electrons and Holes in Electrons, *Phys. Rev.*, vol. 94, pp. 724–725, 1954.

Degen, P. L.: Transistors; N-P Junctions in Semiconductors, *Elec. Rev. London*, vol. 154, pp. 605–609, 1954.

Dorman, D.: Bridge for Junction Transistor Measurements, *Radio-Electronic Eng.*, pp. 10–11, October, 1954.

Dorman, D.: A Bridge Transistor Tester, *Radio-Electronic Eng.*, pp. 5–8, 34, February, 1954.

Dosse, J.: The Transistor and Its Applications, *Convegno di elettronica e televisione*, vol. 2, pp. 617–632, 1954; suppl. to *Ricerca sci.*, vol. 24, 1954.

Dunlap, W. C., Jr.: Diffusion of Impurities in Germanium, *Phys. Rev.*, vol. 94, pp. 1531–1540, 1954.

Dunlap, W. C., Jr.: Germanium Diodes from Spherical Pellets, *J. Appl. Phys.*, vol. 25, pp. 448–451, 1954.

Dunlap, W. C., Jr.: Properties of Zinc-, Copper-, and Platinum-doped Germanium, *Phys. Rev.*, vol. 96, pp. 40–45, 1954.

Early, J. M.: P-N-I-P and N-P-I-N Junction Transistor Triodes, *Bell System Tech. J.*, vol. 33, pp. 517–533, 1954.

Eckart, F.: Conductivity Measurements on Selenium, *Ann. Physik*, vol. 14, pp. 233–252, 1954.

Elliott, R. J.: Theory and Effect of Spin-orbit Coupling on Magnetic Resonance in Some Semiconductors, *Phys. Rev.*, vol. 96, pp. 266–279, 1954.

Ewels, J.: The Measurement of Transistor Characteristics, *Electronic Eng.*, vol. 26, pp. 313–314, 1954.

Fielding, P. E.: The Electrical Properties of Some Complex Compounds. I, *J. Chem. Phys.*, vol. 22, pp. 1153–1155, 1954.

Fielding, P. E., and D. P. Mellor: The Electrical Properties of Some Complex Compounds. II, *J. Chem. Phys.*, vol. 22, pp. 1155–1156, 1954.

Fischer, A.: Thin Semiconducting Layers on Glass, *Z. Naturforsch.*, vol. 9a, pp. 508–511, 1954.

Florida, C. D., F. R. Holt, and J. H. Stephen: Irradiation of Transistors, *Nature*, vol. 173, pp. 397–398, 1954.

Foley, J. S.: Unilateral Four-terminal Circuits, *Electronics*, vol. 27, pp. 186–187, February, 1954.

Ford, A.: Bioelectric Integrator Uses Two Transistors, *Electronics*, vol. 27, pp. 176–177, May, 1954.

Fritzsche, C.: On the Semiconducting Properties of Cuprous Oxide. VIII: The Electrical Conductivity at 0°C as a Function of the Distance inside the Specimen, *Ann. Physik*, vol. 14, pp. 135–140, 1954.

Frohnmeyer, G., E. R. Glocker, and D. Messner: The Dependence of the Electrical Conductivity of Cadmium Sulphide Single Crystals on Wavelength under X-radiation and Gamma-radiation, *Z. Physik*, vol. 137, pp. 117–125, 1954.

Fukuroi, T., S. Tanuma, and Y. Muto: Electrical Properties of Tellurium Crystals at Very Low Temperatures (Experiment with Liquid Helium), *Sci. Repts. Research Insts. Tôhoku Univ.*, vol. 6A, pp. 18–29, 1954.

Fuller, C. S., J. D. Struthers, J. A. Ditzenberger, and K. B. Wolfstirn: Diffusivity and Solubility of Copper in Germanium, *Phys. Rev.*, vol. 93, pp. 1182–1189, 1954.

Gade, D. W.: Feedback in Junction Transistor Circuits, *Electronics*, vol. 27, pp. 174–178, July, 1954.

Garner, L. E.: Transistor Metronome, *Radio Television News*, vol. 51, pp. 50–51, January, 1954.

Garner, L. E.: Transistorized Applause Meter, *Radio Television News*, vol. 51, pp. 82–83, March, 1954.

Garner, L. E.: Transistorized Moisture Detector, *Radio Television News*, vol. 52, pp. 52–53, September, 1954.

Garrett, G. G. B., and W. H. Brattain: Self-powered Semiconductor Amplifier, *Phys. Rev.*, vol. 95, pp. 1091–1092, 1954.

Geballe, T. H., and F. J. Morin: Ionization Energies of Groups III and V Elements in Germanium, *Phys. Rev.*, vol. 95, pp. 1085–1086, 1954.

Germain, J. E.: Kinetic Model of Activated Adsorption on Catalysts Which Are Semiconductors, *Compt. rend.*, vol. 238, pp. 236–238, 1954.

Germain, J. E.: Relation between the Form of the Isotherm, the Kinetics, and the Variation of the Heat of Activated Adsorption on the Semiconductor Catalysts, *Compt. rend.*, vol. 238, pp. 345–347, 1954.

Ghandhi, S. K.: Design Criteria for Transistor Feedback Amplifiers, *Tele-Tech*, vol. 13, pp. 94–95, 158, 161–162, March, 1954.

Ghandhi, S. K.: Design of Transistor Power Amplifiers, *Electronics*, vol. 27, pp. 146–149, March, 1954.

Giacoletto, L. J.: Power Transistor, in Penn State University, Transistor Short Course Proceedings, 1954.

Giacoletto, L. J.: Power Transistors for Audio Output Circuits, *Electronics*, vol. 27, pp. 144–148, January, 1954.

Gibbons, J.: Versatile Transistor Tester, *Radio Television News*, vol. 51, pp. 10–11, 46, June, 1954.

Goldberg, A. E., and G. R. Mitchell: Occurrence of Natural P-N Junctions in Lead Selenide, *J. Chem. Phys.*, vol. 22, pp. 220–222, 1954.

Goldberg, C., and R. E. Davis: New Galvanomagnetic Effect, *Phys. Rev.*, vol. 94, pp. 1121–1125, 1954.

Golden, N. J.: Linear Applications of Transistors, in Penn State University, Transistor Short Course Proceedings, 1954.

Goldsmid, H. J.: On the Thermal and Electrical Conductivity of Semiconductors, *Proc. Phys. Soc. (London)*, vol. 67B, pp. 360–363, 1954.

Goodman, C. H. L.: Semiconducting Compounds and the Scale of Electronegatives, *Proc. Phys. Soc. (London)*, vol. 67B, pp. 258–259, 1954.

Goudal, P.: Experimental Results in the Selection of Germanium Rectifiers, *Cahiers de Phys.*, no. 49, pp. 65–66, 1954.

Grunewald, H.: The Electrical Properties of Fe_2O_3 with Substituted TiO_2, *Ann. Physik*, vol. 14, pp. 129–134, 1954.

Grunewald, H.: On the Dependence of Electrical Conductivity of Titanium Dioxide on the Content of the Ions of a Different Valency, *Ann. Physik*, vol. 14, pp. 121–128, 1954.

Gubanov, A. I.: Towards the Theory of the Effect of Strong Fields in Semiconductors, *Zhur. Tekh. Fiz.*, vol. 24, pp. 308–319, 1954.

Gunn, J. B.: Measurement of the Surface Properties of Germanium, *Proc. Phys. Soc. (London)*, vol. 67B, pp. 409–421, 1954.

Gunn, J. B.: The Theory of Rectification and Injection at a Metal-semiconductor Contact, *Proc. Phys. Soc. (London)*, vol. 67B, pp. 575–581, 1954.

Halverson, G.: Electrical Properties of Microcrystalline Selenium, *Commun. and Electronics*, no. 11, pp. 38–45, 1954.

Harman, T. C., R. K. Willardson, and A. C. Beers: Analysis of Magnetoresistance and Hall Coefficient in P-type Indium-antimonide and P-type Germanium, *Phys. Rev.*, vol. 95, pp. 699–702, 1954.

Harman, T. C., R. K. Willardson, and A. C. Beers: Hall Coefficient in Germanium, *Phys. Rev.*, vol. 94, pp. 1065–1067, 1954.

Harris, B., and A. Macovski: Symmetrical-transistor Phase Detector for Horizontal Synchronization, *RCA Rev.*, vol. 15, pp. 18–26, 1954.

Harrison, S. E.: Conductivity and Hall Effect of ZnO at Low Temperatures, *Phys. Rev.*, vol. 93, pp. 52–62, 1954.

Harten, H. U.: Barrier Contacts between Germanium and Evaporated Metals, *Naturwissenschaften*, vol. 41, p. 162, 1954.

Harten, H. U., W. Koch, H. L. Rath, and W. Schultz: The Barrier-layer Capacitance on the Indium-Germanium Alloy Rectifier, *Z. Physik*, vol. 138, pp. 336–344, 1954.

Hatton, J., and B. V. Rollin: The Electrical Properties of Indium Antimonide at Low Temperatures, *Proc. Phys. Soc. (London)*, vol. 67A, pp. 385–386, 1954.

Heiland, G.: On the Influence of Adsorbed Oxygen on the Conductivity of Zinc Oxide Crystals, *Z. Physik*, vol. 138, pp. 459–464, 1954.

Helsdon, P. B.: Transistorized Megohmmeter, *Wireless World*, vol. 60, pp. 121–123, 1954.

Henisch, H. K., and P. M. Tipple: A Note on the Effect of Temperature Gradients at Point Contacts on Germanium, *Proc. Phys. Soc. (London)*, vol. 67B, pp. 651–652, 1954.

Henkels, H. W., and J. Maczuk: Electrical Properties of Selenium III: Microcrystalline Selenium Metal-doped, *J. Appl. Phys.*, vol. 25, pp. 1–12, 1954.

Henker, H.: Transistor Characteristics with Small Alternating Currents, *Arch. Elekt. Ubertragung*, vol. 8, pp. 213–216, 1954.

Herforth, L., and J. Krumbiegel: Observations on CdS Crystals by Microscopic Examination and Conductivity Measurements, *Z. Naturforsch.*, vol. 9a, pp. 432–434, 1954.

Herman, F.: Speculations on the Energy Band Structure of Ge-Si Alloys, *Phys. Rev.*, vol. 95, pp. 847–848, 1954.

Herold, E. W.: New Advances in the Junction Transistor, *Brit. J. Appl. Phys.*, vol. 5, pp. 115–126, 1954.

Herzog, W.: Raising Transistor Limiting Frequency, *Arch. Elekt. Ubertragung*, vol. 8, pp. 297–300, 1954.

Herzog, W.: The Realization of Maximum Amplification with Unmatched Transistors, *Arch. Elekt. Ubertragung*, vol. 8, pp. 279–282, 1954.

Heywang, W., and H. Henker: Physics and Technology of Rectifiers and Transistors, *Z. Elektrochem.*, vol. 58, pp. 283–321, 1954.

Heywang, W., M. Zerbst, and F. Bischoff: On the Conductivity of Silicon, *Naturwissenschaften*, vol. 41, pp. 301–302, 1954.

Hodgkinson, R. J.: The Effect of Heat Treatment on the Electrical Properties of Germanium, *Gen. Elec. Co. J.*, vol. 21, pp. 63–70, 1954.

Hogarth, C. A.: Current Multiplication Processes in N-type Germanium Point-contact Transistors, *Proc. Phys. Soc. (London)*, vol. 67B, pp. 636–643, 1954.

Hohler, G.: Observations on the Work of B. Seraphin: "The Influence of Temperature and Oxygen on the Rise and Decay of Photoconductivity of Single Crystals of CdS," *Ann. Physik*, vol. 14, pp. 426–427, 1954.

Hollmann, H. E.: Internal Oscillations and Microwaves in Transition, *Naturwissenschaften*, vol. 41, p. 136, 1954.

Hollmann, H. E.: Internal Transistor Oscillations, *Proc. IRE*, vol. 42, p. 1323, 1954.

Hollmann, H. E.: Self Oscillating U. H. F. Transistors, *Tele-Tech*, vol. 13, pp. 75–77, April, 1954.

Hollmann, H. E.: Self Oscillations of Transistors, *Z. Physik*, vol. 138, pp. 1–15, 1954.

Hollmann, H. E.: Vhf Transistor Oscillator, *Electronics*, vol. 27, p. 220, June, 1954.

Homilius, J., and W. Franz: The Spatial Generalization of Zener's Formula for Internal Field Emission, *Z. Naturforsch.*, vol. 9a, pp. 5–14, 1954.

Honig, A.: Polarization of Arsenic Nuclei in a Silicon Semiconductor, *Phys. Rev.*, vol. 96, pp. 234–235, 1954.

Hsieh, H. T., J. M. Goldey, and S. C. Brown: Resonant Cavity Study of Semiconductors, *J. Appl. Phys.*, vol. 25, pp. 302–306, 1954.

Hughes, J. M.: Superregenerative Transistor Receiver, *Radio Television News*, vol. 51, pp. 72–73, March, 1954.

Hunter, F. L., and B. N. Slade: High Frequency Operation of P-type Point Contact Transistors, *RCA Rev.*, vol. 15, pp. 121–134, 1954.

Hunter, L. P.: Graphical Representation of the Semiconductor Hall Effect, *Phys. Rev.*, vol. 94, pp. 1157–1160, 1954.

Hunter, L. P.: Monostable, Bistable, and Astable Operation of Point Contact Transistors, in Penn State University, Transistor Short Course Proceedings, 1954.

James, E. G.: Scientific and Industrial Applications and Implications of Germanium, *Chem. & Ind.*, p. 1227, Oct. 2, 1954.

Jaumann, J., and R. Kessler: The Contribution of Free Charge Carriers in Germanium to Absorption in the Near Infrared, *Z. Naturforsch.*, vol. 9a, p. 476, 1954.

Johnson, J. B., and K. G. McKay: Secondary Electron Emission from Germanium, *Phys. Rev.*, vol. 93, pp. 668–672, 1954.

Johnson, R., D. Humez, and G. Knight, Jr.: Precision Transistor Test Equipment, *Tele-Tech*, vol. 13, pp. 74–75, 179–183, February, 1954.

Kaiser, W., and H. Y. Fan: Infrared Absorption, Photoconductivity, and Impurity States in Germanium, *Phys. Rev.*, vol. 93, pp. 977–980, 1954.

Kanai, Y.: On the A. C. Characteristics of Silicon P-N Junction Alloy Diodes, *J. Phys. Soc. Japan*, vol. 9, pp. 143–144, 1954.

Kanai, Y.: On the Electrical Properties of Silicon Single Crystals. I. *J. Phys. Soc. Japan*, vol. 9, pp. 132–133, 1954.

Kanai, Y.: Temperature Dependency of the Surface Recombination Velocity in Germanium, *J. Phys. Soc. Japan*, vol. 9, pp. 292–293, 1954.

Kelly, S.: The Transistor in Hearing Aids, *Wireless World*, vol. 60, pp. 56–59, 159–162, 1954.

Kendall, J. T.: Electronic Conduction in Grey Tin, *Phil. Mag.*, vol. 45, pp. 141–157, 1954.

Kenn, V., and N. Sokal: Transistorized Light-beam Communications System, *Radio Television News*, vol. 51, pp. 52–53, May, 1954.

Keonjian, E.: Temperature-compensated D.C. Transistor Amplifier, *Proc. IRE*, vol. 42, pp. 661–671, 1954.

Kernahan, J. J. J.: A Digital Code Wheel, *Bell Labs. Record*, vol. 32, pp. 126–131, 1954.

Kerr, J. S. S., J. S. Schaffner, and J. J. Suran: Effect of a Transverse Electric Field on Carrier Diffusion in the Base Region of a Transistor, *J. Appl. Phys.*, vol. 25, pp. 1293–1297, 1954.

Kikuchi, M., and T. Onishi: The "Photo-aftereffect" of Germanium Crystal Rectifiers, *J. Phys. Soc. Japan*, vol. 9, pp. 130–131, 1954.

Kingston, R. H.: Point Emitter-junction Collector Transistor, *J. Appl. Phys.*, vol. 25, pp. 513–515, 1954.

Kingston, R. H.: Switching Time in Junction Diodes and Junction Transistors, *Proc. IRE*, vol. 42, pp. 829–834, 1954.

Kingston, R. H.: Water Vapor and the "Channel" Effect in N-P-N Junction Transistors, *Phys. Rev.*, vol. 93, pp. 346–347, 1954.

Klass, P.: Carrier's Test New Transistorized Mike, *Aviation Week*, vol. 60, pp. 65–66, Jan. 25, 1954.

Klass, P.: New Transistor Easy to Mass Produce, *Aviation Week*, vol. 60, pp. 50–52, Jan. 4, 1954.

Klein, D., and W. Slusher: A Transistor Self-powered C. W. Monitor, *QST*, vol. 38, pp. 28–29, January, 1954.

Klinger, M. I.: The Investigation of the Energetic Spectrum of an Electron in an Ionic Semiconductor for Superposed Electric and Magnetic Fields, *Zhur. Eksptl. Teort. Fiz.*, vol. 26, pp. 159–167, 1954.

Klinger, M. I.: The Investigation of the Polarization of a Semiconductor for Superposed Electric and Magnetic Fields, *Zhur. Eksptl. Teort. Fiz.*, vol. 26, pp. 168–172, 1954.

Kluge, W., and A. Schulz: A Reversible Fatigue Phenomenon of Secondary Emission from Glow Cathodes with Semiconducting Component Layers, *Z. Physik*, vol. 137, pp. 392–400, 1954.

Knausenberger, G.: Equivalent Circuits and Matrices for Transistor Circuits, in Penn State University, Transistor Short Course Proceedings, 1954.

Koehler, J. S., and F. Seitz: Radiation Disarrangement of Crystals, *Z. Physik*, vol. 138, pp. 238–245, 1954.

Kohn, W., and J. M. Luttinger: Quantum Theory of Cyclotron Resonance in Semiconductors, *Phys. Rev.*, vol. 96, pp. 529–530, 1954.

Kolb, E. R.: Modulator for Low Frequency Tape Recording, *Electronics*, vol. 27, p. 220, August, 1954.

Kramer, N. H.: Tester for Transistor Selection, *Electronics*, vol. 27, p. 240, June, 1954.

Kramer, S. I.: Designing Transistor Relaxation Oscillators, *Tele-Tech*, vol. 13, pp. 78–79, May, 1954.

Krause, C. A.: Gain Stabilized Transistor Amplifier, *Electronics*, vol. 27, pp. 183–185, February, 1954.

Krause, C. A.: Transistor Negative Resistance Characteristics by Means of Graphical Analysis, *Radio-Electronic Eng.*, pp. 17–18, 43–44, May, 1954.

Kretzmer, E. R.: Amplitude Stabilized Transistor Oscillator, *Proc. IRE*, vol. 42, pp. 391–401, 1124, 1954.

Kromer, H.: P-N Junctions and Transistors, *Fernmeldetech Z.*, vol. 7, pp. 86–93, 1954.

Kromer, H.: Theory of Diffusion and Drift Transistors, *Arch. Elekt. Ubertragung*, vol. 8, pp. 363–369, 1954.

Kromer, H.: Theory of Diffusion Type and Drift Type Transistors. I: The Quadripole Matrix for Low Frequencies, *Arch. Elekt. Ubertragung*, vol. 8, pp. 223–228, 1954.

Krugman, L. M.: "Fundamentals of Transistors," John Francis Rider, Publishers, Inc., New York, 1954.

Krull, A. R.: Transistors and Their Applications (A Bibliography, 1948–1953), *Trans. IRE*, vol. ED-1, pp. 40–77, August, 1954.

Kummer, O.: A Transistor Frequency Scanner, *IRE Convention Record*, part 10, pp. 81–87, 1954.

Laendle, K. W.: A Presentation of Transistor Test Equipment, in Penn State University, Transistor Short Course Proceedings, 1954.

Lafferty, R. E.: Transistor Gun for TV, *Electronics*, vol. 27, p. 137, May, 1954.

Lagrenaudie, J.: Comparison of Compounds of the MoS_2 Family (Structure and Optical and Electrical Properties). *J. phys. radium*, vol. 15, pp. 299–300, 1954.

Landauer, R.: Bound States in Dislocations, *Phys. Rev.*, vol. 94, pp. 1386–1388, 1954.

Laplace, J.: Calculation of the Combination Current at the Surface of a Fused Junction Transistor, *Compt. rend.*, vol. 238, pp. 1107–1109, 1954.

Laplume, J.: Calculation of the Current Gain in a Junction Transistor Made by Fusion, *Compt. rend.*, vol. 238, pp. 1300–1301, 1954.

Lappe, F.: Irreversible Changes of Electron Mobility in Thin CdO Layers, *Z. Physik*, vol. 137, pp. 380–382, 1954.

Law, J. T.: Mechanism for Water Induced Excess Reverse Dark Current on Growth Germanium N-P Junctions, *Proc. IRE*, vol. 42, pp. 1367–1370, 1954.

Lawrance, R., A. F. Gibson, and J. W. Granville: On the Current Gain of Germanium Filamentary Transistors, *Proc. Phys. Soc. (London)*, vol. 67B, pp. 625–635, 1954.

Lawrance, R.: The Temperature Dependence of the Drift Mobility on Injected Holes in Germanium, *Proc. Phys. Soc. (London)*, vol. 67A, pp. 18–27, 1954.

Lawson, T. R.: Semiconductors; Their Characteristics and Principles, *Westinghouse Engr.*, vol. 14, pp. 178–182, 1954.

Lawson, T. R.: Semiconductors; What They Are, How They Work, *Materials & Methods*, vol. 40, pp. 92–95, July, 1954.

Lax, B., H. J. Zeigler, R. N. Dexter, and E. S. Rosenblum: Directional Properties of the Cyclotron Resonance in Germanium, *Phys. Rev.*, vol. 93, p. 1418, 1954.

Lebow, I. L., and R. H. Baker: Transient Response of Transistor Switching Circuits, *Proc. IRE*, vol. 42, pp. 938–943, 1954.

Lehman, G. J., and C. A. Meuleau: Temperature Regulator Used in Producing Germanium Crystals, *Elect. Commun.*, vol. 31, pp. 19–26, 1954.

Lehovec, K., and J. Broder: Semiconductors as Solid Electrolytes in Electrochemical Systems, *Electrochem. Soc. J.*, vol. 101, pp. 208–209, 1954.

Leifer, H. N., and W. C. Dunlap, Jr.: Some Properties of the P-type Gallium Antimonide between 15°K. and 925°K., *Phys. Rev.*, vol. 95, pp. 51–56, 1954.

Lempicki, A., and C. Wood: Observations on a Form of Breakdown in Germanium Diodes, *Proc. Phys. Soc. (London)*, vol. 67B, pp. 328–337, 1954.

Lennartz, H.: Recorder for Transistor Characteristics, *Funk u. Ton*, vol. 8, pp. 25–29, 1954.

Letaw, H., Jr., and J. Bardeen: Electrolytic Analog Transistor, *J. Appl. Phys.*, vol. 25, pp. 600–606, 1954.

Levitas, A., C. C. Wang, and B. H. Alexander: Energy Gap of Germanium-silicon Alloys, *Phys. Rev.*, vol. 95, p. 846, 1954.

Linvill, J. G.: RC Active Filters in Which the Negative Impedance Converter Uses Transistors, *Proc. IRE*, vol. 42, pp. 555–564, 1954.

Logan, R. A., and M. Schwartz: Thermal Effects on Lifetime of Minority Carriers in Germanium, *Phys. Rev.*, vol. 96, p. 46, 1954.

Lomer, W. M.: The Direct Conversion of Beta-irradiation Energy into Low-voltage Electrical Energy, *Harwell Atomic Energy Research Estab. Memo.* T/M 108, 1954.

Lovett, C. M.: Some Measurements of the Electrical Conductivity, Thermoelectric Power and Other Properties of the Coating in the Oxide-coated Cathode, *Proc. Phys. Soc. (London)*, vol. 67B, pp. 387–394, 1954.

Low, G. G. E.: Properties of Point Contacts on Cobaltite, *Proc. Phys. Soc. (London)*, vol. 67B, pp. 589–590, 1954.

McKay, K. G.: Avalanche Breakdown in Silicon, *Phys. Rev.*, vol. 94, pp. 877–884, 1954.

McKelvey, J. P., and R. L. Longini: Volume and Surface Recombination Rates for Injected Carriers in Germanium, *J. Appl. Phys.*, vol. 25, pp. 634–641, 1954.

McMahon, R. E., I. L. Lebow, and R. H. Baker: Transistors Convert Sine Waves to Pulses, *Electronics*, vol. 27, pp. 160–161, May, 1954.

McWhorter, A. L., and R. H. Kingston: Channels and Excess Reverse Current in Grown Germanium P-N Junction Diodes, *Proc. IRE*, vol. 42, pp. 1376–1380, 1954.

Machlop, S.: Noise in Semiconductors; Spectrum of a Two-parameter Random Signal, *J. Appl. Phys.*, vol. 25, pp. 341–343, 1954.

Madelung, O., and H. Weiss: The Electrical Properties of Indium Antimonide. II. *Z. Naturforsch.*, vol. 9a, pp. 527–534, 1954.

Madelung, O.: On the Theory of Conductivity in Isotropic Semiconductors, *Z. Naturforsch.*, vol. 9a, pp. 667–674, 1954.

Madsen, J. F.: Transistorized Oscillator, *Electronics*, vol. 27, p. 171, September, 1954.

Mallery, P.: Transistors and Their Circuits in 4A Toll Crossbar Switching System, *Elec. Eng.*, vol. 73, p. 129, 1954; *Electronics*, vol 27, p. 216, July, 1954.

Malsch, J.: Equivalent Circuits of Transistors and Their Physical Basis, *Arch. Elekt. Ubertragung*, vol. 8, pp. 179–189, 1954.

Many, A.: Measurement of Minority Carrier Lifetime and Contact Injection Ratio on Transistor Materials, *Proc. Phys. Soc. (London)*, vol. 67B, pp. 9–17, 1954.

Matare, H. F.: Electronic Behavior of Certain Grain Boundaries in Perfect Crystals, *Z. Naturforsch*, vol. 9a, p. 698, 1954.

Mayburg, S.: Vacancies and Interstitials in Heat Treated Germanium, *Phys. Rev.*, vol. 95, pp. 38–43, 1954.

Meiboom, S., and B. Abeles: Theory of the Galvanomagnetic Effects in N-germanium, *Phys. Rev.*, vol. 93, p. 1121, 1954.

Meinnel, J.: On the Existence of Absorption Bands in the Hertzian Spectrum for the Monatomic Semiconductors (Boron, Selenium), *J. phys. radium*, vol. 15, pp. 124–125, 1954.

Mitchell, W. M.: Techniques for Making Stable Non-rectifying Contacts to Germanium and Other Semiconductors, *J. Sci. Instr.*, vol. 31, pp. 147–148, 1954.

Mollwo, E.: The Effect of Hydrogen on the Conductivity and Luminescence of Zinc Oxide Crystals, *Z. Physik*, vol. 138, pp. 478–488, 1954.

Moore, A. R., and J. I. Pankove: Effect of Junction Shape and Surface Recombination on Transistor Current Gain, *Proc. IRE*, vol. 42, pp. 907–913, 1954.

Morin, F. J., and J. P. Maita: Conductivity and Hall Effect in the Intrinsic Range of Germanium, *Phys. Rev.*, vol. 94, pp. 1525–1529, 1954.

Morin, F. J., and J. P. Maita: Electrical Properties of Silicon Containing Arsenic and Boron, *Phys. Rev.*, vol. 96, pp. 28–35, 1954.

Morin, F. J.: Lattice-scattering Mobility in Germanium, *Phys. Rev.*, vol. 93, pp. 62–63, 1954.

Mueller, C. W., and J. I. Pankove: P-N-P Triode Alloy-junction Transistor for Radio Frequency Amplification, *Proc. IRE*, vol. 42, pp. 386–391, 1954.

Newman, R.: Photoconductivity in Gold-germanium Alloys, *Phys. Rev.*, vol. 94, pp. 278–285, 1954.

Nifontoff, N.: Hysteresis Phenomena at Rectifying Contacts and in Thin Films, *Compt. rend.*, vol. 239, pp. 31–33, 1954.

Nifontoff, N.: Remarks on the Comparison between the Study of an Imperfect Contact and the Experimental Results Concerning Thin Metal Films, *Compt. rend.*, vol. 238, pp. 1200–1202, 1954.

Nifontoff, N.: Tentative Explanation of the Mechanism of Conductivity of Thin Granular Metallic Films, *Compt. rend.*, vol. 238, pp. 1870–1872, 1954.

Nijland, L. M.: Some Investigations on the Electrical Properties of Hexagonal Selenium, *Philips Research Repts.*, vol. 9, pp. 259–294, 1954.

Nussbaum, A.: Electrical Properties of Pure Tellurium and Tellurium-Selenium Alloys, *Phys. Rev.*, vol. 94, pp. 337–342, 1954.

Oakes, J. B.: Analysis of Junction Transistor Audio Oscillator Circuits, *Proc. IRE*, vol. 42, pp. 1235–1238, 1954.

Oakes, J. B.: Junction Transistor Pulse-forming Circuits, *Electronics*, vol. 27, pp. 165–167, September, 1954.

Ozarow, V.: Some Electrical Properties of Germanium Crystals Containing Compensated Impurities, *Phys. Rev.*, vol. 93, pp. 371–372, 1954.

Palmer, W.: Electrical Properties of MnSe and MnTe, *J. Appl. Phys.*, vol. 25, p. 125, 1954.

Pankove, J. I.: Recrystallization of Germanium from Indium Solution, *RCA Rev.*, vol. 15, pp. 75–85, 1954.

Parrott, J. E.: The Effects of Heat Flow on Thermoelectric Power in Semiconductors, *Proc. Phys. Soc. (London)*, vol. 67B, pp. 587–588, 1954.

Paul, W., and H. Brooks: Pressure Dependence of the Resistivity of Germanium, *Phys. Rev.*, vol. 94, pp. 1128–1133, 1954.

Pearlman, A. R.: Transistor Power Supply for Geiger Counters, *Electronics*, vol. 27, pp. 144–145, August, 1954.

Pearson, G. L., W. T. Read, Jr., and F. J. Morin: Dislocations in Plastically-deformed Germanium, *Phys. Rev.*, vol. 93, pp. 666–667, 1954.

Pearson, G. L., and C. S. Fuller: Silicon P-N Junction Power Rectifiers and Lightning Protectors, *Proc. IRE*, vol. 42, p. 760, 1954.

Pennsylvania State University: Transistor Short Course Proceedings, 1954.

Phillips, J. P., and R. W. Keown: Phototube Circuit with Transistors, *J. Chem. Educ.*, vol. 31, p. 605, 1954.

Pick, H., and W. Wissman: Electronic Conduction of Naphthalene Single Crystals, *Z. Physik*, vol. 138, pp. 436–440, 1954.

Pittman, G. F., Jr.: Transistor Control of Magnetic Amplifiers, *Radio-Electronic Eng.*, pp. 13–15, 30–31, February, 1954.

Prince, M. B.: Drift Mobilities in Semiconductors. II: Silicon, *Phys. Rev.*, vol. 93, pp. 1204–1206, 1954.

Pritchard, R. L.: Frequency Variations of Junction Transistor Parameters, *Proc. IRE*, vol. 42, pp. 786–799, 1954.

Pritchard, R. L., and W. N. Coffey: Small-signal Parameters of Grown-junction Transistors at High Frequencies, *IRE Convention Record*, part 3, pp. 89–98, 1954.

Prugh, T. A., and J. W. Keller: Thyratron-type Transistor Circuit, *Electronics*, vol. 27, p. 190, August, 1954.

Prugh, T. A., and J. W. Keller: Transistor Pulse Supply, *Electronics*, vol. 27, pp. 188, 190, 192, 194, 197, July, 1954.

Ransom, P., and F. W. G. Rose: On the Relation between the Sum of Donor and Acceptor Concentration and Lifetime in Single Crystal Germanium, *Proc. Phys. Soc. (London)*, vol. 67B, pp. 646–650, 1954.

Rappaport, P.: The Electron-voltaic Effect in P-N Junctions Induced by Beta-particle Bombardment, *Phys. Rev.*, vol. 93, pp. 246–247, 1954.

Rath, H. L.: Capacitance Measurements on Alloyed Germanium-Indium Rectifiers, *Naturwissenschaften*, vol. 41, pp. 161–162, 1954.

Read, W. T., Jr.: Theory of Dislocations in Germanium, *Phil. Mag.*, vol. 45, pp. 775–796, 1954.

Rebstock, H., and K. Seiler: Very High Frequency Conductivity of Hexagonal Selenium, *Z. Naturforsch.*, vol. 9a, pp. 49–55, 1954.

Reeves, A. H.: "Positive Gap" Germanium Diode—New Tool for Pulse Techniques, *Onde élect.*, vol. 34, pp. 32–37, 1954.

Reichardt, W.: A Model for Optical Transistions in Impurity Semiconductors, *Z. Physik*, vol. 137, pp. 503–515, 1954.

Remeika, J. P.: A Method for Growing Barium Titanate Single Crystals, *J. Am. Chem. Soc.*, vol. 76, pp. 940–941, 1954.

Richman, D.: The D. C. Quadricorrelator: A Two-mode Synchronization System, *Proc. IRE*, vol. 42, pp. 288–299, 1954.

Riddle, F. M.: Transistors in Telemetry, *Electronics*, vol. 27, pp. 178–180, January, 1954.

Riddle, R. L.: Practical Two Stage Transistor Amplifiers, *Electronics*, vol. 27, pp. 169–171, April, 1954.

Rittner, E. S.: Extension of the Theory of the Junction Transistor, *Phys. Rev.*, vol. 94, pp. 1161–1171, 1954.

Roka, E. G., R. E. Buck, and W. G. Reiland: Developmental Germanium Power Transistors, *Proc. IRE*, vol. 42, pp. 1247–1250, 1954.

Rollin, B. V., and I. M. Templeton: Noise in Germanium Filaments at Very Low Frequencies, *Proc. Phys. Soc. (London)*, vol. 67B, p. 271, 1954.

Rothstein, J.: Possible Macroscopic Effects of Single Lattice Defects, *Phys. Rev.*, vol. 95, pp. 370–371, 1954.

Ruth, R. P., and J. W. Moyer: Power Efficiency for the Photovoltaic Effect in a Germanium Grown Junction, *Phys. Rev.*, vol. 95, pp. 562–564, 1954.

Ryder, E. J., I. M. Ross, and D. A. Kleinman: Electron Multiplication in Germanium at Low Temperature, *Phys. Rev.*, vol. 95, pp. 1342–1343, 1954.

Ryder, R. M., and W. R. Sittner: Transistor Reliability Studies, *Proc. IRE*, vol. 42, pp. 414–419, 1954.

Saby, J. S.: Mobilities and Diffusion in Semiconductors, in Penn State University, Transistor Short Course Proceedings, 1954.

Sakata, T., and S. Munesue: Magneto-resistance of Cs_3Sb Photocathodes, *J. Phys. Soc. Japan*, vol. 9, pp. 141–142, 1954.

Salow, H., and A. Hahnlein: Germanium Single-crystals for Transistor Preparation, *Fernmeldetech. Z.*, vol. 7, pp. 235–241, 1954.

Schaeffer, N. M., and G. W. Wood: Application of Some Semiconductors as Logarithmic Elements, *Proc. IRE*, vol. 42, pp. 1113–1116, 1954.

Schaffner, J. S., and J. J. Suran: Steady-state Solution of the Two Dimensional Diffusion Equation for Transistors, *J. Appl. Phys.*, vol. 25, pp. 863–867, 1954.

Schaffner, J. S.: Transistor Applications, *Gen. Elec. Rev.*, vol. 57, pp. 50–54, March, 1954; *Machine Design*, vol. 26, p. 282, May, 1954.

Schloemilch, J.: Germanium Diodes and Germanium Transistors, *Siemens-Z.*, vol. 28, pp. 171–175, 1954.

Schmidt, P.: On the Semiconducting Properties of Cuprous Oxide. IX: Hall Effect Measurements at Low Temperatures, *Ann. Physik*, vol. 14, pp. 265–289, 1954.

Schooley, A. H.: Transistor Amplifiers Reduce Delay Line Attenuation, *Electronics*, vol. 27, pp. 181–183, May, 1954.

Schreiber, F.: Pulse Distortion and Inertia Effects with Point Contact Transistors, *Frequenz*, vol. 8, pp. 215–220, 1954.

Schulze, A., and D. Bender: The Dependence of the Gold-chromium Standard Resistors on Loading, *Z. angew. Physik*, vol. 6, pp. 132–136, 1954.

Scott, T. R.: Transistors, Diodes, and Printed Circuits, *Convegno di elettronica e televisione*, vol. 2, pp. 633–644, 1954, suppl. to *Ricerca sci.*, vol. 24, 1954.

Seed, R. G.: Photosensitive Germanium Devices and Some Device Applications, *IRE Convention Record*, part 10, pp. 70–80, 1954.

Seraphin, B.: On a One Dimensional Model of the Semiconducting Compounds of the Type $A_{III}B_V$, *Z. Naturforsch.*, vol. 9a, pp. 450–456, 1954.

Shea, R. F.: Graphical Methods Speed Transistor Power Amplifier Design, *Tele-Tech*, vol. 13, pp. 116–119, 192, June, 1954; pp. 72–74, July, 1954.

Shea, R. F.: High Frequency Applications of Point Contact Transistors, in Penn State University, Transistor Short Course Proceedings, 1954.

Shea, R. F.: Large Signal Operation, in Penn State University, Transistor Short Course Proceedings, 1954.

Shea, R. F.: Transistor Application Fundamentals; Tube and Transistor Circuits Compared, *Elec. Eng.*, vol. 73, pp. 360–365, 1954.

Shea, R. F.: Transistors vs Tubes, *Instruments & Automation*, vol. 27, pp. 771–772, 1954.

Shekel, J.: Reciprocity Relations in Active Three-terminal Elements, *Proc. IRE*, vol. 42, pp. 1268–1270, 1954.

Shibuya, M: Magnetoresistance Effect in Cubic Semiconductors with Spheroidal Energy Surfaces, *Phys. Rev.*, vol. 95, pp. 1385–1393, 1954; *J. Phys. Soc. Japan*, vol. 9, pp. 134–135, 1954.

Shockley, W., and W. P. Mason: Dissected Amplifiers Using Negative Resistance, *J. Appl. Phys.*, vol. 25, p. 677, 1954.

Shockley, W.: Negative Resistance Arising from Transit Time in Semiconductor Diodes, *Bell System Tech. J.*, vol. 33, pp. 799–826, 1954.

Shockley, W.: Transistor Electronics: Imperfections, Unipolar and Analog Transistors, in Penn State University, Transistor Short Course Proceedings, 1954.

Silverman, S. J., and H. Levinstein: Electrical Properties of Single Crystals and Thin Films of PbSe and PbTe, *Phys. Rev.*, vol. 94, pp. 871–876, 1954.

Slocum, A., and J. N. Shive: Shot Dependence of P-N Junction Phototransistors Noise, *J. Appl. Phys.*, vol. 25, p. 406, 1954.

Smith, C. S.: Piezoresistance Effect in Germanium and Silicon, *Phys. Rev.*, vol. 93, pp. 42–49, 1954.

Smolczyk, H. G.: Antimony Content and Semiconduction Properties of Synthetic Lead Sulphide Photoconductive Layers, *Naturwissenschaften*, vol. 41, p. 84, 1954.

Sokal, N. O., and R. G. Seed: Phototransistorized Photoelectric Counter, *Radio Television News*, vol. 51, pp. 52–53, June, 1954.

Soule, D. E., and R. J. Cashman: Bulk Photoconductivity in Lead Sulphide, *Phys. Rev.*, vol. 93, pp. 635–636, 1954.

Stansel, F. R.: An Improved Method of Measuring the Current Amplification Factor of Junction-type Transistors, *Trans. IRE*, no. PGI-3, pp. 41–49, April, 1954.

Steele, E. L.: Charge Storage in Junction Diodes, *J. Appl. Phys.*, vol. 25, pp. 916–918, 1954.

Stockman, H.: Multi-electrode Transistor Tube Analogy, *Proc. IRE*, vol. 42, p. 1023, 1954.

Stockmann, F.: Saturation Photocurrents in Semiconductors, *Z. Physik*, vol. 138, pp. 404–410, 1954.

Strutt, M. J. O.: "Transistoren; Wirkungsweise, Eigenschaften und Anwendungen," S. Hirzel Verlag, Leipzig, 1954. (Monographien der elektrischen Nachrichtentechnik, Band 19.)

Stuetzer, O. M.: Energies Associated with P-N Junctions, in Penn State University, Transistor Short Course Proceedings, 1954.

Stuke, J.: The Optical Absorption Constant of Cadmium Oxide, *Z. Physik*, vol. 137, pp. 401–415, 1954.

Sutherland, J. J.: Germanium in Transistors, *Can. Mining J.*, vol. 75, p. 62, July, 1954.

Swanson, J. A.: Diode Theory in the Light of Hole Injection, *J. Appl. Phys.*, vol. 25, pp. 314–323, 1954.

Taft, E. A., and F. H. Horn: Gold As a Donor in Silicon, *Phys. Rev.*, vol. 93, p. 64, 1954.

Talley, R. M., and D. P. Enright: Photovoltaic Effect in InAs, *Phys. Rev.*, vol. 95, pp. 1092–1094, 1954.

Tanuma, S.: The Effect of Thermally Produced Lattice Defects on the Electrical Properties of Tellurium, *Sci. Repts. Research Insts. Tôhoku Univ.*, vol. 6A, pp. 159–171, 1954.

Tate, H. J.: Temperature Stabilized Transistor Amplifiers, *Electronics*, vol. 27, pp. 144–147, June, 1954.

Tauc, J.: Theory of Thermoelectric Power in Semiconductors, *Phys. Rev.*, vol. 95, p. 1394, 1954.

Tellerman, J.: Measuring Transistor Temperature Rise, *Electronics*, vol. 27, pp. 185–187, April, 1954.

Teszner, S.: Theories of Systems, Rectifiers and Complexes of Semiconductors According to Recent Researches, *Rev. gén. élect.*, vol. 63, pp. 319–334, 1954.

Tewordt, L.: On the Theory of Radiationless Recombination in Nonpolar Semiconductors, *Z. Physik*, vol. 137, pp. 604–616, 1954.

Thomas, D. E.: A Point-contact Transistor VHF FM Transmitter, *Trans. IRE*, vol. ED-1, pp. 43–52, April, 1954.

Thomas, D. E.: Single Transistor F.M. Transmitter, *Electronics*, vol. 27, pp. 130–133, February, 1954.

Toth, D. H.: Tester for Measuring Small Signal Impedances of Transistors, *Rev. Sci. Instr.*, vol. 25, pp. 96–98, 1954.

Trousil, Z.: The Effect of Environment on the Production of Thermal Lattice Defects in Crystals, *Czech J. Phys.*, vol. 4, pp. 98–99, 1954.

Turner, R. J.: Surface-barrier Transistor Measurements and Applications, *Tele-Tech*, vol. 13, pp. 78–80, August, 1954.

Turner, R. P.: "Transistors: Theory and Practice," Gernsback Publications, New York, 1954. (Gernsback Library, no. 51.)

Valdes, L. B.: Resistivity Measurements on Germanium for Transistors, *Proc. IRE*, vol. 42, pp. 420–427, 1954.

van der Maas, G. J.: A Simplified Calculation for Dolph-Tchebycheff Arrays, *J. Appl. Phys.*, vol. 25, pp. 121–125, 1954.

van der Ziel, A.: Note on Shot and Partition Noise in Junction Transistors, *J. Appl. Phys.*, vol. 25, pp. 815–816, 1954.

van Roosbroeck, W., and W. Shockley: Photon-radiative Recombination of Electrons and Holes in Germanium, *Phys. Rev.*, vol. 94, pp. 1558–1560, 1954.

van Vliet, K. M., C. J. van Leeuwen, J. Blok, and C. Ris: Measurements on Current Noise in Carbon Resistors and in Thermistors, *Physica*, vol. 20, pp. 481–496, 1954.

Verwey, E. J. W.: Oxide Systems Possessing Interesting Electrical and Magnetic Properties, *Z. angew. Chem.*, vol. 66, no. 7, pp. 189–192, 1954.

Visvanathan, S., and J. F. Battey: Some Problems in the Diffusion of Minority Carriers in a Semiconductor, *J. Appl. Phys.*, vol. 25, pp. 99–102, 1954.

Vogel, F. L., W. T. Read, and L. C. Lovell: Recombination of Holes and Electrons at Lineage Boundaries in Germanium, *Phys. Rev.*, vol. 94, p. 1791, 1954.

Volger, J.: Further Experimental Investigations on Some Ferromagnetic Oxidic Compounds of Manganese with Perovskite Structure, *Physica*, vol. 20, pp. 49–66, 1954.

Warfield, G.: Energies Associated in Point Contacts, in Penn State University, Transistor Short Course Proceedings, 1954.

Warfield, G.: Junction Transistors, in Penn State University, Transistor Short Course Proceedings, 1954.

Webster, W. M.: On the Variation of Junction-transistor Current Amplification Factor with Emitter Current, *Proc. IRE*, vol. 42, pp. 914–920, 1954.

Wick, R. F.: Solution of the Field Problem of the Germanium Gyrator, *J. Appl. Phys.*, vol. 25, pp. 741–756, 1954.

Willardson, R. K.: Electrical Properties of AlSb, *Elec. Soc. J.*, vol. 101, pp. 354–358, 1954.

Wlerick, G.: Interpretation of the Anomalous Variation of the Photoconductivity of Cadmium Sulphide As a Function of Exciting Intensity, *Compt. rend.*, vol. 238, pp. 2514–2516, 1954.

Wlerick, G.: Role of Deep Traps in the Formation of the Photoelectric Signal of Thin Layers of Cadmium Sulphide, *Compt. rend.*, vol. 239, pp. 257–259, 1954.

Wolfe, R.: On the Theory of Optical Absorption in Metals and Semiconductors, *Proc. Phys. Soc. (London)*, vol. 67A, pp. 74–84, 1954.

Wolff, P. A.: Theory of Electron Multiplication in Silicon and Germanium, *Phys. Rev.*, vol. 95, pp. 1415–1420, 1954.

Woods, L. J.: First Surface Barrier Transistor Developed for Military and Civilian Use, *Elec. Eng.*, vol. 73, p. 185, 1954.

Wright, J. H.: Transient Response Limitations of Various Semiconductor Diodes, in Penn State University, Transistor Short Course Proceedings, 1954.

Yamaka, E., and K. Sawamoto: Electrical Conductivity of Magnesium Oxide Single Crystals, *Phys. Rev.*, vol. 95, pp. 848–850, 1954.

Young, R. L., Jr., and R. Steffens: "Guide to Transistor Literature," Glenn L. Martin Co., Baltimore, 1954.

Zawels, J.: Physical Theory of New Circuit Representation for Junction Transistors, *J. Appl. Phys.*, vol. 25, pp. 976–981, 1954.

Zawels, J.: Transistor As a Mixer, *Proc. IRE*, vol. 42, pp. 542–548, 1954.

Zierdt, C. H., Jr.: A Hermetically Sealed P-N-P Fused Junction Transistor for Medium Power Applications, *Trans. IRE*, vol. ED-1, pp. 47–54, February, 1954.

Zucchino, M. B.: Transistor Preamplifier Drives Magnetic Servo, *Electronics*, vol. 27, pp. 168–171, March, 1954.

All Transistor Calculator Shown by IBM, *Elec. World News*, vol. 142, p. 60, Oct. 25, 1954.

Chemicals Smash the Vacuum Tube, *Chem. Week*, vol. 75, pp. 106–108, Oct. 2, 1954.

Commercial Tetrode Transistors, *Tele-Tech*, vol. 13, p. 83, May, 1954.

Critical Look at Transistors, *Tele-Tech*, vol. 13, p. 128, January, 1954.

Electroplated Transistors Announced, *Electronics*, vol. 27, p. 10, January, 1954.

Kaiser Opens Conductor Lab at Spokane, *Elec. World*, vol. 142, p. 143, Sept. 6, 1954.

New Compounds for Transistor Research, *Electronics*, vol. 27, p. 238, March, 1954.

Philco Develops Surface Barrier Transistor, *Tele-Tech*, vol. 13, p. 87, January, 1954.

Philco's Surface Barrier Transistor, *Radio Television News*, vol. 51, p. 78, February, 1954.

Point-contact Resistor, *Electronics*, vol. 27, p. 200, March, 1954.

Premium for Purity: Silicon Transistor, *Chem. Week*, vol. 74, pp. 43–44, Jan. 30, 1954.

Rate Grown Junction Transistor Production, *Radio Television News*, vol. 52, p. 38, October, 1954.

Semiconductor Manufacture: Controlling the Infinitesimal, *Westinghouse Eng.*, vol. 14, p. 182, 1954.

Silicon Surface Barrier Transistors, *Electronics*, vol. 27, p. 194, May, 1954.

Silicon Transistor Announced, *Electronics*, vol. 27, p. 6, February, 1954.
Transistor Amplifiers, *Electronics*, vol. 27, pp. 224–227, July, 1954.
Transistor Characteristics, in Penn State University, Transistor Short Course Proceedings, 1954.
Transistorized Magnetic Microphone, *Tele-Tech*, vol. 13, p. 91, March, 1954.
Transistorized Wrist Radio, *Tele-Tech*, vol. 13, p. 79, February, 1954.
Transistors, Gossip's Nemesis? *Materials & Methods*, vol. 39, p. 302, May, 1954.
Transistors: Pass Trial by Fire and Water with New Type Crystals, *Iron Age*, vol. 173, p. 82, Mar. 18, 1954.
Transistors Simplify Telephone Plant, *Electronics*, vol. 27, p. 192, May, 1954.
Transistors; Their Use and Operation, *Engineering*, vol. 177, p. 347, Mar. 12, 1954.
Transistors Used in Receivers of Personnel Paging System, *Elec. Eng.*, vol. 73, pp. 480–481, 1954.
Will Transistors Oust Receiving Valves? *Elec. Rev.*, vol. 154, p. 38, Jan. 1, 1954.
Wireless Transistor Microphone Bows, *Electronics*, vol. 27, p. 8, August, 1954.
Zone-melting Process Provides Method for Refining Germanium, *Elec. Eng.*, vol. 73, pp. 484–485, 1954.

1955

Aronson, A. I.: A Transistorized Magnetic Tape Recorder, *Audio Eng. Soc. J.*, vol. 3, no. 4, pp. 198–201, October, 1955.
Avery, D. G., and J. B. Gunn: The Use of a Modulated Light Spot in Semiconductor Measurements, *Proc. Phys. Soc. (London)*, vol. 68B, part 11, pp. 918–921, November, 1955.
Bargellini, P. M., and M. B. Herscher: Investigations of Noise in Audio Frequency Amplifiers Using Junction Transistors, *Proc. IRE*, vol. 43, pp. 217–226, 1955.
Barlow, H. E. M.: Application of the Hall Effect in a Semiconductor to the Measurement of Power in an Electromagnetic Field, *Proc. Inst. Elec. Engrs. (London)*, vol. 102, part B, pp. 179–185, 1955; discussion, pp. 199–203.
Barlow, H. E. M.: Design of Semi-conductor Wattmeters for Power-frequency and Audio-frequency Applications, *Proc. Inst. Elec. Engrs. (London)*, vol. 102, part B, pp. 186–191, 1955; discussion, pp. 199–203.
Bentley, A. D., S. K. Ghandi, and V. P. Mathis: Simplified Transistor Test Equipment, *Tele-Tech*, vol. 14, pp. 56–57, September, 1955.
Bess, L.: Relative Influence of Majority and Minority Carriers on Excess Noise in Semiconductor Filaments, *J. Appl. Phys.*, vol. 26, pp. 1377–1381, 1955.
Beter, R. H., W. E. Bradley, R. B. Brown, and M. Rubinoff: Directly Coupled Transistor Circuits, *Electronics*, vol. 28, pp. 132–136, June, 1955.
Borel, J. P., C. Manus, and R. Mercier: Spectral Analysis of the Intensity of Fluctuations in Germanium Diodes at Low Frequencies, *Helv. Phys. Acta*, vol. 28, no. 5–6, pp. 454–458, 1955.
Borneman, E. H., R. F. Schwarz, and J. J. Stickler: Rectification Properties of Metal Semiconductor Contacts, *J. Appl. Phys.*, vol. 26, pp. 1021–1028, 1955.
Braunbeck, J., and J. Zakovsky: The Dependence of the Barrier Photo-effect on X-irradiation, *Naturwissenschaften*, vol. 42, no. 22, pp. 602–603, 1955.
Braunstein, R.: Radiative Transitions in Semiconductors, *Phys. Rev.*, vol. 99, pp. 1892–1893, 1955.
Bray, R.: Minority Carrier Extraction in Germanium, *Phys. Rev.*, vol. 100, no. 4, pp. 1047–1059, November 15, 1955.
Bree, A., D. J. Carswell, and L. E. Lyons: Photo- and Semi-conductance of Organic Crystals; Photo-effects in Tetracene and Anthracene, *Chem. Soc. J.*, pp. 1728–1733, June, 1955.
Brewer, S. T., and G. Hecht: Telephone Switching Network and Its Electronic Controls, *Bell System Tech. J.*, vol. 34, pp. 361–402, 1955.
Bridgers, H. E., and E. D. Kolb: Rate-grown Germanium Crystals for High-frequency Transistors, *J. Appl. Phys.*, vol. 26, pp. 1188–1189, 1955.
Bright, R. L.: Junction Transistors Used as Switches, *Trans. AIEE*, part 1, vol. 74, pp. 111–121, 1955.
Bright, R. L., and A. P. Kruper: Transistor Choppers for Stable D-C Amplifiers, *Electronics*, vol. 28, pp. 135–137, April, 1955.
Brophy, J. J.: Preliminary Study of the Electrical Properties of a Semiconducting Diamond, *Phys. Rev.*, vol. 99, pp. 1336–1337, 1955.
Brophy, J. J., and N. Rostoker: Hall Effect Noise, *Phys. Rev.*, vol. 100, pp. 754–756, 1955.
Brown, W. L.: Surface Potential and Surface Charge Distribution from Semiconductor Field Effect Measurements, *Phys. Rev.*, vol. 100, pp. 590–591, 1955.
Bruce, G. D., and J. C. Logue: Experimental Transistorized Calculator, *Elec. Eng.*, vol. 74, pp. 1044–1048, 1955.

Bryant, A. V.: Introduction to the Transistor, *Elec. J.*, vol. 154, p. 334, 1955.

Bryant, A. V.: Semi-conductors, *Elec. J.*, vol. 155, pp. 766–769, 933–936, 1084–1087, 1955.

Bube, R. H.: Photoconductivity of the Sulfide, Selenide, and Telluride of Zinc or Cadmium, *Proc. IRE*, vol. 43, no. 12, pp. 1836–1850, December, 1955.

Budinský, J.: Characteristic Parameters of Transistors, *Slaboproudý Obzor*, vol. 16, no. 8, pp. 403–416, 1955.

Burgess, R. E.: The A-C Admittance of Temperature-dependent Circuit Elements, *Proc. Phys. Soc. (London)*, vol. 68B, part 10, pp. 766–774, October, 1955.

Burgess, R. E.: Electrical Oscillations in Thermistors and Germanium Point-contact Rectifiers, *J. Electronics*, vol. 1, no. 3, pp. 297–302, November, 1955.

Burgess, R. E.: Reduction of Noise in Photoconductive Cells, *Brit. J. Appl. Phys.*, vol. 6, no. 11, pp. 385–387, November, 1955.

Burgess, R. E.: The Turnover Phenomenon in Thermistors and in Point-contact Germanium Rectifiers, *Proc. Phys. Soc. (London)*, vol. 68B, part 11, pp. 908–917, November, 1955.

Butler, F.: Transistor Waveform Generators, *Electronic Eng.*, vol. 27, pp. 170–173, 1955.

Butterworth, J.: Surface Recombination and the "Light-disc" Method of Measuring Bulk-lifetime in Semiconductors, *J. Electronics*, vol. 1, no. 3, pp. 293–296, November, 1955.

Campbell, E. L.: Transistorized Little Gem, *QST*, vol. 39, pp. 16–17, August, 1955.

Carswell, D. J., and L. E. Lyons: Photo- and Semi-conductance of Organic Crystals; Spectral Dependence, Quantum Efficiency, and a Relation between Semi- and Photo-effects in Anthracene, *Chem. Soc. J.*, pp. 1734–1740, June, 1955.

Chambers, R. W., and L. G. Coleman: High-voltage Transistor Power Supply, *Radio Television News*, vol. 54, pp. 76ff., October, 1955.

Chaplin, G. B. B., R. E. Hayes, and A. R. Owens: Transistor Digital Fast Multiplier with Magnetostrictive Storage, *Proc. Inst. Elec. Engrs. (London)*, vol. 102, part B, pp. 412–425, 1955.

Chase, F. H.: Junction Transistors and Diodes for Power Regulation, *Bell Labs. Record*, vol. 33, no. 9, pp. 344–349, September, 1955.

Cheng, C. C.: Neutralization and Unilateralization, *IRE Trans. on Circuit Theory*, vol. CT-2, no. 2, pp. 138–145, June, 1955.

Cheng, C. C.: Simplified Design Procedures for Tuned Transistor Amplifiers, *RCA Rev.*, vol. 16, pp. 339–359, 1955.

Chow, W. F., and A. P. Stern: Automatic Gain Control of Transistor Amplifiers, *Proc. IRE*, vol. 43, pp. 1119–1127, 1955.

Chu, G. Y.: Unilateralization of Junction-transistor Amplifiers at High Frequencies, *Proc. IRE*, vol. 43, pp. 1001–1006, 1955.

Clarke, E. N.: Nature of the Water-vapor-induced Excess Current and Grown Germanium P-N Junctions, *Phys. Rev.*, vol. 99, pp. 1899–1900, 1955.

Coale, F. S.: A Switch-detector Circuit, *IRE Trans. Microwave Theory and Tech.*, vol. MTT-3, no. 6, pp. 59–61, December, 1955.

Cocking, W. T.: Transistor Equivalent Circuits. I. Introductory Derivation of Valve Circuit, *Wireless World*, vol. 61, pp. 331–334, 1955.

Colander, R. E., and C. M. Kortman: A Transistorized FM/FM Telemetering System, *IRE Trans. on Telemetry and Remote Control*, vol. TRC-1, no. 2, pp. 20–24, May, 1955.

Cooper, B. F. C.: Bridge for Measuring Audio-frequency Transistor Parameters, *Proc. IRE*, vol. 43, pp. 796–805, 1955.

Crenshaw, R. M.: Application of Germanium Power Rectifiers, *Trans. AIEE*, part II, vol. 74, pp. 48–52, 1955.

Crenshaw, R. M.: Transistors at Work for Industry, *Elec. West*, vol. 114, pp. 71–72, April, 1955.

Cruel, R.: The Transistor and Its Operational Application in the Studio, *Tech. Hausmitt. Nordwestdent. Rundfunks.*, vol. 7, no. 5–6, pp. 89–94, 1955.

Cutler, M.: Forward Characteristic of Germanium Point Contact Rectifiers, *J. Appl. Phys.*, vol. 26, pp. 949–954, 1955.

Dacey, G. C., and I. M. Ross: Field Effect Transistor, *Bell System Tech. J.*, vol. 34, pp. 1149–1189, 1955.

Dauphinee, T. M., and E. Mooser: Apparatus for Measuring Resistivity and Hall Coefficient of Semiconductors, *Rev. Sci. Instr.*, vol. 26, pp. 660–664, 1955.

Decker, R. O.: Transistor Demodulator for Magnetic Amplifier in A-C Servo Applications, *Elec. Eng.*, vol. 74, pp. 590–592, 1955.

Deutsch, S.: Optimum Crystal Mixer Operation—the IN82 Crystal, *IRE Trans. on Broadcast and Television Receivers*, vol. BTR-1, no. 1, pp. 10–28, January, 1955.

Diemer, G., H. A. Klasens, and J. G. van Santen: Solid-state Image Intensifiers, *Philips Research Repts.*, vol. 10, no. 6, pp. 401–424, December, 1955.

Dingle, R. B.: Theory of the Infrared Absorption by Carriers in Semiconductors, *Phys. Rev.*, vol. 99, pp. 1901–1902, 1955.

Dosse, J.: "The Transistor—a New Amplifier Element" (Der Transistor—ein neues Verstärkerelement), R. Oldenbourg, München, 1955.

Douglas, R. W.: No-man's Land between Conductors and Insulators, *Elec. Rev. (London)*, vol. 156, p. 890, May 20, 1955.

Dreyfus-Alain, B.: Junction Diodes, *Onde élect.*, vol. 35, pp. 237–242, 1955.

Drouilhet, P. R., Jr.: Predictions Based on the Maximum Oscillator Frequency of a Transistor, *IRE Trans. on Circuit Theory*, vol. CT-2, no. 2, pp. 178–183, June, 1955.

Dunkuls, A., and E. Zwicker: Potential Distribution as a Function of Current in the Spherical Diode, *J. Appl. Phys.*, vol. 26, p. 779, 1955.

Ebers, J. J., and S. L. Miller: Design of Alloyed Junction Germanium Transistors for High-speed Switching, *Bell System Tech. J.*, vol. 34, pp. 761–781, 1955.

Eckess, W. S., J. E. Davenport, and K. I. Sherman: Transistor Pulse Generators, *Electronics*, vol. 28, pp. 132–133, November, 1955.

Edelman, B.: Practical Transistor Preamp, *Radio Television News*, vol. 53, pp. 39ff., May, 1955.

Ellis, S. G.: Dislocations in Germanium, *J. Appl. Phys.*, vol. 26, pp. 1140–1146, 1955.

Ettinger, G. M.: Transistor Amplifiers for Analog Computers, *Electronics*, vol. 28, pp. 119–121, July, 1955.

Ettinger, G. M.: Transistor Modulator for Flight Trainers, *Electronics*, vol. 28, pp. 126–127, September, 1955.

Ettinger, G. M.: A Voltage-controlled Attenuator, *Electronic Eng.*, vol. 27, pp. 458–459, October, 1955.

Finnegan, F.: Evaluation of Junction Diodes, *Tele-Tech*, vol. 14, pp. 76–77, 141–142, 144–146, May, 1955.

Firle, T. E., M. E. McMahon, and J. F. Roach: Recovery Time Measurements on Point-contact Germanium Diodes, *Proc. IRE*, vol. 43, pp. 603–607, 1955.

Fleming, L.: Broadcast-band Test Oscillator Using Transistors, *Radio Television News*, vol. 54, pp. 48–50, October, 1955.

Fletcher, N. H.: Self-bias Cutoff Effect in Power Transistors, *Proc. IRE*, vol. 43, p. 1669, 1955.

Fletcher, N. H.: Some Aspects of the Design of Power Transistors, *Proc. IRE*, vol. 43, pp. 551–559, 1955.

Flood, J. E.: Junction-transistor Trigger Circuits, *Wireless Eng.*, vol. 32, pp. 122–130, 1955.

Fowler, A., and P. Levesque: Optical Determination of Base Width in Grown N-P-N Silicon Crystals, *J. Appl. Phys.*, vol. 26, pp. 641–642, 1955.

Frank, H.: On the Question of the Static Rectification Characteristics of Germanium P-N Junctions, *Czechoslov. J. Phys.*, vol. 5, no. 3, pp. 389–392, August, 1955.

Frank, H., V. Snejdar, and V. Izberg: Point-contact Transistors, *Slaborproudy Obzor*, vol. 16, pp. 350–357, 1955.

Frank, L. G.: Emergency Portable Broadcast Receiver, *Radio Television News*, vol. 54, pp. 140–141, September, 1955.

Freedman, L. A., T. O. Stanley, and D. D. Homes: Experimental Automobile Receiver Employing Transistors, *Proc. IRE*, vol. 43, pp. 671–678, 1955.

Fritzsche, H.: Electrical Properties of Germanium Semiconductors at Low Temperatures, *Phys. Rev.*, vol. 99, pp. 406–419, 1955.

Furman, N. H., L. J. Sayegh, and R. N. Adams: Constant Current Sources Based on Transistors, *Anal. Chem.*, vol. 27, pp. 1423–1425, 1955.

Garner, L. E., Jr.: Universal Counter, *Radio Television News*, vol. 53, pp. 54–55ff., February, 1955.

Garreta, O.: Temperature Variation of the Punch-through Voltage of a Transistor, *Compt. rend.*, vol. 241, no. 14, pp. 857–859, October 3, 1955.

Garrett, C. G. B., and W. H. Brattain: Physical Theory of Semiconductor Surfaces, *Phys. Rev.*, vol. 99, pp. 376–387, 1955.

Germann, F., and E. Schroter: Selenium Rectifiers Controlled by Magnetic Amplifiers, *AEG Mitt.*, vol. 45, pp. 85–90, 1955.

Giacoletto, L. J.: Comparative High-frequency operation of Junction Transistors Made of Different Semiconductor Materials, *RCA Rev.*, vol. 16, pp. 34–42, 1955.

Gibson, A. F., J. W. Granville, and W. Bardsley: A Germanium Point-contact Transistor to Operate at High Ambient Temperatures, *Brit. J. Appl. Phys.*, vol. 6, pp. 251–254, 1955.

Golde, E., and W. Jentsch: Control of Rectifiers by Means of Magnetic and Electronic Amplifiers, *AEG Mitt.*, vol. 45, pp. 91–96, 1955.

Goodrich, H. C.: Transistorized Sync Separator Circuits for Television Receivers, *RCA Rev.*, vol. 16, no. 4, pp. 533–550, December, 1955.

Gorton, H. C., T. S. Shilliday, and F. K. Eggleston: High-temperature Area-type Titanium-dioxide Rectifiers, *Elec. Eng.*, vol. 74, no. 10, pp. 904–907, October, 1955.

Gossick, B. R.: Transient Behavior of Semiconductor Rectifiers, *J. Appl. Phys.*, vol. 26, pp. 1356–1365, 1955.

Gottlieb, I.: Germanium Diode Oscillator, *Radio Television News*, vol. 53, pp. 55ff., May, 1955.

Grandsen, M. M.: Ultra-pure Solids for Electronics, *Can. Chem. Process*, vol. 39, pp. 43–44, November, 1955.

Granville, J. W., W. Bardsley, and A. F. Gibson: Forming Procedures for Silicon Point-contact Transistors, *Brit. J. Appl. Phys.*, vol. 6, pp. 206–210, 1955.

Greatbatch, W., and W. Hirtreiter: Germanium Transistor Amplifiers Stable to 95°C, *Proc. IRE*, vol. 43, no. 12, p. 1974, December, 1955.

Groendijk, H., and K. S. Knol: Characterization of the Noise of Tubes and Transistors by Four Measurable Quantities, *Tijschr. Ned. Radiogenoot.*, vol. 20, no. 4, pp. 243–256, July, 1955.

Grosvalet, J.: A Method of Measuring the Surface Recombination Velocity of Semiconductors Using the Photomagnetoelectric Effect in the Sinusoidal Regime, *Ann. radioélec.*, vol. 10, pp. 344–347, October, 1955.

Guggenbühl, W.: Contributions to the Knowledge of Semiconductor Noise, with Particular Reference to Crystal Diodes and Transistors, Dissertation E. T. H. Zurich, no. 2515, 1955.

Guggenbühl, W., and M. J. O. Strutt: Experimental Investigation and Separation of the Noise Sources in Junction Transistors, *Arch. Elekt. Ubertragung*, vol. 9, no. 6, pp. 259–269, June, 1955.

Guggenbühl, W., and M. J. O. Strutt: Experimental Verification of the Schottky Noise Formulae with Recent Semiconductor Junction Diodes in the Region of the White Noise Spectrum, *Arch. Elekt. Ubertragung*, vol. 9, pp. 103–108, 1955.

Guggenbühl, W., and M. J. O. Strutt: Measurements of the Spontaneous Fluctuations in Currents with Various Carriers in Semiconductor Barrier Layers, *Helv. Phys. Acta*, vol. 28, no. 7, pp. 694–704, 1955.

Gummel, H., and M. Lax: Thermal Ionization and Capture of Electrons Trapped in Semiconductors, *Phys. Rev.*, vol. 97, pp. 1469–1470, 1955.

Hanningsberg, C.: Low Power Transistor Amplifier, *Onde élect.*, vol. 35, pp. 264–277, 1955.

Hanson, G. H.: Shot Noise in P-N-P Transistors, *J. Appl. Phys.*, vol. 26, pp. 1388–1389, 1955.

Heckelsberg, L. F., G. C. Bailey, and A. Clark: Determination of N- or P-type Conductivity by the Effect Produced by Hydrogen Adsorption on Electrical Conductivity, *J. Am. Chem. Soc.*, vol. 77, pp. 1373–1374, 1955.

Henle, R. A.: Multistable Transistor Circuit, *Elec. Eng.*, vol. 74, pp. 570–572, 1955.

Henry, R. M.: Point-contact Germanium Crystal Diodes, *Rev. tech. C.F.T.H.*, no. 20, pp. 49–59, September, 1955.

Herlet, A., and E. Spenke: Rectifiers with the P-I-N and P-S-N Structure under D. C. Loading, *Z. angew. Physik*, vol. 7, pp. 99–107, 149–163, 195–212, 1955.

Herold, E. W.: Semiconductors and the Transistor, *J. Franklin Inst.*, vol. 259, pp. 87–106, 1955.

Herring, C.: Transpost Properties of a Many-valley Semiconductor, *Bell System Tech. J.*, vol. 34, pp. 237–290, 1955.

Hill, R. S.: Point-contact Transistor Test Set, *Elec. Eng.*, vol. 74, pp. 59–62, 1955.

Hillbourne, R. A.: Measurement and Display of the Current Gain of a Transistor as a Function of the Emitter Current, *J. Sci. Instr.*, vol. 32, pp. 83–85, 1955.

Hillbourne, R. A., and D. D. Jones: Transistor Power Amplifiers, *Proc. Inst. Elec. Engrs. (London)*, vol. 102, part B, pp. 763–774, 1955; discussion, pp. 786–792.

Hollmann, H.: Transistor Receivers and Transmitters Which Operate Directly from Free Power Radiated by Broadcast Stations, *Aviation Week*, vol. 63, p. 95, Sept. 19, 1955.

Hollmann, H. E.: Transistors and Electronic Valves, *Elektron. Rundschau*, vol. 9, no. 8, pp. 277–282, August, 1955.

Holmes, D. D., T. O. Stanley, and L. A. Freedman: Developmental Pocket-size Broadcast Receiver Employing Transistors, *Proc. IRE*, vol. 43, pp. 662–670, 1955.

Holonyak, N., Jr.: Observation of Circular Patterns in the Vicinity of Small-area Alloyed Germanium P-N Junctions, *J. Appl. Phys.*, vol. 26, pp. 121–123, 1955.

Holonyak, N., Jr., and H. Letaw: Sparked Hydrogen Treatment of Germanium Surfaces, *J. Appl. Phys.*, vol. 26, p. 355, 1955.

Holt, A. W.: Diode Amplifier, *Radio Television News* (Radio-Electronic Engineering Section), vol. 53, pp. 18ff., January, 1955.

Hupert, J. J., and T. Szubski: Transistorized F-M Signal Generator, *Electronics*, vol. 28, pp. 133–135, February, 1955.

Hurley, E. B.: Predictable Design of Transistor Amplifiers, *Tele-Tech*, vol. 14, pp. 74–75, August, 1955.

Isaacson, G. O.: Selenium Rectifiers for High-temperature Operation, *Trans. AIEE*, part I. vol. 74, pp. 552–557, 1955.

Jackson, W. D.: Transistor Electronics, *J. Inst. Elec. Engrs. (London)*, vol. 1, pp. 306–307, May, 1955.

Joiner, H. R., and D. R. Woodward: A High-speed Decade Counter Using Germanium Diodes in the Feedback Loops, *Electronic Eng.*, vol. 27, pp. 404–405, September, 1955.

Jones, D. V.: Junction Transistor Test Set, *Radio Television News* (Radio-Electronic Engineering Section), vol. 24, pp. 7ff., March, 1955.

Kabell, L. J., and W. E. Evans: A Transistor Subcarrier Generator for Color Receivers, *IRE Trans. on Broadcast and Television Receivers*, vol. BTR-1, no. 3, pp. 9–13, July, 1955.

Kasai, T.: Improved Instantaneous Compandors Using Metal Rectifiers, *J. Inst. Elect. Commun. Engrs. (Japan)*, vol. 38, no. 8, pp. 602–607, August, 1955.

Kazan, B., and F. H. Nicoll: An Electroluminescent Light-amplifying Picture Panel, *Proc. IRE*, vol. 43, no. 12, pp. 1888–1897, December, 1955.

Kellermann, A.: Barrier-layer Photocells, II, *Arch. tech. Messen*, no. 229, pp. 45–48, February, 1955.

Keonjian, E.: Stable Transistor Oscillator, *Elec. Eng.*, vol. 74, pp. 672–675, 1955.

Keonjian, E., and J. J. Suran: Transistors Generate Multiwaveforms, *Electronics*, vol. 28, pp. 138–139, July, 1955.

Kidd, M. C., W. Hasenberg, and W. M. Webster: Delayed Collector Conduction, a New Effect in Junction Transistors, *RCA Rev.*, vol. 16, pp. 16–33, 1955.

Kikuchi, M., and Y. Tarui: "Step" and "Oscillation" Phenomena in the Collector of A-Type Transistors, *Phys. Soc. Japan J.*, vol. 10, p. 722, 1955.

Kingston, R. H., and S. F. Neustadter: Calculation of the Space Charge, Electric Field, and Free Carrier Concentration at the Surface of a Semiconductor, *J. Appl. Phys.*, vol. 26, pp. 718–720, 1955.

Kinman, T. H., G. A. Carrick, R. G. Hibberd, and A. J. Blundell: Germanium and Silicon Power Rectifiers, *Proc. IRE*, vol. 103A, paper 1936U, pp. 89–112, October, 1955.

Klass, P. J.: Old Idea Used to Cool New Transistors, *Aviation Week*, vol. 62, pp. 33ff., May 23, 1955.

Klass, P. J.: Trend to Transistors Seen Slowed by Military Procurement Policies, *Aviation Week*, vol. 63, pp. 36ff., Aug. 1, 1955.

Klass, P. J.: Vacuum Tubes Face Fast-rising Thread; Transistors Replacing Tubes in Avionic Equipment, *Aviation Week*, vol. 63, pp. 50ff., July 25, 1955.

Knorr, P., and J. Strubbe: Selenium Rectifier Installations, *AEG Mitt.*, vol. 45, no. 5–6, pp. 269–280, May–June, 1955.

Knott, R. D., and J. I. Missen: The EW54 Germanium Junction Rectifier, *G.E.C. Journal*, vol. 22, no. 4, pp. 197–208, October, 1955.

Koch, P.: Some Applications of the Nonlinear Characteristic of Germanium Crystal Diodes, *Bull. assoc. suisse élec.*, vol. 46, pp. 361–372, Apr. 16, 1955.

Kohn, G.: Considerations on the Transition between the Forward and Reverse Bias Regions in the Equivalent Circuit for Slow Germanium Diodes, *Arch. Elekt. Übertragung*, vol. 9, pp. 241–245, 1955.

Kohn, W., and D. Schechter: Theory of Acceptor Levels in Germanium, *Phys. Rev.*, vol. 99, pp. 1903–1904, 1955.

Krenitsky, P.: Decade Counter Employs Silicon Transistors, *Electronics*, vol. 28, pp. 112–113, August, 1955.

Lammers, H. H.: The Type V-79 Light-weight Programme-input Amplifiers Equipped with Transistors, *Tech. Hausmitt. Nordwest-deut. Rundfunks.*, vol. 7, no. 5–6, pp. 94–100, 1955.

Lampert, M. A.: Ground State of Impurity Atoms in Semiconductors Having Anisotropic Energy Surfaces, *Phys. Rev.*, vol. 97, pp. 352–353, 1955.

Laplume, J.: Influence of Polarizing Current on the Operation of Direct Detector Crystals, *Rev. tech. C.F.T.H.*, no. 20, pp. 87–109, September, 1955.

Laplume, J.: Reverse Saturation Current in Semiconductor Diodes, *Rev. tech. C.F.T.H.*, no. 20, pp. 111–122, September, 1955.

Law, J. T., and P. S. Meigs: Effect of Water Vapor on Grown Germanium and Silicon N-P Junction Units, *J. Appl. Phys.*, vol. 26, pp. 1265–1273, 1955.

Lax, B., and L. M. Roth: Propagation and Plasma Oscillation in Semi-conductors with Magnetic Fields, *Phys. Rev.*, vol. 98, pp. 548–549, 1955.

Lederhandler, S. R., and L. J. Giacoletto: Measurement of Minority Carrier Lifetime and Surface Effects in Junction Devices, *Proc. IRE*, vol. 43, pp. 477–483, 1955.

Ledig, G.: Linear Characteristics of the Transistor, *Fernmeldetech. Z.*, vol. 8, pp. 221–228, 1955.

Ledig, G.: Tensor Analysis of Transistor Feedback Circuits, *Arch. Elekt. Ubertragung*, vol. 9, pp. 162–167, 1955.

Lees, J., and S. Walton: The Influence of Pressure on Metal-Germanium Contacts, *Proc. Phys. Soc. (London)*, vol. 68B, part 11, pp. 922–928, November, 1955.

Lees, J., and S. Walton: Surface States on Germanium, *Proc. Phys. Soc. (London)*, vol. 68B, part 12, pp. 1152–1153, December, 1955.

Light, L. H.: Transistor Power Supplies; Circuits for Obtaining H.T. and E.H.T. from Low-voltage Sources, *Wireless World*, vol. 61, no. 12, pp. 582–586, December, 1955.

Light, L. H., and F. H. Hooker: Transistor D. C. Convertors, *Proc. IRE*, vol. 102, part B, pp. 775–786, 1955; discussion, pp. 786–792.

Linvill, J. G.: Nonsaturating Pulse Circuits Using Two Junction Transistors, *Proc. IRE*, vol. 43, pp. 826–834, 1955.

Linvill, J. G., and R. H. Mattson: Junction Transistor Blocking Oscillators, *Proc. IRE*, vol. 43, pp. 1632–1639, 1955.

Loeb, H. W., and N. W. Morgalla: Displayed Transistor Characteristics, *A.T.E.J.*, vol. 11, pp. 38–48, January, 1955.

Loebner, E. E.: Opto-electronic Devices and Networks, *Proc. IRE*, vol. 43, no. 12, pp. 1897–1906, December, 1955.

McKelvey, J. P., and R. L. Longini: Recombination of Injected Carriers at Dislocation Edges in Semiconductors, *Phys. Rev.*, vol. 99, pp. 1227–1232, 1955.

Majewski, Z.: Germanium and Silicon, *Przeglad Elektrotech.*, vol. 31, no. 10–11, pp. 717–728, 1955.

Mallery, P.: Transistors in the 4A Crossbar System, *Bell Labs. Record*, vol. 33, no. 6 pp. 215–219, June, 1955.

Manfrino, R.: Surface Preparation and Resistivity Measurement on Semiconductor Crystals, *Alta frequenza*, vol. 24, no. 4–5, pp. 390–420, August–October, 1955.

Many, A., E. Harnik, and D. Gerlich: Semiconductivity of Crystalline Aromatic Substances, *J. Chem. Phys.*, vol. 23, pp. 1733–1734, 1955.

Maple, T. G., L. Bess, and H. A. Gebbie: Variation of Noise with Ambient in Germanium Filaments, *J. Appl. Phys.*, vol. 26, pp. 490–491, 1955.

Meinke, H., and A. Rihaczek: Crystal Diodes in Voltage Dividers, with Particular Reference to the Linearization and Steepening of Static and Dynamic Characteristics. *Fernmeldetech. Z.*, vol. 8, pp. 272–276, 1955.

Millar, B.: Transistor Circuit Analysis, *Wireless Eng.*, vol. 32, p. 196, 1955.

Miller, L. E., and J. H. Forster: Accelerated Power Aging with Lithium-doped Point Contact Transistors, *IRE Trans. on Electron Devices*, vol. ED-2, no. 3, pp. 4–6, July, 1955.

Miller, S. L.: Avalanche Breakdown in Germanium, *Phys. Rev.*, vol. 99, pp. 1234–1241, 1955.

Miller, S. L., and J. J. Ebers: Alloyed Junction Avalanche Transistors, *Bell System Tech. J.*, vol. 34, pp. 883–902, 1955.

Milnes, A. G.: Phase-locking of Switching-transistor Converters for Polyphase Power Supplies, *Trans. AIEE*, part I, vol. 74, pp. 587–592, 1955.

Misawa, T.: Diffusion Capacitances and High-injection Level Operation of Junction Transistor, *Proc. IRE*, vol. 43, pp. 749–750, 1955.

Moll, J. L.: Junction Transistor Electronics, *Proc. IRE*, vol. 43, no. 12, pp. 1807–1819, December, 1955.

Moore, A. R., and W. M. Webster: Effective Surface Recombination of a Germanium Surface with a Floating Barrier, *Proc. IRE*, vol. 43, pp. 427–435, 1955.

Moss, T. S.: Lead Salt Photoconductors, *Proc. IRE*, vol. 43, no. 12, pp. 1869–1881, December, 1955.

Moss, T. S.: Measurements on P-N Junctions in Lead Sulphide, *Proc. Phys. Soc. (London)*, vol. 68B, part 10, pp. 697–700, October, 1955.

Moulon, J. M.: Basic Properties of Transistors, *Onde élect.*, vol. 35, pp. 243–263, 1955.

Muss, D. R.: Capacitance Measurements on Alloyed Indium-Germanium Junction Diodes, *J. Appl. Phys.*, vol. 26, pp. 1514–1517, 1955.

Nicoll, G. R.: Noise in Silicon Microwave Diodes, *Proc. Inst. Elec. Engrs. (London)*, vol. 101, part 3, pp. 317–324, 1954; discussion, vol. 102, part B, pp. 786–792, 1955.

Nishizawa, J.: Silicon Wide P-N Junction, *Rept. Research Inst. Elec. Commun.*, *Tôhoku Univ.*, vol. 6B, no. 3–4, pp. 183–215, 1955.

Nussbaum, A.: Electrical Characteristics of Power Transistors, *Proc. IRE*, vol. 43, pp. 315–322, 1955.

Oatley, C. W.: Electrical Conduction in Non-metallic Solids, *Proc. Inst. Elec. Engrs. (London)*, vol. 102, part B, pp. 7–10, 1955.

Packham, B. E.: Transistorized Control Unit, *QST*, vol. 39, pp. 32ff., November, 1955.

Palombo, P.: Solid-state Electronics—Transistors, *Elettrotecnica*, vol. 42, no. 11, pp. 590–597, November 10–25, 1955.

Pankove, J. I.: Methods for Revealing P-N Junctions and Inhomogeneities in Germanium Crystals, *RCA Rev.*, vol. 16, pp. 398–402, 1955.

Pearlman, A. R.: Some Properties and Circuit Applications of Superalpha Composite Transistors, *IRE Trans. on Electron Devices*, vol. ED-2, no. 1, pp. 25–43, January, 1955.

Pearson, G. L., and W. H. Brattain: History of Semiconductor Research, *Proc. IRE*, vol. 43, no. 12, pp. 1794–1806, December, 1955.

Pederson, D. O.: Regeneration Analysis of Junction Transistor Multivibrators, *IRE Trans. on Circuit Theory*, vol. CT-2, no. 2, pp. 171–178, June, 1955.

Pell, E. M.: Reverse Current and Carrier Lifetime as a Function of Temperature in Germanium Junction Diodes, *J. Appl. Phys.*, vol. 26, pp. 658–665, 1955.

Penfield, P., Jr.: Transistorized Headlight Dimmer, *Radio Television News*, vol. 54, pp. 56–57, August, 1955.

Penn, W. D.: Simplified Transistor Circuit Equations, *Tele-Tech*, vol. 14, no. 12, pp. 76–77, 149, 151, 153, 155, December, 1955.

Piatti, L.: Technological Processes for the Production of Transistors and Their Influence on the Properties of the Transistors, *Convegno di elettronica e televisione*, vol. 2, pp. 645–666, 1954, suppl. to *Ricerca sci.*, vol. 24, 1954.

Pistoulet, B.: Oscillographic Display of Transistor Characteristics and Measurement of Their Noise Factor, *Rev. tech. C.F.T.H.*, no. 20, pp. 123–134, September, 1955.

Pittman, G. F., Jr.: High-accuracy Static Time-delay Device Utilizing Transistors, *Elec. Eng.*, vol. 74, pp. 498–501, 1955.

Poganski, S.: Low-capacitance Selenium Rectifiers, *AEG Mitt.*, vol. 45, pp. 257–260, 1955.

Pound, G. M., and G. Derge: New Approach to Liquid Structure; Semiconduction in Liquids May Provide New Metallurgical Processes, *Chem. Eng. News*, vol. 33, pp. 1292ff., 1955.

Prince, M. B.: High-frequency Silicon-Aluminium Alloy Junction Diodes, *IRE Trans. on Electron Devices*, vol. ED-2, no. 4, pp. 8–9, October, 1955.

Pritchard, R. L.: Effect of Base-contact Overlap and Parasitic Capacities on Small-signal Parameters of Junction Transistors, *Proc. IRE*, vol. 43, pp. 38–40, 1955.

Pritchard, R. L.: Frequency Response of Theoretical Models of Junction Transistors, *IRE Trans. on Circuit Theory*, vol. CT-2, no. 2, pp. 183–191, June, 1955.

Pritchard, R. L.: High-frequency Power Gain of Junction Transistors, *Proc. IRE*, vol. 43, pp. 1075–1085, 1955.

Prugh, T. A.: Junction Transistor Switching Circuits, *Electronics*, vol. 28, pp. 168–171, January, 1955.

Pucel, R. A.: Design Considerations of Junction Transistors at Higher Frequencies, *Proc. IRE*, vol. 43, no. 7, pp. 878–879, July, 1955.

Reeves, A. H., and R. B. W. Cooke: Germanium Positive-gap Diode; New Tool for Pulse Techniques, *Elec. Commun.*, vol. 32, pp. 112–117, 1955.

Reiss, H., and C. S. Fuller: Ionization and Solubility in Semiconductors, *Phys. Rev.*, vol. 97, pp. 559–560, 1955.

Riddle, R. L.: High Fidelity Transistor Power Amplifier, *Electronics*, vol. 28, pp. 174ff., September, 1955.

Robberson, E.: Make Ready for Transistors, *Radio Television News*, vol. 53, pp. 40ff., April, 1955.

Rose, A.: Performance of Photoconductors, *Proc. IRE*, vol. 43, no. 12, pp. 1850–1869, December, 1955.

Rose, A.: Recombination Processes in Insulators and Semiconductors, *Phys. Rev.*, vol. 97, pp. 322–333, 1727, 1955.

Ross, I. M.: The Field-effect Transistor, *Bell Labs. Record*, vol. 33, pp. 167–172, 1955.

Ross, I. M.: Field-effect Transistor Raises Semiconductor Frequency Range, *Aviation Week*, vol. 62, pp. 50–51, June 27, 1955.

Royer, G. H.: A Switching Transistor D. C. to A. C. Convertor Having an Output Frequency Proportional to the D. C. Input Voltage, *Trans. AIEE*, part I, vol. 74, pp. 322–326, 1955.

Rubin, L. G., and W. D. Straub: High-voltage Silicon Diodes, *Proc. IRE*, vol. 43, p. 490, 1955.

Rugare, A. S.: Germanium and Silicon for Electronic Devices, *Metal Progr.*, vol. 67, pp. 87–91, February, 1955.

Rutz, R. F.: Two-emitter Transistor with a High Adjustable Alpha, *Proc. IRE*, vol. 43, pp. 834–837, 1955.

Sakai, Y., T. Mitsuzuka, and S. Kitajima: Conduction and Its Stability in Copper Oxide, *J. Inst. Elec. Engrs. (Japan)*, vol. 75, pp. 459–464, May, 1955.

Sassier, M.: Germanium Power Rectifiers, *Rev. tech. C.F.T.H.*, no. 20, pp. 75–85, September, 1955.

Sato, A.: A New Bridge Method for Transistor Parameters, *J. Inst. Elec. Commun. Engrs. Japan*, vol. 38, pp. 182–188, March, 1955.

Schaefer, D. H.: A Static Magnetic Transistor Analogue Divider, *Trans. AIEE*, part I, vol. 74, pp. 652–655, 1955.

Schaffner, J. S.: Variation of Junction Transistor Parameters, *Tele-Tech*, vol. 14, pp. 64ff., January, 1955.

Schaffner, J. S., and R. F. Shea: Variation of the Forward Characteristics of Junction Diodes with Temperature, *Proc. IRE*, vol. 43, p. 101, 1955.

Schmidt, G.: Photoeffects in Semiconductors, *Nachrichtentechnik*, vol. 5, no. 10, pp. 468–470, October, 1955.

Schrieffer, J. R.: Effective Carrier Mobility in Surface-space Charge Layers, *Phys. Rev.*, vol. 97, pp. 641–646, 1955.

Schuegraf, K.: Junction Transistors of the OC100 Series, *SEG Nachr.*, vol. 3, no. 1, pp. 45–48, 1955.

Sheehan, W. E., and J. H. Ivers: Design of Transistorized High-gain Portable, *Electronics*, vol. 28, pp. 159–161, March, 1955.

Sherr, S., and T. Kwap: Stabilizing Transistors against Temperature Variations, *Tele-Tech*, vol. 14, pp. 74–76, 145–146, March, 1955.

Shibuya, M.: Hot Electron Problem in Semiconductors with Spheroidal Energy Surfaces, *Phys. Rev.*, vol. 99, pp. 1189–1191, 1955.

Shields, J.: Silicon Alloy Junction Diodes for Power Supply Application, *Engineer*, vol. 199, pp. 801–803, June 10, 1955.

Shive, J. N., and P. Zuk: Junction Phototransistors, *Bell Labs. Record*, vol. 33, no. 12, pp. 445–449, December, 1955.

Shockley, W.: Transistor Physics, *Elec. J.*, vol. 154, p. 1383, 1955; *Elec. Rev. (London)*, vol. 156, p. 737, 1955.

Shotov, A. P.: The Breakdown of P-N Junctions in Ge at the Collision (Avalanche) Voltage, *Zhur. Tekh. Fiz.*, vol. 26, no. 8, pp. 1634–1645, 1955.

Shulman, R. G., J. M. Mays, and D. W. McCall: Nuclear Magnetic Resonance in Semiconductors; Exchange Broadening in InSb and GaSb, *Phys. Rev.*, vol. 100, pp. 692–699, 1955.

Skalicky, M.: The Equations and Equivalent Circuit of the Transistor, *Elektrotech. u. Maschinenbau*, vol. 72, no. 17, pp. 422–423, September 1, 1955.

Skipper, R. E.: Transistor Operating Points, *Tele-Tech*, vol. 14, pp. 104–105, 174, 176, 178, 182, June, 1955.

Slaughter, D. W.: Feedback-stabilized Transistor Amplifier, *Electronics*, vol. 28, pp. 174–175, May, 1955.

Smith, D. H.: Suitability of the Silicon Alloy Junction Diode as a Reference Standard in Regulated Metallic Rectifier Circuits (abstract), *Elec. Eng.*, vol. 74, p. 43, 1955.

Smith, K. D.: Grown Junction Transistor Development, *Bell Labs. Record*, vol. 33, no. 10, pp. 374–378, October, 1955.

Soldi, M., and M. Valeriani: Transistor Circuit for Multiplying Q-Factor, *Alta frequenza*, vol. 24, no. 4–5, pp. 375–389, August–October, 1955.

Somos, I.: Special Properties of Selenium Rectifiers, *Elektrotechnika*, vol. 48, no. 8, pp. 229–239, August, 1955.

Spitzer, W. G., and H. Y. Fan: Infrared Absorption in Indium Antimonide, *Phys. Rev.*, vol. 99, no. 6, pp. 1893–1894, September, 15, 1955.

Spitzer, W. G., T. E. Firle, M. Cutler, R. G. Shulman, and M. Becker: Measurement of the Lifetime of Minority Carriers in Germanium, *J. Appl. Phys.*, vol. 26, pp. 414–417, 1955.

Statz, H., E. A. Guillemin, and R. A. Pucel: Design Considerations of Junction Transistors at Higher Frequencies, *Proc. IRE*, vol. 42, pp. 1620–1628, 1954; discussion, vol. 43, pp. 878–879, 1955.

Stephenson, W. L.: Measurements of Junction-transistor Noise in the Frequency Range 7–50 kc/s, *Proc. Inst. Elec. Engrs. (London)*, vol. 102, part B, pp. 753–756, 1955; discussion, pp. 786–792.

Stern, A. P., C. A. Aldridge, and W. F. Chow: Internal Feedback and Neutralization of Transistor Amplifiers, *Proc. IRE*, vol. 43, pp. 838–847, 1955.

Stevenson, D. T., and R. J. Keyes: Measurement of Carrier Lifetimes in Germanium and Silicon, *J. Appl. Phys.*, vol. 26, pp. 190–195, 1955.

Stone, E. F.: Chemical Aspects of Semi-conductors, *Chem. Ind.*, pp. 561–562, May 14, 1955.

Stripp, K. F., and A. R. Moore: Effects of Junction Shape and Surface Combination on Transistor Current Gain, *Proc. IRE*, vol. 43, pp. 856–866, 1955.

Strosche, H.: On the Action of Cadmium Selenide Layers in the Selenium Rectifier, *Z. Physik*, vol. 140, no. 4, pp. 409–413, 1955.

Suits, C. G.: Improved Transistors Can Be Used in High Frequency Applications, *Elec. Eng.*, vol. 74, p. 633, 1955.

Suran, J. J.: Double Base Expands Diode Applications, *Electronics*, vol. 28, pp. 198–202, March, 1955.

Suran, J. J.: Low-frequency Circuit Theory of the Double-base Diode, *IRE Trans. on Electron Devices*, vol. ED-2, no. 2, pp. 40–48, April, 1955.

Suran, J. J., and E. Keonjian: Semiconductor Diode Multivibrator, *Proc. IRE*, vol. 43, pp. 814–820, 1955.

Swanson, J. A.: Saturation Hall Constant of Semiconductors, *Phys. Rev.*, vol. 99, pp. 1799–1807, 1955.

Tanenbaum, M., L. B. Valdes, E. Buehler, and N. B. Hannay: Silicon N-P-N Grown Junction Transistors, *J. Appl. Phys.* vol. 26, pp. 686–692, 1955.

Taylor, J. W., Jr., and T. M. Moore: Transistor C-R Tube Deflection Circuit, *Electronics*, vol. 28, pp. 146–149, July, 1955.

Tiffany, G. B., and N. O. Sokal: Transistorized Light-beam Audio Transmitter, *Radio Television News*, vol. 53, pp. 35–37, June, 1955.

Tolpygo, K. B., and I. G. Zaslavskaya: Ambipolar Diffusion in Semiconductors at Large Currents, *Zhur. Tekh. Fiz.*, vol. 25, no. 6, pp. 955–977, 1955.

Treacy, J. B.: Automatic Flight Control; Transistors, *SAE Jour.*, vol. 63, p. 96, April, 1955.

Turner, R. P.: Survey of Power Transistor Currently Available, *Tele-Tech*, vol. 14, p. 112, June, 1955.

Turner, R. P.: Transistor Dip Oscillator, *Radio Television News*, vol. 54, p. 51, July, 1955.

Tweet, A. G.: Electrical Properties of Plastically Deformed Germanium, *Phys. Rev.*, vol. 99, pp. 1245–1248, 1955.

Uchrin, G. C., and W. O. Taylor: New Self-excited Square-wave Transistor Power Oscillator, *Proc. IRE*, vol. 43, p. 99, 1955.

Uhlir, A., Jr.: Potentials of Infinite Systems of Sources and Numerical Solutions of Problems in Semiconductor Engineering, *Bell System Tech. J.*, vol. 34, pp. 105–128, 994, 1955.

Van Allen, R. L.: Four-quadrant Multiplication with Transistors and Magnetic Cores, *Trans. AIEE*, part I, vol. 74, pp. 643–648, 1955.

van der Ziel, A.: Theory of Shot Noise in Junction Diodes and Junction Transistors, *Proc. IRE*, vol. 43, pp. 1639–1646, 1955.

van Roosbroeck, W.: Injected Current Carrier Transport in a Semi-infinite Semiconductor and the Determination of Lifetimes and Surface Recombination Velocities, *J. Appl. Phys.*, vol. 26, pp. 380–391, 1955.

Vasseur, J. P.: Principles of Transistor Circuits, *Ann. radioélec.*, vol. 10, pp. 99–162, April, 1955.

Vavilov, V. S.: Semiconductor Converters of Radiant Energy, *Uspekhi Fiz. Nauk*, vol. 56, no. 1, pp. 111–130, 1955.

Volkers, W. K., and N. E. Pedersen: The "Hushed" Transistor Amplifier, I, *Tele-Tech*, vol. 14, no. 12, pp. 82–84, 156–158, December, 1955.

Waddell, J. M., S. E. Mayer, and S. Kaye: A Germanium Diffused-junction Photo-electric Cell, *Proc. Inst. Elec. Engrs. (London)*, vol. 102B, paper 1860R, pp. 757–762, 786–792, May, 1955.

Wallace, R. L.: Junction Tetrode Transistor, *Bell Labs. Record*, vol. 33, pp. 121–124, 1955.

Waltz, M. C.: Electrical Contacts for Transistors and Diodes, *Bell Labs. Record*, vol. 33, no. 7, pp. 260–263, July, 1955.

Wanlass, C. L.: Transistor Circuitry for Digital Computers, *IRE Trans. on Electronic Computers*, vol. EC-4, no. 1, pp. 11–16, March, 1955.

Webster, R. R.: How to Design I-F Transistor Transformers; Reference Sheet, *Electronics*, vol. 28, pp. 156–158, August, 1955; p. 399, October, 1955.

Webster, W. M.: Saturation Current in Alloy Junctions, *Proc. IRE*, vol. 43, pp. 277–280, 1955.

Welker, H.: New Materials with Large Hall-effect and Large Resistance-change in a Magnetic Field, *Elektrotech. Z.*, vol. 76A, pp. 513–517, 1955.

White, A. G.: Transistor as a Thermometer, *J. Sci. Instr.*, vol. 32, pp. 451–452, 1955.

Wiesner, R., and E. Groschwitz: Temperature Dependence of Photocurrents in P-N Junctions, *Z. angew. Phys.*, vol. 7, no. 10, pp. 496–499, October, 1955.

Williams, C. E.: Transistor Amplifier Performance, *Electronics*, vol. 28, pp. 196ff., February, 1955.

Wilson, D. K.: Semiconductor Diodes, *Bell Labs. Record*, vol. 33, no. 6, pp. 227–231, June, 1955.

Woods, L. J.: Surface-barrier Transistor Makes Small Computer Possible, *Elec. Eng.*, vol. 74, pp. 555–556, 1955.

Wulfsberg, C. N.: Zener-voltage Breakdown Uses in Silicon Diodes, *Electronics*, vol. 28, pp. 182ff., December, 1955.

Yamaguchi, J.: Zinc Oxide Rectifiers, *J. Inst. Elec. Engrs. (Japan)*, vol. 1, no. 2, pp. 67–68, June, 1955.

Zawels, J.: Natural Equivalent Circuit of Junction Transistors, *RCA Rev.*, vol. 16, pp. 360–378, 1955.

Air-actuated Machine Makes Catwhiskers for Germanium Wafers, *Electronics*, vol. 28, pp. 210ff., August, 1955.
All-transistor Automobile Receiver, *Radio Television News*, vol. 54, p. 50, July, 1955, *Mech. Eng.*, vol. 77, pp. 603–604, 1955.
All-transistor Calculator, *Mech. Eng.*, vol. 77, pp. 38–39, 1955.
Bell Telephone Laboratories Develops All-transistor Computer for Air Force, *Elec. Eng.*, vol. 74, pp. 447–448, 1955.
Experimental Transistors Are Assembled by Robot Device, *Elec. Eng.*, vol. 74, p. 361, 1955.
Finder Accelerates Tetrode Transistor Production, *Electronics*, vol. 28, pp. 12ff., March, 1955.
Future of Vacuum Tubes and Transistors, *Product Eng.*, vol. 26, pp. 12–15, mid-October, 1955.
General Electric High-frequency Germanium Point-contact Transistor, *Engineer*, vol. 199, pp. 680–681, May 13, 1955.
High-power Transistor, *Mech. Eng.*, vol. 77, p. 433, 1955.
Higher Power Transistors May Replace Dynamotors, *Machine Design*, vol. 27, pp. 12ff., May, 1955.
Improved Transistors, *J. Franklin Inst.*, vol. 260, p. 106, 1955.
Improved Transistors Announced by G. E., *Radio Television News*, vol. 54, p. 112, August, 1955.
Japanese Transistor Broadcast Receiver, *Electronics*, vol. 28, p. 174, December, 1955.
Koldweld Process Seals Semiconductor Parts; G.E.C. Ltd. of England, *Iron Age*, vol. 176, pp. 137–138, Oct. 20, 1955.
Liquid Semiconductor, *Mech. Eng.*, vol. 77, p. 343, 1955.
Machine to Produce Transistors; Mr. Meticulous, *J. Franklin Inst.*, vol. 259, p. 334, 1955.
Magnistors Promise to Supplant Transistors, *Electronics*, vol. 28, pp. 10ff., May, 1955.
Manufacture of Germanium Power Diodes, *Elec. Commun.*, vol. 32, pp. 146–164, 1955.
Manufacturers Plug New Computer Models, *Electronics*, vol. 28, pp. 12ff., April, 1955.
Mysteries of Electricity Deepen as Science Uncovers New Behaviors, *Product Eng.*, vol. 26, pp. 163–166, January, 1955.
New Avionic Diode Simplifies Design, *Aviation Week*, vol. 62, pp. 82ff., Apr. 25, 1955.
New Hearts for Transistors, *Chem. Eng. News*, vol. 33, pp. 2499–2500, June 13, 1955.
New Transistor Performs at Record-high Frequencies, *J. Franklin Inst.*, vol. 260, p. 445, 1955.
New Transistor Radio Hits Market, *Electronics*, vol. 28, pp. 7–8, June, 1955.
New Triumphs Are Chalked Up by the Transistor, *Business Week*, p. 192, Nov. 12, 1955.
1955 Transistor Specification Chart, *Tele-Tech*, vol. 14, sec. 2, pp. 1ff., September, 1955.
Philco Announces Transistor Computer, *Tele-Tech*, vol. 14, p. 16, May, 1955.
Philco Develops Transistor Circuitry, *Elec. World*, new edition, vol. 143, pp. 56ff., Mar. 28, 1955.
Physics of Transistors, *Engineering*, vol. 179, p. 628, 1955.
Research on Semiconductors: 2d International Conference, Amsterdam, *Science*, vol. 121, pp. 718–719, 1955.
Semi-conductor Devices, *Elec. Rev. (London)*, vol. 156, p. 846, 1955; discussion, pp. 889–890.
Simple Explanation of Transistor "h" Parameters, *Mullard Tech. Commun.*, vol. 2, pp. 58–63, July, 1955.
They Save Space, Weight, Heat, *Business Week*, p. 108, Sept. 17, 1955.
Transistor Code Practice Oscillator, *Radio Television News*, vol. 54, p. 147, November, 1955.
Transistor Portables Boost Output, *Electronics*, vol. 28, p. 10, February, 1955.
Transistor Quality Improves, *Electronics*, vol. 28, p. 16, March, 1955.
Transistorized Automobile Radio, *J. Franklin Inst.*, vol. 260, p. 86, 1955.
Transistorized Portable Phonograph, *Radio Television News*, vol. 54, p. 41, October, 1955.
Transistorized Portable Receiver, *Radio Television News*, vol. 53, p. 39, April, 1955.
Transistors; Growing Up Fast, *Business Week*, pp. 86–87, Feb. 5, 1955.
Transistors Invade More Consumer Products, *Electronics*, vol. 28, p. 12, August, 1955.
Wrist Radio Uses Three Transistors, *Electronics*, vol. 28, p. 10, December, 1955.

1956

Abaulina-Zavaritskaya, É. I.: Electrical Properties of Ge at Very Low Temperatures, *Zhur. Eksptl. i Teort. Fiz.*, vol. 30, no. 6, pp. 1158–1160, 1956.
Adirovich, É. I., and G. M. Guro: Characteristic Times of Processes in Semiconductors, *Doklady Akad. Nauk S.S.S.R.*, vol. 108, no. 3, pp. 417–420, 1956.
Adirovich, É. I., and V. G. Kolotilova: On the Theory of Transport Processes in Semiconducting Triodes, *Doklady Akad. Nauk S.S.S.R.*, vol. 108, no. 4, pp. 629–632, 1956.
Agakhanyan, T. M.: Reduction of Pulse Front Distortion in Transistor Video Amplifiers, *Radiotekhnika*, vol. 11, no. 9, pp. 54–58, 1956.

Agakhanyan, T. M., and Yu. A. Volkov: Practical Circuits of Transistor Video Amplifiers, *Radiotekhnika*, vol. 11, no. 11, pp. 38–44, 1956.

Amakasu, K., and M. Asano: Temperature Dependence of Flicker Noise of P-N-P Junction Transistors, *J. Appl. Phys.*, vol. 27, no. 10, p. 1249, October, 1956.

Anastassiades, M., and D. Ilias: On the Anomalous Rectification of Cuprous Sulphide Detectors, *Proc. Phys. Soc. (London)*, vol. 69B, part 9, pp. 958–960, September, 1956.

Angell, J. B., and M. M. Fortini: Computer Switching with Micro-alloy Transistors, *Electronic Inds.*, vol. 15, no. 12, pp. 38–39, 123–124, 126, December, 1956.

Armistead, M. A., E. G. Spencer, and R. D. Hatcher: Microwave Semiconductor Switch, *Proc. IRE*, vol. 44, no. 12, p. 1875, December, 1956.

Armstrong, H. L.: On Open Circuit Transient Effects in Point-contact Rectifiers, *J. Appl. Phys.*, vol. 27, no. 4, pp. 420–421, April, 1956.

Armstrong, H. L.: A Treatment of Cascaded Active Four-terminal Networks, with Application to Transistor Circuits, *IRE Trans. on Circuit Theory*, vol. CT-3, no. 2, pp. 138–140, June, 1956.

Armstrong, H. L., E. D. Metz, and I. Weiman: Design Theory and Experiments for Abrupt Hemispherical P-N Junction Diodes, *IRE Trans. on Electron Devices*, vol. ED-3, no. 2, pp. 86–92, April, 1956.

Armstrong, L. D., C. L. Carlson, and M. Bentivegna: P-N-P Transistors Using High-emitter-efficiency Alloy Materials, *RCA Rev.*, vol. 17, no. 1, pp. 37–45, March, 1956.

Arthur, J. B., A. F. Gibson, and J. B. Gunn: Current Gain at L-H Junctions in Germanium, *Proc. Phys. Soc. (London)*, vol. 69B, part 7, pp. 705–711, July, 1956.

Austin, I. G., C. H. L. Goodman, and A. E. Pengelly: New Semiconductors with the Chalcopyrite Structure, *J. Electrochem. Soc.*, vol. 103, no. 11, pp. 609–610, November, 1956.

Ballentyne, D. W. G.: Relation between the Brightness of Electroluminescent Cells and the Applied Power, *J. phys. radium*, vol. 17, no. 8–9, pp. 759–762, August–September, 1956.

Barnes, R. C. M., G. A. Howells, and E. H. Cooke-Yarborough: Transistor Arithmetic Circuits for an Interleaved-digit Computer, *Proc. Inst. Elec. Engrs. (London)*, paper 1992M, February, 1956.

Bashkow, T. R.: D-C Graphical Analysis of Junction Transistor Flip-flops, *Trans. AIEE*, part I, vol. 75, pp. 1–7, 1956.

Bashkow, T. R.: Effect of Nonlinear Collector Capacitance on Collector Current Rise Time, *IRE Trans. on Electron Devices*, vol. ED-3, no. 4, pp. 167–172, October, 1956.

Bataille, M.: Study of the Equilibrium States of a Bi-stable Switch to Give Long and Reliable Working, *Onde élect.*, vol. 36, pp. 94–103, February, 1956.

Becherer, H.: Experimental Results on the Production of an Ideal Blocking Characteristic in Crystal Diodes, *Nachrtech. Fachberichte*, vol. 5, pp. 10–14, 1956.

Beck, K. H.: An N-stage Series Transistor Circuit, *IRE Trans. on Circuit Theory*, vol. CT-3, no. 1, pp. 44–51, March, 1956.

Beneking, H.: The Analogy between Thermionic Tubes and Transistors, *Arch. Elekt. Ubertragung*, vol. 10, no. 5, pp. 214–221, May, 1956.

Beneking, H., K. H. Kupferschmidt, and H. Wolf: D-C Measuring Amplifier Using Transistors, *Elektron. Rundschau*, vol. 10, no. 10, pp. 268–269, October, 1956.

Benton, B. M.: Servo Amplifiers Use Power Transistors, *Electronics*, vol. 29, no. 9, pp. 153–155, September, 1956.

Berger, W.: Photovoltaic Cell in the Technique of Measurement, *Lichttechnik*, vol. 8, no. 1, pp. 16–19, January, 1956.

Blake, L. R., and A. R. Eames: Transistor Frequency Meters, *Electronic Eng.*, vol. 28, pp. 322–327, August, 1956.

Blakemore, J. S.: Photoconductivity in Indium-doped Silicon, *Can. J. Phys.*, vol. 34, no. 9, pp. 938–948, September, 1956.

Blecher, F. H.: Transistor Circuits for Analog and Digital Systems, *Bell System Tech. J.*, vol. 35, no. 2, pp. 295–332, March, 1956.

Blet, G.: Long Time Constants in Selenium Photocells, *J. phys. radium*, vol. 17, no. 5, pp. 430–439, May, 1956.

Bloem, J.: P-N Junctions in Photosensitive PbS Layers, *Appl. Sci. Research*, vol. 6, part B, no. 1–2, pp. 92–100, 1956.

Bonch-Bruevich, V. L.: On the Question of Surface Recombination, *Zhur. Tekh. Fiz.*, vol. 26, no. 6, pp. 1137–1140, 1956.

Booth, A. M.: Transistorized Receiver for Mobile FM, *Electronics*, vol. 29, no. 11, pp. 158–161, November, 1956.

Borg, L.: High-voltage Selenium Rectifiers, *ASEA Journal*, vol. 29, no. 1–2, pp. 3–10, 1956.

Brattain, W. H., and C. G. B. Garrett: Combined Measurements of Field Effect, Surface Photo-voltage and Photoconductivity, *Bell System Tech. J.*, vol. 35, no. 5, pp. 1019–1040, September, 1956,

Braunbeck, J.: High-gain Transistor Audio Amplifier, *Radio-Electronics*, vol. 27, no. 6, pp. 30–32, June, 1956.

Bridgers, H. E.: Formation of P-N Junctions in Semiconductors by the Variation of Crystal Growth Parameters, *J. Appl. Phys.*, vol. 27, no. 7, pp. 746–751, July, 1956.

Bridgers, H. E., and E. D. Kolb: Distribution Coefficient of Boron in Germanium, *J. Chem. Phys.*, vol. 25, no. 4, pp. 648–650, October, 1956.

Brophy, J. J.: Excess Noise in Deformed Germanium, *J. Appl. Phys.*, vol. 27, no. 11, pp. 1383–1384, November, 1956.

Bruun, G.: Common-emitter Transistor Video Amplifiers, *Proc. IRE*, vol. 44, no. 11, pp. 1561–1572, November, 1956.

Bube, R. H.: Photoconductivity Speed of Response for High Intensity Excitation in Cadmium Sulfide and Selenide, *J. Appl. Phys.*, vol. 27, no. 10, pp. 1237–1242, October, 1956.

Burgess, R. E.: Emitter-base Impedances of Junction Transistors, *J. Electronics*, vol. 2, no. 3, pp. 301–302, November, 1956.

Burgess, R. E.: The Statistics of Charge Carrier Fluctuations in Semiconductors, *Proc. Phys. Soc. (London)*, vol. 69B, part 10, pp. 1020–1027, October, 1956.

Burton, L. W.: Germanium Power Rectifiers, *Direct Current*, vol. 3, no. 1, pp. 3–8, June, 1956.

Burton, L. W.: Germanium Rectifiers for Industrial Applications, *Trans. AIEE*, part I, vol. 75, pp. 41–44, 1956.

Carroll, J. M.: Diffusion Transistors Raise Frequency Limits, *Electronics*, vol. 29, no. 2, pp. 137–139, February, 1956.

Chaplin, G. B. B.: A Point-contact Transistor Scaling Circuit with 0.4 Microsec. Resolution, *Proc. Inst. Elec. Engrs. (London)*, paper 2064R, March, 1956.

Chaplin, G. B. B., and A. R. Owens: A Junction-transistor Scaling Circuit with 2 Microsec. Resolution, *Proc. Inst. Elec. Engrs. (London)*, vol. 103B, paper 2076R, pp. 510–515, 516–518, March, 1956.

Chen, K., and A. J. Schiewe: A Single-transistor Magnetic-coupled Oscillator, *Trans. AIEE*, part I, vol. 75, pp. 396–400, 1956.

Cheng, C. C.: Frequency Stability of Point-contact Transistor Oscillators, *Proc. IRE*, vol. 44, no. 2, pp. 219–223, February, 1956.

Chow, W. F.: Transistor Power Gain Meter, *Tele-Tech*, vol. 15, no. 6, pp. 104–105, 355–359, June, 1956.

Coffey, W. N.: Measuring R-F Parameters of Junction Transistors, *Electronics*, vol. 29, no. 2, pp. 152–155, February, 1956.

Cohrs, T.: The Transistor as a Low-frequency Amplifier for Small Signals, *Tele* (Swedish ed.), no. 4, pp. 209–220, 1956.

Cole, G. H.: Transistorized Indicator Measures Jet Exhaust, *Electronics*, vol. 29, no. 12, pp. 143–145, December, 1956.

Cooke-Yarborough, E. H., R. C. M. Barnes, J. Stephen, and G. A. Howells: A Transistor Digital Computer, *Proc. Inst. Elec. Engrs. (London)*, paper 1964M, 7, January, 1956.

Cooper, B. F. C.: The Application of Transistors to AM Receivers, *Proc. IRE, Australia*, vol. 17, no. 10, pp. 331–340, October, 1956.

Crenshaw, R. M.: Industrial Uses of Germanium Rectifiers, *Elec. Eng.*, vol. 75, no. 8, pp. 719–721, August, 1956.

Curtin, W. A.: Application of Junction Transistors to Carrier-frequency Computing Amplifiers, *Trans. AIEE*, part I, vol. 75, pp. 746–752, 1956.

Curtis, O. L., Jr., and B. R. Gossick: Direct Method of Measuring the Contact Injection Ratio, *Rev. Sci. Instr.*, vol. 27, no. 10, pp. 828–829, October, 1956.

Curtis, O. L., Jr., and B. R. Gossick: Experimental Investigation of the Transient Behavior of Gold-Germanium Surface Barriers, *IRE Trans. on Electron Devices*, vol. ED-3, no. 4, pp. 163–167, October, 1956.

Dawirs, H. N., and E. K. Damon: Measurement of Crystal Impedances at Low Levels, *IRE Trans. on Microwave Theory and Tech.*, vol. MTT-4, no. 2, pp. 94–96, April, 1956.

Della Pergola, G., and D. Sette: Apparatus for Measuring the Hall and Magneto-resistive Effects in Semiconductors, *Alta frequenza*, vol. 25, no. 2, pp. 140-151, April, 1956.

DeSautels, A. N.: A Comparison of Three Common Emitter Transistor Servo Preamplifiers, *Trans. AIEE*, part I, vol. 75, pp. 17–25, 1956.

Deuitch, D. E.: Transistor Circuits for Digital Computers, *Electronics*, vol. 29, no. 5, pp. 160–161, May, 1956.

Dixit, K. R.: Rectification and Crystal Structure, *Indian J. Phys.*, vol. 30, no. 1, pp. 10–15, January, 1956.

Dorin, V. A., and D. N. Nasledov: An Electron Diffraction Study of the Sub-electrode Layer in Selenium Rectifiers with a Cadmium Electrode, *Zhur. Tekh. Fiz.*, vol. 26, no. 2, pp. 284–292, 1956.

Dorn, C. G.: Fast Rise Pulse Generator with High Pulse Repetition Frequency, *Rev. Sci. Instr.*, vol. 27, no. 5, pp. 283–284, May, 1956.

Dorn, C. G.: Forward Transients in Point Contact Diodes, *IRE Trans. on Electron Devices*, vol. ED-3, no. 3, pp. 153–156, July, 1956.

Dreyfus-Alain, B.: Germanium Junction Power Diodes, *Onde élect.*, vol. 36, pp. 220–223, March, 1956.

Ebers, J. J.: Alloyed-junction Transistor Development, *Bell Labs. Record*, vol. 34, no. 1, pp. 8–12, January, 1956.

Evans, D. M.: Measurements on Alloy-type Germanium Transistors and Their Relation to Theory, *J. Electronics*, vol. 1, no. 5, pp. 461–476, March, 1956.

Evans, D. M.: The Temperature Dependence of the Mobility of Electrons in Germanium, *Proc. Phys. Soc. (London)*, vol. 69B, part 8, pp. 845–846, August, 1956.

Feaster, W. C., and E. E. Scheneman: Application of Transistors in Power-line Carrier Relaying, *Trans. AIEE*, part III, vol. 75, pp. 976–979, 1956.

Finkelstein, M. B.: Transistorized Vertical Deflection for Television Receivers, in RCA Laboratories, "Transistors," vol. I, Princeton, N.J., pages 579–597, 1956.

Fleming, L.: Transistorized R. F. Capacitance Meter, *Radio Television News*, vol. 55, no. 5, pp. 65–67, 153, May, 1956.

Fletcher, N. H.: Note on "The Variation of Junction Transistor Current Amplification Factor with Emitter Current," *Proc. IRE*, vol. 44, no. 10, pp. 1475–1476, October, 1956.

Flietner, H., and G. Hesse: Impedance Measurements on H. F. Diodes as a Function of Bias Voltage, *Hochfrequenztech. u. Elektroakust.*, vol. 65, no. 2, pp. 41–46, September, 1956.

Forster, J. H., and L. E. Miller: The Effect of Surface Treatments on Point-contact Transistor Characteristics, *Bell System Tech. J.*, vol. 35, no. 4, pp. 767–812, July, 1956.

Francini, G.: Resistance-Capacitance Transistor Oscillator, *Alta frequenza*, vol. 25, no. 3–4, pp. 198–210, July–August, 1956.

Frank, H.: Germanium Junction Transistors (of Czech Manufacture), *Slaboproudý Obzor*, vol. 17, no. 12, pp. 680–687, 1956.

Franklin, E., and J. B. James: The Application of Transistors to the Trigger, Ratemeter and Power-supply Circuits of Radiation Monitors, *Proc. Inst. Elec. Engrs. (London)*, vol. 103B, paper 2049M, pp. 497–504, 516–518, March, 1956.

Freymann, R., Y. Balcou, M. L. Blanchard, H. Corneteau, M. Freymann, B. Hagéne, M. Hagéne, M. Lepage, J. Meinnel, and R. Rohmer: Electrical and Optical Properties of Some Semiconductors: Zinc Oxide, Zinc Sulphide, Selenium, *J. phys. radium*, vol. 17, no. 8–9, pp. 806–812, August–September, 1956.

Frisch, E., and W. Herzog: Contributions to the Theory of Oscillators, I, *NTZ-Nachrtech. Z.*, vol. 9, no. 7, pp. 310–314, July, 1956.

Frisch, E., and W. Herzog: Contributions to the Theory of Oscillators, II, *NTZ-Nachrtech. Z.*, vol. 9, no. 9, pp. 420–423, September, 1956.

Garrett, C. G. B., and W. H. Brattain: Distribution and Cross-sections of Fast States on Germanium Surfaces, *Bell. System Tech. J.*, vol. 35, no. 5, pp. 1041–1058, September, 1956.

Garrett, C. G. B., and W. H. Brattain: Some Experiments on, and a Theory of, Surface Breakdown, *J. Appl. Phys.*, vol. 27, no. 3, pp. 299–306, March, 1956.

Gaschi, J.: The Equivalent Circuits of the Transistor, *Onde élect.*, vol. 36, pp. 268–276, March, 1956.

Gasson, D. B.: A Four-point Probe Apparatus for Measuring Resistivity, *J. Sci. Instr.*, vol. 33, no. 2, p. 85, February, 1956.

Geist, D.: Self-oscillations of Transistors, *Z. angew. Phys.*, vol. 8, no. 7, pp. 337–339, 1956.

Gerlich, D.: Hole Injection at Metal-semiconductor Point Contact, *Proc. Phys. Soc. (London)*, vol. 69B, part 12, pp. 1350–1351, December, 1956.

Giacoletto, L. J.: Performance of a Radio-frequency Alloy Junction Transistor in Different Circuits, in RCA Laboratories, "Transistors," vol. I, Princeton, N.J., pp. 431–457, 1956.

Giacoletto, L. J., and J. O'Connell: A Variable-capacitance Germanium Junction Diode for UHF, *RCA Rev.*, vol. 17, no. 1, pp. 68–85, March, 1956.

Gianola, U. F.: Photovoltaic Noise in Silicon Broad Area P-N Junctions, *J. Appl. Phys.*, vol. 27, no. 1, pp. 51–54, January, 1956.

Gibson, A. F., and J. W. Granville: The Measurement of Drift Mobility in Germanium at High Electric Fields, *J. Electronics*, vol. 2, no. 3, pp. 259–266, November, 1956.

Glinchuk, K. D., E. G. Miselyuk, and É. I. Rashba: Measurement of Carrier Recombination Velocity by Conductivity Modulation, *Zhur. Tekh. Fiz.*, vol. 26, no. 12, pp. 2607–2613, 1956.

Gornyĭ, N. B.: Distortion of Secondary Emission Current-Voltage Curves at Positive Values of Collector Potential, *Zhur. Tekh. Fiz.*, vol. 26, no. 4, pp. 723–725, 1956.

Gossick, B. R.: A Note on the Small Amplitude Transient Response of P-N Junctions, *Proc. IRE*, vol. 44, no. 2, p. 259, February, 1956.

Gossick, B. R.: On the Transient Behavior of Semiconductor Rectifiers, *J. Appl. Phys.*, vol. 27, no. 8, pp. 905–911, August, 1956.

Gott, E.: High-speed Counter Uses Surface-barrier Transistor, *Electronics*, vol. 29, no. 3, pp. 174–178, March, 1956.

Granville, J. W.: A Junction Transistor with High Current Gain, *J. Electronics*, vol. 1, no. 6, pp. 565–579, May, 1956.

Grimm, V. R., and D. N. Nasledov: A Study of the Rectifying Properties of P-N Junctions between Selenium and the Sulphides and Selenides of Tin, *Zhur. Tekh. Fiz.*, vol. 26, no. 4, pp. 707–715, 1956.

Grinich, V. H.: An Eighty-volt-output Transistor Video Amplifier, *IRE Trans. on Circuit Theory*, vol. CT-3, no. 1, pp. 61–62, March, 1956.

Grinich, V. H.: Stagger-tuned Transistor Video Amplifiers, *IRE Trans. on Broadcast and Television Receivers*, vol. BTR-2, no. 3, pp. 53–56, October, 1956.

Grinich, V. H.: Two Representations for a Junction Transistor in the Common-collector Configuration, *IRE Trans. on Circuit Theory*, vol. CT-3, no. 1, pp. 63–64, March, 1956.

Guggenbühl, W.: Theoretical Consideration on the Physical Basis of the Equivalent Circuit of Semiconductor Diodes at High Current Densities, *Arch. Elekt. Ubertragung*, vol. 10, no. 11, pp. 483–485, November, 1956.

Guggenbühl, W., and B. Schneider: The Stabilization of the D-C Operating Point of D-C Transistors, *Arch. Elekt. Ubertragung*, vol. 10, no. 9, pp. 361–375, September, 1956.

Guggenbühl, W., B. Schneider, and M. J. O. Strutt: Measurements of High-frequency Noise in Transistors, *Nachrtech. Fachberichte*, vol. 5, pp. 34–36, 1956.

Guggenbühl, W., and M. J. O. Strutt: Theory of High-frequency Noise in Transistors at Small Current Densities, *Nachrtech. Fachberichte*, vol. 5, pp. 30–33, 1956.

Gunn, J. B.: Avalanche Injection in Semiconductors, *Proc. Phys. Soc. (London)*, vol. 69B, pt. 8, pp. 781–789, August, 1956.

Gunn, J. B.: The Field-dependence of Electron Mobility in Germanium, *J. Electronics*, vol. 2, no. 1, pp. 87–94, July, 1956.

Haneman, D.: Current Gain in Formed Point Contact N-type Germanium Transistors, *Proc. Phys. Soc. (London)*, vol. 69B, part 7, pp. 712–720, July, 1956.

Harman, T. C., H. L. Goering, and A. C. Beer: Electrical Properties of N-Type InAs, *Phys. Rev.*, vol. 104, no. 6, pp. 1562–1564, December 15, 1956.

Harrick, N. J.: Lifetime Measurements of Excess Carriers in Semiconductors, *J. Appl. Phys.*, vol. 27, no. 12, pp. 1439–1442, December, 1956.

Hasenberg, W.: Evaluation of Transistors for Class-B Power Output Amplifiers, in RCA Laboratories, "Transistors," vol. I, Princeton, N.J., pp. 361–368, 1956.

Hauri, E. R.: On the Question of the Dependence of the Current Gain of Junction Transistors on the Emitter Current, *Tech. Mitt. PTT*, vol. 34, no. 11, pp. 441–451, 1956.

Hayes, A. E., Jr., and W. W. Wells: A Simplified Procedure for the Design of Transistor Audio Amplifiers, *IRE Conv. Record*, vol. 4, pt. 7, pp. 45–61, 1956.

Heinlein, W.: An Equivalent Circuit for Germanium Diodes with Large Inertia, *Nachrtech. Fachberichte*, vol. 5, pp. 37–39, 1956.

Heinz, O., E. M. Gyorgy, and R. S. Ohl: Solid-state Detector for Low-energy Ions, *Rev. Sci. Instr.*, vol. 27, no. 1, pp. 43–47, January, 1956.

Henszey, R. T.: Push-Pull Transistor Servo Amplifier, *Electronics*, vol. 29, no. 12, pp. 155–157, December, 1956.

Herbert, N. J.: Point-contact Transistor Development, *Bell Labs. Record*, vol. 34, no. 2, pp. 46–50, February, 1956.

Herlet, A.: The Behaviour of P-N Junctions at High Current Densities, *Z. Naturforsch.*, vol. 11a, no. 6, pp. 498–510, June, 1956.

Heywang, W., and M. Zerbst: The Determination of Volume and Surface Recombination in Semiconductors, *Nachrtech. Fachberichte*, vol. 5, pp. 27–29, 1956.

Hicks, W.: Transistor Phase-shift Oscillator, *Tele-Tech*, vol. 15, no. 7, pp. 55–56, July, 1956.

Hoffman, G. R.. and M. A. Maclean: Quiescent Core-transistor Counters, *Proc. Inst. Elec. Engrs. (London)*, part B, suppl. 3, paper 2122M, pp. 418–421, 422–424, March, 1956.

Hogarth, C. A.: On the Measurement of Minority Carrier Lifetimes in Silicon, *Proc. Phys. Soc. (London)*, vol. 69B, part 8, pp. 791–795, August, 1956.

Holec, V. P.: The Use of Transistors in Airborne Audio Equipment, *IRE Trans. on Audio*, vol. AU-4, no. 4, pp. 90–93, July–August, 1956.

Hollmann, H. E.: Applications for Tandem Transistors, *Tele-Tech*, vol. 15, no. 2, pp. 58–59, 113–114, February, 1956.

Hollmann, H. E.: Passive Transistor Receivers, *Frequenz*, vol. 10, no. 10, pp. 329–331, October, 1956.

Holmes, D. D., and T. O. Stanley: Stability Considerations in Transistor Intermediate-frequency Amplifiers, in RCA Laboratories, "Transistors," vol. I, Princeton, N.J., pp. 403–421, 1956.

Hooper, D. E., and A. E. Jackets: Current Derived Resistance-capacitance Oscillators Using Junction Transistors, *Electronic Eng.*, vol. 28, pp. 333–337, August, 1956.

Hrostowski, H. J.: Intermetallic Semiconductors, *Bell Labs. Record*, vol. 34, no. 7, pp. 246–250, July, 1956.

Huang, C., M. Marshall, and B. H. White: Field-effect Transistor Applications, *Trans. AIEE*, part I, vol. 75, pp. 323–329, 1956.

Huang, C., and E. Slobodzinski: Power Transistor Switching Circuit, *Trans. AIEE*, part I, vol. 75, pp. 290–296, 1956.

Hurley, R. B.: Bias Stabilization of Tandem Transistors, *Electronic Inds.*, vol. 15, no. 11, pp. 71, 139–141, 143, November, 1956.

Hurley, R. B.: Transistorized Low-level Chopper-circuits, *Electronic Inds.*, vol. 15, no. 12, pp. 42–43, 108, 110, 112, December, 1956.

Hyde, F. J.: Measurement of Noise Spectra of a Germanium P-N Junction Diode, *Proc. Phys. Soc. (London)*, vol. 69B, part 2, pp. 231–241, February, 1956.

Ilberg, V., and S. Vojtášek: Photodiodes and Phototransistors Compared with the (Electron) Emission Photocells, *Slaboproudý Obzor*, vol. 17, no. 10, pp. 564–566, 1956.

Jackets, A. E.: Multivibrator Circuits Using Junction Transistors, *Electronic Eng.*, vol. 28, pp. 184–189, May, 1956.

Jackson, R. W.: Simple Method of Revealing P-N Junctions in Germanium, *J. Appl. Phys.*, vol. 27, no. 3, pp. 309–310, March, 1956.

Jenny, D. A., J. J. Loferski, and P. Rappaport: Photovoltaic Effect in GaAs P-N Junctions and Solar Energy Conversion, *Phys. Rev.*, vol. 101, no. 3, pp. 1208–1209, February 1, 1956.

Jones, M. E., and J. R. MacDonald: Checking D-C Parameters of Transistors, *Electronic Inds.*, vol. 15, no. 10, pp. 56–58, 82, 84, 86, 89, 90, October, 1956.

Kalashnikov, S. G.: Recombination of Electrons and Holes in the Presence of Traps of Different Types, *Zhur. Tekh. Fiz.*, vol. 26, no. 2, pp. 241–250, 1956.

Karlovský, J., and M. Valúšek: Silicon Mixer Diodes, *Slaboproudý Obzor*, vol. 17, no. 12, pp. 672–680, 1956.

Keonjian, E.: Micropower Audio Amplifier, *IRE Trans. on Circuit Theory*, vol. CT-3, no. 1, p. 68, March, 1956.

Keonjian, E.: Micro-power Operation of Silicon Transistors, *Tele-Tech*, vol. 15, no. 5, pp. 76–78, 138–140, 142, May, 1956.

Keonjian, E.: Stable Transistor Oscillator, *IRE Trans. on Circuit Theory*, vol. CT-3, no. 1, pp. 38–44, March, 1956.

Kerfoot, B. P.: Transistors in Current-analog Computing, *IRE Trans. on Electronic Computers*, vol. EC-5, no. 2, pp. 86–93, June, 1956.

Kikuchi, M.: Some Experiments on the Germanium Surface Layer, *J. Phys. Soc. Japan*, vol. 11, no. 8, p. 898, August, 1956.

Kikuchi, M., Y. Tarui, and N. Narukami: Deterioration of Transistors, *Researches Electrotech. Lab. (Tokyo)*, no. 555, September, 1956.

Kilburn, T., R. L. Grimsdale, and D. C. Webb: A Transistor Digital Computer with a Magnetic-drum Store, *Proc. Inst. Elec. Engrs. (London)*, paper 2043M, March, 1956.

Kinkel, J. F., and M. C. Wilson: Vibration Meter Uses Transistors, *Electronics*, vol. 29, no. 4, pp. 127–129, April, 1956.

Kircher, R. J., and I. P. Kaminow: Superregenerative Transistor Oscillator, *Electronics*, vol. 29, no. 7, pp. 166–167, July, 1956.

Kleinman, D. A.: The Forward Characteristic of the P-I-N Diode, *Bell System Tech. J.*, vol. 35, no. 3, pp. 685–706, May, 1956.

Klier, E.: Alternating Current Measurements on Cadmium Sulphide Cells, *Ann. Physik*, vol. 18, no. 3–4, pp. 163–170, 1956.

Kolomiets, B. T., and A. O. Olesk: Characteristics of Photoresistors of Polycrystalline Cadmium Sulphide, *Elektrichestvo*, no. 6, pp. 35–38, 1956.

Konorov, P. I.: Electrical Properties of the Chalco-genides of Bismuth. I. Electrical Properties of Bismuth Sulphide Bi_2S_3, *Zhur. Tekh. Fiz.*, vol. 26, no. 5, pp. 1126–1128, 1956.

Konorov, P. I.: Electrical Properties of the Chalco-genides of Bismuth. II. Electrical Properties of Bi_2Se_3, *Zhur. Tekh. Fiz.*, vol. 26, no. 7, pp. 1394–1399, 1956.

Konorov, P. I.: Electrical Properties of the Chalco-genides of Bismuth. III. Electrical Properties of Bi_2Te_3, *Zhur. Tekh. Fiz.*, vol. 26, no. 7, pp. 1400–1405, 1956.

Koval'chik, T. L., and Yu. P. Maslakovets: The Influence of Impurities on the Electrical Properties of Lead Telluride, *Zhur. Tekh. Fiz.*, vol. 26, no. 11, pp. 2417–2431, 1956.

Kover, F.: Electrical Properties of Aluminum Antimonide, *Compt. rend.*, vol. 243, no. 7, pp. 648–650, August 13, 1956.

Kroemer, H.: The Apparent Contact Potential of a Pseudo-abrupt P-N Junction, *RCA Rev.*, vol. 17, no. 4, pp. 515–521, December, 1956.

Krüger, B.: The Transistor in Linear Power Amplifiers, *Tele* (Swedish ed.), no. 4, pp. 221–227, 1956.

Kuehn, R. L.: Signal Triggered Sweep Magnifies Pulse Widths, *Electronics*, vol. 29, no. 4, pp. 146–147, April, 1956.

Kuhrt, F.: Properties and Applications of Hall Generators, *V.D.E. Fachber.*, vol. 19 (I), pp. 1–8, 1956.

Kyte, D. J.: Anomalous Characteristics of Silicon Point Contact Rectifiers, *J. Electronics*, vol. 2, no. 3, pp. 247–258, November, 1956.

Lacy, J. W., and P. D. Davis, Jr.: Servo Amplifier Uses Silicon Power Transistors, *Electronics*, vol. 29, no. 1, pp. 136–137, January, 1956.

Landsberg, P. T.: Note on Turnover in Germanium Contacts, *Proc. Phys. Soc. (London)*, vol. 69B, part 7, pp. 763–765, July, 1956.

Lebedev, A. A., V. I. Stafeev, and V. M. Tuchkevich: Some Characteristics of Germanium Diodes with Gold Admixture, *Zhur. Tekh. Fiz.*, vol. 26, no. 10, pp. 2131–2141, 1956.

Leblond, A.: On a Special Form of the Equations Which Govern the Propagation of Free Carriers in a One-dimensional Junction Structure in a Homogeneous Crystal, *Compt. rend.*, vol. 242, no. 1, pp. 85–87, January 4, 1956.

Leblond, A.: Theoretical Study of the Current-voltage Characteristics of a P-I-P Semiconductor Structure, Taking the Ionization of the Central Region by the Carriers into Account, *Compt. rend.*, vol. 242, no. 15, pp. 1856–1859, April 9, 1956.

Leblond, A., and R. Gentner: Note on a Particular Structure for Obtaining High-frequency (Electrical) Oscillations, *Compt. rend.*, vol. 242, no. 5, pp. 621–623, January 30, 1956.

Ledig, G.: Design and Analysis of a Voltage-feedback Transistor Oscillator, *Frequenz*, vol. 10, pp. 178–185, June, 1956.

Ledig, G.: Junction Transistor-amplifier Valve: A Comparative Study, *Arch. Elekt. Ubertragung*, vol. 10, no. 1, pp. 1–9, January, 1956.

Lee, C. A.: A High-frequency Diffused Base Germanium Transistor, *Bell System Tech. J.*, vol. 35, no. 1, pp. 23–34, January, 1956.

Lehovec, K., A. Marcus, and K. Schoeni: Current-voltage Characteristic and Hole Injection Factor of Point Contact Rectifiers in the Forward Direction, *IRE Trans. on Electron Devices*, vol. ED-3, no. 1, pp. 1–6, January, 1956.

Leine, P. O.: The Dependence of the Transistor on Temperature, Current and Voltage, *Tele* (Swedish ed.), no. 4, pp. 203–209, 1956.

Levesque, P.: Visual Evidence of Inversion Layers on Semiconductor Materials, *J. Appl. Phys.*, vol. 27, no. 9, pp. 1104–1105, September, 1956.

Lin, H. C.: Quasi-complementary Transistor Amplifier, *Electronics*, vol. 29, no. 9, pp. 173–175, September, 1956.

Lin, H. C., and A. A. Barco: Temperature Effects in Circuits Using Junction Transistors, in RCA Laboratories, "Transistors," vol. I, pp. 369–402, Princeton, N.J., 1956.

Linvill, J. G., and L. G. Schimpf: The Design of Tetrode Transistor Amplifiers, *Bell System Tech. J.*, vol. 35, no. 4, pp. 813–840, July, 1956.

Litvinov, I. I.: Equivalent Circuit of a Semiconducting Triode at High Frequencies, *Radiotekhnika*, vol. 11, no. 10, pp. 25–29, 1956.

Loferski, J. J.: Theoretical Considerations Governing the Choice of the Optimum Semiconductor for Photo-voltaic Solar Energy Conversion, *J. Appl. Phys.*, vol. 27, no. 7, pp. 777–784, July, 1956.

Lovering, W. F., and D. B. Britten: A Simple Transformer Bridge for the Measurement of Transistor Characteristics, *Proc. Inst. Elec. Engrs. (London)*, paper 2247M, December, 1956.

Lukes, F.: The Photoelectric Properties of Gallium Antimonide, *Czechoslov. J. Phys.*, vol. 6, no. 4, pp. 359–363, August, 1956.

Lüscher, J., and P. Choquard: A Circuit Equivalent to a Transistor, *Tech. Mitt. PTT*, vol. 34, no. 5, pp. 193–197, 1956.

McCarthy, W. A.: One-third Watt Phonograph Amplifier, *Electronics*, vol. 29, no. 9, pp. 202, 204, 206, 208, September, 1956.

Macdonald, J. R.: Solution of a Transistor Transient Response Problem, *IRE Trans. on Circuit Theory*, vol. CT-3, no. 1, pp. 54–57, March, 1956.

Mahlman, G. W.: Photoconductivity of Lead Sulfide Films, *Phys. Rev.*, vol. 103, no. 6, pp. 1619–1630, September 15, 1956.

Marcus, A., and J. J. Oberly: Four-probe Resistivity Measurements on Rectangular Semiconductor Filaments, *IRE Trans. on Electron Devices*, vol. ED-3, no. 3, pp. 161–162, July, 1956.

Maslakovets, Yu. P., S. A. Poltinnikov, G. B. Dubrovskiĭ, and V. K. Subashiev: Photoelectric Converters of Solar Energy Made from P-type Silicon, *Zhur. Tekh. Fiz.*, vol. 26, no. 10, pp. 2396–2397, 1956.

Mason, D. E., A. A. Shepherd, and W. M. Walbank: Silicon Junction Power Diodes, *J. Brit. Inst. Radio Engrs.*, vol. 16, no. 8, pp. 431–441, August, 1956.

Mataré, H. F.: Grain Boundary Transistors, *Elektron. Rundschau*, vol. 10, no. 8, pp. 209–211, August; no. 9, pp. 253–255, September, 1956.

Merrill, L. C., and T. L. Slater: Linear Sweep-voltage Generators and Precision Amplitude Comparator Using Transistors, *Elec. Commun.*, vol. 33, no. 3, pp. 228–233, September, 1956.

Meyer, N. I.: Non-linear Distortion in Transistor Amplifiers at Low Signal Levels and Low Frequencies, *Proc. Inst. Elec. Engrs. (London)*, vol. 104C, monograph 209R, pp. 208–216, November, 1956.

Meyer-Brötz, G.: Limits of Application of Junction Transistors to Circuitry, *V.D.E. Fachber.*, vol. 19 (II), pp. 123–126, 1956.

Meyer-Brötz, G.: Neutralization in the Selective Transistor Amplifier, *Arch. Elekt. Ubertragung*, vol. 10, no. 9, pp. 391–397, September, 1956.

Meyer-Brötz, G.: The Quadripole Parameters of the Junction Transistor in the Three Fundamental Configurations, *Telefunken. Ztg.*, vol. 29, pp. 21–28, March, 1956.

Meyer-Brötz, G., and K. Felle: The Design of Wide-band Transistor Amplifiers, *NTZ-Nachrtech. Z.*, vol. 9, no. 11, pp. 498–503, November, 1956.

Middlebrook, R. D., and R. M. Scarlett: An Approximation to Alpha of a Junction Transistor, *IRE Trans. on Electron Devices*, vol. ED-3, no. 1, pp. 25–29, January, 1956.

Miller, L. E.: Negative Resistance Regions in the Collector Characteristics of the Point-contact Transistor, *Proc. IRE*, vol. 44, no. 1, pp. 65–72, January, 1956.

Miller, W., K. Bewig, and B. Salzberg: Note on the Reduction of Carrier Lifetime in P-N Junction Diodes by Electron Bombardment, *J. Appl. Phys.*, vol. 27, no. 12, pp. 1524–1527, December, 1956.

Milnes, A. G.: Transistor Power Amplifiers with Switched Mode of Operation, *Trans. AIEE*, part I, vol. 75, pp. 368–372, 1956.

Misawa, T.: A Note on the Extended Theory of the Junction Transistor, *J. Phys. Soc. Japan*, vol. 11, no. 7, pp. 728–739, July, 1956.

Moll, J. L., and I. M. Ross: The Dependence of Transistor Parameters on the Distribution of Base Layer Resistivity, *Proc. IRE*, vol. 44, no. 1, pp. 72–78, January, 1956.

Moore, A. R.: The Preparation of Single and Multiple P-N Junctions in Single Crystals of Germanium, in RCA Laboratories, "Transistors," vol. I, pp. 77–81, Princeton, N.J., 1956.

Moore, A. R., and H. Nelson: Surface Treatment of Silicon for Low Recombination Velocity, *RCA Rev.*, vol. 17, no. 1, pp. 5–12, March, 1956.

Moortgat-Pick, W.: High-frequency Amplification with Transistors, *Nachrtech. Fachberichte*, vol. 5, pp. 40–44, 1956.

Mueller, C. W., and N. H. Ditrick: Uniform Planar Alloy Junctions for Germanium Transistors, *RCA Rev.*, vol. 17, no. 1, pp. 46–56, March, 1956. ,

Myers, G. H.: Gain Chart for Transistor Amplifiers, *Electronics*, vol. 29, no. 10, pp. 224, 226, October, 1956.

Nadzhakov, G., B. Andreïchin, C. Balabanov, and Yu. Stanislavova: Barrier-layer Photovoltaic Elements of Evaporated CdS, *Compt. rend. acad. bulgare sci.*, vol. 9, no. 2, pp. 1–4, April–June, 1956.

Neale, D. M., and F. Oakes: Transistor D-C Amplifier, *Wireless World*, vol. 62, no. 11, pp. 529–532, November, 1956.

Nekrashevich, I. G.: On the Audio-frequency Performance of Selenium Rectifiers, *Zhur. Tekh. Fiz.*, vol. 26, no. 3, pp. 560–567, 1956.

Niemiaho, H.: Contact Rectifiers, *Kraft o. Ljus*, vol. 29, no. 12, pp. 261–270, December, 1956.

Nosovitskiï, Yu. E.: Calculations on a Selenium Rectifier with Capacitance Filter, *Radiotekhnika*, vol. 11, no. 5, pp. 65–72, 1956.

Onoe, M., and A. Ushirokawa: Inductive A-C Admittance of Junction Transistor, *Proc. IRE*, vol. 44, no. 10, p. 1475, October, 1956.

Pankove, J. I.: Transistor Fabrication by the Melt-quench Process, *Proc. IRE*, vol. 44, no. 2, pp. 185–188, February, 1956.

Paynter, D. A.: An Unsymmetrical Square-wave Power Oscillator, *IRE Trans. on Circuit Theory*, vol. CT-3, no. 1, pp. 64–65, March, 1956.

Pearson, G. L., H. C. Montgomery, and W. L. Feldmann: Noise in Silicon P-N Junction Photocells, *J. Appl. Phys.*, vol. 27, no. 1, pp. 91–92, January, 1956.

Pell, E. M., and G. M. Roe: Reverse Current and Carrier Lifetime as a Function of Temperature in Silicon Junction Diodes, *J. Appl. Phys.*, vol. 27, no. 7, pp. 768–772, July, 1956.

Penfield, P., Jr.: Transistorized Guitar Amplifier, *Radio Television News*, vol. 56, no. 1, pp. 43–45, July, 1956.

Perry, G. H., G. R. Hoffman, and E. W. Shallow: A New and Simple Type of Digital Circuit Technique Using Junction Transistors and Magnetic Cores, *Proc. Inst. Elec. Engrs. (London)*, part B, suppl. 3, paper 2112M, pp. 412–417, 422–424, March, 1956.

Petritz, R. L.: Theory of Photoconductivity in Semiconductor Films, *Phys. Rev.*, vol. 104, no. 6, pp. 1508–1516, December 15, 1956.

Pfister, H.: X-ray Photoeffect in GaAs P-N Junctions, *Z. Naturforsch.*, vol. 11a, no. 6, pp. 434–439, June, 1956.

Pincherle, L., and J. M. Radcliffe: Semiconducting Intermetallic Compounds, *Advances in Phys.*, vol. 5, pp. 271–322, July, 1956.

Piwkowski, T.: PbSe and PbTe Infra Red Detectors, *Acta Phys. Polon.*, vol. 15, no. 4, pp. 271–274, 1956.

Plummer, A. R. F.: Observations on the Growth of Excess Current in Germanium P-N Junctions, *Proc. Phys. Soc. (London)*, vol. 69B, part 5, pp. 539–547, May, 1956.

Pozhela, Yu. K.: On the Question of the Effect of a Strong (Electric) Field in Semiconductors, *Zhur. Tekh. Fiz.*, vol. 26, no. 2, pp. 277–280, 1956.

Prince, M. B.: Diffused P-N Junction Silicon Rectifiers, *Bell System Tech. J.*, vol. 35, no. 3, pp. 661–684, May, 1956.

Prince, M. B.: Silicon Power Diode Development, *Bell Labs. Record*, vol. 34, no. 5, pp. 161–164, May, 1956.

Pritchard, R. L.: Electric-network Representation of Transistors—A Survey, *IRE Trans. on Circuit Theory*, vol. CT-3, no. 1, pp. 5–21, March, 1956.

Pritchard, R. L.: Measurement Considerations in High-frequency Power Gain of Junction Transistors, *Proc. IRE*, vol. 44, no. 8, pp. 1050–1051, August, 1956.

Prom, G. J., and R. L. Crosby: Junction Transistor Switching Circuits for High-speed Digital Computer Applications, *IRE Trans. on Electronic Computers*, vol. EC-5, no. 4, pp. 192–196, December, 1956.

Prugh, T. A.: Minimizing Gain Variations with Temperature in RC Coupled Transistor Amplifiers, *Proc. IRE*, vol. 44, no. 12, p. 1880, December, 1956.

Raabe, G.: Determination of the Stable Modes of Oscillation of Transistor Oscillator Circuits, *Nachrichtentechnik*, vol. 6, no. 7, pp. 295–302, July, 1956.

Rall, B.: The Application of the Junction Transistor in Counter Circuits, *Nachrtech. Fachberichte*, vol. 5, pp. 50–56, 1956.

Raper, J. A. A.: A Transistorized Tuned Amplifier-limiter, *IRE Trans. on Circuit Theory*, vol. CT-3, no. 1, p. 67, March, 1956.

Rapp, A. K., and S. Y. Wong: Transistor Flip-Flops Have High Speed, *Electronics*, vol. 29, no. 12, pp. 180–181, December, 1956.

Rappaport, P., J. J. Loferski, and E. G. Linder: The Electron-voltaic Effect in Germanium and Silicon P-N Junctions, *RCA Rev.*, vol. 17, no. 1, pp. 100–128, March, 1956.

Rashba, É. I.: Diffusion of Current Carriers in a Semiconductor in the Presence of an External Electric Field, *Zhur. Tekh. Fiz.*, vol. 26, no. 7, pp. 1415–1418, 1956.

Rashba, É. I., and K. B. Tolpýgo: Forward Current-Voltage Characteristic of a Planar Rectifier at Large Currents, *Zhur. Tekh. Fiz.*, vol. 26, no. 7, pp. 1419–1427, 1956.

Rathe, H. L.: What Are the Potentialities of Photoconductivity Measurements at Blocking Layers?, *Nachrtech. Fachberichte*, vol. 5, pp. 15–26, 1956.

Read, W. T., Jr.: Theory of the Swept Intrinsic Structure, *Bell System Tech. J.*, vol. 35, no. 6, pp. 1239–1284, November, 1956.

Reiss, H.: P-N Junction Theory by the Method of σ Functions, *J. Appl. Phys.*, vol. 27, no. 5, pp. 530–538, May, 1956.

Rejmánek, M.: A Transistor Receiver, *Slaboproudý Obzor*, vol. 17, no. 12, pp. 668–672, 1956.

Reynolds, D. C., L. C. Greene, and L. L. Antes: Properties of a Cadmium Sulfide Photorectifier, *J. Chem. Phys.*, vol. 25, no. 6, pp. 1177–1179, December, 1956.

Riethmüller, J.: Measurement of the Parameters Determining the Functioning of Transistors at High Frequencies, *Ann. radioélec.*, vol. 11, pp. 239–248, July, 1956.

Rittmann, A. D., and T. J. Miles: High-frequency Silicon Alloy Transistor, *IRE Trans. on Electron Devices*, vol. ED-3, no. 2, pp. 78–82, April, 1956.

Rizkin, A. A.: A Regenerative Method for the Design of Transistor Amplifying Stages, *Radiotekhnika*, vol. 11, no. 5, pp. 56–64, 1956.

Rolfe, J.: The Determination of Base Thickness in Alloy Junction Transistors by Etching, *Brit. J. Appl. Phys.*, vol. 7, no. 3, p. 109, March, 1956.

Rosenberg, W.: Properties and Application of Junction Transistors, I, *Nachrichtentechnik*, vol. 6, no. 11, pp. 492–495, November, 1956.

Rosiński, W.: Transistors, *Rozprawy Elektrotech.*, vol. 1, no. 5, pp. 303–398, 1956.

Rzhanov, A.: The Effect of Impurities on the Lifetime of Excess Charge Carriers in Ge, *Zhur. Tekh. Fiz.*, vol. 26, no. 7, pp. 1389–1393, 1956.

Rzhanov, A.: The Relationship between Surface and Volume Recombination in Germanium Triodes with Alloyed P-N Junctions, *Zhur. Tekh. Fiz.*, vol. 26, no. 1, pp. 239–240, 1956.

Rzhanov, A., I. G. Neizvestnÿĭ, and V. V. Roslyakov: Investigations of Surface Conductivity and Surface Recombination in Specimens of Germanium, *Zhur. Tekh. Fiz.*, vol. 26, no. 10, pp. 2142–2153, 1956.

Saija, L.: Supply Units of Large D-C Power with Semiconductor (Selenium) Rectifiers, *Ind. Ital. Elettrotec.*, vol. 9, no. 9, pp. 127–135, April, 1956.

Salow, H., and W. v. Münch: On a Switching Transistor with Short Response Times, *Z. angew. Phys.*, vol. 8, no. 3, pp. 114–119, 1956.

Sassier, M.: Germanium Power Rectifiers, *Onde élect.*, vol. 36, pp. 224–229, March, 1956.

Scheler, T., and H. W. Becke: A Contribution to the Mathematical and Experimental (Measurements) Treatment of the Transistor as a Linear Quadripole, *Frequenz.*, vol. 10, no. 4, pp. 107–116, April, 1956.

Schenkel, H., and H. Statz: Junction Transistors with Alpha Greater than Unity, *Proc. IRE*, vol. 44, no. 3, pp. 360–371, March, 1956.

Schultz, W.: The Influence of the Surface on the Electrical Properties of Rectifiers and Transistors, *Nachrtech. Fachberichte*, vol. 5, pp. 3–9, 1956.

Schwaibold, E.: The Hall Effect and Its Technical Applications. I. Basic Theory; Hall Generators, *Arch. tech. Messen*, no. 246 (ref. V 943-2), pp. 153–156, July, 1956.

Schwartz, S.: Transistor Characteristics for Circuit Designers, *Electronics*, vol. 29, no. 1, pp. 161–172, 174, January, 1956.

Sharpless, W. M.: Wafer-type Millimeter Wave Rectifiers, *Bell System Tech. J.*, vol. 35, no. 6, pp. 1385–1402, November, 1956.

Shields, J.: Silicon P-N Junction Diodes, *Direct Current*, vol. 3, no. 2, pp. 44–52, September, 1956.

Shigetomi, S., and S. Mori: Electrical Properties of Bi₂Te₃, *J. Phys. Soc. Japan*, vol. 11, no. 9, pp. 915–919, September, 1956.

Shilliday, T. S.: High-temperature Selenium Rectifiers—A Survey of Manufacturers' Data, *Trans. AIEE*, part I, vol. 75, pp. 248–252, 1956.

Shockley, W.: "Transistor Physics," the Forty-sixth Kelvin Lecture, *Proc. Inst. Elec. Engrs. (London)*, vol. 103B, paper 1946, pp. 23–41, January, 1956.

Simkins, Q. W., and J. H. Vogelsong: Transistor Amplifiers for Use in a Digital Computer, *Proc. IRE*, vol. 44, no. 1, pp. 43–55, January, 1956.

Slade, B. N.: Recent Advances in Power Junction Transistors, in RCA Laboratories, "Transistors," vol. I, pp. 153–171, Princeton, N.J., 1956.

Slaughter, D. W.: The Emitter-coupled Differential Amplifier, *IRE Trans. on Circuit Theory*, vol. CT-3, no. 1, pp. 51–53, March, 1956.

Smith, E. C.: Transistor Remote Amplifier, *Tele-Tech*, vol. 15, no. 8, pp. 74, 125, August, 1956.

Smits, F. M., and R. C. Miller: Rate Limitations at the Surface for Impurity Diffusion in Semiconductors, *Phys. Rev.*, vol. 104, no. 5, pp. 1242–1245, December 1, 1956.

Smollett, M., and J. A. Jenkins: The Lead Sulphide Photoconductive Cell, *Electronic Eng.*, vol. 28, pp. 373–375, September, 1956.

Sorokin, O. V.: On the Measurement of Lifetime, Diffusion Coefficient and Surface Recombination Velocity of Minority Current Carriers in Thin Semiconducting Specimens, *Zhur. Tekh. Fiz.*, vol. 26, no. 11, pp. 2473–2479, 1956.

Sorokin, O. V.: Measurement of Surface Recombination Velocity in a Thin Semiconductor Sample with Qualitatively Different Faces, *Zhur. Tekh. Fiz.*, vol. 26, no. 11, pp. 2467–2472, 1956.

Sparks, M., and W. J. Pietenpol: Diffusion in Solids—A Breakthrough in Semiconductor Device Fabrication, *Bell Labs. Record*, vol. 34, no. 12, pp. 441–446, December, 1956.

Spenke, E.: Forward and Reverse Characteristics of a P-I-metal Rectifier, *Z. Naturforsch.*, vol. 11a, no. 6, pp. 440–456, 1956.

Stafeev, V. I., V. M. Tuchkevich, and N. S. Yakovchuk: Operation of a Crystal Amplifier with (Minority Carrier) Depletion, *Zhur. Tekh. Fiz.*, vol. 26, no. 1, pp. 15–21, 1956.

Stanton, J. W.: A Transistorized D-C Amplifier, *IRE Trans. on Circuit Theory*, vol. CT-3, no. 1, pp. 65–66, March, 1956.

Stieltjes, F. H., and L. J. Tummers: Simple Theory of the Junction Transistor, *Philips Tech. Rev.*, vol. 17, no. 9, pp. 233–246, March, 1956.

Stöckmann, F.: On the Effect of Boundary Layers on Photoconduction, *Z. Physik*, vol. 146, no. 4, pp. 407–422, 1956.

Stolz, H.: On the Theory of the Electrical Conductivity of Semiconductors at High Frequencies, *Ann. Physik*, vol. 19, no. 6–8, pp. 394–400, 1956.

Strosche, H.: On the Mode of Action of Cadmium Selenide Layers in the Selenium Rectifier. II. (Further) Contribution, *Z. Physik*, vol. 145, no. 5, pp. 597–610, 1956.

Stuart-Monteith, G.: Temperature Stability of Transistor Amplifiers, *Electronic Eng.*, vol. 28, pp. 544–547, December, 1956.

Suits, G. H., W. D. Schmitz, and R. W. Terhune: Excess Noise in InSb, *J. Appl. Phys.*, vol. 27, no. 11, p. 1385, November, 1956.

Suran, J. J., and F. A. Reibert: Two-terminal Analysis and Synthesis of Junction Transistor Multivibrators, *IRE Trans. on Circuit Theory*, vol. CT-3, no. 1, pp. 26–38, March, 1956.

Svechnikov, S. V.: Properties of Cadmium Sulphide Photocells Irradiated by γ- and β-rays, *Zhur. Tekh. Fiz.*, vol. 26, no. 8, pp. 1646–1650, 1956.

Sylvan, T. P.: Logarithmic Attenuators Using Silicon Junction Diodes, *IRE Trans. on Circuit Theory*, vol. CT-3, no. 1, pp. 69–70, March, 1956.

Taeger, W.: The Different Quadripole Representations of the Transistor, *Frequenz*, vol. 10, no. 6, pp. 186–189, June, 1956.

Tanenbaum, M., and D. E. Thomas: Diffused Emitter and Base Silicon Transistors, *Bell System Tech. J.*, vol. 35, no. 1, pp. 1–22, January, 1956.

Tarbes, P.: Industrial Cadmium Sulphide Photoresistors, *Bull. soc. franç. élect.*, vol. 6, pp. 73–82, January, 1956.

Tavernier, J.: Contribution to the Study of the Mobility of the Charge Carriers in InSb, *Compt. rend.*, vol. 242, no. 23, pp. 2707–2710, June 4, 1956.

Templeton, I. M.: A Chart for the Evaluation of Crystal Rectifier Constants, *Electronic Eng.*, vol. 28, p. 172, April, 1956.

Tendick, F. H., Jr.: Transistor Pulse Regenerative Amplifiers, *Bell System Tech. J.*, vol. 35, no. 5, pp. 1085–1114, September, 1956.

Tharma, P.: Pocket Transistor Receiver, *Wireless World*, vol. 62, no. 11, pp. 538–540, November, 1956.

Thomas, D. E.: Miniature FM Transistor Transmitter, *Bell Labs. Record*, vol. 34, no. 2, pp. 56–59, February, 1956.

Thomas, D. E., and G. C. Dacey: Applications Aspects of the Germanium Diffused Base Transistor, *IRE Trans. on Circuit Theory*, vol. CT-3, no. 1, pp. 22–25, March, 1956.

Tolstoĭ, N. A., B. T. Kolomiets, O. I. Golikova, and M. Ya. Tsenter: Photoconductivity and Luminescence of Polycrystalline CdS (Cu), *Zhur. Eksptl. i Teort. Fiz.*, vol. 30, no. 3, pp. 575–576, 1956.

Torisaki, S.: Crystal Oscillators with Junction Transistors, *J. Inst. Elec. Commun. Engrs. (Japan)*, vol. 39, no. 5, pp. 470–475, May, 1956.

Toscano, P. M., and J. B. Heffner: C.R.T. Power Supply Uses Transistor Oscillator, *Electronics*, vol. 29, no. 9, pp. 162–165, September 1956.

Trokhimenko, Ya. K.: Feedback in Crystal Triode Circuits, *Radiotekhnika*, vol. 11, no. 9, pp. 46–53, 1956.

Trokhimenko, Ya. K.: Method of Analyzing Composite Circuits with Crystal Triodes, *Radiotekhnika*, vol. 11, no. 3, pp. 16–22, 1956.

Trousil, Z.: Bulk Photovoltaic Phenomenon, *Czechoslov. J. Phys.*, vol. 6, no. 1, pp. 96–98, January, 1956.

Tsykin, G. S.: Calculation of the Coefficient and the Basic Characteristics of Amplification of a Stage Using a Semiconducting Triode, *Radiotekhnika*, vol. 11, no. 2, pp. 70–73, 1956.

Uchrin, G. C.: Transistor Power Converter Capable of 250 Watts D-C Output, *Proc. IRE*, vol. 44, no. 2, pp. 261–262, February, 1956.

Uhlir, A., Jr.: Two-terminal P-N Junction Devices for Frequency Conversion and Computation, *Proc. IRE*, vol. 44, no. 9, pp. 1183–1191, September, 1956.

Ukhanov, Yu. I.: A Pulse Method for the Study of Photoelectric Properties of P-N Junctions in Germanium, *Doklady Akad. Nauk S.S.S.R.*, vol. 111, no. 6, pp. 1238–1241, 1956.

Umarov, S. U., and L. G. Gurvich: Theory of the Metal-Semiconductor Contact, *Zhur. Tekh. Fiz.*, vol. 26, no. 10, pp. 2179–2184, 1956.

Upham, J. L., Jr., and A. I. Dranetz: Transistor Modulator for Airborne Recording, *Electronics*, vol. 29, no. 6, pp. 166–169, June, 1956.

Valdes, L. B.: The Frequency Response of Bipolar Transistors with Drift Fields, *Proc. IRE*, vol. 44, no. 2, pp. 178–184, February, 1956.

Vallese, L. M.: Temperature Stabilization of Transistor Amplifiers, *Trans. AIEE*, part I, vol. 75, pp. 379–384, 1956.

Varícak, M.: Oscillographic Measurement of V-I Diagrams of Semiconductors, *Period. Math.-Phys. Astrong. (Zagreb)*, vol. 11, no. 1, pp. 69–70, 1956.

Vasseur, J. P.: Calculation of Circuits Using Junction Transistors at High Frequencies, *Ann. radioélec.*, vol. 11, pp. 125–144, April, 1956.

Vasseur, J. P.: Maximum Powers of Semiconductor Junction Devices, *Ann. radioélec.*, vol. 11, pp. 1–28, January, 1956.

Vasseur, J. P.: Measurement of the High-frequency Parameters of Transistors, *Nachrtech. Fachberichte*, vol. 5, pp. 45–46, 1956.

Veloric, H. S., M. B. Prince, and M. J. Eder: Avalanche Breakdown Voltage in Silicon Diffused P-N Junctions as a Function of Impurity Gradient, *J. Appl. Phys.*, vol. 27, no. 8, pp. 895–899, August, 1956.

Vith, J.: Transistor and Valve, *V.D.E. Fachber.*, vol. 19 (II), pp. 170–173, 1956.

Voishvillo, G. V., and V. S. Davydov: A Graphical Method for Finding the Temperature Compensation in D-C Transistor Amplifiers, *Radiotekhnika*, vol. 11, no. 10, pp. 18–24, 1956.

Vul, B. M.: On the Breakdown of Junction Layers in Semiconductors, *Zhur. Tekh. Fiz.*, vol. 26, no. 11, pp. 2403–2416, 1956.

Wahl, A. J., and J. J. Kleimack: Factors Affecting Reliability of Alloy Junction Transistors, *Proc. IRE*, vol. 44, no. 4, pp. 494–502, April, 1956.

Walles, J.: Transistor Characteristics, *Nachrichtentechnik*, vol. 6, no. 5, pp. 105–113, March, 1956.

Wang, S.: Field-effect Measurements and Application to Semiconductor Surface Studies, *Sylvania Technologist*, vol. 9, no. 4, pp. 111–114, October, 1956.

Warner, R. M., and W. C. Hittinger: A Developmental Intrinsic-barrier Transistor, *IRE Trans. on Electron Devices*, vol. ED-3, no. 3, pp. 157–160, July, 1956.

Watkins, T. B.: Slow Relaxation Phenomena in Junction Diodes, *Proc. Phys. Soc. (London)*, vol. 69B, part 12, pp. 1353–1355, December, 1956.

Weber, H.: Pulse Amplification with Transistors, *Nachrtech. Fachberichte*, vol. 5, pp. 47–49, 1956.

Webster, R. R.: A Tetrode Transistor Amplifier for 5–40 Mc., *Electronic Inds.*, vol. 15, no. 11, pp. 62–64, 124, 126, 128, November, 1956.

Weinreich, G.: Transit Time Transistor, *J. Appl. Phys.*, vol. 27, no. 9, pp. 1025–1027, September, 1956.

Weiss, H.: On the Electrical Properties of Mixed Crystals of the Form In (As_yP_{1-y}), *Z. Naturforsch.*, vol. 11a, no. 6, pp. 430–434, June, 1956.

Wertheim, G. K.: Carrier Lifetime in Indium Antimonide, *Phys. Rev.*, vol. 104, no. 3, pp. 662–664, November 1, 1956.

Wertheim, G. K., and W. M. Augustyniak: Measurement of Short Carrier Lifetimes, *Rev. Sci. Instr.*, vol. 27, no. 12, pp. 1062–1064, December, 1956.

Westerberg, G.: The Transistor as a High-frequency Amplifier, *Tele* (Swedish ed.), no. 4, pp. 227–234, 1956.

Westerberg, G.: The Transistor in Pulse Circuits, *Tele* (Swedish ed.), no. 4, pp. 242–248, 1956.

Weyrick, R. C.: Transistor Analogue Computing Amplifiers for Flight Simulators, *Trans. AIEE*, part I, vol. 75, pp. 338–342, 1956.

Winiger, F.: Fundamentals of Semiconductors and Transistors, *Bull. assoc. suisse élec.*, vol. 47, no. 21, pp. 953–964, October 13, 1956.

Woods, J.: Changes in Conductivity Resulting from Breakdown in Cadmium Sulphide Single Crystals, *Proc. Phys. Soc. (London)*, vol. 69B, part 10, pp. 975–980, October, 1956.

Wrathall, L. R.: Transistorized Binary Pulse Regenerator, *Bell System Tech. J.*, vol. 35, no. 5, pp. 1059–1084, September, 1956.

Wulfsberg, P. G.: Transistors Up Reliability of Broadcast Remotes, *Electronics*, vol. 29, no. 1, pp. 122–125, January, 1956.

Yajima, T.: Emitter Current Noise in Junction Transistor, *J. Phys. Soc. Japan*, vol. 11, no. 10, pp. 1126–1127, October, 1956.

Yamaguchi, J.: On the Inductive Reactance and Negative Resistance on the Transistor, *J. Phys. Soc. Japan*, vol. 11, no. 6, pp. 717–718, June, 1956.

Zeller, H. R., Jr.: Transistor Preamplifier Feeds Tubeless Servo, *Electronics*, vol. 29, no. 2, pp. 168–169, February, 1956.

Zerbst, M., and W. Heywang; The Drift Mobility of the Charge Carriers in Very Pure Silicon, *Z. Naturforsch.*, vol. 11a, no. 7, pp. 608–609, July, 1956.

Zinsli, G.: A Crystal-diode Wattmeter, *Bull. assoc. suisse élec.*, vol. 47, no. 20, pp. 893–901, September 29, 1956.

Circuit Design for Transistor Blocking Oscillators, *Mullard Tech. Commun.*, vol. 2, pp. 235–239, April, 1956.

IRE Standards on Letter Symbols for Semiconductor Devices, *Proc. IRE*, vol. 44, no. 7, pp. 934–937, July, 1956.

IRE Standards on Solid-state Devices: Methods of Testing Transistors, 1956, *Proc. IRE*, vol. 44, no. 11, pp. 1542–1561, November, 1956.

Meltback Process Increases Transistor Range, *Electronics*, vol. 29, no. 8, pp. 190, 192, 194, August, 1956.

The Transistor Amplifier, *Wireless Engr.*, vol. 33, no. 2, pp. 31–32, February, 1956.
Transistor Amplifier Packaged in Steatite, *Electronics*, vol. 29, no. 10, pp. 272, 274, October, 1956.
Transistor Circuitry in Japan, *Electronics*, vol. 29, no. 7, pp. 120–124, July, 1956.
A Transistor Tester, *Mullard Tech. Commun.*, vol. 2, pp. 248–253, July, 1956.
Transistorized Magnetic-core Memory, *Electronics*, vol. 29, no. 9, pp. 210, 212, 214, 216, 218, September, 1956.
Transistors Increase Relay Sensitivity, *Brit. Commun. and Electronics*, vol. 3, no. 4, p. 173, April, 1956.
"Transistors," vol. I, RCA Laboratories, Princeton, N.J., 1956.
A 200 Mw Amplifier Employing Transistors, *Mullard Tech. Commun.*, vol. 2, pp. 210–216, April, 1956.

1957

Abraham, R. P.: A Wide-band Transistor Feedback Amplifier, *IRE WESCON Conv. Record*, vol. 1, part 2, pp. 10–19, 1957.
Adirovich, E. I., and V. G. Kolotilova: The Influence of Emitter Efficiency (γ) on the Transient Characteristics of Semiconducting Triodes, *Zhur. Tekh. Fiz.*, vol. 27, no. 3, pp. 473–477, 1957.
Airapetyants, A. V., A. V. Kogan, N. M. Reinov, S. M. Ryvkin, and I. A. Sokolov: On the Use of Germanium N-P (Junctions in) Alpha-particle Counters at Low Temperatures, *Zhur. Tekh. Fiz.*, vol. 27, no. 7, pp. 1599–1600, 1957.
Almond, J., and R. J. McIntyre: The Equivalent Circuit of the Drift Transistor, *RCA Rev.*, vol. 18, no. 3, pp. 361–384, September, 1957.
Amos, S. W.: Portable Transistor Receiver, I, *Wireless World*, vol. 63, no. 5, pp. 241–246, May, 1957.
Amos, S. W.: Portable Transistor Receiver, II. Circuit Details, *Wireless World*, vol. 63, no. 7, pp. 340–346, July, 1957.
Andresciani, V., and G. Della Pergola: Experimental Determination of the Lifetime of Minority Carriers in Semiconductors, *Ricerca sci.*, vol. 27, no. 9, pp. 2663–2673, September, 1957.
Anouchi, A. Y., and W. F. Palmer: Randomly Selected Transistor Output Pairs, *IRE WESCON Conv. Record*, vol. 1, part 2, pp. 27–53, 1957.
Aoyagi, K., K. Miyawaki, and J. Sasaki: Nonsaturating Junction-transistor Flip-flop Circuits, *J. Inst. Elec. Commun. Engrs. (Japan)*, vol. 40, no. 11, pp. 1196–1202, November, 1957.
Armstrong, H. L.: On the Switching Transient in the Forward Conduction of Semiconductor Diodes, *IRE Trans. on Electron Devices*, vol. ED-4, no. 2, pp. 111–113, April, 1957.
Armstrong, H. L.: A Theory of Voltage Breakdown of Cylindrical P-N Junctions, with Applications, *IRE Trans. on Electron Devices*, vol. ED-4, no. 1, pp. 15–16, January, 1957.
Armstrong, H. L.: Transistor Tuned Oscillators, *Electronics*, vol. 30, no. 2, pp. 218, 220, 222, 224, February 1, 1957.
Aronson, A. I., and C. F. Chong: Monovibrator Has Fast Recovery Time, *Electronics*, vol. 30, no. 12, pp. 158–159, December 1, 1957.
Avery, D. G., D. W. Goodwin, and A. E. Rennie: New Infra-red Detectors Using Indium, *J. Sci. Instr.*, vol. 34, no. 10, pp. 394–395, October, 1957.
Baker, D. W.: High-frequency Circuits Use Meltback Tetrodes, *Electronics*, vol. 30, no. 6, pp. 177–179, June 1, 1957.
Baker, R. H.: Boosting Transistor Switching Speed, *Electronics*, vol. 30, no. 3, pp. 190–193, March 1, 1957.
Balabanova, L. A., and M. M. Bredov: The Thermal Conversion of Germanium by Irradiation with Electrons, *Zhur. Tekh. Fiz.*, vol. 27, no. 7, pp. 1401–1407, 1957.
Barsukov, Yu. K.: Blocking Junction Process in Planar Germanium Diodes DG-Ts, *Zhur. Tekh. Fiz.*, vol. 27, no. 10, pp. 2252–2261, 1957.
Barsukov, Yu. K.: The Problem of the Representation of a Semiconductor Diode in the Form of the Series Connection of Two Non-linear Inertia Elements and the Applicability of the Pulse Method of Voltage Division, *Zhur. Tekh. Fiz.*, vol. 27, no. 10, pp. 2262–2267, 1957.
Bartz, G., and G. Weissenberg: Depicting P-N Junctions in Semiconductors by Means of Reflection Electron Microscopy, *Naturwissenschaften*, vol. 44, no. 7, p. 229, 1957.
Beale, J. R. A.: Alloy-diffusion: A Process for Making Diffused-base Junction Transistors, *Proc. Phys. Soc. (London)*, vol. 50B, part 11, pp. 1087–1089, November, 1957.
Beale, J. R. A., W. L. Stephenson, and E. Wolfendale: A Study of High-speed Avalanche Transistors, *Proc. Inst. Elec. Engrs. (London)*, vol. 104B, paper 2367R, pp. 394–402, July, 1957.

Beaufoy, R., and J. J. Sparkes: The Junction Transistor as a Charge-controlled Device, *A.T.E. J.*, vol. 13, no. 4, pp. 310–327, October, 1957.

Beckley, J. C., O. J. Edwards, L. H. Light, and P. Tharma: Car Radio Receiver with Transistor Output Operating from a 14-volt H.T. Line, *Mullard Tech. Commun.*, vol. 3, pp. 142–150, June, 1957.

Bell, J. H.: Noise in Semiconductor Materials and Devices, *Proc. Natl. Electronics Conf.*, vol. 13, pp. 218–234, 1957.

Beneking, H.: The Influence of Closely Spaced Connections on the D-C and A-C Behaviour of P-N Junctions, *Z. angew. Phys.*, vol. 9, no. 12, pp. 626–631, December, 1957.

Beneking, H.: Measurement of the Working Temperature of Transistors, *Arch. Elekt. Ubertragung*, vol. 11, no. 12, pp. 504–508, December, 1957.

Bereskin, A. B.: A High Power, High Quality Transistor Audio Power Amplifier, *IRE Natl. Conv. Record*, vol. 5, part 7, pp. 149–161, 1957.

Bereskin, A. B.: A Transistorized Decade Amplifier for Low-level Audio-frequency Applications, *IRE Trans. on Audio*, vol. AU-5, no. 5, pp. 138–142, September-October, 1957.

Berestnev, P. D.: Simplified Circuit Analysis of H.F. Self-excited Junction-transistor Oscillators, *Radiotekhnika*, vol. 12, no. 4, pp. 39–44, 1957.

Berman, L. S.: Increase of Power Output of a Tuned Transistor Amplifier by Improvement of Its Efficiency Coefficient, I, *Radiotekhnika*, vol. 12, no. 11, pp. 62–65, 1957.

Berman, L. S.: Use of the Hall Effect in Semiconductors for Electric Power Measurements, *Zhur. Tekh. Fiz.*, vol. 27, no. 6, pp. 1192–1196, 1957.

Berman, L. S., S. S. Raikhman, and Z. A. Khalfin: Balance Modulator Based on the Hall Effect in Semiconductors, *Zhur. Tekh. Fiz.*, vol. 27, no. 7, pp. 1597–1598, 1957.

Bernard, M.: Measurements of the Current in N-P Germanium Junctions as a Function of the Temperature, *J. Electronics*, vol. 2, no. 6, pp. 579–596, May, 1957.

Bhattacharyya, J. C.: An Analysis of Transient Response of Junction Transistor Amplifiers: *J. Inst. Telecommun. Engrs. (New Delhi)*, vol. 3, no. 4, pp. 297–303, September, 1957.

Bichara, M.: Determination of the Frequency of a Transistor Multivibrator between 4 and 4000 c/s, *Compt. rend.*, vol. 245, no. 9, pp. 896–898, August 26, 1957.

Billig, E., and D. B. Gasson: Preparation of Large-area P-N Junctions (Monocrystalline) Silicon by Surface Melting, *J. Appl. Phys.*, vol. 28, no. 11, pp. 1242–1245, November, 1957.

Bir, G. L., and G. E. Pikus: The Influence of Surface Recombination on the Efficiency of P-N Junction Photocells, *Zhur. Tekh. Fiz.*, vol. 27, no. 3, pp. 467–472, 1957.

Bittmann, C. A., and G. Bemski: Lifetime in Pulsed Silicon Crystals, *J. Appl. Phys.*, vol. 28, no. 12, pp. 1423–1426, December, 1957.

Blakemore, J. S.: Properties of Gallium Indium Antimonide, *Can. J. Phys.*, vol. 35, no. 1, pp. 91–97, January, 1957.

Blatt, F. J.: Hall and Drift Mobilities; Their Ratio and Temperature Dependence in Semiconductors, *Phys. Rev.*, vol. 105, no. 4, pp. 1203–1205, February 15, 1957.

Blecher, F. H.: Design Principles for Single Loop Transistor Feedback Amplifiers, *IRE Trans. on Circuit Theory*, vol. CT-4, no. 3, pp. 145–156, September, 1957.

Blecher, F. H.: Transistor Multiple Loop Feedback Amplifiers, *Proc. Natl. Electronics Conf.*, vol. 13, pp. 19–34, 1957.

Blet, G.: Effect of Temperature on the Height of the Potential Barrier in Selenium Photocells, *Compt. rend.*, vol. 244, no. 13, pp. 1754–1756, March 25, 1957.

Bogolyubov, V. F.: Application to the Investigation of Contact Potentials of Semiconductors, *Radiotekh. i Elektron.*, vol. 2, no. 3, pp. 323–327, 1957.

Bogomolov, V. N., and V. D. Vasil'ev: An Attempt to Use the Linear Hall Effect Detector for Measurement Purposes, *Zhur. Tekh. Fiz.*, vol. 27, no. 2, pp. 260–261, 1957.

Bonch-Bruevich, V. L.: Remarks on the Theory of Electron Plasma in Semiconductors, *Zhur. Eksptl. i Teort. Fiz.*, vol. 32, no. 5, pp. 1092–1097, 1957.

Bond, W. L.: The Depth of Diffused Layers, *Bell Labs. Record*, vol. 35, no. 1, pp. 1–5, January, 1957.

Booth, G. W., and T. P. Bothwell: Basic Logic Circuits for Computer Applications, *Electronics*, vol. 30, no. 3, pp. 196–200, March 1, 1957.

Boxall, F. S.: Base Current Feedback in Transistor Power Amplifier Design, *IRE WESCON Conv. Record*, vol. 1, part 2, pp. 20–26, 1957.

Bradshaw, S. E., and A. I. Mlavsky: The Control of the Properties of Single Crystal Silicon, pp. 21–26 in "Report of the Meeting (April, 1956) on Semiconductors," The Physical Society, London, 1957.

Brophy, J. J.: Excess Noise in N-type Germanium, *Phys. Rev.*, vol. 106, no. 4, pp. 675–678, May 15, 1957.

Brostrup-Jensen, P.: An Underground-cable Detector Using Transistors, *Teleteknik* (Danish ed.), vol. 8, no. 3–4, pp. 220–225, December, 1957.

Brown, J. S.: Some Useful Techniques for Transistor Power Gain Measurements, *Proc. Natl. Electronics Conf.*, vol. 13, pp. 403–408, 1957.

Brunson, G. S.: Transistorized Photomultiplier Has 0.1 μ Sec. Resolution, *Nucleonics*, vol. 15, no. 7, pp. 86–87, July, 1957.

Budínský, J.: Determination of the Characteristics with a Negative-resistance Region in Point-contact Transistors, *Slaboproudý Obzor*, vol. 18, no. 7, pp. 432–438, 1957.

Budínský, J.: Negative Resistance in the Input and Output Circuits of a Point-contact Transistor, *Slaboproudý Obzor*, vol. 18, no. 4, pp. 186–191, 1957.

Bürger, A.: The Behaviour of Germanium Transistors and Diodes in Magnetic Fields, *Slaboproudý Obzor*, vol. 18, no. 11, pp. 746–755, 1957.

Burgess, R. E.: A Millisecond Relaxation Process in the Reverse Current of Germanium Point-contact Diodes, *Brit. J. Appl. Phys.*, vol. 8, no. 2, pp. 62–63, February, 1957.

Burr, R. P.: Transistor Feedback Preamplifiers, *IRE Trans. on Broadcast and Television Receivers*, vol. BTR-3, no. 1, pp. 35–39, June, 1957.

Burton, J. A.: Electron Emission from Avalanche Breakdown in Silicon, *Phys. Rev.*, vol. 108, no. 5, pp. 1342–1343, December 1, 1957.

Burton, P. L.: A Transistor D-C Chopper Amplifier, *Electronic Eng.*, vol. 29, pp. 393–397, August, 1957.

Byczkowski, M., and J. R. Madigan: Minority Carrier Lifetime in P-N Junction Devices, *J. Appl. Phys.*, vol. 28, no. 8, pp. 878–881, August, 1957.

Cagle, W. B., and W. H. Chen: A New Method of Designing Low Level, High-speed Semiconductor Logic Circuits, *IRE WESCON Conv. Record*, vol. 1, part 2, pp. 3–9, 1957.

Čermák, J.: The Equivalent Circuit of a Junction Transistor, *Slaboproudý Obzor*, vol. 18, no. 5, pp. 299–303, 1957.

Chang, S. S. L.: Relation between Ratio of Diffusion Lengths of Minority Carriers and Ratio of Conductivities, *Proc. IRE*, vol. 45, no. 7, pp. 1019–1020, July, 1957.

Chaplin, G. B. B., and A. R. Owens: Some Transistor Input Stages for High-gain D-C Amplifiers, *Proc. Inst. Elec. Engrs. (London)*, vol. 105B, paper 2382M, pp. 249–257, July, 1957.

Chaplin, G. B. B., and A. R. Owens: A Transistor High-gain Chopper-type D-C Amplifier, *Proc. Inst. Elec. Engrs. (London)*, vol. 105B, paper 2442M, pp. 258–265, 266–271, November, 1957.

Chisholm, H. C.: High-reliability Transistorized Counter, *Electronics*, vol. 30, no. 6, pp. 171–173, June 1, 1957.

Chow, W. F.: Superregenerative Transistor Transceiver, *Electronics*, vol. 30, no. 4, pp. 181–182, April 1, 1957.

Chow, W. F., and D. A. Paynter: Series Tuned Methods in Transistor Radio Circuitry, *IRE Trans. on Circuit Theory*, vol. CT-4, no. 3, pp. 174–178, September, 1957.

Chynoweth, A. G., and K. G. McKay: Internal Field Emission in Silicon P-N Junctions, *Phys. Rev.*, vol. 106, no. 3, pp. 418–426, May 1, 1957.

Chynoweth, A. G., and K. G. McKay: Threshold Energy for Electron-hole Pair-production by Electrons in Silicon, *Phys. Rev.*, vol. 108, no. 1, pp. 29–34, October 1, 1957.

Cimagalli, V.: The Junction-transistor, a Stable Multivibrator, *Alta frequenza*, vol. 27, no. 2–3, pp. 159–184, April–June, 1957.

Clark, J. W.: Effects of Radiation on Semiconductors, *Electronic Inds.*, vol. 16, no. 8, pp. 80–81, 169–172, August, 1957.

Clark, J. W., H. L. Wiser, and M. D. Petroff: Radiation Effects on Silicon Diodes, *IRE WESCON Conv. Record*, vol. 1, part 9, pp. 43–51, 1957.

Clarke, D. H.: Semiconductor Lifetime as a Function of Recombination State Density, *J. Electronics and Control*, vol. 3, no. 4, pp. 375–386, October, 1957.

Coblenz, A.: Semiconductor Compounds Open New Horizons, *Electronics*, vol. 30, no. 11, pp. 144–149, November 1, 1957.

Coffey, W. N.: Measuring Transistor "Power Gain" at High Frequencies, *Electronic Inds.*, vol. 16, no. 10, pp. 66–68, 167–169, October, 1957.

Collins, C. B., R. O. Carlson, and C. J. Gallagher: Properties of Gold-doped Silicon, *Phys. Rev.*, vol. 105, no. 4, pp. 1168–1173, February 15, 1957.

Cooke-Yarborough, E. H.: "An Introduction to Transistor Circuits," Interscience Publishers, New York, 1957.

Cramwinckel, A.: Transistor Operating Point Stabilization, *Philips Telecommun. Rev.*, vol. 17, no. 3, pp. 100–107, January, 1957.

Cridlan, D. E., and J. E. Thwaites: A Small Quartz Clock with Transistor Drive, *Post Off. Elec. Engrs. J.*, vol. 50, part 3, pp. 189–191, October, 1957.

Cripps, L. G.: Low-frequency Transistor Oscillators, *Mullard Tech. Commun.*, vol. 3, pp. 44–58, March, 1957.

Cronemeyer, D. C.: Hall and Drift Mobility in High-resistivity Single-crystal Silicon, *Phys. Rev.*, vol. 105, no. 2, pp. 522–523, January 15, 1957.

Curtis, O. L., Jr., J. W. Cleland, J. H. Crawford, Jr., and J. G. Pigg: Effect of Irradiation on the Hole Lifetime of N-type Germanium, *J. Appl. Phys.*, vol. 28, no. 10, pp. 1161–1165, October, 1957.

Cutler, M.: Point Contact Rectifier Theory, *IRE Trans. on Electron Devices*, vol. ED-4, no. 3, pp. 201–206, July, 1957.

Cutler, M., and H. M. Bath: Surface Leakage Current in Silicon Fused Junction Diodes, *Proc. IRE*, vol. 45, no. 1, pp. 39–43, January, 1957.

Czeija, E.: Measurement of Rectified Values with Vacuum-diodes and Barrier-layer Rectifiers: Peak-value Measurements and Circuit Characteristics, *Arch. tech. Messen*, no. 257 (ref. J82–12), pp. 137–140, June, 1957.

Davidson, J. J.: Low Noise Transistor Microphone Amplifier, *IRE Natl. Conv. Record*, vol. 5, part 7, pp. 162–168, 1957.

Davies, L. W.: Low-High Conductivity Junctions in Semiconductors, *Proc. Phys. Soc. (London)*, vol. 70B, part 9, pp. 885–889, September, 1957.

DeCastro, E.: D-C Phase Invertors and Balanced Amplifiers Using Transistors, *Elettrotecnica*, vol. 44, no. 12, pp. 701–709, December 10–25, 1957.

Denda, S., and M. Kikuchi: Fundamental Characteristics of the Avalanche Transistor, *Bull. Electrotech. Lab. (Tokyo)*, vol. 21, no. 4, pp. 250–256, April, 1957.

Diebold, E. J.: Temperature Rise of Solid Junctions under Pulse Load, *Commun. and Electronics*, no. 33, November, 1957.

Dill, F., Jr., and L. Depian: Applications of Semiconductor Junction Capacitance, *IRE Natl. Conv. Record*, vol. 5, part 2, pp. 134–136, 1957.

Divoire, E., and A. Dumont: The Parameters of Transistors at High Frequencies; Calculations for a 455 Kc/s Amplifier, *Rev. HF*, vol. 3, no. 10, pp. 339–358, 1957.

Dobrinski, P., H. Knabe, and H. Muller: Zener-diodes with Silicon, *NTZ-Nachrtech. Z.*, vol. 10, no. 4, pp. 195–199, April, 1957.

Donovan, B., and N. H. March: On the Absorption by Free Carriers in Semiconductors, *Proc. Phys. Soc. (London)*, vol. 70B, part 9, pp. 883–885, September, 1957.

Dorin, V. A., and D. N. Nasledov: On the Problem of the Structure of the Upper, Adjacent to the Electrode, Layer of a Selenium Rectifier, *Zhur. Tekh. Fiz.*, vol. 27, no. 1, pp. 90–94, 1957.

Dorn, D.: On the Temperature Dependence of the Mobility in Non-polar Semiconductors, *Z. Naturforsch.*, vol. 12a, no. 1, pp. 18–22, January, 1957.

Dortort, I. K.: A New Voltage-divider Circuit for Semiconductor Rectifiers, *Trans. AIEE*, part I, vol. 76, pp. 356–358, 1957.

Drabble, J. R., and R. Wolfe: Geometrical Effects in Transverse Magnetoresistance Measurements, *J. Electronics and Control*, vol. 3, no. 3, pp. 259–266, September, 1957.

Dunham, B.: The Multipurpose Bias Device. I. The Commutator Transistor, *I.B.M. J. Research Develop.*, vol. 1, no. 2, pp. 116–129, April, 1957.

Dunn, M. V., and K. Mukhopadhyay: An Artificial Traffic Equipment for Calcutta Director Exchanges, *Telecommunications (Jabalpur)*, vol. 7, no. 1, pp. 19–28, June, 1957.

Easley, J. W.: The Effect of Collector Capacity on the Transient Response of Junction Transistors, *IRE Trans. on Electron Devices*, vol. ED-4, no. 1, pp. 6–14, January, 1957.

Eddins, W. T.: A Unique Wide-band Transistorized Pulse Amplifier, *IRE Natl. Conv. Record*, vol. 5, part 5, pp. 70–74, 1957.

Edwards, O. J.: Heat Sinks for Power Transistors, *Mullard Tech. Commun.*, vol. 3, pp. 59–61, March, 1957.

Edwards, O. J.: A 200 Mw Amplifier Employing Transistors Operated from a 6 V Supply, *Mullard Tech. Commun.*, vol. 3, pp. 32–33, February, 1957.

Edwards, O. J., and L. H. Light: Audio Stages for All-transistor Portables, *Mullard Tech. Commun.*, vol. 3, pp. 188–194, October, 1957.

Eichholz, G. G., G. E. Alexander, and A. H. Bettens: All-transistor Circuits for Portable Detectors, *Nucleonics*, vol. 15, no. 11, pp. 90–93, November, 1957.

Elpat'evskaya, O. D., and A. R. Regel': Some Peculiarities of the Electrical Properties of Films of HgSe-HgTe, *Zhur. Tekh. Fiz.*, vol. 27, no. 1, pp. 45–50, 1957.

Engler, A. R., and C. J. Kevane: Direct Reading Minority Carrier Lifetime Measuring Apparatus, *Rev. Sci. Instr.*, vol. 28, no. 7, pp. 548–551, July, 1957.

Enslein, K.: Characteristics of Silicon Junction Diodes as Precision Voltage Reference Devices, *IRE Trans. on Instrumentation*, vol. I-6, no. 2, pp. 105–118, June, 1957.

Erdmann, R. G.: A Transistor Marker Beacon Receiver, *IRE Trans. on Aeronaut. Navigational Electronics*, vol. ANE-4, no. 3, pp. 130–135, September, 1957.

Eriksen, W. T., H. Statz, and G. A. deMars: Excess Surface Currents on Germanium and Silicon Diodes, *J. Appl. Phys.*, vol. 28, no. 1, pp. 133–139, January, 1957.

Evans, D. M.: Measurements on Alloy-type Transistors with Varying Collector Voltage, *Brit. J. Appl. Phys.*, vol. 8, no. 1, pp. 44–45, January, 1957.

Evans, J.: High-frequency Junction Transistors, *Direct Current*, vol. 3, no. 3, pp. 74–84, January, 1957.

Farber, R. J., A. Proudfit, K. M. St. John, and C. R. Wilhe'msen: Tetrajunction Transistor Simplifies Receiver Design, *Electronics*, vol. 30, no. 4, pp. 148–151, April 1, 1957.

Fedorowski, M.: A Transformerless Class-B Power Amplifier Using Identical Transistors, *Prace Inst. Tele-i Radiotech.*, vol. 1, no. 3, pp. 57–77, 1957.

Filiński, I.: Modulation of Light Reflected from Germanium by Injected Current Carriers, *Phys. Rev.*, vol. 107, no. 4, p. 1193, August 15, 1957.

Filippov, A. G.: Frequency Characteristics of Composite Semiconductor Triodes, *Radiotekhnika*, vol. 12, no. 8, pp. 21–27, 1957.

Firle, T. E.: Some Silicon Junction Diode Recovery Phenomena, *IRE WESCON Conv. Record*, vol. 1, part 3, pp. 90–99, 1957.

Fisher, M. E.: A Wide Band Analogue Multiplier Using Crystal Diodes and Its Application to the Study of a Non-linear Differential Equation, *Electronic Eng.*, vol. 29, pp. 580–585, December, 1957.

Fleming, L.: Silicon Diode Chopper Stabilizes D-C Amplifier, *Electronics*, vol. 30, no. 1, pp. 178–179, January 1, 1957.

Fletcher, N. H.: General Semiconductor Junction Relations, *J. Electronics*, vol. 2, no. 6, pp. 609–610, May, 1957.

Fletcher, N. H.: The High Current Limit for Semiconductor Junction Devices, *Proc. IRE*, vol. 45, no. 6, pp. 862–872, June, 1957.

Fletcher, N. H.: A Junction Transistor for Kilowatt Pulses, *Proc. IRE*, vol. 45, no. 4, p. 544, April, 1957.

Follingstad, H. G.: Complete Linear Characterization of Transistors from Low through Very High Frequencies, *IRE Trans. on Instrumentation*, vol. I-6, no. 1, pp. 49–63, March, 1957.

Forshaw, G., and N. W. Morgalia: Junction Transistors in Switching Applications, *A.T.E. J.*, vol. 13, no. 1, pp. 3–27, January, 1957.

Foster, W. H.: Completely Transistorized Strain Gage Oscillator, *IRE Natl. Conv. Record*, vol. 5, part 5, pp. 75–87, 1957.

Freedman, L. A.: Design Considerations in the First Stage of Transistor Receivers, *RCA Rev.*, vol. 18, no. 2, pp. 145–162, June, 1957.

Fukuroi, T., and C. Yamanouchi: Electrical Properties of P-type Indium Antimonide, *Sci. Repts. Research Insts. Tôhoku Univ.*, ser. A, vol. 9, no. 4, pp. 262–266, August, 1957.

Fukuroi, T., and C. Yamanouchi: The Relationship between the Hall Coefficient and the Resistivity of Semiconductors, Taking Various Scattering Mechanisms of the Charge Carriers into Account, *sci. Repts. Research Insts. Tôhoku Univ.*, ser. A, vol. 9, no. 4, pp. 267–272, August, 1957.

Fuller, C. S., and R. A. Logan: Effect of Heat Treatment upon the Electrical Properties of Silicon Crystals, *J. Appl. Phys.*, vol. 28, no. 12, pp. 1427–1436, December, 1957.

Fuller, E. J.: Pulse Generator Uses Junction Transistors, *Electronics*, vol. 30, no. 9, pp. 176–179, September 1, 1957.

Garlick, G. F. J.: Solid State Image Amplifiers, *J. Sci. Instr.*, vol. 34, no. 12, pp. 473–479, December, 1957.

Garrett, C. G. B.: High-frequency Relaxation Processes in the Field-effect Experiment, *Phys. Rev.*, vol. 107, no. 2, pp. 478–487, July 15, 1957.

Gärtner, W. W.: Design Theory for Depletion Layer Transistors, *Proc. IRE*, vol. 45, no. 10, pp. 1392–1400, October, 1957.

Gärtner, W. W.: Temperature Dependence of Junction Transistor Parameters, *Proc. IRE*, vol. 45, no. 5(1), pp. 662–680, May, 1957.

Garver, R. V., E. G. Spencer, and R. C. LeCraw: High-speed Microwave Switching of Semiconductors, *J. Appl. Phys.*, vol. 28, no. 11, pp. 1336–1338, November, 1957.

Ghandhi, S. K.: Bias Considerations in Transistor Circuit Design, *IRE Trans. on Circuit Theory*, vol. CT-4, no. 3, pp. 194–202, September, 1957.

Ghandhi, S. K.: Darlington's Compound Connection for Transistors, *IRE Trans. on Circuit Theory*, vol. CT-4, no. 3, pp. 291–292, September, 1957.

Giacoletto, L. J.: Junction Capacitance and Related Characteristics Using Graded Impurity Semiconductors, *IRE Trans. on Electron Devices*, vol. ED-4, no. 3, pp. 207–215, July, 1957.

Giacoletto, L. J.: Transistorized RC Phase-shift Power Oscillator, *IRE Trans. on Audio*, vol. AU-5, no. 3, pp. 59–62, May–June, 1957.

Gillis, R. C., and J. W. Tarzwell: Resistance of Silicon Transistors to Neutron Bombardment, *IRE WESCON Conv. Record*, vol. 1, part 3, pp. 48–72, 1957.

Giustini, S.: Direct-coupled Amplifiers Employing Junction Transistors, *Alta frequenza*, vol. 26, no. 4, pp. 196–225, August, 1957.

Glaser, W.: Quantitative Treatment of the Transistor Stage with Feedback, *Nachrichtentechnik*, vol. 7, no. 4, pp. 159–162, April, 1957.

Glinchuk, K. D., E. G. Miselyuk, and N. N. Fortunatova: The Effect of Annealing on the Local Energy Levels and the Lifetime of the Non-equilibrium Current Carriers in Iron-doped Germanium, *Zhur. Tekh. Fiz.*, vol. 27, no. 11, pp. 2666–2667, 1957.

Glinchuk, K. D., E. G. Miselyuk, and N. N. Fortunatova: Investigation of the Recombination of Current Carriers in Germanium with Iron Impurity, *Zhur. Tekh. Fiz.*, vol. 27, no. 11, pp. 2451–2457, 1957.

Goffaux, R.: Properties of Silicon Carbide under the Action of Electric Pulses, *Rev. gén. élec.*, vol. 66, no. 9, pp. 463–472, September, 1957.

Golde, W.: Duality and Analogies between Transistor and Valve Circuits, *Arch. Elektrotech.* (*Warsaw*), vol. 6, no. 3, pp. 307–341, 1957.

Goldstein, B.: Electron Mobility in the Germanium-Silicon Alloys, *RCA Rev.*, vol. 18, no. 4, pp. 458–465, December, 1957.

Goodman, C. H. L.: A New Group of Compounds with Diamond-type (Chalcopyrite) Structure, *Nature*, vol. 179, pp. 828–829, April 20, 1957.

Goodwin, D. W.: Cooled Photoconductive Detectors Using Indium Antimonide, *J. Sci. Instr.*, vol. 34, no. 9, pp. 367–368, September, 1957.

Gordon, S. H.: Compensating Silicon Transistor Amplifiers, *Electronics*, vol. 30, no. 7, pp. 184–185, July 1, 1957.

Gorton, R.: Effects of Irradiation upon Diodes of the Silicon Junction Type, *Nature*, vol. 179, p. 864, April 27, 1957.

Green, G. W., C. A. Hogarth, and F. A. Johnson: Some Observations of the Effects of Oxygen on the Minority Carrier Lifetime and Optical Absorption of Silicon Crystals Pulled in Vacuo, *J. Electronics and Control*, vol. 3, no. 2, pp. 171–182, August, 1957.

Green, M.: Drift Mobility Measurements, *J. Appl. Phys.*, vol. 28, no. 12, pp. 1473–1478, December, 1957.

Gribnikov, Z. S., and K. B. Tolpy̆go: Injection Coefficient and Direct Volt-Ampere Characteristic of a Spherical Contact, *Zhur. Tekh. Fiz.*, vol. 27, no. 4, pp. 625–629, 1957.

Gröneveld, E. W.: Some Transistor Circuits in Pulse Technique, *Ned. Tijdschr. Natuurk.*, vol. 23, no. 3, pp. 69–77, March, 1957.

Gudmundsen, R. A., and J. Maserjian, Jr.: Semiconductor Properties of Recrystallized Silicon in Aluminum Alloy Junction Diodes, *J. Appl. Phys.*, vol. 28, no. 11, pp. 1308–1316, November, 1957.

Guggenbühl, W., and M. J. O. Strutt: Theory and Experiments on Shot Noise in Semiconductor Junction Diodes and Transistors, *Proc. IRE*, vol. 45, no. 6, pp. 839–854, June, 1957.

Guggenbühl, W., and W. Wunderlin: Experimental Determination of Extrinsic Base and Emitter Resistances of Alloyed Junction Transistors by Means of Low Frequency Measurements, *Arch. Elekt. Ubertragung*, vol. 11, no. 9, pp. 355–358, September, 1957.

Guggi, W. B.: CRT Deflection Circuit Has High Efficiency, *Electronics*, vol. 30, no. 4, pp. 172–175, April 1, 1957.

Gurnett, K. W., and R. A. Hilbourne: Distortion Due to the Mismatch of Transistors in Push-Pull Audio-frequency Amplifiers, *Proc. Inst. Elec. Engrs.* (*London*), monograph 232R, April, 1957.

Guro, G. M.: Decay Law for Concentration of Non-equilibrium Charge Carriers in Semiconductors, *Zhur. Eksptl. i Teort. Fiz.*, vol. 33, no. 1(7), pp. 158–165, 1957.

Gutzwiller, F. W.: Rating and Application of Germanium and Silicon Rectifiers, *Commun. and Electronics*, no. 28, January, 1957.

Halsted, R. E.: Temperature Consideration in Solar Battery Development, *J. Appl. Phys.*, vol. 28, no. 10, p. 1131, October, 1957.

Haneman, D., and A. J. Mortlock: Point Contact Transistor Studies Using Radioactive Collectors, *Proc. Phys. Soc.* (*London*), vol. 70B, part 1, pp. 145–147, January, 1957.

Hanson, G. H., and A. van der Ziel: Shot Noise in Transistors, *Proc. IRE*, vol. 45, no. 11, pp. 1538–1542, November, 1957.

Harris, H. F., and T. E. Smith: Low Level Transistorized Chopper Amplifiers, *IRE Trans. on Telemetry and Remote Control*, vol. TRC-3, no. 1, paper 3–5, April, 1957.

Hasiguti, R. R., E. Matsuura, and S. Ishino: Lifetime Measurements of Minority Carriers in Deuteron Irradiated Germanium Crystals, *J. Phys. Soc. Japan*, vol. 12, no. 12, pp. 1351–1354, December, 1957.

Heinlein, W.: The Time Lag of Pulse-controlled Semiconductor Diodes and Its Physical Interpretation, *Arch. Elekt. Ubertragung*, vol. 11, no. 101, pp. 387–396, October, 1957.

Henderson, J. C., and J. R. Tillman: Minority-carrier Storage in Semiconductor Diodes, *Proc. Inst. Elec. Engrs.* (*London*), paper 2293R, January, 1957.

Hendrick, R. W., Jr.: Measuring Parameters of Junction Transistors, *Electronics*, vol. 30, no. 8, pp. 174–176, August 1, 1957.

Henisch, H. K.: "Rectifying Semiconductor Contacts," Oxford University Press, London, 1957 (International Series of Monographs on Physics).

Henkels, H. W.: The Fused Silicon Rectifier, *Commun. and Electronics*, no. 28, January, 1957.

Henkels, H. W.: Transistor High Level Injection and High Current Switches, *Proc. Natl. Electronics Conf.*, vol. 13, pp. 235–245, 1957.

Henkels, H. W., and G. Strull: Very High-power Transistors with Evaporated Aluminum Electrodes, *IRE Trans. on Electron Devices*, vol. ED-4, no. 4, pp. 291-294, October, 1957.

Herlet, A.: Determination of Diffusion Length (L) and Carrier Density in the Inversion Layer (n_i) from the Forward Characteristic of Alloyed-junction Silicon Rectifiers, *Z. angew. Phys.*, vol. 9, no. 4, pp. 155–158, April, 1957.

Herzog, W.: Transistor Oscillators and Their Independence of Load, *NTZ-Nachrtech. Z.*, vol. 10, no. 11, pp. 564–569, November, 1957.

Hilsum, C., and I. M. Ross: An Infrared Photocell Based on the Photo-electromagnetic Effect in Indium Antimonide, *Nature*, vol. 179, p. 146, January 19, 1957.

Hlȳnchuk, K. D., H. K. Ivanova, and O. H. Miselyuk: On the Effect on Ge Point Triodes of the Lifetime of Minority Carriers, *Ukraïn. Fiz. Zhur.*, vol. 2, no. 4, pp. 338–346, 1957.

Hobstetter, J. N., and P. Breidt, Jr.: Detection of Both Vacancies and Interstitials in Deformed Germanium, *J. Appl. Phys.*, vol. 28, no. 10, pp. 1214–1215, October, 1957.

Holford, K.: D-C Amplifier Using Transistors and a Silicon Bridge Modulator, *Mullard Tech. Commun.*, vol. 3, pp. 126–137, June, 1957.

Hollmann, H. E.: Tandem-transistors with the Properties of Electron Tubes, *Hochfrequenztech. u. Elecktrokust.*, vol. 65, no. 5, pp. 149–159, March, 1957.

Holmes, D. D.: A Six-transistor Portable Receiver Employing a Complementary Symmetry Output Stage, *IRE Natl. Conv. Record*, vol. 5, part 3, pp. 193–198, 1957.

Hrostowski, H. J., and R. H. Kaiser: Infrared Absorption of Oxygen in Silicon, *Phys. Rev.*, vol. 107, no. 4, pp. 966–972, August 15, 1957.

Hughes, H. E., J. H. Wiley, and P. Zuk: Diffused Silicon Diodes—Design, Characteristics and Aging Data, *IRE WESCON Conv. Record*, vol. 1, part 3, pp. 80–89, 1957.

Humphrey, J. N., and R. L. Petritz: Photoconductivity in Lead Selenide: Theory of the Dependence and Sensitivity on Film Thickness and Absorption Coefficients, *Phys. Rev.*, vol. 105, no. 4, pp. 1192–1197, February 15, 1957.

Humphrey, J. N., and R. L. Petritz: Photoconductivity of Lead Selenide: Theory of the Mechanism of Sensitization, *Phys. Rev.*, vol. 105, no. 6, pp. 1736–1740, March 15, 1957.

Hurley, R. B.: Avalanche Flow Line Analysis, *Electronic Inds.*, vol. 16, no. 6, pp. 101–102, 437–438, June, 1957.

Hurley, R. B.: Flow Line Analysis, *Electronic Inds.*, vol. 16, no. 4, pp. 52–54, 136, 138, 140, April, 1957.

Hurtig, C. R.: Sensory Aid Defines Lights and Marks, *Electronics*, vol. 30, no. 2, pp. 162–163, February 1, 1957.

Hyde, F. J., and R. W. Smith: Transistor Relaxation Oscillations, *Electronic Eng.*, vol. 29, pp. 234–236, May, 1957.

Iglitsȳn, M. I., Yu. A. Kontsevoĭ, and V. D. Kudin: Measurement of the Charge-carrier Lifetime in Monocrystalline Silicon, *Zhur. Tekh. Fiz.*, vol. 27, no. 7, pp. 1425–1430, 1957.

Iglitsȳn, M. I., Yu. A. Kontsevoĭ, V. D. Kudin, and A. A. Meĭer: Measurement of the Charge-carrier Lifetime in Semiconductors, *Zhur. Tekh. Fiz.*, vol. 27, no. 7, pp. 1414–1424, 1957.

Iglitsȳn, M. I., Yu. A. Kontsevoĭ, and A. I. Sidorov: Distribution of Non-equilibrium Charge Carriers in the Base Region of a P-N Junction with a High Injection Coefficient, *Zhur. Tekh. Fiz.*, vol. 27, no. 11, pp. 2458–2460, 1957.

Iglitsȳn, M. I., Yu. A. Kontsevoĭ, and A. I. Sidorov: Lifetime of Non-equilibrium Charge Carriers in Germanium for Arbitrary Injection Levels, *Zhur. Tekh. Fiz.*, vol. 27, no. 11, pp. 2461–2468, 1957.

Inuishi, Y.: Noise from Ge PN Junction and γ-ray Irradiation Effect, *J. Phys. Soc. Japan*, vol. 12, no. 4, p. 439, April, 1957.

Jackson, R. B., and A. K. Walton: Abnormal Noise in Junction Transistors during Secondary Ionization, *Proc. Phys. Soc. (London)*, vol. 70B, part 2, p. 251, February, 1957.

Jacobsen, A. B.: Factors in the Reliability of Germanium Power Transistors, *IRE Trans. on Reliability and Quality Control*, no. RQC-10, pp. 43–48, June, 1957.

Jacobsen, A. B., and C. G. Tinsley: Test Equipment for Transistor Production, *Electronics*, vol. 30, no. 10, pp. 148–151, October 1, 1957.

Jansson, L. E.: Equivalent Circuits for Junction Transistors, *Mullard Tech. Commun.*, vol. 3, pp. 151–160, June, 1957.

Jansson, L. E.: High-frequency Amplification Using Junction Transistors, *Mullard Tech. Commun.*, vol. 3, pp. 174–187, October, 1957.

Jensen, J. L.: An Improved Square-wave Oscillator Circuit, *IRE Trans. on Circuit Theory*, vol. CT-4, no. 3, pp. 276–279, September, 1957.

Johnson, E. O.: Comparison of the Semiconductor Surface and Junction Photovoltages, *RCA Rev.*, vol. 18, no. 4, pp. 556–577, December, 1957.

Johnson, E. O.: Measurement of Minority Carrier Lifetimes with the Surface Photovoltage, *J. Appl. Phys.*, vol. 28, no. 11, pp. 1349–1353, November, 1957.

Johnson, E. O.: Simplified Treatment of Electric Charge Relations at a Semiconductor Surface, *RCA Rev.*, vol. 18, no. 4, pp. 525–555, December, 1957.

Johnson, L. B., and P. Vermes: D-C Stabilisation of Junction Transistors, *Mullard Tech. Commun.*, vol. 3, pp. 67–96, April, 1957.

Jones, A. R.: Noise in Transistor Nucleonic Pulse Amplifiers, *IRE Natl. Conv. Record*, vol. 5, part 9, pp. 78–84, 1957.

Jonscher, A. K.: Diffusion of Minority Carriers in the Presence of Trapping, *Proc. Phys. Soc. (London)*, vol. 70B, part 2, pp. 230–234, February, 1957.

Jonscher, A. K.: Drift of Minority Carriers in the Presence of Trapping, *Proc. Phys. Soc. (London)*, vol. 70B, part 2, pp. 223–229, February, 1957.

Jonscher, A. K.: P-N-P-N Switching Diodes, *J. Electronics and Control*, vol. 3, no. 6, pp. 573–586, December, 1957.

Kaiser, W.: Electrical and Optical Properties of Heat-treated Silicon, *Phys. Rev.*, vol. 105, no. 6, pp. 1751–1756, March 15, 1957.

Kazan, B.: An Improved High-gain Panel Light Amplifier, *Proc. IRE*, vol. 45, no. 10, pp. 1358–1364, October, 1957.

Keister, G. L., and H. V. Stewart: The Effect of Nuclear Radiation on Selected Semiconductor Devices, *Proc. IRE*, vol. 45, no. 7, pp. 931–937, July, 1957.

Keizer, E. O.: A Carrier-energized Bistable Circuit Using Variable-capacitance Diodes, *RCA Rev.*, vol. 18, no. 4, pp. 475–485, December, 1957.

Kelen, A., and P. Svedberg: The Thermoelectric Transistor; a Possible Batteryless Amplifying Semiconductor Device, *Appl. Sci. Research*, vol. 6B, no. 5, pp. 369–378, 1957.

Keonjian, E., and J. J. Suran: Unijunction Transistor Forms Flip-Flop, *Electronics*, vol. 30, no. 9, pp. 165–167, September, 1957.

Kestenbaum, A. L., and N. H. Ditrick: Design, Construction, and High-frequency Performance of Drift Transistors, *RCA Rev.*, vol. 18, no. 1, pp. 12–23, March, 1957.

Kidd, M. C.: Transistor Receiver Video Amplifiers, *RCA Rev.*, vol. 18, no. 3, pp. 308–321, September, 1957.

Kikuchi, M.: Peripheral Inhomogeneities of the Alloyed Germanium P-N Junction, *J. Phys. Soc. Japan*, vol. 12, no. 2, pp. 133–139, February, 1957.

Kikuchi, M.: Some Experiments on the Surface Field Effect in Germanium Single Crystals, *J. Phys. Soc. Japan*, vol. 12, no. 7, pp. 756–762, July, 1957.

Kingston, R. H. (editor), with assistance from K. Burstein, A. L. McWhorter, P. H. Miller, Jr., D. T. Stevenson, and P. B. Weisz: "Semiconductor Surface Physics," University of Pennsylvania Press, Philadelphia, 1957.

Kobayashi, A., and S. Kawaji: Free Bonds on the Clean Surfaces of Germanium Single Crystals, *J. Phys. Soc. Japan*, vol. 12, no. 9, p. 1054, September, 1957.

Kolm, C., S. A. Kulin, and B. L. Averbach: Studies on Group III–V Intermetallic Compounds, *Phys. Rev.*, vol. 108, no. 4, pp. 965–971, November 15, 1957.

Kolomiets, B. T., I. T. Sheftel', and E. V. Kurlina: Electrical Properties of Certain Compound Oxide Semiconductors, *Zhur. Tekh. Fiz.*, vol. 27, no. 1, pp. 51–72, 1957.

Kolotilova, V. G.: Propagation of Single and Periodic Pulses of Current through a Semiconducting Triode, *Zhur. Tekh. Fiz.*, vol. 27, no. 4, pp. 630–637, 1957.

Kontorova, T. A.: On the Question of the Scattering of Current Carriers in Semiconductors with the Ionic Type of Bond, *Zhur. Tekh. Fiz.*, vol. 27, no. 2, pp. 269–274, 1957.

Kosenko, V. E.: A Study of the Characteristics of Wafer-type Germanium Diodes, *Zhur. Tekh. Fiz.*, vol. 27, no. 3, pp. 452–460, 1957.

Kover, F., and A. Quilliet: Electrical and Optical Properties of Aluminum Antimonide; Effect of Lithium, *Compt. rend.*, vol. 244, no. 13, pp. 1739–1741, March 25, 1957.

Kozhevin, V. E., and V. E. Lashkarev: Effect of External Voltage and Other Factors on the Condenser Photo-response of Semiconductors, *Radiotekh. i Elektron.*, vol. 2, no. 3, pp. 260–268, 1957.

Kretschmar, G. G., and L. E. Schilberg: Preparation and Photoconductive Properties of Cadmium Telluride Films, *J. Appl. Phys.*, vol. 28, no. 8, pp. 865–867, August, 1957.

Kretzman, B. H.: Fork-driven Dual Tone Standard, *Electronics*, vol. 3, no. 2, pp. 196, 198, 200, 202, 204, February 1, 1957.

Kroemer, H.: Quasi-electric and Quasi-magnetic Fields in Nonuniform Semiconductors, *RCA Rev.*, vol. 18, no. 3, pp. 332–342, September, 1957.

Kroemer, H.: Theory of a Wide-gap Emitter for Transistors, *Proc. IRE*, vol. 45, no. 11, pp. 1535–1537, November, 1957.

Kuhrt, F., and W. Hartel: The Hall Generator as a Quadripole, *Arch. Elektrotech.*, vol. 43, no. 1, pp. 1–15, 1957.

Kulke, B., and S. L. Miller: Accurate Measurement of Emitter and Collector Series Resistances in Transistors, *Proc. IRE*, vol. 45, no. 1, p. 90, January, 1957.

Kurnosov, B. D.: Germanium Rectifiers at High Frequencies, *Elektrichestvo*, no. 12, pp. 54–56, 1957.

Kurov, G. A., S. A. Semiletov, and Z. G. Pinsker: The Electrical Properties and Real Structure of Single-crystal Films of Germanium Obtained by Vacuum Evaporation, *Kristallografiya*, vol. 2, no. 1, pp. 59–63, 1957.

Kvasnitskaya, A. N., E. B. Mertens, E. G. Miselyuk, and A. I. Skopenko: Point-contact Germanium Triodes with Short Minority Current-carrier Lifetime, *Zhur. Tehk. Fiz.*, vol. 27, no. 3, pp. 437–440, 1957.

Labuntsov, V. A., and Yu. N. Pienkin: Ring Counter Circuits with Transistors, *Elektrichestvo*, no. 8, pp. 48–53, 1957.

Landsberg, P. T.: Lifetimes of Excess Carriers in InSb, *Proc. Phys. Soc. (London)*, vol. 70B, part 12, pp. 1175–1176, December, 1957.

Lashkarev, V. E., V. G. Litovchenko, N. M. Omel'yanovskaya, R. N. Bondarenko, and V. I. Strikha: Dependence of the Lifetime of Injected Current Carriers on the Concentration of Antimony Impurity in Germanium, *Zhur. Tekh. Fiz.*, vol. 27, no. 11, pp. 2437–2439, 1957.

Lashkarev, V. E., E. A. Sal'kov, G. A. Fedorus, and M. K. Sheinkman: On the Shape of the Spectral Distribution of Photoconductivity of CdS Monocrystals, *Doklady Akad. Nauk S.S.S.R.*, vol. 114, no. 6, pp. 1203–1205, 1957.

Lasser, M., C. Wysocki, and B. Bernstein: Effects of Thick Oxides on Germanium Surface Properties, *Phys. Rev.*, vol. 105, no. 2, pp. 491–494, January 15, 1957.

Launay, J.: Hall Effect and Magnetoresistance of Thin Films of Indium Antimonide, *Compt. rend.*, vol. 245, no. 14, pp. 1122–1124, September 30, 1957.

Lee, P. A.: Determination of the Impurity Concentrations in a Semiconductor from Hall Coefficient Measurements, *Brit. J. Appl. Phys.*, vol. 8, no. 8, pp. 340–343, August, 1957.

Lehovec, K., and A. Levitas: Fabrication of Multiple Junctions in Semiconductors by Surface Melt and Diffusion in the Solid State, *J. Appl. Phys.*, vol. 28, no. 1, pp. 106–109, January, 1957.

Lehovec, K., K. Shoeni, and R. Zuleeg: Evaporation of Impurities from Semiconductors, *J. Appl. Phys.*, vol. 28, no. 4, pp. 420–423, April, 1957.

Lenkowski, J.: The Region of Amplification of a Transistor Amplifier at High Frequencies, *Arch. Elektrotech. (Warsaw)*, vol. 6, no. 3, pp. 361–369, 1957.

Light, L. H.: Transistor Class B Push-Pull Stages, *Mullard Tech. Commun.*, vol. 3, pp. 98–101, May, 1957.

Lin, H. C., and R. E. Crosby, Jr.: A Determination of Thermal Resistance of Silicon Junction Diodes, *IRE Natl. Conv. Record*, vol. 5, part 3, pp. 22–25, 1957.

Lin, L. Y.: Study of Injecting and Extracting Contacts on Germanium Single Crystals, *Rev. Sci. Instr.*, vol. 28, no. 3, pp. 187–188, March, 1957.

Lindsay, J. E.: A Decade Ring Counter Using Avalanche-operated Junction Transistors, *IRE Trans. on Circuit Theory*, vol. CT-4, no. 3, pp. 262–267, September, 1957.

Lomakina, G. A., Yu. A. Vodakov, G. P. Naumov, and Yu. P. Maslakovets: Flat Photocell of Cadmium Telluride, *Zhur. Tekh. Fiz.*, vol. 27, no. 7, p. 1594, 1957.

Long, D.: Low Injection Level Behavior and Base Width Measurement in Junction Transistors, *J. Appl. Phys.*, vol. 28, no. 10, pp. 1219–1220, October, 1957.

Lucas, W. J., and P. B. Barber: Computation of Crystal Admittance, *Electronic Radio Engr.*, vol. 34, no. 12, pp. 454–458, December, 1957.

Lummis, F. L., and R. L. Petritz: Noise, Time-constant and Hall Studies on Lead Sulfide Photoconductive Films, *Phys. Rev.*, vol. 105, no. 2, pp. 501–508, January 15, 1957.

MacIntyre, R. M.: A Transistorized, Multi-channel, Airborne Voltage-to-digital Converter, *IRE WESCON Conv. Record*, vol. 1, part 4, pp. 284–292, 1957.

McKelvey, J. P.: Experimental Determination of Injected Carrier Recombination Rates at Dislocations in Semiconductors, *Phys. Rev.*, vol. 106, no. 5, pp. 910–917, June 1, 1957.

McKinley, D. W. R., and R. S. Richards: Transistor Amplifier for Medical Recording, *Electronics*, vol. 30, no. 8, pp. 161–163, August 1, 1957.

McMullen, C. W., R. Aschenbrenner, and M. Slana: A Transistorized Magnetic Tape to Paper Tape Buffer, *Proc. Natl. Electronics Conf.*, vol. 13, pp. 666–672, 1957.

Macnee, A. B.: Approximating the Alpha of a Junction Transistor, *Proc. IRE*, vol. 45, no. 1, p. 91, January, 1957.

MacWilliams, W. H., Jr.: A Transistor Gating Matrix for a Simulated Warfare Computer, *Bell Labs. Record*, vol. 35, no. 3, pp. 94–99, March, 1957.

Magnusson, B. G.: Transistors as Change-over Switches in Pulse Circuits, *Tek. Tidsskr.*, vol. 87, no. 25, pp. 571–579, June 19, 1957.

Makovskiĭ, F. A., and E. P. Usachev: The Effect of Surface Treatment on the Properties of Copper Oxide Rectifiers, *Zhur. Tekh. Fiz.*, vol. 27, no. 12, pp. 2786–2788, 1957.

Maloff, I. G.: Heat Transfer in Power Transistor, *Electronic Inds.*, vol. 16, no. 12, pp. 54–55, 152–157, December, 1957.

Manukyan, É. M.: Nomogram for Transistor H-parameters, *Radiotekhnika*, vol. 12, no. 12, pp. 29–35, 1957.

Many, A., and D. Gerlich: Distribution and Cross-sections of Fast States on Germanium Surfaces in Different Gaseous Ambients, *Phys. Rev.*, vol. 107, no. 2, pp. 404–411, July 15, 1957.

Mason, D. E.: Silicon Junction Diodes, *Brit. Commun. and Electronics*, vol. 4, no. 1, pp. 10–14, January, 1957.

Matakura, Y.: Carrier Concentration Changes in p-Si Induced by Heat Treatment, *J. Phys. Soc. Japan*, vol. 12, no. 1, pp. 103–104, January, 1957.

Matthei, W. G., and F. A. Brand: On the Injection of Carriers into a Depletion Layer, *J. Appl. Phys.*, vol. 28, no. 4, pp. 513–514, April, 1957.

Matz, A. W.: Thermal Turnover in Germanium P-N Junctions, *Proc. Inst. Elec. Engrs. (London)*, vol. 104B, paper 2431R, pp. 555–564, November, 1957.

Maupin, J. T.: The Tetrode Power Transistor, *IRE Trans. on Electron Devices*, vol. ED-4, no. 1, pp. 1–5, January, 1957.

Maynard, F. B., and E. L. Steele: A High Frequency P-N-P Switching Transistor, *Proc. Natl. Electronics Conf.*, vol. 13, pp. 246–253, 1957.

Melehy, M. A.: Accurate Measurement of r_c and α_0 for Transistors, *Proc. IRE*, vol. 45, no. 12, pp. 1739–1740, December, 1957.

Melehy, M. A.: Transistor Push-Pull Audio Amplifier Theory, *Proc. Natl. Electronics Conf.*, vol. 13, pp. 69–76, 1957.

Melehy, M. A., and M. B. Reed: Junction-transistor Oscillators, *Proc. Natl. Electronics Conf.*, vol. 13, pp. 35–39, 1957.

Mendelson, K. S., and R. Bray: Field Dependence of Mobility in P-type Germanium, *Proc. Phys. Soc. (London)*, vol. 70B, part 9, pp. 899–900, September, 1957.

Merson, L. N.: Transistors Boost Video for TV Studio Monitors, *Electronics*, vol. 30, no. 10, p. 205, October 1, 1957.

Mesnard, G., and A. Dolce: On the Current-voltage Characteristics of Rectifying Metal-Germanium Contacts, *Compt. rend.*, vol. 244, no. 15, pp. 2025–2028, April 8, 1957.

Mesnard, G., and A. Dolce: On the Minority-carrier Current across Rectifying Metal-Germanium Contacts, *Compt. rend.*, vol. 245, no. 1, pp. 42–44, July 1, 1957.

Mesnard, G., and A. Dolce: The Variation of the Reverse Current of Rectifying Metal-Germanium Contacts When the Concentrations of Carriers in the Semiconductor Interior Depart from Their Thermal Equilibrium Values. *Compt. rend.*, vol. 244, no. 16, pp. 2141–2143, April 15, 1957.

Messenger, G. C., and C. T. McCoy: Theory and Operation of Crystal Diodes as Mixers, *Proc. IRE*, vol. 45, no. 9, pp. 1269–1283, September, 1957.

Meyer, N.: Equivalent Diagrams and Quadripole Parameters for Transistors, and Their Adaptation to the Physical Characteristics of the Transistor, *Ingeniøren*, vol. 66B, no. 13, pp. 290–297, March 30, 1957.

Meyer, N.: Intermetallic Compounds with Semiconducting Properties, *Ingeniøren*, vol. 66B, no. 26, pp. 697–702, October 1, 1957.

Meyer, N.: Switching Time in P-N Junction Diodes with Built-in Drift Field, *Acta Polytech.*, no. 210 (*Phys. Nucleonics Ser.*, vol. 3, no. 9), 1957.

Meyer-Brötz, G.: The Properties of Zener Diodes and Their Application as Reference Potentials, *Elektron. Rundschau*, vol. 11, no. 12, pp. 376–377, December, 1957.

Meyer-Brötz, G., and K. Felle: Non-linear Distortions in Transistor Amplifiers, *Elektron. Rundschau*, vol. 11, no. 10, pp. 297–301, October, 1957.

Meyerhoff, A. J., and R. M. Tillman: A High-speed Two-winding Transistor-magnetic-core Oscillator, *IRE Trans. on Circuit Theory*, vol. CT-4, no. 3, pp. 228–236, September, 1957.

Middlebrook, R. D.: A New Junction-transistor High-frequency Equivalent Circuit, *IRE Natl. Conv. Record*, vol. 5, part 2, pp. 120–133, 1957.

Mikula, J.: Feedback in Transistor Circuits, *Slaboproudý Obzor*, vol. 18, no. 8, pp. 533–538, 1957.

Mikula, J.: The Temperature Stabilization of Transistors, *Slaboproudý Obzor*, vol. 18, no. 5, pp. 303–309, 1957.

Miller, S. L.: Ionization Rates for Holes and Electrons in Silicon, *Phys. Rev.*, vol. 105, no. 4, pp. 1246–1249, February 15, 1957.

Milnes, A. G.: Transistor Circuits and Applications, *Proc. Inst. Elec. Engrs. (London)*, vol. 104B, paper 2368R, pp. 565–584, May, 1957.

Minton, R.: Circuit Considerations for Audio-output Stages Using Power Transistors, *IRE Natl. Conv. Record*, vol. 5, part 7, pp. 169–180, 1957.

Misawa, T.: Impedance of Bulk Semiconductor in Junction Diode, *J. Phys. Soc. Japan*, vol. 12, no. 8, pp. 882–890, August, 1957.

Mochan, I. V., Yu. N. Obraztsov, and T. V. Krÿlova: Investigation of Thermomagnetic Effects in P-type Germanium, *Zhur. Tekh. Fiz.*, vol. 27, no. 2, pp. 242–259, 1957.

Moïzhes, B. Ya.: Calculation of the Voltage for the Kikoin-Noskov Photomagnetic Effect and the Dember Effect in Strong Magnetic Fields, *Zhur. Tekh. Fiz.*, vol. 27, no. 3, pp. 495–501, 1957.

Molozzi, A. R., D. F. Page, and A. R. Boothroyd: Measurement of High-frequency Equivalent Circuit Parameters of Junction and Surface Barrier Transistors, *IRE Trans. on Electron Devices*, vol. ED-4, no. 2, pp. 120–125, April, 1957.

Molyneux, L.: A Transistor Cardiotachometer, *Electronic Eng.*, vol. 29, pp. 125–127, March, 1957.

Montgomery, G. F.: Transistor Beta Tester, *Electronics*, vol. 30, no. 5, pp. 198, 200, May 1, 1957.

Montgomery, H. C.: Field Effect in Germanium at High Frequencies, *Phys. Rev.*, vol. 106, no. 3, pp. 441–445, May 1, 1957.

Morgan, L. P., and W. L. Stephenson: Decade Counters Using Junction Transistors, *Mullard Tech. Commun.*, vol. 3, pp. 2–10, February, 1957.

Moriguchi, Y., and Y. Koga: Electrical Properties of GeTe, *J. Phys. Soc. Japan*, vol. 12, no. 1, p. 100, January, 1957.

Mortenson, K. E.: Transistor Junction Temperature as a Function of Time, *Proc. IRE*, vol. 45, no. 4, pp. 504–513, April, 1957.

Münch, W. v.: Theory of the Switch-transistor, *Z. angew. Phys.*, vol. 9, no. 12, pp. 621–625, December, 1957.

Murray, J. S.: Transistor Bias Stabilization, *Electronic Radio Engr.*, vol. 34, no. 5, pp. 161–165, May, 1957.

Murray, R. P.: Emitter Bypassing in Transistor Circuits, *IRE Trans. on Audio*, vol. AU-5, no. 3, pp. 71–72, May–June, 1957.

Murray, R. P.: Systematic Design of Transistor Bias Circuits, *Electronic Inds.*, vol. 16, no. 11, pp. 75–77, 147–148, November, 1957.

Muser, H. A.: Thermodynamic Treatment of Electronic Processes in Semiconductor Surface Layers, *Z. Physik*, vol. 148, no. 3, pp. 380–390, 1957.

Nambiar, K. P. P., and A. R. Boothroyd: Junction-transistor Bootstrap Linear-sweep Circuits, *Proc. Inst. Elec. Engrs. (London)*, vol. 104B, paper 2228R, pp. 293–306, 333–336, January, 1957.

Nelson, J. T., J. E. Iwersen, and F. Keywell: A Five-watt Ten-megacycle Transistor, *IRE WESCON Conv. Record*, vol. 1, part 3, pp. 28–39, 1957.

Newhouse, V. L., N. R. Kornfield, and M. M. Kaufman: A Transistorized Ferrite Plate Memory, *Proc. Natl. Electronics Conf.*, vol. 13, pp. 641–652, 1957.

Newman, R.: Recombination Radiation from Deformed and Alloyed Germanium P-N Junctions at 80°K, *Phys. Rev.*, vol. 105, no. 6, pp. 1715–1720, March 15, 1957.

Nielsen, E. G.: Behavior of Noise Figure in Junction Transistors, *Proc. IRE*, vol. 45, no. 7, pp. 957–963, July, 1957.

Nijland, L. M., and L. J. van der Pauw: The Effect of Heat Treatment on the Bulk Lifetime of Excess Charge Carriers in Silicon, *J. Electronics and Control*, vol. 3, no. 4, pp. 391–395, October, 1957.

Nixon, J. D., and P. C. Banbury: Junctions Induced in Germanium Surfaces by Transverse Electric Fields, *Proc. Phys. Soc. (London)*, vol. 70B, part 5, pp. 481–485, May, 1957.

Noordanus, J.: The Balanced Transistor D-C Converter, *Philips Telecommun. Rev.*, vol. 18, no. 3, pp. 125–136, September, 1957.

Oakes, F.: Design Consideration of Junction-transistor Oscillators for the Conversion of Power from Direct to Alternating Current, *Proc. Inst. Elec. Engrs. (London)*, paper 2299R, vol. 104B, pp. 307–317, 333–336, January, 1957.

Oatley, C. W., and T. E. Everhart: The Examination of P-N Junctions with the Scanning Electron Microscope, *J. Electronics*, vol. 2, no. 6, pp. 568–570, May, 1957.

Okada, J.: On the Carrier Recombination through Nickel Impurities in Germanium, *J. Phys. Soc. Japan*, vol. 12, no. 6, p. 741, June, 1957.

Okamura, S., and T. Ohkoshi: The Efficiency of the Microwave Frequency Multiplier Using a Crystal Diode, *J. Inst. Elec. Commun. Engrs. (Japan)*, vol. 40, no. 11, pp. 1190–1196, November, 1957.

Oliver, D. J.: Current Noise in Indium Antimonide, *Proc. Phys. Soc. (London)*, vol. 70B, part 3, pp. 331–332, March, 1957.

Oliver, D. J.: Fluctuations in the Number of Electrons and Holes in a Semiconductor, *Proc. Phys. Soc. (London)*, vol. 70B, part 2, pp. 244–247, February, 1957.

Olschewski, R.: Portable Receivers Using Transistors, *Elektrotech. Z.*, vol. 78A, no. 1, pp. 20–25, January, 1957.

Oroshnik, J.: A Precision Two-point Probe for Measuring Resistivity of Semiconductors and Metal-to-semiconductor Contact Resistance, *Sylvania Technologist*, vol. 10, no. 1, pp. 17–20, January, 1957.

O'Toole, J. B.: Logic Design Symbolism for Direct-coupled Transistor Circuits in Digital Computers, *IRE WESCON Conv. Record*, vol. 1, part 4, pp. 251–258, 1957.

Paige, E. G. S.: The Isothermal Reverse Voltage-current Characteristics of Small Area Alloy Contacts on Germanium, *J. Electronics*, vol. 2, no. 4, pp. 378–386, January, 1957.

Palmer, W. F., and G. Schiess: Transistorized Television Vertical Deflection System, *IRE Trans. on Broadcast and Television Receivers*, vol. BTR-3, no. 2, pp. 98–105, October, 1957.

Paranjape, B. V.: Field Dependence of Mobility in Semiconductors, *Proc. Phys. Soc. (London)*, vol. 70B, part 6, pp. 628–629, June, 1957.

Patraiko, J.: Transistorized Strobe Measures Shaft Torque, *Electronics*, vol. 30, no. 6, pp. 147–149, June 1, 1957.

Pearson, G. L.: Conversion of Solar to Electrical Energy, *Am. J. Phys.*, vol. 25, no. 9, pp. 591–598, December, 1957.

Pearson, W. B.: Discussion of the Electrical Properties of Compounds with the Nickel Arsenide Structure, *Can. J. Phys.*, vol. 35, no. 8, pp. 886–891, August, 1957.

Pell, E. M.: Influence of Electric Field in Diffusion Region upon Breakdown in Germanium N-P Junctions, *J. Appl. Phys.*, vol. 28, no. 4, pp. 459–466, April, 1957.

Peppercorn, A. E.: A High-quality Transistor Receiver, *Proc. IRE Australia*, vol. 18, no. 12, pp. 457–462, December, 1957.

Philips, A. B., and A. M. Intrator: A New High Frequency NPN Silicon Transistor, *IRE Natl. Conv. Record*, vol. 5, part 3, pp. 3–13, 1957.

Pignedoli, A.: On a Certain Problem of Temperature Redistribution of Interest in Transistor Junction Theory, *Rend. accad. nazl. Lincei*, vol. 23, no. 5, pp. 257–262, November, 1957.

Pilat, I. M.: Electrical Properties of the Intermetallic Compound CdSb, *Zhur. Tekh. Fiz.*, vol. 27, no. 1, pp. 119–122, 1957.

Presnov, V. A., and V. F. Sÿnorov: Preparation and Investigation of Intermetallic Compounds in the Form of Thin Layers, *Zhur. Tekh. Fiz.*, vol. 27, no. 1, pp. 123–126, 1957.

Pritchard, R. L.: Transistor Tests Predict High Frequency Performance, *Electronic Inds.*, vol. 16, no. 3, pp. 62–63, 130, 132, 134, 140, 142, 144, March, 1957.

Rashba, É. I., and A. I. Nosar': Current-voltage Characteristics of High-power Semiconductor Rectifiers, *Zhur. Tekh. Fiz.*, vol. 27, no. 7, pp. 1431–1445, 1957.

Rediker, R. H., and D. E. Sawyer: Very Narrow Base Diode, *Proc. IRE*, vol. 45, no. 7, pp. 944–953, July, 1957.

Richardson, J. M., and J. J. Faris: Excess Noise in Microwave Crystal Diodes Used as Rectifiers and Harmonic Generators, *IRE Trans. on Microwave Theory and Tech.*, vol. MTT-5, no. 3, pp. 208–212, July, 1957.

Richardson, J. M., and R. B. Riley: Performance of Three-millimeter Harmonic Generators and Crystal Detectors, *IRE Trans. on Microwave Theory and Tech.*, vol. MTT-5, no. 2, pp. 131–135, April, 1957.

Riddle, R. L.: How Transistors Operate under Atomic Radiation, *Electronics*, vol. 30, no. 12, pp. 125–127, December 1, 1957.

Roberts, D. H., P. H. Stephens, and P. H. Hunt: Effect of Oxygen on the Carrier Lifetime in Silicon, *Nature*, vol. 180, pp. 665–666, September 28, 1957.

Rohr, H.: Characteristics of Junction Transistors, *Nachrichtentechnik*, vol. 7, no. 6, pp. 257–259, June, 1957.

Rose, D. J.: Microplasmas in Silicon, *Phys. Rev.*, vol. 105, no. 2, pp. 413–418, January 15, 1957.

Rose, F. W. G.: On the Impact Ionization in the Space-charge Region of P-N Junctions, *J. Electronics and Control*, vol. 3, no. 4, pp. 396–400, October, 1957.

Rose, F. W. G., E. Billig, and J. E. Parrott: A Simple Derivation of the Thermoelectric Voltage in a Non-degenerative Semiconductor, *J. Electronics and Control*, vol. 3, no. 5, pp. 481–486, November, 1957.

Rosiński, W.: The Technology of Junction Transistors, *Prace Inst. Łączności*, vol. 4, no. 2(8), pp. 1–31, 1957.

Ross, I. M., E. W. Saker, and N. A. C. Thompson: The Hall-effect Compass, *J. Sci. Instr.*, vol. 34, no. 12, pp. 479–484, December, 1957.

Rowe, W. D., and G. H. Royer: Transistor "NOR" Circuit Design, *Trans. AIEE*, part I, vol. 76, pp. 263–267, 1957.

Rozner, F.: Transistor Pulse Generator, Use of Complementary Transistors, *Electronic Radio Engr.*, vol. 34, no. 1, pp. 8–10, January, 1957.

Rubinoff, M.: A New Family of Transistor Switching Circuits, *Commun. and Electronics*, no. 31, July, 1957.

Rudenberg, H. G., and G. Franzen: An Alloy Type Medium Power Silicon Transistor, *IRE Natl. Conv. Record*, vol. 5, part 3, pp. 26–31, 1957.

Rutz, R. F.: Two-collector Transistor for Binary Full Addition, *IBM J. Research Develop.*, vol. 1, no. 3, pp. 212–222, July, 1957.

Rўvkin, S. M., and Yu. A. Makhalov: The Distribution of Minority Current-carrier Concentration Due to Motion of the Injection Region and the Presence of a Field (on a "Null" Method for the Measurement of Mobility), *Zhur. Tekh. Fiz.*, vol. 27, no. 3, pp. 441–451, 1957.

Rўvkin, S. M., N. B. Strokan, V. M. Tuchkevich, and V. E. Chelnokov: Silicon Photodiodes, *Zhur. Tekh. Fiz.*, vol. 28, no. 6, pp. 1165–1168, 1957.

Rzhanov, A. V., Yu. F. Novototskiĭ-Vlasov, and I. G. Neizvestnyĭ: Investigation of the Field Effect and of Surface Recombination in Germanium Specimens, *Zhur. Tekh. Fiz.*, vol. 27, no. 11, pp. 2440–2450, 1957.

Saby, J. S.: Junction Rectifier Theory, "Semiconductor Meeting Report," pp. 39–48, The Physical Society, London, 1957.

Sacks, I. S.: A Low-noise Transistorized Seismic Preamplifier, *J. Geophys. Research*, vol. 62, no. 2, pp. 267–278, June, 1957.

Sah, Chih-Tang, R. N. Noyce, and W. Shockley: Carrier Generation and Recombination in P-N Junctions and P-N Junction Characteristics, *Proc. IRE*, vol. 45, no. 9, pp. 1228–1243, September, 1957.

Salzberg, B., and E. W. Sard: Fast Switching by Use of Avalanche Phenomena in Junction Diodes, *Proc. IRE*, vol. 45, no. 8, pp. 1149–1151, August, 1957.

Sands, W. F., and H. K. Schlegelmilch: Design Considerations of Transistor I.F. Amplifiers for TV Receivers, *Proc. Natl. Electronics Conf.*, vol. 13, pp. 433–441, 1957.

Sasaki, W., and E. Yoshida: Acoustoelectric Effect in N-type Germanium, *J. Phys. Soc. Japan*, vol. 12, no. 8, p. 979, August, 1957.

Satterthwaite, C. B., and R. W. Ure, Jr.: Electrical and Thermal Properties of Bi$_2$Te$_3$, *Phys. Rev.*, vol. 108, no. 5, pp. 1164–1170, December 1, 1957.

Scanlon, W. W.: Lifetime of Carriers in Lead Sulfide Crystals, *Phys. Rev.*, vol. 106, no. 4, pp. 718–720, 1957.

Scheib, R., Jr.: Transistors Stabilize Missile Ships, *Electronics*, vol. 30, no. 6, pp. 138–143, June 1, 1957.

Scheler, T., and H. W. Becke: Negative Resistances, Transistors and Feedback Circuits and Their Mutual Dependencies, *Frequenz*, vol. 11, no. 7, pp. 207–217, July, 1957.

Schmidt, J. D., H. N. Putschi, and E. Keonjian: Transistorized Special Purpose Computer, *Proc. Natl. Electronics Conf.*, vol. 13, pp. 624–634, 1957.

Schmidt, P. F.: Hydrogen Doping as the Mechanism of Electrolytic Rectification, *J. Appl. Phys.*, vol. 28, no. 2, pp. 278–279, February, 1957.

Schubert, J.: Transistor Noise in the Low Frequency Region, *Arch. Elekt. Ubertragung*, vol. 11, no. 8, pp. 331–340, August; no. 9, pp. 379–385, September; no. 10, pp. 416–423, October, 1957.

Schultz, B. H.: Storage of Injected Carriers at Surfaces of Germanium, *Philips Research Repts.*, vol. 12, no. 1, pp. 82–96, February, 1957.

Schwetzoff, V.: The Optical Sensitization of Photoconductors of the Lead Salts Group, *Compt. rend.*, vol. 245, no. 2, pp. 149–152, July 8, 1957.

Scism, W. A.: Computer Delay Unit Uses Semiconductors, *Electronics*, vol. 30, no. 7, p. 173, July 1, 1957.

Shabanskiĭ, V. P.: Heating of the Electron Gas and Transport Processes in Conductors, *Fiz. Metal. i Metallove. Akad. Nauk S.S.S.R.*, vol. 5, no. 2, pp. 193–202, 1957.

Shea, R. F. (editor): "Transistor Circuit Engineering," John Wiley & Sons, Inc., New York, and Chapman and Hall, London, 1957.

Shields, J.: The Elemental Semiconductors—Silicon and Germanium, I–III, *Elec. Energy*, vol. 1, no. 14, pp. 428–433, October; no. 15, pp. 477–482, November; no. 16, pp. 501–503, December, 1957.

Shockley, W.: Unique Properties of the Four-layer Diode, *Electronic Inds.*, vol. 16, no. 8, pp. 56–60, 161–165, August, 1957.

Shtenbek, M., and P. I. Baranskiĭ: A Study of the Motion of Minority Current Carriers in the Bulk in Germanium, *Zhur. Tekh. Fiz.*, vol. 27, no. 2, pp. 221–232, 1957.

Sichling, G., and E. Rohloff: The Switching Transistor, *Siemens Rev.*, vol. 24, no. 5–6, pp. 162–166, December, 1957.

Sim, A. C.: A Quantitative Theory of the Electroformation of Metal-Germanium Point Contacts, *J. Electronics and Control*, vol. 3, no. 2, pp. 139–159, August, 1957.

Singer, K.: A Transistorized Seven-position Portable Mixer, *J. Soc. Motion Picture Television Engrs.*, vol. 66, no. 6, pp. 334–337, June, 1957.

Skvortsova, N. E.: Investigation of the Input Impedances and Experimental Verification of the Equivalent Circuit of Germanium Detectors in the 1000–10,000 Mc/s Band, *Radiotekh. i Elektron.*, vol. 2, no. 3, pp. 296–310, 1957.

Smirnov, L. S.: Measurement of Short Lifetimes of Charge Carriers in Germanium, *Zhur. Tekh. Fiz.*, vol. 27, no. 11, pp. 2469–2471, 1957.

Smith, R. A.: Physics and the New Electronics, *J. Sci. Instr.*, vol. 34, no. 10, pp. 377–382, October, 1957.

Sodha, M. S.: Variation of Mobility with Electric Field in Non-degenerate Semiconductors, *Phys. Rev.*, vol. 107, no. 5, pp. 1266–1271, September 1, 1957.

Sodha, M. S., and P. C. Eastman: Effect of Neutral Impurities on Mobility in Non-degenerate Semiconductors, *Phys. Rev.*, vol. 108, no. 6, pp. 1373–1375, December 15, 1957.

Sorokin, O. V.: A Method of Measuring the Bulk Lifetime and Diffusion Coefficient of Charge Carriers by the Measurement of the Change of Resistance of a Semiconductor in a Magnetic Field, *Zhur. Tekh. Fiz.*, vol. 27, no. 12, pp. 2774–2776, 1957.

Sosnowski, L.: Contribution of Current Carriers in the Reflection of Light from Semiconductors, *Phys. Rev.*, vol. 107, no. 4, pp. 1193–1194, August 15, 1957.

Sparks, J. J., and R. Beaufoy: The Junction Transistor as a Charge Controlled Device, *Proc. IRE*, vol. 45, no. 12, pp. 1740–1742, December, 1957.

Spear, W. E.: Transit Time Measurements of Charge Carriers in Amorphous Selenium Films, *Proc. Phys. Soc. (London)*, vol. 70B, part 7, pp. 669–675, July, 1957.

Speiser, A. P.: Digital Circuits with Transistors, *Scientia Electrica*, vol. 3, no. 4, pp. 121–126, December, 1957.

Spescha, G. A., and M. J. O. Strutt: Theoretical and Experimental Research on the Distortions in the Low-frequency Junction Transistor Fourpole, *Arch. Elekt. Ubertragung*, vol. 11, no. 8, pp. 307–320, August, 1957.

Spilker, J. J., Jr.: A Multi-stage Video Amplifier Design Method, *IRE WESCON Conv. Record*, vol. 1, part 2, pp. 54–59, 1957.

Sprinks, M. E., G. T. G. Robinson, and B. G. Bosch: The Frequency Dependence of Noise Temperature Ratio in Microwave Mixer Crystals, *Brit. J. Appl. Phys.*, vol. 8, no. 7, pp. 275–277, July, 1957.

Stafeev, V. I.: Current Multiplication of Minority Carriers in a Non-ideal P-N Junction, *Zhur. Tekh. Fiz.*, vol. 27, no. 10, pp. 2195–2211, 1957.

Standiford, D. J.: Carrier Lifetime in Semiconductors for Transient Conditions, *Phys. Rev.*, vol. 105, no. 2, p. 524, January 15, 1957.

Starkiewicz, J., G. Bate, H. Bennett, and C. Hilsum: A Single Crystal Photodiode of Lead Sulphide, *Proc. Phys. Soc. (London)*, vol. 70B, part 2, pp. 258–259, February, 1957.

Stasior, R. A.: Pulse Applications of a New Semiconductor Device, *IRE Natl. Conv. Record*, vol. 5, part 2, pp. 137–141, 1957.

Statz, H., and R. A. Pucel: The Spacistor, a New Class of High-frequency Semiconductor Devices, *Proc. IRE*, vol. 45, no. 3, pp. 317–324, March, 1957.

Statz, H., R. A. Pucel, and C. Lanza: High-frequency Semiconductor Spacistor Tetrodes, *Proc. IRE*, vol. 45, no. 11, pp. 1475–1483, November, 1957.

Steele, E. L.: Descriptive Theory of Semiconductors, *Am. J. Phys.*, vol. 25, no. 3, pp. 174–179, March, 1957.

Stern, A. P.: Stability and Power Gain of Tuned Transistor Amplifiers, *Proc. IRE*, vol. 45, no. 3, pp. 335–343, March, 1957.

Stewart, R. F.: High Performance Silicon Tetrode Transistors, *Proc. IRE*, vol. 45, no. 7, p. 1019, July, 1957.

Stil'bans, L. S.: The Commutation (Kommutatsiya) of Semiconducting Thermoelements, *Zhur. Tekh. Fiz.*, vol. 27, no. 1, pp. 212–213, 1957.

Strutt, M. J. O., and S. F. Sun: Experimental and Theoretical Investigation of Semiconductor Hall-effect Oscillators, *Arch. Elekt. Ubertragung*, vol. 11, no. 6, pp. 261–265, June, 1957.

Suran, J. J.: Design of Junction Transistor Flip-flops by Driving-point Impedance Methods, *IRE Natl. Conv. Record*, vol. 5, part 2, pp. 142–147, 1957.

Suran, J. J.: Small-signal Wave Effects in the Double-base Diode, *IRE Trans. on Electron Devices*, vol. ED-4, no. 1, pp. 34–43, January, 1957.

Suran, J. J., and B. K. Eriksen: Transient Response Characteristics of Unijunction Transistors, *IRE Trans. on Circuit Theory*, vol. CT-4, no. 3, pp. 267–275, September, 1957.

Svechnikov, S. V., and V. T. Aleksandrov: Some Photoelectric Properties of CdSe and CdTe Single Crystals, *Zhur. Tekh. Fiz.*, vol. 27, no. 5, pp. 919–920, 1957.

Sylvan, T. P.: Conversion Formulas for Hybrid Parameters, *Electronics*, vol. 30, no. 4, pp. 188, 190, April 1, 1957.

Taeger, W.: Progress in the Development of Semiconductors (Devices), *Frequenz*, vol. 11. no. 11, pp. 333–342, November, 1957.

Tauc, J.: Generation of an E.M.F. in Semiconductors with Nonequilibrium Current Carrier Concentrations, *Rev. Mod. Phys.*, vol. 29, no. 3, pp. 308–324, July, 1957.

Tauc, J., and A. Abraham: Thermal Breakdown in Silicon P-N Junctions, *Phys. Rev.*, vol. 108, no. 4, pp. 936–937, November 15, 1957.

Téboul, M., and N. Nifontoff: On the Effect of Fluctuations in Selenium Photovoltaic Cells, *Compt. rend.*, vol. 244, no. 12, pp. 1631–1633, March 18, 1957.

Tharma, P.: Compensation for Changes in Base to Emitter Voltage with Temperature, *Mullard Tech. Commun.*, vol. 3, pp. 106–109, May, 1957.

Tharma, P.: Distortion in Transistor Amplifiers, *Mullard Tech. Commun.*, vol. 3, pp. 62–64, March, 1957.

Theriault, G. E., and H. M. Wasson: Determination of Transistor Performance Characteristics at V.H.F., *IRE Trans. on Broadcast and Television Receivers*, vol. BTR-3, no. 1, pp. 40–48, June, 1957.

Theuerer, H. C., J. M. Whelan, H. E. Bridgers, and E. Buehler: Heat Treatment of Silicon Using Zone Heating Techniques, *J. Electrochem. Soc.*, vol. 104, no. 12, pp. 721–723, December, 1957.

Thompson, P. M., and J. Mitchell: Some Solutions to Problems of Operating Germanium Transistor Servo Amplifiers at High Ambient Temperatures, *IRE Trans. on Circuit Theory*, vol. CT-4, no. 3, pp. 190–193, September, 1957

Thornton, C., J. Roschen, and T. Miles: Design for an Improved High-frequency Transistor, *Electronic Inds.*, vol. 16, no. 7, pp. 47–49, 124, July, 1957.

Todd, C D.: Transistor Null Detector Has High Sensitivity, *Electronics*, vol. 30, no. 2, pp. 184–185, February 1, 1957.

Tolpygo, K. B.: The Dependence of the Injection Efficiency of a P-N Junction on Its Structure and Operating Conditions, *Zhur. Tekh. Fiz.*, vol. 27, no. 5, pp. 884–898, 1957.

Treharne, R. F.: Collector Bias, the Transistor Equivalent of Cathode Bias, and Some Applications, *Proc. IRE, Australia*, vol. 18, no. 5, pp. 149–159, May, 1957.

Tsykin, G. S.: Semiconductor D-C Convertor, *Radiotekhnika*, vol. 12, no. 12, pp. 56–62, 1957.

Turner, R. J., and P. Hermann: Transistor Design for Picture I.F. Stages, *IRE Trans. on Broadcast and Television Receivers*, vol. BTR-3, no. 2, pp. 76–80, October, 1957.

Uda, S.: Transistor Characteristics at Very Low Temperatures, *J. Inst. Telecommun. Engrs. (New Delhi)*, vol. 3, no. 2, pp. 97–109, March, 1957.

Valeev, Kh. S., and M. D. Mashkovich: Nonlinear Semiconductors Based upon $ZnO-TiO_2$, *Zhur. Tekh. Fiz.*, vol. 27, no. 8, pp. 1649–1651, 1957.

Vallese, L. M.: Unilateralized Common Collector Transistor Amplifier, *Proc. Natl. Electronics Conf.*, vol. 13, pp. 55–68, 1957.

van der Ziel, A.: Theory of Shot Noise in Junction Diodes and Junction Transistors, *Proc. IRE*, vol. 45, no. 7, p. 1011, July, 1957.

Vavilov, V. S., V. M. Malovetskaya, G. N. Galkin, and A. P. Landsman: Silicon Solar Batteries as Sources of Electrical Supply for Artificial Earth Satellites, *Uspekhi Fiz. Nauk*, vol. 63, no. 1a, pp. 123–129, 1957.

Veloric, H. S., and M. B. Prince: High-voltage Conductivity-modulated Silicon Rectifier, *Bell System Tech. J.*, vol. 36, no. 4, pp. 975–1004, July, 1957.

Veloric, H. S., and K. D. Smith: Silicon Diffused Junction "Avalanche" Diodes, *J. Electrochem. Soc.*, vol. 104, no. 4, pp. 222–226, April, 1957.

Vengel', T. N., and B. T. Kolomiets: Vitreous Semiconductors; Some Properties of Materials in the System $As_2Se_3-As_2Te_3$, II, *Zhur. Tekh. Fiz.*, vol. 27, no. 11, pp. 2484–2491, 1957.

Volokobinskiĭ, Yu. M.: The Tunnel Effect in Sulphide Rectifiers, *Doklady Akad. Nauk S.S.S.R.*, vol. 113, no. 6, pp. 1239–1242, 1957.

von Horn, H. B., and W. Y. Stevens: Determination of Transient Response of a Drift Trans'stor Using the Diffusion Equation, *IBM J. Research Develop.*, vol. 1, no. 2, pp. 189–191, April, 1957.

Vul, B. M., and A. P. Shotov: Edge Breakdown of P-N Junctions in Germanium, *Zhur. Tekh. Fiz.*, vol. 27, no. 10, pp. 2189–2194, 1957.

Vul, B. M., and A. P. Shotov: Surface Discharges at P-N Junctions, *Zhur. Tekh. Fiz.*, vol. 27, no. 1, pp. 211–212, 1957.

Vyatkin, A. P.: On the Origin of the Fluctuations of Crystal Triode Parameters. I. Triodes of the P-N-P Type, *Zhur. Tekh. Fiz.*, vol. 27, no. 6, pp. 1197–1204, 1957.

Vyatkin, A. P., and V. A. Ĕĭchin: On the Origin of the Fluctuations of Crystal Triode Parameters. II. Triodes of the N-P-N Type, *Zhur. Tekh. Fiz.*, vol. 27, no. 6, pp. 1205–1208, 1957.

Wahl, A. J.: A Three-dimensional Analytic Solution for Alpha of Alloy Junction Transistors, *IRE Trans. on Electron Devices*, vol. ED-4, no. 3, pp. 216–222, July, 1957.

Wahl, R. E.: Direct-water-cooled Germanium Power Rectifier, *Commun. and Electronics*, no. 28, January, 1957.

Waldhauer, F. D.: Wide-band Feedback Amplifiers, *IRE Trans. on Circuit Theory*, vol. CT-4, no. 3, pp. 178–190, September, 1957.

Walker, A. H. B., and R. G. Martin: Dynamic Methods of Testing Semiconductor Rectifier

Elements and Power Diodes, I–II, *Electronic Eng.*, vol. 29, pp. 150–157, April; pp. 220–224, May, 1957.

Walker, J. M., R. E. Smith, and E. M. Williams: Noise Figures in Semiconductor Dielectric Amplifiers, *IRE Natl. Conv. Record*, vol. 5, part 3, pp. 14–21, 1957.

Walker, W. C., and E. Y. Lambert: Ohmic and Rectifying Contacts to Semiconducting CdS Crystals, *J. Appl. Phys.*, vol. 28, no. 5, pp. 635–636, May, 1957.

Wallmark, J. T.: Influence of Surface Oxidation on Alpha$_{cb}$ of Germanium P-N-P Transistors, *RCA Rev.*, vol. 18, no. 2, pp. 255–271, June, 1957.

Wallmark, J. T.: A New Semiconductor Photocell Using Lateral Photoeffect, *Proc. IRE*, vol. 45, no. 4, pp. 474–483, April, 1957.

Wallmark, J. T., and R. R. Johnson: Influence of Hydration-Dehydration of the Germanium Oxide Layer on the Characteristics of P-N-P Transistors, *RCA Rev.*, vol. 18, no. 4, pp. 512–524, December, 1957.

Wang, S., and G. Wallis: Field Effect on an Illuminated Ge Surface and Investigation of the Surface Recombination Process, *Phys. Rev.*, vol. 105, no. 5, pp. 1459–1464, March 1, 1957.

Wannlund, A. L., and W. P. Waters: A Silicon PNP Fused-junction Transistor, *IRE WESCON Conv. Record*, vol. 1, part 3, pp. 3–13, 1957.

Ward, E. E.: Measurements of the Impedance Parameters of Junction Transistors, *Brit. J. Appl. Phys.*, vol. 8, no. 8, pp. 329–331, August, 1957.

Weiser, K.: Effect of Annealing in Various Gases on the Bulk Lifetime of Germanium, *J. Appl. Phys.*, vol. 28, no. 2, pp. 271–272, February, 1957.

Wertheim, G. K., and G. L. Pearson: Recombination in Plastically Deformed Germanium, *Phys. Rev.*, vol. 107, no. 3, pp. 694–698, August 1, 1957.

Westberg, R. W., and T. R. Robillard: Complementary High-speed Power Transistors for Computer and Transmission Applications, *IRE WESCON Conv. Record*, vol. 1, part 3, pp. 14–21, 1957.

Wheeler, A. J.: Thermistors Compensate Transistor Amplifiers, *Electronics*, vol. 30, no. 1, pp. 169–171, January 1, 1957.

Williams, H. P.: Transistor Impedance Matching: A Note on a Fundamental Property, *Electronic Radio Engr.*, vol. 34, no. 4, pp. 128–129, April, 1957.

Witt, S. N., Jr.: Designing Oscillators for Greater Stability, *Electronics*, vol. 30, no. 11, pp. 180–182, November 1, 1957.

Wolfendale, E., L. P. Morgan, and W. L. Stephenson: The Junction Transistor as a Computing Element, I–III, *Electronic Eng.*, vol. 29, pp. 2–7, January; pp. 83–87, February; pp. 136–139, March, 1957.

Wurst, E. C., Jr., and E. H. Borneman: Rectification Properties of Metal-Silicon Contacts, *J. Appl. Phys.*, vol. 28, no. 2, pp. 235–240, February, 1957.

Wyatt, D. G.: Improving the Linearity of Barrier-layer Photocells, *J. Sci. Instr.*, vol. 34, no. 3, pp. 106–108, March, 1957.

Yagodin, O. G.: On Switching Processes in Pulse Circuits with Point Contact Transistors, *Radiotekhnika*, vol. 12, no. 1, pp. 43–57, 1957.

Yamanaka, I. C., and T. Suita: Multiplication of Charge Carriers and Breakdown in Ge P-N Junction, *J. Phys. Soc. Japan*, vol. 12, no. 3, p. 310, March, 1957.

Yanai, H., and T. Sugano: Effect of Surface Recombination on the Current Amplification Factor of Alloy-junction and Surface-barrier Transistors, *J. Inst. Elec. Commun. Engrs. (Japan)*, vol. 40, no. 8, pp. 883–892, August, 1957.

Yii, R.: Triggering Electronic Flip-flops from Mechanical Switches, *Control Eng.*, vol. 4, no. 10, pp. 71–73, October, 1957.

Yoshida, U., and A. Suzuki: On the Surface Phenomena of a Selenium Photovoltaic Cell, *Bull. Fac. Eng. Yokohama Natl. Univ.*, vol. 6, pp. 33–37, March, 1957.

Younker, E. L.: A Transistor-driven Magnetic-core Memory, *IRE Trans. on Electronic Computers*, vol. EC-6, no. 1, pp. 14–20, March, 1957.

Yuditskiĭ, S. B.: Power Semiconductor Rectifiers and Their Application in Industry, *Elektrichestvo*, no. 4, pp. 1–7, 1957.

Yunovich, A. É.: On Determining the Relaxation Times of Surface States in Germanium, *Soviet Phys., JETP*, vol. 2, no. 8, pp. 1587–1592, August, 1957.

Zawels, J.: Base-width Modulation and the High-frequency Equivalent Circuit of Junction Transistors, *IRE Trans. on Electron Devices*, vol. ED-4, no. 1, pp. 17–22, January, 1957.

Zen'iti, K., K. Husimi, K. Kataoka, and K. Yamanaka: Parametric Excitation Using Barrier-capacitance of Semiconductor, *J. Inst. Elec. Commun. Engrs. (Japan)*, vol. 40, no. 2, pp. 162–169, February, 1957.

IRE Standards on Graphical Symbols for Semiconductor Devices, *Proc. IRE*, vol. 45, no. 12, pp. 1612–1617, December, 1957.

A Portable Transistor Receiver, *Mullard Tech. Commun.*, vol. 3, pp. 198–208, December, 1957.

Report of the Meeting on Semiconductors, The Physical Society, London (April, 1956, meeting), 1957.

Telefunken High frequency Transistors, OC 612 and OC 613, *Telefunken Ztg.*, vol. 30, pp. 214–216, September, 1957.

Temperature-stable Transistor Circuit Based on the Half Supply Voltage Principle, *Electronic Appl. Bull.*, vol. 18, no. 1, pp. 1–11, 1957–1958.

Transistor Circuits Based on the Half Supply Voltage Principle, *Electronic Appl. Bull.*, vol. 18, no. 3, pp. 85–98, 1957–1958.

Transistor Technology, *Nature*, vol. 180, pp. 1329–1330, December 14, 1957.

1958

Adirovich, É. I., Yu. S. Ryabinkin, and K. V. Temko: The Equilibrium Distribution of Potential, Field and Carrier Concentrations in Alloyed Junctions, *Zhur. Tekh. Fiz.*, vol. 28, no. 1, pp. 55–66, 1958.

Agakhanyan, T. M.: Approximate Amplitude and Phase Characteristics of Current Gain of Junction Transistors, *Radiotekhnika*, vol. 13, no. 2, pp. 3–13, 1958.

Agakhanyan, T. M., and L. N. Patrikeev: Determination of the Cut-off Frequency of Current Transmission Coefficient of a Junction Transistor, *Radiotekhnika*, vol. 13, no. 4, pp. 45–52, 1958.

Aigrain, P.: Recombination Processes in Semiconductors, *Nuovo cimento*, suppl., vol. 7, no. 2, pp. 724–729, 1958.

Aitchison, R. E.: An Oscilloscope Accessory for the Display of Transistor Characteristic Curves, *Proc. IRE, Australia*, vol. 19, no. 7, pp. 370–373, July, 1958.

Alcock, B. J.: A Four-pole Analysis for Transistors, *Electronic Eng.*, vol. 30, pp. 592–594, October, 1958.

Aldrich, R. W., and N. Holonyak, Jr.: Multi-terminal P-N-P-N Switches, *Proc. IRE*, vol. 46, no. 6, pp. 1236–1239, June, 1958.

Aldrich, R. W., R. H. Lanzl, D. E. Maxwell, J. O. Percival, and M. Waldner: An 85 Watt Dissipation Silicon Power Transistor, *IRE Trans. on Electron Devices*, vol. ED-5, no. 4, pp. 211–215, October, 1958.

Allred, W. P., B. Paris, and M. Genser: Zone Melting and Crystal Pulling Experiments with AlSb, *J. Electrochem. Soc.*, vol. 105, no. 2, pp. 93–96, February, 1958.

Anderson, L. K., and A. Hendry: An Investigation of the Properties of Germanium Mixer Crystals at Low Temperatures, *IRE Trans. on Microwave Theory and Tech.*, vol. MTT-6, no. 4, pp. 393–398, October, 1958.

Anderson, W. P., and N. A. Godel: Latching Counters. I. Development of Four-phase Circuit. II. Non-binary Counters and Transistor Circuits, *Electronic Radio Engr.*, vol. 35, no. 10, pp. 362–367, October; no. 11, pp. 425–436, November, 1958.

Andres, R. J., and E. L. Steele: Medium-power Silicon Rectifiers, *Electronic Inds.*, vol. 17, no. 3, pp. 62–65, March, 1958.

Angello, S. J.: Review of Other Semiconductor Devices, *Proc. IRE*, vol. 46, no. 6, pp. 968–973, June, 1958.

Anouchi, A. Y.: Measuring Noise Figures of Transistor Amplifiers, *Proc. IRE*, vol. 46, no. 3, p. 619, March, 1958.

Antista, B. A.: A High-speed Transistorized Digital-to-analog Decoder, *Proc. Natl. Electronics Conf.*, vol. 14, pp. 776–788, 1958.

Arends, E.: AEG Silicon Power Rectifiers, *AEG Mitt.*, vol. 48, no. 2–3, pp. 61–65, February–March, 1958.

Armstrong, H. L.: On Avalanche Multiplication in Semiconductor Devices, *J. Electronics and Control*, vol. 5, no. 2, pp. 97–104, August, 1958.

Armstrong, H. L.: On Impact Ionization in Semiconductors, *J. Electronics and Control*, vol. 4, no. 4, pp. 355–357, April, 1958.

Armstrong, H. L.: On Junctions between Semiconductors Having Different Energy Gaps, *Proc. IRE*, vol. 46, no. 6, pp. 1307–1308, June, 1958.

Armstrong, H. L.: Some Reasons for Nonsaturation of Reverse Current in Junction Diodes, *IRE Trans. on Electron Devices*, vol. ED-5, no. 2, pp. 66–68, April, 1958.

Arthur, J. B., A. F. Gibson, J. W. Granville, and E. G. S. Paige: The Diffusion Constant, Mobility and Lifetime of Minority Carriers in Germanium Containing Parallel Arrays of Dislocations, *Phil. Mag.* (8th ser.), vol. 3, pp. 940–949, September, 1958.

Asanabe, S., and A. Okazaki: Electrical Properties of Germanium Telluride GeTe, *Mem. Fac. Sci. Kyūsyū Univ.*, vol. 2, no. 4, pp. 136–140, January, 1958.

Averkieva, G. K., and O. V. Emel'yanenko: The Influence of Impurities on the Electrical Properties of Gallium Arsenide, *Zhur. Tekh. Fiz.*, vol. 28, no. 9, pp. 1945–1947, 1958.

Awender, H., and A. Ludloff: Quartz-controlled Transistor Oscillators, *Elektron. Rundschau*, vol. 12, no. 3, pp. 75–80, March, 1958.

Bachmann, A. E.: Low Noise Transistor Amplifier with High Input Impedance, *Arch. Elekt. Ubertragung*, vol. 12, no. 7, pp. 331–334, July, 1958.

Backenstoss, G.: Conductivity Mobilities of Electrons and Holes in Heavily Doped Silicon, *Phys. Rev.*, vol. 108, no. 6, pp. 1416–1419, December 15, 1958.

Backenstoss, G.: Evaluation of the Surface Concentration of Diffused Layers in Silicon, *Bell System Tech. J.*, vol. 37, no. 3, pp. 699–710, May, 1958.

Baranskiĭ, P. I.: Mobility of the Minority Current Carriers in Collinear Electrical and Magnetic Fields, *Zhur. Tekh. Fiz.*, vol. 28, no. 4, pp. 694–703, 1958.

Barnes, F. S.: The Forward Switching Transient in Semiconductor Diodes at Large Currents, *Proc. IRE*, vol. 46, no. 7, pp. 1427–1428, July, 1958.

Barnes, G. A., and P. C. Banbury: Electrical Properties of Clean Germanium Surfaces, *Proc. Phys. Soc. (London)*, vol. 71, part 6, pp. 1020–1021, June, 1958.

Bath, H. M., and M. Cutler: Measurement of Surface Recombination Velocity in Silicon by Steady-state Photoconductance, *J. Phys. Chem. Solids*, vol. 5, no. 3, pp. 171–179, May, 1958.

Beale, J. R. A., D. E. Thomas, and T. B. Watkins: A Method of Studying Surface Barrier Height Changes on Transistors, *Proc. Phys. Soc. (London)*, vol. 72, part 5, pp. 910–914, November, 1958.

Bechtold, N. F., and C. L. Hanks: Failure-rate Studies on Silicon Rectifiers, *Trans. AIEE*, part I, vol. 77, pp. 49–56, 1958.

Behrens, W. V., and J. M. Shaull: The Effects of Short Duration Neutron Radiation on Semiconductor Devices, *Proc. IRE*, vol. 46, no. 3, pp. 601–605, March, 1958.

Beijersbergen, J. P., M. Beun, and J. te Winkel: The Junction Transistor as a Network Element at Low Frequencies. I. Characteristics and h Parameters, *Philips Tech. Rev.*, vol. 19, no. 1, pp. 15–27; II. Equivalent Circuits and Dependence of the h Parameters on Operating Point, no. 3, pp. 98–105, 1957–1958; III. Stabilization of the Operating Point, in Particular with Regard to Temperature Changes, vol. 20, no. 5, pp. 122–134, 1958–1959.

Bell, D. A.: Semiconductor Noise as a Queuing Problem, *Proc. Phys. Soc. (London)*, vol. 72, part 1, pp. 27–32, July, 1958.

Bemski, G.: Recombination in Semiconductors, *Proc. IRE*, vol. 46, no. 6, pp. 990–1004, June, 1958.

Bemski, G., and J. D. Struthers: Gold in Silicon, *J. Electrochem. Soc.*, vol. 105, no. 10, pp. 588–591, October, 1958.

Beneking, H.: The D-C and A-C Properties of Point-contact Diodes, *Z. angew. Phys.*, vol. 10, no. 5, pp. 216–225, May, 1958.

Benny, A. H., and F. D. Morten: The Measurement of Surface Recombination Velocity on Silicon, *Proc. Phys. Soc. (London)*, vol. 72, part 6, pp. 1007–1012, December, 1958.

Berestnev, P. D.: Self-oscillation Criteria and Oscillation Frequency of Junction Transistor Oscillators, *Radiotekhnika*, vol. 13, no. 2, pp. 36–43, 1958.

Berman, L. S.: Increase of Power Output of a Tuned Transistor Amplifier by Improvement of Its Efficiency Coefficient, *Radiotekhnika*, vol. 13, no. 3, pp. 70–73, 1958.

Bernard, M.: Recombination in Traps at Two Levels in Semiconductors, *J. Electronics and Control*, vol. 5, no. 1, pp. 15–18, July, 1958.

Berry, J. F., and L. E. Jansson: Transistor 20 Kc/s Oscillator with 50 Mw Output, *Mullard Tech. Commun.*, vol. 4, pp. 122–127, November, 1958.

Berz, F.: On the Theory of Surface Recombination in Semiconductors for Large Potential Differences between Surface and Bulk, *Proc. Phys. Soc. (London)*, vol. 71, part 2, pp. 275–280, February, 1958.

Birebent, M., and R. Morelière: Temperature Variation of the Cut-off Frequency of Junction Transistors Operated in the Common-emitter Connection, *Compt. rend.*, vol. 246, no. 6, pp. 909–911, February 10, 1958.

Birnstingle, D. W.: A Transistor Operated Self-balancing Radiation Pyrometer, *Electronic Eng.*, vol. 30, pp. 189–191, April, 1958.

Bisson, D. K.: A Medium Power Silicon Controlled Rectifier, *IRE WESCON Conv. Record*, vol. 2, part 3, pp. 166–171, 1958.

Black, J., S. M. Ku, and H. T. Minden: Some Semiconducting Properties of HgTe, *J. Electrochem. Soc.*, vol. 105, no. 12, pp. 723–728, December, 1958.

Blackburne, N. F.: Capacitance Bridges for Semiconductor Measurements, *A.T.E. J.*, vol. 14, no. 3, pp. 166–175, July, 1958.

Blakemore, J. S.: The Fermi Level in Germanium at High Temperatures, *Proc. Phys. Soc. (London)*, vol. 71, part 4, pp. 692–694, April, 1958.

Blakemore, J. S.: Lifetime in p-Type Silicon, *Phys. Rev.*, vol. 110, no. 6, pp. 1301–1308, June 15, 1958.

Bley, H.: Shot Noise in Semiconductors, Particularly in Germanium Point Diodes at 1 Kc/s to 10 Mc/s, *NTZ-Nachrtech. Z.*, vol. 11, no. 7, pp. 349–359, July, 1958.

Bohan, W. A., M. G. Chasanov, and E. N. Schroeder: An Effect of Pulse Type Radiation on Transistors Packaged in a Moist Atmosphere, *Proc. IRE*, vol. 46, no. 12, pp. 1953–1954, December, 1958.

Bonch-Bruevich, V. L.: On the Theory of the Field Effect, *Zhur. Tekh. Fiz.*, vol. 28, no. 1, pp. 70–76, 1958.

Booher, C.: Increased Cooling for Power Transistors, *Electronic Inds.*, vol. 17, no. 8, pp. 66–68, August, 1958.

Borkan, H., and P. K. Weimer: Differential Method of Lag Compensation in Photoconductive Devices, *RCA Rev.*, vol. 19, no. 1, pp. 62–76, March, 1958.

Bose, K. K.: The Effect of a Magnetic Field on Point-contact Transistors, *Electronic Eng.*, vol. 30, pp. 639–641, November, 1958.

Brophy, J. J.: Experiment Showing the Influence of Surfaces on 1/f Noise in Germanium, *J. Appl. Phys.*, vol. 29, no. 9, pp. 1377–1378, September, 1958.

Brown, D. A. H.: Majority Carrier Lifetime in Copper Doped Germanium at 20°K, *J. Electronics and Control*, vol. 4, no. 4, pp. 341–349, April, 1958.

Browne, G. D.: A. F. C. in Band II FM Receivers Using a Junction Diode, *Mullard Tech. Commun.*, vol. 4, pp. 152–157, November, 1958.

Bube, R. H., and E. L. Lind: Photoconductivity of Zinc Selenide Crystals and a Correlation of Donor and Acceptor Levels in II-VI Photoconductors, *Phys. Rev.*, vol. 110, no. 5, pp. 1040–1049, June 1, 1958.

Burwen, R. S.: Portable Transistor Music System, *Audio Eng. Soc. J.*, vol. 6, no. 1, pp. 10–18, January, 1958.

Busch, G. A.: Semiconducting Compounds, *Nuovo cimento*, suppl., vol. 7, no. 2, pp. 696–712, 1958.

Butler, F.: Transistor Audio Amplifier, *Wireless World*, vol. 64, no. 11, pp. 529–535, November, 1958.

Buznea, D.: Oscillating Conditions for Transistor Oscillators, *Telecomunicatii*, vol. 2, no. 5, pp. 210–214, September–October, 1958.

Cabannes, F.: Observation of Photovoltaic Effects with Thin Layers of Cadmium Sulphide, *Compt. rend.*, vol. 246, no. 2, pp. 257–260, January 13, 1958.

Caldwell, J. W., and T. C. G. Wagner: Boosting Power Transistor Efficiency, *Electronics*, vol. 31, no. 47, pp. 86–88, November 21, 1958.

Campling, C. H. R.: Magnetic Inverter Uses Tubes or Transistors, *Electronics*, vol. 31, no. 11, pp. 158–161, March 14, 1958.

Card, W. H.: Transistor-oscillator Induction-motor Drive, *Commun. and Electronics*, no. 38, September, 1958.

Carlsen, R. A.: Transistor-diode Logic, *Proc. Natl. Electronics Conf.*, vol. 14, pp. 56–64, 1958.

Cattermole, K. W.: Transistor Pulse Generators for Time-division Multiplex, *Proc. Inst. Elec. Engrs. (London)*, paper 2577R, March, 1958.

Čermák, J.: Transistor Noise, *Slaboproudý Obzor*, vol. 19, no. 7, pp. 428–433, 1958.

Chaplin, G. B. B., and R. Williamson: Dekatrons and Electro-mechanical Registers Operated by Transistors, *Proc. Inst. Elec. Engrs. (London)*, paper 2440M, November, 1958.

Chasmar, R. P., and E. Cohen: An Electrical Multiplier Utilizing the Hall Effect in Indium Arsenide, *Electronic Eng.*, vol. 30, pp. 661–664, November, 1958.

Chenette, E. R.: Measurement of the Correlation between Flicker Noise Sources in Transistors, *Proc. IRE*, vol. 46, no. 6, page 1304, June, 1958.

Cherne, Kh. I.: Relationships between Transistor Parameters in the Various Circuit Modes, *Radiotekhnika*, vol. 13, no. 2, pp. 69–78, 1958.

Chuenkov, V. A.: The Behaviour of the Germanium-type Valence Semiconductors in Strong Electric Fields, *Zhur. Tekh. Fiz.*, vol. 28, no. 3, pp. 470–479, 1958.

Chynoweth, A. G.: Ionization Rates for Electrons and Holes in Silicon, *Phys. Rev.*, vol. 109, no. 5, pp. 1537–1540, March 1, 1958.

Chynoweth, A. G., and G. L. Pearson: Effect of Dislocations on Breakdown in Silicon P-N Junctions, *J. Appl. Phys.*, vol. 29, no. 7, pp. 1103–1110, July, 1958.

Clark, M. A.: Power Transistors, *Proc. IRE*, vol. 46, no. 6, pp. 1185–1204, June, 1958.

Cleland, J. W., and J. H. Crawford, Jr.: Low-temperature Irradiation of N-Type Germanium, *J. Appl. Phys.*, vol. 29, no. 2, pp. 149–151, February, 1958.

Cloot, P. L.: A Basic Transistor Circuit for the Construction of Digital-computing Systems, *Proc. Inst. Elec. Engrs. (London)*, vol. 105B, paper 2585M, pp. 213–220, May, 1958.

Coffey, W. N.: Behaviour of Noise Figure in Junction Transistors, *Proc. IRE*, vol. 46, no. 2, pp. 495–496, February, 1958.

Conwell, E. M.: Properties of Silicon and Germanium, *Proc. IRE*, vol. 46, no. 6, pp. 1281–1300, June, 1958.

Cooke, H.: FM Tuner Uses Four Transistors, *Electronics*, vol. 31, no. 31, pp. 72–73, August 1, 1958.

Cooper, B. J.: The Measurement of Transistor Voltage-current Characteristics Using Pulse Techniques, *Electronic Eng.*, vol. 30, pp. 440–441, July, 1958.

Corson, A. J.: On the Application of Zener Diodes to Expanded Scale Instruments, *Commun. and Electronics*, no. 38, September, 1958.

Cote, A. J., Jr.: Evaluation of Transistor Neutralization Networks, *IRE Trans. on Circuit Theory*, vol. CT-5, no. 2, pp. 95–103, June, 1958.

Cote, A. J., Jr.: Matrix Analysis of Oscillators and Transistor Applications, *IRE Trans. on Circuit Theory*, vol. CT-5, no. 3, pp. 181–188, September, 1958.

Credle, A. B.: Effects of Low Temperatures on Transistor Characteristics, *IBM J. Research Develop.*, vol. 2, no. 1, pp. 54–71, January, 1958.

Cripps, L. G.: Transistor Cutoff Frequency Measurement, *Proc. IRE*, vol. 46, no. 4, pp. 781–782, April, 1958.

Crump, L. R.: Radio Waves Power Transistor Circuits, *Electronics*, vol. 31, no. 19, pp. 63–65, May 9, 1958.

Davis, E. M., Jr.: Comparisons between Multiple Loop and Single-loop Transistor Feedback Amplifiers, *IRE WESCON Conv. Record*, vol. 2, part 2, pp. 78–86, 1958.

Davýdov, V. S.: Graphic Analysis of Thermal Stabilization of Emitter Followers, *Radiotekhnika*, vol. 13, no. 2, pp. 23–27, 1958.

Deb, S., and A. N. Daw: On the Lifetime and Diffusion Constant of the Injected Carriers and the Emitter Efficiency of a Junction Transistor, *J. Electronics and Control*, vol. 5, no. 6, pp. 514–530, December, 1958.

Denda, S.: Germanium P-N-P-N Switches, *J. Inst. Elec. Commun. Engrs. (Japan)*, vol. 41, no. 7, pp. 701–705, July, 1958.

Depian, L., and R. E. Smith: A Stabilized D-C Differential Transistor Amplifier, *Trans. AIEE*, part I, vol. 77, pp. 157–159, 1958.

Dion, D. F.: Common Emitter Transistor Amplifiers, *Proc. IRE*, vol. 46, no. 5(1), p. 920, May, 1958.

Dirksen, H. J.: Photoconductivity in Cadmium Selenide (Fotogeleiding in Cadmium-Selenide), University of Delft dissertation, 1958.

Dorda, G.: The Effect of the Irradiation of Germanium with α-particles on the Recombination of Current Carriers, *Czechoslov. J. Phys.*, vol. 8, no. 2, pp. 181–185, 1958.

Dorph-Petersen, P.: Megohmmeter with Transistor–D-C Converter, *Ingeniøren*, vol. 67B, no. 7, pp. 236–238, April 1, 1958.

Drabble, J. R.: The Effect of Strain on the Thermoelectric Properties of a Many-valley Semiconductor, *J. Electronics and Control*, vol. 5, no. 4, pp. 362–372, October, 1958.

Drechsel, W.: Investigation of Germanium Diode Impedances and of Diode Circuits, *Nachrichtentechnik*, vol. 8, no. 11, pp. 482–488, November, 1958.

Drechsel, W.: The Noise of (Semiconductor) Diodes, *Nachrichtentechnik*, vol. 8, no. 12, pp. 538–541, December, 1958.

Dulberger, L. H.: Transistor Oscillator Supplies Stable Signal, *Electronics*, vol. 31, no. 5, p. 43, January 31, 1958.

Dykast, K.: Neutralization of Transistor Amplifiers, *Slaboproudý Obzor*, vol. 19, no. 11, pp. 732–737, 1958.

Early, J. M.: Structure-determined Gain-band Product of Junction Triode Transistors, *Proc. IRE*, vol. 46, no. 12, pp. 1924–1927, December, 1958.

Easley, J. W.: Comparison of Neutron Damage in Germanium and Silicon Transistors, *IRE WESCON Conv. Record*, vol. 2, part 3, pp. 148–156, 1958.

Easley, J. W.: Transistor Characteristics for Direct-coupled Transistor Logic Circuits, *IRE Trans. on Electronic Computers*, vol. EC-7, no. 1, pp. 6–16, March, 1958.

Efimov, E. A., and I. G. Erusalimchik: The Germanium Electrode with a P-N Junction, *Doklady Akad. Nauk S.S.S.R.*, vol. 122, no. 4, pp. 632–634, 1958.

Emeis, R., and A. Herlet: The Blocking Capability of Alloyed Silicon Power Transistors, *Proc. IRE*, vol. 46, no. 6, pp. 1216–1220, June, 1958.

Emeis, R., A. Herlet, and E. Spenke: The Effective Emitter Area of Power Transistors, *Proc. IRE*, vol. 46, no. 6, pp. 1220–1229, June, 1958.

Engbert, W.: Junction Transistors; Characteristics and Production Problems, *Telefunken Ztg.*, vol. 31, pp. 175–178, September, 1958.

Eriksen, W. T.: Field Modulation of Liquid Induced Excess Surface Currents on Germanium P-N Junctions, *J. Appl. Phys.*, vol. 29, no. 4, pp. 730–732, April, 1958.

Esaki, L.: New Phenomenon in Narrow Germanium P-N Junctions, *Phys. Rev.*, vol. 109, no. 2, pp. 603–604, January 15, 1958.

Ettinger, G. M.: Some Methods of Measuring Power Loss in Switching Transistors, *Proc. Natl. Electronics Conf.*, vol. 14, pp. 464–477, 1958.

Evans, D. M.: The Dependence of Minority Carrier Lifetime on Majority Carrier Density, *Proc. IRE*, vol. 46, no. 12, pp. 1962–1963, December, 1958.

Evans, J.: Silicon Switching Diodes, *Direct Current*, vol. 4, no. 3, pp. 68–71, December, 1958.

Faĭnshteĭn, S. M., and O. S. Lýsogorov: The Effect of Ionic Bombardment on the Current-voltage Characteristics of Silicon Point-contact Diodes, *Zhur. Tekh. Fiz.*, vol. 28, no. 3, pp. 493–497, 1958.

Fan, H. Y.: Properties of Semiconductors, *Nuovo cimento*, suppl., vol. 7, no. 2, pp. 661–695, 1958.

Feldman, E. J.: Recent Developments in Microwave Diodes, *Sylvania Technologist*, vol. 11, no. 2, pp. 71–75, April, 1958.

Fewer, D. R.: Transistor Non-linearity—Dependence on Emitter Bias Current in P-N-P Alloy Junction Transistors, *IRE Trans. on Audio*, vol. AU-6, no. 2, pp. 41–44, March–April, 1958.

Fischer, A.: "Problems of P-N Electroluminescence in the Visible Spectral Region, Semiconductors and Phosphors," pp. 551–553, Vieweg, Brunswick, 1958.

Fix, H.: The Application of Transistors to Video-frequency Equipment, *Rundfunktech. Mitt.*, vol. 2, no. 1, pp. 10–17, February, 1958.

Flaherty, P., G. Freedman, P. Kaufmann, D. Root, D. Spittlehouse, W. Waring, P. Whoriskey, and J. Williams: A New Five-watt, Class A, Silicon Power Transistor, *IRE Natl. Conv. Record*, vol. 6, part 3, pp. 77–83, 1958.

Fleming, R. F.: Design of a Transistorized Record-playback Amplifier for Dictation Machine Application, *IRE Natl. Conv. Record*, vol. 6, part 7, pp. 95–117, 1958.

Flesher, G. T.: Transistor Pulse Width Control Amplifier with Reactive Load, *Proc. Natl. Electronics Conf.*, vol. 14, pp. 454–463, 1958.

Fletcher, N. H.: Power Transistors, *Proc. IRE, Australia*, vol. 19, no. 7, pp. 311–315, July, 1958.

Florida, C. D.: A New Bistable Element Suitable for Use in Digital Computers, I-II, *Electronic Eng.*, vol. 30, pp. 71–77, February; pp. 148–153, March, 1958.

Florine, J.: Practical Applications of Semiconductors (in Transistor Amplifiers), *Rev. HF*, vol. 4, no. 4, pp. 89–102, 1958.

Fonger, W. H., J. J. Loferski, and P. Rappaport: Radiation Induced Noise in P-N Junctions, *J. Appl. Phys.*, vol. 29, no. 3, pp. 588–591, March, 1958.

Forster, J. H., and H. S. Veloric: Effect of Variations in Surface Potential on Junction Characteristics, *J. Appl. Phys.*, vol. 30, no. 6, pp. 906–914, June, 1958.

Forster, J. H., and P. Zuk: Millimicrosecond Diffused Silicon Computer Diodes, *IRE WESCON Conv. Record*, vol. 2, part 3, pp. 122–130, 1958.

Foster, W. H.: Completely Transistorized Strain Gage Oscillator, *Electronics*, vol. 31, no. 5, pp. 40–42, January 31, 1958.

Frerichs, R., and E. Muly: The Response of a Germanium Phototransistor to Light Pulses of Very High Intensity and Short Duration, *Proc. Natl. Electronics Conf.*, vol. 14, pp. 331–342, 1958.

Fujimura, Y.: High-frequency Characteristics of Transistor Video Amplifiers, *J. Inst. Elec. Commun. Engrs. (Japan)*, vol. 41, no. 10, pp. 957–965, October, 1958.

Garmash, E. N.: Analysis of Transistor Circuits, *Radiotekhnika*, vol. 13, no. 7, pp. 47–54, 1958.

Gärtner, W. W.: Large-signal Rise-times in Junction Transistors, *IRE Trans. on Electron Devices*, vol. ED-5, no. 4, p. 316, October, 1958.

Gärtner, W. W., R. Hanel, R. Stampfl, and F. Caruso: The Current Amplification of a Junction Transistor as a Function of Emitter Current and Junction Temperature, *Proc. IRE*, vol. 46, no. 11, pp. 1876–1877, November, 1958.

Geib, C. C., and W. E. Brown: A High-current-density Selenium Rectifier, *Appl. and Ind.*, no. 34, January, 1958.

Gelder, E.: Single Transistor D-C Convertor, *Radio Mentor*, vol. 24, no. 1, pp. 27–32, January, 1958.

Gentry, F. E.: Forward Current Surge Failure in Semiconductor Rectifiers, *Commun. and Electronics*, no. 39, November, 1958.

Gereth, R., and H. A. Müser: Test Equipment for Photoconductors, *Z. angew. Phys.*, vol. 10, no. 9, pp. 419–424, September, 1958.

Gerlich, D.: Temperature Dependence of Point Contact Injection Ratio in Germanium, *Proc. Phys. Soc. (London)*, vol. 72, part 2, pp. 264–267, August, 1958.

Giacoletto, L. J.: Analog Solution of Space-charge Regions in Semiconductors, *Proc. IRE*, vol. 46, no. 6, pp. 1083–1085, June, 1958.

Giacoletto, L. J.: Power Amplification × Bandwidth Figure of Merit for Transducers Including Transistors, *J. Electronics and Control*, vol. 4, no. 6, pp. 515–522, June, 1958.

Gibson, A. F., and E. G. S. Paige: An Interpretation of Certain Transport Properties in Germanium Containing Parallel Arrays or Edge Dislocations, *Phil. Mag.* (8th ser.), vol. 3, pp. 950–960, September, 1958.

Giguere, W. J.: A Transistorized 150-Mc FM Receiver, *Proc. IRE*, vol. 46, no. 4, pp. 693–699, April, 1958.

Gill, A.: Matching Transistor-diodes, *Electronics*, vol. 31, no. 3, p. 75, January 17, 1958.

Giorgis, J., and C. C. Thompson: Silicon Transistor Performance in a Chopper Application, *Appl. and Ind.*, no. 37, July, 1958.

Glicksman, M.: Mobility of Electrons in Germanium-Silicon Alloys, *Phys. Rev.*, vol. 111, no. 1, pp. 125–128, July 1, 1958.

Gobeli, G. W.: Alpha-particle Irradiation of Ge at 4.2°K, *Phys. Rev.*, vol. 112, no. 3, pp. 732–739, November 1, 1958.

Gordeev, G. V.: On Electrical Conductivity of Amorphous Semiconductors, *Zhur. Tekh. Fiz.*, vol. 28, no. 3, pp. 539–541, 1958.

Görlich, P., A. Krohs, and W. Lang: Photo-resistors, Photo-diodes and Photo-transistors, *Arch. tech. Meesen*, no. 272 (ref. J394-1), pp. 189–192, September; no. 274 (ref. J394-2), pp. 235–238, November; no. 275 (ref. J394-3), pp. 247–250, December, 1958.

Gosar, P.: On the Lateral Photovoltaic Effect in P-N Junctions, *Compt. rend.*, vol. 247, no. 22, pp. 1975–1978, December 1, 1958.

Gosar, P., and H. Ménaché: The Influence of Surface State on the Measurement of Diffusion Length in Silicon, *J. phys. radium*, vol. 19, no. 12, pp. 930–938, December, 1958.

Gottlieb, E.: Transistor Reflex Circuit Trims Receiver Costs, *Electronics*, vol. 31, no. 1, pp. 66–68, January 3, 1958.

Goulding, F. S.: Transistorized Radiation Monitors, *IRE Trans. on Nuclear Sci.*, vol. NS-5, no. 2, pp. 38–43, August, 1958.

Graveson, R. T., and H. Sadowski: Pulse Amplifiers Using Transistor Circuits, *IRE Trans. on Nuclear Sci.*, vol. NS-5, no. 3, pp. 179–182, December, 1958.

Graveson, R. T., and H. Sadowski: Transistorization of Nuclear Counting Circuits, *IRE Trans. on Nuclear Sci.*, vol. NS-5, no. 2, pp. 33–38, August, 1958.

Greenberg, L. S., and R. C. Wonson: Capacity Neutralization of H. F. Transistors, *Electronic Inds.*, vol. 17, no. 9, pp. 82–86, September, 1958.

Gremmelmaier, R.: Irradiation of P-N Junctions with Gamma Rays: A Method for Measuring Diffusion Lengths, *Proc. IRE*, vol. 46, no. 6, pp. 1045–1049, June, 1958.

Grimsdell, G.: Diode Hole Storage and "Turn-on" and "Turn-off" Time, *Electronic Eng.*, vol. 30, pp. 645–646, November, 1958.

Grimsdell, G.: New Types of Germanium Diodes and Their Circuit Applications, *Electronic Eng.*, vol. 30, pp. 709–710, December, 1958.

Grinberg, A. A.: Theory of Transient Response of Transistors, *Radiotekhnika*, vol. 13, no. 2, pp. 51–53, 1958.

Grinich, V. H., and R. N. Noyce: Switching Time Calculations for Diffused Base Transistors, *IRE WESCON Conv. Record*, vol. 2, part 3, pp. 141–147, 1958.

Griswold, D. M., and V. J. Cadra: Use of the RCA 2N384 Drift Transistor as a Linear Amplifier, *IRE Natl. Conv. Record*, vol. 6, part 3, pp. 49–56, 1958.

Grosvalet, J.: Some Properties of Small-area Silicon Alloy Junction Diodes. I. Avalanche and Breakdown Voltage, *Ann. radioélec.*, vol. 13, pp. 162–166, April, 1958.

Grover, N. B., and E. Harnik: Sweep-out Effects in the Phase Shift Method of Carrier Lifetime Measurements, *Proc. Phys. Soc. (London)*, vol. 72, part 2, pp. 267–269, August, 1958.

Gruber, P.: Crystal Converter for Tropo-scatter Receivers, *Electronics*, vol. 31, no. 15, pp. 78–82, April 11, 1958.

Gudmundsen, R. A.: The Emitter Tetrode, *IRE Trans. on Electron Devices*, vol. ED-5, no. 4, pp. 223–225, October, 1958.

Guggenbühl, W., and W. Wunderlin: Experimental and Theoretical Investigations of the Equivalent Circuits of Modern High-frequency Transistors, in Particular, Drift Transistors, *Arch. Elekt. Ubertragung*, vol. 12, no. 5, pp. 193–202, May, 1958.

Gunn, J. B.: On Carrier Accumulation, and the Properties of Certain Semiconductor Junctions, *J. Electronics and Control*, vol. 4, no. 1, pp. 17–50, January, 1958.

Günther, K. G.: Evaporated Layers of Semiconducting III-V Compounds, *Naturwissenschaften*, vol. 45, no. 17, pp. 415–416, 1958.

Gutzwiller, F. W.: The Silicon Controlled Rectifier—A Semiconductor Power Switch with Microsecond Response, *Elec. Mfg.*, vol. 62, no. 6, pp. 62–65, 109, December, 1958.

Haidekker, A.: Several Criteria for the Reliable Operation of Transistorized Pulse-forming Circuits in Industrial Switching Technique, *Elektron. Rundschau*, vol. 12, no. 3, pp. 93–94, March, 1958.

Haidekker, A.: Transistorized Counter Circuits with Visual Indication, *Elektronik*, vol. 7, no. 7, pp. 211–213, July, 1958.

Hake, E. A.: A 10 Kw Germanium Rectifier for Automatic Power Plants, *Appl. and Ind.*, no. 34, January, 1958.

Hall, R. A.: A 1 Kc/s Junction Transistor T-parameter Measurement Set, *Electronic Eng.*, vol. 30, pp. 82–85, February, 1958.

Hall, R. A.: 1 Kc/s Transistor High-gain Tuned Amplifier, *Electronic Eng.*, vol. 30, pp. 192–195, April, 1958.

Hall, R. N.: Electrical Contacts to Silicon Carbide, *J. Appl. Phys.*, vol. 29, no. 6, pp. 914–917, June, 1958.

Halpern, J., and R. H. Rediker: Out-diffusion as a Technique for the Production of Diodes and Transistors, *Proc. IRE*, vol. 46, no. 6, pp. 1068–1076, June, 1958.

Hamilton, D. J.: A Transistor (Emitter-coupled) Univibrator with Stabilized Pulse Duration, *IRE Trans. on Circuit Theory*, vol. CT-5, no. 1, pp. 69–73, March, 1958.

Hamilton, D. J.: A Transistor Pulse Generator for Digital Systems, *IRE Trans. on Electronic Computers*, vol. EC-7, no. 3, pp. 244–249, September, 1958.

Harnik, E., A. Many, and N. B. Grover: Phase Shift Method of Carrier Lifetime Measurements in Semiconductors, *Rev. Sci. Instr.*, vol. 29, no. 10, pp. 889–891, October, 1958.

Harrick, N. J.: Characteristics of Junctions in Germanium, *J. Appl. Phys.*, vol. 29, no. 5, pp. 764–770, May, 1958.

Harris, J. R.: Direct-coupled Transistor Logic Circuitry, *IRE Trans. on Electronic Computers*, vol. EC-7, no. 1, pp. 2–6, March, 1958.

Hasenberg, W.: Power Transistor Test Set, *Electronic Inds.*, vol. 17, no. 5, pp. 58–60, May, 1958.

Hauri, E. R.: A Low Noise Transistor Amplifier for Acoustic Measurements, *Tech. Mitt. PTT*, vol. 36, no. 4, pp. 142–144, 1958.

Hauri, E. R.: Present-day Limiting Properties of Transistors, *Bull. assoc. suisse élec.*, vol. 49, no. 17, pp. 809–810, 827–833, August 16, 1958.

Hayashi, K.: Characteristics and Applications of Silicon Solar Battery, *J. Inst. Elec. Commun. Engrs. (Japan)*, vol. 41, no. 8, pp. 780–786, August, 1958.

Hazel, W. C.: Use of Operational Amplifiers in the Measurement of Transistor Parameters, *Rev. Sci. Instr.*, vol. 29, no. 3, pp. 235–237, March, 1958.

Heasell, E. L., N. R. Howard, and E. W. Timmins: An Apparatus for Measuring the Electrical Resistivity of Silicon, *BTH Activities*, vol. 29, no. 4, pp. 147–149, July–August, 1958.

Heinlein, W.: Inertia in Germanium Diodes and Its Effect in Simple Rectifier and Limiter Circuits, *Frequenz*, vol. 12, no. 5, pp. 159–163, May; no. 6, pp. 191–197, June, 1958.

Heinlein, W.: The Inertia of P-N Junction Diodes When Strongly Driven with Sinusoidal Voltages, *Arch. Elekt. Übertragung*, vol. 12, no. 11, pp. 510–514, November, 1958.

Hellerman, H.: A Generalized Theory of Transistor Bias Circuits, *Trans. AIEE*, part I, vol. 76, pp. 694–697, 1958.

Hellstrom, M. J.: Transistor Thermal Stability, *IRE Trans. on Broadcast and Television Receivers*, vol. BTR-4, no. 4, pp. 42–50, September, 1958.

Helsdon, P. B.: Transistor Video Amplifiers, *Marconi Rev.*, vol. 21, pp. 56–75, 2d quarter, 1958.

Henkels, H. W.: Germanium and Silicon Rectifiers, *Proc. IRE*, vol. 46, no. 6, pp. 1086–1098, June, 1958.

Henkels, H. W., and T. P. Nowalk: High Power Silicon Transistors, *IRE WESCON Conv. Record*, vol. 2, part 3, pp. 157–165, 1958.

Henle, R. A., and J. L. Walsh: The Application of Transistors to Computers, *Proc. IRE*, vol. 46, no. 6, pp. 1240–1254, June, 1958.

Herczog, A., R. R. Haberecht, and A. E. Middleton: Preparation and Properties of Aluminum Antimonide, *J. Electrochem. Soc.*, vol. 105, no. 9, pp. 533–540, September, 1958.

Herrman, G. F., M. Uenohara, and A. Uhlir, Jr: Noise Figure Measurements on Two Types of Variable Reactance Amplifiers Using Semiconductor Diodes, *Proc. IRE*, vol. 46, no. 6, pp. 1301–1303, June, 1958.

Herscher, M. B.: Designing Transistor A-F Power Amplifiers, *Electronics*, vol. 31, no. 15, pp. 96–99, April, 1958.

Herscher, M. B.: High Power Transistor Audio Amplifiers, *Audio Eng. Soc. J.*, vol. 6, no. 1, pp. 42–48, January, 1958.

Heywang, W., and M. Zerbst: Properties of High-purity Silicon, *Siemens Rev.*, vol. 25, no. 2, pp. 44–50, April, 1958.

Hill, J. E., and K. M. van Vliet: Ambipolar Transport of Carrier Density Fluctuations in Germanium, *Physica*, vol. 24, no. 9, pp. 709–720, September, 1958.

Hill, J. E., and K. M. van Vliet: Generation Recombination Noise in Intrinsic and Near-intrinsic Germanium Crystals, *J. Appl. Phys.*, vol. 29, no. 2, pp. 177–182, February, 1958.

Hilsum, C.: Multiplication by Semiconductors, *Electronic Eng.*, vol. 30, pp. 664–666, November, 1958.

Hilsum, C., and R. Barrie: Properties of p-type Indium Antimonide. I. Electrical Properties, *Proc. Phys. Soc. (London)*, vol. 71, part 4, pp. 676–685, April, 1958.

Hinrichs, K., and B. B. Weekes: "Squarved" (Squashed and Starved) Input Stages for Low-level Transistor Amplifiers, *IRE WESCON Conv. Record*, vol. 2, part 2, pp. 104–114, 1958.

Hochwald, W., and F. H. Gerhard: A Drift Compensated Operational D-C Amplifier Employing a Low-level Silicon Transistor Chopper, *Proc. Natl. Electronics Conf.*, vol. 14, pp. 798–810, 1958.

Hoerni, J. A.: Carrier Mobilities at Low Injection Levels, *Proc. IRE*, vol. 46, no. 2, p. 502, February, 1958.

Hoffmann, A.: On the Mode of Action of N-P-N Phototransistors, *Z. angew. Phys.*, vol. 10, no. 9, pp. 416–418, September, 1958.

Hofmeister, E., and E. Groschwitz: The Influence of the Geometrical and Physical Conditions at the Point Contact of Germanium Diodes on the (Current-voltage) Characteristics, *Z. angew. Phys.*, vol. 10, no. 3, pp. 109–114, March, 1958.

Hogarth, C. A., and P. J. Hoyland: Radial Variation of Minority Carrier Lifetime in Vacuum-grown Germanium Single Crystals, *J. Electronics and Control*, vol. 4, no. 1, pp. 60–62, January, 1958.

Hoge, H. H.: Diode Cuts Transistor Cutoff-current Drift, *Electronics*, vol. 31, no. 29, p. 83, July 18, 1958.

Holford, K., and L. M. Newall: Video Amplifiers Using Alloy Junction Transistors, *Mullard Tech. Commun.*, vol. 4, pp. 94–105, October, 1958.

Horn, I.: An Emitter-follower-coupled, High-speed Binary Counter, *IRE WESCON Conv. Record*, vol. 2, part 4, pp. 54–61, 1958.

Hufner, W.: Transistor Oscillators of High Frequency-stability for Carrier-frequency Techniques, *Nachrichtentechnik*, vol. 8, no. 3, pp. 117–122, March, 1958.

Huldt, L., and T. Staflin: Infrared Absorption of Photogenerated Free Carriers in Germanium, *Phys. Rev. Letters*, vol. 1, no. 7, pp. 236–237, October 1, 1958.

Hulscher, F. R.: A Transistor Multimeter, *Proc. IRE, Australia*, vol. 19, no. 4, pp. 168–173, April, 1958.

Humphreys, T. I.: Transistor Unit Detects Foetal Heart Sounds, *Electronics*, vol. 31, no. 17, pp. 52–53, April 25, 1958.

Hyde, F. J.: The Internal Current Gain of Drift Transistors, *Proc. IRE*, vol. 46, no. 12, pp. 1963–1964, December, 1958.

Hyde, F. J.: A Method for Measuring Transistor Current Gain at Radio Frequencies, *J. Sci. Instr.*, vol. 35, no. 3, p. 115, March, 1958.

Hyde, F. J.: Some Measurements on Commercial Transistors and Their Relation to Theory, *Proc. Inst. Elec. Engrs. (London)*, vol. 105B, paper 2438R, pp. 45–52, January, 1958.

Hyde, F. J., and R. W. Smith: An Investigation of the Current Gain of Transistors at Frequencies up to 105 Mc/s, *Proc. Inst. Elec. Engrs. (London)*, vol. 105B, paper 2548R, pp. 221–228, May, 1958.

Hykes, G. R.: Transistorized Airborne Frequency Standard, *IRE Natl. Conv. Record*, vol. 6, part 5, pp. 131–135, 1958.

Iles, P. A., and P. J. Coppen: On the Delineation of P-N Junctions in Silicon, *J. Appl. Phys.*, vol. 29, no. 10, p. 1514, October, 1958.

Ilisavskii, Yu. V.: The Current-voltage Characteristic of a Metal-Aluminium Antimonide Point Contact, *Zhur. Tekh. Fiz.*, vol. 28, no. 5, pp. 965–973, 1958.

Irons, H. R.: A Transistor–Magnetic Core Binary Counter, *Proc. IRE*, vol. 46, no. 12, pp. 1967–1968, December, 1958.

Ivanov, Yu. L., and S. M. Rўvkin: Generation of an Oscillating Current in Germanium Specimens Placed in Electric and Longitudinal Magnetic Fields, *Zhur. Tekh. Fiz.*, vol. 28, no. 4, pp. 774–775, 1958.

Izumi, H., and T. Hayashi: Channel Effects of Silicon Diodes, *J. Inst. Elec. Commun. Engrs. (Japan)*, vol. 41, no. 11, pp. 1108–1113, November, 1958.

Jackets, A. E.: A Method for Sharpening the Output Waveform of Junction Transistor Multivibrator Circuits, *Electronic Eng.*, vol. 30, pp. 371–374, June, 1958.

Jenny, D. A.: A Gallium Arsenide Microwave Diode, *Proc. IRE*, vol. 46, no. 4, pp. 717–722, April, 1958.

Jenny, D. A.: The Status of Transistor Research in Compound Semiconductors, *Proc. IRE*, vol. 46, no. 6, pp. 959–968, June, 1958.

Jenny, D. A., and R. Braunstein: Some Properties of Gallium Arsenide–Germanium Mixtures, *J. Appl. Phys.*, vol. 29, no. 3, pp. 596–597, March, 1958.

Jochems, P. J. W., O. W. Memelink, and L. J. Tummers: Construction and Electrical Properties of a Germanium Alloy–diffused Transistor, *Proc. IRE*, vol. 46, no. 6, pp. 1161–1165, June, 1958.

Johnston, R. C.: Transient Response of Drift Transistors, *Proc. IRE*, vol. 46, no. 5(1), pp. 830–838, May, 1958.

Jonscher, A. K.: Analysis of Current Flow in a Planar Junction Diode at a High Forward Bias, *J. Electronics and Control*, vol. 5, no. 1, pp. 1–14, July, 1958.

Joshi, M. V.: Design of an Emitter Current Controlled Common Emitter Transistor I.F. Amplifier Stage, *J. Inst. Telecommun. Engrs. (New Delhi)*, vol. 5, no. 1, pp. 17–22, December, 1958.

Kaganov, I. L.: Engineering Calculations (Methods) of Low-frequency Semiconductor Amplifiers, *Elektrichestvo*, no. 9, pp. 8–15, 1958.

Kambouris, G. N.: Low Frequencies Vary T-parameters (of Transistors), *Electronic Inds.*, vol. 17, no. 12, pp. 69–71, December, 1958.

Kampf, H. A.: Transistors and Diodes in Strong Magnetic Fields, *Electronic Inds.*, vol. 17, no. 3, pp. 71–73, March, 1958.

Kanai, Y.: Electrical Conductivity in P-type InSb under Strong Electric Field, *J. Phys. Soc. Japan*, vol. 13, no. 9, pp. 1065–1066, September, 1958.

Kazan, B.: A Solid-state Amplifying Fluoroscope Screen, *RCA Rev.*, vol. 19, no. 1, pp. 19–34, March, 1958.

Kemhadjian, H.: A Stable Gain Transformer Coupled Transistor A.F. Amplifier, *Mullard Tech. Commun.*, vol. 3, pp. 245–251, January, 1958.

Kemhadjian, H.: Transistor Amplifiers for D-C Signals, *Mullard Tech. Commun.*, vol. 4, pp. 162–172, December, 1958.

Kendall, J. T.: Manufacture of Silicon Transistors, an Assessment of the Present State of Technology, *Electronic Radio Engr.*, vol. 35, no. 6, pp. 202–207, June, 1958.

Keywell, F.: Improved Diffusion Boundary Junction in Silicon Due to Scratch-free Polishing, *J. Appl. Phys.*, vol. 29, no. 5, pp. 871–872, May, 1958.

Kikuchi, M.: Observation of the Lateral Photovoltage by Surface Field Effect, *J. Phys. Soc. Japan*, vol. 13, no. 9, p. 1061, September, 1958.

Kikuchi, M.: On the Backward Leakage Current in the Alloyed Germanium P-N Junction, *J. Phys. Soc. Japan*, vol. 13, no. 4, pp. 350–362, April, 1958.

Klein, M. L.: Techniques for Stabilizing D-C Transistor Amplifiers, *IRE WESCON Conv.*, vol. 2, part 2, pp. 94–103, 1958.

Klein, O.: New SAF High-power Selenium Rectifiers, *SEG Nachr.*, vol. 6, no. 1, pp. 69–71, 1958.

Kloss, A.: Design of Germanium Power Rectifiers, *Elektrotech. Obzor*, vol. 47, no. 3, pp. 149–153, 1958.

Knowles, C. H.: New Transistor Design—The "Mesa," *Electronic Inds.*, vol. 17, no. 8, pp. 55–60, August, 1958.

Koenig, S. H.: Rate Processes and Low-temperature Electrical Conduction in N-type Germanium, *Phys. Rev.*, vol. 110, no. 4, pp. 986–988, May 15, 1958.

Kolomiets, B. T., and V. N. Larichev: An Investigation of the Photoelectric Properties of the Lead Sulphide Group of Semiconductors by the Condenser Method, *Zhur. Tekh. Fiz.*, vol. 28, no. 5, pp. 921–924, 1958.

Komatsubara, K.: Study on the Correlation between the Noise by Hole Generation and Surface Recombination Velocity at Ge Fused Junction, *J. Phys. Soc. Japan*, vol. 13, no. 11, pp. 1409–1410, November, 1958.

Komatsubara, K., and U. Hashimoto: Study on Annealing of Radiation Induced 1/f Noise in Ge P-N Junction, *J. Phys. Soc. Japan*, vol. 13, no. 9, p. 1062, September, 1958.

Konopiński, T., and M. Politowski: Design of D-C Push-Pull Transistor Converters, *Prace Inst. Tele i Radiotech.*, vol. 2, no. 3, pp. 3–16, 1958.

Kramar, J., and V. Horacek: Properties of Germanium Diodes Designed for Parallel and Series Arrangement, *Elektrotech. Obzor*, vol. 47, no. 11, pp. 558–564, 1958.

Krause, C. A., and R. R. Lowe: Design of A-C Computing Amplifiers Using Transistors, *IRE Trans. on Electronic Computers*, vol. EC-7, no. 3, pp. 191–195, September, 1958.

Krekule, I.: Test and Measurement Methods for Germanium Diodes and Transistors, *Slaboproudý Obzor*, vol. 19, no. 11, pp. 729–732, 1958.

Krinitz, A.: Transistor–Magnetic Pulse Generator, *Proc. Natl. Electronics Conf.*, vol. 14, pp. 37–55, 1958.

Krüger, B.: Basic Characteristics of Transistor Power Oscillators and D-C Convertors, *Elteknik*, vol. 1, no. 8, pp. 129–134, October, 1958.

Krugman, L. M.: Designing Transistor Narrow Band Amplifiers, *Electronic Inds.*, vol. 17, no. 10, pp. 78–81, October, 1958.

Kubat, M.: Czechoslovak Germanium Power Rectifiers, *Elektrotech. Obzor*, vol. 47, no. 5, pp. 233–241, 1958.

Kuz'min, V. A., and V. I. Shveikin: The Operation of Transistors in the Saturation Region, *Radiotekh. i Elektron.*, vol. 3, no. 10, pp. 1269–1273, October, 1958.

Labutin, V. K.: The h_{11}/Z_{11} Transistor Parameter and Generalized Gain and Impedance Characteristics, *Radiotekhnika*, vol. 13, no. 2, pp. 59–68, 1958.

Lamming, J. S.: A High Frequency Germanium Drift Transistor by Post Alloy Diffusion, *J. Electronics and Control*, vol. 4, no. 3, pp. 227–236, March, 1958.

Lecorguillier, J.: Semiconductors and Gas-filled Tubes in Heavy Current Techniques, *Bull. soc. franç. élec.*, vol. 8, pp. 553–562, September, 1958.

Ledig, G.: The H. F. Transistor and Its Complex Characteristics in the Frequency Range: 0–2 Mc/s, *Frequenz*, vol. 12, no. 5, pp. 137–148, May, 1958.

Lefkowitz, H.: Transistor A-C Amplifier Uses Multiple Feedback, *Electronics*, vol. 31, no. 21, pp. 84–85, May 23, 1958.

Lesk, I. A., and R. E. Gonzalez: Germanium and Silicon Transistor Structures by the Diffused Meltback Process Employing Two or Three Impurities, *IRE Trans. on Electron Devices*, vol. ED-5, no. 3, pp. 121–126, July, 1958.

Lesk, I. A., and R. E. Gonzalez: Selective Electrolytic Etching of Germanium and Silicon Junction Transistor Structures, *J. Electrochem. Soc.*, vol. 105, no. 8, pp. 469–472, August, 1958.

Lindemann, W. W., and R. K. Mueller: Grain Boundary Photo-detector, *J. Appl. Phys.*, vol. 29, no. 12, pp. 1770–1771, December, 1958.

Lindsay, J. E., and H. J. Woll: Design Considerations for Direct-coupled Transistor Amplifiers, *RCA Rev.*, vol. 19, no. 3, pp. 433–454, September, 1958.

Linvill, J. G.: Lumped Models of Transistors and Diodes, *Proc. IRE*, vol. 46, no. 6, pp. 1141–1152, June, 1958.

Lippmann, H. J., and F. Kuhrt: The Effect of Geometry on Hall and Magnetoresistive Effects in Rectangular Semiconductor Specimens, *Naturwissenschaften*, vol. 45, no. 7, pp. 156–157, 1958.

Litvinov, I. I.: Effect of Frequency-dependent Operating Characteristics of a Transistor on the (Pulse) Front Duration, *Radiotekhnika*, vol. 13, no. 2, pp. 54–58, 1958.

Lloyd, D. J.: A Simple Transistor Amplifier for Energizing a Hall Multiplier, *Electronic Eng.*, vol. 30, pp. 560–561, September, 1958.

Loferski, J. J.: Analysis of the Effect of Nuclear Radiation on Transistors, *J. Appl. Phys.*, vol. 29, no. 1, pp. 35–40, January, 1958.

Loferski, J. J., and P. Rappaport: The Effect of Radiation on Silicon Solar-energy Converters, *RCA Rev.*, vol. 19, no. 4, pp. 536–554, December, 1958.

Loferski, J. J., and P. Rappaport: Radiation Damage in Ge and Si Detected by Carrier Lifetime Changes: Damage Thresholds, *Phys. Rev.*, vol. 111, no. 2, pp. 432–439, July 15, 1958.

Löfgren, L.: Analog Multiplier Based on the Hall Effect, *J. Appl. Phys.*, vol. 29, no. 2, pp. 158–166, February, 1958.

Lunze, K.: Design Methods for the Stabilization of Transistor Circuits over a Temperature Range, *Nachrichtentechnik*, vol. 8, no. 3, pp. 98–108, March, 1958.

Lyubin, V. M.: Semiconductor RC Generators with Phase Reversal, *Radiotekhnika*, vol. 13, no. 2, pp. 44–50, 1958.

McKelvey, J. P.: Volume and Surface Recombination of Injected Carriers in Cylindrical Semiconductor Ingots, *IRE Trans. on Electron Devices*, vol. ED-5, no. 4, pp. 260–264, October, 1958.

Mackintosh, I. M.: The Electrical Characteristics of Silicon P-N-P-N Triodes, *Proc. IRE*, vol. 46, no. 6, pp. 1229–1235, June, 1958.

MacNichol, E. F., Jr., and T. Bickart: The Use of Transistors in Physiological Amplifiers, *IRE Trans. on Med. Electronics*, no. PGME-10, pp. 15–24, March, 1958.

McSpadden, W. R., and E. Eberhard: Graphical Designing of Transistor Oscillators, *Electronics*, vol. 31, no. 49, pp. 90–93, December 5, 1958.

Makovskiï, F. A., and E. P. Usachev: The Effect of the Upper Electrode Material on the Electrical Properties of Copper Oxide Rectifiers, *Zhur. Tekh. Fiz.*, vol. 28, no. 4, pp. 788–789, 1958.

Makovskiï, L. L.: Calculation of the Dependence of Current Amplification Factor on Emitter Current in Germanium Alloy Transistors for Injection and Extraction at High Temperatures, *Zhur. Tekh. Fiz.*, vol. 28, no. 1, pp. 52–54, 1958.

Malakhov, A. N.: Resistance Fluctuations of Semiconductor Detectors, *Radiotekh. i Elektron.*, vol. 3, no. 4, pp. 547–551, 1958.

Maloff, I. G.: Bilateral Conductivity in Power Transistors, *Electronic Inds.*, vol. 17, no. 7, pp. 82, 88–89, 122; July, 1958.

Manoogian, H. A.: Transistor Photoflash Power Converters, *Electronics*, vol. 31, no. 35, pp. 29–31, August 29, 1958.

Marcovitz, M. W., and E. Seif: Analytical Design of Resistor-coupled Transistor Logical Circuits, *IRE Trans. on Electronic Computers*, vol. EC-7, no. 2, pp. 109–119, June, 1958.

Margolin, M. G.: Relationships between Parameters of Thermionic Values and of Transistors, *Radiotekhnika*, vol. 13, no. 2, pp. 79–85, 1958.

Marshall, J. A., and V. N. Stewart: Silicon Power Rectifier Equipments, *Appl. and Ind.*, no. 34, January, 1958.

Maslov, A. A.: Alloyed Transistor Amplifiers, *Elektrichestvo*, no. 2, pp. 46–51, 1958.

Mason, D. R., and J. C. Sarace: Bonding Materials for Making Contacts to p-type Silicon, *J. Electrochem. Soc.*, vol. 105, no. 10, pp. 594–598, October, 1958.

Matsuzawa, T., and M. Kikuchi: Some Technical Problems on a Large-area P-N Junction Made by the Alloying Process, *Bull. Electrotech. Lab. (Tokyo)*, vol. 22, no. 2, pp. 81–84, February, 1958.

Matz, A. W.: Variation of Junction Transistor Current Amplification Factor with Emitter Current, *Proc. IRE*, vol. 46, no. 3, pp. 616–617, March, 1958.

Maynard, F. B.: Half-adders Drive Simultaneous Computer, *Electronics*, vol. 31, no. 29, pp. 80–82, July 18, 1958.

Meinhardt, J.: The Basic Theory of L.F. Small-signal Amplifiers Using Junction Transistors, *Nachrichtentechnik*, vol. 8, no. 9, pp. 415–422, September, 1958.

Meinhardt, J.: The Germanium Diode in the Demodulator Circuit, *Nachrichtentechnik*, vol. 8, no. 11, pp. 489–495, November, 1958.

Melehy, M. A.: A Wide-range Junction Transistor Audio Oscillator, *IRE WESCON Conv. Record*, vol. 2, part 2, pp. 74–77, 1958.

Melehy, M. A., and A. E. Smith: Class-C Transistor Amplifiers, *IRE Trans. on Circuit Theory*, vol. CT-5, no. 3, p. 227, September, 1958.

Mel'nik, V. G., I. G. Mel'nik, and S. S. Gutin: On P-N Junction in Solid Point-contact Rectifiers, *Doklady Akad. Nauk S.S.S.R.*, vol. 121, no. 5, pp. 852–854, 1958.

Memelink, O. S.: The Deplistor, a Semiconductor Switching Device, *Philips Research Repts.*, vol. 13, no. 5, pp. 485–488, October, 1958.

Mercouroff, W.: Statistics of Divalent Compensated Impurities in Semiconductors, *Compt. rend.*, vol. 246, no. 8, pp. 1175–1177, February 24, 1958.

Messenger, G. C.: New Concepts in Microwave Mixer Diodes, *Proc. IRE.*, vol. 46, no. 6, pp. 1116–1121, June, 1958.

Messenger, G. C.: Physical Mechanisms Leading to Deterioration of Transistor Life, *IRE Trans. on Electron Devices*, vol. ED-5, no. 3, pp. 147–151, July, 1958.

Messenger, G. C., and J. P. Spratt: The Effects of Neutron Irradiation on Germanium and Silicon, *Proc. IRE*, vol. 46, no. 6, pp. 1038–1044, June, 1958.

Meyer, N. I.: On the Variation of Transistor Small-signal Parameters with Emitter Current and Collector Voltage, *J. Electronics and Control*, vol. 4, no. 4, pp. 305–334, April, 1958.

Meyer-Brötz, G.: Problems and Possibilities of Applying Junction Transistors, *Telefunken Ztg.*, vol. 31, pp. 162–174, September, 1958.

Mikula, J.: The Junction Transistor as a High-frequency Amplifier, *Slaboproudý Obzor*, vol. 19, no. 7, pp. 433–436, 1958.

Mikula, J.: Spread of Transistor Parameters and the Possibility of the Reduction of Its Effect, *Slaboproudý Obzor*, vol. 19, no. 5, pp. 288–292, 1958.

Millea, M. F., and T. C. Hall: Surface Mobility in Germanium and Silicon, *Phys. Rev. Letters*, vol. 1, no. 8, pp. 278–279, October, 1958.

Miller, L. E.: The Design and Characteristics of a Diffused Silicon Logic Amplifier Transistor, *IRE WESCON Conv. Record*, vol. 2, part 3, pp. 132–140, 1958.

Miller, L. G., and W. R. Hodgson: Germanium Rectifier Equipment for Electrolytic Processes, *Appl. and Ind.*, no. 34, January, 1958.

Milnes, A. G.: High-efficiency Push-Pull Magnetic Amplifiers with Transistors as Switched Rectifiers, *Commun. and Electronics*, no. 37, July, 1958.

Misawa, T.: Theory of the P-N Junction Device Using Avalanche Multiplication, *Proc. IRE*, vol. 46, no. 12, p. 1954, December, 1958.

Missen, J. I.: A Method for Testing and Establishing the Rating of Semiconductor Rectifiers under Dynamic Conditions, *Proc. Inst. Elec. Engrs. (London)*, vol. 106C, monograph 310M, pp. 3–10, August, 1958.

Mitchell, A., and L. Lapidus: High-current Switching Times for a PNP Drift Transistor: Numerical Analysis on the IBM 704 Digital Computer, *IRE Natl. Conv. Record*, vol. 6, part 3, pp. 57–67, 1958.

Moizhes, B. Ya: The Effect of Surface and Volume Recombination on Alpha and the Reverse Collector Current of Alloy Crystal Triodes, *Zhur. Tekh. Fiz.*, vol. 28, no. 11, pp. 2402–2409, 1958.

Moll, J. L.: The Evolution of the Theory for the Voltage-current Characteristics of P-N Junctions, *Proc. IRE*, vol. 46, no. 6, pp. 1076–1082, June, 1958.

Moll, J. L., A. Uhlir, Jr., and B. Senitzky: Microwave Transients from Avalanching Silicon Diodes, *Proc. IRE*, vol. 46, no. 6, pp. 1306–1307, June, 1958.

Morcerf, F. J., and L. F. Roehm: Automatic Transistor Classifier, *IRE Natl. Conv. Record*, vol. 6, part 6, pp. 3–11, 1958.

Morgan, R. E.: A New Control Amplifier Using a Saturable Current Transformer and a Switching Transistor, *Trans. AIEE*, part I, pp. 557–562, 1958.

Mueller, C. W., and J. Hilibrand: The "Thyristor"—A New High-speed Switching Transistor, *IRE Trans. on Electron Devices*, vol. ED-5, no. 1, pp. 2–5, January, 1958.

Muller, A., and J. de Sartre: Transistor Push-Pull D-C Converters, *Ann. radioélec.*, vol. 13, pp. 252–266, July, 1958.

Münch, W. v.: Electrical Properties of Switching Transistors Used for Storage, *NTZ-Nachrtech. Z.*, vol. 11, no. 11, pp. 565–571, November, 1958.

Münch, W. v.: A Transistor with Thyratron Characteristics and Related Devices, *J. Brit. Inst. Radio Engrs.*, vol. 18, no. 11, pp. 645–652, November, 1958.

Münch, W. v., and H. Salow: A Storing and Switching Transistor, *NTZ-Nachrtech. Z.*, vol. 11, no. 6, pp. 293–299, June, 1958.

Murray, R. P.: Design of Transistor RC Amplifiers, *IRE Trans. on Audio*, vol. AU-6, no. 3, pp. 67–76, May–June, 1958.

Muss, D. R., and R. F. Greene: Reverse Breakdown in In-Ge Alloy Junctions, *J. Appl. Phys.*, vol. 29, no. 11, pp. 1534–1537, November, 1958.

Nambiar, K. P. P.: Junction Transistor Sawtooth Waveform Generators, *Electronic Eng.*, vol. 30, pp. 61–65, February, 1958.

Nanavati, R. P., and R. A. Johnson: Turn-on Delay Time and Its Prediction, *Proc. Natl. Electronics Conf.*, vol. 14, pp. 25–31, 1958.

Nasledov, D. N., and S. V. Slobodchikov: Investigation of the Electrical and Thermoelectric Properties of Aluminium Antimonide, *Zhur. Tekh. Fiz.*, vol. 28, no. 4, pp. 715–724, 1958.

Nelson, H.: The Preparation of Semiconductor Devices by Lapping and Diffusion Techniques, *Proc. IRE*, vol. 46, no. 6, pp. 1062–1067, June, 1958.

Nelson, J. T., and J. E. Iwersen: Measurement of Internal Temperature Rise of Transistors, *Proc. IRE*, vol. 46, no. 6, pp. 1207–1208, June, 1958.

Nelson, J. T., J. E. Iwersen, and F. Keywell: A Five-watt, Ten-megacycle Transistor, *Proc. IRE*, vol. 46, no. 6, pp. 1209–1215, June, 1958.

Nelson, R. C.: Organic Photoconductors. IV. Sign of the Charge Carrier, *J. Chem. Phys.*, vol. 29, no. 2, pp. 388–390, August, 1958.

Nesvadba, O., O. Kwaczek, and F. Machala: Geometrical Model of Alloyed P-N-P Junction, *Slaboproudý Obzor*, vol. 19, no. 11, pp. 755–758, 1958.

Newell, A. F.: The Design of Logical Circuits Using Transistors and Square-loop Ferrite Cores, *Mullard Tech. Commun.*, vol. 4, pp. 110–120, October, 1958.

Newell, A. F.: An Introduction to the Use of Transistors in Inductive Circuits; Delayed Switch-off Effect, *Mullard Tech. Commun.*, vol. 4, pp. 157–160, November, 1958.

Nicoll, F. H.: A Hysteresis Effect in Cadmium Selenide and Its Use in a Solid-state Image Storage Device, *RCA Rev.*, vol. 19, no. 1, pp. 77–85, March, 1958.

Nikolaenko, N. S.: Transistor Amplifier with D-C Coupling (Directly Coupled Transistor Amplifier), *Radiotekhnika*, vol. 13, no. 2, pp. 14–22, 1958.

Nishina, Y., and W. J. Spry: Measurement of the Hall Mobility in N-type Germanium at 9,121 Megacycles, *J. Appl. Phys.*, vol. 29, no. 2, pp. 230–231, February, 1958.

Nosov, Yu. R., and B. I. Khazanov: Thermal Stabilization of Transistor Voltage Amplifiers, *Radiotekhnika*, vol. 13, no. 2, pp. 28–35, 1958.

Novophashennyĭ, G. N., and P. V. Novitskiĭ: Simplification of the Design of Semiconductor Triode Amplifiers, *Elektrichestvo*, no. 6, pp. 47–49, 1958.

Oliferenko, G. I.: Calculation of the Sawtooth Current Retrace in a Transistor Oscillator, *Radiotekhnika*, vol. 13, no. 10, pp. 51–56, 1958.

Ollington, D. R.: Transistorized Vehicle Speedmeter, *Electronic Radio Engr.*, vol. 35, no. 9, pp. 322–324, September, 1958.

Orr, B. E.: Direct Drive Amplifier for Two-speed Servos, *Electronics*, vol. 31, no. 11, pp. 146–147, March 14, 1958.

Oshima, S., Y. Nakagome, and R. Inohana: Signal Input and Output Circuits for Parametron Using Transistors and Their Applications, *J. Inst. Elec. Commun. Engrs. (Japan)*, vol. 41, no. 9, pp. 856–861, September, 1958.

Page, D. F.: A Design Basis for Junction Transistor Oscillator Circuits, *Proc. IRE*, vol. 46, no. 6, pp. 1271–1280, June, 1958.

Paranjape, B. V.: Field Dependence of Mobility in Semiconductors, *Rept. Brit. Elec. Research Assoc.*, rep. L/T372, 1958.

Paul, R. J.: The Conditions for the Onset of Oscillations in Transistor Oscillators, *Nachrichtentechnik*, vol. 8, no. 3, pp. 109–116, March, 1958.

Pawling, J. F., and P. Tharma: A 4.5W Sliding-bias Amplifier Using an OC16, *Mullard Tech. Commun.*, vol. 4, pp. 19–28, July, 1958.

Pederson, D. O., and M. S. Ghausi: The Root Locus Design of Transistor Feedback Amplifiers, *IRE WESCON Conv. Record*, vol. 2, part 2, pp. 87–93, 1958.

Penfield, P., Jr.: Protecting Power Transistors from Thermal Runaway, *Electronic Inds.*, vol. 17, no. 2, pp. 79–80, 137, February, 1958.

Penin, N. A., and N. E. Skvortsova: The Impedance of the Rectifying Contact of Germanium and Silicon Detectors, at Ultra High Frequencies, *Radiotekh. i Elektron.*, vol. 3, no. 2, pp. 267–275, 1958.

Pensak, L.: High-voltage Photovoltaic Effect, *Phys. Rev.*, vol. 109, no. 2, p. 601, January 15, 1958.

Petritz, R. L.: Theory of an Experiment for Measuring the Mobility and Density of Carriers in the Space-charge Region of a Semiconductor Surface, *Phys. Rev.*, vol. 110, no. 6, pp. 1254–1262, June 15, 1958.

Pett, A. S.: A Transistorized I.F. Amplifier for Communication Receivers, *Proc. IRE Australia*, vol. 19, no. 7, pp. 351–357, July, 1958.

Philips, J., and H. C. Chang: Germanium Power Switching Devices, *IRE Trans. on Electron Devices*, vol. ED-5, no. 1, pp. 13–18, January, 1958.

Pinciroli, A., and S. Fubini: The Advantage of Considering the Transistor as an Active Quadripole, *Ricerca sci.*, vol. 28, no. 1, pp. 152–159, January, 1958.

Plummer, A. R.: The Effect of Heat Treatment on the Breakdown Characteristics of Silicon PN Junctions, *J. Electronics and Control*, vol. 5, no. 5, pp. 405–416, November, 1958.

Poelman, E. E. P.: Stabilization of the Operating Point of Transistors, *Tijdschr. Ned. Radiogenoot.*, vol. 23, no. 1, pp. 1–7, January, 1958.

Pornaro, M.: Evolution of the Rectifiers and Electronic Apparatus during the Sixty Years' Life of the A.E.I., *Elettrotecnica*, vol. 45, no. 3, pp. 162–178, April 7, 1958.

Price, P. J.: On the Statistical Mechanics of Impurity Conduction in Semiconductors, *IBM J. Research Develop.*, vol. 2, no. 2, pp. 123–129, April, 1958.

Prince, M. B., and M. Wolf: New Developments in Silicon Photovoltaic Devices, *J. Brit. Inst. Radio Engrs.*, vol. 18, no. 10, pp. 583–595, October, 1958.

Prior, A. C.: Avalanche Multiplication and Electron Mobility in Indium Antimonide at High Electric Fields, *J. Electronics and Control*, vol. 4, no. 2, pp. 165–169, February, 1958.

Pritchard, R. L.: Advances in the Understanding of the P-N Junction Triode, *Proc. IRE*, vol. 46, no. 6, pp. 1130–1141, June, 1958.

Pritchard, R. L.: Two-dimensional Current Flow in Junction Transistors at High Frequencies, *Proc. IRE*, vol. 46, no. 6, pp. 1152–1160, June, 1958.

Provost, F.: Silicon Junction Diodes, *Onde élect.*, vol. 38, pp. 347–352, May, 1958.

Purton, R. F.: Common Emitter Transistor Amplifiers, *Proc. IRE*, vol. 46, no. 12, pp. 1961–1962, December, 1958.

Purton, R. F.: Transistor Amplifiers: Common Base versus Common Emitter, *A.T.E. J.*, vol. 14, no. 2, pp. 157–163, April, 1958.

Ranachowski, J., and J. Wehr: Testing the Structure of Electrical Insulating Materials by Ultrasonic Methods, *Przeglad Elektrotech.*, vol. 34, no. 1, pp. 20–26, January, 1958.

Rath, H. L.: Physical and Electrical Properties of Silicon Rectifiers for the Communications Field, *Elektron. Rundschau*, vol. 12, no. 4, pp. 119–122, April, 1958.

Read, W. T., Jr.: A Proposed High-frequency, Negative-resistance Diode, *Bell System Tech. J.*, vol. 37, no. 2, pp. 401–446, March, 1958.

Redin, R. D., R. G. Morris, and G. C. Danielson: Semiconducting Properties of Mg₂Ge Single Crystals, *Phys. Rev.*, vol. 109, no. 6, pp. 1916–1920, March 15, 1958.

Redington, R. W.: Maximum Performance of High-resistivity Photoconductors, *J. Appl. Phys.*, vol. 29, no. 2, pp. 189–193, February, 1958.

Reich, B.: Measurement of Transistor Thermal Resistance, *Proc. IRE*, vol. 46, no. 6, pp. 1204–1207, June, 1958.

Reich, B.: Temperature Sensitivity of Current Gain in Power Transistors, *IRE Trans. on Electron Devices*, vol. ED-5, no. 3, pp. 180–182, July, 1958.

Reid, F. J., and R. K. Willardson: Carrier Mobilities in InP, GaAs, and AlSb, *J. Electronics and Control*, vol. 5, no. 1, pp. 54–61, July, 1958.

Reynolds, W. N., M. T. Lilburne, and R. M. Dell: Some Properties of Semiconducting Indium Phosphide, *Proc. Phys. Soc. (London)*, vol. 71, part 3, pp. 416–421, March, 1958.

Ridley, B. K.: Measurement of Lifetime by the Photoconductive Decay Method, *J. Electronics and Control*, vol. 5, no. 6, pp. 549–558, December, 1958.

Rigaux, C., and J. M. Thuillier: Measurement and Recording of the Speed of Surface Recombination, of Bulk Lifetimes and of Differences in Contact Potential, *J. Electronics and Control*, vol. 4, no. 2, pp. 175–178, February, 1958.

Risch, R.: Measurement of the Voltage Drop of Semiconductor Rectifier Cells, *Bull. assoc. suisse élec.*, vol. 49, no. 26, pp. 1219–1222, December 20, 1958.

Rittmann, A. D., G. C. Messenger, R. A. Williams, and E. Zimmerman: Microalloy Transistor, *IRE Trans. on Electron Devices*, vol. ED-5, no. 2, pp. 49–54, April, 1958.

Roberts, D. H., and B. L. H. Wilson: The Performance of Infra-red Photoconductive Cells, *Brit. J. Appl. Phys.*, vol. 9, no. 7, pp. 291–299, July, 1958.

Rodionov, L. I.: Calculation of the Potentiometer Circuit for Thermal Stabilization of Transistor Operating Point, *Radiotekhnika*, vol. 13, no. 10, pp. 57–63, 1958.

Rollett, J. M.: The Characteristic Frequencies of a Junction Transistor, *J. Electronics and Control*, vol. 5, no. 4, pp. 344–347, October, 1958.

Roschen, J., and C. G. Thornton: Solid-state Dissolution of Germanium by Indium in Semiconductor Devices, *J. Appl. Phys.*, vol. 29, no. 6, pp. 923–928, June, 1958.

Rose, F. W. G.: On the Mass-action Laws in Degenerate Semiconductors, *Proc. Phys. Soc. (London)*, vol. 71, part 4, pp. 699–701, April, 1958.

Rosenthal, J. E., and W. W. Gärtner: Design Theory for Depletion Layer Transistors, *Proc. IRE*, vol. 46, no. 7, pp. 1422–1423, July, 1958.

Rosier, G.: Transistors in Medium-frequency and Detector Circuits for Radio Communication Apparatus, *Tijdschr. Ned. Radiogenoot.*, vol. 23, no. 1, pp. 9–16, January, 1958.

Rowe, W. D.: A Transistorized Digital-to-analog Converter, *IRE Trans. on Instrumentation*, vol. I-7, no. 1, pp. 22–28, March, 1958.

Rudenberg, H. G.: On the Effect of Base Resistance and Collector-to-base Overlap on the Saturation Voltages of Power Transistors, *Proc. IRE*, vol. 46, no. 6, pp. 1304–1305, June, 1958.

Ryvkin, S. M., and N. B. Strokan: The Kinetics of Photo-triodes, *Zhur. Tekh. Fiz.*, vol. 28, no. 6, pp. 1169–1173, 1958.

Sah, Chih-Tang, and W. Shockley: Electron-hole Recombination Statistics in Semiconductors through Flaws with Many Charge Conditions, *Phys. Rev.*, vol. 109, no. 4, pp. 1103–1115, February 15, 1958.

Salaman, R. G.: Receiver Video Transistor Amplifiers, *IRE Trans. on Broadcast and Television Receivers*, vol. BTR-4, no. 4, pp. 68–77, September, 1958.

Samoilenko, V. I.: Theory and Calculation of FM Modulators by Means of Semiconductor Elements, *Radiotekhnika*, vol. 13, no. 5, pp. 64–71, 1958.

Sandiford, D. J.: Temperature Dependence of Carrier Lifetime in Silicon, *Proc. Phys. Soc. (London)*, vol. 71, part 6, pp. 1002–1006, June, 1958.

Santilli, R. A.: Design Considerations for Transistorized Automobile Receivers, *IRE Natl. Conv. Record*, vol. 6, part 7, pp. 125–131, 1958.

Sardella, J. J., and R. C. Wonson: A New High-frequency Diffused Base NPN Silicon Transistor, *IRE Natl. Conv. Record*, vol. 6, part 3, pp. 68–76, 1958.

Sato, A., S. Kanai, and T. Tominaga: The New Double-base Diode with Hook Structure, *J. Inst. Elec. Commun. Engrs. (Japan)*, vol. 41, no. 11, pp. 1101–1108, November, 1958.

Sauer, J., and O. Werner: Supervision of Mutator Plant with Transistor Fault Indicators, *Elektrotech. Z.*, B, vol. 10, no. 6, pp. 229–233, June 21, 1958.

Sawyer, D. E., and R. H. Rediker: Narrow Base Germanium Photodiodes, *Proc. IRE*, vol. 46, no. 6, pp. 1122–1130, June, 1958.

Schaffhauser, H.: Description of Stabilized Low-frequency LC Transistor Oscillator, *Scientia Electrica*, vol. 4, no. 1, pp. 22–30, 1958.

Schenck, E.: On the Attainable Accuracy in Pulse Amplitude Modulation and Pulse Length Modulation with Transistors, *NTZ-Nachrtech. Z.*, vol. 11, no. 4, pp. 191–196, April, 1958.

Schenkerman, S.: Designing Stability into Transistor Circuits, *Electronics*, vol. 31, no. 7, pp. 122–124, February 14, 1958.

Schenkerman, S.: Designing Transistor D-C to A-C Converters, *Electronics*, vol. 31, no. 39, pp. 78–80, September 26, 1958.

Schmid, H.: A Transistorized, All-electronic Cosine/Sine Function Generator, *IRE WESCON Conv. Record*, vol. 2, part 4, pp. 89–107, 1958.

Schneider, B., and M. J. O. Strutt: The Characteristics and Noise of Silicon P-N Diodes and Silicon Transistors, *Arch. Elekt. Ubertragung*, vol. 12, no. 10, pp. 429–440, October, 1958.

Schröter, E.: Rectifiers for Feeding Arcs, *Bull. sci. A.I.M. (Belg.)*, vol. 71, no. 1, pp. 25–46, 47–50, January, 1958.

Schubert, J.: Design of Low-noise Input Stages of L.F. Amplifiers Using the OC603 Transistor, *Frequenz*, vol. 12, no. 9, pp. 285–293, September, 1958.

Schuster, D.: D-C Transistor Amplifier for High-impedance Input, *Electronics*, vol. 31, no. 9, pp. 64–65, February 28, 1958.

Seiwatz, H.: Low-frequency Rotational Hysteresis Losses in Ferrites, *J. Appl. Phys.*, vol. 29, no. 6, pp. 994–995, June, 1958.

Selivanov, A. S.: A Storage Computer Unit Using Transistors, *Radiotekhnika*, vol. 13, no. 11, pp. 67–71, 1958.

Senitzky, B., and J. L. Moll: Breakdown in Silicon, *Phys. Rev.*, vol. 110, no. 3, pp. 612–620, May 1, 1958.

Sharpless, W. M.: Wafer-type Rectifiers for Millimeter Waves, *Bell Labs. Record*, vol. 36, no. 1, pp 21–24, January, 1958.

Shattes, W. J., and H. A. R. Wegener: Lifetime and Nickel Precipitation in Silicon, *J. Appl. Phys.*, vol. 29, no. 5, p. 866, May, 1958.

Shaw, D.: A New Photoconductive Device, *B.T.H. Activities*, vol. 29, no. 6, pp. 229–234, November–December, 1958.

Sherov-Ignat'ev, G. P.: Nomograph Determination of H. F. Parameters of Transistors by Their Transient Characteristics, *Radiotekhnika*, vol. 13, no. 10, pp. 45–50, 1958.

Sherr, S.: Rapid Conversion of Hybrid Parameters, *Electronics*, vol. 31, no. 13, pp. 76–77, March 28, 1958.

Shields, J.: Avalanche Breakdown Voltage in Hemispherical (P-N) Junctions, *J. Electronics and Control*, vol. 4, no. 1, pp. 58–60, January, 1958.

Shockley, W.: Electrons, Holes, and Traps, *Proc. IRE*, vol. 46, no. 6, pp. 973–990, June, 1958.

Shotov, A. P.: Collision Ionization in Germanium P-N Junctions, *Zhur. Tekh. Fiz.*, vol. 28, no. 3, pp. 437–446, 1958.

Sichling, G.: Transistor as Energy Driving Switch, *Elektronik*, vol. 7, no. 12, pp. 369–371, December, 1958.

Silverman, S. J., and J. B. Singleton: Technique for Preserving Lifetime in Diffused Silicon, *J. Electrochem. Soc.*, vol. 105, no. 10, pp. 591–594, October, 1958.

Silvey, G. A.: Zn_3As_2, A semiconducting Intermetallic Compound, *J. Appl. Phys.*, vol. 29, no. 2, pp. 226–227, February, 1958.

Sim, A. C.: A Note on Surface Recombination Velocity and Photoconductive Decays, *J. Electronics and Control*, vol. 5, no. 3, pp. 251–255, September, 1958.

Slade, B. N., and J. Printon: Large-area Germanium Power Transistors, *RCA Rev.*, vol. 19, no. 1, pp. 98–108, March, 1958.

Smits, F. M.: Formation of Junction Structures by Solid-state Diffusion, *Proc. IRE*, vol. 46, no. 6, pp. 1049–1061, June, 1958.

Smits, F. M.: Measurement of Sheet Resistivities with the Four-point Probe, *Bell System Tech. J.*, vol. 37, no. 3, pp. 711–718, May, 1958.

Sodha, M. S., and P. C. Eastman: Mobility of Electrons in Nondegenerate Semiconductors Considering Electron-Electron Scattering, *Z. Physik*, vol. 150, no. 2, pp. 242–246, 1958.

Sokolov, F. F.: Heat Loss of Rectifier Posts Consisting of Large Selenium (Rectangular) Elements, *Elektrichestvo*, no. 1, pp. 58–63, 1958.

Soltamov, U. B., and E. S. Grishin: Investigation of the Effect of Low-energy Electronics on the P-N Junction in Germanium, *Zhur. Tekh. Fiz.*, vol. 28, no. 7, pp. 1394–1398, 1958.

Špány, V.: Design and Experimental Investigation of a Monostable Circuit with Junction Transistors, *Slaboproudý Obzor*, vol. 19, no. 10, pp. 667–669, 1958.

Špány, V.: A Sawtooth Voltage Generator with Junction Transistors, *Slaboproudý Obzor*, vol. 19, no. 12, pp. 817–819, 1958.

Sparkes, J. J.: Measurement of Junction Transistor Equivalent Circuit Parameters, *A.T.E. J.*, vol. 14, no. 3, pp. 176–187, July, 1958.

Sparkes, J. J.: Voltage Feedback and Thermal Resistance in Junction Transistors, *Proc. IRE*, vol. 46, no. 6, pp. 1305–1306, June, 1958.

Spenke, E.: The Inductive Behaviour of P-N Rectifiers at High Forward Currents, *Z. angew. Phys.*, vol. 10, no. 2, pp. 65–88, February, 1958.

Stafeev, V. I.: The Effect of the Bulk Resistance of the Semiconductor on the Form of the Current-voltage Characteristic of a Diode, *Zhur. Tekh. Fiz.*, vol. 28, no. 8, pp. 1631–1641, 1958.

Stanek, M., and B. Medvezov: An Instrument for Measurement of Input Parameters of Transistors, *Slaboproudý Obzor*, vol. 19, no. 3, pp. 128–132, 1958.

Statz, H., and G. A. deMars: Electrical Conduction via Slow Surface States on Semiconductors, *Phys. Rev.*, vol. 111, no. 1, pp. 169–182, July 1, 1958.

Stephenson, W. L.: A Four-transistor D-C Converter Circuit for Use with Relatively High-voltage Supplies, *Mullard Tech. Commun.*, vol. 4, pp. 191–192, December, 1958.

Stephenson, W. L.: Transistor Cut-off Frequency, *Electronic Radio Engr.*, vol. 35, no. 2, pp. 69–71, February, 1958.

Stier, F., and H. Blessing: Silicon Rectifier with Regulating Transformer Compared with Leonard Converter, *Elektrotech. Z.*, vol. 79A, no. 8, pp. 280–282, April 11, 1958.

Strack, W.: Pocket-radio Signaling, *Bell Labs. Record*, vol. 36, no. 1, pp. 9–12, January, 1958.

Stratton, R.: On the Hot Electron Effect in n-type Germanium, *J. Electronics and Control*, vol. 5, no. 2, pp. 157–161, August, 1958.

Straub, C. L., and H. G. Wiest: Metallic Rectifiers for Shipboard Electric Systems, *Appl. and Ind.*, no. 36, May, 1958.

Stubb, T.: A Contribution to the Study of the Efficiency in a Photon Excited P-N Junction in Silicon, *Comment. Phys.-Math. (Helsinki)*, vol. 21, no. 1–8, 1958.

Suran, J. J.: Transistor Monostable Multivibrators for Pulse Generation, *Proc. IRE*, vol. 46, no. 6, pp. 1260–1271, June, 1958.

Susini, A.: A Function Generator Using Diodes, *Elettrotecnica*, vol. 45, no. 11, pp. 626–629, November 10–25, 1958.

Svechnikov, S. V.: On the Peculiarities of Photoconductivity in Cadmium Selenide, *Zhur. Eksptl. i Teort. Fiz.*, vol. 34, no. 3, pp. 548–554, 1958.

Svechnikov, S. V., and V. I. Dvortsin: Some Noise Characteristics of Cadmium Sulphide Photoresistors, *Radiotekh. i Elektron.*, vol. 3, no. 3, pp. 409–414, 1958.

Sylvan, T. P.: Bistable Circuits Using Unijunction Transistors, *Electronics*, vol. 31, no. 51, pp. 89–91, December 19, 1958.

Szerlip, A.: Transistorized Decade Counter, *IRE WESCON Conv. Record*, vol. 2, part 6, pp. 181–187, 1958.

Takeya, K., and K. Nakamura: Current Amplification by Electron Bombardment in the Semiconductor Barrier Layer, *J. Phys. Soc. Japan*, vol. 13, no. 2, p. 223, February, 1958.

Talley, H. E.: A Family of Diffused-base Germanium Transistors, *IRE WESCON Conv. Record*, vol. 2, part 3, pp. 115–121, 1958.

Tauc, J.: Electron Emission from Silicon P-N Junctions, *Nature*, vol. 181, p. 38, January, 1958.

Taylor, T. C.: Crack-free Alloyed Junctions in Silicon Using Pure Aluminum, *J. Appl. Phys.*, vol. 29, no. 5, pp. 865–866, May, 1958.

Teitler, S.: Generation-recombination Noise in a Two-level Impuirty Semiconductor, *J. Appl. Phys.*, vol. 29, no. 11, pp. 1585–1587, November, 1958.

Teszner, S.: On a New Method of Amplification of Electric Power and Voltage at High Frequency, *Compt. rend.*, vol. 246, no. 1, pp. 72–73, January 6, 1958.

Teszner, S., and M. Thue: The Tecnetron, New Stage in the Development of Semiconductor Devices, *Bull. soc. franç. élec.*, vol. 8, pp. 683–700, October, 1958.

Tewksbury, J. M.: Transistorized P-A System Adjusts to Aircraft Noise, *Electronics*, vol. 31, no. 7, pp. 106–107, February, 1958.

Tharma, P.: 15W Public Address Amplifiers Using OC16 Transistors, *Mullard Tech. Commun.*, vol. 4, pp. 30–32, August, 1958.

Tharma, P.: Temperature Stability of Transistor Class B Amplifiers, *Mullard Tech. Commun.*, vol. 3, pp. 265–277, March, 1958.

Thomas, D. F., and J. L. Moll: Junction Transistor Short-circuit Current Gain and Phase Determination, *Proc. IRE*, vol. 46, no. 6, pp. 1177–1184, June, 1958.

Thornton, C. G., and J. B. Angell: Technology of Micro-alloy Diffused Transistors, *Proc. IRE*, vol. 46, no. 6, pp. 1166–1176, June, 1958.

Thornton, C. G., and C. D. Simmons: A New High Current Mode of Transistor Operation, *IRE Trans. on Electron Devices*, vol. ED-5, no. 1, pp. 6–10, January, 1958.

Towles, W. B.: Transistorized Analog-digital Converter, *Electronics*, vol. 31, no. 31, pp. 90–93, August 1, 1958.

Trokhimenko, Ya. K.: Single-stage, Multi-element RC Oscillator Using a Transistor, *Radiotekhnika*, vol. 13, no. 11, pp. 44–51, 1958.

Trumbore, F. A., and A. A. Tartaglia: Resistivities and Hole Mobilities in Very Heavily Doped Germanium, *J. Appl. Phys.*, vol. 29, no. 10, p. 1511, October, 1958.

Tuchkevich, V. M., and V. E. Chelnokov: Current-voltage Characteristics of Diffused Silicon P-N Junctions, *Zhur. Tekh. Fiz.*, vol. 28, no. 10, pp. 2115–2123, 1958.

Uhlir, A.: Junction Diodes in Microwave Circuits, *Proc. Inst. Elec. Engrs. (London)*, vol. 105, part B, suppl. 11, pp. 661, 672–673, 1958.

Uhlir, A., Jr.: The Potential of Semiconductor Diodes in High-frequency Communications, *Proc. IRE*, vol. 46, no. 6, pp. 1099–1115, June, 1958.

Ukhanov, Yu. I.: A Study of the Induced Absorption of Infrared Radiation in a Germanium Diode, *Zhur. Tekh. Fiz.*, vol. 28, no. 11, pp. 2410–2416, 1958.

Van Allen, R. L.: Time Interval Generation with Transistor Switches and Magnetic Cores, *Proc. Natl. Electronics Conf.*, vol. 14, pp. 884–897, 1958.

van Bergen, H., and K. Binge: Measurement of the Peak-voltage of High-voltage A-C Using Germanium Diodes and a Moving-coil Meter, *Elektrotech. Z.*, vol. 79A, no. 9, pp. 310–313, May 1, 1958.

van der Pauw, L. J.: A Method of Measuring Specific Resistivity and Hall Effect of Discs of Arbitrary Shape, *Philips Research Repts.*, vol. 13, no. 1, pp. 1–9, February, 1958.

van der Ziel, A., and A. G. T. Becking: Theory of Junction Diode and Junction Transistor Noise, *Proc. IRE*, vol. 46, no. 3, pp. 589–594, March, 1958.

van Vessem, J. C.: The Transistor, Seen from Within, *Tijdschr. Ned. Radiogenoot.*, vol. 23, no. 4, pp. 177–194, July, 1958.

van Vliet, K. M.: Noise in Semiconductors and Photoconductors, *Proc. IRE*, vol. 46, no. 6, pp. 1004–1018, June, 1958.

Varecha, K., and F. Mandys: Equipment for Measurement of the Noise Temperature of Silicon Diodes, *Slaboproudý Obzor*, vol. 19, no. 2, pp. 67–72, 1958.

Vasseur, J. P.: "Properties and Applications of Transistors" (Proprietés et applications des transistors), Société Française de Documentation Electronique, Paris, 1958.

Vertsner, V. N., and L. N. Malakhov: Application of the Electron Shadow Microscope Technique to the Study of the Distribution of Potential in P-N Junctions, *Doklady Akad. Nauk S.S.S.R.*, vol. 118, no. 2, pp. 266–268, 1958.

Vojtášek, S., and V. Ilberg: Oscillographic Display of Transistor Characteristics, *Slaboproudý Obzor*, vol. 19, no. 4, pp. 201–205, 1958.

Vul, B. M., and B. I. Segal: Theory of the P-N Junctions in Semiconductors, *Zhur. Tekh. Fiz.*, vol. 28, no. 4, pp. 681–688, 1958.

Wahl, A. J.: An Analysis of Base Resistance for Alloy Junction Transistors, *IRE Trans. on Electron Devices*, vol. ED-5, no. 3, pp. 131–139, July, 1958.

Wallis, G., and J. F. Battey: High-field Emission in Germanium Point-contact Diodes, *IRE Trans. on Electron Devices*, vol. ED-5, no. 1, pp. 19–21, January, 1958.

Warman, J. B., and D. M. Bibb: Transistor Circuits for Use with Gas-filled Multi-cathode Counter Valves, *Electronic Eng.*, vol. 30, pp. 136–139, March, 1958.

Warner, R. M., Jr.: A New Passive Semiconductor Component, *IRE Natl. Conv.*, vol. 6, part 3, pp. 43–48, 1958.

Warner, R. M., Jr., J. M. Early, and G. T. Loman: Characteristics, Structure, and Performance of a Diffused-base Germanium Oscillator Transistor, *IRE Trans. on Electron Devices*, vol. ED-5, no. 3, pp. 127–130, July, 1958.

Weiser, K.: Decomposition Method for Producing P-N Junctions in InP, *J. Appl. Phys.*, vol. 29, no. 2, pp. 229–230, February, 1958.

Weisner, L. E.: Transistor Count-rate Systems, *Elec. Eng.*, vol. 77, no. 7, pp. 623–625, July, 1958.

Weitzsch, F.: Some Criteria for the Thermal Stability of Transistors, *Frequenz*, vol. 12, no. 3, pp. 65–71, March, 1958.

Wernick, J. H., S. Geller, and K. E. Benson: New Semiconductors, *J. Phys. Chem. Solids*, vol. 4, no. 1–2, pp. 154–155, 1958.

Wertheim, G. K.: Electron-bombardment Damage in Silicon, *Phys. Rev.*, vol. 110, no. 6, pp. 1272–1279, June 15, 1958.

Wheaton, R. N.: Techniques of Transistor Production, *Proc. IRE, Australia*, vol. 19, no. 7, pp. 358–369, July, 1958.

Widl, H.: A Curve-tracer for Transistor Parameters, *Arch. tech. Messen*, no. 266, R29-R33, March, 1958.

Wilk, W. E., and W. B. Sander: Development of a Transistorized Voltage Controllable Frequency Source, *IRE WESCON Conv. Record*, vol. 2, part 5, pp. 86–97, 1958.

Williams, R. H.: Transistor Chopper Drives Accurate Clock, *Electronics*, vol. 31, no. 21, pp. 64–65, May 23, 1958.

Williams, R. L.: Properties of Cadmium Sulphide Photoconductive Cells, *Can. J. Phys.*, vol. 36, no. 5, pp. 1536–1550, November, 1958.

Wilson, B. L. H.: Transistor Noise: Its Origin, Measurement and Behaviour, *J. Brit. Inst. Radio Engrs.*, vol. 18, no. 4, pp. 207–225, April, 1958.

Winkler, G.: The Transistor Noise Equivalent Circuit, *Nachrichtentechnik*, vol. 8, no. 12, pp. 542–547, December, 1958.

Wolsky, S. P.: Preparation and Regeneration of Clean Germanium Surfaces, *J. Appl. Phys.*, vol. 29, no. 7, pp. 1132–1133, July, 1958.

Wright, D. A.: Photoconductivity, *Brit. J. Appl. Phys.*, vol. 9, no. 6, pp. 205–214, June, 1958.

Wucherer, W.: Measuring with Crystal Rectifiers, *Arch. tech. Messen.*, no. 265 (ref. Z52-11), pp. 41–44, February, 1958.

Yajima, T., and L. Esaki: Excess Noise in Narrow Germanium P-N Junctions, *J. Phys. Soc. Japan*, vol. 13, no. 11, pp. 1281–1287, November, 1958.

Yakovlev, V. N.: Calculation of Pulse Duration in a Transistor Blocking Oscillator, *Radiotekh. i Elektron.*, vol. 3, no. 9, pp. 1167–1171, 1958.

Yamaguchi, J., and Y. Hamakawa: Forward Characteristics of Germanium P-N Junctions, *Technol. Repts. Osaka Univ.*, vol. 8, pp. 29–34, March, 1958.

Yunovich, A. É.: Frequency Dependence of the Field Effect in Semiconductors, *Zhur. Tekh. Fiz.*, vol. 28, no. 4, pp. 689–693, 1958.

Yurkov, B. Ya.: On the Theory of Semiconductor Energy Converters, *Zhur. Tekh. Fiz.*, vol. 28, no. 7, pp. 1365–1370, 1958.

Zawels, J.: High-frequency Parameters of Transistors and Valves, *Electronic Eng.*, vol. 30, pp. 15–17, January, 1958.

Zawels, J.: A Wide-band Bridge Yielding Directly the Device Parameters of Junction Transistors, *IRE Trans. on Electron Devices*, vol. ED-5, no. 1, pp. 21–25, January, 1958.

Zemanek, H.: "Manilüfterl," a Decimal, Fully Transistorized Automatic Computer, *Elektrotech. u. Maschinenbau*, vol. 75, no. 15–16, pp. 453–463, August 1, 1958.

Zemel, J. N., and R. L. Petritz: Magneto-surface Experiments on Germanium, *Phys. Rev.*, vol. 110, no. 6, pp. 1263–1271, June 15, 1958.

Zhuze, V. P., V. M. Sergeeva, and E. L. Shtrum: New Semiconducting Compounds, *Zhur. Tekh. Fiz.*, vol. 28, no. 2, pp. 233–236, 1958.

Zuleeg, R.: Effective Collector Capacitance in Transistors, *Proc. IRE*, vol. 46, no. 11, pp. 1878–1879, November, 1958.

IRE Standards on Solid-state Devices: Methods of Testing Point-contact Transistors for Large-signal Applications, *Proc. IRE*, vol. 46, no. 5(1), pp. 878–888, May, 1958.

"Semiconductors and Phosphors" (Halbleiter und Phosphore), Vieweg, Brunswick, 1958.

1959

Abdyukhanov, M. A.: A Note on the Limits of Applicability of the Small Signal Theory for Transistors, *Radiotekh. i Elektron.*, vol. 4, no. 7, pp. 1094–1102, July, 1959.

Acker, R. C.: 70-Watt Transistorized Public Address Equipment, *Audio Eng. Soc. J.*, vol. 7, no. 4, pp. 239–242, October, 1959.

Adirovich, É. I.: Conductivity and Voltage Transfer Coefficient of a Semiconductor Diode in the Non-stationary Regime, *Fiz. Tverdogo Tela*, vol. 1, no. 7, pp. 1115–1124, July, 1959.

Agakhanyan, T. M.: Transient and Phase-frequency Characteristics of Current Gain or Drift Transistors, *Radiotekhnika*, vol. 14, no. 12, pp. 38–43, December, 1959.

Ahlstrom, E., W. G. Matthei, and W. W. Gärtner: Use of Surface-barrier Photodiodes as Fast Response Photocapacitors, *Rev. Sci. Instr.*, vol. 30, no. 7, pp. 592–593, July, 1959.

Airoldi, G., Z. Fuhrman, and E. Germagnoli: Annealing of Electron Irradiated Germanium, *Nuovo cimento*, vol. 14, no. 2, pp. 452–453, October 16, 1959.

Aitchison, R. E.: Transistor Circuit Design Using Modified Hybrid Parameters, *Proc. IRE, Australia*, vol. 20, no. 11, pp. 673–679, November, 1959.

Akgün, M., and M. J. O. Strutt: Cross Modulation and Non-linear Distortion in R.F. Transistor Amplifiers, *IRE Trans. on Electron Devices*, vol. ED-6, no. 4, pp. 457–467, October, 1959.

Akimov, I. A.: The Effect of Illumination on the Contact Potential of Some Semiconductors, *Doklady Akad. Nauk S.S.S.R.*, vol. 128, no. 4, pp. 691–694, October 1, 1959.

Aldrich, R. W., and N. Holonyak, Jr.: Silicon-controlled Rectifiers from Oxide-masked Diffused Structures, *Trans. AIEE*, part I, vol. 77, pp. 952–954, 1959.

Aldrich, R. W., and N. Holonyak, Jr.: Two-terminal Asymmetrical and Symmetrical Silicon Negative Resistance Switches, *J. Appl. Phys.*, vol. 30, no. 11, pp. 1819–1824, November, 1959.

Alekseeva, V. G., I. V. Karpova, and S. G. Kalashnikov: Dependence of the Electron and Hole Lifetimes in Germanium on Carrier Density, *Fiz. Tverdogo Tela*, vol. 1, no. 4, pp. 529–534, April, 1959.

Alferov, Zh. I., and E. V. Silina: The Influence of the State of the Surface on the Breakdown Voltage of Silicon Diodes, *Fiz. Tverdogo Tela*, vol. 1, no. 12, pp. 1878–1879, December, 1959.

Allen, J. W.: The Reverse Characteristics of Gallium Arsenide P-N Junctions, *J. Electronics and Control*, vol. 7, no. 3, pp. 254–260, September, 1959.

Allen, J. W., and P. E. Gibbons: Breakdown and Light Emission in Gallium Phosphide Diodes, *J. Electronics and Control*, vol. 7, no. 6, pp. 518–522, December, 1959.

Amick, J. A., and B. Goldstein: Delineation of Junctions in Semiconductors by Electroscopic Powders, *J. Appl. Phys.*, vol. 30, no. 9, pp. 1471–1472, September, 1959.

Amith, A.: Photoconductive and Photoelectromagnetic Lifetime Determination in Presence of Trapping. I. Small Signals, *Phys. Rev.*, vol. 116, no. 4, pp. 793–802, November 15, 1959.

Anderson, J. C., and T. Winer: A Temperature-stabilized Photo-transistor Relay Circuit, *Electronic Eng.*, vol. 31, pp. 36–37, January, 1959.

Anderson, J. S., E. A. Faulkner, and D. F. Klemperer: Analysis of Composite Spectral-sensitivity Functions, *Austral. J. Phys.*, vol. 12, no. 4, pp. 469–470, December, 1959.

Andreev, A. A., and N. S. Nikolaenko: Transistorized Amplifiers for Automatic Measuring Instruments, *Instr. Construct.*, no. 9, pp. 6–8, September, 1959.

Angell, J. B.: Direct-coupled Logic Circuitry, in Proceedings of the Western Joint Computer Conference, pp. 22–27, AIEE, New York, March, 1959.

Applebaum, M., and E. Midgley: A Domestic FM Receiver Using Diffused Base Mesa Transistors, *Electronic Eng.*, vol. 31, pp. 448–453, August, 1959.

Armstrong, H. L.: On Calculating the Current Gain of Junction Transistors with Arbitrary Doping Distributions, *IRE Trans. on Electron Devices*, vol. ED-6, no. 1, pp. 1–5, January, 1959.

Armstrong, H. L.: On the Usefulness of Transconductance as a Transistor Parameter, *Proc. IRE*, vol. 47, no. 1, pp. 83–84, January, 1959.

Armstrong, L. D., and H. D. Harmon: A Simple and Flexible Method of Fabricating Diffused N-P-N Silicon Power Transistors, *IRE Natl. Conv. Record*, vol. 7, part 3, pp. 18–21. 1959.

Aschner, J. F., C. A. Bittmann, W. F. J. Hare, and J. J. Kleimack: A Double-diffused Silicon High-frequency Switching Transistor Produced by Oxide Masking Techniques, *J. Electrochem. Soc.*, vol. 106, no. 5, pp. 415–417, May, 1959.

Aukerman, L. W.: Electron Irradiation of Indium Arsenide, *Phys. Rev.*, vol. 115, no. 5, pp. 1133–1135, September 1, 1959.

Avis, G. G.: Application of Transistors to D-C/D-C Convertors, *Proc. Inst. Elec. Engrs.*

(*London*), (International Convention on Transistors and Associated Semiconductor Devices), paper 2924E, May, 1959.

Bachmann, A. E.: Transistor Active Filters Using Twin-T Rejection Networks, *Proc. Inst. Elect. Engrs.* (*London*), vol. 106B, paper 2787R, pp. 170–174, March, 1959.

Bachmann, A. E.: Transistor Amplifier for Magnetic Tape and Drum Playback, *Electronic Eng.*, vol. 31, pp. 213–217, April, 1959.

Bagaev, V. S., B. M. Vul, A. A. Sherebstova, and S. B. Yuditskii: Investigation of Large Germanium Rectifiers, *Elektrichestvo*, no. 10, pp. 21–26, October, 1959.

Bagley, J. H.: The Measurement of Transistor Characteristics at Very High Frequencies, *Proc. Inst. Elec. Engrs.* (*London*), (International Convention on Transistors and Associated Semiconductor Devices), vol. 106B, suppl. 17, paper 3019E, pp. 945–950, 1009–1011, 1959.

Bakanowski, A. E., N. G. Granna, and A. Uhlir, Jr.: Diffused Silicon Nonlinear Capacitors, *IRE Trans. on Electron Devices*, vol. ED-6, no. 4, pp. 384–390, October, 1959.

Baker, A. N., J. M. Goldey, and I. M. Ross: Recovery Time of P-N-P-N Diodes, *IRE WESCON Conv. Record*, vol. 3, part 3, pp. 43–48, 1959.

Baker, R. H.: Symmetrical Transistor Logic, in Proceedings of the Western Joint Computer Conference, pp. 27–33, AIEE, New York, March, 1959.

Baker, T. E., Jr., E. U. Cohler, M. I. Crystal, and J. E. Monahan: Circuit Designs for a General Purpose Computer, *Sylvania Technologist*, vol. 12, no. 3, pp. 68–79, July, 1959.

Baldinger, E.: Application of Transistors in Pulse Techniques, *Bull. assoc. suisse élec.*, vol. 50, no. 1, pp. 2–9, January 3, 1959.

Baldinger, E., H. Bilger, and M. A. Nicolet: Experimental Investigations of the Influence and the Production of Lattice Defects in Junction Transistors, *Helv. Phys. Acta*, vol. 32, no. 1, pp. 78–88, 1959.

Barney, H. L.: Unitary Transistorized Artificial Larynx, *IRE WESCON Conv. Record*, vol. 3, part 8, pp. 26–34, 1959.

Barney, H. L., F. E. Haworth, and H. K. Dunn: An Experimental Transistorized Artificial Larynx, *Bell System Tech. J.*, vol. 38, no. 6, pp. 1337–1356, November, 1959.

Barry, J. N., and S. F. Fisher: The Measurement of Semiconductor Diode Switching, *Brit. Commun. and Electronics*, vol. 6, no. 11, pp. 788–791, November, 1959.

Barry, J. N., and D. M. Leakey: Transistorized Pulse Amplifier; Design of a High-speed Type, *Electronic Radio Engr.*, vol. 36, no. 6, pp. 200–207, June, 1959.

Barry, J. N., and F. J. Nixon: The Use of Semiconductor Devices in P.A.M. System Demodulations, *Proc. Inst. Elec. Engrs.* (*London*), (International Convention on Transistors and Associated Semiconductor Devices), part B, suppl. 16, paper 2961E, pp. 577–586, 633–636, May, 1959.

Barsukov, Yu. K.: Investigation of the P-N Junction for High Current Densities, *Fiz. Tverdogo Tela*, vol. 1, no. 11, pp. 1659–1667, November, 1959.

Barsukov, Yu. K.: Theory of the Pulse Method of Voltage Separation in Semiconductor Diodes, *Fiz. Tverdogo Tela*, vol. 1, no. 6, pp. 886–894, June, 1959.

Barsukov, Yu. K.: The Transistor Switching of a Semiconductor Junction Diode at High Currents, *Fiz. Tverdogo Tela*, vol. 1, no. 4, p. 602, April, 1959.

Bassett, H. G.: An Apparatus for the Measurement of Current Gain in the Range 1–300 Mc/s, *Proc. Inst. Elec. Engrs.* (*London*), (International Convention on Transistors and Associated Semiconductor Devices), part B, suppl. 15, paper 2949E, pp. 532–535, 567, May, 1959.

Bassett, H. G., D. Thomason, and P. E. Greenaway: The Application of Junction Transistors to Audio-frequency Telephone Line Amplifiers, *Proc. Inst. Elec. Engrs.* (*London*), paper 2764R, pp. 290–293, 294–298, May, 1959.

Battye, C. K., and R. E. George: Transistors as Low-noise Amplifiers, *Proc. Inst. Elec. Engrs.* (*London*), (International Convention on Transistors and Associated Semiconductor Devices), paper 2933E, May, 1959.

Baxandall, P. J.: Transistor Sine-wave LC Oscillators, *Proc. Inst. Elec. Engrs.* (*London*), (International Convention on Transistors and Associated Semiconductor Devices), vol. 106B, suppl. 16, paper 2978E, pp. 748–758, 1959.

Bazhan, A. N., and L. N. Kaitsov: A Transistor Oscillator with Limitation in the Saturation Region, *Radiotekh. i Elektron.*, vol. 4, no. 9, pp. 1549–1556, September, 1959.

Beale, J. R. A.: The Factors that Determine the High-frequency Performance of Transistors, *Proc. Inst. Elec. Engrs.* (*London*), (International Convention on Transistors and Associated Semiconductor Devices), vol. 106B, suppl. 17, paper 3123E, pp. 903–905, 937–938, 1959.

Beale, J. R. A., D. E. Thoams, and T. B. Watkins: The Application of Surface-measurement Techniques to Transistors, *Proc. Inst. Elec. Engrs.* (*London*), (International Convention on Transistors and Associated Semiconductor Devices), vol. 106B, suppl. 17, paper 3081E, pp. 1004–1008, 1009–1011, 1959.

Beatie, R. N.: A Lumped Model Analysis of Noise in Semiconductor Devices, *IRE Trans. on Electron Devices*, vol. ED-6, no. 2, pp. 133–140, April, 1959.

Beaufoy, R.: Transistor Switching-circuit Design Using the Charge-control Parameters, *Proc. Inst. Elec. Engrs. (London)*, (International Convention on Transistors and Associated Semiconductor Devices), paper 2970E, May, 1959.

Beeson, R. H., I. Haas, and V. H. Grinich: Thermal Response of Transistors in the Avalanche Mode, *Proc. Natl. Electronics Conf.*, vol. 15, pp. 546–556, 1959.

Beneking, H.: On Narrow Band Amplification with Transistors, *NTZ-Nachrtech. Z.*, vol. 12, no. 11, pp. 543–546, November, 1959.

Beneking, H.: A Transistor Mixer Equivalent Circuit, *Arch. Elekt. Ubertragung*, vol. 13, no. 7, pp. 313–319, July, 1959.

Bijl, A.: Transistorized Oscillograph, *Proc. Inst. Elec. Engrs. (London)*, (International Convention on Transistors and Associated Semiconductor Devices), vol. 106B, suppl. 18, paper 2921E, pp. 1303–1310, 1334–1338, 1959.

Bilinski, J. R., and R. Merrill: Selecting Transistors for Radiation Environment, *Electronics*, vol. 32, no. 52, pp. 38–40, December 25, 1959.

Bilotti, A., and L. Garlatti: Thermal Instability in Junction Transistors, I, *Rev. electrotéc.*, vol. 45, no. 1, pp. 6–17, January, 1959.

Bir, G. L.: The Influence of Surface Recombinations on Photoconductivity of Semiconductors, *Fiz. Tverdogo Tela*, vol. 1, no. 1, pp. 67–76, 1959.

Bisson, D. K., and R. F. Dyer: A Silicon-controlled Rectifier. I. Characteristics and Ratings, *Trans. AIEE*, part I, vol. 78, pp. 102–106, 1959.

Bitovskii, N. A., T. V. Mashovets, and S. M. Ryvkin: The Determination of the Number of Acceptor Levels of Defects Produced in Germanium by the Action of γ-rays, *Fiz. Tverdogo Tela*, vol. 1, no. 9, pp. 1381–1384, September, 1959.

Blackburne, N. F., and R. A. Spears: A Transistorized Crystal Chronometer, *A.T.E. J.*, vol. 15, no. 4, pp. 303–312, October, 1959.

Blanks, H. S.: The Parallel and Series Operation of Germanium Rectifiers, *Proc. IRE Australia*, vol. 20, no. 7, pp. 406–412, July, 1959.

Bloem, J., C. Haas, and P. Penning: Properties of Oxygen in Germanium, *J. Phys. Chem. Solids*, vol. 12, no. 1, pp. 22–27, December, 1959.

Bobisch, P., and C. Sondhauss: Influence of the Time Dependent Series Resistance of the Capacitance Diode in the Mavar Up-converters, *J. Electronics and Control*, vol. 7, no. 4, pp. 344–366, October, 1959.

Bockemuehl, R. R.: Transistor Rectifier Gives D-C of Either Polarity, *Electronics*, vol. 32, no. 25, p. 76, June 19, 1959.

Boensel, D. W.: Computing Transistor Switching Dissipation, *Electronics*, vol. 32, no. 48, pp. 74–76, November 27, 1959.

Boensel, D. W.: Switching Circuits for Missile Count-downs, *Electronics*, vol. 32, no. 31, pp. 76–78, July 31, 1959.

Bogomolov, V. N., N. S. Nikolaenko, and V. P. Fedotov: D-C–A-C Convertor Utilizing the Hall Effect, *Pribory i Tekh. Eksperimenta*, no. 2, pp. 134–135, March–April, 1959.

Boite, R.: Minority Carrier Injection and Extraction Phenomena in a Nearly Intrinsic Semiconductor, *Rev. HF*, vol. 4, no. 7, pp. 151–156, 1959.

Böke, K., J. B. M. Spaapen, and N. B. Speyer: Diffusion Capacitance in Transistors, *Philips Research Repts.*, vol. 14, no. 2, pp. 111–122, April, 1959.

Borne, J.: Transistorized Waveform Generator for the 819-line Television Standard, *Onde élect.*, vol. 39, pp. 100–102, February, 1959.

Bowar, G. I.: Design Considerations for Large Industrial Semiconductor Rectifiers, *Appl. and Ind.*, no. 41, March, 1959.

Bowes, R. C.: A New Linear Delay Circuit Based on an Emitter-coupled Multivibrator, *Proc. Inst. Elec. Engrs. (London)*, (International Convention on Transistors and Associated Semiconductor Devices), paper 2951E, 1959.

Bowes, R. C., and J. C. Gill: An All-transistor Digital Voltmeter, *Proc. Inst. Elec. Engrs. (London)*, (International Convention on Transistors and Associated Semiconductor Devices), vol. 106B, suppl. 18, paper 2927E, pp. 1311–1314, 1334–1338, 1959.

Bowes, R. C., and M. E. Piggott: A Transistor Linear Time-base Circuit for a High-current Electromagnetic Deflection System, *Proc. Inst. Elec. Engrs. (London)*, (International Convention on Transistors and Associated Semiconductor Devices), paper 2911E, May, 1959.

Bramson, B. M.: Starved Transistors Raise D-C Input Resistance, *Electronics*, vol. 32, no. 5, pp. 54–55, January 30, 1959.

Bray, D., and A. Conway: A Transistorized Magnetic-core Store, *Proc. Inst. Elec. Engrs. (London)*, (International Convention on Transistors and Associated Semiconductor Devices), paper 2954E, May, 1959.

Brill, P. H., and R. F. Schwarz: Radiative Recombination and Lifetime in Germanium, *J. Phys. Chem. Solids*, vol. 8, pp. 75–77, 85–86, January, 1959.

Brookes, G. A., G. W. Read, and E. W. Templin: A Low Cost Transistorized Re-recording Mixer, *J. Soc. Motion Picture Television Engrs.*, vol. 68, no. 9, pp. 589–593, September, 1959.

Brouwer, G.: Three-dimensional Electric-circuit Model of the High-frequency Phenomena in a Junction Transistor, *Philips Research Repts.*, vol. 14, no. 2, pp. 132–142, April, 1959.

Brown, W. L., W. M. Augustyniak, and T. R. Waite: Annealing of Radiation Defects in Semiconductors, *J. Appl. Phys.*, vol. 30, no. 8, pp. 1258–1268, August, 1959.

Brückner, E.: Frequency Stability of a Transistorized Astable Multivibrator, *NTZ-Nachrtech. Z.*, vol. 12, no. 10, pp. 509–513, October, 1959.

Bube, R. H., and L. A. Barton: The Achievement of Maximum Photoconductivity Performance in Cadmium Sulfide Crystals, *RCA Rev.*, vol. 20, no. 4, pp. 564–598, December, 1959.

Budínský, J.: Bistable Semiconductor Elements, *Slaboproudý Obzor*, vol. 20, no. 2, pp. 99–109, 1959.

Budínský, J.: Dynamic Properties of Junction Transistors in Pulse Operation, *Slaboproudý Obzor*, vol. 20, no. 12, pp. 747–753, 1959.

Budínský, J.: Static Characteristics of Junction Transistors under Pulsed Conditions, *Slaboproudý Obzor*, vol. 20, no. 9, pp. 570–577, 1959.

Burgess, R. E.: Statistical Theory of Avalanche Breakdown in Silicon, *Can. J. Phys.*, vol. 37, no. 6, pp. 730–738, June, 1959.

Butler, F.: A Regenerative Modulator Frequency Divider Using Transistors, *Electronic Eng.*, vol. 31, pp. 72–75, February, 1959.

Butler, F.: A Transistor Blocking Oscillator Frequency Divider, *Electronic Eng.*, vol. 31, pp. 611–612, October, 1959.

Butler, F.: Transistor Invertors and Rectifier-filter Units, *Electronic Eng.*, vol. 31, pp. 412–418, July, 1959.

Calle, M. J., B. Dale, and C. A. P. Foxell: The Design and Performance of a High-speed Silicon Diode, *Proc. Inst. Elec. Engrs. (London)*, (International Convention on Transistors and Associated Semiconductor Devices), paper 2910E, May, 1959.

Callendar, M. V.: Junction Diodes as Limiters and Oscillators, *Electronic Radio Engr.*, vol. 36, no. 12, p. 466, December, 1959.

Capper, B. H., and B. Lowe: Transistor Circuits for Use with Magnetic Drum-controlled Data-handling Systems, *Proc. Inst. Elec. Engrs. (London)*, (International Convention on Transistors and Associated Semiconductor Devices), vol. 106B, suppl. 18, paper 2966E, pp. 1216–1225, 1289–1291, 1959.

Carasso, J. I.: Environmental Effects on the Growth of Excess Reverse Current in Germanium P-N Junctions, *Proc. Inst. Elec. Engrs. (London)*, (International Convention on Transistors and Associated Semiconductor Devices), vol. 106B, suppl. 17, paper 3080E, pp. 964–967, 1009–1011, 1959.

Card, W. H.: Four Transistor Inverter Drives Induction Motor, *Electronics*, vol. 32, no. 8, pp. 60–61, February 20, 1959.

Carlson, A. W.: Static Characteristics of Transistors, *Semiconductor Prods.*, vol. 2, no. 6, pp. 31–35, June, 1959.

Carstaedt, J.: The Transistor as an U.H.F. Oscillator, *Radio Mentor*, vol. 25, no. 4, pp. 235–239, April, 1959.

Cashen, J. F., and A. Harel: The Usefulness of Transconductance as a Transistor Parameter, *Proc. IRE*, vol. 47, no. 5, pp. 990–991, May, 1959.

Cawley, J. H.: A Transistorized Nuclear Reactor Count Rate Channel, *IRE Natl. Conv. Record*, vol. 7, part 9, pp. 183–189, 1959.

Čermák, J.: Internal Feedback in Transistors, *Slaboproudý Obzor*, vol. 20, no. 3, pp. 150–156, 1959.

Chang, K. K. N.: Low-noise Tunnel-diode Amplifier, *Proc. IRE*, vol. 47, no. 7, pp. 1268–1269, July, 1959.

Chao, S. C.: A Generalized Resistor-transistor Logic Circuit and Some Applications, *IRE Trans. on Electronic Computers*, vol. EC-8, no. 1, pp. 8–12, March, 1959.

Chaplin, G. B. B., and C. J. N. Candy: A Transistor Circuit for Fast Coincidence Measurements, *Nuclear Instr. and Methods*, vol. 5, no. 4, pp. 242–246, October, 1959.

Chaplin, G. B. B., C. J. N. Candy, and A. J. Cole: Transistor Stages for Wide-band Amplifiers, *Proc. Inst. Elec. Engrs. (London)*, (International Convention on Transistors and Associated Semiconductor Devices), paper 2892E, May, 1959.

Chaplin, G. B. B., and A. R. Owens: A Method of Designing Avalanche Transistor Trigger Circuits, *Proc. Inst. Elec. Engrs. (London)*, (International Convention on Transistors and Associated Semiconductor Devices), paper 2944E, May, 1959.

Chaplin, G. B. B., A. R. Owens, and A. J. Cole: A Sensitive Transistor Oscillograph with DC to 300 Mc/s Response, *Proc. Inst. Elec. Engrs. (London)*, (International Convention on Transistors and Associated Semiconductor Devices), part B, suppl. 16, paper 2943E, pp. 815–823, 840, May, 1959.

Chenette, E. R.: The Influence of Inductive Source Reactance on the Noise Figure of a Junction Transistor, *Proc. IRE*, vol. 47, no. 3, pp. 448–449, March, 1959.

Cheroff, G., R. C. Enck, and S. P. Keller: Effects of Polarized Light on Photocurrents and Photovoltages in ZnS, *Phys. Rev.*, vol. 116, no. 5, pp. 1091–1093, December 1, 1959.

Chevýchelov, A. D.: The Current-voltage Characteristic of an N-P Junction Calculated with Allowance for the Generation and Recombination of Current Carriers in the Space-charge Layer, *Fiz. Tverdogo Tela*, vol. 1, no. 8, pp. 1205–1212, August, 1959.

Chow, W. F.: Crystal Controlled High-frequency Transistor Oscillators, *Semiconductor Prods.*, vol. 2, no. 9, pp. 21–27, September, 1959.

Chuenkov, V. A.: A Theory of the Electrical Breakdown of Semiconductors, *Fiz. Tverdogo Tela*, Sbornik (suppl.) I, pp. 200–208; II, pp. 209–214, 1959.

Chynoweth, A. G., and K. G. McKay: Light Emission and Noise Studies of Individual Microplasmas in Silicon P-N Junctions, *J. Appl. Phys.*, vol. 30, no. 11, pp. 1811–1813, November, 1959.

Cihelka, J., L. Cerný, V. Husa, J. Kriz, and J. Ladnar: A New Technology for Production of Germanium Power Diodes, *Direct Current*, vol. 4, no. 4, pp. 112–115, March, 1959.

Claussen, B. H.: The Influence of Surface Properties on the Characteristics of Formed Point Contacts on p-type Germanium, *Proc. Inst. Elec. Engrs. (London)*, (International Convention on Transistors and Associated Semiconductor Devices), paper 2935E, May, 1959.

Clayton, P. S., and G. E. Snazell: Semiconductor Rectifiers for High Power Electrochemical Duty, *Engineer*, vol. 207, pp. 408–412, March 13, 1959.

Cobbold, R. S. C.: The Charge Storage in a Junction Transistor during Turn-off in the Active Region, *Electronic Eng.*, vol. 31, pp. 275–277, May, 1959.

Cobbold, R. S. C., and D. A. Goodings: Approximation to α for Diffusion Transistors, *Proc. Inst. Elec. Engrs. (London)*, (International Convention on Transistors and Associated Semiconductor Devices), vol. 106B, suppl. 17, paper 2976E, pp. 1018–1025, 1072–1074, May, 1959.

Collinge, B.: A Transistor Scaling Circuit with a Short Resolving Time, *Electronic Eng.*, vol. 31, pp. 604–605, October, 1959.

Connett, J., and P. Cooke: Transistor Applications in a High-speed Parallel Computer, *Proc. Inst. Elec. Engrs. (London)*, (International Convention on Transistors and Associated Semiconductor Devices), paper 2909E, May, 1959.

Conway, A. C.: A Fast Random-access Diode-capacitor Store Using Transistors, *Proc. Inst. Elec. Engrs. (London)*, (International Convention on Transistors and Associated Semiconductor Devices), paper 2952E, May, 1959.

Cooke, H. F.: Transistor Eyeglass Radio, *Electronics*, vol. 32, no. 39, p. 88, September 26, 1959.

Cooke-Yarborough, E. H.: The Use of Transistors in Instrumentation, *Proc. Inst. Elec. Engrs. (London)*, (International Convention on Transistors and Associated Semiconductor Devices), vol. 106B, suppl. 18, paper 3060E, pp. 1292–1294, 1334–1338, 1959.

Cooper, B. F. C., and W. J. Payten: Pulse Modulators Using Transistors and Switching Reactors, *Proc. IRE, Australia*, vol. 20, no. 3, pp. 148–152, March, 1959.

Cooper, H. K.: Circuit Losses in the Transistor A.F. Amplifier, *Electronic Inds.*, vol. 18, no. 2, pp. 74–77, February, 1959.

Crawford, J. H., Jr., and J. W. Cleland: Nature of Bombardment Damage and Energy Levels in Semiconductors, *J. Appl. Phys.*, vol. 30, no. 8, pp. 1204–1213, August, 1959.

Cripps, L. G.: Some Aspects of Small-signal High-frequency Equivalent Circuits for Transistors, *Proc. Inst. Elec. Engrs. (London)*, (International Convention on Transistors and Associated Semiconductor Devices), vol. 106B, suppl. 17, paper 3009E, pp. 1026–1032, 1072–1074, 1959.

Cripps, L. G.: Transistor High-frequency Parameter f_1, *Electronic Radio Engr.*, vol. 36, no. 9, pp. 341–346, September, 1959.

Cundall, C. M., J. K. Saggerson, and G. Shaw: A Transistor D-C Amplifier for Use in Analogue Computers, *Proc. Inst. Elec. Engrs. (London)*, vol. 106B, suppl. 18, paper 3038E, pp. 1354–1364, 1394, 1959.

Curtis, O. L., Jr.: Radiation Effects on Recombination in Germanium, *J. Appl. Phys.*, vol. 30, no. 8, pp. 1174–1180, August, 1959.

Das, M. B., and A. R. Boothroyd: On the Determination of the Minority Carrier Lifetime in the Base Region of Transistors, *J. Electronics and Control*, vol. 7, no. 6, pp. 534–539, December, 1959.

Das, M. B., and A. R. Boothroyd: Measurement of Equivalent Circuit Parameters of Transistors at V.H.F., *Proc. Inst. Elec. Engrs. (London)*, (International Convention on Transistors and Associated Semiconductor Devices), vol. 106B, suppl. 15, paper 3077E, pp. 536–549, 567–570, 1959.

D'Asaro, L. A.: A Stepping Transistor Element, *IRE WESCON Conv. Record*, vol. 3, part 3, pp. 37–42, 1959.

Davis, W. D.: Lifetimes and Capture Cross-sections in Gold-doped Silicon, *Phys. Rev.*, vol. 114, no. 4, pp. 1006–1008, May 15, 1959.

Deb, S., and A. N. Daw: Determination of Physical Parameters and Geometry of a Junction Transistor, *Proc. Inst. Elec. Engrs. (London)*, (International Convention on Transistors and Associated Semiconductor Devices), vol. 106B, suppl. 17, paper 3041E, pp. 1033–1037, 1072–1074, 1959.

Deb, S., and A. N. Daw: The Physical Interpretation of Measurements on Transistors, *J. Electronics and Control*, vol. 6, no. 6, pp. 552–553, June, 1959.

Deb, S., and J. K. Sen: Variation of Input Conductance of a Grounded Base Junction Transistor, *Electronic Eng.*, vol. 31, pp. 753–755, December, 1959.

Della Riccia, J.: Theory of Transistor Gain and Carrier Distribution in the Base, *Ann. radioélec.*, vol. 14, pp. 366–374, October, 1959.

Dement'ev, E. P.: Calculation of Automatic Gain Control in Transistor Amplifiers, *Radiotekhnika*, vol. 14, no. 6, pp. 39–44, June, 1959.

Dement'ev, E. P.: Non-linear Distortion in Semiconductor Triode Amplifiers Using Automatic Gain Control (A.G.C.), *Radiotekhnika*, vol. 14, no. 11, pp. 58–66, November, 1959.

Denda, S.: Three-terminal Germanium P-N-P-N Switches, *J. Inst. Elec. Commun. Engrs. (Japan)*, vol. 42, no. 12, pp. 1199–1203, December, 1959.

DeSautels, A. N.: Power Switching with Junction Transistors, *Control Eng.*, vol. 6, no. 11, pp. 113–117, November, 1959.

DeSautels, A. N.: Servo Preamplifiers Using Direct-coupled Transistors, *Electronics*, vol. 32, no. 20, p. 74, May 15, 1959.

Deschamps, R.: Double Diffusion Germanium N-P-N Transistors, *Onde élect.*, vol. 39, pp. 74–87, February, 1959.

Dessoulavy, R.: Some Aspects of Feedback in Transistor Amplifiers, *Bull. assoc. suisse élec.*, vol. 50, no. 6, pp. 233–239, March 14, 1959.

Dew-Hughes, D., A. H. Jones, and G. E. Brock: Improved Automatic Four-point Resistivity Probe, *Rev. Sci. Instr.*, vol. 30, no. 10, pp. 920–922, October, 1959.

Dezoteux, J.: Wide-band Transistor Amplifiers, *Onde élect.*, vol. 39, pp. 726–732, September, 1959.

Dick, J. O.: High-temperature Capabilities of Germanium Transistors, *Elec. Mfg.*, vol. 63, no. 1, pp. 149–151, 204, January, 1959.

Dimmer, R. P., and E. L. Roback: A New Transistorized Negative-impedance Telephone Repeater, *Commun. and Electronics*, no. 45, November, 1959.

Dorendorf, H.: Investigation of P-N Junctions in Germanium with Various Densities of Recombination Centers, *Z. angew. Phys.*, vol. 11, no. 5, pp. 162–164, May, 1959.

Dousmanis, G. C.: Effects of Carrier Injection on the Recombination Velocity in Semiconductor Surfaces, *J. Appl. Phys.*, vol. 30, no. 2, pp. 180–184, February, 1959.

Dunnet, W. J., E. P. Auger, and A. C. Scott: Analysis of Transistor-resistor-logic Circuit Propagation Delay, *Sylvania Technologist*, vol. 12, no. 4, pp. 123–133, October, 1959.

Dunnet, W. J., and A. G. Lemack: Transistor–Magnetic Core Bilogical Computer Element, in Proceedings of the Western Joint Computer Conference, pp. 144–149, AIEE, New York, March, 1959.

Dusek, J.: Measurement of the Hall Coefficient and Electrical Conductivity in Semiconductors by the Method of an Alternating Magnetic Field and Alternating Current, *Czechoslov. J. Phys.*, vol. 9, no. 2, pp. 250–255, 1959.

Early, J. M.: Maximum Rapidly Switchable Power Density in Junction Triodes, *IRE Trans. on Electron Devices*, vol. ED-6, no. 3, pp. 322–325, July, 1959.

Eckhardt, K.: Suitability of Germanium Photodiodes and Phototransistors for Photometry, *Lichttechnik*, vol. 11, no. 9, pp. 478–482, September, 1959.

Edwards, K. A., O. Golubjatnikov, and D. J. Brady: Transistor Phase-locked Oscillators, *Commun. and Electronics*, no. 40, January, 1959.

Egorov, V.: The Recombination of Charge Carriers in Semiconductors for a Large Trap Concentration, *Fiz. Tverdogo Tela*, vol. 1, no. 5, pp. 832–833, May, 1959.

Emden, K.: Note on the Stabilization of the Operating Point for Transistors, *Arch. Elekt. Ubertragung*, vol. 13, no. 5, pp. 219–220, May, 1959.

Endler, H., A. D. Berk, and W. L. Whirry: Relaxation Phenomena in Diode Parametric Amplifiers, *Proc. IRE*, vol. 47, no. 8, pp. 1376–1378, August, 1959.

Enemark, D.: Transistors Improve Telemeter Transmitter, *Electronics*, vol. 32, no. 11, pp. 136–137, March 13, 1959.

Eng, S. T., and W. P. Waters: A Gold-bonded Germanium Diode for Parametric Amplification, *Proc. Natl. Electronic Conf.*, vol. 15, pp. 83–91, 1959.

Epstein, M., L. J. Greenstein, and H. M. Sachs: Principles and Applications of Hall-effect Devices, *Proc. Natl. Electronics Conf.*, vol. 15, pp. 241–252, 1959.

Erofeev, A. V., and A. A. Lukin: Transistorized Amplifier for Electronic Self-balancing Bridges and Potentiometers, *Proborostroenie*, no. 7, July, 1959.

Ettinger, G. M., and B. J. Cooper: The Design of High-power Switched Transistor Amplifiers, *Proc. Inst. Elec. Engrs. (London)*, vol. 106B, suppl. 18, paper 3092, pp. 1285–1288, 1289–1291, 1959.

Evans, A. D.: Increasing the Input Impedance in Transistor Amplifiers, *Electronic Inds.*, vol. 18, no. 3, pp. 84–86, March, 1959.

Evans, D. M.: The Measurement of the Temperature Dependence of the Mobility and Effective Lifetime of Minority Carriers in the Base Region of Silicon Transistors, *J. Electronics and Control*, vol. 6, no. 3, pp. 204–208, March, 1959.

Evans, D. M.: The Temperature Dependence of the Low-level Lifetime and Conductivity Mobility of Carriers in Silicon, *J. Electronics and Control*, vol. 7, no. 2, pp. 112–122, August, 1959.

Evans, J., D. S. Ridler, and R. W. A. Scarr: Bidirectional Transistors and Their Uses in Switching Circuits, *Proc. Inst. Elec. Engrs. (London)*, paper 2972E, May, 1959.

Feuillade, G.: Study of the Preparation of N-P Junctions by the Diffusion of Boron and Phosphorus into Silicon, *J. Chem. Phys.*, vol. 56, no. 6, pp. 593–608, June, 1959.

Finch, T. R.: Transistor Resistor Logic Circuits for Digital Data Systems, in Proceedings of the Western Joint Computer Conference, pp. 17–22, AIEE, New York, March, 1959.

Firle, T. E., and O. E. Hayes: Some Reactive Effects in Forward Biased Junctions, *IRE Trans. on Electron Devices*, vol. ED-6, no. 3, pp. 330–334, July, 1959.

Fleming, G. C.: Transistors and Saturable-core Transformers as Square Wave Oscillators, *Electronic Eng.*, vol. 31, pp. 543–545, September, 1959.

Fortini, M. M., and J. Vilms: Solid-state Generator for Microwave Power, *Electronics*, vol. 32, no. 36, pp. 42–43, September 4, 1959.

Freestone, R.: A Method of Preparing Semiconductor P-N-P-N Switching Devices, *Proc. Inst. Elec. Engrs. (London)*, paper 2886E, May, 1959.

Frei, A. H., and M. J. O. Strutt: Analog Computer Measurements on Saturation Currents, Admittances, and Transfer Efficiencies of Semiconductor Junction Diodes and Transistors, *Proc. IRE*, vol. 47, no. 7, pp. 1245–1252, July, 1959.

Friese, T.: Quasilogarithmic Impulse Indication with Transistors, *Elektron. Rundschau*, vol. 13, no. 8, pp. 283–285, August, 1959.

Fulop, W.: Design Considerations of a Graded-base Transistor with Improved Emitter-base Breakdown Voltage, *Proc. Inst. Elec. Engrs. (London)*, paper 2918E, May, 1959.

Gair, F. C., R. C. V. Macario, and R. L. Rouse: A Resistance-network Analysis of the Current Gain of Junction Transistors, *Proc. Inst. Elec. Engrs. (London)*, vol. 106B, suppl. 14, pp. 1038–1045, 1072–1074, 1959.

Galkina, T. I.: Application of the Photogalvanomagnetic Effect in Measuring the Surface Recombination Rate, *Fiz. Tverdogo Tela*, vol. 1, no. 2, pp. 216–217, February, 1959.

Gariano, W. F.: Transient Analysis of Junction Transistors, *IRE Trans. on Electron Devices*, vol. ED-6, no. 1, pp. 90–100, January, 1959.

Garmash, E. N.: Equivalent Y-parameters of a Transistor with Resistivity Emitter Load, *Radiotekhnika*, vol. 14, no. 11, pp. 67–72, November, 1959.

Garreta, O.: Contribution to the Study of Small Semiconductor Structures at Low Temperatures, *Ann. radio-élec.*, vol. 14, pp. 47–72, January, 1959.

Garside, A. E., and P. Harvey: The Characteristics of Silicon-voltage-reference Diodes, *Proc. Inst. Elec. Engrs. (London)*, (International Convention on Transistors and Associated Semiconductor Devices), vol. 106B, suppl. 17, paper 3055E, pp. 982–990, 1009–1011, 1959.

Gärtner, W. W.: Depletion-layer Photoeffects in Semiconductors, *Phys. Rev.*, vol. 116, no. 1, pp. 84–87, October 1, 1959.

Garver, R. V.: High-speed Microwave Switching of Semiconductors, *IRE Trans. on Microwave Theory and Tech.*, vol. MTT-7, no. 2, pp. 272–276, April, 1959.

Garwin, R. L., A. M. Patlach, and H. A. Reich: Transistorized, Crystal-controlled Marginal Oscillator, *Rev. Sci. Instr.*, vol. 30, no. 2, pp. 79–80, February, 1959.

Gasstrom, R. V.: A Transistorized Coincidence Unit with Nanosecond Resolution, *Proc. Inst. Elec. Engrs. (London)*, vol. 106B, suppl. 16, paper 3113E, pp. 834–839, 840–842, 1959.

Gay, M. J.: The Design of Apparatus to Measure Transistor Small-signal Parameters, *Proc. Inst. Elec. Engrs. (London)*, part B, suppl. 15, paper 2956E, pp. 550–554, 567, May, 1959.

Gay, M. J.: Measurements of Transistor Parameters Using Bridge Techniques, *Brit. Commun. and Electronics*, vol. 6, no. 6, pp. 430–432, June, 1959.

George, R. E.: A Transistor Stimulator for Physiological Use, *Electronic Eng.*, vol. 31, pp. 530–533, September, 1959.

Gerasimov, S. M.: Temperature Dependence of Power Characteristics of Transistor Oscillators, *Radiotekhnika*, vol. 14, no. 7, pp. 33–39, July, 1959.

Gerlach, A.: Automatically Switched Transistor Vibrator in Electronic Flash Apparatus, *Radio Mentor*, vol. 25, no. 1, pp. 34–35, January 19, 1959.

Giacoletto, L. J.: Avalanche Controlled Semiconductor Amplifier, *Proc. IRE*, vol. 47, no. 8, pp. 1379–1381, August, 1959.

Giacoletto, L. J.: Transistor Equivalent Circuit Modification Due to Non-equipotential Base, *J. Electronics and Control*, vol. 7, no. 3, pp. 233–242, September, 1959.

Gibson, A. F.: The Mobility, Diffusion Constant, and Lifetime of Minority Carriers in Heavily Dislocated Germanium, *J. Phys. Chem. Solids*, vol. 8, pp. 147–149, 164–171, January, 1959.

Giguere, W. J., and J. H. Jamison: Transistor Pulse Circuits for 160 Mc Clock Rates. I Pulse Regeneration; II. Parallel-to-serial Multiplexing, by J. C. Noll; *IRE Trans. on Electronic Computers*, vol. EC-8, no. 4, pp. 432–435, 436–438, December, 1959.

Gilland, J. R.: Transistor Circuitry for Radiation Counting, *Rev. Sci. Instr.*, vol. 30, no. 6, pp. 479–484, June, 1959.

Ginsbach, K. H.: The Initial Region of the Characteristics of a Transistor in the Common-emitter Connection, *Proc. Inst. Elec. Engrs. (London)*, (International Convention on Transistors and Associated Semiconductor Devices), vol. 106B, suppl. 17, paper 3043E, pp. 991–997, 1009–1011, 1959.

Giralt, G.: On the Stability Factor and Static Gain of Transistor Amplifiers, *Compt. rend.*, vol. 248, no. 24, pp. 3415–3417, June 15, 1959.

Gisina, F. A.: Relaxation Characteristics of Semiconductor Photo-resistors and Photo-elements, *Fiz. Tverdogo Tela*, vol. 1, no. 9, pp. 1434–1440, September, 1959.

Gleghorn, P.: An Analogue Electronic Multiplier Using Transistors as Square-wave Modulators, *Proc. Inst. Elec. Engrs. (London)*, vol. 107B, paper 2962M, pp. 94–100, 1959.

Glicksman, M., and M. C. Steele: Plasma Pinch Effects in Indium Antimonide, *Phys. Rev. Letters*, vol. 2, no. 11, pp. 461–463, June 1, 1959.

Glinchuk, K. D., E. G. Miselyuk, and N. N. Fortunatova: A Study of Silver and Gold Local Levels in Germanium, *Fiz. Tverdogo Tela*, vol. 1, no. 9, pp. 1345–1350, September, 1959.

Glucharoff, T., and C. P. Gilbert: The Use of Silicon Diodes in D-C Modulators and Their Applications to Drift Correctors for Computing Amplifiers, *Proc. Inst. Elec. Engrs. (London)*, monograph 346M, October, 1959.

Goda, B. T., W. R. Johnston, S. Markowitz, M. Rosenberg, and R. Stuart-Williams: All-transistor Magnetic-core Memories, *Commun. and Electronics*, no. 45, November, 1959.

Goldie, V. W., R. G. Amicone, and C. T. Davey: Generating Pulses with Solid-state Thyratrons, *Electronics*, vol. 32, no. 33, p. 70, August 14, 1959.

Gordeev, G. V.: Ionization by Collision at N-P Junctions, *Fiz. Tverdogo Tela*, vol. 1, no. 6, pp. 851–860, June, 1959.

Gordonov, A. Yu.: Transient Processes in a Transistor in Common Emitter Circuits, *Fiz. Tverdogo Tela*, Sbornik (suppl.) II, pp. 319–325, 1959.

Gorodetsky, A. F., V. G. Mel'nik, and I. G. Mel'nik: A Method of Producing Ohmic Contacts with Silicon, *Fiz. Tverdogo Tela*, vol. 1, no. 1, pp. 173–174, 1959.

Gosmand, R.: Static Convertors Using Transistors, *Rev. tech. C.F.T.H.*, no. 31, pp. 63–94, September, 1959.

Gosslau, K., and K. Braun: Transistorized Switching Circuits in Data Processing Systems, *Elektron. Rechenanlagen*, vol. 1, no. 1, 1959.

Götz, E., H. C. Heinzerling, and H. G. Lott: Transistors in Control Systems with Logical Switching Elements, *Elektrotech. Z.*, vol. 80A, no. 15, pp. 487–492, August 1, 1959.

Götzberger, A.: The Voltage-dependence of Reverse Current in Alloy Transistors, *Z. angew. Phys.*, vol. 11, no. 1, pp. 6–9, January, 1959.

Gowthorpe, A., and P. Jefferson: Transistorized Power Supplies for Travelling-wave Tubes, Cathode-ray Tubes, and Klystrons, *Proc. Inst. Elec. Engrs. (London)*, (International Convention on Transistors and Associated Semiconductor Devices), vol. 106B, suppl. 18, paper 3093E, pp. 1325–1333, 1334–1338, 1959.

Graveson, R. T.: A Transistorized Pulse Height Analyzer for Gamma Spectroscopy, *IRE Natl. Conv. Record*, vol. 7, part 9, pp. 202–213, 1959.

Gray, M. G.: Using Silicon Diodes in Radarmodulators, *Electronics*, vol. 32, no. 24, pp. 70–72, June 12, 1959.

Gray, P. E.: On Direct Coupled Transistor Amplifier Stages, *Proc. IRE*, vol. 47, no. 4, pp. 591–592, April, 1959.

Green, D. A.: Transistor Equivalent Circuit; Alloyed Junction Types at High Frequencies, *Electronic Radio Engr.*, vol. 36, no. 3, pp. 108–114, March, 1959.

Green, M.: Space Charge in Semiconductors Resulting from Low-level Injection, *J. Appl. Phys.*, vol. 30, no. 5, pp. 744–747, May, 1959.

Gremmelmaier, R., and H. J. Henkel: GaAs Tunnel Diodes, *Z. Naturforsch.*, vol. 14a, no. 12, pp. 1072–1073, December, 1959.

Grinich, V. H., and I. Haas: P-N-π-N Triode Switching Applications, *IRE Trans. on Electronic Computers*, vol. EC-8, no. 2, pp. 108–113, June, 1959.

Groschwitz, E., and R. Ebhardt: The Effective Contact Area of Point Contact Crystal Rectifiers, *Z. angew. Phys.*, vol. 11, no. 9, pp. 342–346, September, 1959.

Grosvalet, J.: Study of a Drift-type High-frequency Transistor, *Onde élect.*, vol. 39, pp. 68–73, February, 1959.

Grover, D. J., and J. M. C. Dukes: Transistorized Central Pulse Generator for Digital Equipment, *Proc. Inst. Elec. Engrs. (London)*, (International Convention on Transistors and Associated Semiconductor Devices), part B, suppl. 16, paper 2893E, pp. 824–827, 840, May, 1959.

Grubbs, W. J.: Hall Effect Devices, *Bell System Tech. J.*, vol. 38, no. 3, pp. 853–876, May, 1959.

Grybowski, T. M., and W. G. Vieth: A Transistorized 20-channel Carrier Telegraph Terminal, *Trans. AIEE*, part I, vol. 78, pp. 260–265, 1959.

Guggenbühl, W.: Voltage Breakdown in Junction Transistors under General Circuit Conditions, *Arch. Elekt. Ubertragung*, vol. 13, no. 11, pp. 451–461, November, 1959.

Gullen, M. A.: The Transistor as a 4-terminal Network, *Can. Electronics Eng.*, vol. 3, pp. 25–28, April; pp. 34–37, 41, May, 1959.

Gumowski, I.: Concerning a Non-linear Effect in Transistor Amplifiers with Feedback, *Compt. rend.*, vol. 249, no. 23, pp. 2514–2516, December 9, 1959.

Gunn, J. B.: Effect of Electron and Impurity Density on the Field-dependence of Mobility in Germanium, *J. Phys. Chem. Solids*, vol. 8, pp. 239–241, 262–263, January, 1959.

Hadley, C. P., and E. Fischer: Sintered Cadmium Sulfide Photoconductive Cells, *RCA Rev.*, vol. 20, no. 4, pp. 635–647, December, 1959.

Halpern, J., and R. H. Rediker: Millimicrosecond Switching Diodes, *Electronics*, vol. 32, no. 23, pp. 66–68, June 5, 1959.

Hamilton, D. J., J. F. Gibbons, and W. Shockley: Physical Principles of Avalanche Transistor Pulse Circuits, *Proc. IRE*, vol. 47, no. 6, pp. 1102–1108, June, 1959.

Hammerslag, J.: Circuit Design Using Silicon Capacitors, *Electronics*, vol. 32, no. 38, pp. 48–50, September 18, 1959.

Hanel, R., R. A. Stampfl, and F. Caruse: Bias Considerations in D-C Transistor Amplifiers, *Proc. Inst. Elec. Engrs. (London)*, vol. 106B, suppl. 18, paper 3063E, pp. 1365–1372, 1394, 1959.

Hangstefer, J. B., and L. H. Dixon, Jr.: Triggered Bistable Semiconductor Circuits, *Electronics*, vol. 32, no. 35, pp. 58–59, August 28, 1959.

Harel, A., and J. F. Cashen: Unified Representation of Junction Transistor Transient Response, *RCA Rev.*, vol. 20, no. 1, pp. 136–152, March, 1959.

Harmans, J., and H. Neumann: I. F. Problems in Transistor AM-FM Receivers, *Radio Mentor*, vol. 25, no. 4, pp. 214–218, April, 1959.

Harnden, J. D., Jr.: The Controlled Rectifiers: Key to the Continuing Control Renaissance, *Trans. AIEE*, part I, vol. 77, pp. 1006–1012, 1959.

Harrick, N. J.: Effect of the Metal-to-semiconductor Potential on the Semiconductor Surface Barrier Height, *J. Phys. Chem. Solids*, vol. 8, pp. 106–108, 121–122, January, 1959.

Harrick, N. J.: Metal to Semiconductor Contacts: Injection or Extraction for Either Direction of Current Flow, *Phys. Rev.*, vol. 115, no. 4, pp. 876–882, August 15, 1959.

Harrick, N. J.: Properties of a Semiconductor Surface as Determined from a Modified Drift Mobility Experiment, *Phys. Rev. Letters*, vol. 2, no. 5, pp. 199–200, March 1, 1959.

Harrick, N. J.: Technique for Measuring Particle Drift Mobilities in Near Intrinsic and Narrow Band Gap Semiconductors, *J. Appl. Phys.*, vol. 30, no. 3, pp. 451–452, March, 1959.

Harten, H. U.: The Recombination of Excess Carriers at a Silicon-Electrolyte Interface, *Proc. Inst. Elec. Engrs. (London)*, (International Convention on Transistors and Associated Semiconductor Devices), paper 2877E, May, 1959.

Harten, H. U.: Surface Recombination of Silicon, *Philips Research Repts.*, vol. 14, no. 4, pp. 346–360, October, 1959.

Haug, A.: Simplified Design of Push-Pull Transistor Inverters, *Radio Mentor*, vol. 25, no. 12, pp. 964–966, December, 1959.

Hayashi, T.: Field Emission in Germanium, *J. Inst. Elec. Commun. Engrs. (Japan)*, vol. 42, no. 12, pp. 1180–1186, December, 1959.

Hellerman, H.: Some Stability Consideration in the Design of Large Feedback Junction Transistor Amplifiers, *Semiconductor Prods.*, vol. 2, no. 6, pp. 25–31, June, 1959.

Helsdon, P. B.: Transistor Line Deflection Circuits for Television, *Marconi Rev.*, vol. 22, pp. 38–70, 1st quarter, 1959.

Helsdon, P. B.: Transistors in Video Equipment, *J. Brit. Inst. Radio Engrs.*, vol. 19, no. 12, pp. 753–768, December, 1959.

Herman, R.: Transistor Storage and Logic Circuits for Binary Data Processing, *Proc. Inst. Elec. Engrs.* (*London*), (International Convention on Transistors and Associated Semiconductor Devices), paper 2958E, May, 1959.

Herring, C.: Transport, *J. Phys. Chem. Solids*, vol. 8, pp. 543–549, January, 1959.

Heywang, W., and M. Zerbst: Theory of the Trapping Mechanism in Semiconductors, *Z. Naturforsch.*, vol. 14a, no. 7, pp. 641–645, July, 1959.

Hierholzer, F. J., Jr.: Linear Power Amplifiers Using Dynistors or Trinistors, *Trans. AIEE*, part I, vol. 77, pp. 892–898, 1959.

Hilberg, W.: Method of Operation of Transistorized Blocking Oscillators and Review of Their Basic Arrangements, *Elektron. Rundschau*, vol. 13, no. 9, pp. 330–335, September, 1959.

Hilberg, W.: The Realization of Switches for Both Directions of Current Flow Using Junction Transistors, *Elektron. Rundschau*, vol. 13, no. 12, pp. 438–440, December, 1959.

Hilbourne, R. A., and D. D. Jones: The Maximum Voltage, Current and Power Ratings of Junction Transistors, *Proc. Inst. Elec. Engrs.* (*London*), (International Convention on Transistors and Associated Semiconductor Devices), vol. 106B, suppl. 17, paper 3048E, pp. 998–1003, 1009–1011, 1959.

Hilibrand, J., and W. R. Beam: Semiconductor Diodes in Parametric Sub-harmonic Oscillators, *RCA Rev.*, vol. 20, no. 2, pp. 229–253, June, 1959.

Hilibrand, J., C. W. Mueller, C. F. Stocker, and R. D. Gold: Semiconductor Parametric Diodes in Microwave Computers, *IRE Trans. on Electronic Computers*, vol. EC-8, no. 3, pp. 287–297, September, 1959.

Hilsenbeck, K.: The Semiconductor Rectifier, a New Construction Element for Railway Operation, *Glasers Ann.*, vol. 83, no. 4, pp. 102–107, April, 1959.

Hirsch, P.: Linear-phase Transistor Amplifier, *Elec. Eng.*, vol. 78, no. 12, pp. 1184–1189, December, 1959.

Hoehm, G. L., Jr.: Semiconductor Comparator Circuits, *IRE WESCON Conv. Record*, vol. 3, part 2, pp. 102–110, 1959.

Hoffman, T. R.: Effect of Emitter Bypass Capacitance on Frequency Response of a Grounded Emitter Transistor Amplifier Stage, *Semiconductor Prods.*, vol. 2, no. 7, p. 2709, July, 1959.

Hoffman, T. R.: Feedback Design for Transistor Amplifier Stages, *Electronics*, vol. 32, no. 33, pp. 52–54, August 14, 1959.

Hogarth, C. A., A. Langridge, and J. M. Ziman: Thermal-resistance Considerations in the Design of Semiconductor Devices, *Proc. Inst. Elec. Engrs.* (*London*), (International Convention on Transistors and Associated Semiconductor Devices), paper 2968E, May, 1959.

Hoge, R. R.: Transistorized Source-range Reactor Instrumentation, *IRE Natl. Conv. Record*, vol. 7, part 9, pp. 190–195, 1959.

Hoge, R. R., and D. J. Niehaus: Transistorized Reactor Instrumentation and Protective Circuits, *IRE Trans. on Nuclear Sci.*, vol. NS-6, no. 2, pp. 42–48, June, 1959.

Holford, K.: Transistor LC Oscillator Circuits for Low-frequency, Low-power Operation, *Mullard Tech. Commun.*, vol. 5, pp. 17–25, December, 1959.

Holonyak, N., Jr., I. A. Lesk, R. N. Hall, J. J. Tiemann, and H. Ehrenreich: Direct Observation of Phonons during Tunnelling in Narrow Junction Diodes, *Phys. Rev. Letters*, vol. 3, no. 4, pp. 167–168, August 15, 1959.

Homolius, K.: Locked Detection with Transistors, *Arch. tech. Messen*, no. 281 (ref. Z52-12), pp. 129–132, June, 1959.

Horsley, G. S.: Three Layer Compensated Avalanche Diodes, *IRE WESCON Conv. Record*, vol. 3, part 3, pp. 56–63, 1959.

Huang, C.: A Physical Theory of Junction Transistors in the Collector-voltage-saturation Region, *IRE Trans. on Electron Devices*, vol. ED-6, no. 2, pp. 141–153, April, 1959.

Huang, C., C. M. Chang, and M. Weissenstern: Surface and Geometry Effects on Large Signal Base Input Voltage and Input Resistance of Junction Transistors, *IRE Trans. on Electron Devices*, vol. ED-6, no. 2, pp. 154–161, April, 1959.

Hughes, H. E., T. R. Robillard, and R. W. Westberg: Medium Power High-speed Germanium Alloy Transistors, *IRE Trans. on Electron Devices*, vol. ED-6, no. 3, pp. 311–314, July, 1959.

Huldt, L.: Determination of Free Carrier Lifetimes in Semiconductors from the Relaxation Time of Photo-excited Infrared Absorption, *Arkiv Fysik*, vol. 15, paper 19, pp. 229–236, 1959.

Huldt, L.: Optical Method for Determining Carrier Lifetimes in Semiconductors, *Phys. Rev. Letters*, vol. 2, no. 1, pp. 3–5, Jan. 1, 1959.

Hull, J. E.: Flip-flop Circuit Using Saturated Transistors, *Electronic Inds.*, vol. 18, no. 9, pp. 88–91, September; no. 10, pp. 103–106, October, 1959.

Hulme, V. B.: Some Switching-circuit Applications of Transistors and Saturable Magnetic Cores, *Proc. Inst. Elec. Engrs.* (*London*), (International Convention on Transistors and Associated Semiconductor Devices), paper 2953E, May, 1959.

Hunter, W. H.: An Ultra Stable Diffused Voltage Reference Diode, *IRE WESCON Conv. Record*, vol. 3, part 6, pp. 113–117, 1959.

Husa, V., J. Cihelka, and L. Černý: The Problems of Overvoltage in Circuits with Germanium Diodes and Protection against Overvoltage, *Elektrotech. Obzor*, vol. 48, no. 9, pp. 478–482, 1959.

Husa, V., and J. Kriz: Measurement of Lifetimes in Silicon, *Slaboproudý Obzor*, vol. 20, no. 10, pp. 615–617, 1959.

Husa, V., J. Kriz, and J. Ladnar: P*-P-N* Junction in Silicon, *Slaboproudý Obzor*, vol. 20, no. 5, pp. 284–287, 1959.

Hutchins, R., and J. D. Martin: Transistor "h" Parameters, *Electronic Radio Engr.*, vol. 36, no. 10, pp. 383–387, October, 1959.

Hyde, F. J.: The Current Gains of Diffusion and Drift Types of Junction Transistors, *Proc. Inst. Elec. Engrs.* (*London*), (International Convention on Transistors and Associated Semiconductor Devices), paper 2937E, May, 1959.

Hyde, F. J.: High-frequency Power Gain of the Drift Transistors, *Proc. Inst. Elec. Engrs.* (*London*), vol. 106B, paper 2857R, pp. 405–407, July, 1959.

Hyde, F. J.: An Investigation of the Current Gain of a Drift Transistor at Frequencies Up to 105 Mc/s, *Proc. Inst. Elec. Engrs.* (*London*), vol. 106B, paper 2856R, pp. 397–404, July, 1959.

Hyde, F. J.: An Investigation of the Dependence of the Current Gain of a Plane-alloy-junction Transistor on Emitter Current and Frequency, *Proc. Inst. Elec. Engrs.* (*London*), vol. 106B, paper 2855R, pp. 391–396, July, 1959.

Hyde, F. J.: The Physical Interpretation of Measurements on Transistors, *J. Electronics and Control*, vol. 6, no. 4, pp. 362–364, April, 1959.

Hyde, F. J.: Radio-frequency Measurements on Transistors, *Proc. Inst. Elec. Engrs.* (*London*), (International Convention on Transistors and Associated Semiconductor Devices), vol. 106B, suppl. 17, paper 3127E, pp. 942–944, 1009–1011, 1949.

Hyde, F. J., and T. E. Price: Measurement of the High-frequency Base Resistance and Collector Capacitance of Drift Transistors, *J. Electronics and Control*, vol. 6, no. 4, pp. 347–355, April, 1959.

Ingraham, R. C., and R. E. Hunt: Molten Dot Technique for Alloy Junction Fabrication, *IRE WESCON Conv. Record*, vol. 3, part 3, pp. 50–55, 1959.

Ivanov, S. N., N. E. Skvortsova, and Yu. F. Sokolov: Germanium Diodes for Parametric Amplifiers, *Radiotekh. i Elektron.*, vol. 4, no. 9, pp. 1538–1542, September, 1959.

Iwersen, J. E., and J. T. Nelson: An R. F. Power Transistor, *Bell Labs. Record*, vol. 37, no. 10, pp. 390–393, October, 1959.

Iyer, T. S. K. V.: Analysis of a Direct Coupled Astable Transistor Multivibrator, *J. Inst. Telecommun. Engrs.* (*New Delhi*), vol. 5, no. 2, pp. 93–97, March, 1959.

Jakits, O.: Measurement of the Thermal Behaviour of Semiconductor Diodes, *Elektrotech. Z.*, vol. 80A, no. 15, pp. 518–520, August 1, 1959.

Jankowski, T.: Transistors in Pulse Operation, *Rozprawy Elektrotech.*, vol. 5, no. 1, pp. 121–162, 1959.

Jenny, D. A., and J. J. Wysocki: Temperature Dependence and Lifetime in Semiconductor Junctions, *J. Appl. Phys.*, vol. 30, no. 11, pp. 1692–1698, November, 1959.

Joffe, A.: Properties of Various Semiconductors, *J. Phys. Chem. Solids*, vol. 8, pp. 6–12, 20, January, 1959.

Johnson, E. O., and A. Rose: Simple General Analysis of Amplifier Devices with Emitter, Control, and Collector Functions, *Proc. IRE*, vol. 47, no. 3, pp. 407–418, March, 1959.

Johnson, R. R., and R. D. Lohman, and R. R. Painter: A New Technique for Measuring Transistor Switching Times, *Semiconductor Prods.*, vol. 2, no. 6, pp. 35–37, May, 1959.

Jones, A. M.: The Effects of Variations in Transistor Parameters on the Overall Performance of a Radio Receiver, *Proc. Inst. Elec. Engrs.* (*London*), vol. 106B, suppl. 18, paper 3026E, pp. 1194–1197, 1207, 1959.

Jones, D. D.: Rectification and Power Supplies, *Proc. Inst. Elec. Engrs.* (*London*), (International Convention on Transistors and Associated Semiconductor Devices), vol. 106B, suppl. 18, paper 3062E, pp. 1300–1302, 1334–1338, 1959.

Jones, D. H.: Intermodulation Distortion in an Experimental Group Amplifier Using Transistors, *Proc. Inst. Elec. Engrs.* (*London*), (International Convention on Transistors and Associated Semiconductor Devices), paper 2878E, May, 1959.

Jones, D. L.: Directly Coupled Transistor Hearing Aid, *Mullard Tech. Commun.*, vol. 5, pp. 2–9, December, 1959.

Jones, D. V.: Applying the Transistor in a Stereophonic Tape System, *Audio Eng. Soc. J.*, vol. 7, no. 3, pp. 133–134, July, 1959.

Jones, D. V.: Silicon Controlled Rectifier-triggering and Turn-off Circuitry for Inverter Applications, *IRE WESCON Conv. Record*, vol. 3, part 6, pp. 122–128, 1959.

Jones, R. C.: Phenomenological Description of the Response and Detecting Ability of Radiation Detectors, *Proc. IRE*, vol. 47, no. 9, pp. 1495–1502, September, 1959.

Jonscher, A. K.: Emitter Efficiency and Injection Level in Diffused Structures, *Proc. Inst. Elec. Engrs. (London)*, (International Convention on Transistors and Associated Semiconductor Devices), paper 2894E, May, 1959.

Joshi, M. V.: Design of Transistor I.F. Amplifier Detector Stages with Stabilized Band-pass Characteristics, *J. Inst. Telecommun. Engrs. (New Delhi)*, vol. 5, no. 4, pp. 223–229, September, 1959.

Junga, F. A., and G. M. Enslow: Radiation Effects in Silicon Solar Cells, *IRE Trans. on Nuclear Sci.*, vol. NS-6, no. 2, pp. 49–53, June, 1959.

Kaiser, W., and G. H. Wheatley: Hot Electrons and Carrier Multiplication in Silicon at Low Temperature, *Phys. Rev. Letters*, vol. 3, no. 7, pp. 334–336, October 1, 1959.

Kaitsov, L. N., K. Ya. Senatorov, and O. I. Poilavskaya: The Problem of the Establishment of Oscillations in Transistor Oscillators, *Radiotekh. i Elektron.*, vol. 4, no. 9, pp. 1557–1562, September, 1959.

Kalashnikov, S. G., and A. I. Morozov: The Temperature Dependence of the Trapping Coefficient of Electrons at Neutral Levels of Copper in Germanium, *Fiz. Tverdogo Tela*, vol. 1, no. 8, pp. 1294–1296, August, 1959.

Kampf, H. A.: Increasing Counting System Reliability, *Electronics*, vol. 32, no. 37, pp. 112–113, September 11, 1959.

Kaposi, A. A.: Transistor Blocking Oscillator for Use in Digital Systems, *Electronic Eng.*, vol. 31, pp. 480–484, August, 1959.

Karandeev, K. B., M. G. Mizyuk, and N. I. Smirnov: D-C Millivoltmeter Employing Transistors, *Pribory i Tekh. Eksperimenta*, no. 2, pp. 65–67, March–April, 1959.

Kasprzhak, G. M., and E. L. Orkina: Transient Processes in Transistorized D-C Amplifiers, *Elektrichestvo*, no. 12, pp. 55–60, December, 1959.

Kaufmann, P.: Static Current Gain as Function of Emitter Current of Transistors with Homogeneous and Diffused Bases, *Arch. Elekt. Ubertragung*, vol. 13, no. 4, pp. 141–151, April, 1959.

Kaufmann, P.: Types of Construction and Doping Profiles in Junction Transistors, *Scientia Electrica*, vol. 5, no. 1, pp. 19–39, April, 1959.

Kaufmann, P., and G. Freedman: An Analysis of Impurity Distributions and Their Relation to Electrical Behavior of Conventional Transistor Constructions, I–II, *Semiconductor Prods.*, vol. 2, no. 4, pp. 17–24, April; no. 5, pp. 26–31, May, 1959.

Kaufmann, P., and J. J. Klein: Flow Graph Analysis of Transistor Feedback Networks, *Semiconductor Prods.*, vol. 2, no. 10, pp. 37–41, October, 1959.

Kawana, Y., and T. Misawa: A Silicon P-N-P-N Power Triode, *J. Electronics and Control*, vol. 6, no. 4, pp. 324–332, April, 1959.

Kawasaki, K., K. Kanou, and Y. Sekita: Interaction of Water Vapour with Germanium Real Surface, *J. Phys. Soc. Japan*, vol. 14, no. 2, pp. 233–234, February, 1959.

Keller, W.: Measurement of Carrier Lifetime in Silicon Monocrystals with High Frequencies, *Z. angew. Phys.*, vol. 11, no. 9, pp. 351–352, September, 1959.

Kelso, R. J., and J. C. Groce: Encoder Measures Random Event Time Intervals, *Electronics*, vol. 32, no. 12, pp. 48–51, March 20, 1959.

Kendall, J. T., and J. S. Walker: High-frequency Tetrode Transistors, *Brit. Commun. and Electronics*, vol. 6, no. 6, pp. 438–442, June, 1959.

Kihn, H., and W. E. Barnette: The Megacoder—A High-speed, Large-capacity Microminiature Decoder for Selective Communication, *RCA Rev.*, vol. 20, no. 1, pp. 153–179, March, 1959.

Kilby, J. S.: Semiconductor Solid Circuits, *Electronics*, vol. 32, no. 32, pp. 110–111, August 7, 1959.

Kim, C. S.: Four Terminal Equivalent Circuits of Parametric Diodes, *IRE WESCON Conv. Record*, vol. 3, part 2, pp. 91–101, 1959.

Kirvalidze, I. D.: The Effect of Heat Treatment and Ion Bombardment on the Properties of Silicon Point-contact Diodes, *Fiz. Tverdogo Tela*, Sbornik (suppl.) I, pp. 155–158, 1959.

Kirvalidze, I. D.: The Effect of Pressure on the Sign of Photocurrent through a Contact of a Metal Point with a Semiconductor, *Fiz. Tverdogo Tela*, Sbornik (suppl.) I, pp. 76–77, 1959.

Kita, S., and K. Sugiyama: The Nonlinear Barrier Capacitance of Silver-bonded Diode, *J. Inst. Elec. Commun. Engrs. (Japan)*, vol. 42, no. 12, pp. 1186–1192, December, 1959.

Kitchen, L. D.: A Cardiac Ratemeter Using Transistors, *Electronic Eng.*, vol. 31, pp. 44–45, January, 1959.

Klein, A. G., and A. W. Pryor: The Application of Transistors to Nucleonic Instrumentation, *Proc. IRE, Australia,* vol. 20, no. 7, pp. 388–405, July, 1959.

Klein, M., and A. P. Kordalewski: Germanium PNPN Thyratron, *IBM J. Research Develop.,* vol. 3, no. 4, pp. 377–379, October, 1959.

Klimek, A.: Semiconductor Power Switching and Controlling P-N-P-N and P-N-P-M Elements, *Elektrotech. Obzor,* vol. 48, no. 7, pp. 367–372, 1959.

Ko, W. H., and F. E. Brammer: Semiconductor Diode Amplifiers and Pulse Modulators, *IRE Trans. on Electron Devices,* vol. ED-6, no. 3, pp. 341–347, July, 1959.

Kobayashi, M., Y. Ishikawa, and K. Hayashi: Solar Batteries for Use as the Power Source of Unattended V.H.F. Repeaters, *Proc. Inst. Elec. Engrs. (London),* (International Convention on Transistors and Associated Semiconductor Devices), part B, suppl. 16, paper 2960E, pp. 726–730, 746–747, May, 1959.

Koc, S.: Measurements of the Lifetime of the Minority Current Carriers in Semiconductors by Means of the Many Bridge with a Differential Amplifier, *Slaboproudý Obzor,* vol. 20, no. 12, pp. 744–747, 1959.

Komatsubara, K.: Change of Surface Recombination Velocity of Germanium by X-ray Irradiation, *J. Phys. Soc. Japan,* vol. 14, no. 3, pp. 383–384, March, 1959.

Konopinski, T.: Design of D-C–D-C Push-Pull Transistor Convertors, *Proc. Inst. Elec. Engrs. (London),* (International Convention on Transistors and Associated Semiconductor Devices), paper 2969E, May, 1959.

Kontsevoi, Yu. A.: The Determination of the Capture Cross-sections for Recombination at Multiply Charged Centers, *Fiz. Tverdogo Tela,* vol. 1, no. 8, pp. 1289–1293, August, 1959.

Kopylovskii, B. D.: Phase Method of Measuring Lifetime and Surface Recombination Speed of Unbalanced Charge Carriers in Semiconductors, *Pribory i Tekh. Eksperimenta,* no. 2, pp. 75–78, March–April, 1959.

Kornfel'd, M. I., and D. N. Mirlin: The Temperature Dependence of Low Frequency Conductivity Fluctuations in Germanium, *Fiz. Tverdogo Tela,* vol. 1, no. 12, pp. 1866–1868, December, 1959.

Kossov, O. A.: The Behaviour of a Semiconductor Switch under Various Loading Conditions, *Elektrichestvo,* no. 5, pp. 60–65, May, 1959.

Kossov, O. A.: A Transistor-magnetic Amplifier, *Avtomat. i Telemekh.,* vol. 20, no. 7, pp. 988–991, 1959.

Kozintsova, L. P.: Calculation of R.F. Characteristics of Transistor Amplifiers. *Radiotekhnika,* vol. 14, no. 4, pp. 29–34, April, 1959.

Krajewski, I.: Transistor Circuits for a 1 Mc/s Digital Computer, *Electronic Eng.,* vol. 31, pp. 403–407, July, 1959.

Kreuder, N. L.: The Dynamics of Toggle Action, in Proceedings of the Western Joint Computer Conference, pp. 46–50, AIEE, New York, March, 1959.

Kroczek, J.: How the Selenium Rectifier Can Compete with Germanium and Silicon Rectifiers, *Elektrotech. Obzor,* vol. 48, no. 10, pp. 507–510, 1959.

Kruger, B.: Design and Analysis of Transistor Power Oscillators and D.C. Convertors, *Elteknik,* vol. 2, no. 2, pp. 25–31, February; no. 3, pp. 45–52, March, 1959.

Kruithof, A.: Transient Response of Junction Transistors and Its Graphical Representation, *Proc. Inst. Elec. Engrs. (London),* (International Convention on Transistors and Associated Semiconductor Devices), vol. 106B, paper 3003E, pp. 1092–1107, 1119–1121, 1959.

Kubátová, J.: Photoelectric Resistors of Sintered Cadmium Sulphide, *Slaboproudý Obzor,* vol. 20, no. 9, pp. 556–559, 1959.

Kulikov, S. V.: Contactless Polarized Relay Using Transistors, *Instr. Construct.,* no. 9, pp. 8-11, September, 1959.

Kurkin, Yu. L., and A. A. Sokolov: Calculation of a Compound Transistor Equivalent Circuit, *Elektrichestvo,* no. 8, pp. 62–64, August, 1959.

Kurokawa, K., and J. Hamasaki: An Analysis of Periodically Distributed Parametric Amplifiers, *J. Inst. Elec. Commun. Engrs. (Japan),* vol. 42, no. 6, pp. 579–585, June, 1959.

Ladany, I.: D-C Characteristics of a Junction Diode, *Proc. IRE,* vol. 47, no. 4, p. 589, April, 1959.

Lampert, M. A., F. Herman, and M. C. Steele: Role of Single Phonon Emission in Low-field Breakdown of Semiconductors at Low Temperatures, *Phys. Rev. Letters,* vol. 2, no. 9, pp. 394–397, May 1, 1959.

Landsberg, P. T.: A Review of Recombination Mechanisms in Semiconductors, *Proc. Inst. Elec. Engrs. (London),* (International Convention on Transistors and Associated Semiconductor Devices), paper 2964E, May, 1959.

Landy, A., Jr.: Minimum Transistor Logic Modules for Airborne Control Applications, in Proceedings of the Western Joint Computer Conference, pp. 141–144, AIEE, New York, March, 1959.

Larrabee, R. D.: Drift Velocity Saturation in P-type Germanium, *J. Appl. Phys.*, vol. 30, no. 6, pp. 857–859, June, 1959.

Larrabee, R. D.: High-field Effect in Boron-doped Silicon, *Phys. Rev.*, vol. 116, no. 2, pp. 300–301, October 15, 1959.

Larrabee, R. D.: Theory and Application of a Minority Carrier Sweep-out Effect, *J. Appl. Phys.*, vol. 30, no. 10, pp. 1535–1538, October, 1959.

Lavet, M.: Electrical Maintaining of Chronometric Balances: New Applications of Transistors, *Rev. gén. élec.*, vol. 68, no. 3, pp. 191–201, March, 1959.

Lawrance, R.: Cadmium Sulphide Photoconductive Layers, *Brit. J. Appl. Phys.*, vol. 10, no. 6, pp. 298–300, June, 1959.

Lebedev, V. V.: Matching Problems in Transistor Tuned Amplifiers, *Radiotekhnika*, vol. 14, no. 9, pp. 40–44, September, 1959.

Leberwurst, K.: Calculation of the Trigger Characteristics of a P-N-P-N-P-N Combination, *Nachrichtentechnik*, vol. 9, no. 6, pp. 246–253, June, 1959.

Lee, C. A., and G. Kaminsky: Investigation of the Temperature Variation of Noise in Diode and Transistor Structures, *J. Appl. Phys.*, vol. 30, no. 12, pp. 1849–1855, December, 1959.

Lee, C. A., and G. Kaminsky: Preparation and Electrical Properties of Alloyed P-N Junctions of InSb, *J. Appl. Phys.*, vol. 30, no. 12, pp. 2021–2022, December, 1959.

Lee, H. C.: Transistor Television Picture I.F. Double-tuned Amplifiers, *IRE Trans. on Broadcast and Television Receivers*, vol. BTR-5, no. 2, pp. 25–32, May, 1959.

Leenov, D., and A. Uhlir, Jr.: Frequency Multiplication and Division by Semiconductor Diodes at Microwave Frequencies, *Semiconductor Prods.*, vol. 2, no. 10, pp. 25–28, October, 1959.

Leenov, D., and A. Uhlir, Jr.: Generation of Harmonics and Subharmonics at Microwave Frequencies with P-N Junction Diodes, *Proc. IRE*, vol. 47, no. 10, pp. 1724–1729, October, 1959.

Lesk, I. A.: Germanium P-N-P-N Switches, *IRE Trans. on Electron Devices*, vol. ED-6, no. 1, pp. 28–35, January, 1959.

Lesk, I. A., N. Holonyak, Jr., and U. S. Davidsohn: The Tunnel Diode—Circuits and Applications, *Electronics*, vol. 32, no. 48, pp. 60–64, November 27, 1959.

Lesk, I. A., N. Holonyak, Jr., U. S. Davidsohn, and M. W. Aarons: Germanium and Silicon Tunnel Diodes—Design Operation, and Application, *IRE WESCON Conv. Record*, vol. 3, part 3, pp. 9–31, 1959.

Leslie, R. E., and D. T. Hess: Neutralizing Wide Band H.F. Transistor Amplifiers, *Electronic Inds.*, vol. 18, no. 12, pp. 95–98, December, 1959.

Levinstein, H.: Impurity Photoconductivity in Germanium, *Proc. IRE*, vol. 47, no. 9, pp. 1478–1481, September, 1959.

Levitas, A., and I. Ladany: Semiconductor-Semiconductor "Point Contact" Diode, *J. Appl. Phys.*, vol. 30, no. 2, pp. 267–268, February, 1959.

Lin, H. C.: Some Rating and Application Considerations for Silicon Diodes, *IRE Trans. on Component Parts*, vol. CP-6, no. 4, pp. 269–273, December, 1959.

Lin, H. C., and W. F. Jordan, Jr.: Effect of Transient Voltages on Transistors, *IRE Trans. on Electron Devices*, vol. ED-6, no. 1, pp. 79–83, January, 1959.

Lin, H. C., and B. H. White: Single-ended Amplifiers, *Electronics*, vol. 32, no. 22, pp. 86–87, May 29, 1959.

Lipsky, S. E., and J. F. Siegel: Design Considerations for Wide Band Transistorized V.H.F. Amplifiers, *Semiconductor Prods.*, vol. 2, no. 12, pp. 30–34, December, 1959.

Lisitzkaya, I. N., and A. N. Svenson: Counting Circuit with Germanium Triodes, *Pribory i Tekh. Eksperimenta*, no. 3, pp. 136–137, May–June, 1959.

Litovchenko, V. G., and V. I. Lyashenko: An Investigation of Fast Surface States in Germanium, *Fiz. Tverdogo Tela*, vol. 1, no. 10, pp. 1609–1621, October, 1959.

Litvinov, I. I.: The Effect of the Circuit and Semiconductor Triode Parameters on the Duration of the Edges in a Single-action, Pulse Generator, *Radiotekhnika*, vol. 14, no. 1, pp. 55–61, 1959.

Lochinger, R. B., and M. J. O. Strutt: Applications of Electroluminescent Cells as Electrical Circuit Elements, *Scientia Electrica*, vol. 5, no. 3, pp. 77–92, September, 1959.

Long, D., C. D. Motchenbacher, and J. Myers: Impurity Compensation and Magnetoresistance in P-type Silicon, *J. Appl. Phys.*, vol. 30, no. 3, pp. 353–362, March, 1959.

Long, D., and J. Myers: Ionized-impurity Scattering-mobility of Electrons in Silicon, *Phys. Rev.*, vol. 115, no. 5, pp. 1107–1118, September, 1959.

Long, J. D.: A Practical Approach to Transistor Circuit Design, *Semiconductor Prods.*, vol. 2, no. 11, pp. 19–23, November, 1959.

Lotsch, H.: Investigation of the Intermodulation Behaviour of H.F. Transistors, *Elektron. Rundschau*, vol. 13, no. 8, pp. 290–294, August, 1959.

Lowry, H. R.: Industrial Applications of Silicon Controlled Rectifiers, *Proc. Inst. Elec.*

Engrs. (*London*), (International Convention on Transistors and Associated Semiconductor Devices), vol. 106B, suppl. 18, paper 3061E, pp. 1295–1299, 1334–1338, May, 1959.

Luscher, J., and P. Dome: Transistor Simulator, *Rev. Sci. Instr.*, vol. 30, no. 8, pp. 656–659, August, 1959.

Lysakovskii, G. I., and V. Kh. Shtern: New Bracket Pin Insulators, *Elekt. Stantizii*, no. 3, pp. 62–63, March, 1959.

Macario, R. C. V.: Avalanche Transistors: An Appraisal of Their Properties and Uses, *Electronic Eng.*, vol. 31, pp. 262–267, May, 1959.

MacDonald, W., D. Schultz, and J. R. Madigan: Variable Capacitance Diffused Junction Diodes, *Semiconductor Prods.*, vol. 2, no. 11, pp. 29–34, November, 1959.

McMahon, M. E., and L. S. Chase: Voltage-variable Capacitors—State of the Art, *Electronic Inds.*, vol. 18, no. 12, pp. 90–94, December, 1959.

McMullen, C. W.: Transistorized Distributed Amplifier, *Rev. Sci. Instr.*, vol. 30, no. 12, pp. 1109–1113, December, 1959.

Macpherson, A. C.: The Germanium Microwave Crystal Rectifier, *IRE Trans. on Electron Devices*, vol. ED-6, no. 1, pp. 83–90, January, 1959.

Macpherson, J. D.: Low-noise Hydrophone Preamplifier, *Rev. Sci. Instr.*, vol. 30, no. 7, pp. 533–535, July, 1959.

McWorter, A. L., and R. H. Rediker: The Cryosar—A New Low-temperature Computer Component, *Proc. IRE*, vol. 47, no. 7, pp. 1207–1213, July, 1959.

Madelung, O.: Hall Effect in Semiconductors with P-N Transitions, *Z. Naturforsch.*, vol. 14a, no. 11, pp. 951–958, November, 1959.

Madigan, J. R.: Thermal Characteristics of Silicon Diodes, *Electronic Inds.*, vol. 18, no. 12, pp. 80–88, December, 1959.

Majewski, Z., S. Sikorski, and J. Swiderski: On the Relation between Anomalous Resistivity and Concentration Gradient of Carriers in Germanium, *Bull. acad. polon. sci.*, *Classe III*, vol. 7, no. 6, pp. 401–406, 1959.

Mandelkorn, J.: Electrical Characteristics of Some Gallium Phosphide Devices, *Proc. IRE*, vol. 47, no. 11, pp. 2012–2013, November, 1959.

Martin, A. V. J.: A Theory of the Tecnetron, *IRE Natl. Conv. Record*, vol. 7, part 3, pp. 9–17, 1959.

Martinengo, R.: Considerations in Transistor Automobile Receiver Front End Design, *IRE Natl. Conv. Record*, vol. 7, part 7, pp. 70–76, 1959.

Maserjian, J.: Determination of Avalanche Breakdown in P-N Junctions, *J. Appl. Phys.*, vol. 30, no. 10, pp. 1613–1614, October, 1959.

Massey, R. P.: Transistor-core Converter for High Input Voltages, *Proc. Natl. Electronics Conf.*, vol. 15, pp. 666–673, 1959.

Matakura, Y.: Germanium-silicon Alloy Junctions, *J. Phys. Soc. Japan*, vol. 14, no. 3, p. 374, March, 1959.

Matz, A. W.: A Modification of the Theory of the Variation of Junction Transistor Current Gain with Operating Point and Frequency, *J. Electronics and Control*, vol. 7, no. 2, pp. 133–152, August, 1959.

Matz, A. W.: A Review of Semiconductor Switching Devices and Associated Design Requirements, *A.T.E. J.*, vol. 15, no. 1, pp. 61–82, January, 1959.

Matzen, W. T., and J. R. Biard: Differential Amplifier Features D-C Stability, *Electronics*, vol. 32, no. 3, pp. 60–62, January 16, 1959.

Mayenc, G.: Construction of Low-power Convertor Using Transistors, *Rev. tech. C.F.T.H.*, no. 30, pp. 59–64, March, 1959.

Mayer, J. W.: Performance of Germanium and Silicon-surface Barrier Diodes as Alphaparticle Spectrometers, *J. Appl. Phys.*, vol. 30, no. 12, pp. 1937–1944, December, 1959.

Mayerhofer, W. A.: The 4-layer Diode—A Bistable Semiconductor 2-pole, *Elektron. Rundschau*, vol. 13, no. 2, pp. 51–54, February, 1959.

Mercier, J.: Influence of Technology and of Diffusion on the Characteristics of a Drift Transistor, *Ann. radioélec.*, vol. 14, pp. 322–338, October, 1959; *Onde élect.*, vol. 39, pp. 869–875, November; pp. 897–907, December, 1959.

Mercier, J. M.: Survey of Present-day Manufacturing Techniques of Transistors, *Proc. Inst. Elec. Engrs.* (*London*), (International Convention on Transistors and Associated Semiconductor Devices), vol. 106B, suppl. 17, paper 3109E, pp. 1155–1159, 1181, May, 1959.

Mercurio, J. F., Jr.: Stable, Low-cost One Mc Oscillator, *Electronics*, vol. 32, no. 6, pp. 50–51, February 6, 1959.

Meth, M.: TV Sound Detector Uses Drift Transistor, *Electronics*, vol. 32, no. 8, pp. 62–64, February 20, 1959.

Meunier, R., and J. Teiger: A Three-diode Fast Coincidence Circuit, *Nuclear Instr. and Methods*, vol. 5, no. 3, pp. 148–151, September, 1959.

Meyer, D.: Transistor O. T. L. (Output Transformerless Amplifier) Delivers 8 Watts, *Radio-Electronics*, vol. 30, no. 10, pp. 34–38, October, 1959.

Meyer, N. I.: Non-linear Distortion in Transistor Class A Amplifiers at Low and Medium Frequencies, *Proc. Inst. Elec. Engrs. (London)*, (International Convention on Transistors and Associated Semiconductor Devices), paper 289E, May, 1959.

Michels, A., J. Van Eck, S. Machlup, and C. A. Ten Seldam: Pressure-dependence of the Resistivity of Germanium, *J. Phys. Chem. Solids*, vol. 10, no. 1, pp. 12–18, April, 1959.

Middlebrook, R. D.: A Modern Approach to Semiconductor and Vacuum Device Theory, *Proc. Inst. Elec. Engrs. (London)*, (International Convention on Transistors and Associated Semiconductor Devices), vol. 106B, paper 3180E, pp. 887–902, 937–938, 1959.

Mikula, J.: Neutralization of an L.F. Transistor Amplifier, *Slaboproudý Obzor*, vol. 20, no. 1, pp. 31–37, 1959.

Miller, R. H.: Simplified Coincidence Circuits Using Transistors and Diodes, *Rev. Sci. Instr.*, vol. 30, no. 6, pp. 395–398, June, 1959.

Minton, R.: Designing High-quality A.-F. Transistor Amplifiers, *Electronics*, vol. 32, no. 24, pp. 60–61, June 12, 1959.

Mira, C.: On the Calculation of Bistable Circuits Using Junction Transistors, *Compt. rend.*, vol. 248, no. 23, pp. 3284–3286, June 8, 1959.

Misawa, T.: Turn-on Transient of P-N-P-N Triode, *J. Electronics and Control*, vol. 7, no. 6, pp. 523–533, December, 1959.

Missen, J. I.: The Power Rating of Semiconductor Rectifiers, *Proc. Inst. Elec. Engrs. (London)*, (International Convention on Transistors and Associated Semiconductor Devices), vol. 106B, suppl. 17, paper 3068E, pp. 968–981, 1009–1011, 1959.

Mitchell, W. B.: Power Dissipation in Diode Clippers, *Semiconductor Prods.*, vol. 2, no. 10, pp. 45–47, October, 1959.

Model', E. I., and A. G. Aleksenko: Temperature Compensation in Transistor Flip-flops, *Radiotekhnika*, vol. 14, no. 7, pp. 40–48, July, 1959.

Moizhes, B. Ya.: The Cut-off Frequency of the Drift Transistor, Allowance Being Made for the Drift Field Variation and for the Carrier Mobility in the Base, *Fiz. Tverdogo Tela*, vol. 1, no. 8, pp. 1308–1311, August, 1959.

Moll, J. L.: Avalanche Transistors as Fast Pulse Generators, *Proc. Inst. Elec. Engrs. (London)*, (International Convention on Transistors and Associated Semiconductor Devices), vol. 106B, suppl. 17, paper 3065E, pp. 1082–1085, 1119–1121, 1959.

Moody, N. F., and R. G. Harrison: Millimicrosecond Digital Computer Logic, *Electronic Eng.*, vol. 31, pp. 526–529, September, 1959.

Mooers, H. T., and R. J. Zelinka: The Advantages of Tetrode Geometry for Power Transistors; Stability and Control of Amplified Leakage Current, *Semiconductor Prods.*, vol. 2, no. 4, pp. 29–34, April, 1959.

Moortgat-Pick, W.: Equivalent Circuit and Amplifier Performance of Junction Transistors, *Arch. Elekt. Ubertragung*, vol. 13, no. 1, pp. 33–48, January, 1959.

Morgan, J. V., and E. O. Kane: Observation of Direct Tunneling in Germanium, *Phys. Rev. Letters*, vol. 3, no. 10, pp. 466–468, November 15, 1959.

Morgan, R. E.: Controlled D-C to D-C Voltage Step-up with a Single Transistor, *Proc. Natl. Electronics Conf.*, vol. 15, pp. 674–678, 1959.

Morgan, T. N.: The Mobility of Electrons Heated by Microwave Fields in N-type Germanium, *J. Phys. Chem. Solids*, vol. 8, pp. 245–249, 262–263, January, 1959.

Moriguchi, Y.: Selenium Rectifiers with Artificial Layers of Selenides of Cadmium, Tin, Bismuth and Lead, *J. Phys. Soc. Japan*, vol. 14, no. 2, pp. 152–167, February, 1959.

Mortenson, K. E.: Alloyed, Thin-base Diode Capacitors for Parametric Amplification, *J. Appl. Phys.*, vol. 30, no. 10, pp. 1542–1548, October, 1959.

Mortenson, K. E.: High-level Transistor Operation and Transport Capacitance, *IRE Trans. on Electron Devices*, vol. ED-6, no. 2, pp. 174–189, April, 1959.

Movshovich, M. E.: Problems of Applying P-N-P and N-P-N Transistors in Full Wave Output Stages, *Radiotekhnika*, vol. 14, no. 2, pp. 57–62, 1959.

Mroziewicz, B.: The Technological Effects of the Shape of P-N Alloy Junctions, *Arch. Elektrotech. (Warsaw)*, vol. 8, no. 1, pp. 169–200, 1959.

Mueller, R. K.: Capacitance and Barrier Height in Grain Boundaries, *J. Appl. Phys.*, vol. 30, no. 4(1), pp. 546–550, April, 1959.

Mueller, R. K.: Transient Response of Grain Boundaries and Its Application for a Novel Light Sensor, *J. Appl. Phys.*, vol. 30, no. 7, pp. 1004–1010, July, 1959.

Mueller, R. K., and R. L. Jacobson: Grain Boundary Photovoltaic Cell, *J. Appl. Phys.*, vol. 30, no. 1, pp. 121–122, January, 1959.

Mushinsky, V. P.: Semiconducting Properties of Aluminium Selenide, *Fiz. Tverdogo Tela,* vol. 1, no. 3, pp. 515–517, March, 1959.

Nambiar, K. P. P.: Some Problems in the Design of Transistor Amplifiers, *J. Inst. Telecommun. Engrs. (New Delhi),* vol. 5, no. 3, pp. 152–162, June, 1959.

Nanavati, R. P.: Analysis and Design of a Transistor Linear-delay Circuit, *Trans. AIEE,* part I, vol. 78, pp. 577–580, 1959.

Nanavati, R. P.: The Influence of Nonlinear Junction Capacitance on Transistor Rise and Fall Times, *Proc. Natl. Electronics Conf.,* vol. 15, pp. 557–565, 1959.

Narud, J. A., and M. R. Aaron: Analysis and Design of a Transistor Blocking Oscillator Including Inherent Nonlinearities, *Bell System Tech. J.,* vol. 36, no. 3, pp. 785–852, May, 1959.

Nash, H., and W. Luft: Improved Silicon Photovoltaic Cells, *Electronic Inds.,* vol. 18, no. 8, pp. 91–95, 106, August, 1959.

Nasledov, D. N., and S. V. Slobodchikov: Electrical Properties of N-type AlSb, *Fiz. Tverdogo Tela,* vol. 1, no. 5, pp. 748–754, May, 1959.

Nasledov, D. N., N. N. Smirnova, and B. V. Tsarenkov: Point-contact Gallium Arsenide Diodes, *Fiz. Tverdogo Tela,* Sbornik (suppl.) II, pp. 96–98, 1959.

Nasledov, D. N., and B. V. Tsarenkov: P-N Junctions in Gallium Arsenide, *Fiz. Tverdogo Tela,* Sbornik (suppl.) I, pp. 78–88, 1959.

Nasledov, D. N., and B. V. Tsarenkov: Spectral Characteristics of GaAs Photocells, *Fiz. Tverdogo Tela,* vol. 1, no. 9, pp. 1467–1470, September, 1959.

Navon, D., and P. Debeurs: An Alloy-diffuse Silicon High-current Transistor with Fast-switching Possibilities, *IRE Trans. on Electron Devices,* vol. ED-6, no. 2, pp. 169–173, April, 1959.

Nelson, H.: Surface-immune Transistor Structure, *Proc. Inst. Elec. Engrs. (London),* (International Convention on Transistors and Associated Semiconductor Devices), paper 2870E, May, 1959.

Nelson, J. T., and J. C. Irvin: Visible Light from a Germanium Reverse Biased P-N Junction, *J. Appl. Phys.,* vol. 30, no. 11, p. 1847, November, 1959.

Nelson, R. E.: Point-contact Diodes in Terms of P-N Junction Theory, *IRE Trans. on Electron Devices,* vol. ED-6, no. 3, pp. 270–277, July, 1959.

Neumann, L.: Transistorized Generator for Pulse Circuit Design, *Electronics,* vol. 32, no. 14, pp. 47–49, April 3, 1959.

Newell, W. E., L. Depian, and A. G. Milnes: Frequency Characteristics of a Semiconductor Rectifier at Voltages Greater Than kT/q, *IRE Trans. on Electron Devices,* vol. ED-6, no. 2, pp. 125–132, April, 1959.

Nicholls, M. R.: Zener Diode Characteristics, *Electronic Eng.,* vol. 31, p. 559, September, 1959.

Nicolet, M. A.: Limits of Validity and Physical Models of the Equivalent Circuit of Junction Transistors, *Helv. Phys. Acta,* vol. 32, no. 1, pp. 58–77, 1959.

Nitsche, E., and F. Pokorny: The Silicon Rectifier in Rectifier Engineering, *Elektrotech. Z.,* vol. 80A, no. 15, pp. 506–512, August 1, 1959.

Nitzan, D.: Graphical Evaluation of Magnetic Amplifier Performance Based on Constant-voltage Reset Test, *Trans. AIEE,* part I, vol. 78, pp. 891–898, 1959.

Nixon, J. D., and P. C. Banbury: Time Dependent Changes in Excess Carrier Concentrations in the Presence of Surface Recombination, *Proc. Phys. Soc. (London),* vol. 73, part 1, pp. 54–58, January, 1959.

Nosov, Yu. R.: Semiconductor Diodes Operated in the Range of Breakdown of the Voltage-current Characteristic in Order to Raise the Speed of Action of Pulse Circuits, *Instr. Construct.,* no. 9, pp. 14–16, September, 1959.

Nowalk, T. P.: A Twenty-ampere Switching Transistor, *IRE Natl. Conv. Record,* vol. 7, part 3, pp. 22–26, 1959.

Nowicki, J. R.: A 4-watt 500 Kc/s Transistor Transmitter, *Mullard Tech. Commun.,* vol. 4, pp. 250–259, May, 1959.

O'Connor, B.: Electrical Characteristics of Thin-base Semiconductor Diodes, *Proc. Inst. Elec. Engrs. (London),* (International Convention on Transistors and Associated Semiconductor Devices), paper 2920E, May, 1959.

Ohl, R. S., P. P. Budenstein, and C. A. Burrus: Improved Diode for the Harmonic Generation of Millimeter and Submillimeter Waves, *Rev. Sci. Instr.,* vol. 30, no. 9, pp. 765–774, September, 1959.

Pajgrt, M.: Measurement of the Stability of Transistor Feedback Amplifiers, *Slaboproudý Obzor,* vol. 20, no. 9, pp. 542–548, 1959.

Palmer, P. R., and J. E. Scheibner: Tra-Decom, a Transistorized P. A. M. Decommutator, National Telemetering Conference, Denver, Colo., pp. 206–211, 1959.

Paul, R.: The High-frequency Equivalent Circuit of Transistors, *Nachrichtentechnik,* vol. 9, no. 7, pp. 296–300, July, 1959.

Paz, H. J.: A New Approach to Low Distortion in a Transistor Power Amplifier, *IRE Natl. Conv. Record*, vol. 7, part 7, pp. 140–145, 1959.

Paz, H. J.: A Transistor Preamplifier Design for Magnetic Pickups, *Audio Eng. Soc. J.*, vol. 5, no. 4, pp. 208–214, October, 1959.

Pearson, A., and Y. J. Fokkinga: Logarithmic-amplifier Period Meter, *Nucleonics*, vol. 17, no. 2, pp. 82, 84, 86, 88, February, 1959.

Pearson, G. L., and R. P. Riesz: High-speed Switching Diodes from Plastically Deformed Germanium, *J. Appl. Phys.*, vol. 30, no. 3, pp. 311–312, March, 1959.

Pederson, D. O., and R. S. Pepper: An Evaluation of Transistor Lowpass Broad-banding Techniques, *IRE WESCON Conv. Record*, vol. 3, part 2, pp. 111–126, 1959.

Perova, L. Ya.: Threshold Sensitivity and Noise Spectrum of Germanium Junction Photo-diodes, *Radiotekh. i Elektron.*, vol. 4, no. 2, pp. 330–331, February, 1959.

Petin, G. P.: A Schmitt Trigger Using Junction Triodes, *Radiotekhnika*, vol. 14, no. 9, pp. 25–28, September, 1959.

Petitclerc, A.: Control of Relays by Transistors and Zener Diodes, *Schweiz. Tech. Z.*, vol. 56, no. 8–9, pp. 143–150, February 26, 1959.

Petrak, J. R.: An Improved Transistorized Wave Analyzer, *Proc. Natl. Electronics Conf.*, vol. 15, pp. 874–883, 1959.

Petrusevich, V. A.: The Effect of Surface Treatment on the Photoconductivity Spectrum of N-type Silicon, *Fiz. Tverdogo Tela*, vol. 1, no. 11, pp. 1695–1696, November, 1959.

Pfann, W. G., and C. G. B. Garrett: Semiconductor Varactors Using Surface Space-charge Layers, *Proc. IRE*, vol. 47, no. 11, pp. 2011–2012, November, 1959.

Pfyffer, H.: Local Feedback in Transistor Amplifiers, *Electronic Eng.*, vol. 31, pp. 550–555, September, 1959.

Phylip-Nones, G.: Stability Conditions in Tuned Common-Emitter Transistor Amplifiers, *Proc. Inst. Elec. Engrs. (London)*, (International Convention on Transistors and Associated Semiconductor Devices), vol. 106B, suppl. 15, paper 3053E, pp. 505–517, 1959.

Pies, J. R.: A New Semiconductor for Temperature Measuring, *ISA Journal*, vol. 6, no. 8, pp. 50–54, August, 1959.

Pittman, P. F.: The Trinistor Switch—A Solid-state Power Relay, *IRE Trans. on Nuclear Sci.*, vol. NS-6, no. 2, pp. 69–73, June, 1959.

Pitts, W. J., D. E. A. Harvey, and J. R. Baron: Design Considerations of Transistorized Broadcast Receivers, *Proc. Inst. Elec. Engrs. (London)*, vol. 106B, suppl. 18, paper 2977E, pp. 1198–1205, 1206–1207, 1959.

Plagemann, H. H.: Surface Problems with Semiconductor Rectifiers, *Nachrichtentechnik*, vol. 9, no. 7, pp. 292–295, July, 1959.

Pohl, R. G.: The Nesistor—A Semiconductor Negative Resistance Device, *IRE Trans. on Electron Devices*, vol. ED-6, no. 3, pp. 278–287, July, 1959.

Pokorny, F.: Heavy-duty Silicon Rectifiers, *Bull. sci. A.I.M. (Belg.)*, vol. 72, no. 6–7, pp. 379–403, June–July, 1959.

Porter, J. H.: Pulse-sorting with Transistors and Ferrites, *Electronics*, vol. 32, no. 20, pp. 64–65, May 15, 1959.

Potekhina, N. D.: Calculation of Relaxation Processes of a Phototriode at Small Illumination Intensities, *Fiz. Tverdogo Tela*, vol. 1, no. 10, pp. 1509–1515, October, 1959.

Prener, J. S., and F. E. Williams: Some Characteristics of Large Band Gap Compound Semiconductors, *J. Phys. Chem. Solids*, vol. 8, pp. 461–464, 484–485, January, 1959.

Principi, P., and V. Svelto: Transistorized-Collinge-Huxtable Binary Circuit, *Energia nucleare (Milan)*, vol. 6, no. 10, pp. 365–366, October, 1959.

Pritchard, R. L.: Transition Capacitance of P-N Junctions, *Semiconductor Prods.*, vol. 2, no. 8, pp. 31–35, August, 1959.

Pritchard, R. L.: Transistor Equivalent Circuits, *Proc. Inst. Elec. Engrs. (London)*, (International Convention on Transistors and Associated Semiconductor Devices), vol. 106B, suppl. 17, paper 3097E, pp. 1012–1017, 1072–1074, 1959.

Pumper, E. Ya.: Controlled Semiconductor Rectifier, *Elektrichestvo*, no. 8, pp. 65–68, August, 1959.

Putley, E. H.: Electrical Conduction in N-type InSb between 2°K and 300°K, *Proc. Phys. Soc. (London)*, vol. 73, part 2, pp. 280–290, February, 1959.

Pye, T. R.: Design of Transistor Power Converters, *Electronics*, vol. 32, no. 36, pp. 56–58, September 4, 1959.

Pye, T. R.: High-power Transistor D-C Converters; Designs for Silicon and Germanium Transistors, *Electronic Radio Engr.*, vol. 36, no. 3, pp. 96–105, March, 1959.

Raillard, H., and J. J. Suran: Speed vs. Circuit Power Dissipation in Flip-flops (Using Transistors), *Proc. IRE*, vol. 47, no. 1, pp. 96–97, January, 1959.

Ramsa, A. P., H. Jacobs, and F. A. Brand: Microwave Techniques in Measurement of Lifetime in Germanium, *J. Appl. Phys.*, vol. 30, no. 7, pp. 1054–1060, July, 1959.

Redington, R. W.: Gain Band-width Product of Photoconductors, *Phys. Rev.*, vol. 115, no. 4, pp. 894–896, August 15, 1959.

Redington, R. W., and P. J. Van Heerden: Doped Silicon and Germanium Photoconductors as Targets for Infrared Television Camera Tubes, *J. Opt. Soc. Amer.*, vol. 49, no. 10, pp. 997–1001, October, 1959.

Reich, B., and W. Orloff: Performance of Transistors as Tuned Power Amplifiers at V.H.F., *Semiconductor Prods.*, vol. 2, no. 5, pp. 32–34, May, 1959.

Reichenbaum, G.: Improved Semiconductor-to-copper Soldered Contact, *Brit. J. Appl. Phys.*, vol. 10, no. 10, pp. 469–470, October, 1959.

Retzinger, L. P.: High-speed Circuit Techniques Utilizing Minority Carrier Storage to Enhance Transient Response, in Proceedings of the Western Joint Computer Conference, pp. 149–155, AIEE, New York, March, 1959.

Richmond, I. J.: Solid-state Devices, *Research (London)*, vol. 12, no. 10–11, pp. 374–380, October–November, 1959.

Roberts, C. S., and V. H. Grinich: The Annealing of Neutron Damage in Silicon Mesa Transistors, *IRE WESCON Conv. Record*, vol. 3, part 3, pp. 64–70, 1959.

Roberts, D. H., and B. L. H. Wilson: Some Effects of Oxygen on Resistivity in Silicon, *J. Appl. Phys.*, vol. 30, no. 3, pp. 447–448, March, 1959.

Roberts, F. F., J. C. Henderson, and R. A. Hastie: An Accelerated Aging Experiment on Germanium P-N-P Alloy Type Transistors, *Proc. Inst. Elec. Engrs. (London)*, (International Convention on Transistors and Associated Semiconductor Devices), vol. 106B, suppl. 17, paper 3008E, pp. 958–963, 1009–1011, 1959.

Robinson, P. B.: A Precision, Continuous Voltage Reference for Industrial Recorders, AIEE Analog and Digital Instrumentation Conference paper, pp. 43–48, 1959.

Robson, R. C., A. Goodier, and R. G. Penn: Fully Transistorized Frequency Modulated Indicator for Field Tests, *Engineer*, vol. 207, pp. 374–377, March 6; pp. 412–414 March 13, 1959.

Roehr, W. D.: Characteristics of Degenerative Amplifiers Having a Base-emitter Shunt Impedance, *IRE Trans. on Audio*, vol. AU-7, no. 6, pp. 165–169, November–December, 1959.

Roehr, W. D.: A Two-watt Transistor Audio Amplifier, *IRE Trans. on Audio*, vol. AU-7, no. 5, pp. 125–128, September–October, 1959.

Rohan, J. J., N. E. Pickering, and J. Kennedy: Diffusion of Radioactive Antimony in Silicon, *J. Electrochem. Soc.*, vol. 106, no. 8, pp. 705–709, August, 1959.

Rohr, H.: Four-pole Locus-diagrams of the Transistor as Bases for Circuit Design, *Nachrichtentechnik*, vol. 9, no. 6, pp. 253–260, June, 1959.

Rollett, J. M.: Another Approximation for the Alpha of a Junction Transistor, *Proc. IRE*, vol. 47, no. 10, pp. 1784–1785, October, 1959.

Rollett, J. M.: The Characteristic Frequencies of a Drift Transistor, *J. Electronics and Control*, vol. 7, no. 3, pp. 193–213, September, 1959.

Roschen, J., T. J. Miles, and C. G. Thornton: Alloying with Controlled Spreading in Silicon Transistors, *Semiconductor Prods.*, vol. 2, no. 8, pp. 41–45, August, 1959.

Rose, F. W. G.: A Comparison of the Theory of Impact Ionization with Measurements on Silicon P-N Junctions, *J. Electronics and Control*, vol. 6, no. 1, pp. 70–73, January, 1959.

Rosenberg, A. J., and T. C. Harman: Cd_3As_2—A Non-cubic Semiconductor with Unusually High Electron Mobility, *J. Appl. Phys.*, vol. 30, no. 10, pp. 1621–1622, October, 1959.

Ross, I. M.: Switching Transistors, in Proceedings of the Western Joint Computer Conference, pp. 93–95, AIEE, New York, March, 1959.

Rowley, G. C.: Transistor Circuits for a Digital Differential Analyzer, *Proc. Inst. Elec. Engrs. (London)*, (International Convention on Transistors and Associated Semiconductor Devices), vol. 106B, suppl. 16, paper 2993E, pp. 685–687, 698–701, 1959.

Rozner, F., and P. Pengelly: Transistors and Cores in Counting Circuits, *Electronic Eng.*, vol. 31, pp. 272–274, May, 1959.

Rudenberg, H. G.: Optimum Figures of Merit of Varactors, *Proc. Natl. Electronics Conf.*, vol. 15, pp. 79–82, 1959.

Ruppel, W., and R. W. Smith: A CdS Analog Diode and Triode, *RCA Rev.*, vol. 20, no. 4, pp. 702–714, December, 1959.

Rutz, R. F.: A 3000 Mc Lumped-parameter Oscillator Using an Esaki Negative-resistance Diode, *IBM J. Research Develop.*, vol. 3, no. 4, pp. 372–374, October, 1959.

Rutz, R. F., and D. F. Singer: Some Properties of Experimental 1000-mc Transistors, *IBM J. Research Develop.*, vol. 3, no. 3, pp. 230–236, July, 1959.

Ryabinkin, Yu. S.: Electric Field in the Base of a Junction Transistor at Low Injection Levels, *Fiz. Tverdogo Tela*, Sbornik (suppl.) I, pp. 159–169, 1959.

Ryvkin, S. M., and N. B. Strokan: On the Problem of Relaxation of Non-equilibrium Conductivity on Recombination at Traps, *Doklady Akad. Nauk S.S.S.R.*, vol. 124, no. 5, pp. 1034–1037, 1959.

Rzhanov, A. V.: On the Correlation between the Capture Cross-section Ratio and the Energy Levels of the Surface Recombination Centers in Germanium, *Fiz. Tverdogo Tela*, vol. 1, no. 3, pp. 522–524, March, 1959.

Rzhanov, A. V., Yu. F. Novototski-Vlasov, and I. G. Neizvestny: The Nature of Surface Recombination Centers in Germanium, *Fiz. Tverdogo Tela*, vol. 1, no. 9, pp. 1471–1474, September, 1959.

Rzhevkin, K. S., and V. I. Shveikin: The Saturation State in Junction Transistors, *Radiotekh. i Elektron.*, vol. 4, no. 7, pp. 1164–1172, July, 1959.

Sadowski, H., and M. E. Cassidy: Transistorized Cold Cathode Decade Counter, *IRE Natl. Conv. Record*, vol. 7, part 9, pp. 214–221, 1959.

Saito, S.: Transmission Line Involving Parametric Elements, Especially on Periodically Distributed Parametric Amplifiers, *J. Inst. Elec. Commun. Engrs. (Japan)*, vol. 42, no. 6, pp. 573–579, June, 1959.

Salaman, R. G.: Designing Transistorized Video Amplifiers, I, *Electronic Inds.*, vol. 18, no. 5, pp. 79–83, May, 1959.

Sal'kov, E. A., G. A. Fedorus, and M. K. Sheinkman: On the Effect of Surface Treatment on Certain Characteristics of the Photoconductivity of CdS Single Crystals, *Fiz. Tverdogo Tela*, vol. 1, no. 4, pp. 579–582, April, 1959.

Sandiford, D. J.: Heat Treatment Centers and Bulk Currents in Silicon P-N Junctions, *J. Appl. Phys.*, vol. 30, no. 12, pp. 1981–1986, December, 1959.

Santilli, R. A., and C. F. Wheatley: A Five-transistor Automobile Receiver Employing Drift Transistors, *IRE Natl. Conv. Record*, vol. 7, part 7, pp. 77–84, 1959.

Saunders, W. F., III: Easing Transistor Loads, *Electronics*, vol. 32, no. 2, p. 68, January 9, 1959.

Sawyer, D. E.: Surface-dependent Losses in Variable Reactance Diodes, *J. Appl. Phys.*, vol. 30, no. 11, pp. 1689–1691, November, 1959.

Saxena, B. S.: Common Emitter Characteristics of Transistors at Very Low Temperatures, *J. Sci. Ind. Research (India)*, vol. 18B, no. 1, pp. 1–7, January, 1959.

Scarlett, R. M.: Space-charge Layer Width in Diffused Junctions, *IRE Trans. on Electron Devices*, vol. ED-6, no. 4, pp. 405–408, October, 1959.

Scarr, R. W. A.: Applications of Photo-sensitive Devices, *Proc. Inst. Elec. Engrs. (London)*, vol. 106B, suppl. 18, paper 3067E, pp. 1342–1345, 1394, 1959.

Schaffer, J., and D. W. Furby: A Precision Transistorized Television Wave-form and Pattern Generator, *Proc. Inst. Elec. Engrs. (London)*, (International Convention on Transistors and Associated Semiconductor Devices), vol. 106B, suppl. 18, paper 2959E, pp. 1260–1266, 1289–1291, 1959.

Schauwecker, H. E.: Maximum Power Dissipation in Transistors, *Semiconductor Prods.*, vol. 2, no. 12, pp. 35–39, December, 1959.

Schmeltzer, R. A.: Stabilization of Transistor Gain over Wide Temperature Ranges, *RCA Rev.*, vol. 20, no. 2, pp. 284–292, June, 1959.

Schmidt, L. W., and J. I. Davis: Infrared Detector Silicon Solar Cell Power Supply, *Proc. IRE*, vol. 47, no. 9, pp. 1519–1520, September, 1959.

Schmitz, N. I., and T. Bernstein: Reversible-polarity D-C Power Amplifier Using Magnetic-amplifier-controlled Switched Transistors, *Commun. and Electronics*, no. 40, January, 1959.

Schneider, B., and M. J. O. Strutt: Noise in Germanium and Silicon Transistors in the High Current Range, *Arch. Elekt. Ubertragung*, vol. 13, no. 12, pp. 495–502, December, 1959.

Schneider, B., and M. J. O. Strutt: Theory and Experiments on Shot Noise in Silicon P-N Junction Diodes and Transistors, *Proc. IRE*, vol. 47, no. 4, pp. 546–554, April, 1959.

Schöninger, E.: Monostable Flip-flop Circuits Using Transistors, *Radio Mentor*, vol. 25, no. 6, pp. 444–446, June, 1959.

Schroter, E.: The Application of Magnetic Amplifiers in Semiconductor Rectifier Equipment, *AEG Mitt.*, vol. 49, no. 10–11, pp. 488–492, October–November, 1959.

Seeger, K.: Microwave Induced Carrier Multiplication in Germanium, *J. Appl. Phys.*, vol. 30, no. 30, pp. 443–444, March, 1959.

Senatorov, K. Ya., and A. I. Gomonova: Some Features of Transistor Transient Characteristics with Small Signals, *Radiotekh. i Elektron.*, vol. 4, no. 7, pp. 1153–1163, July, 1959.

Senitzky, B.: Electron Emission from Silicon P-N Junctions, *Phys. Rev.*, vol. 116, no. 4, pp. 874–879, November 15, 1959.

Senitzky, B., and P. D. Radin: Effect of Internal Heating on the Breakdown Characteristics of Silicon P-N Junctions, *J. Appl. Phys.*, vol. 30, no. 12, pp. 1945–1950, December, 1959.

Shah, R.: European Developments in Transistor (V.H.F. Radio Receiver) Circuits, *Electronics*, vol. 32, no. 21, pp. 41–43, May 22, 1959.

Sharpless, W. M.: High-frequency Gallium Arsenide Point-contact Rectifiers, *Bell System Tech. J.*, vol. 38, no. 1, pp. 259–269, January, 1959.

Shea, R. F.: Transistors Demonstrate Reliability in Critical Nuclear Instrumentation, *Elec. Mfg.*, vol. 63, no. 5, pp. 111–115, May, 1959.

Sheehan, W. E., and W. H. Ryer: Special Circuits for Transistor Receivers, *Electronics*, vol. 32, no. 2, pp. 56–57, January 9, 1959.

Sherr, S., and S. King: Avalanche Noise in P-N Junctions, *Semiconductor Prods.*, vol. 2, no. 5, pp. 21–25, May, 1959.

Shields, J.: Breakdown in Silicon P-N Junctions, *J. Electronics and Control*, vol. 6, no. 2, pp. 130–148, February, 1959.

Shields, J.: The Forward Characteristics of P+-N-N+ Diodes in Theory and Experiment, *Proc. Inst. Elec. Engrs. (London)*, paper 2938E, May, 1959.

Shockley, W., and J. Gibbons: Theory of Transient Build-up in Avalanche Transistors, *Commun. and Electronics*, no. 40, January, 1959.

Shul'man, S. G.: Germanium Diode Inverse Current as a Function of the Voltage Pulse Repetition Frequency, *Fiz. Tverdogo Tela*, vol. 1, no. 4, pp. 597–601, April, 1959.

Sim, A. C.: The Dark-spot Method for Measuring the Diffusion Constant and Length of Excess Charge Carriers in Semiconductors, *Proc. Inst. Elec. Engrs. (London)*, (International Convention on Transistors and Associated Semiconductor Devices), vol. 106B, suppl. 15, paper 2997E, pp. 28–34, 1959.

Sim, A. C.: A Note on the Use of Filters in Photoconductive Decay Measurements, *Proc. Inst. Elec. Engrs. (London)*, (International Convention on Transistors and Associated Semiconductor Devices), paper 2885E, May, 1959.

Simkins, Q. W.: Transistor Resistor Logic, *Semiconductor Prods.*, vol. 2, no. 4, pp. 34–38, April, 1959.

Simmons, B. D., and D. M. Bibb: Digital Circuits Operating at 1 Mc/s Using Transistors, *Proc. Inst. Elec. Engrs. (London)*, (International Convention on Transistors and Associated Semiconductor Devices), paper 2942E, May, 1959.

Sirven, P.: Control of Relays by Transistors, *Electricien (Paris)*, vol. 87, pp. 11–13, January, 1959.

Sklar, B.: The Tunnel Diode—Its Action and Properties, *Electronics*, vol. 32, no. 45, pp. 54–57, November 6, 1959.

Slatter, J. A. G.: An Analogue of a Diffused-base Transistor, *Proc. Inst. Elec. Engrs. (London)*, (International Convention on Transistors and Associated Semiconductor Devices), vol. 106B, suppl. 17, paper 3101E, pp. 1067–1071, 1072–1074, 1959.

Slotnicky, J.: A Characteristic Curve Tracer for Transistors, *Slaboproudý Obzor*, vol. 20, no. 10, pp. 626–630, 1959.

Smirnov, N. I.: Frequency Response Analysis of a Transistor Amplifier, *Radiotekhnika*, vol. 14, no. 9, pp. 70–74, September, 1959.

Smith, F. P.: Transistorized Receiver for Marker Beacon Use, *Electronics*, vol. 32, no. 46, pp. 76–78, November 13, 1959.

Smith, R. W., and F. J. Hyde: Transistor Current Gain, *Electronic Radio Engr.*, vol. 36, no. 7, pp. 249–252, July, 1959.

Snitko, O. V.: The Effect of an External Electric Field on the Surface Recombination and Capacitor Phota E.M.F. of N-type Silicon, *Fiz. Tverdogo Tela*, vol. 1, no. 6, pp. 980–983, June, 1959.

Sofronov, K.: An Instrument for Measuring the H-parameters of Transistors, *Slaboproudý Obzor*, vol. 20, no. 3, pp. 157–164, 1959.

Sohm, J. C.: Impact Ionization of Impurities in Silicon at Low Temperatures, *Compt. rend.*, vol. 249, no. 25, pp. 2737–2739, December 21, 1959.

Solms, S. J.: Logarithmic Amplifier Design, *IRE Trans. on Instrumentation*, vol. I-8, no. 3, pp. 91–96, December, 1959.

Sommers, H. S.: Tunnel Diodes as High-frequency Devices, *Proc. IRE*, vol. 47, no. 7, pp. 1201–1206, July, 1959.

Sommers, H. S., K. K. N. Chang, H. Nelson, R. Steinhoff, and P. Schnitzler: Tunnel Diodes for Low Noise Amplification, *IRE WESCON Conv. Record*, vol. 3, part 3, pp. 3–8, 1959.

Sorger, G. U., and B. O. Weinschel: Comparison of Deviations from Square Law for R.F. Crystal Diodes and Barretters, *IRE Trans. on Instrumentation*, vol. I-8, no. 3, pp. 103–111, December, 1959.

Sorokin, O. V.: Equipment for the Investigation of Transient Processes on Semiconductor Surfaces, *Pribory i Tekh. Eksperimenta*, no. 2, pp. 68–75, March–April, 1959.

Spany, V.: Design of a Junction-transistor Divider Chain and the Indication of Its States, *Slaboproudý Obzor*, vol. 20, no. 6, pp. 378–381, 1959.

Spany, V.: A Novel Approximate Method of Designing the Blocking Oscillator with Junction Transistors, *Slaboproudý Obzor*, vol. 20, no. 7, pp. 429–435, 1959.

Spany, V.: A Pulse Frequency-divider Based on a Diode Storage Integrator and a Junction-transistor Blocking Oscillator, *Slaboproudý Obzor*, vol. 20, no. 9, pp. 565–570, 1959.

Sparkes, J. J.: The Effect of Carrier Storage in the Emitter on Transistor Input Admittance, *Proc. Inst. Elec. Engrs. (London)*, (International Convention on Transistors and Associated Semiconductor Devices), vol. 106B, suppl. 17, paper 3007, pp. 1102–1107, 1119–1121, 1959.

Spector, C. J.: A Design Theory for the High-frequency P-N Junction Variable Capacitor, *IRE Trans. on Electron Devices*, vol. ED-6, no. 3, pp. 347–351, July, 1959.

Spescha, G., and M. J. O. Strutt: Definition and Measurements of the Noise Figure of Semiconductor Photodiodes, *Scientia Electrica*, vol. 5, no. 4, pp. 121–132, December, 1959.

Spicer, W. E.: Relationship between Signal-to-noise Ratio and Threshold of Response of Infrared Photoconductors Limited by Generation-recombination Noise, *J. Appl. Phys.*, vol. 30, no. 9, pp. 1381–1384, September, 1959.

Spindler, K.: Calculations and Measurements for the Optimum Design of Low-noise Transistor Amplifiers, *NTZ-Nachrtech. Z.*, vol. 12, no. 5, pp. 250–256, May, 1959.

Spradlin, B. C.: Effects of Operation of Germanium Alloy Junction Transistors above Rated Conditions, *Commun. and Electronics*, no. 44, September, 1959.

Stafeev, V. I.: The Current-voltage Characteristics of Diodes under Extremely High Injection Rates, *Fiz. Tverdogo Tela*, vol. 1, no. 6, pp. 848–850, June, 1959.

Stafeev, V. I.: Modulation of the Diffusion Length as a New Working Principle of Semiconducting Devices, *Fiz. Tverdogo Tela*, vol. 1, no. 6, pp. 841–847, June, 1959.

Stark, G. W. E.: Charts for Deriving Transistor R-parameters from H-parameters. *Electronic Eng.*, vol. 31, pp. 592–593, October, 1959.

Steele, M. C.: Low-field Electrical Breakdown in N-Indium Phosphide, *J. Phys. Chem. Solids*, vol. 9, no. 1, pp. 93–94, January, 1959.

Steele, M. C., L. Pensak, and R. D. Gold: Pulse Amplification Using Impact Ionization in Germanium, *Proc. IRE*, vol. 47, no. 6, pp. 1109–1117, June, 1959.

Stefanescu, S.: Applications of Quadripole Theory to the Calculation of Transistor Circuits, *Telecomunicatii*, vol. 3, no. 5, pp. 204–213, September–October, 1959.

Steiger, W.: A Transistor Temperature Analysis and Its Application to Differential Amplifiers, *IRE Trans. on Instrumentation*, vol. I-8, no. 3, pp. 82–91, December, 1959.

Steinke, L.: The Gain-controlled Transistor, *Nachrichtentechnik*, vol. 9, no. 6, pp. 261–264, June, 1959.

Stephenson, J.: An Investigation into the Use of Transistors in a Stabilized Klystron Power Supply, *Proc. Inst. Elec. Engrs. (London)*, (International Convention on Transistors and Associated Semiconductor Devices), paper 2940E, May, 1959.

Stephenson, L. M., and H. E. M. Barlow: Power Measurement at 4 Gc/s by the Application of the Hall Effect in a Semiconductor, *Proc. Inst. Elec. Engrs. (London)*, vol. 106B, paper 2748R, pp. 27–30, January, 1959.

Stephenson, W. L., L. P. Morgan, and T. H. Brown: The Design of Transistor Push-Pull D-C Convertor, *Electronic Eng.*, vol. 31, pp. 585–589, October, 1959.

Stern, S.: Cooling Power Transistors, *Electronic Inds.*, vol. 18, no. 9, pp. 77–82, September, 1959.

Stewart, J. J.: The Noise Figure of Junction Transistors, *Proc. Inst. Elec. Engrs. (London)*, (International Convention on Transistors and Associated Semiconductor Devices), paper 2973E, May, 1959.

Stierhof, H.: A Simple Pulse Generator and a Pulse Distributor Employing Transistors, *Rundfunktech. Mitt.*, vol. 3, no. 2, pp. 81–90, April, 1959.

Stinton, H.: A Monostable Circuit Using a Transistor, *Electronic Eng.*, vol. 31, pp. 80–81, February, 1959.

Stockmann, F.: Physics and Applications of Photoconductivity, *Z. angew. Phys.*, vol. 11, no. 2, pp. 68–80, February, 1959.

Stone, H. A., Jr.: The Field Effect Tetrode, *IRE Natl. Conv. Record*, vol. 7, part 3, pp. 3–8, 1959.

Stone, H. A., Jr.: Theory and Use of Field Effect Tetrodes, *Electronics*, vol. 32, no. 20, pp. 66–68, May 15, 1959.

Strickland, P. R.: The Thermal Equivalent Circuit of a Transistor, *IBM J. Research Develop.*, vol. 3, no. 1, pp. 35–45, January, 1959.

Strom, R. L.: Radio Noise in Semiconductor Devices, *Semiconductor Prods.*, vol. 2, no. 10, pp. 41–44, October, 1959.

Strutt, M. J. O., and S. F. Sun: Polyphase Wattmeter Based on the Magnetically Induced Change of Resistance of Semiconductors, *Bull. assoc. suisse élec.*, vol. 50, no. 10, pp. 452–458, May 9, 1959.

Sugano, T.: Alpha Cut-off Frequency of Transistors with Curved Junctions, *J. Inst. Elec. Commun. Engrs. (Japan)*, vol. 42, no. 9, pp. 838–843, September, 1959.

Svedberg, P.: Choice of Semiconductor Diodes, *Tek. Tidsskr.*, vol. 89, no. 36, pp. 949–951, October 2, 1959.

Svedberg, P.: Measurement of Thermal Properties of Silicon Power Diodes, *Elteknik*, vol. 2, no. 1, pp. 11–14, January, 1959.

Sylvan, T. P.: Large Signal Characteristics of the Silicon Unijunction Transistor, *Semiconductor Prods.*, vol. 2, no. 10, pp. 29–35, October, 1959.

Szarvas, G.: Shift Registers Containing Transistors in Each Stage, *Proc. Inst. Elec. Engrs. (London)*, (International Convention on Transistors and Associated Semiconductor Devices), vol. 106B, suppl. 18, paper 3129E, pp. 1277–1284, 1289–1291, 1959.

Taeger, W.: Design Considerations for Transistor D-C Convertors ("Transvertors"), *Frequenz*, vol. 13, no. 3, pp. 90–93, March, 1959.

Tager, A. S., and A. D. Gladun: Use of Cyclotron Resonance in Semiconductors for the Amplification and Generation of Microwaves, *Soviet Phys. JETP*, vol. 35(8), no. 3, pp. 560–561, March, 1959.

Tailleur, M. A.: A Transistor-regulated D-C–D-C Converter, *Onde élect.*, vol. 39, pp. 795–801, October, 1959.

Takada, S., Y. Onishi, H. Majima, F. Ando, S. Shimada, and Y. Itachida: A Transistor-operated Magnetic-core Memory, *J. Inst. Elec. Commun. Engrs. (Japan)*, vol. 42, no. 11, pp. 1057–1064, November, 1959.

Tarui, Y.: Accurate Measurement of Transistor Cut-off Frequency, *Electronic Eng.*, vol. 31, pp. 284–287, May, 1959.

Tauc, J.: Electron Impact Ionization in Semiconductors, *J. Phys. Chem. Solids*, vol. 8, pp. 219–223, 262–263, January, 1959.

Tauc, J., and M. Zivutovi: Photo-piezoelectric Effect in Semiconductors, *Czechoslov. J. Phys.*, vol. 9, no. 5, pp. 572–577, 1959.

Taylor, A. H.: Full Bridge Amplifiers, *Proc. IRE*, vol. 47, no. 3, pp. 444–445, March, 1959.

Thomas, D. E.: Some Design Considerations for High-frequency Transistor Amplifiers, *Bell System Tech. J.*, vol. 38, no. 6, pp. 1551–1580, November, 1959.

Thomas, D. E., and J. M. Klein: How to Construct a Miniature FM Transmitter, *Electronics*, vol. 32, no. 31, pp. 80–81, July 31, 1959.

Thomas, M. J. B., and E. J. Zdanuk: Cadmium Sulfide Photoconductive Sintered Layers, *J. Electrochem. Soc.*, vol. 106, no. 11, pp. 964–971, November, 1959.

Thompson, P. M., and J. Bateson: Transistor Switching Speed, *Wireless World*, vol. 65, no. 11, pp. 530–533, December, 1959.

Thorne, D., and R. V. Fournier: Improvements in Detection, Gain-control and Audio-driver Circuits of Transistorized Broadcast-band Receivers, *IRE Natl. Conv. Record*, vol. 7, part 7, pp. 85–92, 1959.

Thwaite, H., and E. Aspinall: A Transistor Hearing Aid, *Post Off. Elec. Engrs. J.*, vol. 52, part 3, pp. 163–169, October, 1959.

Tink, E. M.: Portable Transistor Amplifier for News Recording Applications, *J. Soc. Motion Picture Television Engrs.*, vol. 68, no. 2, pp. 83–86, February, 1959.

Tink, E. M.: Transistorizing 16 Mm. TV Remote Film Camera, *Electronics*, vol. 32, no. 3, pp. 58–59, January 16, 1959.

Tolk, A.: The Transistor Amplifiers for the Reporter Magnetic Recorder Type R20, *Tech. Mitt. BRF*, vol. 3, no. 1–2, pp. 21–25, October, 1959.

Tomlinson, T. B.: Switching Circuits Using Bi-directional Non-linear Impedances, *J. Brit. Inst. Radio Engrs.*, vol. 19, no. 9, pp. 571–591, September, 1959.

Towers, T. D.: Practical Design Problems in Transistor D-C/D-C Convertors and D-C/A-C Inverters, *Proc. Inst. Elec. Engrs. (London)*, vol. 106B, suppl. 18, paper 2984E, pp. 1373–1383, 1394, 1959.

Trainor, A., and P. T. Harris: The Control of Resistivity in Pulled Silicon Crystals, *Proc. Phys. Soc. (London)*, vol. 74, part 5, pp. 669–670, November, 1959.

Trivedi, P. C., and G. P. Srivastava: Transistors in Magnetic Fields—Effect on Characteristics, *Electronic Radio Engr.*, vol. 36, no. 10, pp. 368–370, October, 1959.

Turner, D. R.: Junction Delineation on Silicon in Electrochemical Displacement Plating Solutions, *J. Electrochem. Soc.*, vol. 106, no. 8, pp. 701–705, August, 1959.

Ugai, Ya. A., and T. N. Vigutove: A New Intermetallic Semiconductor, *Fiz. Tverdogo Tela*, vol. 1, no. 12, pp. 1786–1788, December, 1959.

Uhlir, A., Jr.: Junction-diode Amplifiers, *Sci. American*, vol. 200, no. 6, pp. 118–120, 123–124, 126–127, 129, June, 1959.

Uvarov, A. I.: The Influence of the Space Charge of Mobile Carriers on the Electrical Breakdown of a Highly Asymmetrical P-N Junction, *Fiz. Tverdogo Tela*, vol. 1, no. 9, pp. 1457–1459, September, 1959.

Valdes, L. B.: Proposes Microwave Mixer Diode of Improved Conversion Efficiency, *J. Appl. Phys.*, vol. 30, no. 3, pp. 436–439, March, 1959.

Vallese, L. M.: Transistor Bias Design from Thermal Incremental Properties, *Electronic Eng.*, vol. 31, pp. 88–93, February, 1959.

Vallese, L. M.: Unilateralized Transistor Amplifier, *IRE Trans. on Audio*, vol. AU-7, no. 2, pp. 36–39, March–April, 1959.

Van Dong, N., and A. Barraud: Influence of Fast Neutrons on the Recombination of Electron-hole Pairs in Germanium, *Compt. rend.*, vol. 249, no. 21, pp. 2181–2183, November 23, 1959.

Van Dong, N., and A. Barraud: Recombination Centers Produced in Ge by Fast Neutrons, *J. Electronics and Control*, vol. 7, no. 3, pp. 275–288, September, 1959.

Van Tol, M., and F. Bregman: A Transistorized Radiation Monitor, *Philips Tech. Rev.*, vol. 21, no. 7, pp. 201–206, 1959.

Van Vessem, J. C.: Effect of Device Design on Performance and Quality, *Proc. Inst. Elec. Engrs.* (*London*), (International Convention on Transistors and Semiconductor Devices), vol. 106B, suppl. 17, paper 3096E, pp. 1122–1124, 1153–1154, 1959.

Vapaille, A.: Measurement of the Lifetime of Carriers Produced in Silicon by Electron Bombardment, *Compt. rend.*, vol. 249, no. 5, pp. 648–650, August 3, 1959.

Varnerin, L. J.: Stored Charge Method of Transistor Base Transit Analysis, *Proc. IRE*, vol. 47, no. 4, pp. 523–527, April, 1959.

Vavilov, V. S., L. S. Smirnov, and V. M. Patskevich: The Diffusion Length of the Charge Carriers in Silicon Photo-elements, *Fiz. Tverdogo Tela*, vol. 1, no. 9, pp. 1465–1467, September, 1959.

Vdovin, Yu. A., B. M. Grafov, and V. A. Myamlin: The Rectifying Effect of an Electrolyte–N-type Semiconductor Contact, *Doklady Akad. Nauk S.S.S.R.*, vol. 129, no. 4, pp. 827–830, December 1, 1959.

Vdovin, Yu., V. G. Levich, and V. A. Myamlin: Current Voltage Characteristics of an Electrolyte-semiconductor Junction, *Doklady Akad. Nauk S.S.S.R.*, vol. 124, no. 2, pp. 350–353, 1959.

Veazie, C. E.: Transistorized Radar Sweep Circuits Using Low Power, *Electronics*, vol. 32, no. 26, pp. 46–47, June 26, 1959.

Vigneron, B.: Functional Transistor Units, *Onde élect.*, vol. 39, pp. 88–99, February, 1959.

Vitovskii, N. A., P. I. Maleev, and S. M. Ryvkin: The Optimum State for Using Photodiodes in Recording Small Signals, *Radiotekh. i Elektron.*, vol. 4, no. 8, pp. 1387–1392, August, 1959.

Vitrikhovskii, N. I., and I. B. Mizetskaya: The Preparation of Mixed CdS-CdTe Monocrystals and Some of Their Characteristics, *Fiz. Tverdogo Tela*, vol. 1, no. 6, pp. 996–999, June, 1959.

Volodin, V. S., E. D. Larin, M. A. Rozenblatt, and G. V. Subbotina: High-speed Push-Pull Magnetic-transistor Amplifier for a Servodrive, *Avtomat. i Telemekh.*, vol. 20, no. 3, pp. 323–330, 1959.

Vook, F. L., and R. W. Balluffi: Length and Resistivity Changes in Germanium upon Low-temperature Deuteron Irradiation and Annealing, *Phys. Rev.*, vol. 113, no. 1, pp. 62–69, January 1, 1959.

Vorobeva, E. F.: The Stability of a Junction Transistor Tuned Amplifier in Common Emitter and Common Base Operation, *Radiotekhnika*, vol. 14, no. 6, pp. 45–51, June, 1959.

Vul, B. M.: P-N Junctions at Low Temperatures, *Doklady Akad. Nauk S.S.S.R.*, vol. 129, no. 1, pp. 61–63, November 1, 1959.

Vul, B. M., and A. P. Shotov: Impact Ionization in Silicon P-N Junctions, *Fiz. Tverdogo Tela*, Sbornik (suppl.) I, pp. 150–154, 1959.

Waddington, D. E. O. N.: Transistor Stopwatch, *Wireless World*, vol. 65, no. 10, pp. 521–524, November, 1959.

Wade, E. J., and D. S. Davidson: Transistor Amplifiers for Reactor Control, *Electronics*, vol. 32, no. 31, pp. 52–53, May 22, 1959.

Wade, E. J., and D. S. Davidson: Transistorized Log-period Amplifier, *IRE Trans. on Nuclear Sci.*, vol. NS-6, no. 2, pp. 53–56, June, 1959.

Waldner, M.: Measurement of Minority Carrier Diffusion Length and Lifetime by Means of the Photovoltaic Effect, *Proc. IRE*, vol. 47, no. 5, pp. 1004–1005, May, 1959.

Walker, R. I., F. A. Cunnell, C. H. Gooch, and J. J. Low: A Gallium Arsenide Switching Diode, *J. Electronics and Control*, vol. 7, no. 3, pp. 268–269, September, 1959.

Wallis, G., and S. Wang: Effect of Various Etches on Recombination Centers at Germanium Surfaces, *J. Electrochem. Soc.*, vol. 106, no. 3, pp. 231–238, March, 1959.

Wallmark, J. T., and S. M. Marcus: Integrated Devices Using Direct-coupled Unipolar Transistor Logic, *IRE Trans. on Electronic Computers*, vol. EC-8, no. 2, pp. 98–107, June, 1959.

Wallmark, J. T., and S. M. Marcus: Semiconductor Devices for Microminiaturization, *Electronics*, vol. 32, no. 26, pp. 35–37, June 26, 1959.

Wang, S., and T. T. Wu: On the Theory of D-C Amplification Factor of Junction Transistors, *IRE Trans. on Electron Devices*, vol. ED-32, no. 2, pp. 162–169, April, 1959.

Waring, J.: How to Design Reflexed Transistor Receivers, *Electronics*, vol. 32, no. 19, pp. 70–72, May 8, 1959.

Warner, R. E., and H. Yemm: An Investigation of the Alloying Technique for the Fabrication of Germanium P-N-P Transistors, *Proc. Inst. Elec. Engrs.* (*London*), (International Convention on Transistors and Associated Semiconductor Devices), paper 2906E, May, 1959.

Warner, R. M., Jr., W. H. Jackson, E. I. Doucette, and H. A. Stone, Jr.: A Semiconductor Current Limiter, *Proc. IRE*, vol. 47, no. 1, pp. 44–56, January, 1959.

Warnier, A.: Ultra-low-frequency Noise Generator, *Rev. tech. C.F.T.H.*, vol. 30, pp. 65–69, March, 1959.

Watkins, T. B.: 1/f Noise in Germanium Devices, *Proc. Phys. Soc.* (*London*), vol. 73, part 1, pp. 59–68, January 1, 1959.

Webb, G. N., and R. N. Glackin: Transistor Waveform Generators, *IRE Natl. Conv. Record*, vol. 7, part 9, pp. 51–55, 1959.

Webber, K. L.: Temperature Stabilization of Transistors in Call B. Amplifiers, *Proc. IRE, Australia*, vol. 20, no. 12, pp. 726–733, December, 1959.

Weber, S.: New Transistor Works at Cryogenic Temperatures, *Electronics*, vol. 32, no. 4, p. 34, January 23, 1959.

Wedlock, B. D.: Stabilities of Common Emitter and Emitter Follower Transistor Amplifiers, *Proc. IRE*, vol. 47, no. 9, pp. 1657–1658, September, 1959.

Wegener, H. A. R.: The Cylindrical Field-effect Transistor, *IRE Trans. on Electron Devices*, vol. ED-6, no. 4, pp. 442–449, October, 1959.

Weinreich, O. A., H. Matare, and B. Reed: The Grain-boundary Amplifier, *Proc. Phys. Soc.* (*London*), vol. 73, part 6, pp. 969–972, June, 1959.

Weitzsch, F.: The Thermal Stability of Transistors under Dynamic Conditions, *Arch. Elekt. Ubertragung*, vol. 13, no. 5, pp. 185–198, May, 1959.

Wertheim, G. K.: Recombination Properties of Bombardment Defects in Semiconductors, *J. Appl. Phys.*, vol. 30, no. 8, pp. 1166–1174, August, 1959.

Wiencek, Z., and J. E. Bridges: An Analysis of a Transistorized Class "B" Vertical Deflection System, *IRE Natl. Conv. Record*, vol. 7, part 7, pp. 56–69, 1959.

Willardson, R. K.: Transport Properties in Silicon and Gallium Arsenide, *J. Appl. Phys.*, vol. 30, no. 8, pp. 1158–1165, August, 1959.

Williams, B. E.: A Delta Modulation System Using Junction Transistors, *Electronic Eng.*, vol. 31, pp. 674–680, November, 1959.

Willis, J., and C. C. Richardson: A High-performance 100 Kc/s Amplifier and Discriminator, *Proc. Inst. Elec. Engrs.* (*London*) (International Convention on Transistors and Associated Semiconductor Devices), part B, suppl. 16, paper 2988E, pp. 780–788, 789–792, May, 1959.

Winkel, J.: Drift Transistors Simplified Electrical Characterization, *Electronic Radio Engr.*, vol. 36, no. 8, pp. 280–288, August, 1959.

Winkel, J.: Transmission-line Analogue of a Drift Transistor, *Philips Research Repts.*, vol. 14, no. 1, pp. 52–64, February, 1959.

Winter, J.: A Single Equivalent Circuit of a Junction Transistor under Consideration of Temperature Dependence, *Frequenz*, vol. 13, no. 11, pp. 351–359, November, 1959.

Wion, F. W.: A Transistor outside Broadcast Amplifier, *Proc. IRE, Australia*, vol. 20, no. 4, pp. 193–197, April, 1959.

Wolf, M.: The Solar Battery, *Proc. Natl. Electronics Conf.*, vol. 15, pp. 226–240, 1959.

Wolfendale, E.: D-C Amplifiers, *Proc. Inst. Elec. Engrs.* (*London*), vol. 106B, suppl. 18, paper 3066E, pp. 1339–1341, 1394, 1959.

Wood, P. W.: Transistorized FM Oscillator, *Electronics*, vol. 32, no. 5, p. 64, January 30, 1959.

Worcester, J. A.: One-transistor "Push-Pull," *Electronics*, vol. 32, no. 24, p. 74, June 12, 1959.

Yakovlev, V. N.: The Starting Conditions of Avalanche Processes in Relaxation Oscillators Using Point-contact Transistors, *Radiotekh. i Elektron.*, vol. 4, no. 1, pp. 70–74, January, 1959.

Yamaguchi, J., and Y. Hamakawa: Barrier Temperature at Turnover in Germanium P-N Junction, *J. Phys. Soc. Japan*, vol. 14, no. 2, pp. 232–233, February, 1959.

Yamaguchi, J., and Y. Hamakawa: Electrical Breakdown in Germanium P-N Junction, *Proc. Inst. Elec. Engrs.* (*London*), (International Convention on Transistors and Associated Semiconductor Devices), paper 2916E, May, 1959.

Yamaguchi, J., and Y. Hamakawa: High Electric Field Effects in Germanium P-N Junction, *J. Phys. Soc. Japan*, vol. 14, no. 1, pp. 15–21, January, 1959.

Yarrow, C. J.: Transistor Convertors for the Generation of High-voltage, Low-current D-C Supplies, *Proc. Inst. Elec. Engrs.* (*London*), (International Convention on Transistors and Associated Semiconductor Devices), paper 2929E, May, 1959.

Yates, G. G.: A Simple Transistor Tester, *Electronic Eng.*, vol. 31, pp. 602–603, October, 1959.

Yee, R., J. Murphy, A. D. Kurtz, and H. Bernstein: Avalanche Breakdown in N-P Germanium Diffused Junctions, *J. Appl. Phys.*, vol. 30, no. 4, pp. 596–597, April, 1959.

Young, F. J.: Equivalent Base Resistance of Point Contact Transistors, *Appl. Sci. Res.*, vol. 7B, no. 5, pp. 361–365, 1959.

Yunovich, A. E.: The Kinetics of Electron Exchange between the Surface and Interior in Germanium, *Fiz. Tverdogo Tela*, vol. 1, no. 6, pp. 908–912, June, 1959.

Zakrzewski, J. T., and D. H. Mehrtens: Use of the Silicon Resistor in the D-C Stabilization of Transistor Circuits, *Nature*, vol. 184, pp. 811–812, September 12, 1959.

Zelikman, G. A., Ya. S. Levenberg, I. P. Lukashova, Yu. I. Sidorov, and S. V. Fronk: Silicon Junction Diodes, *Elektrichestvo*, no. 1, pp. 64–68, January, 1959.

Zerbst, M., and W. Heywang: Experimental Investigation of Trapping Centres in Silicon, *Z. Naturforsch.*, vol. 14a, no. 7, pp. 645–649, July, 1959.

Zerbst, M., G. Winstel, and W. Heywang: Carrier Recombination in Semiconductors after High Excitation, *Z. Naturforsch.*, vol. 14a, no. 11, pp. 958–962, November, 1959.

Zielasek, G.: A New Semiconductor Component for Electronic Circuits, *Elektrotech. Z.*, vol. 11B, no. 5, pp. 227–228, May 21, 1959.

Zima, V., and K. Stika: Relationships between the Quadripole Parameters of the Basic Transistor Configurations, *Slaboproudý Obzor*, vol. 20, no. 6, pp. 372–378, 1959.

Zins, W. A.: How to Design a Video Amplifier with a 30 Mc Bandwidth, *Electronic Inds.*, vol. 18, no. 9, pp. 84–87, September, 1959.

Zoldan, G.: On the Frequency Response of Certain Equivalent Circuits of Junction Transistors, *Elettrotecnica*, vol. 46, no. 12, pp. 853–857, December, 1959.

Zotova, N. V., and D. N. Nasledov: Indium Arsenide Hall Effect Probes for Measuring the Magnetic Field Intensity, *Fiz. Tverdogo Tela*, vol. 1, no. 11, pp. 1690–1694, November, 1959.

Application of Transistors in Calculating Apparatus. I. Application of Transistor Circuits in Binary Calculators, by G. Ozenne, *Rev. tech. C.F.T.H.*, no. 30, pp. 13–23; II. Utilization of Transistors in Traffic-control Installations (for Railways), by H. Suzan, pp. 25–37; III. Analogue Circuits Using Transistors, by P. Boyer, pp. 39–47, March, 1959.

Proceedings of the 1958 Conference on Semiconductors, *J. Phys. Chem. Solids*, vol. 8, 552 pp., January, 1959.

Proceedings of the Western Joint Computer Conference, AIEE, New York, March, 1959.

A Temperature-stable 8-watt Transistor Amplifier for High-quality Stereo Reproducing Equipment, *Elektron. Rundschau*, vol. 13, no. 4, pp. 134–136, April, 1959.

Transient Behavior and Fundamental Transistor Parameters, *Electronic Appl.* (Netherlands), vol. 20, no. 2, pp. 56–83, 1959–1960.

Transistor Amplifiers for Sound Broadcasting, *B.B.C. Eng. Monograph*, no. 26, pp. 5–19, August, 1959.

1960

Abboud, F. L.: Transistorized Vertical Scan System for Magnetic Deflection, *IRE Trans. on Broadcast and Television Receivers*, vol. BTR-6, no. 1, pp. 33–38, May, 1960.

Abraham, R. P.: Transistor Behavior at High Frequencies, *IRE Trans. on Electron Devices*, vol. ED-7, no. 1, pp. 59–69, January, 1960.

Achuthan, M. K.: The Junction Transistor: Basic Operating Mode, *Electronic Technol.*, vol. 37, no. 6, pp. 238–240, June, 1960.

Aigrain, P., and G. M. Phillipe: Other Semiconductor (Device) Structures, *Rev. E*, vol. 3, no. 3, pp. 93–102, 1960.

Aigrain, P., and G. M. Phillipe: Theoretical Limitations to Transistor Performance, *Rev. E*, vol. 3, no. 2, pp. 83–91, 1960.

Aitchison, R. E.: Approximate Expressions for the Alpha Cut-off Frequency of the Drift Transistor, *Proc. IRE, Australia*, vol. 21, no. 6, pp. 413–414, June, 1960.

Alford, C. H., Jr.: Analysis and Design of the Twin-tunnel-diode Logic Circuit, *IRE WESCON Conv. Record*, vol. 4, part 2, pp. 94–101, 1960.

Alfrey, G. F., and C. S. Wiggins: Carrier Concentration and Hole Mobility in P-type Gallium Phosphide, *Z. Naturforsch.*, vol. 15a, no. 3, pp. 267–268, March, 1960.

Allen, J. W.: Gallium Arsenide as a Semi-insulator, *Nature*, vol. 187, pp. 403–405, July 30, 1960.

Ambroziak, A., and A. Kobus: Transient Phenomena Connected with the Accumulation of the Minority Carriers in a Gold-bonded Diode, *Przeglad Electrotech.* (*Poland*), vol. 1, no. 1, pp. 50–55, January–March, 1960.

Anders, H.: Preamplifiers with Drift Transistors for Vidicon Cameras, *Rundfunktech. Mitt.*, vol. 4, no. 2, pp. 66–73, April, 1960.

Anderson, R. L.: Germanium–Gallium Arsenide Hetero-junctions, *IBM J. Research Develop.*, vol. 4, no. 3, pp. 283–287, July, 1960.

Anderson, R. L., and M. J. O'Rourke: A Vapor-grown Variable Capacitance Diode, *IBM J. Research Develop.*, vol. 4, no. 3, pp. 264–268, July, 1960.

Armstrong, A. J.: A Pulse-code Modulator Using Junction Transistors, *Proc. Inst. Elec. Engrs.* (*London*), (International Convention on Transistors and Associated Semiconductor Devices), part B, suppl. 16, paper 3088E, pp. 571–576, 1960.

Armstrong, F. E.: Battery-powered Portable Scaler, *Electronics*, vol. 33, no. 19, pp. 74–75, May, 1960.

Arnoldt, P.: A Cascode Trigger Circuit Using a PNP and NPN Transistor, *Electronic Eng.*, vol. 32, pp. 620–623, October, 1960.

Aschner, J. F., C. A. Bittmann, W. F. J. Hare, and J. J. Kleimack: A Silicon Medium-power Transistor for High-current High-speed Switching Applications, *IRE Trans. on Electron Devices*, vol. ED-7, no. 4, pp. 251–256, October, 1960.

Ashley, R. B.: Linearization of a Transistorized Vertical Deflection System, *IRE Trans. on Broadcast and Television Receivers*, vol. BTR-6, no. 1, pp. 39–48, May, 1960.

Ashton, G., and M. H. Issott: The Preparation of Single-crystal Silicon for the Production of Voltage-reference Diodes, *Proc. Inst. Elec. Engrs.* (*London*), (International Convention of Transistors and Associated Semiconductor Devices), part B, suppl. 15, paper 3083E, pp. 273–276, 1960.

Atalla, M. M., and E. Tannenbaum: Impurity Redistribution and Junction Formation in Silicon by Thermal Oxidation, *Bell System Tech. J.*, vol. 39, no. 4, pp. 933–946, July, 1960.

Audebert, M: The Design of Transistor Video Amplifiers, *Acta Electronica*, vol. 4, no. 2, pp. 215–228, April, 1960.

Bachle, E.: A Transistor Relaxation Oscillator and Its Application, *Elektronik*, vol. 9, no. 3, pp. 68–72, March, 1960.

Bakanowski, A. E., and J. H. Forster: Electrical Properties of Gold-doped Diffused Silicon Computer Diodes, *Bell System Tech. J.*, vol. 39, no. 1, pp. 87–104, January, 1960.

Baker, A. N.: Charge Analysis of Transistor Operation, *Proc. IRE*, vol. 48, no. 5, pp. 959–960, May, 1960.

Baker, L. R.: Construction and Performance of a Position-sensitive Photo-transistor, *Optica Acta* (*Paris*), vol. 7, no. 2, pp. 191–198, April, 1960.

Baker, S. C., H. G. Jackson, and D. A. Mack: Transistor Counting Systems for Scintillation Detectors, *IRE Trans. on Nuclear Sci.*, vol. NS-7, no. 2–3, pp. 89–95, June–September, 1960.

Bapat, Ya. N., and I. L. Kaganov: High-speed Semiconductor Switch and Trigger for Electronic Computers, *Elektrichestvo*, no. 6, pp. 76–81, June, 1960.

Barry, J. N.: Switching Transistors; Analysis of Performance at High-current Levels, *Electronic Technol.*, vol. 37, no. 12, pp. 442–449, December, 1960.

Barson, F., M. J. Dyett, C. Karan, and W. E. Mutter: A Controlled Diffusion Process for Indium in N-type Germanium, *J. Electrochem. Soc.*, vol. 107, no. 5, pp. 469–471, May, 1960.

Basov, N. G., O. N. Krokhin, and Yu. M. Popov: Semiconductor Amplifiers and Generators with Carriers Having Negative Effective Mass, *Zhur. Eksptl. i Teort. Fiz.*, vol. 38, no. 3, pp. 1001–1003, March, 1960.

Batdorf, R. L., A. G. Chynoweth, G. C. Dacey, and P. W. Foy: Uniform Silicon P-N Junctions. I. Broad-area Breakdown, *J. Appl. Phys.*, vol. 31, no. 7, 1153–1160, July, 1960.

Batdorf, R. L., G. C. Dacey, R. L. Wallace, and D. J. Walsh: Esaki Diode in InSb, *J. Appl. Sci.*, vol. 31, no. 3, pp. 613–614, March, 1960.

Bayer, R., and H. U. Knauer: The "Director" Intercomm-sets, *SEL Nachr.*, vol. 8, no. 1, pp. 20–23, 1960.

Beale, J. R. A., and L. J. Varnerin: The Calculation of Transit Times in Junction Transistors When the Mobilities Are Not Constant, *Proc. IRE*, vol. 48, no. 7, pp. 1341–1342, July, 1960.

Beauchamp, K. G.: A Sensitive Transistor Recording Pen Amplifier, *Electronic Eng.*, vol. 32, pp. 444–445, July, 1960.

Bell, C. V., and G. Wade: Iterative Traveling-wave Parametric Amplifiers, *IRE Trans. on Circuit Theory*, vol. CT-7, no. 1, pp. 4–11, March, 1960.

Bell, J. S., and P. G. Wright: Stabilized Voltage Supplies Using Transistors, *Electronic Eng.*, vol. 32, pp. 758–761, December, 1960.

Belova, N. A., A. N. Kovalev, and N. A. Penin: The Effect of Carrier Generation in the Barrier Layer on the Reverse Current-voltage Characteristics of Germanium Diodes, *Fiz. Tverdogo Tela*, vol. 2, no. 10, pp. 2647–2654, October, 1960.

Benz, W.: Equivalent Circuits for Transistors Driven as Linear Amplifiers, *Elektron. Rundschau*, vol. 34, no. 2, pp. 59–64, February, 1960.

Bereskin, A. B.: A Transistorized Stereo Preamplifier and Tone Control for Magnetic Cartridges, *IRE Trans. on Electronic Computers*, vol. EC-9, no. 4, pp. 430–438, December, 1960.

Bergman, R. H.: Tunnel Diode Logic Circuits, *IRE Trans. on Electronic Computers*, vol. EC-9, no. 4, pp. 17–20, January–February, 1960.

Berkovskii, F. M., S. M. Rўvkin, and N. B. Strokan: Volt-amp Characteristics of the Depletion Layer of a Germanium P-N Junction in Forward Direction, *Fiz. Tverdogo Tela*, vol. 2, no. 8, pp. 1956–1961, August, 1960.

Berlock, M. D., and H. Jefferson: Transistor Inverters and Converters, I–III, *Wireless World*, vol. 66, no. 8, pp. 299–402, August; no. 9, pp. 461–465, September; no. 10, pp. 507–509, October, 1960.

Berman, L. S., and V. K. Subashiev: Investigation of the Barrier Capacitance of Diffused P-N Junctions in Silicon, *Fiz. Tverdogo Tela*, vol. 2, no. 8, pp. 1962–1965, August, 1960.

Bernard, M.: Study of Recombination and Generation Phenomena in Germanium P_0-N_0 Junctions, *Ann. Telecommun.*, vol. 15, no. 1–2, pp. 2–26, January–February, 1960.

Bernard, M., and B. Leduc: Germanium P-N Junction Plasticly Deformed, *J. Phys. Chem. Solids*, vol. 13, no. 1–2, pp. 2–26, January–February, 1960.

Bhide, V. G.: Surface Sensitivity of Rectification, *J. Phys. Chem. Solids*, vol. 14, pp. 150–154, July, 1960.

Bickart, T. A.: Transistorized Slicer Analyzes Signal Amplitude, *Electronics*, vol. 33, no. 5, pp. 70–72, January, 1960.

Bickley, J.: Measurement of Transistor Characteristic Frequencies in the 20–1000 Mc/s Range, *Proc. Inst. Elec. Engrs. (London)*, vol. 107B, paper 3206M, pp. 301–305, May, 1960.

Bloom, M.: Microwave Switching with Computer Diodes, *Electronics*, vol. 33, no. 3, pp. 85–87, January 15, 1960.

Bochemuehl, R. R.: Cadmium Sulfide Field Effect Phototransistor, *Proc. IRE*, vol. 48, no. 5, pp. 875–882, May, 1960.

Bochemuehl, R. R.: Circuit Applications of Field Effect Transistors, *Electronics*, vol. 33, no. 33, pp. 132–135, August 15, 1960.

Bochemuehl, R. R.: Field-effect Modulation of Photoconductance in a Quasi-intrinsic Semiconductor, *J. Appl. Phys.*, vol. 31, no. 12, pp. 2255–2259, December, 1960.

Bogle, A. G.: Transistor Matching Impedances, *Electronic Technol.*, vol. 37, no. 1, pp. 28–30, January, 1960.

Bogomolov, V. N., and V. A. Myasnikov: The Use of Hall-elements as Phase-sensitive Detectors, *Automation and Remote Control*, vol. 20, no. 6, pp. 774–782, February, 1960.

Bohan, W. A., J. D. Maxey, and R. P. Pecoraro: Some Effects of Pulse Irradiation on Semiconductor Devices, *Proc. Inst. Elec. Engrs. (London)*, (International Convention on Transistors and Associated Semiconductor Devices), part B, suppl. 15, paper 3124E, pp. 361–367, 1960.

Bok, J.: Study of Charge Carriers in Semiconductors Subjected to an Intense Electric Field, *Ann. radioélec.*, vol. 15, pp. 120–146, April, 1960.

Boltaks, B. I., G. S. Kulikov, and R. Sh. Malkovich: The Effect of Gold on the Electrical Properties of Silicon, *Fiz. Tverdogo Tela*, vol. 2, no. 3, pp. 181–191, February, 1960.

Booth, A. D.: High-speed Track Selection for a Magnetic Drum Store, *Electronic Eng.*, vol. 32, no. 4, pp. 209–211, April, 1960.

Borne, J.: A Transistorized Generator of Television Synchronizing and Blanking Signals, *Acta Electronica*, vol. 4, no. 2, pp. 247–256, April, 1960.

Bossard, B. B., E. Frost, and W. Fishbein: X-band Super-regenerative Parametric Amplifier, *Proc. IRE*, vol. 48, no. 7, pp. 1329–1330, July, 1960.

Bouscasse, M. J.: Transistor Switches and Static Switching Circuits, *Bull. soc. franç. élect.*, vol. 1, pp. 227–239, April, 1960.

Brandqvist, L.: Design of Transistor Choppers, *Elteknik*, vol. 3, no. 1, November, 1960.

Breitzer, D. I.: Noise Figure of Tunnel Diode Mixer, *Proc. IRE*, vol. 48, no. 5, pp. 935–936, June, 1960.

Brini, D., A. Gandolfi, and G. L. Tabellini: Transistorized Apparatus for Accumulation and Binary-decimal Conversion, *Nuclear Instr. and Methods (Intern.)*, vol. 8, no. 1, pp. 46–54, 1960.

Brockman, H. P.: Sweep Generator Design, *Electronics*, vol. 33, no. 3, p. 92, January 15, 1960.

Brodie, J. H.: Matrix Solution to Transistor Amplifier Problems, *J. Inst. Engrs. Australia*, vol. 32, no. 6, pp. 117–122, June, 1960.

Brophy, J., and R. J. Robinson: Current Noise Due to Ohmic Contacts on Cadmium Sulfide, *J. Appl. Phys.*, vol. 31, no. 8, pp. 1343–1344, August, 1960.

Brophy, J., and R. J. Robinson: Frequency Factor and Energy Distribution of Shallow Traps in Cadmium Sulfide, *Phys. Rev.*, vol. 118, no. 4, pp. 959–966, May 15, 1960.

Brown, D. C., and J. E. Baughen: A Pulse Width Modulator, *Electronic Eng.*, vol. 32, pp. 302–303, May, 1960.

Brown, T. H., and W. L. Stephenson: Transistor Monostable Circuits, *Mullard Tech. Commun.*, vol. 5, pp. 89–95, April, 1960.

Bube, R. H.: Saturation of Photocurrent with Light Intensity, *J. Appl. Phys.*, vol. 31, no. 7, pp. 1301–1302, July, 1960.

Buelow, F. K.: Improvements to Current Switching, *IRE Trans. on Electronic Computers*, vol. EC-9, no. 4, pp. 415–418, December, 1960.

Burgess, R. E.: Negative Resistance in Semiconductor Devices, *Can. J. Phys.*, vol. 38, no. 3, pp. 369–375, March, 1960.

Burman, D. F., L. J. Fey, and D. G. W. Ingram: Transistor Feedback Amplifiers in Carrier Telephone Systems, *Proc. Inst. Elec. Engrs. (London)*, (International Convention on Transistors and Associated Semiconductor Devices), part B, suppl. 16, paper 3023E, pp. 587–595, 1960.

Cain, A. L., P. Swift, and A. T. Watts: The Use of Transistors in a Digital Correlator for Processing Radar Information, *Proc. Inst. Elec. Engrs. (London)*, (International Convention on Transistors and Associated Semiconductor Devices), part B, suppl. 16, paper 3037E, pp. 649–656, 1960.

Calawa, A. R., R. H. Rediker, B. Lax, and A. L. McWhorter: Magneto-tunneling in InSb, *Phys. Rev. Letters*, vol. 5, no. 2, pp. 555–557, July 15, 1960.

Caldwell, J. H.: A Transistor Push-Pull Amplifier without Transformers, *IRE Trans. on Audio*, vol. AU-8, no. 6, pp. 202–205, November–December, 1960.

Campbell, C. M., Jr.: A New Technique for Computer Switching, *Semiconductor Prods.*, vol. 3, no. 2, pp. 40–43, February, 1960.

Carbonel, M.: A New Theory of the Transistor in the Saturated Regime-switching Problems, *Ann. radioélec.*, vol. 15, no. 1, pp. 78–96, January, 1960.

Carlson, A. W.: Temperature Effects and Stability Factor, *Semiconductor Prods.*, vol. 3, no. 1, pp. 25–29, January, 1960.

Carlson, R. D.: Steering Circuit Control Reversible Counters, *Electronics*, vol. 33, no. 1, pp. 86–88, January 1, 1960.

Carson, D. N., and S. K. Dhawan: Data Conversion Circuits for Earth Satellite Telemetry, *Electronics*, vol. 33, no. 3, pp. 82–84, January 15, 1960.

Caussin, C.: Techniques for Using Semiconductors in Power Installations, *Bull. soc. franç. élec.*, vol. 1, no. 11, pp. 770–776, May 11, 1960.

Champlin, K. S.: Generation-recombination Noise in Semiconductors—The Equivalent Circuit, *IRE Trans. on Electron Devices*, vol. ED-7, no. 1, pp. 29–38, January, 1960.

Chandler, J. A.: The Characteristics and Applications of Zener (Voltage Reference) Diodes, *Electronic Eng.*, vol. 32, pp. 78–86, February, 1960.

Chang, H. C.: Silicon Carbide and Its Use in High Temperature Rectifiers, *Semiconductor Prods.*, vol. 3, no. 1, pp. 29–34, January, 1960.

Chang, K. K. N., G. H. Helmeier, and H. J. Prager: Low-noise Tunnel-diode Down Converter Having Conversion Gain, *Proc. IRE*, vol. 48, no. 5, pp. 854–858, May, 1960.

Charles, T. G., and D. Hartman: Reliability of Transistors, *Tek. Tidsskr.*, vol. 90, no. 5, pp. 119–124, January 22, 1960.

Chenette, E. R.: Frequency Dependence of the Noise and the Current Amplification Factor of Silicon Transistors, *Proc. IRE*, vol. 48, no. 1, pp. 111–112, January, 1960.

Chidambaram, R., and S. Krishman: The Single-ended Diode Phase-sensitive Detector, *Electronic Eng.*, vol. 32, pp. 158–159, March, 1960.

Chirlian, P. M.: A Technique for Cascading Tunnel-diode Amplifiers, *Proc. IRE*, vol. 48, no. 6, p. 1156, June, 1960.

Chow, W. F.: Tunnel Diode Digital Circuitry, *IRE Trans. on Electronic Computers*, vol. EC-9, no. 3, pp. 295–301, September, 1960.

Chow, W. F.: Tunnel Diode Logic Circuits, *Electronics*, vol. 33, no. 26, pp. 103–107, June 24, 1961.

Christiansen, H. M., and M. Schlichte: P. P. M. 60—A Transistorized P. P. M. System for 60 Channels, *NTZ-Nachrtech. Z.*, vol. 13, no. 8, pp. 392–399, August, 1960.

Chynoweth, A. G.: Uniform Silicon P-N Junctions. II. Ionization Rates for Electrons, *J. Appl. Phys.*, vol. 31, no. 7, pp. 1161–1165, July, 1960.

Chynoweth, A. G., W. L. Fieldmann, C. A. Lee, R. A. Logan, and G. L. Pearson: Internal Field Emission at Narrow Silicon and Germanium P-N Junctions, *Phys. Rev.*, vol. 118, no. 2, pp. 425–434, April 15, 1960.

Chynoweth, A. G., and R. A. Logan: Internal Field Emission at Narrow P-N Junctions in Indium Antimonide, *Phys. Rev.*, vol. 118, no. 6, pp. 1470–1473, June 15, 1960.

Closser, W. H.: Drift Mobility in Neutron Irradiated N-type Germanium, *J. Appl. Phys.*, vol. 31, no. 7, p. 1693, September, 1960.

Cobbold, R. S. C.: On the Application of the Base Charge Concept to the Design of Transistor Switch-in Circuits, *IRE Trans. on Circuit Theory*, vol. CT-7, no. 1, pp. 12–18, March, 1960.

Cohen, R. M.: The Reliability of Transistors in Battery Portable Radio Receivers, *IRE Trans. on Reliability and Quality Control*, vol. RQC-9, no. 2, pp. 11–16, September, 1960.

Coleman, D. R.: Some Performance Parameters of Silicon Junction Power Rectifiers, *Electronic Eng.*, vol. 32, pp. 98–102, February, 1960.

Conrad, G., K. K. N. Chang, and R. Hughes: The Diode-loaded Helix as a Microwave Amplifier, *Proc. IRE*, vol. 48, no. 5, pp. 939–940, 1960.

Cooke, H. F.: Designing TV Tuners with Mesa Transistors, *Electronics*, vol. 33, no. 15, pp. 64–69, April 8, 1960.

Cooper, B. J., and R. B. Ireland: Life-testing of Germanium Power Transistors, *Brit. Commun. and Electronics*, vol. 7, no. 1, pp. 14–20, January, 1960.

Corbyn, D. B., and N. L. Potter: The Characteristics and Protection of Semiconductor Rectifiers, *Proc. Inst. Elec. Engrs. (London)*, vol. 107A, paper 3135U, 1960.

Corey, P. D., and W. O. Hansen: A Transistorized D-C Voltage Regulator for Direct Replacement of Carbon-pile Regulators, *Appl. and Ind.*, no. 49, July, 1960.

Corning, J. J.: Aspects of Reliability in Transistorized Home Radios, *IRE Trans. on Reliability and Quality Control*, vol. RQC-9, no. 2, pp. 23–28, September, 1960.

Cox, F. B., and P. R. Johannessen: Application for Switching Transistors and Saturable Reactors in a High-performance Servo, *Trans. AIEE*, part II, vol. 78, no. 1, pp. 466–474, 1960.

Cox, L. G.: A Tunnel Diode Crystal Calibrator, *J. Brit. Inst. Radio Engrs.*, vol. 20, no. 8, pp. 621–623, August, 1960.

Culligan, G., and N. H. Lipman: Fast Transistorized Time-to-pulse-height Converter, *Rev. Sci. Instr.*, vol. 31, no. 11, pp. 1209–1214, November, 1960.

Curll, A. R.: A Transistorized Portable Television Receiver, *IRE Trans. on Broadcast and Television Receivers*, vol. BTR-6, no. 1, pp. 9–16, May, 1960.

Curtis, O. L., Jr., and J. W. Cleland: Monoenergetic Neutron Irradiation of Germanium, *J. Appl. Phys.*, vol. 31, no. 11, pp. 423–427, February, 1960.

Dachert, F.: Theory of Parametric Amplification with Diodes, *Ann. radioélec.*, vol. 15, pp. 109–119, April, 1960.

Dallemague, R., and P. Caniquit: The Feedback Transistor Amplifier, *Cables & Transmission (Paris)*, vol. 13, no. 4, pp. 230–239, October, 1960.

Dandl, R. A., and F. T. May: Some Interesting Transistor Characteristics in the Millimicroampere Region, *Rev. Sci. Instr.*, vol. 31, no. 5, pp. 575–576, May, 1960.

Daniel, A. F.: Solar Batteries, *Proc. IRE*, vol. 48, no. 4, pp. 636–641, April, 1960.

Darré, A.: The Transistor as a Passive Circuit Element, *Frequenz*, vol. 14, no. 1, pp. 6–10, January, 1960.

Das, M. B.: On the Determination of the Extrinsic Equivalent Circuit Parameters of Drift Transistors, *J. Electronics and Control*, vol. 8, no. 5, pp. 351–363, May, 1960.

Das, M. B., and A. R. Boothroyd: On the Frequency Dependence of the Magnitude of Common-emitter Current Gain of Graded-base Transistors, *Proc. IRE*, vol. 48, no. 2, pp. 240–241, February, 1960.

Davidson, J. J.: Transistor A-C Amplifier with High Input Impedance, *Semiconductor Prods.*, vol. 3, no. 3, pp. 42–50, March, 1960.

Davies, L. W.: Recombination Radiation from Hot Electrons in Silicon, *Phys. Rev. Letters*, vol. 4, no. 1, pp. 11–12, January, 1960.

Davis, B. A. I., and D. L. Lynton: Sectioning and Fault Analysis of Junction Transistors, *Proc. Inst. Elec. Engrs. (London)*, (International Convention on Transistors and Associated Semiconductor Devices), part B, suppl. 15, paper 2994E, pp. 445–446, 1960.

Demidenko, Z. A., and K. B. Tolpygo: (Carrier) Injection on the Passage of a Current through an Inhomogeneous Semiconductor, *Fiz. Tverdogo Tela*, vol. 2, no. 11, pp. 2753–2761, November, 1960.

Denda, S.: Germanium P-N-P-N Switches, *Direct Current*, vol. 4, no. 8, pp. 232–235, March, 1960.

Deschamps, R.: Conditions for Obtaining Germanium Transistors by Double Diffusion, *Compt. rend.*, vol. 250, no. 19, pp. 3137–3139, May 9, 1960.

Deschamps, R.: Properties of Germanium Transistors Made by Double Diffusion, *Compt. rend.*, vol. 250, no. 26, pp. 4307–4309, June 27, 1960.

Dewey, C. G., and M. E. Hodges: Transistorized Phase-comparison Relaying, Principles and Circuits, *Power App. Systems*, no. 49, August, 1960.

Diehl, M. H.: A Transistorized Vidicon Camera for Industrial Use, *J. Soc. Motion Picture Television Engrs.*, vol. 69, no. 11, pp. 795–800, November, 1960.

Dietrich, A. F., and W. M. Goodall: Solid State Generator for 2×10^{-10} Second Pulses, *Proc. IRE*, vol. 48, no. 4, pp. 791–792, April, 1960.

Dill, H. G., and M. R. MacPherson: Tracing Tunnel Diode Curves, *Electronics*, vol. 33, no. 32, pp. 62–64, August 5, 1960.

Diven, L.: Solid-state Modulator Feeds Subminiature Transponder, *Electronics*, vol. 33, no. 27, pp. 48–51, July 1, 1960.

Domenico, R. J., and R. A. Henle: All-purpose Computer Circuits, *Electronics*, vol. 33, no. 24, pp. 56–58, August 19, 1960.

Dovzhikov, E. E.: The Effects of Parameters of a Transistor Blocking Oscillator on Its Pulse Shape, *Radiotekhnika*, vol. 15, no. 9, pp. 40–46, September, 1960.

Drechsel, W.: The Physical Foundations of Amplifiers with Negative Masses, *Nachrichtentechnik*, vol. 10, no. 3, pp. 115–122, March, 1960.

Drugunescu, M.: Matz Theory of the Junction Transistor at High Injection Levels, *J. Electronics and Control*, vol. 8, no. 6, pp. 459–463, June, 1960.

Dubrovskii, G. B.: The Quantum Yield of P-N Junction CdTe Photocells in the Ultraviolet Region, *Fiz. Tverdogo Tela*, vol. 2, no. 4, pp. 569–570, April, 1960.

Dubrovskii, G. B., and V. K. Subashiev: Determination of the Recombination Parameters from the Spectral Response of a Photocell with a P-N Junction, *Fiz. Tverdogo Tela*, vol. 2, no. 7, pp. 1562–1571, July, 1960.

Dumas, G.: Fabrication and Electrical Characteristics of Low- and High-power Silicon Diodes, *Bull. soc. franc. élec.* (ser. 8), vol. 1, no. 11, pp. 750–769, November, 1960.

Dunnet, W. J., and Yu-Chi Ho: Statistical Analysis of Transistor-resistor Logic Networks, *IRE Intern. Conv. Record*, vol. 8, part 2, pp. 11–40, 1960.

Easley, J. W., and R. R. Blair: Fast Neutron Bombardment of Germanium and Silicon Esaki Diodes, *J. Appl. Phys.*, vol. 31, no. 10, pp. 1772–1774, October, 1960.

Easley, J. W., and J. A. Dooley: On the Neutron Bombardment Reduction of Transistor Current Gain, *J. Appl. Phys.*, vol. 31, no. 6, pp. 1024–1028, June, 1960.

Eckess, W. S., and P. G. Ducker: Measurement of Diode Switching Characteristics, *Electronics*, vol. 33, no. 15, pp. 59–61, April 8, 1961.

Edmond, J. T.: Heat Treatment of Gallium Arsenide, *J. Appl. Phys.*, vol. 31, no. 8, pp. 1428–1430, August, 1960.

Ekiss, J. A.: Transistor A-C Amplifiers with High Input Impedance: A Survey, *Audio Eng. Soc. J.*, vol. 8, no. 1, pp. 18–22, January, 1960.

Ekiss, J. A.: Transistor Choppers, *Semiconductor Prods.*, vol. 3, no. 10, pp. 23–27, October, 1960.

Ekiss, J. A., and C. D. Simmons: Calculation of the Rise and Fall Times of an Alloy Junction Transistor Switch, *Proc. IRE*, vol. 48, no. 8, pp. 1487–1488, August, 1960.

Elsner, R., L. Pungs, and K. H. Steiner: The Parametric Amplifier, *Frequenz*, vol. 14, no. 2, pp. 59–67, February, 1960.

Emms, E. T.: A Novel Single Transistor RC Oscillator, *Electronic Eng.*, vol. 32, pp. 506–508, August, 1960.

Eng, S. T., and R. Solomon: Frequency Dependence of the Equivalent Series Resistance for a Germanium Parametric Amplifier Diode, *Proc. IRE*, vol. 48, no. 3, pp. 358–359, March, 1960.

English, A. C., and W. H. Tobin: A Nondestructive Breakdown Phenomenon, *Commun. and Electronics*, no. 47, March, 1960.

Enselme, L.: Transistor Preamplifier for Television Camera, *Acta Electronica*, vol. 4, no. 2, pp. 229–245, April, 1960.

Eremenko, V. V.: Investigation of the Spectral Dependence of the Photoconductivity of Monocrystalline CdSe at 77° and 20°K, *Fiz. Tverdogo Tela*, vol. 2, no. 10, pp. 2596–2601, October, 1960.

Faizulaev, B. N.: Pulsed Emitter-follower, *Radiotekhnika*, vol. 15, no. 1, pp. 60–67, January, 1960.

Ferguson, A. E.: Circuit Analysis of Feedback Transistor Amplifiers, *Proc. IRE, Australia*, vol. 21, no. 6, pp. 394–397, June, 1960.

Fischer, A. I.: Transistor Broad-band Amplifier, *Nachrichtentechnik*, vol. 10, no. 2, pp. 83–87, February, 1960.

Fischer, T. L.: Wideband FM Receiver for Remote Aircraft Control, *Electronics*, vol. 33, no. 40, pp. 85–87, September 30, 1960.

Fishman, D., H. C. P. Kinge, and J. G. Litterick: Design Considerations in the Development of Silicon Power Rectifiers, *Proc. Inst. Elec. Engrs. (London)*, (International Convention on Transistors and Associated Semiconductor Devices), part B, suppl. 15, paper 3099E, pp. 419–425, 1960.

Fistul, V. I., and D. G. Andrianov: Change of the Surface Conductivity of Germanium Due to Absorption, *Doklady Akad. Nauk S.S.S.R.*, vol. 130, no. 2, pp. 374–376, January 11, 1961.

Fistul, V. I., and O. B. Orzhevskii: Conductivity of Electron-hole Junctions in Reverse Direction, *Fiz. Tverdogo Tela*, vol. 2, no. 9, pp. 2214–2217, September, 1960.

Fitzgerald, P. M., T. H. Lee, M. S. Moy, E. J. Powers, and J. J. Younger: A Non-linear Capacitor Harmonic Generator Suitable for Space-vehicle Applications, *IRE WESCON Conv. Record*, vol. 4, part 2, pp. 43–61, 1960.

Flaschen, S. S., A. D. Pearson, and I. L. Kalnins: Improvement of Semiconductor Surfaces by Low Melting Glasses, Possibly Functioning as Ion Getters, *J. Appl. Phys.*, vol. 31, no. 2, pp. 431–432, February, 1960.

Flood, J. E., and W. B. Deller: The P-N-P-N Diode as a Cross-point for Electronic Telephone Exchanges, *Proc. Inst. Elec. Engrs. (London)*, paper 3377E, November, 1960.

Flowers, T. H.: Transistor V. F. Signal Receivers, *Proc. Inst. Elec. Engrs. (London)*, (International Convention on Transistors and Associated Semiconductor Devices), part B, suppl. 16, paper 3100E, pp. 625–632, 1960.

Forest, M. L. N.: Avalanche Carrier Multiplication in Junction Transistors and Its Implications in Circuit Design, *J. Brit. Inst. Radio Engrs.*, vol. 20, no. 6, pp. 429–439, June, 1960.

Forshufvud, R., and P. O. Leine: Linear Amplifiers Using Transistors, *Tek. Tidsskr.*, vol. 90, no. 5, pp. 93–111, January 29, 1960.

Frank, H.: Semiconductor Compounds, *Slaboproudý Obzor*, vol. 21, no. 7, pp. 426–432, 1960.

Frazier, H. D.: Hypersensitive Voltage Variable Capacitor, *Semiconductor Prods.*, vol. 3, no. 3, pp. 56–59, March, 1960.

Frykman, R. W.: Radio Command Set for High-altitude Balloons, *Electronics*, vol. 33, no. 35, August 26, 1960.

Fujimura, Y.: Synthesis of Multi-stage Feedback Amplifier with Inverse Root-locus Method, *J. Inst. Elec. Commun. Engrs. (Japan)*, vol. 43, no. 5, pp. 604–611, May, 1960.

Fujimura, Y., and N. Mii: Automatic Frequency Circuitry with Reactance Transistors, *Electronics*, vol. 33, no. 40, pp. 97–99, September 30, 1960.

Fujimura, Y., and N. Mii: Reactance Transistor, *Proc. IRE*, vol. 48, no. 1, p. 118, January, 1960.

Fullwood, R.: On the Use of 2N504 Transistors in the Avalanche Mode for Nuclear Instrumentation, *Rev. Sci. Instr.*, vol. 31, no. 11, pp. 1186–1189, November, 1960.

Galkin, G. N., N. S. Rytova, and V. S. Vavilov: Volume Recombination of Carriers in N-Type Silicon Containing Radiation Defects, *Fiz. Tverdogo Tela*, vol. 2, no. 9, pp. 2025–2030, September, 1960.

Gardner, L. B.: A Silicon Transistorized Scaling Stage, *IRE Trans. on Instrumentation*, vol. I-9, no. 1, pp. 55–59, June, 1960.

Gärtner, W. W.: Tunnel Diodes, *Elektron. Rundschau*, vol. 14, no. 7, pp. 265–271, July, 1960.

Garver, R. V., J. A. Rosado, and E. F. Turner: Theory of the Germanium Diode Microwave Switch, *IRE Trans. on Microwave Theory and Tech.*, vol. MTT-8, no. 1, pp. 108–111, January, 1960.

Gast, T.: A Carrier-frequency Transistor Amplifier for Electric Micro-weighing and Other Measurement Applications, *Z. Instrumentenk.*, vol. 68, no. 2, pp. 30–34, February, 1960.

Geller, I. Kh., and P. V. Sharavskii: The Electrical Characteristics of Some Types of Selenium Rectifiers, *Fiz. Tverdogo Tela*, vol. 2, no. 7, pp. 1441–1449, July, 1960.

Geyger, W. A.: Recent Developments on Magnetic Coupled Multivibrators, *Trans. AIEE*, part I, vol. 79, pp. 106–112, 1960.

Geyling, F. T., and J. J. Forst: Semiconductor Strain Transducers, *Bell System Tech. J.*, vol. 39, no. 3, pp. 705–731, May, 1960.

Giannelli, G., and L. Stanchi: Nonlinear Operations on Pulses by Means of P-N Junctions, *Nuclear Instr. and Methods (Intern.)*, vol. 8, no. 1, pp. 79–91, July, 1960.

Gibbons, J. F., and G. L. Pearson: P-N-P Variable Capacitance Diodes, *Proc. IRE*, vol. 48, no. 2, pp. 253–255, February, 1960.

Glang, R.: Location of Diffused P-N Junctions on Germanium by Electrodeposition of Copper, *J. Electrochem. Soc.*, vol. 107, no. 4, pp. 356–357, April, 1960.

Glang, R., and W. B. Easton: Donor Concentration at the Surface of a Diffused N-type Layer on P-type Germanium, *J. Electrochem. Soc.*, vol. 107, no. 9, pp. 758–763, September, 1960.

Goetzberger, A.: Uniform Avalanche Effect in Silicon Three-layer Diodes, *J. Appl. Phys.*, vol. 31, no. 12, pp. 2260–2261, December, 1960.

Goetzberger, A., and W. Shockley: Metal Precipitates in Silicon P-N Junctions, *J. Appl. Phys.*, vol. 31, no. 10, pp. 1821–1824, October, 1960.

Gohm, L.: Broad-band Neutralization in Transistor Amplifiers, *Elektronik*, vol. 9, no. 5, pp. 149–152, May, 1960.

Goldsmid, H. J., and R. A. Hilbourne: Transistor Operation Aided by Thermoelectric Refrigeration, *Brit. Commun. and Electronics*, vol. 7, no. 1, pp. 26–30, January, 1960.

Goldstein, I.: Some Parametric Amplifier Circuit Configurations and Results, *Proc. IRE*, vol. 48, no. 10, pp. 1783–1784, October, 1960.

Goldstein, I., and J. Zorzy: Some Results on Diode Parametric Amplifiers, *Proc. IRE*, vol. 48, no. 10, p. 1783, October, 1960.

Goldsworthy, W. W.: Transistorized Portable Counting-rate Meter, *Nucleonics*, vol. 18, no. 1, pp. 92, 94, 96, 98, 99, January, 1960.

Goodman, A. M.: Test Set for Displaying the Volt-ampere Characteristics of Tunnel Diodes, *Rev. Sci. Instr.*, vol. 31, no. 3, pp. 286–288, March, 1960.

Goodman, C. H. L.: The Regrown-diffused Transistor, *Solid-state Electronics*, vol. 1, no. 3, pp. 188–193, 1960.

Gordy, E., and G. Sieber: Transistor Pulse Generator, *Nucleonics*, vol. 18, no. 4, pp. 90–92, April, 1960.

Gorton, H. C., J. M. Swartz, and C. S. Peet: Radiative Recombination in Gallium Phosphide Point-contact Diodes, *Nature*, vol. 188, pp. 303–304, October 22, 1960.

Gossick, B. R.: Dipole Mode of Minority Carrier Diffusion with Reference to Point Contact Rectification, *J. Appl. Phys.*, vol. 31, no. 1, pp. 29–35, January, 1960.

Gossick, B. R.: Transistor with Base Containing a Dispersed Colloidal Phase, *J. Appl. Phys.*, vol. 31, no. 4, p. 745, April, 1960.

Goto, E., K. Murata, K. Nakazawa, K. T. Moto-oka, Y. Matusoka, Y. Ishibashi, H. Ishida, T. Soma, and E. Wada: Esaki Diode High-speed Logical Circuits, *IRE Trans. on Electronic Computers*, vol. EC-9, no. 1, pp. 25–29, March, 1960.

Grabowski, K. P., and R. D. Weglein: Coupled-cavity Traveling-wave Parametric Amplifiers: Experiments, *Proc. IRE*, vol. 48, no. 12, pp. 1973–1987, December, 1960.

Grannemann, W. W., C. D. Longerot, R. D. Jones, D. Endsley, T. Summers, T. Lommasson, A. Pope, and D. Smith: Pulse-height-to-digital Signal Converter, *Electronics*, vol. 33, no. 2, pp. 58–60, January, 1960.

Grannemann, W. W., and C. J. Reese: Transient Junction Temperatures in Power Transistors, *Elec. Eng.*, vol. 79, no. 1, pp. 53–57, January, 1960.

Grave, H. F.: Properties and Applications of Semiconductor Diodes, *Elektrotech. Z.*, vol. 81, no. 22, pp. 761–767, October 24, 1960.

Gray, C. R., and T. C. Lawson: Transistorized FM and TV Limiter Design and Performance, *IRE Trans. on Broadcast and Television Receivers*, vol. BTR-6, no. 2, pp. 10–14, July, 1960.

Greene, J. C., and E. W. Sard: Optimum Noise and Gain-band width Performance for a Practical One-port Parametric Amplifier, *Proc. IRE*, vol. 48, no. 9, pp. 1583–1590, 1960.

Gribnikov, Z. S.: Avalanche Breakdown in a Diode with a Limited Space-charge Layer, *Fiz. Tverdogo Tela*, vol. 2, no. 5, pp. 854–856, May, 1960.

Grinberg, A. A.: The Photomagnetic Effect in Isotropic Semiconductors and Its Use in Measuring the Lifetime of Minority Current Carriers, *Fiz. Tverdogo Tela*, vol. 2, no. 5, pp. 836–847, May, 1960.

Grinberg, A. A.: Transient Response of Transistors in Grounded-emitter and Collector Configurations, *Radiotekhnika*, vol. 15, no. 3, pp. 45–52, March, 1960.

Grinberg, A. A., and N. B. Strokan: The Effect of the Surface Recombination Velocity and the Absorption Coefficient on the Transient Characteristics of Diodes, *Fiz. Tverdogo Tela*, vol. 2, no. 7, pp. 1536–1541, July, 1960.

Groschwitz, E.: On the Question of New Possibilities of Amplification by the Movement of Carriers in Semiconductors, *Z. angew. Phys.*, vol. 12, no. 8, pp. 370–372, August, 1960.

Growes, J. R.: Transistor Circuitry for a Very Sensitive Photomultiplier, *Proc. IRE, Australia*, vol. 21, no. 3, pp. 142–147, March, 1960.

Gullen, M. A., and H. H. Schwartz: Graphical Method Permits Checking V. H. F. Transistor Stability, *Can. Electronics Eng.*, vol. 4, no. 11, pp. 44–47, November, 1960.

Gumowski, I.: On a Non-linear Effect in Transistor Amplifiers with Feedback, *Compt. rend.*, vol. 250, no. 5, pp. 822–824, February 1, 1960.

Gumowski, I., J. Lagasse, and Y. Sevely: Establishment of an Equation for the Behavior of a Nonlinear Transistor Amplifier, *Compt. rend.*, vol. 250, no. 11, pp. 1995–1997, March 14, 1960.

Gusa, V., Ya. Tsigelka, and L. Chernyi: The Protection of a Germanium Diode from Overvoltages Excited on Switching, *Elektrichestvo*, no. 6, pp. 82–85, June, 1960.

Gyulai, J.: On the Simultaneous Determination of Lifetime, Diffusivity and Surface Recombination Velocity of Injected Carriers in Semiconductors by the Flying Spot Method, *Acta Phys. Acad. Sci. Hung.*, vol. 12, no. 2, pp. 167–170, 1960.

Hagmeister, H.: Non-destructive Testing of Transistor Switching Characteristics, *Elektronik*, vol. 9, no. 9, pp. 262–264, September, 1960.

Haisty, R. W.: Constant Current Supply for Very High Resistance Loads, *Rev. Sci. Instr.*, vol. 31, no. 12, pp. 1297–1298, December, 1960.

Hall, R. N.: Tunnel Diodes, *IRE Trans. on Electron Devices*, vol. ED-7, no. 1, pp. 1–9, January, 1960.

Halligan, J. W.: Effect of External Base and Emitter Resistors on Noise Figures, *Proc. IRE*, vol. 48, no. 5, pp. 936–937, May, 1960.

Hambleton, K. G., J. J. Low, and R. J. Sherwell: Gallium Arsenide Tunnel Diodes, *Nature*, vol. 185, pp. 676–677, March 5, 1960.

Hamerak, K.: Transistorized Control for Running Two Shafts in Phase, *Elektron. Rundschau*, vol. 14, no. 5, pp. 177–180, May, 1960.

Hamilton, D. J.: Current Build-up in Avalanche Transistors with Resistance Loads, *IRE Trans. on Electronic Computers*, vol. EC-9, no. 4, pp. 456–460, December, 1960.

Handel, S.: The Possibilities of the Tecnetron, *Brit. Commun. and Electronics*, vol. 7, no. 4, pp. 282–285, April, 1960.

Harrick, N. J.: Rectification without Injection at Metal-to-semiconductor Contacts, *Phys. Rev.*, vol. 118, no. 4, pp. 986–987, May 15, 1960.

Harrick, N. J.: Semiconductor Surface Properties Deduced from Free Carrier Absorption and Reflection of Infrared Radiation, *J. Phys. Chem. Solids*, vol. 14, pp. 60–71, July, 1960.

Harris, P. E.: Insuring Stability in Time Delay Multivibrators, *Electronics*, vol. 33, no. 15, p. 73, April 8, 1960.

Harvey, R. V.: Transistor V.H.F./FM Receiver, I–III, *Wireless World*, vol. 66, no. 8, pp. 366–369, August; no. 9, pp. 418–422, September; no. 10, pp. 519–522, October, 1960.

Hauri, E. R.: Transistor Feedback Amplifiers, I–II, *Tech. Mitt. PTT*, vol. 38, no. 6, pp. 185–200; no. 7, pp. 228–235, 1960.

Havel, J.: A Plug-in Transistorized Flip-flop Circuit with Read-out by Means of Neon Indicators, *Slaboproudý Obzor*, vol. 21, no. 7, pp. 409–412, 1960.

Havlik, L.: Present State of the Transistor Measuring Technique, *Slaboproudý Obzor*, vol. 21, no. 2, pp. 89–96, 1960.

Hayashi, T.: A New Type Field-effect Transistor, *J. Inst. Elec. Commun. Engrs. (Japan)*, vol. 43, no. 3, pp. 298–305, March, 1960.

Hegbom, T.: The Hall Multiplier for Measurement and Recording of Single- and Three-phase Powers, *Elektroteknikeren*, vol. 73, no. 7, pp. 124–126, March 5, 1960.

Heilmeier, G. H.: Millimeter Wave Generation by Parametric Methods, *Proc. IRE*, vol. 48, no. 7, pp. 1326–1327, July, 1960.

Hempel, R. A.: A New Type 150 Kc Binary-quinary Decade Counter with Neon Display, *Semiconductor Prods.*, vol. 3, no. 9, pp. 36–39, September, 1960.

Henkels, H. W., and T. P. Nowalk: High Gain Silicon Transistors, *Semiconductor Prods.*, vol. 3, no. 9, pp. 39–42, September, 1960.

Henkels, H. W., and F. S. Stein: Comparison of N-P-N Transistors and N-P-N-P Devices as Twenty-ampere Switches, *IRE Trans. on Electron Devices*, vol. ED-7, no. 1, pp. 39–45, January, 1960.

Herbst, L. J., R. H. Moffett, R. F. Purton, and J. L. Slow: The Application of Transistors to the Generation of Stable-frequency Supplies for Carrier Telephone Equipment, *Proc. Inst. Elec. Engrs. (London)*, (International Convention of Transistors and Associated Semiconductor Devices), part B, suppl. 16, paper 3039E, pp. 613–618, 1960.

Hermsdorf, L., and J. Meinhardt: The Frequency Response of Power Transistors in the Low-frequency Range and Its Effect on the Amplification of Transistor Output Stages, *Nachrichtentechnik*, vol. 10, no. 2, pp. 80–83, February, 1960.

Herndon, M., and A. C. MacPherson: Gallium Arsenide Microwave Diode at X Band, *Proc. IRE*, vol. 48, no. 5, p. 945, May, 1960.

Herwald, S. W., and S. J. Angello: Integration of Circuit Functions into Solids, *Science*, vol. 132, pp. 1127–1133, October 21, 1960.

Heyser, R. C.: A Signal Biasing Output Transformerless Transistor Power Amplifier, *Audio Eng. Soc. J.*, vol. 8, no. 3, pp. 185–192, July, 1960.

Hibbard, F.: Transistor Noise Factor Calculations, *Electronic Eng.*, vol. 32, pp. 163–164, March, 1960.

Hilberg, W.: The Eccles-Jordan Circuit Using Transistors for Very Fast Counters, *Telefunken Ztg.*, vol. 33, pp. 98–108, June, 1960.

Hilibrand, J., and R. D. Gold: Determination of the Impurity Distribution in Junction Diodes from Capacitance-voltage Measurements, *RCA Rev.*, vol. 21, no. 2, pp. 245–252, June, 1960.

Hilibrand, J., and C. F. Stocker: The Design of Varactor Diodes, *RCA Rev.*, vol. 21, no. 2, pp. 457–474, September, 1960.

Hines, M. E.: High-frequency Negative-resistance Circuit Principles for Esaki Diode Applications, *Bell System Tech. J.*, vol. 39, no. 3, pp. 477–513, May, 1960.

Hines, M. E., and W. W. Anderson: Noise Performance Theory of Esaki (Tunnel) Diode Amplifiers, *Proc. IRE*, vol. 48, no. 4, p. 789, April, 1960.

Hiwatashi, K., Y. Fujimura, K. Suzuki, and N. Mii: Applications of Transistors to Video Equipment, I, *Semiconductor Prods.*, vol. 3, no. 5, pp. 45–49, May, 1960.

Hiwatashi, K., Y. Fujimura, K. Suzuki, and N. Mii: Application of Transistors to Video Equipment, II, *Semiconductor Prods.*, vol. 3, no. 6, pp. 44–48, June; III, no. 7, pp. 26–28, July, 1960.

Hoffman, T. R.: Multiple-interval Timers Using Gated Staircase Counters, *Semiconductor Prods.*, vol. 3, no. 4, pp. 47–50, April, 1960.

Hofheimer, R. W.: Transistor-capacitor Shift Register, *Semiconductor Prods.*, vol. 3, no. 7, pp. 31–32, July, 1960.

Hoge, R. R.: A Sensitive Parametric Modulator for D-C Measurements, *IRE Intern. Conv. Record*, vol. 8, part 9, pp. 34–42, 1960.

Holbrook, G. W.: Correcting Nonlinearity of Transistor Amplifiers, *IRE Trans. on Audio*, vol. AU-8, no. 3, pp. 103–104, May–June, 1960.

Hollander, L. E., G. L. Vick, and T. J. Diesel: The Piezoresistive Effect and Its Applications, *Rev. Sci. Instr.*, vol. 31, no. 3, pp. 323–327, March, 1960.

Holonyak, N., Jr., and I. A. Lesk: Gallium Arsenide Tunnel Diodes, *Proc. IRE*, vol. 48, no. 8, pp. 1405–1409, August, 1960.

Horowitz, S. H., A. J. McConnell, and H. T. Seeley: Transistorized Phase-comparison Relaying: Application and Tests, *Power App. Systems*, no. 49, August, 1960.

Humphrey, J. G.: A Transistor TV I-F Amplifier, *IRE Trans. on Broadcast and Television Receivers*, vol. BTR-6, no. 1, pp. 17–20, May, 1960.

Hutcheon, I. C., and D. N. Harrison: A Transistor Quadrature Suppressor for A-C Servo Systems, *Proc. Inst. Elec. Engrs. (London)*, vol. 107B, paper 3134M, pp. 73–82, January, 1960.

Hutcheon, I. C., and D. N. Harrison: A Transistor-thermistor Feedback Quadrature Suppressor, *Electronic Eng.*, vol. 32, pp. 87–91, February, 1960.

Hutcheon, I. C., and D. Summers: A Low-drift Transistor Chopper-type D-C Amplifier with High Gain and Large Dynamic Range, *Proc. Inst. Elec. Engrs. (London)*, vol. 107B, paper 3227M, 1960.

Hutchinson, G. W., R. Rubinstein, and W. H. Wells: A Transistorized Ring Scaler of Resolving Time 0.3, *Nuclear Instr. and Methods (Intern.)*, vol. 7, no. 2, pp. 167–173, May, 1960.

Iglitsyn, M. I., and Yu. A. Kontsevoi: The Determination of the Physical Parameters of the Recombination Centers Produced by Copper in Germanium, *Fiz. Tverdogo Tela*, vol. 2, no. 6, pp. 1148–1151, June, 1960.

Iles, P. A., and P. J. Coppen: Location of P-N Junctions in Semiconductors, *Brit. J. Appl. Phys.*, vol. 11, no. 5, pp. 177–184, May, 1960.

Jacobs, H., F. A. Brand, M. Benanti, J. Meindl, and H. R. Benjamin: A New Semiconductor Microwave Modulator, *IRE Intern. Conv. Record*, vol. EC-9, no. 3, pp. 303–308, September, 1960.

James, J. R.: Analysis of the Transistor Cascode Configuration, *Electronic Eng.*, vol. 32, pp. 44–46, January, 1960.

James, P., and A. F. Newell: Switching Times for Alloy Junction Transistors, Derived from the Large Signal Equivalent Circuit, *Mullard Tech. Commun.*, vol. 5, pp. 159–171, June, 1960.

Jantsch, O.: Inverse Characteristics with the Surface Breakdown of Silicon PSPN Rectifiers, *Z. Naturforsch.*, vol. 15a, no. 4, pp. 302–307, April, 1960.

Jantsch, O.: Inversion Behavior of Silicon Rectifiers in Moist Gases, *Z. Naturforsch.*, vol. 15a, no. 2, pp. 141–149, February, 1960.

Jarvis, D. B., L. P. Morgan, and J. A. Weaver: Transistor Current Switching and Routing Techniques, *IRE Trans. on Electronic Computers*, vol. EC-9, no. 3, pp. 302–308, September, 1960.

Johnson, S. O.: A Performance/Cost Approach to Transistor Design, *Proc. Inst. Elec. Engrs. (London)*, (International Convention on Transistors and Associated Semiconductor Devices), part B, suppl. 15, paper 299E, pp. 370–374, 1960.

Johnston, R. C., and R. L. Burke: Measurement of Switching Transistor Parameters, *Semiconductor Prods.*, vol. 3, no. 2, pp. 43–46, February, 1960.

Jones, D. H., and J. R. Tillman: Some Notes on the Output Capacitance of Transistors, *Proc. Inst. Elec. Engrs. (London)*, (International Convention on Transistors and Associated Semiconductor Devices), part B, suppl. 15, paper 3102E, pp. 490–493, 1960.

Jones, D. V.: Turn-off Circuits for Controlled Rectifiers, *Electronics*, vol. 33, no. 2, pp. 52–55, August 5, 1960.

Joshi, M. V., and T. V. Ramamurti: Transistors in Community Receivers, *J. Inst. Telecommun. Engrs. (New Delhi)*, vol. 6, no. 2, pp. 71–76, February, 1960.

Kaenel, R. A.: Novel Adder-Subtracter Circuit Utilizing Tunnel Diodes, *IRE WESCON Conv. Record*, vol. 4, part 3, pp. 53–64, 1960.

Kalman, J.: Designing Solar Power Supplies for Transistorized Radio Receivers, *IRE Trans. on Broadcast and Television Receivers*, vol. BTR-6, no. 1, pp. 21–24, May, 1960.

Kamal, A. K., and A. J. Holub: Gain Inconsistencies in Low-frequencies Reactance Parametric Up-converters, *Proc. IRE*, vol. 48, no. 10, pp. 1784–1785, October, 1960.

Kane, E. O.: Zener Tunneling in Semiconductors, *J. Phys. Chem. Solids*, vol. 12, no. 2, pp. 181–188, January, 1960.

Kaufman, M. M.: A Tunnel Diode Tenth Microsecond Memory, *IRE Intern. Conv. Record*, vol. 8, part 2, pp. 114–123, 1960.

Kemhadjian, H., and A. F. Newell: A Circuit for the Protection of a Stabilized Transistor Power Supply, *Electronic Eng.*, vol. 32, pp. 228–230, April, 1960.

Kennedy, D. P.: Minority Carrier Current in a Linearly Graded Drift Field, *J. Appl. Phys.*, vol. 31, no. 1, pp. 218–219, January, 1960.

Kennedy, D. P.: Minority Carrier Recombination in a Cylindrical Transistor Base Region, *J. Appl. Phys.*, vol. 31, no. 6, pp. 954–956, June, 1960.

Kennedy, D. P.: Spreading Resistance in Cylindrical Semiconductor Devices, *J. Appl. Phys.*, vol. 31, no. 8, pp. 1490–1497, August, 1960.

Keywell, F., and G. Dorosheski: Measurement of the Sheet Resistivity of a Square Wafer with a Square Four-point Probe, *Rev. Sci. Instr.*, vol. 31, no. 8, pp. 833–837, August, 1960.

Kharlamova, T. E., and G. F. Kholuyanov: Electric Properties of Alloyed Silicon Carbide P-N Junctions, *Fiz. Tverdogo Tela*, vol. 2, no. 3, pp. 426–433, March, 1960.

Kholuyanov, G. F.: Photoelectric Properties of Alloy P-N Junctions in Silicon Carbide, *Fiz. Tverdogo Tela*, vol. 2, no. 8, pp. 1904–1914, August, 1960.

Kibler, L. U.: Parametric Oscillations with Point Contact Diodes at Frequencies Higher Than Pumping Frequency, *Proc. IRE*, vol. 48, no. 2, pp. 239–240, February, 1960.

Kilburn, T., D. B. G. Edwards, and D. Aspinall: A Parallel Arithmetic Unit Using a Saturated-transistor Fast-carry Circuit, *Proc. Inst. Elec. Engrs. (London)*, vol. 107B, paper 3302M, pp. 573–584, November, 1960.

Kirvalidze, I. D., and V. F. Zhukov: The Effect of Heat Treatments on the Electrical Properties of P-type Silicon, *Fiz. Tverdogo Tela*, vol. 2, no. 4, pp. 571–574, April, 1960.

Kita, S., and F. Obata: An X-band Parametric Amplifier Using a Silver Bonded Diode, *Proc. IRE*, vol. 48, no. 9, pp. 1651–1652, September, 1960.

Klein, M.: A Four Terminal P-N-P-N Switching Device, *IRE Trans. on Electron Devices*, vol. ED-7, no. 4, pp. 214–217, October, 1960.

Kling, N.: Space Capsule Oscillator, *Electronics*, vol. 33, no. 38, p. 86, September 16, 1960.

Klose, W.: The P-N Junction in a Thermal Gradient, *Ann. Physik*, vol. 6, no. 1–2, pp. 25–30, 1960.

Knechtli, R. C., and R. D. Weglein: Diode Capacitors for Parametric Amplification, *J. Appl. Phys.*, vol. 31, no. 6, pp. 1134–1135, June, 1960.

Knechtli, R. C., and R. D. Weglein: Low-noise Parametric Amplifier, *Proc. IRE*, vol. 48, no. 7, pp. 1218–1226, July, 1960.

Koc, S.: Measurement of the Lifetime of the Minority Current Carriers in Semiconductors by the Phase Method, *Slaboproudý Obzor*, vol. 21, no. 2, pp. 103–106, 1960.

Koch, L., J. Messier, and Q. Kerns: Measurement of the Coefficient of Charge Collection in P-N Junction Particle Detectors: New Method of Measuring Lifetimes, *J. Electronics and Control*, vol. 8, no. 4, pp. 289–300, April, 1960.

Koehler, E.: Behaviour of P-N Junctions under Pulse Operation, *Nachrichtentechnik*, vol. 10, no. 2, pp. 62–67, February, 1960.

Köhler, K.: P.P.M. Equipment for 60 Voice Circuits, *Siemens-Z.*, vol. 34, no. 1, pp. 26–31, January, 1960.

Koll, A. J., E. Bleckner, and O. C. Srygley: Semiconductor Synchronous Clamp for Millivolt Signal Levels, *IRE Intern. Conv. Record*, vol. 8, part 9, pp. 43–46, 1960.

Köstner, R.: Investigations of Magnetically Coupled Transistor Oscillators, *Nachrichtentechnik*, vol. 10, no. 8, pp. 348–352, August, 1960.

Kotlarski, J. R.: Choosing Transistors for Monostable Multivibrators, *Electronics*, vol. 33, no. 4, pp. 58, 60, January 22, 1960.

Kotzebue, K. L.: Optimum Noise Performance of Parametric Amplifiers, *Proc. IRE*, vol. 48, no. 7, pp. 1324–1325, July, 1960.

Krabbe, U., and N. Meyer: P-N-P-N Semiconductor Components, *Ingeniøren*, vol. 69B, no. 8, pp. 249–258, April 15, 1960.

Krajewski, I.: Use of a Transistor for Setting a Square Loop Magnetic Core, *Electronic Eng.*, vol. 32, pp. 509–511, August, 1960.

Kramareva, S. A., and V. I. Stafeev: An Investigation of Certain "Long" Diode Properties, *Fiz. Tverdogo Tela*, vol. 2, no. 2, pp. 377–379, February, 1960.

Kubát, M., V. Malý, and J. Zika: Protection in Circuits with Semiconductor Power Rectifiers, *Elektrotech. Obzor*, vol. 49, no. 2, pp. 92–101, 1960.

Kuhrt, F.: The Hall-effect Generator and Its Application for the Electrical Measurements, *Elektron. Rundschau*, vol. 14, no. 1, pp. 10–13, January, 1960.

Kuijsten, L. H., and F. A. Vitha: Transistorized Carrier Telephone Equipment, I, *Philips Telecommun. Rev.*, vol. 21, no. 4, pp. 168–182, April, 1960.

Kulikov, S. V.: The Design of a Semiconductor Relay, *Radiotekhnika*, vol. 15, no. 4, pp. 73–80, April, 1960.

Labutin, V. K.: A Hybrid π Equivalent Circuit of a Transistor and Frequency Dependence of Y-parameters, *Radiotekhnika*, vol. 15, no. 5, pp. 33–38, May, 1960.

Ladany, I.: An Analysis of Inertial Inductance in a Junction Diode, *IRE Trans. on Electron Devices*, vol. ED-7, no. 4, pp. 303–310, October, 1960.

Lakshmanan, T. K.: P-N Junction between Semiconductors Having Different Energy Gaps, *Proc. IRE*, vol. 48, no. 9, pp. 1646–1647, September, 1960.

Lamont, K.: Transistors in Audio- and Carrier-frequency Amplifiers, *Electronic Technol.*, vol. 37, no. 8, pp. 292–299, August, 1960.

Langfelder, R.: Design of Static Relays for Signalling and Control, *Electronics*, vol. 33, no. 30, pp. 64–68, July 22, 1960.

Larass, W.: Transistor-stabilized Power Supplies, *Elektron. Rundschau*, vol. 14, no. 2, pp. 51–55, February, 1960.

Larrabee, R. D.: Measurement of Semiconductor Properties through Microwave Absorption, *RCA Rev.*, vol. 21, no. 1, pp. 124–129, March, 1960.

Larrabee, R. D., and M. C. Steele: The Oscillistor—New Type of Semiconductor Oscillator, *J. Appl. Phys.*, vol. 31, no. 9, pp. 1519–1523, September, 1960.

Larsh, A. E., G. E. Gordon, and T. Sikkeland: Use of Silicon P-N Junction Detectors in Studies of Nuclear Reactions Induced by Heavy Ions, *Rev. Sci. Instr.*, vol. 31, no. 10, pp. 1114–1118, October, 1960.

Laskowski, G.: The Frequency Response of Surface-barrier Transistors in Electronic Computers, *Nachrichtentechnik*, vol. 10, no. 2, pp. 68–72, February, 1960.

Lauckner, H.: Analysis of the D-C Characteristic of Selenium Rectifiers, *Z. angew. Phys.*, vol. 12, no. 4, pp. 171–177, April, 1960.

Lawrence, H., and R. M. Warner, Jr.: Diffused Junction Depletion Layer Calculations, *Bell System Tech. J.*, vol. 39, no. 2, pp. 389–403, March, 1960.

Lawson, W. D., F. A. Smith, and A. S. Young: Influence of Crystal Size on the Spectral Response Limit of Evaporated PbTe and PbSe Photoconductive Cells, *J. Electrochem. Soc.*, vol. 107, no. 3, pp. 206–210, March, 1960.

Leberwurst, K.: The Switching Mechanism of a Schmitt Trigger Circuit with Transistors, *Nachrichtentechnik*, vol. 10, no. 12, pp. 519–523, December, 1960.

Lee, C. A., and G. Kaminsky: Anomalous Barrier Capacitance in P-N Junctions of InSb, *J. Appl. Phys.*, vol. 31, no. 10, pp. 1717–1719, October, 1960.

Lee, M. A.: Variation with Temperature of the Distribution Coefficient of Indium in Germanium, *Solid-state Electronics*, vol. 1, no. 3, pp. 194–201, 1960.

Leenov, D., and J. W. Rood: U.H.F. Harmonic Generation with Silicon Diodes, *Proc. IRE*, vol. 48, no. 7, p. 1335, July, 1960.

Lesk, I. A.: The Diffused Shot-melting Technique for Making Germanium and Silicon P-N Junction Devices, *J. Electrochem. Soc.*, vol. 107, no. 6, pp. 534–536, June, 1960.

Lesk, I. A., and J. J. Suran: Tunnel Diode Operation and Application, *Elec. Eng.*, vol. 79, no. 4, pp. 270–277, April, 1960.

Leuttgenau, G., M. V. Duffin, and P. H. Dirnbach: High Power at 1000 Mc/s Using Semiconductor Devices, *IRE WESCON Conv. Record*, vol. 4, part 3, pp. 13–26, 1960.

Levine, I.: High Input Impedance Transistor Circuits, *Electronics*, vol. 33, no. 36, pp. 50–51, September 2, 1960.

Levitan, G. I.: Calculation of Diode Detector Performance, *Radiotekhnika*, vol. 15, no. 6, pp. 22–23, June, 1960.

Levy, D. T.: A Packaged Micromodule Laboratory for Industry, *IRE WESCON Conv. Record*, vol. 4, part 3, pp. 119–124, 1960.

Lin, H. C., A. R. Hlavacek, and B. H. White: Transient Operation of Transistor with Inductive Load, *IRE Trans. on Electron Devices*, vol. ED-7, no. 3, pp. 174–178, July, 1960.

Lindemann, W. W., and R. K. Mueller: Grain-boundary Photoresponse, *J. Appl. Phys.*, vol. 31, no. 10, pp. 1746–1751, October, 1960.

Lob, W. H.: Solid-state Pulse Modulator, *Electronics*, vol. 33, no. 30, pp. 72 and 74, July 22, 1960.

Logan, R. A., and A. J. Peters: Impurity Effects upon Mobility in Silicon, *J. Appl. Phys.*, vol. 31, no. 1, pp. 122–124, January, 1960.

Lombardini, P. P., and R. J. Doviak: Temporary and Permanent Deterioration of Microwave Silicon Crystal Diodes, *Proc. IRE*, vol. 48, no. 1, pp. 119–120, January, 1960.

Lommasson, T. E., and W. W. Grannemann: A Low-level Pulse-height Standard, *Proc. IRE*, vol. 48, no. 3, p. 361, March, 1960.

LoSasso, L. A.: Tunnel Diode as an Interstage Gain Device, *Proc. IRE*, vol. 48, no. 4, pp. 793–794, April, 1960.

Lotsch, H.: Survey of Non-linear Distortions, Including Cross-modulation, in Transistor Stages, *Arch. Elekt. Ubertragung*, vol. 14, no. 5, pp. 204–216, May, 1960.

Lowell, R., and M. J. Kiss: Solid-state Microwave Power Sources Using Harmonic Generation, *Proc. IRE*, vol. 48, no. 7, pp. 1334–1335, July, 1960.

Lowen, J., and R. H. Rediker: Gallium-arsenide Diffused Diodes, *J. Electrochem. Soc.*, vol. 107, no. 1, pp. 26–29, January, 1960.

Lucovsky, G.: Photoeffects in Nonuniformly Irradiated P-N Junctions, *J. Appl. Phys.*, vol. 31, no. 6, pp. 1088–1095, June, 1960.

Luecke, J.: Silicon Transistor-resistor Logic Circuits, *Elec. Mfg.*, vol. 66, no. 2, pp. 113–116, August, 1960.

Luft, W.: Forward Voltage Drop and Power Loss in Silicon Rectifiers, *Appl. and Ind.*, no. 49, July, 1960.

Lynch, J. T., and J. J. Karew: System Application of Hybrid Logic Circuitry, *IRE Trans. on Electronic Computers*, vol. EC-9, no. 4, pp. 418–423, December, 1960.

Lynn, D. K., and D. O. Pederson: Switching and Memory Criteria in Transistor Flip-flops, *IRE Intern. Conv. Record*, vol. 8, part 2, pp. 3–10, 1960.

Lyubin, V. M., and G. A. Fedorova: On the Question of High-voltage Photoelectromotive Forces in Thin Semiconductor Layers, *Doklady Akad. Nauk S.S.S.R.*, vol. 135, no. 4, pp. 833–836, December 1, 1960.

Macario, R. C. V., and N. E. Broadberry: Transformerless Circuits for Broadcast Receivers, *Wireless World*, vol. 66, no. 3, pp. 110–113, March, 1960.

McCaldin, J. O.: Interaction between Arsenic and Aluminum in Germanium, *J. Appl. Phys.*, vol. 31, no. 1, pp. 89–94, January, 1960.

McInnes, I. G.: TV Signal Amplifiers Using Drift Transistors, *Proc. IRE, Australia*, vol. 21, no. 4, pp. 265–270, April, 1960.

MacRae, A. U., and H. Levinstein: Surface-dependent $1/f$ Noise in Germanium, *Phys. Rev.*, vol. 119, no. 1, pp. 62–69, July 1, 1960.

Madey, R., and D. A. Barge: Anti-coincidence Circuit for Use in the Millimicrosecond Region, *Rev. Sci. Instr.*, vol. 31, no. 6, pp. 664–665, June, 1960.

Madigan, J. R.: Thermal Characteristics of Silicon Diodes, *Electronic Inds.*, vol. 19, no. 1, pp. 83–87, January, 1960.

Madigan, J. R., and W. Macdonald: Semiconductor Diode Switching Characteristics, *Semiconductor Prods.*, vol. 3, no. 2, pp. 29–34, February, 1960.

Mahnau, H.: A Transportable Measuring Apparatus with Geiger-Müller Counters, *Elektron. Rundschau*, vol. 14, no. 3, pp. 87–89, March, 1960.

Maissel, L.: Microalloy Junction for Silicon, *J. Electrochem. Soc.*, vol. 107, no. 11, pp. 933–935, November, 1960.

Mancianti, M., and G. Salardi: Transistor Current Amplifiers for Analogue Computation, *Energia Elett.*, vol. 37, no. 3, pp. 216–221, March, 1960.

Mandelkorn, J.: Analysis of Low-level Semiconductor Lifetime Decay Waveshapes, *Rev. Sci. Instr.*, vol. 30, no. 4, p. 455, April, 1960.

Marfaing, T.: Electric Properties of InSb P-N Junctions, *Compt. rend.*, vol. 250, no. 22, pp. 3608–3610, May 30, 1960.

Marinace, J. C.: Tunnel Diodes by Vapor Growth of Ge on Ge and on GaAs, *IBM J. Research Develop.*, vol. 4, no. 3, pp. 280–282, July, 1960.

Marsocci, V. A.: A Survey of Semiconductor Devices and Circuits in Computers, I, *Semiconductor Prods.*, vol. 3, no. 12, pp. 39–43, December, 1960.

Marvin, J. F., W. D. Miller, and M. K. Loken: Transistorized Ratemeter Design, *Rev. Sci. Instr.*, vol. 31, no. 11, pp. 1238–1240, November, 1960.

Masher, D. P.: The Design of Diode-transistor NOR Circuits, *IRE Trans. on Electronic Computers*, vol. EC-9, no. 1, pp. 15–24, March, 1960.

Mead, C. A.: Transistor Switching Analysis, I–III, *Semiconductor Prods.*, vol. 3, no. 9, pp. 43–47, September; no. 10, pp. 38–42, October; no. 11, pp. 28–32, November, 1960.

Mehrtens, D. H., and J. T. Zakrzewski: The Use of the Silicon Resistor in the D-C Stabilization of Transistor Circuits, *Electronic Eng.*, vol. 32, pp. 624–629, October, 1960.

Messenger, G. C.: A Review of Parametric Diode Research, *Semiconductor Prods.*, vol. 3, no. 1, pp. 17–19, January, 1960.

Messiaen, A.: Light-pulse Counter Using Transistors, *Rev. HF*, vol. 4, no. 9, pp. 210–214, 1960.

Meyer, N. I.: "Non-linear Distortion and Small-signal Parameters of Alloyed Junction Transistors," Danish Science Press, Copenhagen, 1960.

Meyer-Brötz, G.: Properties and Applications of the Junction Transistor as a Switch, *Telefunken Ztg.*, vol. 33, pp. 85–98, June, 1960.

Meyers, R. T.: A Transistorized Receiver for 150-Mc Mobile Service, *IRE Trans. on Vehicular Commun.*, vol. VC-9, no. 2, pp. 70–79, August, 1960.

Michelitsch, M.: On the Current Ratio I Max/I Min of Tunnel Diodes, *Naturwissenschaften*, vol. 47, no. 12, p. 247, 1960.

Midgley, D.: The Possibility of a Self-sustaining Corbino Disk, *Nature*, vol. 186, p. 377, April, 1960.

Mikula, J.: Dependence of the Power Gain on the Bandwidth in an Intermediate-frequency Neutralized Transistor Amplifier, *Slaboproudý Obzor*, vol. 21, no. 5, pp. 268–272, 1960.

Miles, T. J., and J. A. Sluss, Jr.: 15-watt Microalloy Diffused-base Transistor, *IRE Intern. Conv. Record*, vol. 8, part 3, pp. 3–9, 1960.

Milevskii, L. S.: The Effect of Quenching on the Minority-carrier Lifetime in Silicon, *Fiz. Tverdogo Tela*, vol. 2, no. 9, pp. 2158–2160, September, 1960.

Miller, E. C.: Audio Volume Compressor, *Electronics*, vol. 33, no. 2, p. 62, January 8, 1960.

Miller, O.: Analysis of the Usefulness of Zawels's Practical Equivalent Circuit, *Elektron. Rundschau*, vol. 14, no. 3, pp. 90–94, March, 1960.

Miller, R. H.: Transistorized Coincidence Circuit for π-e Experiment, *Rev. Sci. Instr.*, vol. 31, no. 10, pp. 1047–1051, October, 1960.

Miller, S. L., M. I. Nathan, and A. C. Smith: Pressure Dependence of the Current-voltage Characteristics of Esaki Diodes, *Phys. Rev. Letters*, vol. 4, no. 2, pp. 60–62, January 15, 1960.

Minner, W.: The Slope of H-F Alloy and Drift Transistors as a Function of Frequency and Working Point, and Its Derivatives, *Arch. Elekt. Ubertragung*, vol. 14, no. 9, pp. 411–420, September, 1960.

Mira, C., and Y. Sevely: A Special Trigger Circuit, *Compt. rend.*, vol. 250, no. 3, pp. 488–490, January 18, 1960.

Möhring, R.: Transistorized Pulse Rate Meter for Portable Geiger-Müller Counter Equipment, *Nachrichtentechnik*, vol. 10, no. 2, pp. 76–77, February, 1960.

Moizhes, B. Ya.: Theory of Photoelements with a P-N Junction, *Fiz. Tverdogo Tela*, vol. 2, no. 2, pp. 221–226, February, 1960.

Mokrytzki, B., and R. A. Stuart: A Magnetic-amplifier-silicon-transistor, Power Supply for Missile Application, *Commun. and Electronics*, no. 46, January, 1960.

Montgomery, G. F.: Efficient Harmonic Generation, *Proc. IRE*, vol. 48, no. 2, pp. 251–252, February, 1960.

Morgan, S. P., and F. M. Smits: Potential Distribution and Capacitance of a Graded P-N Junction, *Bell System Tech. J.*, vol. 39, no. 6, pp. 1573–1602, November, 1960.

Morrison, S. R.: The Evaluation of Germanium Surface Treatments, *J. Phys. Chem. Solids*, vol. 14, pp. 214–219, July, 1960.

Mortenson, K. E.: Comments on "Diode Capacitors for Parametric Amplification" by R. C. Knechtli and R. D. Weglein, *J. Appl. Phys.*, vol. 31, no. 6, p. 1135, June, 1960.

Mortenson, K. E.: Parametric Diode Figure of Merit and Optimization, *J. Appl. Phys.*, vol. 31, no. 7, pp. 1207–1212, July, 1960.

Moss, T. S.: Indium Antimonide, in "Progress in Semiconductors," vol. 5, pp. 189–220, Heywood and Co., London, 1960.

Mueller, C. W., and R. D. Gold: High-frequency Varactor Diodes, *RCA Rev.*, vol. 21, no. 4, pp. 547–557, December, 1960.

Munch, W. v.: Transistor Measurement Techniques, *Fernmelde-Ingenieur*, vol. 14, no. 7, July 15, 1960.

Murray, R. P.: Biasing Methods for Tunnel Diodes, *Electronics*, vol. 33, pp. 82–83, June 3, 1960.

Nagata, M., Z. Abe, and T. Kinoshita: Series-regulated Transistorized Power Supply, *J. Inst. Elec. Commun. Engrs. (Japan)*, vol. 43, no. 2, pp. 173–180, February, 1960.

Nambiar, K. P. P., and A. R. Boothroyd: A Compensation Technique for Reduction of Performance Errors of Operational Amplifiers, *Proc. Inst. Elec. Engrs. (London)*, (International Convention on Transistors and Associated Semiconductor Devices), part B, suppl. 15, paper 3082E, pp. 496–504, 1960.

Nanavati, R. P.: Prediction of Storage Time in Junction Transistors, *IRE Trans. on Electron Devices*, vol. ED-7, no. 1, pp. 9–15, January, 1960.

Nasledov, D., N. N. Smirnova, and B. V. Tsarenkov: The Temperature Dependence of the Principal Parameters of GaAs Point-contact Diodes, *Fiz. Tverdogo Tela*, vol. 2, no. 11, pp. 2762–2769, November, 1960.

Neff, G. W., S. A. Butler, and D. L. Critchlow: Esaki Diode Logic Circuits, *IRE Trans. on Electronic Computers*, vol. EC-9, no. 4, pp. 423–429, December, 1960.

Nelson, D. E., and F. Sterzer: Tunnel-diode Microwave Oscillators with Milliwatt Power Outputs, *IRE WESCON Conv. Record*, vol. 4, part 1, pp. 68–73, 1960.

Nikolenko, N. S.: Graphico-analytical Method of Designing Transistorized Low Frequency Amplifiers, *Radiotekhnika*, vol. 15, no. 7, pp. 51–59, July, 1960.

Norman, P., and E. J. E. Smith: The Design of Transistor Blocking Oscillators, *Proc. Inst. Elec. Engrs. (London)*, (International Convention on Transistors and Associated Semiconductor Devices), vol. 106B, suppl. 18, paper 3013E, pp. 1251–1259, 1289–1291, 1960.

Nossov, Yu. R., and B. I. Khasanov: Thermostability Equation for Transistorized Voltage Amplifiers, *Radiotekhnika*, vol. 15, no. 3, pp. 38–44, March, 1960.

Nowicki, J. R.: New High Power (Transistorized) D-C Converter Circuits, *Mullard Tech. Commun.*, vol. 5, pp. 104–114, April, 1960.

Oakes, F., and C. Thompson: Complementary Transistor Circuits, *Electronic Eng.*, vol. 32, pp. 438–442, July, 1960.

Offner, F.: Transistorized Data Amplifier Has High Gain-stability, *Electronics*, vol. 33, no. 27, pp. 55–57, July 1, 1960.

Okadá, R. H.: Stable Transistor Wide-band D-C Amplifiers, *Commun. and Electronics*, no. 47, March, 1960.

Okazaki, S., and H. Oki: Measurement of Lifetime in Ge from Noise, *Phys. Rev.*, vol. 118, no. 4, pp. 1023–1024, May 15, 1960.

Ord, G., and P. L. Lewis: High-speed Digital-computer Circuits Using Transistors as Bidirectional Switches, *Proc. Inst. Elec. Engrs. (London)*, (International Convention on Transistors and Associated Semiconductor Devices), part B, suppl. 16, paper 2985E, pp. 828–833, 1960.

O'Rourke, M. J., J. C. Marinace, R. L. Anderson, and W. H. White: Electrical Properties of Vapor-grown Ge Junctions, *IBM J. Research Develop.*, vol 4, no. 3, pp. 256–263, July, 1960.

Owen, P. L., and T. R. H. Sizer: An Eight Digit Word Generator Using Surface Barrier Transistors and Direct Coupled Technique, I-II, *Electronic Eng.*, vol. 32, pp. 134–138, March; pp. 212–217, April, 1960.

Padwick, G. C., and A. L. Cain: Transistor Circuits for a Ferrite Store, *Proc. Inst. Elec. Engrs. (London)*, (International Convention on Transistors and Associated Semiconductor Devices), part B, suppl. 16, paper 3027E, pp. 663–674, 1960.

Pajgrt, M.: Design of High-frequency Transistor Amplifiers, *Slaboproudý Obzor*, vol. 21, no. 12, pp. 714–719, 1960.

Pankove, J. I.: Influence of Degeneracy on Recombination Radiation in Germanium, *Phys. Rev. Letters*, vol. 4, no. 1, pp. 20–21, January 1, 1960.

Partridge, G. R.: A Transistorized Pulse Code Repeater, *Commun. and Electronics*, no. 46, January, 1960.

Paul, R.: The Equivalent Circuit for H.F.—Particularly Drift Transistors, *Nachrichtentechnik*, vol. 10, no. 2, pp. 50–55, February, 1960.

Paul, R.: The Frequency Behavior of Alloy Transistors, *Nachrichtentechnik*, vol. 10, no. 8, pp. 340–347, August, 1960.

Paul, R.: The Measurement of Single Elements of the Transistor Equivalent Circuit, *Nachrichtentechnik*, vol. 10, no. 2, pp. 56–61, February, 1960.

Payne, J. B., III: Voltage-controlled Bootstrap Generator, *Electronics*, vol. 33, no. 11, pp. 177–178, March 11, 1960.

Paynter, D. A., B. D. Bedford, and J. D. Harnden, Jr.: Solid-state Power Inversion Techniques, I, *Semiconductor Prods.*, vol. 3, no. 3, pp. 51–56, March, 1960.

Pell, E. M.: Ion Drift in an N-P Junction, *J. Appl. Phys.*, vol. 31, no. 2, pp. 291–302, February, 1960.

Penfield, P., Jr.: Noise Performance of Tunnel-diode Amplifiers, *Proc. IRE*, vol. 84, no. 8, pp. 1478–1479, August, 1960.

Penisten, G. E., and D. B. Hall: 60-Mc I.F. Amplifier Using Silicon Tetrodes, *Semiconductor Prods.*, vol. 3, no. 1, pp. 20–24, January, 1960.

Perrett, R.: Applications of Semiconductor Rectifiers in Large and Medium Power Electrochemical Installations, *Bull. Sci. A.I.M. (Belg.)*, vol. 73, no. 1, pp. 5–66, January, 1960.

Petitclerc, A.: The Silicon Thyratron Transistor, a New Silicon Semiconductor Element for Fast Switching at High Powers, *Onde élect.*, vol. 40, pp. 155–160, February, 1960.

Pettai, R., B. Bossard, and S. Weissbaum: Single-diode Parametric Up-converter with Large Gain-bandwidth Product, *Proc. IRE*, vol. 48, no. 7, pp. 1323–1324, July, 1960.

Pickover, M. B.: Transistorized Motor Speed Controls for Satellite Tape Recorders, *Proc. IRE*, vol. 48, no. 4, pp. 725–728, April, 1960.

Pike, E. R., and J. F. Cochran: Simple Transistor-operated Oven-temperature Regulator, *Rev. Sci. Instr.*, vol. 31, no. 9, pp. 1005–1007, September, 1960.

Pinasco, S. F.: Transistorized Linear Amplifier, *Rev. electrotéc.*, vol. 46, no. 6, pp. 209–211, June, 1960.

Pope, G. J.: Transistor Constant-volume Amplifier, *Wireless World*, vol. 66, no. 2, pp. 88–91, February, 1960.

Poyurovskii, M. E.: Transistor D-C Converter with Built-in Magnetic Stabilization, *Elektrichestvo*, no. 5, pp. 66–70, May, 1960.

Price, C. H., Jr.: High-current Solid-state Switches, *Electronics*, vol. 33, no. 38, pp. 72–73, September 1, 1960.

Prior, A. C.: The Field-dependence of Carrier Mobility in Silicon and Germanium, *J. Phys. Chem. Solids*, vol. 12, no. 2, pp. 175–180, January, 1960.

Pryor, A. W.: The Input Stage of a Transistor Pulse Amplifier, *Nuclear Instr. and Methods (Intern.)*, vol. 6, no. 2, pp. 164–168, January, 1960.

Pulfer, J. K.: Voltage Tuning in Tunnel Diode Oscillators, *Proc. IRE*, vol. 48, no. 6(I), p. 1155, June, 1960.

Raillard, H.: Fundamental Considerations of Power Dissipation Limits in Some Bistable Transistor Pulse Circuits, *Trans. AIEE*, part III, vol. 79, pp. 53–55, 1960.

Rathé, E. J.: Notes on the Development of a Signal Receiver, *Tech. Mitt. PTT*, vol. 38, no. 2, pp. 33–51, 1960.

Read, J. C.: Germanium and Silicon Power Rectifiers, Present Stage of World Development, *Engineer*, vol. 210, pp. 533–536, September 30, 1960.

Reddi, V. G. K.: Applying Transistor "Y" Parameters, *Electronic Inds.*, vol. 19, no. 1, pp. 79–82, January, 1960.

Redmond, K.: Low-cost Transistor Overload Safety Circuit, *Electronics*, vol. 33, no. 42, p. 102, October 14, 1960.

Reich, B., and W. Orloff: Junction Transistor Measurements and Practical Standards, I-II, *Semiconductor Prods.*, vol. 3, no. 3, pp. 59–63, March; no. 4, pp. 39–46, April, 1960.

Richings, W. V., and B. J. White: Transistorized Sound Level Meter, *Electronics*, vol. 33, no. 25, pp. 64–66, July 17, 1960.

Richter, M.: A Two-pulse Generator for Measurements on Transistors, *Nachrichtentechnik*, vol. 10, no. 12, pp. 524–529, December, 1960.

Riggs, R. H.: Analytical Design of Transistor Push-Pull Amplifiers, *Electronics*, vol. 33, no. 24, pp. 60–62, June 10, 1960.

Roach, W. E.: Designing High-power Transistor Oscillators, *Electronics*, vol. 33, no. 2, pp. 52–55, January 8, 1960.

Roach, W. E.: Transistor Scaling Theory, *IRE WESCON Conv. Record*, vol. 4, part 3, pp. 65–71, 1960.

Roberts, G. N.: Tunnel Diodes, *Electronic Technol.*, vol. 37, no. 6, pp. 217–222, June, 1960.

Robinette, S. L.: A Diode Matrix Commutator with Transistor Flip-flop Switching, *IRE Trans. on Instrumentation*, vol. I-9, no. 1, pp. 40–42, June, 1960.

Robinson, B. J., C. L. Seeger, K. J. van Damme, and J. T. de Jager: On Stabilizing the Gain of Varactor Amplifiers, *Proc. IRE*, vol. 48, no. 9, p. 1648, September, 1960.

Roman, G.: The Dependence of Current Amplification on Transistor Geometry and Minority-carrier Lifetime, *Proc. Inst. Elec. Engrs. (London)*, (International Convention on Transistors and Associated Semiconductor Devices), vol. 106B, suppl. 18, paper 3164E, pp. 932–936, 937–938, 1960.

Ronne, J. S.: Computer Switching with High-power Transistors, *Electronics*, vol. 33, no. 10, pp. 44–47, March 4, 1960.

Root, C. D.: Voltages and Electric Fields of Diffused Semiconductor Junctions, *IRE Trans. on Electron Devices*, vol. ED-7, no. 4, pp. 279–282, October, 1960.

Root, C. D., D. P. Lieb, and B. Jackson: Avalanche Breakdown Voltages of Diffused Silicon and Germanium Diodes, *IRE Trans. on Electron Devices*, vol. ED-7, no. 4, pp. 257–262, October, 1960.

Rosi, F. D., D. Meyerhofer, and R. V. Jensen: Properties of p-type GaAs Prepared by Copper Diffusion, *J. Appl. Phys.*, vol. 31, no. 6, pp. 1105–1108, June, 1960.

Rupprecht, G.: Cross-sections of Midgap Surface States in Silicon by Pulsed Field Effect Experiment, *J. Phys. Chem. Solids*, vol. 14, pp. 208–213, July, 1960.

Russell, C. R.: The Parametric Amplifier, I, *Brit. Commun. and Electronics*, vol. 7, no. 2, pp. 94–98, February, 1960.

Russell, R. D., and F. Kollar: Transistorized Power Supplies for a Mass Spectrometer, *Can. J. Phys.*, vol. 38, no. 5, pp. 616–623, May, 1960.

Ruth, R. P., J. C. Marinace, and W. C. Dunlap, Jr.: Vapor-deposited Single-crystal Germanium, *J. Appl. Phys.*, vol. 31, no. 6, pp. 995–1006, June, 1960.

Rȳvkin, S. M., R. F. Konopleva, L. V. Maslova, and O. A. Matveev: Low-inertia Germanium Photodiodes, *Fiz. Tverdogo Tela*, vol. 2, no. 9, pp. 2199–2201, September, 1960.

Rzhanov, A. V.: The Applicability of the Stationary Photoconductivity Method for Studying the Dependence of the Rate of Surface Recombination on the Surface Potential, *Fiz. Tverdogo Tela*, vol. 2, no. 10, pp. 2431–2438, October, 1960.

Sadler, A. J., and P. A. Turner: The Silicon-controlled Rectifier, I-II, *Control*, vol. 3, pp. 101–103, August; pp. 108–110, September, 1960.

Sagar, A.: Piezoresistance in n-type InP, *Phys. Rev.*, vol. 117, no. 1, p. 101, January 1, 1960.

Sager, R. L., G. Strachanov, and G. W. Fyler: Transistorized Deflection Circuit for 110° Picture Tubes, *IRE Trans. on Broadcast and Television Receivers*, vol. BTR-6, no. 2, pp. 3–9, July, 1960.

Saha, A. R.: Transistor Beta-phase-shift Oscillator, *J. Electronics and Control*, vol. 9, no. 2, pp. 113–125, August, 1960.

Salter, F.: High-speed Transistorized Adder for a Digital Computer, *IRE Trans. on Electronic Computers*, vol. EC-9, no. 4, pp. 461–464, December, 1960.

Santilli, R. A., and H. Thanos: Portable Radio Uses Drift-field Transistors, *Electronics*, vol. 33, no. 28, pp. 48–50, July 8, 1960.

Santilli, R. A., and C. F. Wheatley: Transistorized Automobile Receivers Employing Drift Transistors, *Semiconductor Prods.*, vol. 3, no. 6, pp. 29–35, June, 1960.

Sard, E. W.: Tunnel (Esaki) Diode Amplifiers with Unusually Large Bandwidths, *Proc. IRE*, vol. 48, no. 3, pp. 357–358, March, 1960.

Sarkar, G.: A High Power Transistor-magnetic D-C Amplifier, *Electronic Eng.*, vol. 32, pp. 705–711, November, 1960.

Schaffner, G.: A Compact Tunnel-diode Amplifier for Ultra-high Frequencies, *IRE WESCON Conv. Record*, vol. 4, part 2, pp. 86–93, 1960.

Scharf, K.: Photovoltaic Effect Produced in Silicon Solar Cells by X- and Gamma-rays, *J. Research, NBS*, vol. 64A, no. 4, pp. 297–307, July–August, 1960.

Schmeltzer, R. A.: Maximum Stable Collector Voltage for Junction Transistors, *Proc. IRE*, vol. 48, no. 3, pp. 332–340, March, 1960.

Schmid, H.: A Transistor Bidirectional Limiter, *Semiconductor Prods.*, vol. 3, no. 4, pp. 29–32, April, 1960.

Schmidt, P.: Physical Basis for the Frequency Characteristics of Diodes and Transistors, *Nachrichtentechnik*, vol. 10, no. 2, pp. 43–49, February, 1960.

Schmutz, K., and F. Ogay: A Wide-band Amplifier Using Transistors for H-F Radio Telephone Links, *Tech. Mitt. PTT*, vol. 38, no. 12, pp. 425–441, 1960.

Schneider, B., and M. J. O. Strutt: Shot and Thermal Noise in Germanium and Silicon Transistors at High-level Current Injections, *Proc. IRE*, vol. 48, no. 10, pp. 1731–1739, October, 1960.

Schneider, H.: Properties and Application of Transistors in the Measurement Field, *Elektrotech. Z.*, vol. 81A, no. 22, pp. 767–772, October 24, 1960.

Schultz, J. B., and H. B. Yin: Negative-resistance Amplifier Design, *Electronics*, vol. 33, no. 22, pp. 110–112, May 27, 1960.

Schulz, D.: Transient Response of Variable Capacitance Diodes, *IRE Trans. on Component Parts*, vol. CP-7, no. 2, pp. 49–53, June, 1960.

Schwabe, G.: The Dependence of Current Gain on Emitter Current in a Drift Transistor, *Z. angew. Phys.*, vol. 12, no. 7, pp. 314–320, July, 1960.

Schwartz, B., and M. Levy: Field Effect on Silicon Transistors, *Proc. IRE*, vol. 48, no. 3, pp. 317–320, March, 1960.

Segal, R. E.: A Solid-state Video Processor with Pulse-for-pulse A.G.C., *IRE WESCON Conv. Record*, vol. 4, part 2, pp. 35–42, 1960.

Senderikhin, I. M.: Theory of the Thermal Breakdown of Germanium Diodes, *Fiz. Tverdogo Tela*, vol. 2, no. 7, pp. 1506–1517, July, 1960.

Senderikhin, I. M., and P. V. Sharavskii: Investigation of Characteristics of Germanium Diodes, *Fiz. Tverdogo Tela*, vol. 2, no. 7, pp. 1497–1505, July, 1960.

Sensiper, S., and R. D. Weglein: Capacitance and Charge Coefficients for Parametric Diode Devices, *Proc. IRE*, vol. 48, no. 8, pp. 1482–1483, August, 1960.

Seurot, J. P. M.: On the Problems of Cooling Semiconductor Elements, Diodes, and Transistors; Simple Structures and Determination of the Maximum Dissipated Power, *Onde élect.*, vol. 40, pp. 164–182, February, 1960.

Shafer, C. G.: Design and Operation of an S-band Traveling-wave Diode Parametric Amplifier, *IRE WESCON Conv. Record*, vol. 4, part 1, pp. 49–54, 1960.

Sherin, R. J.: Efficient Photoflash Power Converter, *Electronics*, vol. 33, no. 4, p. 57, January 22, 1960.

Showell, H. A., C. W. M. Barrow, and R. E. Collis: Transistorized Magnetostrictive Delay-line Stores, *A.E.I. Eng. Rev.*, vol. 1, no. 2, pp. 58–67, July, 1960.

Sie, J. J.: Absolutely Stable Hybrid Coupled Tunnel-diode Amplifier, *Proc. IRE*, vol. 48, no. 7, p. 1321, July, 1960.

Siegel, K.: Anomalous Reverse Current in Varactor Diodes, *Proc. IRE*, vol. 48, no. 6(I), pp. 1159–1160, June, 1960.

Sim, A. C.: Some Fundamental Aspects of P-N Junctions, *Proc. Inst. Elec. Engrs. (London)*, (International Convention on Transistors and Associated Semiconductor Devices), part B, suppl. 15, paper 2990E, pp. 357–360, 1960.

Simmons, C. D., and C. R. Gray: The Video Processing Circuits of an All Transistor Television Receiver, *IRE Trans. on Broadcast and Television Receivers*, vol. BTR-6, no. 1, pp. 25–32, May, 1960.

Simmons, C. D., J. Specialny, and A. Sfreddo: A Transistor TV Tuner with a 4.5 Db Noise Figure, *IRE Trans. on Broadcast and Television Receivers*, vol. BTR-6, no. 2, pp. 67–71, July, 1960.

Simpson, P. V., and V. Mukai: Design Notes on a Transistorized V.H.F. TV Tuner, *Semiconductor Prods.*, vol. 3, no. 3, pp. 35–42, March, 1960.

Sirven, P.: Current Convertors with Transistors, *Electricien (Paris)*, vol. 88, pp. 86–88, May, 1960.

Sirven, P.: D-C Voltage Regulator Using Transistors, *Electricien (Paris)*, vol. 88, pp. 118–121, June, 1960.

Smith, M. J., E. S. Kirk, and C. W. Spencer: Device for Measurement of the Electrical Properties of Bi_2Se_3 at Elevated Temperatures, *J. Appl. Phys.*, vol. 31, no. 8, pp. 1504–1505, August, 1960.

Sochava, L. S., and D. N. Mirlin: The Relationship between the Excess Noise and the Surface Traps in Germanium, *Fiz. Tverdogo Tela*, vol. 2, no. 1, pp. 23–25, January, 1960.

Solomon, A. H., and F. Sterzer: A Parametric Subharmonic Oscillator Pumped at 34.3 Kmc/s, *Proc. IRE*, vol. 48, no. 7, pp. 1322–1323, July, 1960.

Solomon, R.: Anomalous Surface Channels on Silicon P-N Junctions, *J. Appl. Phys.*, vol. 31, no. 10, pp. 1791–1799, October, 1960.

Somlyody, A.: Transistor Bias Method Raises Breakdown Point, *Electronics*, vol. 33, no. 2, pp. 48–49, January 8, 1960.

Sorokin, O. V., and B. T. Tuseev: A Comparative Study of the Magneto-resistance and Photoelectric Methods of Measuring the Rates of Surface Recombination, *Fiz. Tverdogo Tela*, vol. 2, no. 7, pp. 1533–1535, July, 1960.

Špány, V.: Negative Resistance of Storage Elements Based on Junction Transistors, *Slaboproudý Obzor*, vol. 21, no. 7, pp. 403–408, 1960.

Sparkes, J. J.: The Measurement of Transistor Transient Switching Parameters, *Proc. Inst. Elec. Engrs. (London)*, (International Convention on Transistors and Associated Semiconductor Devices), part B, suppl. 15, paper 3006, pp. 562–566, 567, 1960.

Sparkes, J. J.: A Study of the Charge Control Parameters of Transistors, *Proc. IRE*, vol. 48, no. 10, pp. 1696–1705, October, 1960.

Spear, W. E.: The Hole Mobility in Selenium, *Proc. Phys. Soc. (London)*, vol. 86, part 6, pp. 826–832, December 1, 1960.

Spencer, H. E.: Noise and Signal Response in Lead Sulfide Photoconductive Films, *J. Appl. Phys.*, vol. 31, no. 3, pp. 505–510, March, 1960.

Spiegel, P.: High-speed Scalers Using Tunnel Diodes, *Rev. Sci. Instr.*, vol. 31, no. 7, pp. 754–755, July, 1960.

Staniforth, A., and J. H. Craven: Improvement in the Square Law Operation of IN23B Crystals from 2 to 11 Kmc, *IRE Trans. on Microwave Theory and Tech.*, vol. MTT-8, no. 1, pp. 111–115, January, 1960.

Starke, L.: A Transistor Bridge for Measuring Static Values in Industrial Plants, *Elektronik*, vol. 9, no. 11, pp. 333–335, November, 1960.

Statz, H. N., and R. A. Pucel: Negative Resistance in Transistors Based on Transit-time and Avalanche Effects, *Proc. IRE*, vol. 48, no. 5, pp. 948–949, May, 1960.

Steiger, W.: Transistor Power Amplifiers with Negative Output Impedance, *IRE Trans. on Audio*, vol. AU-8, no. 6, pp. 195–201, November–December, 1960.

Stelzer, I.: Surface Studies on P-N Junctions, *J. Electronics and Control*, vol. 8, no. 1, pp. 39–57, January, 1960.

Stevenson, I. R.: Transistor Ratings and Reliability, *Proc. IRE, Australia*, vol. 21, no. 3, pp. 138–141, March, 1960.

Stitch, M. L., N. O. Robinson, and W. Silvey: Parametric Diodes in a Maser Phase-locked Frequency Divider, *IRE Trans. on Microwave Theory and Tech.*, vol. MTT-8, no. 2, pp. 218–221, March, 1960.

Stopper, H.: Determination of the Code and Logical Circuit of a Decade Counter, *Telefunken Ztg.*, vol. 33, pp. 13–19, March, 1960.

Struzhinskii, V. A.: Germanium H-F Power Transistors, *Fiz. Tverdogo Tela*, vol. 2, no. 3, pp. 420–425, March, 1960.

Stumpe, A. C.: Transistor Inverters, *AEG Mitt.*, vol. 50, no. 1–2, pp. 19–27, January–February, 1960.

Subashiev, V. K.: Determination of the Losses and Efficiency of Various Processes in the Photoelectric Utilization of Solar Energy, *Fiz. Tverdogo Tela*, vol. 2, no. 2, pp. 198–204, February, 1960.

Subashiev, V. K.: Determination of the Recombination Parameters from the Spectral Response of a Photocell with a P-N Junction, *Fiz. Tverdogo Tela*, vol. 2, no. 2, pp. 205–212, February, 1960.

Subashiev, V. K., G. B. Dubrovskii, and V. A. Petrusevich: Determination of the Recombination Constants and Depth of a P-N Junction from the Spectral Characteristics of Photoelements, *Fiz. Tverdogo Tela*, vol. 2, no. 8, pp. 1978–1980, August, 1960.

Subashiev, V. K., and S. A. Poltinnikov: Determination of the Carrier Mobility and Density in the Surface Layer of a Semiconductor, *Fiz. Tverdogo Tela*, vol. 2, no. 6, pp. 1169–1177, June, 1960.

Sugano, T., and H. Yanai: Analytical Studies on Effects of Surface Recombination on the Current Amplification Factor of Alloy Junction and Surface Barrier Transistors, *Proc. IRE*, vol. 48, no. 10, pp. 1739–1749, October, 1960.

Sugarman, R. M.: Nonsaturating Transistor Circuitry for Nanosecond Pulses, *IRE Trans. on Nuclear Sci.*, vol. NS-7, no. 1, pp. 23–28, March, 1960.

Svehaug, O., and J. R. Kobbe: Battery-operated Transistor Oscilloscope, *Electronics*, vol. 33, no. 12, pp. 8–83, March 18, 1960.

Szilágyi, M.: Measurement of the Injection Efficiency of the Emitter Point Contact on Germanium in the Presence of a Drift Field, *Acta Phys. Acad. Sci. Hung.*, vol. 11, no. 4, pp. 401–404, 1960.

Theuerer, H. C., J. J. Kleimack, H. H. Loar, and H. Christensen: Epitaxial Diffused Transistors, *Proc. IRE*, vol. 48, no. 9, pp. 1642–1643, September, 1960.

Thies, A. W.: A Transistor Amplifier with Heavy Feedback for 12-channel Open-wire Carrier Systems, *Proc. IRE, Australia*, vol. 21, no. 2, pp. 91–98, February, 1960.

Tiemann, J. J.: Shot Noise in Tunnel Diode Amplifiers, *Proc. IRE*, vol. 48, no. 8, pp. 1418–1423, August, 1960.

Todd, C. D.: Combining Transistors with Tunnel Diodes, *Electronics*, vol. 33, no. 34, pp. 59–61, August 19, 1960.

Todd, C. D.: Preamplifier Designed for Minimum Power Consumption, *Electronics*, vol. 33, no. 18, pp. 106–107, April 29, 1960.

Todd, C. D.: A Tunnel Diode Monostable Multivibrator, *Semiconductor Prods.*, vol. 3, no. 12, pp. 27–34, December, 1960.

Trenholme, W. M.: A Reactor Safety System Using Transistors and Silicon Controlled Rectifiers, *IRE Trans. on Nuclear Sci.*, vol. NS-7, no. 4, pp. 14–19, December, 1960.

Uenohara, M.: Noise Consideration of the Variable Capacitance Parametric Amplifier, *Proc. IRE*, vol. 48, no. 2, pp. 169–179, February, 1960.

van Biljon, L.: Transistor Avalanche Voltage, *Electronic Technol.*, vol. 37, no. 2, pp. 72–76, February, 1960.

van der Donckt, J.: Application of Transistors to Long Distance Telephony, *Rev. E*, vol. 3, no. 2, pp. 67–78, 1960.

van der Maesen, F.: Determination of Numbers of Injected Holes and Electrons in Semiconductors, *Philips Research Repts.*, vol. 15, no. 2, pp. 107–119, April, 1960.

van der Ziel, A.: Shot Noise in Transistors, *Proc. IRE*, vol. 48, no. 1, pp. 114–115, January, 1960.

van Dievoet, W.: Semiconductor Rectifiers in Electrolysis, *Rev. E*, vol. 3, no. 1, pp. 31–42, 1960.

van Doveren, C. P. L., and J. F. Lansu: Transistorized Carrier Telephone Equipment, *Philips Telecommun. Rev.*, vol. 21, no. 4, pp. 183–193, April, 1960.

van Ligten, R. H., and D. Navon: Base Turn-off of PNPN Switches, *IRE WESCON Conv. Record*, vol. 4, part 3, pp. 49–52, 1960.

Vařecha, K., and J. Pšenička: Equipment for the Measurement of the Conversion Loss of Silicon Diodes, *Slaboproudý Obzor*, vol. 21, no. 1, pp. 11–15, 1960.

Veloric, H. S., and W. J. Greig: Evaluation and Control of Diffused Impurity Layers in Germanium, *RCA Rev.*, vol. 21, no. 3, pp. 437–456, September, 1960.

Venkateswaran, S., and A. R. Boothroyd: Power Gain and Bandwidth of Tuned Transistor Amplifier States, *Proc. Inst. Elec. Engrs. (London)*, (International Convention on Transistors and Associated Semiconductor Devices), part B, suppl. 15, paper 3090E, pp. 518–528, 1960.

Versini, F.: A Comparison of the Properties of Static Logic Circuits Based on Magnetic and Transistor Elements for Industrial Control Applications, *Bull. soc. franç élec.* (ser. 8), vol. 1, no. 10, pp. 711–720, October, 1960.

Vilim, J., M. Kubat, and J. Kroczek: Some Aspects for Testing and Ensuring Reliable Operation of Germanium Power Rectifiers, *Elektrie*, vol. 14, no. 6, pp. 214–216, June, 1960.

Vinopal, J., and G. Pisa: Silicon Rectifiers for Large Power, *Elektrotech. Obzor*, vol. 49, no. 5, pp. 268–271, 1690.

Vodakov, Yu. A., G. A. Lomakina, G. P. Naumov, and Yu. P. Maslakovets: Properties of P-N Junctions in Cadmium Telluride Photocells, *Fiz. Tverdogo Tela*, vol. 2, no. 1, pp. 15–22, January, 1960.

Vodicka, V. W., and R. Zuleeg: Transistor Operation beyond Cutoff Frequency, *Electronics*, vol. 33, no. 35, pp. 56–60, August 26, 1960.

Vogel, J. S., and M. J. O. Strutt: Calculation of Distortion and Interference Effects in Transistor Amplifying Stages on the Basis of Equivalent Circuits, *Arch. Elekt. Ubertragung*, vol. 14, no. 9, pp. 397–404, September, 1960.

Vogel, J. S., and M. J. O. Strutt: The Execution and Discussion of Comparative Life-tests on European Audio Frequency Transistors of Various Makes, *Arch. Elekt. Ubertragung*, vol. 14, no. 3, pp. 121–130, March, 1960.

Völger, H.: Germanium Rectifiers for Electroplating and Electrolytic Processes, *Elektrotech. Z.*, vol. 12B, no. 12, pp. 285–291, June 13, 1960.

Völger, H.: A Silicon Rectifier for Paralleling with Mercury-arc and Contact Rectifiers, *AEG Mitt.*, vol. 50, no. 10–11, pp. 476–480, October–November, 1960.

Vul, B. M., and E. I. Zavaritskaya: Capacitance of P-N Junctions at Low Temperatures, *Zhur. Eksptl. i Teort. Fiz.*, vol. 38, no. 1, pp. 10–17, January, 1960.
Waddell, J. M., and D. R. Coleman: Zener Diodes—Their Properties and Applications, *Wireless World*, vol. 66, no. 1, pp. 17–21, January, 1960.
Wagner, K.: Ring Counter for Forward and Reverse Counting Using Transistors, *Elektron. Rundschau*, vol. 14, no. 4, pp. 121–125, April, 1960.
Wagner, R.: Remarks on the Design of a Fully Transistorized AM/FM Receiver, I, *Elektron. Rundschau*, vol. 14, no. 6, pp. 237–239, June; II, Observations on the Design of a Fully Transistorized AM/FM Receiver, no. 7, pp. 276–282, July, 1960.
Waldner, M., and L. Sivo: Lifetime Preservation in Diffused Silicon, *J. Electrochem. Soc.*, vol. 107, no. 4, pp. 298–301, June, 1960.
Walter, F. J., J. W. T. Dabbs, and L. D. Roberts: Large Area Germanium Surface-barrier Counters, *Rev. Sci. Instr.*, vol. 31, no. 7, pp. 756–762, July, 1960.
Ward, E. E.: The Design of Controlled Rectifiers Using Triode Transistors, *Proc. Inst. Elec. Engrs. (London)*, vol. 107B, paper 3281E, pp. 473–480, September, 1960.
Ward, J. J.: Junction Transistor Circuits; Calculation of Temperature Drift, *Electronic Technol.*, vol. 37, no. 3, pp. 109–115, March, 1960.
Wei, Yin-Min: Ultrasonic Frequency Power Generator Using Transistors, *Commun. and Electronics*, no. 46, January, 1960.
Wertwijn, G.: Design Consideration for a Germanium P-N-P-N Switching Device with Three Contacts and a "Sandwich" Structure, *IRE Trans. on Electron Devices*, vol. ED-7, no. 3, pp. 132–137, July, 1960.
Westerberg, G.: The Transistor in Pulse Circuits, *Tek. Tidsskr.*, vol. 90, no. 5, pp. 111–119, January 29, 1960.
Whelan, J. M., and C. S. Fuller: Precipitation of Copper in Gallium Arsenide, *J. Appl. Phys.*, vol. 31, no. 8, pp. 1507–1508, August, 1960.
Wittig, K.: Transistorized TV and FM Tuners, *Semiconductor Prods.*, vol. 3, no. 7, pp. 19–25, July, 1960.
Wolff, G.: Back-transient Diode Logic, *Commun. and Electronics*, no. 47, March, 1960.
Wonson, R. C., and W. A. McCarthy: An NPN Fusion Alloy Silicon Transistor for "Avalanche Mode" Operation, *IRE Intern. Conv. Record*, vol. 8, part 3, pp. 10–16, 1960.
Wright, M. J.: A Transistor Switching Circuit for Power Regulation Applications, *Electronic Eng.*, vol. 32, pp. 484–487, August, 1960.
Wunderlin, W.: Properties of Transistors with Non-uniform Base-region Impurity Distribution, *Scientia Electrica*, vol. 6, no. 3, pp. 124–139, September, 1960.
Wunderlin, W.: Structure and Production Techniques for Transistors with Non-uniformly Doped Base Layers, *Scientia Electrica*, vol. 6, no. 2, pp. 80–91, June, 1960.
Wysocki, J. J., and P. Rappaport: Effect of Temperature on Photovoltaic Solar Energy Conversion, *J. Appl. Phys.*, vol. 31, no. 3, pp. 571–578, March, 1960.
Yamashita, J.: Theory of Avalanche Multiplication in Non-polar Semiconductors, "Progress in Semiconductors," vol. 4, pp. 63–94, Heywood and Co., London, 1960.
Yariv, A., J. S. Cook, and P. E. Butzien: Operation of an Esaki Diode Microwave Amplifier, *Proc. IRE*, vol. 48, no. 6(1), p. 1155, June, 1960.
Zakharov, A. L.: The Appearance of Instability in a Semiconducting Amplifier with Negative Effective Mass of the Carriers, *Zhur. Eksptl. i Teort. Fiz.*, vol. 38, no. 2, pp. 665–667, February, 1960.
Zehnel, P. G., M. Bräuer, and H. D. Engelke: Silicon Diodes in High-voltage Rectifiers, *Frequenz*, vol. 14, no. 8, pp. 259–263, August, 1960.
Zholkevich, G. A.: The Mechanism of Negative Photoconductivity, *Fiz. Tverdogo Tela*, vol. 2, no. 10, pp. 2480–2483, October, 1960.
Zima, V.: Review of the Formulae for a Chain of Identical Active-quadripoles, *Slaboproudý Obzor*, vol. 21, no. 12, pp. 704–708, 1960.
Zolotarev, V. F., and V. N. Larichev: P-N Junctions in Photosensitive Layers of PbS, *Fiz. Tverdogo Tela*, vol. 2, no. 8, pp. 1741–1750, August, 1960.
Zuleeg, R., and V. W. Vodicka: Parametric Amplification Properties in Transistors, *Proc. IRE*, vol. 48, no. 10, pp. 1785–1786, October, 1960.
Controlled Silicon Rectifiers, I, *Elektronik*, vol. 9, no. 7, pp. 199–200, July, 1960.
"Progress in Semiconductors," vol. 4, edited by A. F. Gibson, F. A. Kröger, and R. E. Burgess, Heywood and Co., London, 1960.
"Progress in Semiconductors," vol. 5, edited by A. F. Gibson, F. A. Kröger, and R. E. Burgess, Heywood and Company, London, 1960.
Single OC26 in Car-radio Output Stages, *Mullard Tech. Commun.*, vol. 5, pp. 74–78, February, 1960.
Transistor Circuits for Magnetic Matrix Stores, *Mullard Tech. Commun.*, vol. 5, pp. 197–207, September, 1960.

Transistor LC Oscillator Circuits Giving Moderate Values of Output Power, *Mullard Tech. Commun.*, vol. 5, pp. 60–70, February, 1960.

Transistor-resistor Logical Circuits, *Mullard Tech. Commun.*, vol. 5, pp. 174–181, September, 1960.

Transistor Three-phase D-C–A-C Inverter, *Mullard Tech. Commun.*, vol. 5, pp. 78–80, February, 1960.

Transistorized Three-circuit Carrier Telephone Equipment for Open-wire Lines. System SPo. 1012, *G.E.C. Telecommun.*, no. 30, pp. 29–38, July, 1960.

1961

Allen, J. W., and R. J. Cherry: Space-charge Currents in Gallium, *Nature*, vol. 189, pp. 297–298, January 28, 1961.

Bates, C. W., Jr.: Tunneling Current in Esaki Diodes, *Phys. Rev.*, vol. 121, no. 4, pp. 1070–1071, February 15, 1961.

Blundell, A. J., A. E. Garside, R. G. Hibberd, and I. Williams: Silicon Power Rectifiers, *Proc. Inst. Elec. Engrs. (London)*, vol. 108B, paper 3362U, 1961.

Cardona, M.: Electron Effective Masses in InAs and GaAs as a Function of Temperature and Doping, *Phys. Rev.*, vol. 121, no. 3, pp. 752–758, February 1, 1961.

Chagnon, P. R.: Low-level Linear Microsecond Gate, *Rev. Sci. Instr.*, vol. 32, no. 1, pp. 68–70, January, 1961.

Chase, R. L., W. A. Higinbotham, and G. L. Miller: Amplifiers for Use with P-N Junction Radiation Detectors, *IRE Trans. on Nuclear Sci.*, vol. NS-8, no. 1, pp. 147–150, January, 1961.

Chynoweth, A. G., W. L. Feldmann, and R. A. Logan: Excess Tunnel Current in Silicon Esaki Junctions, *Phys. Rev.*, vol. 121, no. 3, pp. 684–694, February, 1961.

Das, M. B., and A. R. Boothroyd: Determination of Physical Parameters of Diffusion and Drift Transistors, *IRE Trans. on Electron Devices*, vol. ED-8, no. 1, pp. 15–30, January, 1961.

Deb, S., and A. M. Daw: Variation of L.F. Noise Figure of a Junction Transistor, *J. Brit. Inst. Radio Engrs.*, vol. 21, no. 1, pp. 49–56, January, 1961.

Eckart, P., and G. Jungk: Hall Effect and Conductivity of Evaporated Germanium Films, *Ann. Physik*, vol. 7, no. 3–4, pp. 210–215, 1961.

Evans, J. F. O., D. A. Gill, and B. R. Moffitt: Symmetrical Transistors as A-C and D-C Switches and Their Applications in Modulator and Demodulator Circuits, *J. Brit. Inst. Radio Engrs.*, vol. 21, no. 2, pp. 143–152, February, 1961.

Feldman, D. W., and B. R. McAvoy: A 100 Db Microwave Semiconductor Switch, *Rev. Sci. Instr.*, vol. 32, no. 1, p. 76, January, 1961.

Grinberg, A. A., S. R. Novikov, and S. M. Rўvkin: A New Negative Photoconductivity Effect in a Magnetic Field, *Doklady Akad. Nauk S.S.S.R.*, vol. 136, no. 2, pp. 329–331, January 11, 1961.

Gummel, H. K., and F. M. Smits: Margin Considerations for an Esaki Diode-resistor OR Gate, *Bell System Tech. J.*, vol. 40, no. 1, pp. 213–232, January, 1961.

Harden, B. N., and R. W. Smith: Transistor Measurements; Power-gain and Noise Factor at Frequencies Up to 100 Mc/s, *Electronic Technol.*, vol. 38, no. 2, pp. 58–62, February, 1961.

Henderson, J. C.: Assessment of Transistor Life, *Post Off. Elec. Engrs. J.*, vol. 53, part 4, pp. 236–238, January, 1961.

Hutchins, R.: Selective RC Amplifier Using Transistors, *Electronic Eng.*, vol. 33, pp. 84–87, February, 1961.

Kallmann, H., B. Kramer, E. Haidemenakis, W. J. McAleer, H. Barkemeyer, and P. I. Pollak: Photovoltages in Silicon and Germanium Layers, *J. Electrochem. Soc.*, vol. 108, no. 3, pp. 247–251, March, 1961.

Kane, E. O.: Theory of Tunneling, *J. Appl. Phys.*, vol. 32, no. 1, pp. 83–91, January, 1961.

Koch, L., J. Messier, and Q. Kerns: Nuclear Method of Measurement of Diffusion Length in P-N Junctions, *IRE Trans. on Nuclear Sci.*, vol. NS-8, no. 1, pp. 83–90, January, 1961.

Laff, R. A., and H. Y. Fan: Carrier Lifetime in Indium Antimonide, *Phys. Rev.*, vol. 121, no. 1, pp. 53–62, January 1, 1961.

Lampert, M. A., and A. Rose: Volume-controlled, Two-carrier Currents in Solids: the Injected Plasma Case, *Phys. Rev.*, vol. 121, no. 1, pp. 26–37, January 1, 1961.

Larrabee, R. D.: Current-voltage Characteristics of Forward Biased Long P-I-N Structures, *Phys. Rev.*, vol. 121, no. 1, pp. 37–39, January 1, 1961.

Logan, R. A., J. F. Gilbert, and F. A. Trumbore: Electron Mobilities and Tunneling Currents in Silicon, *J. Appl. Phys.*, vol. 32, no. 1, pp. 131–132, January, 1961.

McCaldin, J. O., and D. B. Wittry: Germanium Saturated with Gallium Antimonide, *J. Appl. Phys.*, vol. 32, no. 1, pp. 65–69, January, 1961.

McCotter, J. D., M. J. Walker, and M. M. Fortini: A Coaxially Packed MADT for Microwave Applications, *IRE Trans. on Electron Devices*, vol. ED-8, no. 1, pp. 8–12, January, 1961.

Marsocci, V. A.: A Survey of Semiconductor Devices and Circuits in Computers, II, *Semiconductor Prods.*, vol. 4, no. 1, pp. 31–37, January, 1961.

Parks, G. H.: Symmetrical Transistors, *J. Brit. Inst. Radio Engrs.*, vol. 21, no. 1, pp. 79–88, January, 1961.

Ratcliffe, S., and J. E. Hughes: The Copper Staining of P-N-P Alloyed Junction Transistor Sections, *Brit. J. Appl. Phys.*, vol. 12, no. 4, pp. 193–194, April, 1961.

Ryan, W. D.: Frequency Division by Carrier Storage, *Electronic Eng.*, vol. 33, pp. 40–41, January, 1961.

Sah, C. T.: Effects of Electrons and Holes on the Transition Layer Characteristics of Linearly Graded P-N Junctions, *Proc. IRE*, vol. 49, no. 3, pp. 603–618, March, 1961.

Shockley, W., and H. J. Queisser: Detailed Balance Limit of Efficiency of P-N Junction Solar Cells, *J. Appl. Phys.*, vol. 32, no. 3, pp. 510–519, March, 1961.

Stocker, H. J.: Current-voltage Characteristics of Alloyed and Diffused P-N Junction Diodes in InSb, *J. Appl. Phys.*, vol. 32, no. 2, p. 322, February, 1961.

Strauss, A. J.: Electrical Properties of n-type GaSb, *Phys. Rev.*, vol. 121, no. 4, pp. 1087–1090, February 15, 1961.

Stubb, T.: An Exponential Generator for Determining the Lifetime of Charge Carriers in Solids, *State Inst. Tech. Research (Finland)*, no. 7, 1961.

Terner, G. E.: Theoretic Curves of Drift Transistor Current Gain, *IRE Trans. on Electron Devices*, vol. ED-8, no. 1, pp. 13–15, January 15, 1961.

Vogl, T. P., J. R. Hansen, and M. Garbuny: Photoconductive Time Constants and Related Characteristics of p-type Gold-doped Germanium, *J. Opt. Soc. Amer.*, vol. 51, no. 1, pp. 70–75, January, 1961.

Weingarten, I. R., and M. Rothberg: Radio-frequency Carrier and Capacitive Coupling Procedures for Resistivity and Lifetime Measurements on Silicon, *J. Electrochem. Soc.*, vol. 108, no. 2, pp. 167–171, February, 1961.

Wiencek, Z.: An Analysis and Representation of Junction Transistors in the Saturation State, *IRE Trans. on Electron Devices*, vol. ED-8, no. 1, pp. 87–95, January, 1961.

Wolfendale, E.: Alloy-diffused Transistors, *Electronic Eng.*, vol. 33, pp. 88–93, February, 1961.

AUTHOR INDEX

In the following index the superscript number affixed to the page number is the number of the reference in the list of references at the end of each section. Thus the entry Beam, W. R., **16**-25[26] indicates that W. R. Beam is the author referred to on page **16**-25 where the reference number 26 occurs.

The page numbers listed without superscript reference numbers are pages on which the author's name explicitly appears, and in general are the page numbers of the lists of references at the end of each section.

SUBJECT INDEX

7